W9-CQY-295

List of the Elements with Their Atomic Symbols and Atomic Weights

Name	Symbol	Atomic Number	Atomic Weight	Name	Symbol	Atomic Number	Atomic Weight
Actinium	Ac	89	227.028	Meitnerium	Mt	109	(268)
Aluminum	Al	13	26.9815	Mendelevium	Md	101	(258)
Americium	Am	95	(243)	Mercury	Hg	80	200.59
Antimony	Sb	51	121.76	Molybdenum	Mo	42	95.94
Argon	Ar	18	39.948	Neodymium	Nd	60	144.24
Arsenic	As	33	74.9216	Neon	Ne	10	20.1797
Astatine	At	85	(210)	Neptunium	Np	93	237.048
Barium	Ba	56	137.327	Nickel	Ni	28	58.693
Berkelium	Bk	97	(247)	Niobium	Nb	41	92.9064
Beryllium	Be	4	9.01218	Nitrogen	N	7	14.0067
Bismuth	Bi	83	208.980	Nobelium	No	102	(259)
Bohrium	Bh	107	(264)	Osmium	Os	76	190.23
Boron	B	5	10.811	Oxygen	O	8	15.9994
Bromine	Br	35	79.904	Palladium	Pd	46	106.42
Cadmium	Cd	48	112.411	Phosphorus	P	15	30.9738
Calcium	Ca	20	40.078	Platinum	Pt	78	195.08
Californium	Cf	98	(251)	Plutonium	Pu	94	(244)
Carbon	C	6	12.011	Polonium	Po	84	(209)
Cerium	Ce	58	140.115	Potassium	K	19	39.0983
Cesium	Cs	55	132.905	Praseodymium	Pr	59	140.908
Chlorine	Cl	17	35.4527	Promethium	Pm	61	(145)
Chromium	Cr	24	51.9961	Protactinium	Pa	91	231.036
Cobalt	Co	27	58.9332	Radium	Ra	88	226.025
Copernicium	Cn	112	(285)	Radon	Rn	86	(222)
Copper	Cu	29	63.546	Rhenium	Re	75	186.207
Curium	Cm	96	(247)	Rhodium	Rh	45	102.906
Darmstadtium	Ds	110	(271)	Roentgenium	Rg	111	(272)
Dubnium	Db	105	(262)	Rubidium	Rb	37	85.4678
Dysprosium	Dy	66	162.50	Ruthenium	Ru	44	101.07
Einsteinium	Es	99	(252)	Rutherfordium	Rf	104	(261)
Erbium	Er	68	167.26	Samarium	Sm	62	150.36
Europium	Eu	63	151.965	Scandium	Sc	21	44.9559
Fermium	Fm	100	(257)	Seaborgium	Sg	106	(266)
Fluorine	F	9	18.9984	Selenium	Se	34	78.96
Francium	Fr	87	(223)	Silicon	Si	14	28.0855
Gadolinium	Gd	64	157.25	Silver	Ag	47	107.868
Gallium	Ga	31	69.723	Sodium	Na	11	22.9898
Germanium	Ge	32	72.61	Strontium	Sr	38	87.62
Gold	Au	79	196.967	Sulfur	S	16	32.066
Hafnium	Hf	72	178.49	Tantalum	Ta	73	180.948
Hassium	Hs	108	(269)	Technetium	Tc	43	(98)
Helium	He	2	4.00260	Tellurium	Te	52	127.60
Holmium	Ho	67	164.930	Terbium	Tb	65	158.925
Hydrogen	H	1	1.00794	Thallium	Tl	81	204.383
Indium	In	49	114.818	Thorium	Th	90	232.038
Iodine	I	53	126.904	Thulium	Tm	69	168.934
Iridium	Ir	77	192.22	Tin	Sn	50	118.710
Iron	Fe	26	55.847	Titanium	Ti	22	47.88
Krypton	Kr	36	83.80	Tungsten	W	74	183.84
Lanthanum	La	57	138.906	Uranium	U	92	238.029
Lawrencium	Lr	103	(260)	Vanadium	V	23	50.9415
Lead	Pb	82	207.2	Xenon	Xe	54	131.29
Lithium	Li	3	6.941	Ytterbium	Yb	70	173.04
Lutetium	Lu	71	174.967	Yttrium	Y	39	88.9059
Magnesium	Mg	12	24.3050	Zinc	Zn	30	65.39
Manganese	Mn	25	54.9381	Zirconium	Zr	40	91.224

Dear students,

There were many factors your instructors took into consideration before choosing the texts for this course: content, instruction, readability, layout, visual effects, and cost. I wanted the best book at a reasonable cost; for this reason, I chose to specifically select the material that matches the topics I will cover and with them, designed this custom text.

I made the decision to remove some of the chapters and combine materials from multiple sources; therefore, you will find that your book is "missing/skipping" some pages. Please be reassured that you do not have a faulty book; instead, you have a book that will serve you well as it covers precisely the course content. Also, as the price has been adjusted to reflect the content removed, I have been able to offer you a more reasonably priced text.

I hope you enjoy the materials and the course and wish you well in your scholastic endeavors.

Sincerely,

Professor Norick

PEARSON

ALWAYS LEARNING

Fundamentals of General, Organic, and Biological Chemistry
Volume I

Custom Edition for Foothill College

Taken from:
Fundamentals of General, Organic, and Biological Chemistry,
Seventh Edition
by John McMurry, David S. Ballantine, Carl A. Hoeger, and Virginia E. Peterson

Study Guide & Full Solutions Manual for *Fundamentals of General, Organic, and Biological Chemistry*, Seventh Edition
by Susan E. McMurry

Pearson Learning Solutions, 501 Boylston Street, Suite 900, Boston, MA 02116
A Pearson Education Company
www.pearsoned.com

Printed in the United States of America

000200010271302996

CB

14 16

ISBN 10: 1-256-89403-6
ISBN 13: 978-1-256-89403-2

About the Authors

John McMurry, educated at Harvard and Columbia, has taught approximately 17,000 students in general and organic chemistry over a 30-year period. A professor of chemistry at Cornell University since 1980, Dr. McMurry previously spent 13 years on the faculty at the University of California at Santa Cruz. He has received numerous awards, including the Alfred P. Sloan Fellowship (1969–71), the National Institute of Health Career Development Award (1975–80), the Alexander von Humboldt Senior Scientist Award (1986–87), and the Max Planck Research Award (1991).

David S. Ballantine received his B.S. in Chemistry in 1977 from the College of William and Mary in Williamsburg, VA, and his Ph.D. in Chemistry in 1983 from the University of Maryland at College Park. After several years as a researcher at the Naval Research Labs in Washington, DC, he joined the faculty in the Department of Chemistry and Biochemistry of Northern Illinois University, where he has been a professor since 1989. He was awarded the Excellence in Undergraduate Teaching Award in 1998 and has been departmental Director of Undergraduate Studies since 2008. In addition, he is the coordinator for the Introductory and General Chemistry programs and is responsible for supervision of the laboratory teaching assistants.

Carl A. Hoeger received his B.S. in Chemistry from San Diego State University and his Ph.D. in Organic Chemistry from the University of Wisconsin, Madison in 1983. After a postdoctoral stint at the University of California, Riverside, he joined the Peptide Biology Laboratory at the Salk Institute in 1985, where he ran the NIH Peptide Facility while doing basic research in the development of peptide agonists and antagonists. During this time he also taught general, organic, and biochemistry at San Diego City College, Palomar College, and Miramar College. He joined the teaching faculty at University of California, San Diego, in 1998. Dr. Hoeger has been teaching chemistry to undergraduates for over 20 years, where he continues to explore the use of technology in the classroom; his current project involves the use of videopodcasts as adjuncts to live lectures. In 2004, he won the Paul and Barbara Saltman Distinguished Teaching Award from UCSD. He is deeply involved with the General Chemistry program at UCSD and also shares partial responsibility for the training and guidance of teaching assistants in the Chemistry and Biochemistry departments.

Virginia E. Peterson received her B.S. in Chemistry in 1967 from the University of Washington in Seattle and her Ph.D. in Biochemistry in 1980 from the University of Maryland at College Park. Between her undergraduate and graduate years she worked in lipid, diabetes, and heart disease research at Stanford University. Following her Ph.D. she took a position in the Biochemistry Department at the University of Missouri in Columbia and is now Professor Emerita. When she retired in 2011 she had been the Director of Undergraduate Advising for the department for 8 years and had taught both senior capstone classes and biochemistry classes for nonscience majors. Although retired, Dr. Peterson continues to advise undergraduates and teach classes. Awards include both the college-level and the university-wide Excellence in Teaching Award and, in 2006, the University's Outstanding Advisor Award and the State of Missouri Outstanding University Advisor Award. Dr. Peterson believes in public service and in 2003 received the Silver Beaver Award for service from the Boy Scouts of America.

Contents

The following content was taken from *Fundamentals of General, Organic, and Biological Chemistry*, Seventh Edition by John McMurry, David S. Ballantine, Carl A. Hoeger, and Virginia E. Peterson.

The following content was taken from *Study Guide & Full Solutions Manual* for *Fundamentals of General, Organic, and Biological Chemistry*, Seventh Edition by Susan E. McMurry.

CHAPTER 1

Matter and Measurements

CONTENTS

◄ Increasing our knowledge of the chemical and physical properties of matter depends on our ability to make measurements that are precise and accurate.

Earth, air, fire, water—the ancient philosophers believed that all matter was composed of these four fundamental substances. We now know that matter is much more complex, made up of nearly 100 naturally occurring fundamental substances, or elements, in millions of unique combinations. Everything you see, touch, taste, and smell is made of chemicals formed from these elements. Many chemicals occur naturally, but others are synthetic, including the plastics, fibers, and medicines that are so critical to modern life. Just as everything you see is made of chemicals, many of the natural changes you see taking place around you are the result of *chemical reactions*—the change of one chemical into another. The crackling fire of a log burning in the fireplace, the color change of a leaf in the fall, and the changes that a human body undergoes as it grows and ages are all results of chemical reactions. To understand these and other natural processes, you must have a basic understanding of chemistry.

As you might expect, the chemistry of living organisms is complex, and it is not possible to understand all concepts without a proper foundation. Thus, the general plan of this book is to gradually increase in complexity, beginning in the first 11 chapters with a grounding in the scientific fundamentals that govern all of chemistry. In the following six chapters, we look at the nature of the carbon-containing substances, or *organic chemicals*, that compose all living things. In the final 12 chapters, we apply what we have learned in the first part of the book to the study of biological chemistry.

We begin in Chapter 1 with an examination of the states and properties of matter and an introduction to the systems of measurement that are essential to our understanding of matter and its behavior.

1.1 Chemistry: The Central Science

Chemistry is often referred to as "the central science" because it is crucial to nearly all other sciences. In fact, as more and more is learned, the historical dividing lines between chemistry, biology, and physics are fading, and current research is more interdisciplinary. Figure 1.1 diagrams the relationship of chemistry and biological chemistry to other fields of scientific study. Whatever the discipline in which you are most interested, the study of chemistry builds the necessary foundation.

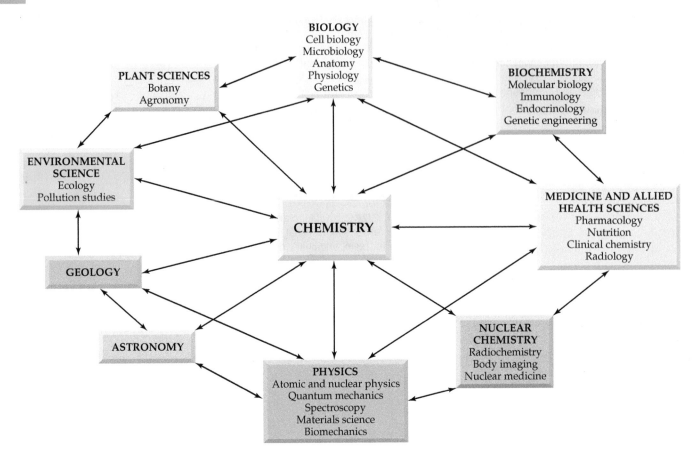

▲ **Figure 1.1**

Some relationships between chemistry—the central science—and other scientific and health-related disciplines.

Chemistry The study of the nature, properties, and transformations of matter.

Matter The physical material that makes up the universe; anything that has mass and occupies space.

Scientific Method The systematic process of observation, hypothesis, and experimentation used to expand and refine a body of knowledge.

Property A characteristic useful for identifying a substance or object.

Physical change A change that does not affect the chemical makeup of a substance or object.

Chemical change A change in the chemical makeup of a substance.

Chemistry is the study of matter—its nature, properties, and transformations. **Matter**, in turn, is a catchall word used to describe anything physically real—anything you can see, touch, taste, or smell. In more scientific terms, matter is anything that has mass and volume. As with our knowledge of all the other sciences, our knowledge of chemistry has developed by application of a process called the **scientific method** (see Chemistry in Action on p. 8). Starting with observations and measurements of the physical world, we form hypotheses to explain what we have observed. These hypotheses can then be tested by more observations and measurements, or experiments, to improve our understanding.

How might we describe different kinds of matter more specifically? Any characteristic that can be used to describe or identify something is called a **property**; size, color, and temperature are all familiar examples. Less familiar properties include *chemical composition*, which describes what matter is made of, and *chemical reactivity*, which describes how matter behaves. Rather than focus on the properties themselves, however, it is often more useful to think about *changes* in properties. Changes are of two types: *physical* and *chemical*. A **physical change** is one that does not alter the chemical makeup of a substance, whereas a **chemical change** is one that *does* alter a substance's chemical makeup. The melting of solid ice to give liquid water, for instance, is a physical change because the water changes only in form but not in chemical makeup. The rusting of an iron bicycle left in the rain, however, is a chemical change because iron combines with oxygen and moisture from the air to give a new substance, rust.

Table 1.1 lists some chemical and physical properties of several familiar substances—water, table sugar (sucrose), and baking soda (sodium bicarbonate). Note in Table 1.1 that the changes occurring when sugar and baking soda are heated are chemical changes, because new substances are produced.

TABLE **1.1** Some Properties of Water, Sugar, and Baking Soda		
Water	**Sugar (Sucrose)**	**Baking Soda (Sodium Bicarbonate)**
Physical properties		
Colorless liquid	White crystals	White powder
Odorless	Odorless	Odorless
Melting point: 0 °C	Begins to decompose at 160 °C, turning black and giving off water.	Decomposes at 270 °C, giving off water and carbon dioxide.
Boiling point: 100 °C	—	—
Chemical properties		
Composition:*	Composition:*	Composition:*
11.2% hydrogen	6.4% hydrogen	27.4% sodium
88.8% oxygen	42.1% carbon	1.2% hydrogen
	51.5% oxygen	14.3% carbon
		57.1% oxygen
Does not burn.	Burns in air.	Does not burn.

Compositions are given by mass percent.

▲ **Burning of potassium in water is an example of a chemical change.**

PROBLEM 1.1

Identify each of the following as a physical change or a chemical change:

(**a**) Grinding of a metal   (**b**) Fruit ripening

(**c**) Wood burning   (**d**) A rain puddle evaporating

1.2 States of Matter

Matter exists in three forms: solid, liquid, and gas. A **solid** has a definite volume and a definite shape that does not change regardless of the container in which it is placed; for example, a wooden block, marbles, or a cube of ice. A **liquid**, by contrast, has a definite volume but an indefinite shape. The volume of a liquid, such as water, does not change when it is poured into a different container, but its shape does. A **gas** is different still, having neither a definite volume nor a definite shape. A gas expands to fill the volume and take the shape of any container it is placed in, such as the helium in a balloon or steam formed by boiling water (Figure 1.2).

Solid A substance that has a definite shape and volume.

Liquid A substance that has a definite volume but assumes the shape of its container.

Gas A substance that has neither a definite volume nor a definite shape.

◄ **Figure 1.2**
The three states of matter—solid, liquid, and gas.

(**a**) Ice: A solid has a definite volume and a definite shape independent of its container.

(**b**) Water: A liquid has a definite volume but a variable shape that depends on its container.

(**c**) Steam: A gas has both variable volume and shape that depend on its container.

State of matter The physical state of a substance as a solid, liquid, or gas.

Change of state The conversion of a substance from one state to another—for example, from liquid to gas.

Many substances, such as water, can exist in all three phases, or **states of matter**—the solid state, the liquid state, and the gaseous state—depending on the temperature. The conversion of a substance from one state to another is known as a **change of state**. The melting of a solid, the freezing or boiling of a liquid, and the condensing of a gas to a liquid are familiar to everyone.

Worked Example 1.1 Identifying States of Matter

Formaldehyde is a disinfectant, a preservative, and a raw material for the manufacturing of plastics. Its melting point is −92 °C and its boiling point is −19.5 °C. Is formaldehyde a gas, a liquid, or a solid at room temperature (25 °C)?

ANALYSIS The state of matter of any substance depends on its temperature. How do the melting point and boiling point of formaldehyde compare with room temperature?

▶▶ The symbol °C means degrees Celsius and will be discussed in Section 1.13.

SOLUTION
Room temperature (25 °C) is above the boiling point of formaldehyde (−19.5 °C), and so the formaldehyde is a gas.

PROBLEM 1.2
Acetic acid, which gives the sour taste to vinegar, has a melting point of 16.7 °C and a boiling point of 118 °C. Predict the physical state of acetic acid when the ambient temperature is 10 °C.

1.3 Classification of Matter

The first question a chemist asks about an unknown substance is whether it is a pure substance or a mixture. Every sample of matter is one or the other. Water and sugar alone are pure substances, but stirring some sugar into a glass of water creates a *mixture*.

Pure substance A substance that has a uniform chemical composition throughout.

Mixture A blend of two or more substances, each of which retains its chemical identity.

Homogeneous mixture A uniform mixture that has the same composition throughout.

Heterogeneous mixture A non-uniform mixture that has regions of different composition.

▶▶ We'll revisit the properties of mixtures in Section 9.1 when we discuss solutions.

What is the difference between a pure substance and a mixture? One difference is that a **pure substance** is uniform in its chemical composition and its properties all the way down to the microscopic level. Every sample of water, sugar, or baking soda, regardless of source, has the composition and properties listed in Table 1.1. A **mixture**, however, can vary in both composition and properties, depending on how it is made. A **homogeneous mixture** is a blend of two or more pure substances having a uniform composition at the microscopic level. Sugar dissolved in water is one example. You cannot always distinguish between a pure substance and a homogeneous mixture just by looking. The sugar–water mixture *looks* just like pure water but differs on a molecular level. The amount of sugar dissolved in a glass of water will determine the sweetness, boiling point, and other properties of the mixture. A **heterogeneous mixture**, by contrast, is a blend of two or more pure substances having non-uniform composition, such as a vegetable stew in which each spoonful is different. It is relatively easy to distinguish heterogeneous mixtures from pure substances.

Another difference between a pure substance and a mixture is that the components of a mixture can be separated without changing their chemical identities. Water can be separated from a sugar–water mixture, for example, by boiling the mixture to drive off the steam and then condensing the steam to recover the pure water. Pure sugar is left behind in the container.

Element A fundamental substance that cannot be broken down chemically into any simpler substance.

▶▶ Elements are explored in the next section of this chapter (Section 1.4).

Pure substances are themselves classified into two groups: those that can undergo a chemical breakdown to yield simpler substances and those that cannot. A pure substance that cannot be broken down chemically into simpler substances is called an **element**. Examples include hydrogen, oxygen, aluminum, gold, and sulfur. At the time this book was printed, 118 elements had been identified, although only 91 of these occur naturally. All the millions of other substances in the universe are derived from them.

Any pure material that *can* be broken down into simpler substances by a chemical change is called a **chemical compound**. The term *compound* implies "more than one" (think "compound fracture"). A chemical compound, therefore, is formed by combining two or more elements to make a new substance. Water, for example, can be chemically changed by passing an electric current through it to produce hydrogen and oxygen. In writing this chemical change, the initial substance, or **reactant** (water), is written on the left; the new substances, or **products** (hydrogen and oxygen), are written on the right; and an arrow connects the two parts to indicate a chemical change, or **chemical reaction**. The conditions necessary to bring about the reaction are written above and below the arrow.

Chemical compound A pure substance that can be broken down into simpler substances by chemical reactions.

Reactant A starting substance that undergoes change during a chemical reaction.

Product A substance formed as the result of a chemical reaction.

Chemical reaction A process in which the identity and composition of one or more substances are changed.

▶▶ We will discuss how chemical reactions are represented in more detail in Section 1.6, and how reactions are classified in Chapter 5.

The classification of matter into mixtures, pure compounds, and elements is summarized in Figure 1.3.

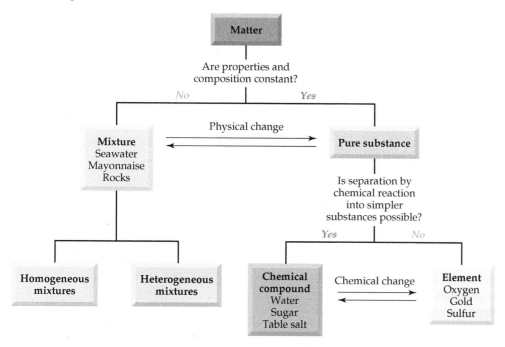

Figure 1.3
◀ A scheme for the classification of matter.

Worked Example 1.2 Classifying Matter

Classify each of the following as a mixture or a pure substance. If a mixture, classify it as heterogeneous or homogeneous. If a pure substance, identify it as an element or a compound.

(a) Vanilla ice cream   **(b)** Sugar

ANALYSIS Refer to the definitions of pure substances and mixtures. Is the substance composed of more than one kind of matter? Is the composition uniform?

SOLUTION

(a) Vanilla ice cream is composed of more than one substance—cream, sugar, and vanilla flavoring. The composition appears to be uniform throughout, so this is a homogeneous mixture.

(b) Sugar is composed of only one kind of matter—pure sugar. This is a pure substance. It can be converted to some other substance by a chemical change (see Table 1.1), so it is not an element. It must be a compound.

PROBLEM 1.3

Classify each of the following as a mixture or a pure substance. If a mixture, classify it as heterogeneous or homogeneous. If a pure substance, identify it as an element or a compound.

(a) Concrete   **(b)** The helium in a balloon   **(c)** A lead weight   **(d)** Wood

PROBLEM 1.4

Classify each of the following as a physical change or a chemical change:

(a) Dissolving sugar in water

(b) Producing carbon dioxide gas and solid lime by heating limestone

(c) Frying an egg

(d) The conversion of salicylic acid to acetylsalicylic acid (see the following Chemistry in Action)

▶▶▶ Prostaglandins are discussed in Section 24.9.

CHEMISTRY IN ACTION

Aspirin—A Case Study

Acetylsalicylic acid, more commonly known as aspirin, is perhaps the first true wonder drug. It is used as an analgesic to reduce fevers and to relieve headaches and body pains. It possesses anticoagulant properties, which in low doses can help prevent heart attacks and min_____. But how was it discovered_____ very" of aspirin is a combin_____own as the scientific meth_____rma-tion of a hypothesis,_____t the hypothesis and furthe_____

Anticoagulant property helps prevent ☐ atta___. & minimize the damage caused by strokes.

The origins of asp_____Greek physician Hippocrates_____k and leaves of the willow_____nowl-edge of the therapeutic properties of these substances was the result of systematic observations and the evaluation of folklore—knowledge of the common people obtained through trial and error. The development of aspirin took another step forward in 1828 when scientists isolated a bitter-tasting yellow extract, called salicin, from willow bark. Experimental evidence identified salicin as the active ingredient responsible for the observed medi-cal effects. Salicin could be easily converted by chemical reaction to salicylic acid (SA), which by the late 1800s was being mass-produced and marketed. SA had an unpleasant taste, however, and often caused stomach irritation and indigestion.

Further experiments were performed to convert salicylic acid to a substance that retained the therapeutic activity of SA, but without the unpleasant side effects. The discovery of acetylsali-cylic acid (ASA), a derivative of SA, has often been attributed to Felix Hoffman, a chemist working for the Bayer pharmaceutical labs, but the first synthesis of ASA was actually reported by a French chemist, Charles Gerhardt, in 1853. Nevertheless, Hoff-man obtained a patent for ASA in 1900, and Bayer marketed the new drug, now called aspirin, in water-soluble tablets.

▲ *Hippocrates.* **The ancient Greek physician prescribed a precursor of aspirin found in willow bark to relieve pain.**

But, how does aspirin work? Once again, experimental data provided insights into the therapeutic activity of aspirin. In 1971, the British pharmacologist John Vane discovered that aspirin suppresses the body's production of prostaglandins, which are responsible for the pain and swelling that accompany inflamma-tion. The discovery of this mechanism led to the development of new analgesic drugs.

Research continues to explore aspirin's potential for prevent-ing colon cancer, cancer of the esophagus, and other diseases.

See Chemistry in Action Problem 1.96 at the end of the chapter.

🔑 KEY CONCEPT PROBLEM 1.5

In the image below, red spheres represent element A and blue spheres represent element B. Identify the process illustrated in the image as a chemical change or a physical change. Explain your answer.

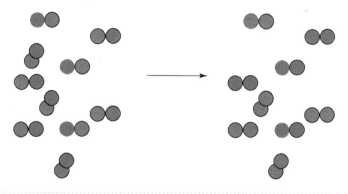

1.4 Chemical Elements and Symbols

As of the date this book was printed, 118 chemical elements have been identified. Some are certainly familiar to you—oxygen, helium, iron, aluminum, copper, and gold, for example—but many others are probably unfamiliar—rhenium, niobium, thulium, and promethium. Rather than write out the full names of elements, chemists use a short-hand notation in which elements are referred to by one- or two-letter symbols. The names and symbols of some common elements are listed in Table 1.2, and a complete alphabetical list is given inside the front cover of this book.

Note that all two-letter symbols have only their first letter capitalized, whereas the second letter is always lowercase. The symbols of most common elements are the first one or two letters of the elements' commonly used names, such as H (hydrogen) and Al (aluminum). Pay special attention, however, to the elements grouped in the last column to the right in Table 1.2. The symbols for these elements are derived from their original Latin names, such as Na for sodium, once known as *natrium*. The only way to learn these symbols is to memorize them; fortunately, they are few in number.

Only 91 of the elements occur naturally; the remaining elements have been produced artificially by chemists and physicists. Each element has its own distinctive properties, and just about all of the first 95 elements have been put to use in some way that takes advantage

▶▶▶ We will discuss the creation of new elements by nuclear bombardment in Chapter 11.

TABLE 1.2 Names and Symbols for Some Common Elements

Elements with Symbols Based on Modern Names						Elements with Symbols Based on Latin Names	
Al	Aluminum	Co	Cobalt	N	Nitrogen	Cu	Copper (*cuprum*)
Ar	Argon	F	Fluorine	O	Oxygen	Au	Gold (*aurum*)
Ba	Barium	He	Helium	P	Phosphorus	Fe	Iron (*ferrum*)
Bi	Bismuth	H	Hydrogen	Pt	Platinum	Pb	Lead (*plumbum*)
B	Boron	I	Iodine	Rn	Radon	Hg	Mercury (*hydrargyrum*)
Br	Bromine	Li	Lithium	Si	Silicon	K	Potassium (*kalium*)
Ca	Calcium	Mg	Magnesium	S	Sulfur	Ag	Silver (*argentum*)
C	Carbon	Mn	Manganese	Ti	Titanium	Na	Sodium (*natrium*)
Cl	Chlorine	Ni	Nickel	Zn	Zinc	Sn	Tin (*stannum*)

TABLE 1.3 Elemental Composition of the Earth's Crust and the Human Body*

Earth's Crust		Human Body	
Oxygen	46.1%	Oxygen	61%
Silicon	28.2%	Carbon	23%
Aluminum	8.2%	Hydrogen	10%
Iron	5.6%	Nitrogen	2.6%
Calcium	4.1%	Calcium	1.4%
Sodium	2.4%	Phosphorus	1.1%
Magnesium	2.3%	Sulfur	0.20%
Potassium	2.1%	Potassium	0.20%
Titanium	0.57%	Sodium	0.14%
Hydrogen	0.14%	Chlorine	0.12%

Mass percent values are given.

Chemical formula A notation for a chemical compound using element symbols and subscripts to show how many atoms of each element are present.

▶▶▶ We'll learn more about the structure of atoms and how they form compounds in Chapter 2.

of those properties. As indicated in Table 1.3, which shows the approximate elemental composition of the earth's crust and the human body, the naturally occurring elements are not equally abundant. Oxygen and silicon together account for nearly 75% of the mass in the earth's crust; oxygen, carbon, and hydrogen account for nearly all the mass of a human body.

Just as elements combine to form chemical compounds, symbols are combined to produce **chemical formulas**, which show by subscripts how many *atoms* (the smallest fundamental units) of each element are in a given chemical compound. For example, the formula H_2O represents water, which contains 2 hydrogen atoms combined with 1 oxygen atom. Similarly, the formula CH_4 represents methane (natural gas), and the formula $C_{12}H_{22}O_{11}$ represents table sugar (sucrose). When no subscript is given for an element, as for carbon in the formula CH_4, a subscript of "1" is understood.

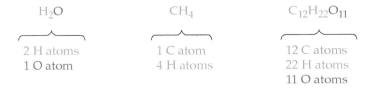

$$H_2O \qquad CH_4 \qquad C_{12}H_{22}O_{11}$$

2 H atoms	1 C atom	12 C atoms
1 O atom	4 H atoms	22 H atoms
		11 O atoms

PROBLEM 1.6
Match the names of the elements described below (a–f) with their elemental symbols (1–6).
(a) Sodium, a major component in table salt
(b) Tungsten, a metal used in light bulb filaments
(c) Strontium, used to produce brilliant red colors in fireworks
(d) Titanium, used in artificial hips and knee-replacement joints
(e) Fluorine, added to municipal water supplies to strengthen tooth enamel
(f) Tin, a metal used in solder

(1) W   **(2)** Na   **(3)** Sn   **(4)** F   **(5)** Ti   **(6)** Sr

PROBLEM 1.7
Identify the elements represented in each of the following chemical formulas, and tell the number of atoms of each element:
(a) NH_3 (ammonia)   **(b)** $NaHCO_3$ (sodium bicarbonate)
(c) C_8H_{18} (octane, a component of gasoline)   **(d)** $C_6H_8O_6$ (vitamin C)

1.5 Elements and the Periodic Table

The symbols of the known elements are normally presented in a tabular format called the **periodic table**, as shown in Figure 1.4 and the inside front cover of this book. We will have much more to say about the periodic table and how it is numbered later, but will note for now that it is the most important organizing principle in chemistry. An enormous amount of information is embedded in the periodic table, information that gives chemists the ability to explain known chemical behavior of elements and to predict new behavior. The elements can be roughly divided into three groups: *metals*, *nonmetals*, and *metalloids* (sometimes called *semimetals*).

Periodic table A tabular format listing all known elements.

▶▶ The organization of the periodic table will be discussed in Chapter 2.

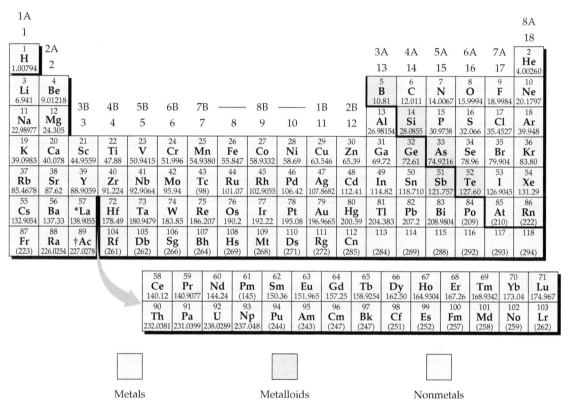

▲ **Figure 1.4**
The periodic table of the elements.
Metals appear on the left, nonmetals on the right, and metalloids in a zigzag band between metals and nonmetals. The numbering system is explained in Section 2.4.

Ninety-four of the currently known elements are metals—aluminum, gold, copper, and zinc, for example. **Metals** are solid at room temperature (except for mercury), usually have a lustrous appearance when freshly cut, are good conductors of heat and electricity, and are malleable rather than brittle. That is, metals can be pounded into different shapes rather than shattering when struck. Note that metals occur on the left side of the periodic table.

Eighteen elements are **nonmetals**. All are poor conductors of heat and electricity. Eleven are gases at room temperature, six are brittle solids, and one is a liquid. Oxygen and nitrogen, for example, are gases present in air; sulfur is a solid found in large underground deposits. Bromine is the only liquid nonmetal. Note that nonmetals occur on the right side of the periodic table.

Only six elements are **metalloids**, so named because their properties are intermediate between those of metals and nonmetals. Boron, silicon, and arsenic are examples. Pure silicon has a lustrous or shiny surface, like a metal, but it is brittle, like a nonmetal, and its electrical conductivity lies between that of metals and nonmetals. Note that metalloids occur in a zigzag band between metals on the left and nonmetals on the right side of the periodic table.

Metal A malleable element, with a lustrous appearance, that is a good conductor of heat and electricity.

Nonmetal An element that is a poor conductor of heat and electricity.

Metalloid An element whose properties are intermediate between those of a metal and a nonmetal.

(a)   (b)   (c)

▲ **Metals: Gold, zinc, and copper.**
(a) Known for its beauty, gold is very unreactive and is used primarily in jewelry and in electronic components. (b) Zinc, an essential trace element in our diets, has industrial uses ranging from the manufacture of brass, to roofing materials, to batteries. (c) Copper is widely used in electrical wiring, in water pipes, and in coins.

(a)   (b)   (c)

▲ **Nonmetals: Nitrogen, sulfur, and iodine.**
(a) Nitrogen, (b) sulfur, and (c) iodine are essential to all living things. Pure nitrogen, which constitutes almost 80% of air, is a gas at room temperature and does not condense to a liquid until it is cooled to −328 °C. Sulfur, a yellow solid, is found in large underground deposits in Texas and Louisiana. Iodine is a dark violet crystalline solid that was first isolated from seaweed.

(a)   (b)

▲ **Metalloids: Boron and silicon.**
(a) Boron is a strong, hard metalloid used in making the composite materials found in military aircraft. (b) Silicon is well known for its use in making computer chips.

Those elements essential for human life are listed in Table 1.4. In addition to the well-known elements carbon, hydrogen, oxygen, and nitrogen, less familiar elements such as molybdenum and selenium are also important.

TABLE 1.4 Elements Essential for Human Life*

Element	Symbol	Function
Carbon	C	
Hydrogen	H	These four elements are present in all living organisms
Oxygen	O	
Nitrogen	N	
Arsenic	As	May affect cell growth and heart function
Boron	B	Aids in the use of Ca, P, and Mg
Calcium*	Ca	Necessary for growth of teeth and bones
Chlorine*	Cl	Necessary for maintaining salt balance in body fluids
Chromium	Cr	Aids in carbohydrate metabolism
Cobalt	Co	Component of vitamin B_{12}
Copper	Cu	Necessary to maintain blood chemistry
Fluorine	F	Aids in the development of teeth and bones
Iodine	I	Necessary for thyroid function
Iron	Fe	Necessary for oxygen-carrying ability of blood
Magnesium*	Mg	Necessary for bones, teeth, and muscle and nerve action
Manganese	Mn	Necessary for carbohydrate metabolism and bone formation
Molybdenum	Mo	Component of enzymes necessary for metabolism
Nickel	Ni	Aids in the use of Fe and Cu
Phosphorus*	P	Necessary for growth of bones and teeth; present in DNA/RNA
Potassium*	K	Component of body fluids; necessary for nerve action
Selenium	Se	Aids vitamin E action and fat metabolism
Silicon	Si	Helps form connective tissue and bone
Sodium*	Na	Component of body fluids; necessary for nerve and muscle action
Sulfur*	S	Component of proteins; necessary for blood clotting
Zinc	Zn	Necessary for growth, healing, and overall health

C, H, O, and N are present in most foods. Other elements listed vary in their distribution in different foods. Those marked with an asterisk are macronutrients, essential in the diet at more than 100 mg/day; the rest, other than C, H, O, and N, are micronutrients, essential at 15 mg or less per day.

LOOKING AHEAD ▶▶▶ The elements listed in Table 1.4 are not present in our bodies in their free forms. Instead, they are combined into many thousands of different chemical compounds. We will talk about some compounds formed by metals in Chapter 3 and compounds formed by nonmetals in Chapter 4.

PROBLEM 1.8

The six metalloids are boron (B), silicon (Si), germanium (Ge), arsenic (As), antimony (Sb), and tellurium (Te). Locate them in the periodic table, and tell where they appear with respect to metals and nonmetals.

PROBLEM 1.9

Locate the element Hg (discussed in the Chemisty in Action on p. 15) in the periodic table. Is it a metal, nonmetal, or metalloid? What physical and chemical properties contribute to the toxicity of mercury and compounds containing mercury?

1.6 Chemical Reactions: An Example of Chemical Change

If we take a quick look at an example of a chemical reaction, we can reinforce some of the ideas discussed in the previous sections. The element *nickel* is a hard, shiny metal, and the compound *hydrogen chloride* is a colorless gas that dissolves in water to give a solution called *hydrochloric acid*. When pieces of nickel are added to hydrochloric acid in a test tube, the nickel is slowly eaten away, the colorless solution turns green, and a gas bubbles out of the test tube. The change in color, the dissolving of the nickel, and the appearance of gas bubbles are indications that a chemical reaction is taking place, as shown in Figure 1.5.

Overall, the reaction of nickel with hydrochloric acid can be either written in words or represented in a shorthand notation using symbols to represent the elements or compounds involved as reactants and products, as shown below.

Reactants ⎯⎯

Products ⎯

Nickel + Hydrochloric acid ⟶ Nickel (II) chloride + Hydrogen

$$[\text{Ni} + 2\,\text{HCl} \longrightarrow \text{NiCl}_2 + \text{H}_2]$$

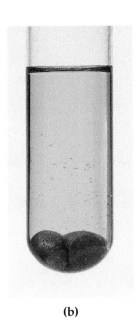

(a)   (b)   (c)

▲ **Figure 1.5**
Reactants and products of a chemical reaction.
(a) The reactants: The flat dish contains pieces of nickel, an element that is a typical lustrous metal. The bottle contains hydrochloric acid, a solution of the chemical compound hydrogen chloride in water. These reactants are about to be combined in the test tube. (b) The reaction: As the chemical reaction occurs, the colorless solution turns green when water-insoluble nickel metal slowly changes into the water-soluble chemical compound nickel (II) chloride. Gas bubbles of the element hydrogen are produced and rise slowly through the green solution. (c) The product: Hydrogen gas can be collected as it bubbles from the solution. Removal of water from the solution leaves behind the other product, a solid green chemical compound known as nickel (II) chloride.

1.7 Physical Quantities

Our understanding of matter depends on our ability to measure the changes in physical properties associated with physical and chemical change. Mass, volume, temperature, density, and other physical properties that can be measured are called **physical quantities** and are described by both a number and a **unit** of defined size:

Physical quantity A physical property that can be measured.

Unit A defined quantity used as a standard of measurement.

Number   Unit

61.2 kilograms

CHEMISTRY IN ACTION

Mercury and Mercury Poisoning

Mercury, the only metallic element that is liquid at room temperature, has fascinated people for millennia. Egyptian kings were buried in their pyramids along with containers of mercury, alchemists during the Middle Ages used mercury to dissolve gold, and Spanish galleons carried loads of mercury to the New World in the 1600s for use in gold and silver mining. Even its symbol, Hg, from the Latin *hydrargyrum,* meaning "liquid silver," hints at mercury's uniqueness.

Much of the recent interest in mercury has concerned its toxicity, but there are some surprises. For example, the mercury compound Hg_2Cl_2 (called *calomel*) is nontoxic and has a long history of medical use as a laxative, yet it is also used as a fungicide and rat poison. Dental amalgam, a solid alloy of approximately 50% elemental mercury, 35% silver, 13% tin, 1% copper, and trace amounts of zinc, has been used by dentists for many years to fill tooth cavities, with little or no adverse effects except in individuals with a hypersensitivity to mercury. Yet exposure to elemental mercury *vapor* for long periods leads to mood swings, headaches, tremors, and loss of hair and teeth. The widespread use of mercuric nitrate, a mercury compound employed to make the felt used in hats, exposed many hatters of the eighteenth and nineteenth centuries to toxic levels of mercury. The eccentric behavior displayed by hatters suffering from mercury poisoning led to the phrase "mad as a hatter."

Why is mercury toxic in some forms but not in others? It turns out that the toxicity of mercury and its compounds is related to solubility. Only soluble mercury compounds are toxic, because they can be transported through the bloodstream to all parts of the body, where they react with different enzymes and interfere with various biological processes. Elemental mercury and insoluble mercury compounds become toxic only when converted

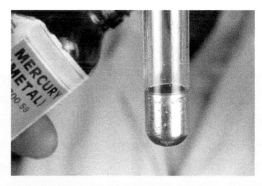

▲ **Elemental Mercury, a liquid at room temperature, forms many toxic compounds.**

into soluble compounds, reactions that are extremely slow in the body. Calomel, for example, is an insoluble mercury compound that passes through the body long before it is converted into any soluble compounds. Mercury alloys were considered safe for dental use because mercury does not evaporate readily from the alloys and it neither reacts with nor dissolves in saliva. Mercury vapor, however, remains in the lungs when breathed, until it is slowly converted into soluble compounds. Soluble organic forms of mercury can be particularly toxic. Trace amounts are found in nearly all seafood, but some larger species such as king mackerel and swordfish contain higher levels of mercury. Because mercury can affect the developing brain and nervous system of a fetus, pregnant women are often advised to avoid consuming them.

Recent events have raised new concerns regarding the safe use of mercury in some other applications. Perhaps the most controversial example is the use of thimerosal, an organic mercury compound, as a preservative in flu vaccines. While there is anecdotal evidence suggesting a link between thimerosal and autism in children, most scientific data seem to refute this claim. In response to these concerns, preservative-free versions of the influenza vaccine are available for use in infants, children, and pregnant women.

See Chemistry in Action Problem 1.97 at the end of the chapter.

The number alone is not much good without a unit. If you asked how much blood an accident victim had lost, the answer "three" would not tell you much. Three drops? Three milliliters? Three pints? Three liters? (By the way, an adult human has only 5–6 liters of blood.)

Any physical quantity can be measured in many different units. For example, a person's height might be measured in inches, feet, yards, centimeters, or many other units. To avoid confusion, scientists from around the world have agreed on a system of standard units, called by the French name *Système International d'Unites* (International System of Units), abbreviated *SI*. **SI units** for some common physical quantities are given in Table 1.5. Mass is measured in *kilograms* (kg), length is measured in *meters* (m), volume is measured in *cubic meters* (m^3), temperature is measured in *kelvins* (K), and time is measured in *seconds* (s, not sec).

SI units are closely related to the more familiar *metric units* used in all industrialized nations of the world except the United States. If you compare the SI and metric units shown in Table 1.5, you will find that the basic metric unit of mass is the *gram* (g) rather than the kilogram (1 g = 1/1000 kg), the metric unit of volume is the *liter* (L) rather than the cubic meter (1 L = 1/1000 m^3), and the metric unit of temperature

SI units Units of measurement defined by the International System of Units.

TABLE 1.5 Some SI and Metric Units and Their Equivalents

Quantity	SI Unit (Symbol)	Metric Unit (Symbol)	Equivalents
Mass	Kilogram (kg)	Gram (g)	1 kg = 1000 g = 2.205 lb
Length	Meter (m)	Meter (m)	1 m = 3.280 ft
Volume	Cubic meter (m³)	Liter (L)	1 m³ = 1000 L = 264.2 gal
Temperature	Kelvin (K)	Celsius degree (°C)	See Section 1.13
Time	Second (s)	Second (s)	—

is the *Celsius degree* (°C) rather than the kelvin. The meter is the unit of length, and the second is the unit of time in both systems. Although SI units are now preferred in scientific research, metric units are still used in some fields. You will probably find yourself working with both.

In addition to the units listed in Table 1.5, many other widely used units are derived from them. For instance, units of *meters per second* (m/s) are often used for *speed*—the distance covered in a given time. Similarly, units of *grams per cubic centimeter* (g/cm³) are often used for *density*—the mass of substance in a given volume. We will see other such derived units in future chapters.

One problem with any system of measurement is that the sizes of the units often turn out to be inconveniently large or small for the problem at hand. A biologist describing the diameter of a red blood cell (0.000 006 m) would find the meter to be an inconveniently large unit, but an astronomer measuring the average distance from the earth to the sun (150,000,000,000 m) would find the meter to be inconveniently small. For this reason, metric and SI units can be modified by prefixes to refer to either smaller or larger quantities. For instance, the SI unit for mass—the kilogram—differs by the prefix *kilo-* from the metric unit gram. *Kilo-* indicates that a kilogram is 1000 times as large as a gram:

$$1 \text{ kg} = (1000)(1 \text{ g}) = 1000 \text{ g}$$

Small quantities of active ingredients in medications are often reported in *milligrams* (mg). The prefix *milli-* shows that the unit gram has been divided by 1000, which is the same as multiplying by 0.001:

$$1 \text{ mg} = \left(\frac{1}{1000}\right)(1 \text{ g}) = (0.001)(1 \text{ g}) = 0.001 \text{ g}$$

▶▶▶ The use of exponents is reviewed in Section 1.10.

A list of prefixes is given in Table 1.6, with the most common ones displayed in color. Note that the exponents are multiples of 3 for *mega-* (10^6), *kilo-* (10^3), *milli-* (10^{-3}), *micro-* (10^{-6}), *nano-* (10^{-9}), and *pico-* (10^{-12}). The prefixes *centi-*, meaning $1/100$, and *deci-*, meaning $1/10$, indicate exponents that are not multiples of 3. *Centi-* is seen most often in the length unit *centimeter* (1 cm = 0.01 m), and *deci-* is used most often in clinical chemistry, where the concentrations of blood components are given in milligrams per deciliter (1 dL = 0.1 L). These prefixes allow us to compare the magnitudes of different numbers by noting how the prefixes modify a common unit.

For example,

$$1 \text{ meter} = 10 \text{ dm} = 100 \text{ cm} = 1000 \text{ mm} = 1,000,000 \text{ } \mu\text{m}$$

Such comparisons will be useful when we start performing calculations involving units in Section 1.12. Note also in Table 1.6 that numbers having five or more digits to the right of the decimal point are shown with thin spaces every three digits for convenience—0.000 001, for example. This manner of writing numbers is becoming more common and will be used throughout this book.

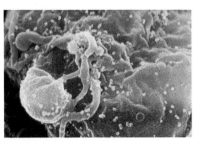

▲ The HIV-1 virus particles (in green) budding from the surface of a lymphocyte have an approximate diameter of 0.000 000 120 m.

TABLE 1.6   Some Prefixes for Multiples of Metric and SI Units

Prefix	Symbol	Base Unit Multiplied By*	Example
mega	M	$1{,}000{,}000 = 10^6$	1 megameter (Mm) = 10^6 m
kilo	k	$1000 = 10^3$	1 kilogram (kg) = 10^3 g
hecto	h	$100 = 10^2$	1 hectogram (hg) = 100 g
deka	da	$10 = 10^1$	1 dekaliter (daL) = 10 L
deci	d	$0.1 = 10^{-1}$	1 deciliter (dL) = 0.1 L
centi	c	$0.01 = 10^{-2}$	1 centimeter (cm) = 0.01 m
milli	m	$0.001 = 10^{-3}$	1 milligram (mg) = 0.001 g
micro	μ	$0.000\ 001 = 10^{-6}$	1 micrometer (μm) = 10^{-6} m
nano	n	$0.000\ 000\ 001 = 10^{-9}$	1 nanogram (ng) = 10^{-9} g
pico	p	$0.000\ 000\ 000\ 001 = 10^{-12}$	1 picogram (pg) = 10^{-12} g
femto	f	$0.000\ 000\ 000\ 000\ 001 = 10^{-15}$	1 femtogram (fg) = 10^{-15} g

*The scientific notation method of writing large and small numbers (for example, 10^6 for 1,000,000) is explained in Section 1.10.

PROBLEM 1.10

Give the full name of the following units and express the quantities in terms of the basic unit (for example, 1 mL = 1 milliliter = 0.001 L):

(a) 1 cm   **(b)** 1 dg   **(c)** 1 km   **(d)** 1 μs   **(e)** 1 ng

1.8 Measuring Mass, Length, and Volume

The terms *mass* and *weight*, though often used interchangeably, really have quite different meanings. **Mass** is a measure of the amount of matter in an object, whereas **weight** is a measure of the gravitational pull that the earth, moon, or other large body exerts on an object. Clearly, the amount of matter in an object does not depend on location. Whether you are standing on the earth or standing on the moon, the mass of your body is the same. On the other hand, the weight of an object *does* depend on location. Your weight on earth might be 140 lb, but it would only be 23 lb on the moon because the pull of gravity there is only about one-sixth as great.

At the same location, two objects with identical masses have identical weights; that is, gravity pulls equally on both. Thus, the *mass* of an object can be determined by comparing the *weight* of the object to the weight of a known reference standard. Much of the confusion between mass and weight is simply due to a language problem: We speak of "weighing" when we really mean that we are measuring mass by comparing two weights. Figure 1.6 shows a two-pan balance in which the mass of objects are measured by comparison with the known masses of standard materials, such as brass weights.

Mass A measure of the amount of matter in an object.

Weight A measure of the gravitational force that the earth or other large body exerts on an object.

◄**Figure 1.6**
The two-pan balance is used to measure the mass of objects, such as the pennies on the left pan, by comparing them with the mass of standard objects, such as the brass weights on the right pan.

One kilogram, the SI unit for mass, is equal to 2.205 lb—too large a quantity for many purposes in chemistry and medicine. Thus, smaller units of mass such as the gram, milligram (mg), and microgram (μg), are more commonly used. Table 1.7 shows the relationships between metric and common units for mass.

The meter is the standard measure of length, or distance, in both the SI and metric systems. One meter is 39.37 inches (about 10% longer than a yard), a length that is much too large for most measurements in chemistry and medicine. Other, more commonly used measures of length are the *centimeter* (cm; 1/100 m) and the *millimeter* (mm; 1/1000 m). One centimeter is a bit less than half an inch—0.3937 inch to be exact. A millimeter, in turn, is 0.03937 inch, or about the thickness of a dime. Table 1.8 lists the relationships of these units.

Volume is the amount of space occupied by an object. The SI unit for volume—the cubic meter, m^3—is so large that the liter (1 L = 0.001 m^3 = 1 dm^3) is much more commonly used in chemistry and medicine. One liter has the volume of a cube 10 cm (1 dm) on edge and is a bit larger than one U.S. quart. Each liter is further divided into

TABLE 1.7 Units of Mass

Unit	Equivalent	Unit	Equivalent
1 kilogram (kg)	= 1000 grams = 2.205 pounds	1 ton	= 2000 pounds = 907.03 kilograms
1 gram (g)	= 0.001 kilogram = 1000 milligrams = 0.035 27 ounce	1 pound (lb)	= 16 ounces = 0.454 kilogram = 454 grams
1 milligram (mg)	= 0.001 gram = 1000 micrograms	1 ounce (oz)	= 0.028 35 kilogram = 28.35 grams
1 microgram (μg)	= 0.000 001 gram = 0.001 milligram		= 28,350 milligrams

TABLE 1.8 Units of Length

Unit	Equivalent
1 kilometer (km)	= 1000 meters = 0.6214 mile
1 meter (m)	= 100 centimeters = 1000 millimeters = 1.0936 yards = 39.37 inches
1 centimeter (cm)	= 0.01 meter = 10 millimeters = 0.3937 inch
1 millimeter (mm)	= 0.001 meter = 0.1 centimeter
1 mile (mi)	= 1.609 kilometers = 1609 meters
1 yard (yd)	= 0.9144 meter = 91.44 centimeters
1 foot (ft)	= 0.3048 meter = 30.48 centimeters
1 inch (in)	= 2.54 centimeters = 25.4 millimeters

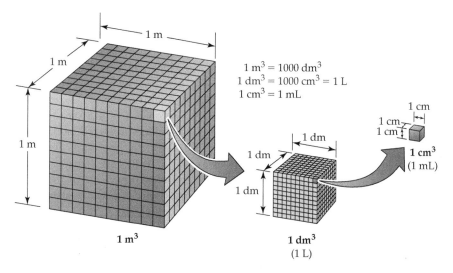

1 m³

1 m³ = 1000 dm³
1 dm³ = 1000 cm³ = 1 L
1 cm³ = 1 mL

1 dm³
(1 L)

1 cm³
(1 mL)

◀ **Figure 1.7**
A cubic meter is the volume of a cube
1 m on edge. Each cubic meter contains 1000 cubic decimeters (liters),
and each cubic decimeter contains
1000 cubic centimeters (milliliters).
Thus, there are 1000 mL in a liter and
1000 L in a cubic meter.

TABLE 1.9 Units of Volume

Unit	Equivalent
1 cubic meter (m³)	= 1000 liters = 264.2 gallons
1 liter (L)	= 0.001 cubic meter = 1000 milliliters = 1.057 quarts
1 deciliter (dL)	= 0.1 liter = 100 milliliters
1 milliliter (mL)	= 0.001 liter = 1000 microliters
1 microliter (μL)	= 0.001 milliliter
1 gallon (gal)	= 3.7854 liters
1 quart (qt)	= 0.9464 liter = 946.4 milliliters
1 fluid ounce (fl oz)	= 29.57 milliliters

1000 *milliliters* (mL), with 1 mL being the size of a cube 1 cm on edge, or 1 cm³. In fact, the milliliter is often called a *cubic centimeter* (cm³ or cc) in medical work. Figure 1.7 shows the divisions of a cubic meter, and Table 1.9 shows the relationships among units of volume.

1.9 Measurement and Significant Figures

How much does a tennis ball weigh? If you put a tennis ball on an ordinary bathroom scale, the scale would probably register 0 lb (or 0 kg if you have a metric scale). If you placed the same tennis ball on a common laboratory balance, however, you might get a reading of 54.07 g. Trying again by placing the ball on an expensive analytical balance like those found in clinical and research laboratories, you might find a mass of 54.071 38 g. Clearly, the precision of your answer depends on the equipment used for the measurement.

Every experimental measurement, no matter how precise, has a degree of uncertainty to it because there is always a limit to the number of digits that can be determined. An analytical balance, for example, might reach its limit in measuring mass to the fifth decimal place, and weighing the tennis ball several times might produce

▲ The tennis ball weighs 54.07 g on this common laboratory balance, which is capable of determining mass to about 0.01 g.

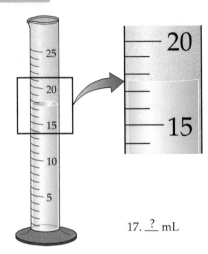

▲ **Figure 1.8**
What is the volume of liquid in this graduated cylinder?

Significant figures The number of meaningful digits used to express a value.

slightly different readings, such as 54.071 39 g, 54.071 38 g, and 54.071 37 g. Also, different people making the same measurement might come up with slightly different answers. How, for instance, would you record the volume of the liquid shown in Figure 1.8? It is clear that the volume of liquid lies between 17.0 and 18.0 mL, but the exact value of the last digit must be estimated.

To indicate the precision of a measurement, the value recorded should use all the digits known with certainty, plus one additional estimated digit that is usually considered uncertain by plus or minus 1 (written as ±1). The total number of digits used to express such a measurement is called the number of **significant figures**. Thus, the quantity 54.07 g has four significant figures (5, 4, 0, and 7), and the quantity 54.071 38 g has seven significant figures. *Remember:* All but one of the significant figures are known with certainty; the last significant figure is only an estimate accurate to ±1.

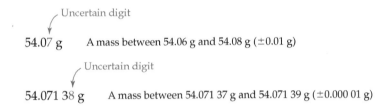

Deciding the number of significant figures in a given measurement is usually simple, but it can be troublesome when zeros are involved. Depending on the circumstances, a zero might be significant or might be just a space-filler to locate the decimal point. For example, how many significant figures does each of the following measurements have?

94.072 g	Five significant figures (9, 4, 0, 7, 2)
0.0834 cm	Three significant figures (8, 3, 4)
0.029 07 mL	Four significant figures (2, 9, 0, 7)
138.200 m	Six significant figures (1, 3, 8, 2, 0, 0)
23,000 kg	*Anywhere* from two (2, 3) to five (2, 3, 0, 0, 0) significant figures

The following rules are helpful for determining the number of significant figures when zeros are present:

RULE 1: Zeros in the middle of a number are like any other digit; they are always significant. Thus, 94.072 g has five significant figures.

RULE 2: Zeros at the beginning of a number are not significant; they act only to locate the decimal point. Thus, 0.0834 cm has three significant figures, and 0.029 07 mL has four.

RULE 3: Zeros at the end of a number and *after* the decimal point are significant. It is assumed that these zeros would not be shown unless they were significant. Thus, 138.200 m has six significant figures. If the value were known to only four significant figures, we would write 138.2 m.

RULE 4: Zeros at the end of a number and *before* an implied decimal point may or may not be significant. We cannot tell whether they are part of the measurement or whether they act only to locate the unwritten but implied decimal point. Thus, 23,000 kg may have two, three, four, or five significant figures. Adding a decimal point at the end would indicate that all five numbers are significant.

Often, however, a little common sense is useful. A temperature reading of 20 °C probably has two significant figures rather than one, because one significant figure would imply a temperature anywhere from 10 °C to 30 °C and would be of little use. Similarly, a volume given as 300 mL probably has three significant figures. On the other hand, a figure of 150,000,000 km for the distance between the earth and the sun has only two or three significant figures because the distance is variable. We will see a better way to deal with this problem in the next section.

One final point about significant figures: some numbers, such as those obtained when counting objects and those that are part of a definition, are *exact* and effectively have an unlimited number of significant figures. Thus, a class might have *exactly* 32 students (not 31.9, 32.0, or 32.1), and 1 foot is defined to have *exactly* 12 inches.

▲ The number of seats in this auditorium is an exact number with an unlimited number of significant figures.

Worked Example 1.3 Significant Figures of Measurements

How many significant figures do the following measurements have?

(a) 2730.78 m   (b) 0.0076 mL   (c) 3400 kg   (d) 3400.0 m²

ANALYSIS All nonzero numbers are significant; the number of significant figures will then depend on the status of the zeros in each case. (Hint: which rule applies in each case?)

SOLUTION

(a) Six (rule 1)   (b) Two (rule 2)
(c) Two, three, or four (rule 4)   (d) Five (rule 3)

PROBLEM 1.11

How many significant figures do the following measurements have?

(a) 3.45 m   (b) 0.1400 kg
(c) 10.003 L   (d) 35 cents

 KEY CONCEPT PROBLEM 1.12

How would you record the temperature reading on the following Celsius thermometer? How many significant figures do you have in your answer?

1.10 Scientific Notation

Rather than write very large or very small numbers in their entirety, it is more convenient to express them using *scientific notation*. A number is written in **scientific notation** as the product of a number between 1 and 10, times the number 10 raised to a power. Thus, 215 is written in scientific notation as 2.15×10^2:

$$215 = 2.15 \times 100 = 2.15(10 \times 10) = 2.15 \times 10^2$$

Notice that in this case, where the number is *larger* than 1, the decimal point has been moved *to the left* until it follows the first digit. The exponent on the 10 tells how many places we had to move the decimal point to position it just after the first digit:

$$2\underset{\curvearrowleft}{15}. = 2.15 \times 10^2$$

Decimal point is moved two places to the left, so exponent is 2.

Scientific notation A number expressed as the product of a number between 1 and 10, times the number 10 raised to a power.

To express a number *smaller* than 1 in scientific notation, we have to move the decimal point *to the right* until it follows the first digit. The number of places moved is the negative exponent of 10. For example, the number 0.002 15 can be rewritten as 2.15×10^{-3}:

$$0.002\ 15 = 2.15 \times \frac{1}{1000} = 2.15 \times \frac{1}{10 \times 10 \times 10} = 2.15 \times \frac{1}{10^3} = 2.15 \times 10^{-3}$$

$$0.002\,15 = 2.15 \times 10^{-3}$$

Decimal point is moved three places to the right, so exponent is −3.

To convert a number written in scientific notation to standard notation, the process is reversed. For a number with a *positive* exponent, the decimal point is moved to the *right* a number of places equal to the exponent:

$$3.7962 \times 10^4 = 37{,}962$$

Positive exponent of 4, so decimal point is moved to the right four places.

For a number with a *negative* exponent, the decimal point is moved to the *left* a number of places equal to the exponent:

$$1.56 \times 10^{-8} = 0.000\ 000\ 015\ 6$$

Negative exponent of −8, so decimal point is moved to the left eight places.

Scientific notation is particularly helpful for indicating how many significant figures are present in a number that has zeros at the end but to the left of a decimal point. If we read, for instance, that the distance from the earth to the sun is 150,000,000 km, we do not really know how many significant figures are indicated. Some of the zeros might be significant, or they might merely act to locate the decimal point. Using scientific notation, however, we can indicate how many of the zeros are significant. Rewriting 150,000,000 as 1.5×10^8 indicates two significant figures, whereas writing it as 1.500×10^8 indicates four significant figures. Scientific notation is not ordinarily used for numbers that are easily written, such as 10 or 175, although it is sometimes helpful in doing arithmetic.

▶▶▶ Rules for doing arithmetic with numbers written in scientific notation are reviewed in Appendix A.

Worked Example 1.4 Significant Figures and Scientific Notation

There are 1,760,000,000,000,000,000,000 molecules of sucrose (table sugar) in 1 g. Use scientific notation to express this number with four significant figures.

ANALYSIS Because the number is larger than 1, the exponent will be positive. You will have to move the decimal point 21 places to the left.

SOLUTION
The first four digits—1, 7, 6, and 0—are significant, meaning that only the first of the 19 zeros is significant. Because we have to move the decimal point 21 places to the left to put it after the first significant digit, the answer is 1.760×10^{21}.

▲ How many molecules are in this 1 g pile of table sugar?

Worked Example 1.5 Scientific Notation

The rhinovirus responsible for the common cold has a diameter of 20 nm, or 0.000 000 020 m. Express this number in scientific notation.

ANALYSIS The number is smaller than 1, and so the exponent will be negative. You will have to move the decimal point eight places to the right.

SOLUTION
There are only two significant figures, because zeros at the beginning of a number are not significant. We have to move the decimal point 8 places to the right to place it after the first digit, so the answer is 2.0×10^{-8} m.

Worked Example 1.6 Scientific Notation and Unit Conversions

A clinical laboratory found that a blood sample contained 0.0026 g of phosphorus and 0.000 101 g of iron.

(a) Give these quantities in scientific notation.

(b) Give these quantities in the units normally used to report them—milligrams for phosphorus and micrograms for iron.

ANALYSIS Is the number larger or smaller than 1? How many places do you have to move the decimal point?

SOLUTION

(a) 0.0026 g phosphorus $= 2.6 \times 10^{-3}$ g phosphorus

$\qquad$ 0.000 101 g iron $= 1.01 \times 10^{-4}$ g iron

(b) We know from Table 1.6 that 1 mg $= 1 \times 10^{-3}$ g, where the exponent is -3. Expressing the amount of phosphorus in milligrams is straightforward because the amount in grams (2.6×10^{-3} g) already has an exponent of -3. Thus, 2.6×10^{-3} g $= 2.6$ mg of phosphorus.

$$(2.6 \times 10^{-3} \ g)\left(\frac{1 \ mg}{1 \times 10^{-3} \ g}\right) = 2.6 \ mg$$

We know from Table 1.6 that 1 μg $= 1 \times 10^{-6}$ g where the exponent is -6. Expressing the amount of iron in micrograms thus requires that we restate the amount in grams so that the exponent is -6. We can do this by moving the decimal point six places to the right:

$$0.000 \ 101 \ g \ iron = 101 \times 10^{-6} \ g \ iron = 101 \ \mu g \ iron$$

PROBLEM 1.13

Convert the following values to scientific notation:

(a) 0.058 g $\qquad$ **(b)** 46,792 m $\qquad$ **(c)** 0.006 072 cm $\qquad$ **(d)** 345.3 kg

PROBLEM 1.14

Convert the following values from scientific notation to standard notation:

(a) 4.885×10^{4} mg $\qquad$ **(b)** 8.3×10^{-6} m $\qquad$ **(c)** 4.00×10^{-2} m

PROBLEM 1.15

Rewrite the following numbers in scientific notation as indicated:

(a) 630,000 with five significant figures

(b) 1300 with three significant figures

(c) 794,200,000,000 with four significant figures

1.11 Rounding Off Numbers

It often happens, particularly when doing arithmetic on a pocket calculator, that a quantity appears to have more significant figures than are really justified. For example, you might calculate the gas mileage of your car by finding that it takes 11.70 gallons of gasoline to drive 278 miles:

$$\text{Mileage} = \frac{\text{Miles}}{\text{Gallons}} = \frac{278 \ \text{mi}}{11.70 \ \text{gal}} = 23.760 \ 684 \ \text{mi/gal (mpg)}$$

Although the answer on a calculator has eight digits, your calculated result is really not as precise as it appears. In fact, as we will see below, your answer is good to only three significant figures and should be **rounded off** to 23.8 mi/gal.

Rounding off A procedure used for deleting nonsignificant figures.

How do you decide how many digits to keep? The full answer to this question is a bit complex and involves a mathematical treatment called *error analysis*, but for many purposes, a simplified procedure using just two rules is sufficient:

RULE 1: In carrying out a multiplication or division, the answer cannot have more significant figures than either of the original numbers. This is just a common-sense rule if you think about it. After all, if you do not know the number of miles you drove to better than three significant figures (278 could mean 277, 278, or 279), you certainly cannot calculate your mileage to more than the same number of significant figures.

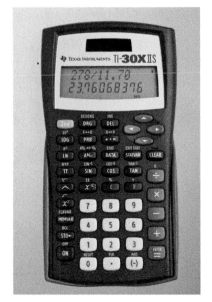

▲ Calculators often display more digits than are justified by the precision of the data.

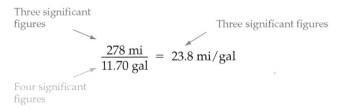

RULE 2: In carrying out an addition or subtraction, the answer cannot have more digits after the decimal point than either of the original numbers. For example, if you have 3.18 L of water and you add 0.013 15 L more, you now have 3.19 L. Again, this rule is just common sense. If you do not know the volume you started with past the second decimal place (it could be 3.17, 3.18, or 3.19), you cannot know the total of the combined volumes past the same decimal place.

Volume of water at start → 3.18? ?? L ← Two digits after decimal point
Volume of water added → + 0.013 15 L ← Five digits after decimal point
Total volume of water → 3.19? ?? L ← Two digits after decimal point

If a calculation has several steps, it is generally best to round off at the end after all the steps have been carried out, keeping the number of significant figures determined by the least precise number in your calculations. Once you decide how many digits to retain for your answer, the rules for rounding off numbers are straightforward:

RULE 1: If the first digit you remove is 4 or less, drop it and all following digits. Thus, 2.4271 becomes 2.4 when rounded off to two significant figures because the first of the dropped digits (a 2) is 4 or less.

RULE 2: If the first digit you remove is 5 or greater, round the number up by adding a 1 to the digit to the left of the one you drop. Thus, 4.5832 becomes 4.6 when rounded off to two significant figures because the first of the dropped digits (an 8) is 5 or greater.

Worked Example 1.7 Significant Figures and Calculations: Addition/Subtraction

Suppose that you weigh 124 lb before dinner. How much will you weigh after dinner if you eat 1.884 lb of food?

ANALYSIS When performing addition or subtraction, the number of significant figures you report in the final answer is determined by the number of digits in the least precise number in the calculation.

SOLUTION

Your after-dinner weight is found by adding your original weight to the weight of the food consumed:

$$
\begin{array}{r}
124 \quad \text{lb} \\
\underline{1.884\ \text{lb}} \\
125.884\ \text{lb (Unrounded)}
\end{array}
$$

Because the value of your original weight has no significant figures after the decimal point, your after-dinner weight also must have no significant figures after the decimal point. Thus, 125.884 lb must be rounded off to 126 lb.

Worked Example **1.8** Significant Figures and Calculations: Multiplication/Division

To make currant jelly, 13.75 cups of sugar was added to 18 cups of currant juice. How much sugar was added per cup of juice?

ANALYSIS For calculations involving multiplication or division, the final answer cannot have more significant figures than either of the original numbers.

SOLUTION

The quantity of sugar must be divided by the quantity of juice:

$$
\frac{13.75 \text{ cups sugar}}{18 \text{ cups juice}} = 0.763\ 888\ 89 \ \frac{\text{cup sugar}}{\text{cup juice}} \text{(Unrounded)}
$$

The number of significant figures in the answer is limited to two by the quantity 18 cups in the calculation and must be rounded to 0.76 cup of sugar per cup of juice.

PROBLEM 1.16

Round off the following quantities to the indicated number of significant figures:

(a) 2.304 g (three significant figures)
(b) 188.3784 mL (five significant figures)
(c) 0.008 87 L (one significant figure)
(d) 1.000 39 kg (four significant figures)

PROBLEM 1.17

Carry out the following calculations, rounding each result to the correct number of significant figures:

(a) 4.87 mL + 46.0 mL   **(b)** 3.4 × 0.023 g
(c) 19.333 m − 7.4 m   **(d)** 55 mg − 4.671 mg + 0.894 mg
(e) 62,911 ÷ 611

1.12 Problem Solving: Unit Conversions and Estimating Answers

Many activities in the laboratory and in medicine—measuring, weighing, preparing solutions, and so forth—require converting a quantity from one unit to another. For example: "These pills contain 1.3 grains of aspirin, but I need 200 mg. Is one pill enough?" Converting between units is not mysterious; we all do it every day. If you run 9 laps around a 400-meter track, for instance, you have to convert between the distance unit "lap" and the distance unit "meter" to find that you have run 3600 m (9 laps times

▲ Currency exchange between the US$ and Euros is another activity that requires a unit conversion.

400 m/lap). If you want to find how many miles that is, you have to convert again to find that 3600 m = 2.237 mi.

The simplest way to carry out calculations involving different units is to use the **factor-label method**. In this method, a quantity in one unit is converted into an equivalent quantity in a different unit by using a **conversion factor** that expresses the relationship between units:

Starting quantity × Conversion factor = Equivalent quantity

As an example, we learned from Table 1.8 that 1 km = 0.6214 mi. Writing this relationship as a fraction restates it in the form of a conversion factor, either kilometers per mile or miles per kilometer.

Since 1 km = 0.6214 mi, then:

Conversion factors between kilometers and miles
$$\frac{1 \text{ km}}{0.6214 \text{ mi}} = 1 \quad \text{or} \quad \frac{0.6214 \text{ mi}}{1 \text{ km}} = 1$$

Note that this and all other conversion factors are numerically equal to 1 because the value of the quantity above the division line (the numerator) is equal in value to the quantity below the division line (the denominator). Thus, multiplying by a conversion factor is equivalent to multiplying by 1 and so does not change the value of the quantity being multiplied:

These two quantities are the same.
$$\frac{1 \text{ km}}{0.6214 \text{ mi}} \quad \text{or} \quad \frac{0.6214 \text{ mi}}{1 \text{ km}}$$
These two quantities are the same.

The key to the factor-label method of problem solving is that units are treated like numbers and can thus be multiplied and divided (though not added or subtracted) just as numbers can. When solving a problem, the idea is to set up an equation so that all unwanted units cancel, leaving only the desired units. Usually, it is best to start by writing what you know and then manipulating that known quantity. For example, if you know there are 26.22 mi in a marathon and want to find how many kilometers that is, you could write the distance in miles and multiply by the conversion factor in kilometers per mile. The unit "mi" cancels because it appears both above and below the division line, leaving "km" as the only remaining unit.

$$26.22 \text{ mi} \times \frac{1 \text{ km}}{0.6214 \text{ mi}} = 42.20 \text{ km}$$

Starting quantity   Conversion factor   Equivalent quantity

The factor-label method gives the right answer only if the equation is set up so that the unwanted unit (or units) cancel. If the equation is set up in any other way, the units will not cancel and you will not get the right answer. Thus, if you selected the incorrect conversion factor (miles per kilometer) for the above problem, you would end up with an incorrect answer expressed in meaningless units:

$$\text{Incorrect} \quad 26.22 \text{ mi} \times \frac{0.6214 \text{ mi}}{1 \text{ km}} = 16.29 \frac{\text{mi}^2}{\text{km}} \quad \text{Incorrect}$$

The main drawback to using the factor-label method is that it is possible to get an answer without really understanding what you are doing. It is therefore best when solving a problem to first think through a rough estimate, or *ballpark estimate*, as a check on your work. If your ballpark estimate is not close to the final calculated solution, there is a misunderstanding somewhere and you should think the problem through again. If, for example, you came up with the answer 5.3 cm³ when calculating the volume of a human cell, you should realize that such an answer could not possibly be right. Cells are too tiny to be distinguished with the naked eye, but a volume of 5.3 cm³ is about the size

---

Factor-label method A problem-solving procedure in which equations are set up so that unwanted units cancel and only the desired units remain.

Conversion factor An expression of the numerical relationship between two units.

of a walnut. The Worked Examples 1.11, 1.12, and 1.13 at the end of this section show how to estimate the answers to simple unit-conversion problems.

The factor-label method and the use of ballpark estimates are techniques that will help you solve problems of many kinds, not just unit conversions. Problems sometimes seem complicated, but you can usually sort out the complications by analyzing the problem properly:

STEP 1: Identify the information given, including units.

STEP 2: Identify the information needed in the answer, including units.

STEP 3: Find the relationship(s) between the known information and unknown answer, and plan a series of steps, including conversion factors, for getting from one to the other.

STEP 4: Solve the problem.

BALLPARK CHECK Make a ballpark estimate at the beginning and check it against your final answer to be sure the value and the units of your calculated answer are reasonable.

Worked Example 1.9 Factor Labels: Unit Conversions

Write conversion factors for the following pairs of units (use Tables 1.7–1.9):

(a) Deciliters and milliliters

(b) Pounds and grams

ANALYSIS Start with the appropriate equivalency relationship and rearrange to form conversion factors.

SOLUTION

(a) Since 1 dL = 0.1 L and 1 mL = 0.001 L, then 1 dL = $(0.1 \text{ L})\left(\dfrac{1 \text{ mL}}{0.001 \text{ L}}\right)$ =

100 mL. The conversion factors are

$$\frac{1 \text{ dL}}{100 \text{ mL}} \quad \text{and} \quad \frac{100 \text{ mL}}{1 \text{ dL}}$$

(b) $\dfrac{1 \text{ lb}}{454 \text{ g}}$ and $\dfrac{454 \text{ g}}{1 \text{ lb}}$

Worked Example 1.10 Factor Labels: Unit Conversions

(a) Convert 0.75 lb to grams.

(b) Convert 0.50 qt to deciliters.

ANALYSIS Start with conversion factors and set up equations so that units cancel appropriately.

SOLUTION

(a) Select the conversion factor from Worked Example 1.9(b) so that the "lb" units cancel and "g" remains:

$$0.75 \text{ lb} \times \frac{454 \text{ g}}{1 \text{ lb}} = 340 \text{ g}$$

(b) In this, as in many problems, it is convenient to use more than one conversion factor. As long as the unwanted units cancel correctly, two or more conversion factors can be strung together in the same calculation. In this case, we can convert first between quarts and milliliters, and then between milliliters and deciliters:

$$0.50 \text{ qt} \times \frac{946.4 \text{ mL}}{1 \text{ qt}} \times \frac{1 \text{ dL}}{100 \text{ mL}} = 4.7 \text{ dL}$$

Worked Example 1.11 Factor Labels: Unit Conversions

A child is 21.5 inches long at birth. How long is this in centimeters?

ANALYSIS This problem calls for converting from inches to centimeters, so we will need to know how many centimeters are in an inch and how to use this information as a conversion factor.

BALLPARK ESTIMATE It takes about 2.5 cm to make 1 in., and so it should take two and a half times as many centimeters to make a distance equal to approximately 20 in., or about 20 in. × 2.5 = 50 cm.

SOLUTION

STEP 1: **Identify given information.**	Length = 21.5 in.
STEP 2: **Identify answer and units.**	Length = ?? cm
STEP 3: **Identify conversion factor.**	$1 \text{ in.} = 2.54 \text{ cm} \rightarrow \dfrac{2.54 \text{ cm}}{1 \text{ in.}}$
STEP 4: **Solve.** Multiply the known length (in inches) by the conversion factor so that units cancel, providing the answer (in centimeters).	$21.5 \text{ in.} \times \dfrac{2.54 \text{ cm}}{1 \text{ in.}} = 54.6 \text{ cm}$ (Rounded off from 54.61)

BALLPARK CHECK How does this value compare with the ballpark estimate we made at the beginning? Are the final units correct? 54.6 cm is close to our original estimate of 50 cm.

Worked Example 1.12 Factor Labels: Concentration to Mass

A patient requires an injection of 0.012 g of a pain killer available as a 15 mg/mL solution. How many milliliters of solution should be administered?

ANALYSIS Knowing the amount of pain killer in 1 mL allows us to use the concentration as a conversion factor to determine the volume of solution that would contain the desired amount.

BALLPARK ESTIMATE One milliliter contains 15 mg of the pain killer, or 0.015 g. Since only 0.012 g is needed, a little less than 1.0 mL should be administered.

▲ **How many milliliters should be injected?**

SOLUTION

STEP 1: **Identify known information.**	Dosage = 0.012 g Concentration = 15 mg/mL
STEP 2: **Identify answer and units.**	Volume to administer = ?? mL
STEP 3: **Identify conversion factors.** Two conversion factors are needed. First, g must be converted to mg. Once we have the mass in mg, we can calculate mL using the conversion factor of mL/mg.	$1 \text{ mg} = .001 \text{ g} \Rightarrow \dfrac{1 \text{ mg}}{0.001 \text{ g}}$ $15 \text{ mg/mL} \Rightarrow \dfrac{1 \text{ mL}}{15 \text{ mg}}$
STEP 4: **Solve.** Starting from the desired dosage, we use the conversion factors to cancel units, obtaining the final answer in mL.	$(0.012 \text{ g})\left(\dfrac{1 \text{ mg}}{0.001 \text{ g}}\right)\left(\dfrac{1 \text{ mL}}{15 \text{ mg}}\right) = 0.80 \text{ mL}$

BALLPARK CHECK Consistent with our initial estimate of a little less than 1 mL.

Worked Example **1.13** Factor Labels: Multiple Conversion Calculations

Administration of digitalis to control atrial fibrillation in heart patients must be carefully regulated because even a modest overdose can be fatal. To take differences between patients into account, dosages are sometimes prescribed in micrograms per kilogram of body weight (μg/kg). Thus, two people may differ greatly in weight, but both will receive the proper dosage. At a dosage of 20 μg/kg body weight, how many milligrams of digitalis should a 160 lb patient receive?

ANALYSIS Knowing the patient's body weight (in kg) and the recommended dosage (in μg/kg), we can calculate the appropriate amount of digitalis.

BALLPARK ESTIMATE Since a kilogram is roughly equal to 2 lb, a 160 lb patient has a mass of about 80 kg. At a dosage of 20 μg/kg, an 80 kg patient should receive 80 $\times$ 20 μg, or about 1600 μg of digitalis, or 1.6 mg.

SOLUTION

STEP 1: **Identify known information.**

STEP 2: **Identify answer and units.**

STEP 3: **Identify conversion factors.** Two conversions are needed. First, convert the patient's weight in pounds to weight in kg. The correct dose can then be determined based on μg digitalis/kg of body weight. Finally, the dosage in μg is converted to mg.

STEP 4: **Solve.** Use the known information and the conversion factors so that units cancel, obtaining the answer in mg.

| |
| Patient weight $=$ 160 lb |
| Prescribed dosage $=$ 20 μg digitalis/kg body weight |
| Delivered dosage $=$?? mg digitalis |

$$1 \text{ kg} = 2.205 \text{ lb} \rightarrow \frac{1 \text{ kg}}{2.205 \text{ lb}}$$

$$1 \text{ mg} = (0.001 \text{ g})\left(\frac{1 \mu\text{g}}{10^{-6} \text{ g}}\right) = 1000 \ \mu\text{g}$$

$$160 \text{ lb} \times \frac{1 \text{ kg}}{2.205 \text{ lb}} \times \frac{20 \ \mu\text{g digitalis}}{1 \text{ kg}} \times \frac{1 \text{ mg}}{1000 \ \mu\text{g}}$$

$$= 1.5 \text{ mg digitalis (Rounded off)}$$

BALLPARK CHECK Close to our estimate of 1.6 mg.

PROBLEM 1.18
Write appropriate conversion factors and carry out the following conversions:
(a) 16.0 oz $=$? g **(b)** 2500 mL $=$? L **(c)** 99.0 L $=$? qt

PROBLEM 1.19
Convert 0.840 qt to milliliters in a single calculation using more than one conversion factor.

PROBLEM 1.20
One international nautical mile is defined as exactly 6076.1155 ft, and a speed of 1 knot is defined as one international nautical mile per hour. What is the speed in meters per second of a boat traveling at a speed of 14.3 knots? (Hint: what conversion factor is needed to convert from feet to meters? From hours to seconds?)

PROBLEM 1.21
Calculate the dosage in milligrams per kilogram body weight for a 135 lb adult who takes two aspirin tablets containing 0.324 g of aspirin each. Calculate the dosage for a 40 lb child who also takes two aspirin tablets.

1.13 Temperature, Heat, and Energy

All chemical reactions are accompanied by a change in **energy**, which is defined in scientific terms as *the capacity to do work or supply heat* (Figure 1.9). Detailed discussion of the various kinds of energy will be included in Chapter 7, but for now we will look at the various units used to describe energy and heat, and how heat energy can be gained or lost by matter.

Energy The capacity to do work or supply heat.

    Temperature, the measure of the amount of heat energy in an object, is commonly reported either in Fahrenheit (°F) or Celsius (°C) units. The SI unit for reporting temperature, however, is the *kelvin* (K). (Note that we say only "kelvin," not "degrees kelvin".)
    The kelvin and the celsius degree are the same size—both are 1/100 of the interval between the freezing point of water and the boiling point of water at atmospheric pressure.

Temperature The measure of the amount of heat energy in an object.

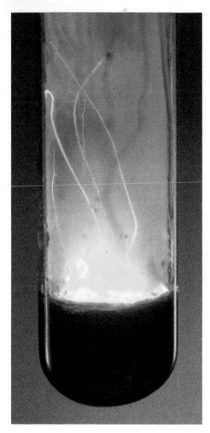

▲ **Figure 1.9**
The reaction of aluminum with bromine releases energy in the form of heat.
When the reaction is complete, the products undergo no further change.

Thus, a change in temperature of 1 °C is equal to a change of 1 K. The only difference between the Kelvin and Celsius temperature scales is that they have different zero points. The Celsius scale assigns a value of 0 °C to the freezing point of water, but the Kelvin scale assigns a value of 0 K to the coldest possible temperature, sometimes called *absolute zero*, which is equal to −273.15 °C. Thus, 0 K = −273.15 °C, and +273.15 K = 0 °C. For example, a warm spring day with a temperature of 25 °C has a Kelvin temperature of 298 K (for most purposes, rounding off to 273 is sufficient):

$$\text{Temperature in K} = \text{Temperature in °C} + 273.15$$
$$\text{Temperature in °C} = \text{Temperature in K} - 273.15$$

For practical applications in medicine and clinical chemistry, the Fahrenheit and Celsius scales are used almost exclusively. The Fahrenheit scale defines the freezing point of water as 32 °F and the boiling point of water as 212 °F, whereas 0 °C and 100 °C are the freezing and boiling points of water on the Celsius scale. Thus, it takes 180 Fahrenheit degrees to cover the same range encompassed by only 100 celsius degrees, and a Celsius degree is therefore exactly 180/100 = 9/5 = 1.8 times as large as a Fahrenheit degree. In other words, a change in temperature of 1.0 °C is equal to a change of 1.8 °F. Figure 1.10 gives a comparison of all three scales.

Converting between the Fahrenheit and Celsius scales is similar to converting between different units of length or volume, but is a bit more complex because two corrections need to be made—one to adjust for the difference in degree size and one to adjust for the different zero points. The degree-size correction is made by using the relationship 1 °C = (9/5) °F and 1 °F = (5/9) °C. The zero-point correction is made by remembering that the freezing point is higher by 32 on the Fahrenheit scale than on the Celsius scale. These corrections are incorporated into the following formulas, which show the conversion methods:

Celsius to Fahrenheit: $\quad °F = \left(\dfrac{9\ °F}{5\ °C} \times °C \right) + 32\ °F$

Fahrenheit to Celsius: $\quad °C = \dfrac{5\ °C}{9\ °F} \times (°F - 32\ °F)$

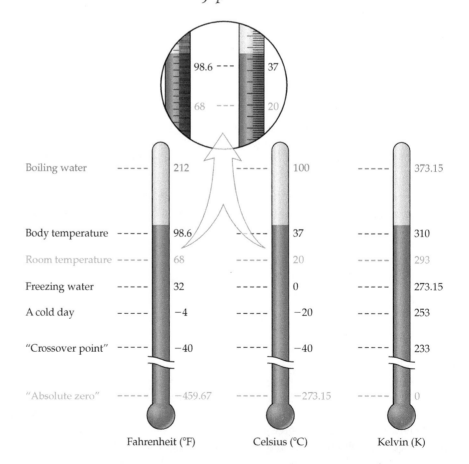

▶ **Figure 1.10**
A comparison of the Fahrenheit, Celsius, and Kelvin temperature scales.
One Fahrenheit degree is 5/9 the size of a kelvin or a celsius degree.

CHEMISTRY IN ACTION

Temperature–Sensitive Materials

Wouldn't it be nice to be able to tell if the baby's formula bottle is too hot without touching it? Or to easily determine if the package of chicken you are buying for dinner has been stored appropriately? Temperature-sensitive materials are already being used in these and other applications. Although these materials have been used previously in many popular "fads," like mood rings or clothes that changed color at different temperatures, more practical applications are emerging.

Most current applications use substances known as thermochromic materials that change color as their temperature increases, and they change from the liquid phase to a semicrystalline ordered state. These "liquid crystals" can be incorporated into plastics or paints and can be used to monitor the temperature of the products or packages in which they are incorporated. For example, some meat packaging now includes a temperature strip that darkens when the meat is stored above a certain temperature, which makes the meat unsafe to eat. Some beverage containers turn color to indicate when the beverage has reached its optimal temperature for consumption. Hospitals and other medical facilities now routinely use strips that, when

placed under the tongue or applied to the forehead, change color to indicate the patient's body temperature. In the future, we may even see road signs that change color to warn us of dangerous icy road conditions.

See Chemistry in Action Problems 1.98 and 1.99 at the end of the chapter.

Energy is represented in SI units by the unit *joule* (J; pronounced "jool"), but the metric unit *calorie* (cal) is still widely used in medicine. In most of this text we will present energy values in both units of calories and joules. One calorie is the amount of heat necessary to raise the temperature of 1 g of water by 1 °C. A *kilocalorie* (kcal), often called a *large calorie (Cal)* or *food calorie* by nutritionists, equals 1000 cal:

$$1000 \text{ cal} = 1 \text{ kcal} \qquad 1000 \text{ J} = 1 \text{ kJ}$$
$$1 \text{ cal} = 4.184 \text{ J} \qquad 1 \text{ kcal} = 4.184 \text{ kJ}$$

Not all substances have their temperatures raised to the same extent when equal amounts of heat energy are added. One calorie raises the temperature of 1 g of water by 1 °C but raises the temperature of 1 g of iron by 10 °C. The amount of heat needed to raise the temperature of 1 g of a substance by 1 °C is called the **specific heat** of the substance. It is measured in units of $\text{cal}/(\text{g} \cdot {}^\circ\text{C})$.

$$\text{Specific heat} = \frac{\text{calories}}{\text{grams} \times {}^\circ\text{C}}$$

Specific heats vary greatly from one substance to another, as shown in Table 1.10. The specific heat of water, $1.00 \text{ cal}/(\text{g} \cdot {}^\circ\text{C})$ (or $4.184 \text{ J/g} \, {}^\circ\text{C}$) is higher than that of most other substances, which means that a large transfer of heat is required to change the temperature of a given amount of water by a given number of degrees. One consequence is that the human body, which is about 60% water, is able to withstand changing outside conditions.

Knowing the mass and specific heat of a substance makes it possible to calculate how much heat must be added or removed to accomplish a given temperature change, as shown in Worked Example 1.15.

$$\text{Heat (cal)} = \text{Mass } (\cancel{g}) \times \text{Temperature change } (\cancel{{}^\circ C}) \times \text{Specific heat}\left(\frac{\text{cal}}{\cancel{g} \cdot \cancel{{}^\circ C}}\right)$$

Specific heat The amount of heat that will raise the temperature of 1 g of a substance by 1 °C.

TABLE **1.10** Specific Heats of Some Common Substances		
Substance	**Specific Heat** [cal/g °C];	[J/g °C]
Ethanol	0.59;	2.5
Gold	0.031;	0.13
Iron	0.106;	0.444
Mercury	0.033;	0.14
Sodium	0.293;	1.23
Water	1.00;	4.18

Worked Example **1.14** Temperature Conversions: Fahrenheit to Celsius

A body temperature above 107 °F can be fatal. What does 107 °F correspond to on the Celsius scale?

ANALYSIS Using the temperature (in °F) and the appropriate temperature conversion equation we can convert from the Fahrenheit scale to the Celsius scale.

BALLPARK ESTIMATE Note in Figure 1.10 that normal body temperature is 98.6 °F, or 37 °C. A temperature of 107 °F is approximately 8 °F above normal; since 1 °C is nearly 2 °F, then 8 °F is about 4 °C. Thus, the 107 °F body temperature is 41 °C.

SOLUTION

STEP 1: **Identify known information.**

STEP 2: **Identify answer and units.**

STEP 3: **Identify conversion factors.** We can convert from °F to °C using this equation.

STEP 4: **Solve.** Substitute the known temperature (in °F) into the equation.

$$\text{Temperature} = 107 \,^\circ\text{F}$$

$$\text{Temperature} = ?? \,^\circ\text{C}$$

$$^\circ\text{C} = \frac{5 \,^\circ\text{C}}{9 \,^\circ\text{F}} \times (^\circ\text{F} - 32 \,^\circ\text{F})$$

$$^\circ\text{C} = \frac{5 \,^\circ\text{C}}{9 \,^\circ\text{F}} \times (107 \,^\circ\text{F} - 32 \,^\circ\text{F}) = 42 \,^\circ\text{C}^*$$

(Rounded off from 41.666 667 °C)

BALLPARK CHECK Close to our estimate of 41 °C.

*It is worth noting that the 5/9 conversion factor in the equation is an exact conversion, and so does not impact the number of significant figures in the final answer.

Worked Example **1.15** Specific Heat: Mass, Temperature, and Energy

Taking a bath might use about 95 kg of water. How much energy (in calories and Joules) is needed to heat the water from a cold 15 °C to a warm 40 °C?

ANALYSIS From the amount of water being heated (95 kg) and the amount of the temperature change (40 °C − 15 °C = 25 °C), the total amount of energy needed can be calculated by using specific heat $[1.00 \text{ cal}/(\text{g} \cdot ^\circ\text{C})]$ as a conversion factor.

BALLPARK ESTIMATE The water is being heated 25 °C (from 15 °C to 40 °C), and it therefore takes 25 cal to heat each gram. The tub contains nearly 100,000 g (95 kg is 95,000 g), and so it takes about 25 × 100,000 cal, or 2,500,000 cal, to heat all the water in the tub.

SOLUTION

STEP 1: **Identify known information.**

STEP 2: **Identify answer and units.**

STEP 3: **Identify conversion factors.** The amount of energy (in cal) can be calculated using the specific heat of water (cal/g · °C), and will depend on both the mass of water (in g) to be heated and the total temperature change (in °C). In order for the units in specific heat to cancel correctly, the mass of water must first be converted from kg to g.

STEP 4: **Solve.** Starting with the known information, use the conversion factors to cancel unwanted units.

$$\text{Mass of water} = 95 \text{ kg}$$

$$\text{Temperature change} = 40 \,^\circ\text{C} - 15 \,^\circ\text{C} = 25 \,^\circ\text{C}$$

$$\text{Heat} = ?? \text{ cal}$$

$$\text{Specific heat} = \frac{1.0 \text{ cal}}{\text{g} \cdot ^\circ\text{C}}$$

$$1 \text{ kg} = 1000 \text{ g} \rightarrow \frac{1000 \text{ g}}{1 \text{ kg}}$$

$$95 \cancel{\text{ kg}} \times \frac{1000 \cancel{\text{ g}}}{\cancel{\text{kg}}} \times \frac{1.00 \text{ cal}}{\cancel{\text{g}} \cdot \cancel{^\circ\text{C}}} \times 25 \cancel{^\circ\text{C}} = 2,400,000 \text{ cal}$$

$$= 2.4 \times 10^6 \text{ cal (or } 1.0 \times 10^7 \text{ J)}$$

BALLPARK CHECK Close to our estimate of 2.5×10^6 cal.

PROBLEM 1.22
The highest land temperature ever recorded was 136 °F in Al Aziziyah, Libya, on
September 13, 1922. What is this temperature on the kelvin scale?

PROBLEM 1.23
The patient in the photo in the Chemistry in Action on page 31 has a temperature of
39 °C. What is the body temperature of the patient in °F?

PROBLEM 1.24
Assuming that Coca-Cola has the same specific heat as water, how much energy in
calories is removed when 350 g of Coca-Cola (about the contents of one 12 oz can) is
cooled from room temperature (25 °C) to refrigerator temperature (3 °C)?

PROBLEM 1.25
What is the specific heat of aluminum if it takes 161 cal (674 J) to raise the temperature of a 75 g aluminum bar by 10.0 °C?

1.14 Density and Specific Gravity

One further physical quantity that we will take up in this chapter is **density**, which
relates the mass of an object to its volume. Density is usually expressed in units of
grams per cubic centimeter (g/cm^3) for solids and grams per milliliter (g/mL) for liquids. Thus, if we know the density of a substance, we know both the mass of a given
volume and the volume of a given mass. The densities of some common materials are
listed in Table 1.11.

Density The physical property that
relates the mass of an object to its
volume; mass per unit volume.

$$\text{Density} = \frac{\text{Mass (g)}}{\text{Volume (mL or } cm^3)}$$

Although most substances contract when cooled and expand when heated, water behaves differently. Water contracts when cooled from 100 °C to 3.98 °C, but
below this temperature it begins to *expand* again. The density of liquid water is
at its maximum of 1.0000 g/mL at 3.98 °C but decreases to 0.999 87 g/mL at 0 °C.
When freezing occurs, the density drops still further to a value of 0.917 g/cm^3 for
ice at 0 °C. Since a less dense substance will float on top of a more dense fluid, ice
and any other substance with a density less than that of water will float in water.
Conversely, any substance with a density greater than that of water will sink in
water.

Knowing the density of a liquid is useful because it is often easier to measure a
liquid's volume rather than its mass. Suppose, for example, that you need 1.50 g of

▲ **The Galileo thermometer
contains several weighted
bulbs which rise or fall as the
density of the liquid changes
with temperature.**

TABLE **1.11** Densities of Some Common Materials at 25 °C			
Substance	**Density***	**Substance**	**Density***
Gases		Solids	
Helium	0.000 194	Ice (0 °C)	0.917
Air	0.001 185	Gold	19.3
		Human fat	0.94
Liquids		Cork	0.22–0.26
Water (3.98 °C)	1.0000	Table sugar	1.59
Urine	1.003–1.030	Balsa wood	0.12
Blood plasma	1.027	Earth	5.54

*Densities are in g/cm^3 for solids and g/mL for liquids and gases.

Specific gravity The density of a substance divided by the density of water at the same temperature.

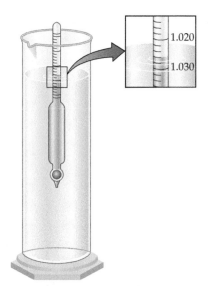

▲ **Figure 1.11**

A hydrometer for measuring specific gravity.

The instrument has a weighted bulb at the end of a calibrated glass tube. The depth to which the hydrometer sinks in a liquid indicates the liquid's specific gravity.

ethanol. Rather than use a dropper to weigh out exactly the right amount, it would be much easier to look up the density of ethanol (0.7893 g/mL at 20 °C) and measure the correct volume (1.90 mL) with a syringe or graduated cylinder. Thus, density acts as a conversion factor between mass (g) and volume (mL).

$$1.50 \text{ g ethanol} \times \frac{1 \text{ mL ethanol}}{0.7893 \text{ g ethanol}} = 1.90 \text{ mL ethanol}$$

For many purposes, ranging from winemaking to medicine, it is more convenient to use *specific gravity* than density. The **specific gravity** (sp gr) of a substance (usually a liquid) is simply the density of the substance divided by the density of water at the same temperature. Because all units cancel, specific gravity is unitless:

$$\text{Specific gravity} = \frac{\text{Density of substance (g/mL)}}{\text{Density of water at the same temperature (g/mL)}}$$

At typical temperatures, the density of water is very close to 1 g/mL. Thus, the specific gravity of a substance is numerically equal to its density and is used in the same way.

The specific gravity of a liquid can be measured using an instrument called a *hydrometer*, which consists of a weighted bulb on the end of a calibrated glass tube, as shown in Figure 1.11. The depth to which the hydrometer sinks when placed in a fluid indicates the fluid's specific gravity: the lower the bulb sinks, the lower the specific gravity of the fluid.

In medicine, a hydrometer called a *urinometer* is used to indicate the amount of solids dissolved in urine. Although the specific gravity of normal urine is about 1.003–1.030, conditions such as diabetes mellitus or a high fever cause an abnormally high urine specific gravity, indicating either excessive elimination of solids or decreased elimination of water. Abnormally low specific gravity is found in individuals using diuretics—drugs that increase water elimination.

Worked Example 1.16 Density: Mass-to-Volume Conversion

What volume of isopropyl alcohol (rubbing alcohol) would you use if you needed 25.0 g? The density of isopropyl alcohol is 0.7855 g/mL at 20 °C.

ANALYSIS The known information is the mass of isopropyl alcohol needed (25.0 g). The density (0.7855 g/mL) acts as a conversion factor between mass and the unknown volume of isopropyl alcohol.

BALLPARK ESTIMATE Because 1 mL of isopropyl alcohol contains only 0.7885 g of the alcohol, obtaining 1 g of alcohol would require almost 20% more than 1 mL, or about 1.2 mL. Therefore, a volume of about 25 × 1.2 mL = 30 mL is needed to obtain 25 g of alcohol.

SOLUTION

STEP 1: **Identify known information.**

STEP 2: **Identify answer and units.**

STEP 3: **Identify conversion factors.** Starting with the mass of isopropyl alcohol (in g), the corresponding volume (in mL) can be calculated using density (g/mL) as the conversion factor.

STEP 4: **Solve.** Starting with the known information, set up the equation with conversion factors so that unwanted units cancel.

BALLPARK CHECK Our estimate was 30 mL.

Mass of rubbing alcohol = 25.0 g
Density of rubbing alcohol = 0.7855 g/mL

Volume of rubbing alcohol = ?? mL

Density = g/mL → 1/density = mL/g

$$25.0 \text{ g alcohol} \times \frac{1 \text{ mL alcohol}}{0.7855 \text{ g alcohol}} = 31.8 \text{ mL alcohol}$$

CHEMISTRY IN ACTION

A Measurement Example: Obesity and Body Fat

According to the U.S. Centers for Disease Control and Prevention, the U.S. population is suffering from a fat epidemic. Over the last 25 years, the percentage of adults 20 years or older identified as obese increased from 15% in the late 1970s to nearly 33% in 2008. Even children and adolescents are gaining too much weight: The number of overweight children in all age groups increased by nearly a factor of 3, with the biggest increase seen among teenagers (from 5% to 18.1%). Of particular concern is the fact that 80% of children who were overweight as teenagers were identified as obese at age 25. Obesity increases the risk for many adverse health conditions, including type 2 diabetes and heart disease.

How do we define obesity, however, and how is it measured? Obesity is defined by reference to *body mass index* (BMI), which is equal to a person's mass in kilograms divided by the square of his or her height in meters. BMI can also be calculated by dividing a person's weight in pounds by the square of her or his height in inches multiplied by 703. For instance, someone 5 ft 7 in. (67 inches; 1.70 m) tall weighing 147 lb (66.7 kg) has a BMI of 23:

$$\text{BMI} = \frac{\text{weight (kg)}}{[\text{height (m)}]^2}, \quad \text{or} \quad \frac{\text{weight (lb)}}{[\text{height (in.)}]^2} \times 703$$

A BMI of 25 or above is considered overweight, and a BMI of 30 or above is obese. By these standards, approximately 61% of the U.S. population is overweight. Health professionals are concerned by the rapid rise in obesity in the United States because of the link between BMI and health problems. Many reports have documented the correlation between health and BMI, including a recent study on more than 1 million adults. The

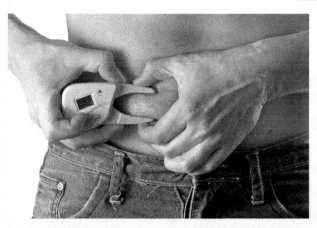

▲ **A person's percentage body fat can be estimated by measuring the thickness of the fat layer under the skin.**

lowest death risk from any cause, including cancer and heart disease, is associated with a BMI between 22 and 24. Risk increases steadily as BMI increases, more than doubling for a BMI above 29.

An individual's percentage of body fat is most easily measured by the skinfold-thickness method. The skin at several locations on the arm, shoulder, and waist is pinched, and the thickness of the fat layer beneath the skin is measured with calipers. Comparing the measured results to those in a standard table gives an estimation of percentage body fat. As an alternative to skinfold measurement, a more accurate assessment of body fat can be made by underwater immersion. The person's underwater body weight is less than her or his weight on land because water gives the body buoyancy. The higher the percentage of body fat, the more buoyant the person and the greater the difference between land weight and underwater body weight. Checking the observed buoyancy on a standard table then gives an estimation of body fat.

See Chemistry in Action Problems 1.100 and 1.101 at the end of the chapter.

Weight (lb)

Height	110	115	120	125	130	135	140	145	150	155	160	165	170	175	180	185	190	195	200
5'0"	21	22	23	24	25	26	27	28	29	30	31	32	33	34	35	36	37	38	39
5'2"	20	21	22	23	24	25	26	27	27	28	29	30	31	32	33	34	35	36	37
5'4"	19	20	21	21	22	23	24	25	26	27	27	28	29	30	31	32	33	33	34
5'6"	18	19	19	20	21	22	23	23	24	25	26	27	27	28	29	30	31	31	32
5'8"	17	17	18	19	20	21	21	22	23	24	24	25	26	27	27	28	29	30	30
5'10"	16	17	17	18	19	19	20	21	22	22	23	24	24	25	26	27	27	28	29
6'0"	15	16	16	17	18	18	19	20	20	21	22	22	23	24	24	25	26	26	27
6'2"	14	15	15	16	17	17	18	19	19	20	21	21	22	22	23	24	24	25	26
6'4"	13	14	15	15	16	16	17	18	18	19	19	20	21	21	22	23	23	24	24

Body Mass Index (numbers in boxes)

▲ The specific gravity of urine, measured by a urinometer, is used to diagnose conditions such as diabetes.

PROBLEM 1.26

A sample of pumice, a porous volcanic rock, weighs 17.4 grams and has a volume of 27.3 cm³. If this sample is placed in a container of water, will it sink or will it float? Explain.

PROBLEM 1.27

Chloroform, once used as an anesthetic agent, has a density of 1.474 g/mL. What volume would you use if you needed 12.37 g?

PROBLEM 1.28

The sulfuric acid solution in an automobile battery typically has a specific gravity of about 1.27. Is battery acid more dense or less dense than pure water?

SUMMARY: REVISITING THE CHAPTER GOALS

1. What is matter and how is it classified? *Matter* is anything that has mass and occupies volume—that is, anything physically real. Matter can be classified by its physical state as *solid, liquid,* or *gas.* A solid has a definite volume and shape, a liquid has a definite volume but indefinite shape, and a gas has neither a definite volume nor a definite shape. Matter can also be classified by composition as being either *pure* or a *mixture.* Every pure substance is either an *element* or a *chemical compound.* Elements are fundamental substances that cannot be chemically changed into anything simpler. A chemical compound, by contrast, can be broken down by chemical change into simpler substances. Mixtures are composed of two or more pure substances and can be separated into component parts by physical means (*see Problems 40–45, 96, 103*).

2. How are chemical elements represented? Elements are represented by one- or two-letter symbols, such as H for hydrogen, Ca for calcium, Al for aluminum, and so on. Most symbols are the first one or two letters of the element name, but some symbols are derived from Latin names—Na (sodium), for example. All the known elements are commonly organized into a form called the *periodic table.* Most elements are *metals,* 18 are *nonmetals,* and 6 are *metalloids* (*see Problems 29–31, 48–57, 96, 102, 103*).

3. What kinds of properties does matter have? A *property* is any characteristic that can be used to describe or identify something: *physical* properties can be seen or measured without changing the chemical identity of the substance (that is, color, melting point), while *chemical* properties can only be seen or measured when the substance undergoes a *chemical change,* such as a chemical reaction (*see Problems 37–39, 42–44, 47, 97, 102, 103*).

4. What units are used to measure properties, and how can a quantity be converted from one unit to another? A property that can be measured is called a *physical quantity* and is described by both a number and a label, or *unit.* The preferred units are either those of the International System of Units (*SI units*) or the *metric system.* Mass, the amount of matter an object contains, is measured in *kilograms* (kg) or *grams* (g). Length is measured in *meters* (m). Volume is measured in *cubic meters* (m³) in the SI system and in *liters* (L) or *milliliters* (mL) in the metric system. Temperature is measured in *kelvins* (K) in the SI system and in *degrees celsius* (°C) in the metric system. A measurement in one unit can be converted to another unit by multiplying by a *conversion factor* that expresses the exact relationship between the units (*see Problems 58–63, 72–82, 100, 101, 104, 105, 107–109, 121*).

5. How good are the reported measurements? When measuring physical quantities or using them in calculations, it is important to indicate the exactness of the measurement by *rounding off* the final answer using the correct number of *significant figures.* All but one of the significant figures in a number is known with certainty; the final digit is estimated to ±1 (*see Problems 32–35, 64–71, 104, 112*).

6. How are large and small numbers best represented? Measurements of small and large quantities are usually written in *scientific notation* as the product of a number between 1 and 10, times a power of 10. Numbers greater than 10 have a positive exponent, and numbers less than 1 have a negative exponent. For example, $3562 = 3.562 \times 10^3$, and $0.003\,91 = 3.91 \times 10^{-3}$ (*see Problems 64–71, 75, 82, 108*).

7. What techniques are used to solve problems? Problems are best solved by applying the *factor-label method,* in which units can be multiplied and divided just as numbers can. The idea is to set up an equation so that all unwanted units cancel, leaving only the desired units. Usually it is best to start by identifying the known and needed information, then decide how to convert the known information to the answer, and finally check to make sure the answer is reasonable both chemically and physically (*see Problems 76–82, 101, 106, 107, 109, 110–112, 114, 115, 118–123*).

8. What are temperature, specific heat, density, and specific gravity? *Temperature* is a measure of how hot or cold an object is. The *specific heat* of a substance is the amount of heat necessary to raise the temperature of 1 g of the substance by 1 °C (1 cal/g °C or 4.184 J/g °C). Water has an unusually high specific heat, which helps our bodies to maintain an even temperature. *Density,* the physical property that relates mass to volume, is expressed in units of grams per milliliter (g/mL) for a liquid or grams per cubic centimeter (g/cm³) for a solid. The *specific gravity* of a liquid is the density of the liquid divided by the density of water at the same temperature. Because the density of water is approximately 1 g/mL, specific gravity and density have the same numerical value (*see Problems 32, 36, 42, 43, 83–89, 90–95, 98, 99, 106, 109, 113, 118–120, 122, 123*).

KEY WORDS

Change of state, *p. 6*

Chemical change, *p. 4*

Chemical compound, *p. 7*

Chemical formula, *p. 10*

Chemical reaction, *p. 7*

Chemistry, *p. 4*

Conversion factor, *p. 26*

Density, *p. 33*

Element, *p. 6*

Energy, *p. 29*

Factor-label method, *p. 26*

Gas, *p. 5*

Heterogeneous mixture, *p. 6*

Homogeneous mixture, *p. 6*

Liquid, *p. 5*

Mass, *p. 17*

Matter, *p. 4*

Metal, *p. 11*

Metalloid, *p. 11*

Mixture, *p. 6*

Nonmetal, *p. 11*

Periodic table, *p. 11*

Physical change, *p. 4*

Physical quantity, *p. 14*

Product, *p. 7*

Property, *p. 4*

Pure substance, *p. 6*

Reactant, *p. 7*

Rounding off, *p. 24*

Scientific Method, *p. 4*

Scientific notation, *p. 21*

SI units, *p. 15*

Significant figures, *p. 20*

Solid, *p. 5*

Specific gravity, *p. 34*

Specific heat, *p. 31*

State of matter, *p. 6*

Temperature, *p. 29*

Unit, *p. 14*

Weight, *p. 17*

UNDERSTANDING KEY CONCEPTS

The problems in this section are intended as a bridge between the Chapter Summary and the Additional Problems that follow. Primarily visual in nature, they are designed to help you test your grasp of the chapter's most important principles before attempting to solve quantitative problems. Answers to all Key Concept problems are at the end of the book following the appendixes.

1.29   The six elements in blue at the far right of the periodic table are gases at room temperature. The red elements in the middle of the table are the so-called coinage metals. Identify each of these elements using the periodic table inside the front cover of this book.

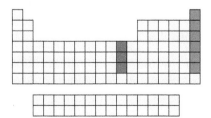

1.30   Identify the three elements indicated on the following periodic table and tell which is a metal, which is a nonmetal, and which is a metalloid.

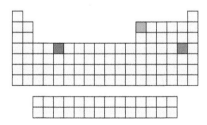

1.31 The radioactive element indicated on the following periodic table is used in smoke detectors. Identify it, and tell whether it is a metal, a nonmetal, or a metalloid.

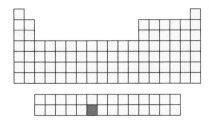

1.32 **(a)** What is the specific gravity of the following solution?

(b) How many significant figures does your answer have?

(c) Is the solution more dense or less dense than water?

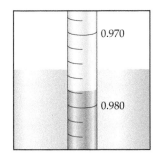

1.33 Assume that you have two graduated cylinders, one with a capacity of 5 mL (a) and the other with a capacity of 50 mL (b). Draw a line in each showing how much liquid you would add if you needed to measure 2.64 mL of water. Which cylinder do you think is more precise? Explain.

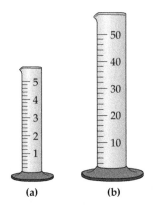

1.34 State the length of the pencil depicted in the accompanying figure in both inches and centimeters using appropriate numbers of significant figures.

1.35 Assume that you are delivering a solution sample from a pipette. Figures (a) and (b) show the volume level before and after dispensing the sample, respectively. State the liquid level (in mL) before and after dispensing the sample, and calculate the volume of the sample.

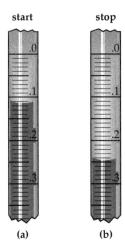

1.36 Assume that identical hydrometers are placed in ethanol (sp gr 0.7893) and in chloroform (sp gr 1.4832). In which liquid will the hydrometer float higher? Explain.

ADDITIONAL PROBLEMS

These exercises are divided into sections by topic. Each section begins with review and conceptual questions, followed by numerical problems of varying levels of difficulty. Many of the problems dealing with more difficult concepts or skills are presented in pairs, with each even-numbered problem followed by an odd-numbered one requiring similar skills. The final section consists of unpaired General Questions and Problems that draw on various parts of the chapter and, in future chapters, may even require the use of concepts from previous chapters. Answers to all even-numbered problems are given at the end of the book following the appendixes.

CHEMISTRY AND THE PROPERTIES OF MATTER

1.37 What is the difference between a physical change and a chemical change?

1.38 Which of the following is a physical change and which is a chemical change?

(a) Boiling water

(b) Decomposing water by passing an electric current through it

(c) Exploding of potassium metal when placed in water

(d) Breaking of glass

1.39 Which of the following is a physical change and which is a chemical change?

(a) Making lemonade (lemons + water + sugar)

(b) Frying eggs

(c) Burning a candle

(d) Whipping cream

(e) Leaves changing color

STATES AND CLASSIFICATION OF MATTER

1.40 Name and describe the three states of matter.

1.41 Name two changes of state, and describe what causes each to occur.

1.42 Sulfur dioxide is a compound produced when sulfur burns in air. It has a melting point of $-72.7\,°C$ and a boiling point of $-10\,°C$. In what state does it exist at room temperature (298 K)? (refer to Figure 1.10).

1.43 Butane (C_4H_8) is an easily compressible gas used in cigarette lighters. It has a melting point of $-138.4\,°C$ and a boiling point of $-0.5\,°C$. Would you expect a butane lighter to work in winter when the temperature outdoors is 25 °F? Why or why not? (refer to Figure 1.10).

1.44 Classify each of the following as a mixture or a pure substance:

(a) Pea soup   (b) Seawater

(c) The contents of a propane tank

(d) Urine   (e) Lead

(f) A multivitamin tablet

1.45 Which of these terms, (i) mixture, (ii) solid, (iii) liquid, (iv) gas, (v) chemical element, (vi) chemical compound, applies to the following substances at room temperature?

(a) Gasoline   (b) Iodine

(c) Water   (d) Air

(e) Blood   (f) Sodium bicarbonate

(g) Gaseous ammonia   (h) Silicon

1.46 Hydrogen peroxide, often used in solutions to cleanse cuts and scrapes, breaks down to yield water and oxygen:

$$\text{Hydrogen peroxide} \longrightarrow \text{Water} + \text{Oxygen}$$

(a) Identify the reactants and products.

(b) Which of the substances are chemical compounds, and which are elements?

1.47 When sodium metal is placed in water, the following change occurs:

$$\text{Sodium} + \text{Water} \longrightarrow \text{Hydrogen} + \text{Sodium hydroxide}$$

(a) Identify the reactants and products.

(b) Which of the substances are elements, and which are chemical compounds?

ELEMENTS AND THEIR SYMBOLS

1.48 Describe the general properties of metals, nonmetals, and metalloids.

1.49 What is the most abundant element in the earth's crust? In the human body? List the name and symbol for each.

1.50 What are the symbols for the following elements?

(a) Gadolinium (used in color TV screens)

(b) Germanium (used in semiconductors)

(c) Technetium (used in biomedical imaging)

(d) Arsenic (used in pesticides)

(e) Cadmium (used in rechargeable batteries)

1.51 Supply the missing names or symbols for the elements in the spaces provided:

(a) N _____   (b) K _____

(c) Cl _____   (d) _____ Calcium

(e) _____ Phosphorus (f) _____ Manganese

1.52 Correct the following statements.

(a) The symbol for bromine is BR.

(b) The symbol for manganese is Mg.

(c) The symbol for carbon is Ca.

(d) The symbol for potassium is Po.

1.53 Correct the following statements.

(a) Carbon dioxide has the formula CO2.

(b) Carbon dioxide has the formula Co_2.

(c) Table salt, NaCl, is composed of nitrogen and chlorine.

1.54 The amino acid glycine has the formula $C_2H_5NO_2$. Which elements are present in glycine? What is the total number of atoms represented by the formula?

1.55 Glucose, a form of sugar, has the formula $C_6H_{12}O_6$. Which elements are included in this compound, and how many atoms of each are present?

1.56 Write the formula for ibuprofen: 13 carbons, 18 hydrogens, and 2 oxygens.

1.57 Given the physical properties of the following elements classify each one as a metal, nonmetal, or metalloid:

(a) a hard, shiny, very dense solid that conducts electricity

(b) a brittle, gray solid that conducts electricity poorly

(c) a brown, crystalline solid that does not conduct electricity

(d) a colorless, odorless gas

PHYSICAL QUANTITIES: DEFINITIONS AND UNITS

1.58 What is the difference between a physical quantity and a number?

1.59 What are the units used in the SI system to measure mass, volume, length, and temperature? In the metric system?

1.60 Give the full name of the following units:

(a) cc   (b) dm   (c) mm

(d) nL   (e) mg   (f) m^3

1.61 Write the symbol for the following units:

(a) nanogram   (b) centimeter

(c) microliter   (d) micrometer

(e) milligram

1.62 How many picograms are in 1 mg? In 35 ng?

1.63 How many microliters are in 1 L? In 20 mL?

SCIENTIFIC NOTATION AND SIGNIFICANT FIGURES

1.64 Express the following numbers in scientific notation with the correct number of significant figures:

(a) 9457   (b) 0.000 07

(c) 20,000,000,000 (four significant figures)

(d) 0.012 345   (e) 652.38

1.65 Convert the following numbers from scientific notation to standard notation:

(a) 5.28×10^3 (b) 8.205×10^{-2}

(c) 1.84×10^{-5} (d) 6.37×10^4

1.66 How many significant figures does each of the following numbers have?

(a) 237,401   (b) 0.300   (c) 3.01

(d) 244.4   (e) 50,000   (f) 660

1.67 How many significant figures are there in each of the following quantities?

(a) Distance from New York City to Wellington, New Zealand, 14,397 km

(b) Average body temperature of a crocodile, 25.6 °C

(c) Melting point of gold, 1064 °C

(d) Diameter of an influenza virus, 0.000 01 mm

(e) Radius of a phosphorus atom, 0.110 nm

1.68 The diameter of the earth at the equator is 7926.381 mi.

(a) Round off the earth's diameter to four significant figures, to two significant figures, and to six significant figures.

(b) Express the earth's diameter in scientific notation.

1.69 Round off each of the numbers in Problem 1.67 to two significant figures, and express them in scientific notation.

1.70 Carry out the following calculations, express each answer to the correct number of significant figures, and include units in the answers.

(a) 9.02 g + 3.1 g   (b) 88.80 cm + 7.391 cm

(c) 362 mL − 99.5 mL

(d) 12.4 mg + 6.378 mg + 2.089 mg

1.71 Carry out the following calculations, express the answers to the correct numbers of significant figures, and include units in the answers.

(a) $5280 \dfrac{ft}{mi} \times 6.2$ mi

(b) 4.5 m $\times$ 3.25 m

(c) 2.50 g $\div 8.3 \dfrac{g}{cm^3}$

(d) 4.70 cm $\times$ 6.8 cm $\times$ 2.54 cm

UNIT CONVERSIONS AND PROBLEM SOLVING

1.72 Carry out the following conversions:

(a) 3.614 mg to centigrams

(b) 12.0 kL to megaliters

(c) 14.4 μm to millimeters

(d) 6.03×10^{-6} cg to nanograms

(e) 174.5 mL to deciliters

(f) 1.5×10^{-2} km to centimeters

1.73 Carry out the following conversions. Consult Tables 1.7–1.9 as needed.

(a) 56.4 mi to kilometers and to megameters

(b) 2.0 L to quarts and to fluid ounces

(c) 7 ft 2.0 in. to centimeters and to meters

(d) 1.35 lb to kilograms and to decigrams

1.74 Express the following quantities in more convenient units by using SI unit prefixes:

(a) 9.78×10^4 g   (b) 1.33×10^{-4} L

(c) 0.000 000 000 46 g   (d) 2.99×10^8 cm

1.75 Fill in the blanks to complete the equivalencies either with appropriate units prefixes or with the appropriate scientific notation. The first blank is filled in as an example.

(a) 125 km = 1.25×10^5 m

(b) 6.285×10^3 mg = _____? _____ kg

(c) 47.35 dL = $4.735 \times$ _____? _____ mL

(d) 67.4 cm = 6.7×10^{-4} _____? _____

1.76 The speed limit in Canada is 100 km/h.

(a) How many miles per hour is this?

(b) How many feet per second?

1.77 The muzzle velocity of a projectile fired from a 9 mm handgun is 1200 ft/s.

(a) How many miles per hour is this?

(b) How many meters per second?

1.78 The diameter of a red blood cell is 6×10^{-6} m.

   (a) How many centimeters is this?

   (b) How many red blood cells are needed to make a line 1 cm long? 1 in. long?

1.79 The Willis Tower in Chicago has an approximate floor area of 418,000 m^2. How many square feet of floor space is this?

1.80 A normal value for blood cholesterol is 200 mg/dL of blood. If a normal adult has a total blood volume of 5 L, how much total cholesterol is present?

1.81 The recommended daily dose of calcium for an 18-year-old male is 1200 mg. If 1.0 cup of whole milk contains 290 mg of calcium and milk is his only calcium source, how much milk should an 18-year-old male drink each day?

1.82 The white blood cell concentration in normal blood is approximately 12,000 cells/mm^3 of blood. How many white blood cells does a normal adult with 5 L of blood have? Express the answer in scientific notation.

ENERGY, HEAT, AND TEMPERATURE

1.83 The boiling point of liquid nitrogen, used in the removal of warts and in other surgical applications, is -195.8 °C. What is this temperature in kelvins and in degrees Fahrenheit? (3.74 J/g °C)

1.84 Diethyl ether, a substance once used as a general anesthetic, has a specific heat of 0.895 cal/(g °C). How many calories and how many kilocalories of heat are needed to raise the temperature of 30.0 g of diethyl ether from 10.0 °C to 30.0 °C? How many Joules and kiloJoules?

1.85 Aluminum has a specific heat of 0.215 cal/(g °C). When 25.7 cal (108.5 J) of heat is added to 18.4 g of aluminum at 20.0°, what is the final temperature of the aluminum?

1.86 Calculate the specific heat of copper if it takes 23 cal (96 J) to heat a 5.0 g sample from 25 °C to 75 °C.

1.87 The specific heat of fat is 0.45 cal/(g·°C) (1.9 J/g °C) and the density of fat is 0.94 g/cm^3. How much energy (in calories and joules) is needed to heat 10 cm^3 of fat from room temperature (25 °C) to its melting point (35 °C)?

1.88 A 150 g sample of mercury and a 150 g sample of iron are at an initial temperature of 25.0 °C. If 250 cal (1050 J) of heat is applied to each sample, what is the final temperature of each? (See Table 1.10.)

1.89 When 100 cal (418 J) of heat is applied to a 125 g sample, the temperature increases by 28 °C. Calculate the specific heat of the sample and compare your answer to the values in Table 1.10. What is the identity of the sample?

DENSITY AND SPECIFIC GRAVITY

1.90 Aspirin has a density of 1.40 g/cm^3. What is the volume in cubic centimeters of a tablet weighing 250 mg?

1.91 Gaseous hydrogen has a density of 0.0899 g/L at 0 °C. How many liters would you need if you wanted 1.0078 g of hydrogen?

1.92 What is the density of lead (in g/cm^3) if a rectangular bar measuring 0.500 cm in height, 1.55 cm in width, and 25.00 cm in length has a mass of 220.9 g?

1.93 What is the density of lithium metal (in g/cm^3) if a cube measuring 0.82 cm $\times$ 1.45 cm $\times$ 1.25 cm has a mass of 0.794 g?

1.94 Ethanol produced by fermentation has a specific gravity of 0.787 at 25 °C. What is the volume of 125 g of ethanol at this temperature? (The density of water at 25 °C is 0.997 g/mL.)

1.95 Ethylene glycol, commonly used as automobile antifreeze, has a specific gravity of 1.1088 at room temperature (25 °C). What is the mass of 1.00 L of ethylene glycol at this temperature?

CHEMISTRY IN ACTION

1.96 The active ingredient in aspirin, acetylsalicylic acid (ASA), has the formula $C_9H_8O_4$ and melts at 140 °C. Identify the elements and how many atoms of each are present in ASA. Is it a solid or a liquid at room temperature? [*Aspirin—A Case Study, p. 8*]

1.97 Calomel (Hg_2Cl_2) is not toxic but methyl mercury chloride (CH_3HgCl) is highly toxic. What physical property explains this difference in toxicity? [*Mercury and Mercury Poisoning, p. 15*]

1.98 A thermochromic plastic chip included in a shipping container for beef undergoes an irreversible color change if the storage temperature exceeds 28 °F. What is this temperature on the Celsius and Kelvin scales? [*Temperature-Sensitive Materials, p. 31*]

1.99 A temperature-sensitive bath toy undergoes several color changes in the temperature range from 37 °C to 47 °C. What is the corresponding temperature range on the Fahrenheit scale? [*Temperature-Sensitive Materials, p. 31*]

1.100 Calculate the BMI for an individual who is

   (a) 5 ft 1 in. tall and weighs 155 lb

   (b) 5 ft 11 in. tall and weighs 170 lb

   (c) 6 ft 3 in. tall and weighs 195 lb

   Which of these individuals is likely to have increased health risks? [*A Measurement Example: Obesity and Body Fat, p. 35*]

1.101 Liposuction is a technique for removing fat deposits from various areas of the body. How many liters of fat would have to be removed to result in a 5.0 lb weight loss? The density of human fat is 0.94 g/mL. [*A Measurement Example: Obesity and Body Fat, p. 35*]

GENERAL QUESTIONS AND PROBLEMS

1.102 The most recently discovered element is number 117, Ununseptium. Based on its location in the periodic table, classify it as a metal, nonmetal, or metalloid and discuss the physical properties (physical state, conductivity, etc.) you would expect it to exhibit.

1.103 A white solid with a melting point of 730 °C is melted. When electricity is passed through the resultant liquid, a brown gas and a molten metal are produced. Neither the metal nor the gas can be broken down into anything simpler by chemical means. Classify each—the white solid, the molten metal, and the brown gas—as a mixture, a compound, or an element.

1.104 Refer to the pencil in Problem 1.34. Using the equivalent values in Table 1.8 as conversion factors, convert the length measured in inches to centimeters. Compare the calculated length in centimeters to the length in centimeters measured using the metric ruler. How do the two values compare? Explain any differences.

1.105 Gemstones are weighed in carats, where 1 carat = 200 mg exactly. What is the mass in grams of the Hope diamond, the world's largest blue diamond, at 44.4 carats?

1.106 The relationship between the nutritional unit for energy and the metric unit is 1 Calorie = 1 kcal.

(a) One donut contains 350 Calories. Convert this to calories and joules.

(b) If the energy in one donut was used to heat 35.5 kg of water, calculate the increase in temperature of the water (in °C).

1.107 Drug dosages are typically prescribed in units of milligrams per kilogram of body weight. A new drug has a recommended dosage of 9 mg/kg.

(a) How many mgs would a 130 lb woman have to take to obtain this dosage?

(b) How many 125 mg tablets should a 40 lb child take to receive the recommended dosage?

1.108 A clinical report gave the following data from a blood analysis: iron, 39 mg/dL; calcium, 8.3 mg/dL; cholesterol, 224 mg/dL. Express each of these quantities in grams per deciliter, writing the answers in scientific notation.

1.109 The Spirit of America Goodyear blimp has a volume of $2.027 \times 10^5 \text{ ft}^3$.

(a) Convert this volume to L.

(b) When in operation it is filled with helium gas. If the density of helium at room temperature is 0.179 g/L, calculate the mass of helium in the blimp.

(c) What is the mass of air occupying the same volume? The density of air at room temperature is 1.20 g/L.

1.110 Approximately 75 mL of blood is pumped by a normal human heart at each beat. Assuming an average pulse of 72 beats per minute, how many milliliters of blood are pumped in one day?

1.111 A doctor has ordered that a patient be given 15 g of glucose, which is available in a concentration of 50.00 g glucose/1000.0 mL of solution. What volume of solution should be given to the patient?

1.112 Reconsider the volume of the sample dispensed by pipette in Problem 1.35. Assuming that the solution in the pipette has a density of 0.963 g/mL, calculate the mass of solution dispensed in the problem to the correct number of significant figures.

1.113 Today, thermometers containing mercury are used less frequently than in the past because of concerns regarding the toxicity of mercury and because of its relatively high melting point (−39 °C). This means that mercury thermometers cannot be used in very cold environments because the mercury is a solid under such conditions. Alcohol thermometers, however, can be used over a temperature range from −115 °C (the melting point of alcohol) to 78.5 °C (the boiling point of alcohol).

(a) What is the effective temperature range of the alcohol thermometer in °F?

(b) The densities of alcohol and mercury are 0.79 g/mL and 13.6 g/mL, respectively. If the volume of liquid in a typical laboratory thermometer is 1.0 mL, what mass of alcohol is contained in the thermometer? What mass of mercury?

1.114 In a typical person, the level of blood glucose (also known as blood sugar) is about 85 mg/100 mL of blood. If an average body contains about 11 pints of blood, how many grams and how many pounds of glucose are present in the blood?

1.115 A patient is receiving 3000 mL/day of a solution that contains 5 g of dextrose (glucose) per 100 mL of solution. If glucose provides 4 kcal/g of energy, how many kilocalories per day is the patient receiving from the glucose?

1.116 A rough guide to fluid requirements based on body weight is 100 mL/kg for the first 10 kg of body weight, 50 mL/kg for the next 10 kg, and 20 mL/kg for weight over 20 kg. What volume of fluid per day is needed by a 55 kg woman? Give the answer with two significant figures.

1.117 Chloral hydrate, a sedative and sleep-inducing drug, is available as a solution labeled 10.0 gr/fluidram. What volume in milliliters should be administered to a patient who is meant to receive 7.5 gr per dose? (1 gr = 64.8 mg ; 1 fluidram = 3.72 mL)

1.118 When 1.0 tablespoon of butter is burned or used by our body, it releases 100 kcal (100 food Calories or 418. 4 kJ) of energy. If we could use all the energy provided, how many tablespoons of butter would have to be burned to raise the temperature of 3.00 L of water from 18.0 °C to 90.0 °C?

1.119 An archeologist finds a 1.62 kg goblet that she believes to be made of pure gold. When 1350 cal (5650 J) of heat is added to the goblet, its temperature increases by 7.8 °C. Calculate the specific heat of the goblet. Is it made of gold? Explain.

1.120 In another test, the archeologist in Problem 1.119 determines that the volume of the goblet is 205 mL. Calculate the density of the goblet and compare it with the density of gold (19.3 g/mL), lead (11.4 g/mL), and iron (7.86 g/mL). What is the goblet probably made of?

1.121 Sulfuric acid (H_2SO_4, density = 1.83 g/mL) is produced in larger amounts than any other chemical: 2.01×10^{11} lb worldwide in 2004. What is the volume of this amount in liters?

1.122 Imagine that you place a piece of cork measuring 1.30 cm × 5.50 cm × 3.00 cm in a pan of water and that on top of the cork you place a small cube of lead measuring 1.15 cm on each edge. The density of cork is 0.235 g/cm^3 and the density of lead is 11.35 g/cm^3. Will the combination of cork plus lead float or sink?

1.123 At a certain point, the Celsius and Fahrenheit scales "cross," and at this point the numerical value of the Celsius temperature is the same as the numerical value of the Fahrenheit temperature. At what temperature does this crossover occur?

Atoms and the Periodic Table

CONTENTS

◄ These basaltic columns at the Devil's Post-pile National Monument in northern California are one example of repeating patterns that can be found in nature.

1. **What is the modern theory of atomic structure?**
   THE GOAL: Be able to explain the major assumptions of atomic theory.

2. **How do atoms of different elements differ?**
   THE GOAL: Be able to explain the composition of different atoms according to the number of protons, neutrons, and electrons they contain.

3. **What are isotopes, and what is atomic weight?**
   THE GOAL: Be able to explain what isotopes are and how they affect an element's atomic weight.

4. **How is the periodic table arranged?**
   THE GOAL: Be able to describe how elements are arranged in the periodic table, name the subdivisions of the periodic table, and relate the position of an element in the periodic table to its electronic structure.

5. **How are electrons arranged in atoms?**
   THE GOAL: Be able to explain how electrons are distributed in shells and subshells around the nucleus of an atom, how valence electrons can be represented as electron-dot symbols, and how the electron configurations can help explain the chemical properties of the elements.

Chemistry must be studied on two levels. In the previous chapter we dealt with chemistry on the large-scale, or *macroscopic*, level, looking at the properties and transformations of matter that we can see and measure. Now we are ready to look at the sub-microscopic, or atomic level, studying the behavior and properties of individual atoms. Although scientists have long been convinced of their existence, only within the past 20 years have powerful new instruments made it possible to see individual atoms. In this chapter, we will look at modern atomic theory and how the structure of atoms influences macroscopic properties.

2.1 Atomic Theory

Take a piece of aluminum foil, and cut it in two. Then, take one of the pieces and cut *it* in two, and so on. Assuming that you have extremely small scissors and extraordinary dexterity, how long can you keep dividing the foil? Is there a limit, or is matter infinitely divisible into ever smaller and smaller pieces? Historically, this argument can be traced as far back as the ancient Greek philosophers. Aristotle believed that matter could be divided infinitely, while Democritus argued (correctly) that there is a limit. The smallest and simplest bit that aluminum (or any other element) can be divided and still be identifiable as aluminum is called an **atom**, a word derived from the Greek *atomos*, meaning "indivisible."

Chemistry is founded on four fundamental assumptions about atoms and matter, which together make up modern **atomic theory**:

- All matter is composed of atoms.
- The atoms of a given element differ from the atoms of all other elements.
- Chemical compounds consist of atoms combined in specific ratios. That is, only whole atoms can combine—one A atom with one B atom, or one A atom with two B atoms, and so on. The enormous diversity in the substances we see around us is based on the vast number of ways that atoms can combine with one another.
- Chemical reactions change only the way that atoms are combined in compounds. The atoms themselves are unchanged.

Atoms are extremely small, ranging from about 7.4×10^{-11} m in diameter for a hydrogen atom to 5.24×10^{-10} m for a cesium atom. In mass, atoms vary from 1.67×10^{-24} g for hydrogen to 3.95×10^{-22} g for uranium, one of the heaviest naturally occurring atoms. It is difficult to appreciate just how small atoms are, although it might help if you realize that a fine pencil line is about 3 million atoms across and that even the smallest speck of dust contains about 10^{16} atoms. Our current understanding

Atom The smallest and simplest particle of an element.

Atomic theory A set of assumptions proposed by the English scientist John Dalton to explain the chemical behavior of matter.

▶▶ We will further explore the topics of chemical compounds in Chapters 3 and 4, and chemical reactions in Chapters 5 and 6.

TABLE 2.1 A Comparison of Subatomic Particles

Name	Symbol	Mass (Grams)	Mass (amu)	Charge (Charge Units)
Proton	p	$1.672\,622 \times 10^{-24}$	$1.007\,276$	$+1$
Neutron	n	$1.674\,927 \times 10^{-24}$	$1.008\,665$	0
Electron	e^-	$9.109\,328 \times 10^{-28}$	$5.485\,799 \times 10^{-4}$	-1

Subatomic particles Three kinds of fundamental particles from which atoms are made: protons, neutrons, and electrons.

Proton A positively charged subatomic particle.

Neutron An electrically neutral subatomic particle.

Electron A negatively charged subatomic particle.

Atomic mass unit (amu) A convenient unit for describing the mass of an atom; 1 amu = $\frac{1}{12}$ the mass of a carbon-12 atom.

▲ The relative size of a nucleus in an atom is the same as that of a pea in the middle of this stadium.

Nucleus The dense, central core of an atom that contains protons and neutrons.

▶ **Figure 2.1**
The structure of an atom.
Protons and neutrons are packed together in the nucleus, whereas electrons move about in the large surrounding volume. Virtually all the mass of an atom is concentrated in the nucleus.

of atomic structure is the result of many experiments performed in the late 1800s and early 1900s (see Chemistry in Action on p. 48).

Atoms are composed of tiny **subatomic particles** called *protons, neutrons,* and *electrons*. A **proton** has a mass of $1.672\,622 \times 10^{-24}$ g and carries a positive $(+)$ electrical charge; a **neutron** has a mass similar to that of a proton $(1.674\,927 \times 10^{-24}$ g$)$ but is electrically neutral; and an **electron** has a mass that is only $1/1836$ that of a proton $(9.109\,328 \times 10^{-28}$ g$)$ and carries a negative $(-)$ electrical charge. In fact, electrons are so much lighter than protons and neutrons that their mass is usually ignored. Table 2.1 compares the properties of the three fundamental subatomic particles.

The masses of atoms and their constituent subatomic particles are so small when measured in grams that it is more convenient to express them on a *relative* mass scale. That is, one atom is assigned a mass, and all others are measured relative to it. The process is like deciding that a golf ball (46.0 g) will be assigned a mass of 1. A baseball (149 g), which is $149/46.0 = 3.24$ times heavier than a golf ball, would then have a mass of about 3.24; a volleyball (270 g) would have a mass of $270/46.0 = 5.87$; and so on.

The basis for the relative atomic mass scale is an atom of carbon that contains 6 protons and 6 neutrons. Such an atom is assigned a mass of exactly 12 **atomic mass units** (**amu;** also called a *dalton* in honor of the English scientist John Dalton, who proposed most of atomic theory as we know it), where 1 amu $= 1.660\,539 \times 10^{-24}$ g. Thus, for all practical purposes, both a proton and a neutron have a mass of 1 amu (Table 2.1). Hydrogen atoms are only about $\frac{1}{12}$th as heavy as carbon atoms and have a mass close to 1 amu, magnesium atoms are about twice as heavy as carbon atoms and have a mass close to 24 amu, and so forth.

Subatomic particles are not distributed at random throughout an atom. Rather, the protons and neutrons are packed closely together in a dense core called the **nucleus**. Surrounding the nucleus, the electrons move about rapidly through a large, mostly empty volume of space (Figure 2.1). Measurements show that the diameter of a nucleus is only about 10^{-15} m, whereas that of the atom itself is about 10^{-10} m. For comparison, if an atom were the size of a large domed stadium, the nucleus would be approximately the size of a small pea in the center of the playing field.

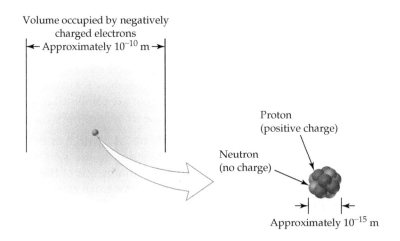

Volume occupied by negatively charged electrons
← Approximately 10^{-10} m →

Proton (positive charge)

Neutron (no charge)

Approximately 10^{-15} m

The structure of the atom is determined by an interplay of different attractive and repulsive forces. Because unlike charges attract one another, the negatively charged electrons are held near the positively charged nucleus. But because like charges repel one another, the electrons also try to get as far away from one another as possible, accounting for the relatively large volume they occupy. The positively charged protons in the nucleus also repel one another, but are nevertheless held together by a unique attraction called the *nuclear strong force*, which we will discuss further in Chapter 11.

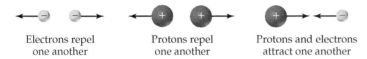

Electrons repel   Protons repel   Protons and electrons
one another   one another   attract one another

Worked Example **2.1** Atomic Mass Units: Gram-to-Atom Conversions

How many atoms are in a small piece of aluminum foil with a mass of 0.100 g? The mass of an atom of aluminum is 27.0 amu.

ANALYSIS We know the sample mass in grams and the mass of one atom in atomic mass units. To find the number of atoms in the sample, two conversions are needed, the first between grams and atomic mass units and the second between atomic mass units and the number of atoms. The conversion factor between atomic mass units and grams is $1 \text{ amu} = 1.660\,539 \times 10^{-24}$ g.

BALLPARK ESTIMATE An atom of aluminum has a mass of 27.0 amu; since $1 \text{ amu} \sim 10^{-24}$ g, the mass of a single aluminum atom is very small ($\approx 10^{-23}$ g). A very *large* number of atoms, therefore, (10^{22} ?) is needed to obtain a mass of 0.100 g.

SOLUTION

STEP 1: Identify known information.

Mass of aluminum foil = 0.100 g
1 Al atom = 27.0 amu

STEP 2: Identify unknown answer and units.

Number of Al atoms = ?

STEP 3: Identify needed conversion factors. Knowing the mass of foil (in g) and the mass of individual atoms (in amu) we need to convert from atoms/amu to atoms/g.

$1 \text{ amu} = 1.660\,539 \times 10^{-24}$ g

$$\rightarrow \frac{1 \text{ amu}}{1.660\,539 \times 10^{-24} \text{ g}}$$

STEP 4: Solve. Set up an equation using known information and conversion factors so that unwanted units cancel.

$$(0.100 \text{ g})\left(\frac{1 \text{ amu}}{1.660\,539 \times 10^{-24} \text{ g}}\right)\left(\frac{1 \text{ Al atom}}{27.0 \text{ amu}}\right)$$
$$= 2.23 \times 10^{21} \text{ Al atoms}$$

BALLPARK CHECK Our estimate was 10^{22}, which is within a factor of 10.

PROBLEM 2.1
What is the mass in grams of 150×10^{12} iron atoms, each having a mass of 56 amu?

PROBLEM 2.2
How many atoms are in each of the following?
(a) 1.0 g of hydrogen atoms, each of mass 1.0 amu
(b) 12.0 g of carbon atoms, each of mass 12.0 amu
(c) 23.0 g of sodium atoms, each of mass 23.0 amu

PROBLEM 2.3
What pattern do you see in your answers to Problem 2.2? (We will return to this very important pattern in Chapter 6.)

PROBLEM 2.4
The atoms in the gold foil used in Rutherford's experiments have an estimated radius of 1.44×10^{-10} m (see Chemistry in Action on p. 48). If we assume that the radius of the nucleus of a gold atom is 1.5×10^{-15} m, what fraction of the volume of the atom is occupied by the nucleus? (Volume $= 4/3\,\pi r^3$)

CHEMISTRY IN ACTION

Are Atoms Real?

Chemistry rests on the premise that matter is composed of the tiny particles we call atoms. Every chemical reaction and every physical law that governs the behavior of matter is explained by chemists in terms of atomic theory. But how do we know that atoms are real and not just an imaginary concept? And how do we know the structure of the atom? The development of our understanding of atomic structure is another example of the scientific method at work.

Dalton's atomic theory was originally published in 1808, but many prominent scientists dismissed it. Over the next century, however, several unrelated experiments provided insight into the nature of matter and the structure of the atom. Nineteenth-century investigations into electricity, for example, demonstrated that matter was composed of charged particles—rubbing a glass rod with a silk cloth would generate "static electricity," the same phenomenon that shocks you when you walk across a carpet and then touch a metal surface. It was also known that passing electricity through certain substances, such as water, decomposed the compounds into their constituent elements (hydrogen and oxygen, in the case of water). Several hypotheses were proposed to explain the nature and origin of these charged particles, but our current understanding of atomic structure developed incrementally from several key experiments.

Experiments performed in 1897 by J. J. Thomson demonstrated that matter contained negatively charged particles that were 1000 times lighter than H^+, the lightest positively charged particles found in aqueous solution, and that the mass-to-charge ratio of these particles was the same regardless of the material used to produce the particles (Section 6.10 and Chapter 10). This result implied that atoms were not the smallest particles of matter but that they could be divided into even smaller particles. In 1909, Robert Millikan determined that the charge associated with the "electron," as these particles were now called, was 1.6×10^{-19} coulombs.

But where did the electron fit in the overall structure of matter? The pieces to this puzzle fell into place as a result of experiments performed in 1910 by Ernest Rutherford. He bombarded a gold foil with positively charged "alpha" particles emitted from radium during radioactive decay. The majority of these particles

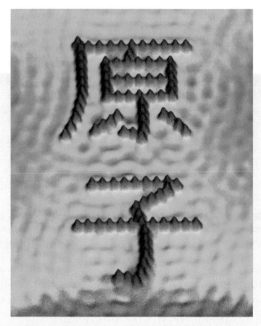

▲ **STM image of the Kanji characters for "atom" formed by iron atoms (radius = 126 pm) deposited on a copper metal surface.**

passed straight through the foil, but a small fraction of them were deflected, and a few even bounced back. From these results, Rutherford deduced that an atom consists mostly of empty space (occupied by the negatively charged electrons) and that most of the mass and all of the positive charges are contained in a relatively small, dense region that he called the "nucleus."

We can now actually "see" and manipulate individual atoms through the use of a device called a *scanning tunneling microscope*, or STM. With the STM, invented in 1981 by a research team at the IBM Corporation, magnifications of up to 10 million have been achieved, allowing chemists to look directly at atoms. The accompanying photograph shows a computer-enhanced representation of iron atoms that have been deposited on a copper surface.

Most present uses of the STM involve studies of surface chemistry, such as the events accompanying the corrosion of metals and the ordering of large molecules in polymers. Work is also underway using the STM to determine the structures of complex biological molecules, such as immunoglobulin G and streptavidin.

See Chemistry in Action Problems 2.84 and 2.85 at the end of the chapter.

2.2 Elements and Atomic Number

Atomic number (Z) The number of protons in atoms of a given element; the number of electrons in atoms of a given element.

Atoms of different elements differ from one another according to how many protons they contain, a value called the element's **atomic number (Z)**. Thus, if we know the number of protons in an atom, we can identify the element. Any atom with 6 protons, for example, is a carbon atom because the atomic number for carbon is 6 ($Z = 6$).

Atoms are neutral overall and have no net charge because the number of positively charged protons in an atom is the same as the number of negatively charged electrons. Thus, the atomic number also equals the number of electrons in every atom of a given element. Hydrogen, $Z = 1$, has only 1 proton and 1 electron; carbon, $Z = 6$, has 6 protons and 6 electrons; sodium, $Z = 11$, has 11 protons and 11 electrons; and so on, up to the element with the largest known atomic number ($Z = 118$). In a periodic table, elements are listed in order of increasing atomic number, beginning at the upper left and ending at the lower right.

The sum of the protons and neutrons in an atom is called the atom's **mass number (A)**. Hydrogen atoms with 1 proton and no neutrons have mass number 1, carbon atoms with 6 protons and 6 neutrons have mass number 12, sodium atoms with 11 protons and 12 neutrons have mass number 23, and so on. Except for hydrogen, atoms generally contain at least as many neutrons as protons and frequently contain more. There is no simple way to predict how many neutrons a given atom will have.

Mass number (A) The total number of protons and neutrons in an atom.

Worked Example 2.2 Atomic Structure: Protons, Neutrons, and Electrons

Phosphorus has the atomic number $Z = 15$. How many protons, electrons, and neutrons are there in phosphorus atoms, which have mass number $A = 31$?

ANALYSIS The atomic number gives the number of protons, which is the same as the number of electrons, and the mass number gives the total number of protons plus neutrons.

SOLUTION
Phosphorus atoms, with $Z = 15$, have 15 protons and 15 electrons. To find the number of neutrons, subtract the atomic number from the mass number:

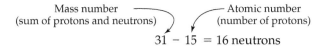

$$\text{Mass number} \qquad \text{Atomic number}$$
$$\text{(sum of protons and neutrons)} \qquad \text{(number of protons)}$$
$$31 - 15 = 16 \text{ neutrons}$$

Worked Example 2.3 Atomic Structure: Atomic Number and Atomic Mass

An atom contains 28 protons and has $A = 60$. Give the number of electrons and neutrons in the atom, and identify the element.

ANALYSIS The number of protons and the number of electrons are the same and are equal to the atomic number Z, 28 in this case. Subtracting the number of protons (28) from the total number of protons plus neutrons (60) gives the number of neutrons.

SOLUTION
The atom has 28 electrons and $60 - 28 = 32$ neutrons. The list of elements inside the front cover shows that the element with atomic number 28 is nickel (Ni).

PROBLEM 2.5
Use the list inside the front cover to identify the following elements:
(a) $A = 186$, with 111 neutrons
(b) $A = 59$, with 21 neutrons
(c) $A = 127$, with 75 neutrons

PROBLEM 2.6
The cobalt used in cancer treatments has $Z = 27$ and $A = 60$. How many protons, neutrons, and electrons are in these cobalt atoms?

2.3 Isotopes and Atomic Weight

All atoms of a given element have the same number of protons, equal to the atomic number (Z) characteristic of that element. But, different atoms of an element can have different numbers of neutrons and therefore different mass numbers. Atoms with identical atomic numbers but different mass numbers are called **isotopes**. Hydrogen, for example, has three isotopes. The most abundant hydrogen isotope, called *protium*, has no neutrons and thus has a mass number of 1. A second hydrogen isotope, called *deuterium*, has one neutron and a mass number of 2; and a third isotope, called *tritium*, has two neutrons and a mass number of 3. Tritium is unstable and does not occur naturally in significant amounts, although it can be made in nuclear reactors.

Isotopes Atoms with identical atomic numbers but different mass numbers.

▶▶▶ We will see that isotopes of the same element have the same *chemical* behavior (Chapter 5), but very different *nuclear* behavior (Chapter 11).

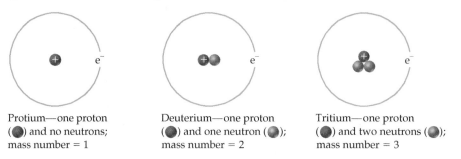

Protium—one proton (⚫) and no neutrons; mass number = 1

Deuterium—one proton (⚫) and one neutron (⚫); mass number = 2

Tritium—one proton (⚫) and two neutrons (⚫); mass number = 3

A specific isotope is represented by showing its mass number (A) as a superscript and its atomic number (Z) as a subscript in front of the atomic symbol, for example, $^A_Z X$, where X represents the symbol for the element. Thus, protium is $^1_1 H$, deuterium is $^2_1 H$, and tritium is $^3_1 H$.

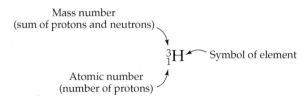

Mass number (sum of protons and neutrons)

$^3_1 H$ ⟵ Symbol of element

Atomic number (number of protons)

Unlike the three isotopes of hydrogen, the isotopes of most elements do not have distinctive names. Instead, the mass number of the isotope is given after the name of the element. The $^{235}_{92} U$ isotope used in nuclear reactors, for example, is usually referred to as uranium-235, or U-235.

Most naturally occurring elements are mixtures of isotopes. In a large sample of naturally occurring hydrogen atoms, for example, 99.985% have mass number $A = 1$ (protium) and 0.015% have mass number $A = 2$ (deuterium). Therefore, it is useful to know the *average* mass of the atoms in a large sample, a value called the element's **atomic weight**. For hydrogen, the atomic weight is 1.008 amu. Atomic weights for all elements are given on the inside of the front cover of this book.

▶▶▶ We will discuss nuclear reactors in Section 11.11.

Atomic weight The weighted average mass of an element's atoms.

To calculate the atomic weight of an element, the individual masses of the naturally occurring isotopes and the percentage of each must be known. The atomic weight can then be calculated as the sum of the masses of the individual isotopes for that element, or

$$\text{Atomic weight} = \Sigma \left[(\text{isotopic abundance}) \times (\text{isotopic mass}) \right]$$

where the Greek symbol Σ indicates the mathematical summing of terms.

Chlorine, for example, occurs on earth as a mixture of 75.77% Cl-35 atoms (mass = 34.97 amu) and 24.23% Cl-37 atoms (mass = 36.97 amu). The atomic weight is found by calculating the percentage of the mass contributed by each isotope. For chlorine, the calculation is done in the following way (to four significant figures), giving an atomic weight of 35.45 amu:

$$\text{Contribution from } ^{35}Cl: (0.7577)(34.97 \text{ amu}) = 26.4968 \text{ amu}$$
$$\text{Contribution from } ^{37}Cl: (0.2423)(36.97 \text{ amu}) = \underline{8.9578 \text{ amu}}$$
$$\text{Atomic weight} = 35.4546 = 35.45 \quad \text{amu}$$
$$(\text{rounded to four significant figures})$$

The final number of significant figures in this case (four) was determined by the atomic masses. Note that the final rounding to four significant figures was not done until *after* the final answer was obtained.

Worked Example 2.4 Average Atomic Mass: Weighted-Average Calculation

Gallium is a metal with a very low melting point—it will melt in the palm of your hand. It has two naturally occurring isotopes: 60.4% is Ga-69 (mass = 68.9257 amu), and 39.6% is Ga-71 (mass = 70.9248 amu). Calculate the atomic weight for gallium.

ANALYSIS We can calculate the average atomic mass for the element by summing up the contributions from each of the naturally occurring isotopes.

BALLPARK ESTIMATE The masses of the two naturally occurring isotopes of gallium differ by 2 amu (68.9 and 70.9 amu). Since slightly more than half of the Ga atoms are the lighter isotope (Ga-69), the average mass will be slightly less than halfway between the two isotopic masses; estimate = 69.8 amu.

SOLUTION

STEP 1: **Identify known information.**	Ga-69 (60.4% at 68.9257 amu) Ga-71 (39.6% at 70.9248 amu)
STEP 2: **Identify the unknown answer and units.**	Atomic weight for Ga (in amu) = ?
STEP 3: **Identify conversion factors or equations.** This equation calculates the average atomic weight as a weighted average of all naturally occurring isotopes.	Atomic weight = $\sum [\,(\text{isotopic abundance}) \times (\text{isotopic mass})\,]$
STEP 4: **Solve.** Substitute known information and solve.	Atomic weight = $(0.604) \times (68.9257 \text{ amu}) = 41.6311$ amu $+ (0.396) \times (70.9248 \text{ amu}) = 28.0862$ amu Atomic weight = 69.7 amu (3 significant figures)
	BALLPARK CHECK Our estimate (69.8 amu) is close!

Worked Example 2.5 Identifying Isotopes from Atomic Mass and Atomic Number

Identify element X in the symbol $^{194}_{78}X$, and give its atomic number, mass number, number of protons, number of electrons, and number of neutrons.

ANALYSIS The identity of the atom corresponds to the atomic number—78.

SOLUTION

Element X has Z = 78, which shows that it is platinum. (Look inside the front cover for the list of elements.) The isotope $^{194}_{78}Pt$ has a mass number of 194, and we can subtract the atomic number from the mass number to get the number of neutrons. This platinum isotope therefore has 78 protons, 78 electrons, and $194 - 78 = 116$ neutrons.

PROBLEM 2.7
Potassium (K) has two naturally occurring isotopes: K-39 (93.12%; mass = 38.9637 amu) and K-41 (6.88%; 40.9618 amu). Calculate the atomic weight for potassium. How does your answer compare with the atomic weight given in the list inside the front cover of this book?

PROBLEM 2.8
Bromine, an element present in compounds used as sanitizers and fumigants (for example, ethylene bromide), has two naturally occurring isotopes, with mass numbers 79 and 81. Write the symbols for both, including their atomic numbers and mass numbers.

PROBLEM 2.9
An element used to sanitize water supplies has two naturally occurring isotopes with mass numbers of 35 and 37, and 17 electrons. Write the symbols for both isotopes, including their atomic numbers and mass numbers.

2.4 The Periodic Table

Ten elements have been known since the beginning of recorded history: antimony (Sb), carbon (C), copper (Cu), gold (Au), iron (Fe), lead (Pb), mercury (Hg), silver (Ag), sulfur (S), and tin (Sn). It is worth noting that the symbols for many of these elements are derived from their Latin names, a reminder that they have been known since the time when Latin was the language used for all scholarly work. The first "new" element to be found in several thousand years was arsenic (As), discovered in about 1250. In fact, only 24 elements were known up to the time of the American Revolution in 1776.

As the pace of discovery quickened in the late 1700s and early 1800s, chemists began to look for similarities among elements that might make it possible to draw general conclusions. Particularly important was Johann Döbereiner's observation in 1829 that there were several *triads*, or groups of three elements, that appeared to have similar chemical and physical properties. For example, lithium, sodium, and potassium were all known to be silvery metals that react violently with water; chlorine, bromine, and iodine were all known to be colored nonmetals with pungent odors.

Numerous attempts were made in the mid-1800s to account for the similarities among groups of elements, but the great breakthrough came in 1869 when the Russian chemist Dmitri Mendeleev organized the elements in order of increasing mass and then grouped elements into columns based on similarities in chemical behavior. His table is a forerunner of the modern periodic table, introduced previously in Section 1.5 and shown again in Figure 2.2. The table has boxes for each element that give the symbol, atomic number, and atomic mass of the element:

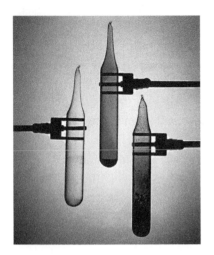

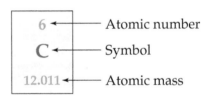

$$6 \longleftarrow \text{Atomic number}$$
$$\text{C} \longleftarrow \text{Symbol}$$
$$12.011 \longleftarrow \text{Atomic mass}$$

Beginning at the upper left corner of the periodic table, elements are arranged by increasing atomic number into seven horizontal rows, called **periods**, and 18 vertical columns, called **groups**. When organized in this way, *the elements in a given group have similar chemical properties.* Lithium, sodium, potassium, and the other elements in group 1A behave similarly. Chlorine, bromine, iodine, and the other elements in group 7A behave similarly, and so on throughout the table.

Note that different periods (rows) contain different numbers of elements. The first period contains only 2 elements, hydrogen and helium; the second and third periods each contain 8 elements; the fourth and fifth periods each contain 18; the sixth and seventh periods contain 32. Note also that the 14 elements following lanthanum (the *lanthanides*) and the 14 following actinium (the *actinides*) are pulled out and shown below the others.

Groups are numbered in two ways, both shown in Figure 2.2. The 2 large groups on the far left and the 6 on the far right are called the **main group elements** and are numbered 1A through 8A. The 10 smaller groups in the middle of the table are called the **transition metal elements** and are numbered 1B through 8B. Alternatively, all 18 groups are numbered sequentially from 1 to 18. The 14 groups shown separately at the bottom of the table are called the **inner transition metal elements** and are not numbered.

Period One of the 7 horizontal rows of elements in the periodic table.

Group One of the 18 vertical columns of elements in the periodic table.

Main group element An element in one of the 2 groups on the left or the 6 groups on the right of the periodic table.

Transition metal element An element in one of the 10 smaller groups near the middle of the periodic table.

Inner transition metal element An element in one of the 14 groups shown separately at the bottom of the periodic table.

Main groups — Transition metal groups — Main groups

Period	1A 1	2A 2	3B 3	4B 4	5B 5	6B 6	7B 7	8	8B 9	10	1B 11	2B 12	3A 13	4A 14	5A 15	6A 16	7A 17	8A 18
1	1 **H** 1.00794																	2 **He** 4.00260
2	3 **Li** 6.941	4 **Be** 9.01218											5 **B** 10.81	6 **C** 12.011	7 **N** 14.0067	8 **O** 15.9994	9 **F** 18.9984	10 **Ne** 20.1797
3	11 **Na** 22.98977	12 **Mg** 24.305											13 **Al** 26.98154	14 **Si** 28.0855	15 **P** 30.9738	16 **S** 32.066	17 **Cl** 35.4527	18 **Ar** 39.948
4	19 **K** 39.0983	20 **Ca** 40.078	21 **Sc** 44.9559	22 **Ti** 47.88	23 **V** 50.9415	24 **Cr** 51.996	25 **Mn** 54.9380	26 **Fe** 55.847	27 **Co** 58.9332	28 **Ni** 58.69	29 **Cu** 63.546	30 **Zn** 65.39	31 **Ga** 69.72	32 **Ge** 72.61	33 **As** 74.9216	34 **Se** 78.96	35 **Br** 79.904	36 **Kr** 83.80
5	37 **Rb** 85.4678	38 **Sr** 87.62	39 **Y** 88.9059	40 **Zr** 91.224	41 **Nb** 92.9064	42 **Mo** 95.94	43 **Tc** (98)	44 **Ru** 101.07	45 **Rh** 102.9055	46 **Pd** 106.42	47 **Ag** 107.8682	48 **Cd** 112.41	49 **In** 114.82	50 **Sn** 118.710	51 **Sb** 121.757	52 **Te** 127.60	53 **I** 126.9045	54 **Xe** 131.29
6	55 **Cs** 132.9054	56 **Ba** 137.33	57 ***La** 138.9055	72 **Hf** 178.49	73 **Ta** 180.9479	74 **W** 183.85	75 **Re** 186.207	76 **Os** 190.2	77 **Ir** 192.22	78 **Pt** 195.08	79 **Au** 196.9665	80 **Hg** 200.59	81 **Tl** 204.383	82 **Pb** 207.2	83 **Bi** 208.9804	84 **Po** (209)	85 **At** (210)	86 **Rn** (222)
7	87 **Fr** (223)	88 **Ra** 226.0254	89 **†Ac** 227.0278	104 **Rf** (261)	105 **Db** (262)	106 **Sg** (266)	107 **Bh** (264)	108 **Hs** (269)	109 **Mt** (268)	110 **Ds** (271)	111 **Rg** (272)	112 **Cn** (285)	113 (284)	114 (289)	115 (288)	116 (292)	117 (293)	118 (294)

Lanthanides	58 **Ce** 140.12	59 **Pr** 140.9077	60 **Nd** 144.24	61 **Pm** (145)	62 **Sm** 150.36	63 **Eu** 151.965	64 **Gd** 157.25	65 **Tb** 158.9254	66 **Dy** 162.50	67 **Ho** 164.9304	68 **Er** 167.26	69 **Tm** 168.9342	70 **Yb** 173.04	71 **Lu** 174.967
Actinides	90 **Th** 232.0381	91 **Pa** 231.0399	92 **U** 238.0289	93 **Np** 237.048	94 **Pu** (244)	95 **Am** (243)	96 **Cm** (247)	97 **Bk** (247)	98 **Cf** (251)	99 **Es** (252)	100 **Fm** (257)	101 **Md** (258)	102 **No** (259)	103 **Lr** (262)

Metals   Metalloids   Nonmetals

▲ **Figure 2.2**
The periodic table of the elements.
Each element is identified by a one- or two-letter symbol and is characterized by an *atomic number.* The table begins with hydrogen (H, atomic number 1) in the upper left-hand corner and continues to the yet unnamed element with atomic number 118. The 14 elements following lanthanum (La, atomic number 57) and the 14 elements following actinium (Ac, atomic number 89) are pulled out and shown below the others.

Elements are organized into 18 vertical columns, or *groups,* and 7 horizontal rows, or *periods.* The 2 groups on the left and the 6 on the right are the *main groups;* the 10 in the middle are the *transition metal groups.* The 14 elements following lanthanum are the *lanthanides,* and the 14 elements following actinium are the *actinides;* together these are known as the *inner transition metals.* Two systems for numbering the groups are explained in the text.

Those elements (except hydrogen) on the left-hand side of the black zigzag line running from boron (B) to tellurium (Te) are *metals* (yellow), those elements to the right of the line are *nonmetals* (blue), and most elements abutting the line are *metalloids* (purple).

PROBLEM 2.10
Locate aluminum in the periodic table, and give its group number and period number.

PROBLEM 2.11
Identify the group 1B element in period 5 and the group 2A element in period 4.

PROBLEM 2.12
There are five elements in group 5A of the periodic table. Identify them, and give the period of each.

▲ **Sodium, an alkali metal, reacts violently with water to yield hydrogen gas and an alkaline (basic) solution.**

Alkali metal An element in group 1A of the periodic table.

2.5 Some Characteristics of Different Groups

To see why the periodic table has the name it does, look at the graph of atomic radius versus atomic number in Figure 2.3. The graph shows an obvious *periodicity*—a repeating rise-and-fall pattern. Beginning on the left with atomic number 1 (hydrogen), the sizes of the atoms increase to a maximum at atomic number 3 (lithium), then decrease to a minimum, then increase again to a maximum at atomic number 11 (sodium), then decrease, and so on. It turns out that the maxima occur for atoms of group 1A elements—Li, Na, K, Rb, Cs, and Fr—and the minima occur for atoms of the group 7A elements.

There is nothing unique about the periodicity of atomic radii shown in Figure 2.3. The melting points of the first 100 elements, for example, exhibit similar periodic behavior, as shown in Figure 2.4, with a systematic trend of peaks and valleys as you progress through the elements in the periodic table. Many other physical and chemical properties can be plotted in a similar way with similar results. In fact, the various elements in a given group of the periodic table usually show remarkable similarities in many of their chemical and physical properties. Look at the following four groups, for example:

- **Group 1A—Alkali metals:** Lithium (Li), sodium (Na), potassium (K), rubidium (Rb), cesium (Cs), and francium (Fr) are shiny, soft metals with low melting points. All react rapidly (often violently) with water to form products that are highly alkaline, or basic—hence the name **alkali metals**. Because of their high reactivity, the alkali metals are never found in nature in the pure state but only in combination with other elements.

▶ **Figure 2.3**

A graph of atomic radius in picometers (pm) versus atomic number shows a periodic rise-and-fall pattern.

The maxima occur for atoms of the group 1A elements (Li, Na, K, Rb, Cs, Fr, in red); the minima occur for atoms of the group 7A elements (blue). Accurate data are not available for the group 8A elements.

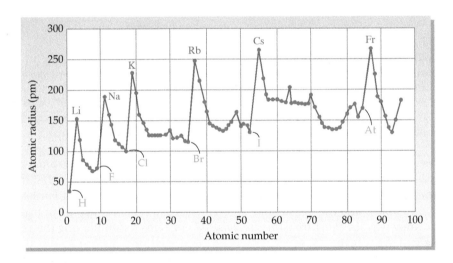

▶ **Figure 2.4**

A graph of melting point versus atomic number shows periodic properties similar to the trend in Figure 2.3.

While the maxima and minima are not as sharp as in Figure 2.3, the change in melting points of the elements still show a similar periodic trend.

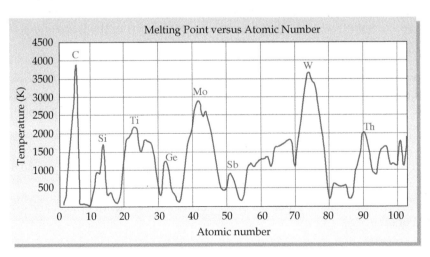

- **Group 2A—Alkaline earth metals:** Beryllium (Be), magnesium (Mg), calcium (Ca), strontium (Sr), barium (Ba), and radium (Ra) are also lustrous, silvery metals, but are less reactive than their neighbors in group 1A. Like the alkali metals, the alkaline earths are never found in nature in the pure state.

- **Group 7A—Halogens:** Fluorine (F), chlorine (Cl), bromine (Br), iodine (I), and astatine (At) are colorful and corrosive nonmetals. All are found in nature only in combination with other elements, such as with sodium in table salt (sodium chloride, NaCl). In fact, the group name **halogen** is taken from the Greek word *hals*, meaning salt.

- **Group 8A—Noble gases:** Helium (He), neon (Ne), argon (Ar), krypton (Kr), xenon (Xe), and radon (Rn) are colorless gases. The elements in this group were labeled the "noble" gases because of their lack of chemical reactivity—helium, neon, and argon don't combine with any other elements, whereas krypton and xenon combine with a very few.

Alkaline earth metal An element in group 2A of the periodic table.

Halogen An element in group 7A of the periodic table.

Noble gas An element in group 8A of the periodic table.

▸▸ ▸ The reason for the similarity in chemical properties of elements within each group will be explained in Section 2.8.

Although the resemblances are not as pronounced as they are within a single group, *neighboring* elements often behave similarly as well. Thus, as noted in Section 1.5 and indicated in Figure 2.2, the periodic table can be divided into three major classes of elements—*metals*, *nonmetals*, and *metalloids* (metal-like). Metals, the largest category of elements, are found on the left side of the periodic table, bounded on the right by a zigzag line running from boron (B) at the top to astatine (At) at the bottom. Nonmetals are found on the right side of the periodic table, and six of the elements adjacent to the zigzag boundary between metals and nonmetals are metalloids.

LOOKING AHEAD ▸▸ ▸ Carbon, the element on which life is based, is a group 4A nonmetal near the top right of the periodic table. Clustered near carbon are other elements often found in living organisms, including oxygen, nitrogen, phosphorus, and sulfur. We will look at the subject of *organic chemistry*—the chemistry of carbon compounds—in Chapters 12–17, and move on to *biochemistry*—the chemistry of living things—in Chapters 18–29.

PROBLEM 2.13

Identify the following elements as metals, nonmetals, or metalloids:

(a) Ti   **(b)** Te

(c) Se   **(d)** Sc

(e) At   **(f)** Ar

PROBLEM 2.14

Locate **(a)** krypton, **(b)** strontium, **(c)** nitrogen, and **(d)** cobalt in the periodic table. Indicate which categories apply to each: (i) metal, (ii) nonmetal, (iii) transition element, (iv) main group element, (v) noble gas.

PROBLEM 2.15

Heavier elements were formed in stars by the fusion of hydrogen and helium nuclei (see Chemistry in Action on p. 56). How many He-4 nuclei would be needed to form a Fe-56 nucleus? What additional particles would be needed?

KEY CONCEPT PROBLEM 2.16

Identify the elements whose nuclei are shown below. For each, tell its group number, its period number, and whether it is a metal, nonmetal, or metalloid.

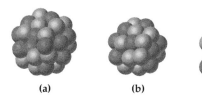

○ Neutron

● Proton

(a)   (b)

CHEMISTRY IN ACTION

The Origin of Chemical Elements

Astronomers believe that the universe began some 15 billion years ago in an extraordinary moment they call the "big bang." Initially, the temperature must have been inconceivably high, but after 1 second, it had dropped to about 10^{10} K and subatomic particles began to form: protons, neutrons, and electrons. After 3 minutes, the temperature had dropped to 10^9 K, and protons began fusing with neutrons to form helium nuclei, $^4_2$He.

Matter remained in this form for many millions of years, until the expanding universe had cooled to about 10,000 K and electrons were then able to bind to protons and to helium nuclei, forming stable hydrogen and helium atoms.

The attractive force of gravity acting on regions of higher-than-average density of hydrogen and helium atoms slowly produced massive local concentrations of matter and ultimately formed billions of galaxies, each with many billions of stars. As the gas clouds of hydrogen and helium condensed under gravitational attraction and stars formed, their temperatures reached 10^7 K, and their densities reached 100 g/cm^3. Protons and neutrons again fused to yield helium nuclei, generating vast amounts of heat and light.

Most of these early stars probably burned out after a few billion years, but a few were so massive that, as their nuclear fuel diminished, gravitational attraction caused a rapid contraction leading to still higher core temperatures and higher densities—up to 5×10^8 K and 5×10^5 g/cm^3. Under such extreme conditions, larger nuclei were formed, including carbon, oxygen, silicon, magnesium, and iron. Ultimately, the stars underwent a gravitational collapse resulting in the synthesis of still heavier

▲ **"Light echoes" illuminate dust around the supergiant star V838 monocerotis, as seen from the Hubble telescope.**

elements and an explosion visible throughout the universe as a *supernova*.

Matter from exploding supernovas was blown throughout the galaxy, forming a new generation of stars and planets. Our own sun and solar system formed about 4.5 billion years ago from matter released by former supernovas. Except for hydrogen and helium, all the atoms in our bodies and our entire solar system were created more than 5 billion years ago in exploding stars. We and our world are made from the ashes of dying stars.

See Chemistry in Action Problems 2.86 and 2.87 at the end of this chapter.

2.6 Electronic Structure of Atoms

Why does the periodic table have the shape it does, with periods of different length? Why are periodic variations observed in atomic radii and in so many other characteristics of the elements? And why do elements in a given group of the periodic table show similar chemical behavior? These questions occupied the thoughts of chemists for more than 50 years after Mendeleev, and it was not until well into the 1920s that the answers were established. Today, we know that *the properties of the elements are determined by the arrangement of electrons in their atoms.*

Our current understanding of the electronic structure of atoms is based on the now accepted *quantum mechanical model*, developed by Austrian physicist Erwin Schrödinger in 1926. One of the fundamental assumptions of the model is that electrons have both particle-like and wave-like properties, and that the behavior of electrons can be described using a mathematical equation called a wave function. One consequence of this assumption is that electrons are not perfectly free to move about in an atom. Instead, each electron is restricted to a certain region of space within the atom, depending on the energy level of the electron. Different electrons have different amounts of energy and thus occupy different regions within the atom.

Furthermore, the energies of electrons are *quantized*, or restricted to having only certain values.

To understand the idea of quantization, think about the difference between stairs and a ramp. A ramp is *not* quantized because it changes height continuously. Stairs, by contrast, *are* quantized because they change height only by a fixed amount. You can climb one stair or two stairs, but you cannot climb 1.5 stairs. In the same way, the energy values available to electrons in an atom change only in steps rather than continuously.

The wave functions derived from the quantum mechanical model also provide important information about the location of electrons in an atom. Just as a person can be found by giving his or her address within a state, an electron can be found by giving its "address" within an atom. Furthermore, just as a person's address is composed of several successively narrower categories—city, street, and house number—an electron's address is also composed of successively narrower categories—*shell, subshell,* and *orbital,* which are defined by the quantum mechanical model.

The electrons in an atom are grouped around the nucleus into **shells**, roughly like the layers in an onion, according to the energy of the electrons. The farther a shell is from the nucleus, the larger it is, the more electrons it can hold, and the higher the energies of those electrons. The first shell (the one nearest the nucleus) can hold only 2 electrons, the second shell can hold 8, the third shell can hold 18, and the fourth shell can hold 32 electrons.

Shell number:	1	2	3	4
Electron capacity:	2	8	18	32

Within shells, electrons are further grouped into **subshells** of four different types, identified in order of increasing energy by the letters *s, p, d,* and *f.* The first shell has only one subshell, of the *s* type. The second shell has two subshells: an *s* subshell and a *p* subshell. The third shell has an *s,* a *p,* and a *d* subshell. The fourth shell has an *s,* a *p,* a *d,* and an *f* subshell. Of the four types, we will be concerned mainly with *s* and *p* subshells because most of the elements found in living organisms use only these. A specific subshell is symbolized by writing the number of the shell, followed by the letter for the subshell. For example, the designation *3p* refers to the *p* subshell in the third shell. Note that the number of subshells in a given shell is equal to the shell number. For example, shell number 3 has 3 subshells.

Finally, within each subshell, electrons are grouped into **orbitals**, regions of space within an atom where the specific electrons are most likely to be found. There are different numbers of orbitals within the different kinds of subshells. A given *s* subshell has only 1 orbital, a *p* subshell has 3 orbitals, a *d* subshell has 5 orbitals, and an *f* subshell has 7 orbitals. Each orbital can hold only two electrons, which differ in a property known as *spin.* If one electron in an orbital has a clockwise spin, the other electron in the same orbital must have a counterclockwise spin. The configuration of shells, subshells, and orbitals is summarized in the figure below.

Shell number:	1	2		3			4			
Subshell designation:	s	s , p		s , p , d			s , p , d , f			
Number of orbitals:	1	1 , 3		1 , 3 , 5			1 , 3 , 5 , 7			

Different orbitals have different shapes and orientations, which are described by the quantum mechanical model. Orbitals in *s* subshells are spherical regions centered about the nucleus, whereas orbitals in *p* subshells are roughly dumbbell-shaped regions (Figure 2.5). As shown in Figure 2.5(b), the three *p* orbitals in a given subshell are oriented at right angles to one another.

The overall electron distribution within an atom is summarized in Table 2.2 and in the following list:

- The first shell holds only 2 electrons. The 2 electrons have different spins and are in a single 1*s* orbital.

▲ Stairs are *quantized* because they change height in discrete amounts. A ramp, by contrast, is not quantized because it changes height continuously.

Shell (electron) A grouping of electrons in an atom according to energy.

Subshell (electron) A grouping of electrons in a shell according to the shape of the region of space they occupy.

Orbital A region of space within an atom where an electron in a given subshell can be found.

▶ **Figure 2.5**
The shapes of s and p orbitals.
(a) The s orbitals and **(b)** the p orbitals. The three p orbitals in a given subshell are oriented at right angles to one another. Each orbital can hold only two electrons.

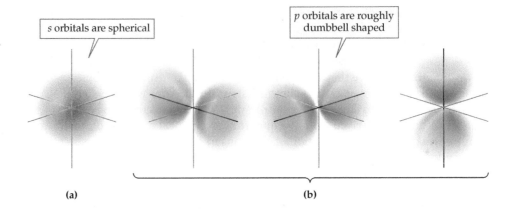

| s orbitals are spherical |
| p orbitals are roughly dumbbell shaped |

(a)   (b)

- The second shell holds 8 electrons. Two are in a 2s orbital, and 6 are in the three different 2p orbitals (two per 2p orbital).
- The third shell holds 18 electrons. Two are in a 3s orbital, 6 are in three 3p orbitals, and 10 are in five 3d orbitals.
- The fourth shell holds 32 electrons. Two are in a 4s orbital, 6 are in three 4p orbitals, 10 are in five 4d orbitals, and 14 are in seven 4f orbitals.

Worked Example **2.6** Atomic Structure: Electron Shells

How many electrons are present in an atom that has its first and second shells filled and has 4 electrons in its third shell? Name the element.

ANALYSIS The number of electrons in the atom is calculated by adding the total electrons in each shell. We can identify the element from the number of protons in the nucleus, which is equal to the number of electrons in the atom.

SOLUTION
The first shell of an atom holds 2 electrons in its 1s orbital, and the second shell holds 8 electrons (2 in a 2s orbital and 6 in three 2p orbitals). Thus, the atom has a total of $2 + 8 + 4 = 14$ electrons and must be silicon (Si).

PROBLEM 2.17
How many electrons are present in an atom in which the first and second shells and the 3s subshell are filled? Name the element.

PROBLEM 2.18
An element has completely filled $n = 1$ and $n = 2$ shells and has 6 electrons in the $n = 3$ shell. Identify the element and its major group (i.e., main group, transition, etc.). Is it a metal or a nonmetal? Identify the orbital in which the last electron is found.

TABLE 2.2 Electron Distribution in Atoms

SHELL NUMBER:	1	2	3	4
Subshell designation:	s	s , p	s , p , d	s , p , d , f
Number of orbitals:	1	1 , 3	1 , 3 , 5	1 , 3 , 5 , 7
Number of electrons:	2	2 , 6	2 , 6 , 10	2 , 6 , 10 , 14
Total electron capacity:	2	8	18	32

2.7 Electron Configurations

The exact arrangement of electrons in an atom's shells and subshells is called the atom's **electron configuration** and can be predicted by applying three rules:

RULE 1: **Electrons occupy the lowest-energy orbitals available, beginning with 1s and continuing in the order shown in Figure 2.6a.** Within each shell, the orbital energies increase in the order *s, p, d, f.* The overall ordering is complicated, however, by the fact that some "crossover" of energies occurs between orbitals in different shells above the 3p level. For example, the 4s orbital is lower in energy than the 3d orbitals, and is therefore filled first. The energy level diagram can be used to predict the order in which orbitals are filled, but it may be hard to remember. The schematic in Figure 2.6b may also be used and is easier to remember.

RULE 2: **Each orbital can hold only two electrons, which must be of opposite spin.**

RULE 3: **Two or more orbitals with the same energy—the three p orbitals or the five d orbitals in a given shell, for example—are each half-filled by one electron before any one orbital is completely filled by addition of the second electron.**

Electron configurations of the first 20 elements are shown in Table 2.3. Notice that the number of electrons in each subshell is indicated by a superscript. For example, the notation $1s^2\,2s^2\,2p^6\,3s^2$ for magnesium means that magnesium atoms have 2 electrons in the first shell, 8 electrons in the second shell, and 2 electrons in the third shell.

8 electrons in second shell

2 electrons in first shell

2 electrons in third shell

Mg (atomic number 12): $1s^2\,2s^2\,2p^6\,3s^2$

Electron configuration The specific arrangement of electrons in an atom's shells and subshells.

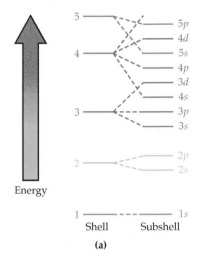

(a)

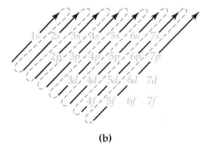

(b)

▲ **Figure 2.6**
Order of orbital energy levels.
(a) An energy-level diagram shows the order in which orbitals will be filled within each shell. Above the 3p level, there is some crossover of energies among orbitals in different shells.
(b) A simple scheme to remember the order in which the orbitals are filled.

TABLE 2.3 Electron Configurations of the First 20 Elements

	Element	Atomic Number	Electron Configuration
H	Hydrogen	1	$1s^1$
He	Helium	2	$1s^2$
Li	Lithium	3	$1s^2\,2s^1$
Be	Beryllium	4	$1s^2\,2s^2$
B	Boron	5	$1s^2\,2s^2\,2p^1$
C	Carbon	6	$1s^2\,2s^2\,2p^2$
N	Nitrogen	7	$1s^2\,2s^2\,2p^3$
O	Oxygen	8	$1s^2\,2s^2\,2p^4$
F	Fluorine	9	$1s^2\,2s^2\,2p^5$
Ne	Neon	10	$1s^2\,2s^2\,2p^6$
Na	Sodium	11	$1s^2\,2s^2\,2p^6\,3s^1$
Mg	Magnesium	12	$1s^2\,2s^2\,2p^6\,3s^2$
Al	Aluminum	13	$1s^2\,2s^2\,2p^6\,3s^2\,3p^1$
Si	Silicon	14	$1s^2\,2s^2\,2p^6\,3s^2\,3p^2$
P	Phosphorus	15	$1s^2\,2s^2\,2p^6\,3s^2\,3p^3$
S	Sulfur	16	$1s^2\,2s^2\,2p^6\,3s^2\,3p^4$
Cl	Chlorine	17	$1s^2\,2s^2\,2p^6\,3s^2\,3p^5$
Ar	Argon	18	$1s^2\,2s^2\,2p^6\,3s^2\,3p^6$
K	Potassium	19	$1s^2\,2s^2\,2p^6\,3s^2\,3p^6\,4s^1$
Ca	Calcium	20	$1s^2\,2s^2\,2p^6\,3s^2\,3p^6\,4s^2$

As you read through the following electron configurations, check the atomic number and the location of each element in the periodic table (Figure 2.2). See if you can detect the relationship between electron configuration and position in the table.

- **Hydrogen ($Z = 1$):** The single electron in a hydrogen atom is in the lowest-energy, $1s$, level. The configuration can be represented in either of two ways:

$$\textbf{H} \qquad 1s^1 \quad \text{or} \quad \overset{\uparrow}{\underset{1s^1}{\rule{1.5em}{0.4pt}}}$$

In the written representation, the superscript in the notation $1s^1$ means that the $1s$ orbital is occupied by one electron. In the graphic representation, the $1s$ orbital is indicated by a line and the single electron in this orbital is shown by an up arrow ($\uparrow$). A single electron in an orbital is often referred to as being *unpaired*.

- **Helium ($Z = 2$):** The two electrons in helium are both in the lowest-energy, $1s$, orbital, and their spins are *paired*, as represented by up and down arrows ($\uparrow\downarrow$):

$$\textbf{He} \qquad 1s^2 \quad \text{or} \quad \overset{\uparrow\downarrow}{\underset{1s^2}{\rule{1.5em}{0.4pt}}}$$

- **Lithium ($Z = 3$):** With the first shell full, the second shell begins to fill. The third electron goes into the $2s$ orbital:

$$\textbf{Li} \qquad 1s^2\,2s^1 \quad \text{or} \quad \overset{\uparrow\downarrow}{\underset{1s^2}{\rule{1.5em}{0.4pt}}}\ \overset{\uparrow}{\underset{2s^1}{\rule{1.5em}{0.4pt}}}$$

Because $[\text{He}]$ has the configuration of a filled $1s^2$ orbital, it is sometimes substituted for the $1s^2$ orbital in depictions of electron pairing. Using this alternative shorthand notation, the electron configuration for Li is written $[\text{He}]\,2s^1$.

- **Beryllium ($Z = 4$):** An electron next pairs up to fill the $2s$ orbital:

$$\textbf{Be} \qquad 1s^2\,2s^2 \quad \text{or} \quad \overset{\uparrow\downarrow}{\underset{1s^2}{\rule{1.5em}{0.4pt}}}\ \overset{\uparrow\downarrow}{\underset{2s^2}{\rule{1.5em}{0.4pt}}} \quad \text{or} \quad [\text{He}]\,2s^2$$

- **Boron ($Z = 5$), Carbon ($Z = 6$), Nitrogen ($Z = 7$):** The next three electrons enter the three $2p$ orbitals, one at a time. Note that representing the configurations with lines and arrows gives more information than the alternative written notations because the filling and pairing of electrons in individual orbitals within the p subshell is shown.

$$\textbf{B} \qquad 1s^2\,2s^2\,2p^1 \quad \text{or} \quad \overset{\uparrow\downarrow}{\underset{1s^2}{\rule{1.5em}{0.4pt}}}\ \overset{\uparrow\downarrow}{\underset{2s^2}{\rule{1.5em}{0.4pt}}}\ \underset{2p^1}{\underbrace{\overset{\uparrow}{\rule{1.2em}{0.4pt}}\ \rule{1.2em}{0.4pt}\ \rule{1.2em}{0.4pt}}} \quad \text{or} \quad [\text{He}]\,2s^2\,2p^1$$

$$\textbf{C} \qquad 1s^2\,2s^2\,2p^2 \quad \text{or} \quad \overset{\uparrow\downarrow}{\underset{1s^2}{\rule{1.5em}{0.4pt}}}\ \overset{\uparrow\downarrow}{\underset{2s^2}{\rule{1.5em}{0.4pt}}}\ \underset{2p^2}{\underbrace{\overset{\uparrow}{\rule{1.2em}{0.4pt}}\ \overset{\uparrow}{\rule{1.2em}{0.4pt}}\ \rule{1.2em}{0.4pt}}} \quad \text{or} \quad [\text{He}]\,2s^2\,2p^2$$

$$\textbf{N} \qquad 1s^2\,2s^2\,2p^3 \quad \text{or} \quad \overset{\uparrow\downarrow}{\underset{1s^2}{\rule{1.5em}{0.4pt}}}\ \overset{\uparrow\downarrow}{\underset{2s^2}{\rule{1.5em}{0.4pt}}}\ \underset{2p^3}{\underbrace{\overset{\uparrow}{\rule{1.2em}{0.4pt}}\ \overset{\uparrow}{\rule{1.2em}{0.4pt}}\ \overset{\uparrow}{\rule{1.2em}{0.4pt}}}} \quad \text{or} \quad [\text{He}]\,2s^2\,2p^3$$

- **Oxygen ($Z = 8$), Fluorine ($Z = 9$), Neon ($Z = 10$):** Electrons now pair up one by one to fill the three $2p$ orbitals and fully occupy the second shell:

$$\textbf{O} \qquad 1s^2\,2s^2\,2p^4 \quad \text{or} \quad \overset{\uparrow\downarrow}{\underset{1s^2}{\rule{1.5em}{0.4pt}}}\ \overset{\uparrow\downarrow}{\underset{2s^2}{\rule{1.5em}{0.4pt}}}\ \underset{2p^4}{\underbrace{\overset{\uparrow\downarrow}{\rule{1.2em}{0.4pt}}\ \overset{\uparrow}{\rule{1.2em}{0.4pt}}\ \overset{\uparrow}{\rule{1.2em}{0.4pt}}}} \quad \text{or} \quad [\text{He}]\,2s^2\,2p^4$$

$$\textbf{F} \qquad 1s^2\,2s^2\,2p^5 \quad \text{or} \quad \overset{\uparrow\downarrow}{\underset{1s^2}{\rule{1.5em}{0.4pt}}}\ \overset{\uparrow\downarrow}{\underset{2s^2}{\rule{1.5em}{0.4pt}}}\ \underset{2p^5}{\underbrace{\overset{\uparrow\downarrow}{\rule{1.2em}{0.4pt}}\ \overset{\uparrow\downarrow}{\rule{1.2em}{0.4pt}}\ \overset{\uparrow}{\rule{1.2em}{0.4pt}}}} \quad \text{or} \quad [\text{He}]\,2s^2\,2p^5$$

$$\textbf{Ne} \qquad 1s^2\,2s^2\,2p^6 \quad \text{or} \quad \overset{\uparrow\downarrow}{\underset{1s^2}{\rule{1.5em}{0.4pt}}}\ \overset{\uparrow\downarrow}{\underset{2s^2}{\rule{1.5em}{0.4pt}}}\ \underset{2p^6}{\underbrace{\overset{\uparrow\downarrow}{\rule{1.2em}{0.4pt}}\ \overset{\uparrow\downarrow}{\rule{1.2em}{0.4pt}}\ \overset{\uparrow\downarrow}{\rule{1.2em}{0.4pt}}}}$$

At this point, we may use the shorthand notation $[\text{Ne}]$ to represent the electron configuration for a completely filled set of orbitals in the second shell.

- **Sodium to Calcium $(Z = 11 - 20)$:** The pattern seen for lithium through neon is seen again for sodium $(Z = 11)$ through argon $(Z = 18)$ as the 3s and 3p sub-shells fill up. For elements having a third filled shell, we may use $[Ar]$ to represent a completely filled third shell. After argon, however, the first crossover in subshell energies occurs. As indicated in Figure 2.6, the 4s subshell is lower in energy than the 3d subshell and is filled first. Potassium $(Z = 19)$ and calcium $(Z = 20)$ therefore have the following electron configurations:

K $1s^2 2s^2 2p^6 3s^2 3p^6 4s^1$ or $[Ar]4s^1$ **Ca** $1s^2 2s^2 2p^6 3s^2 3p^6 4s^2$ or $[Ar]4s^2$

Worked Example **2.7** Atomic Structure: Electron Configurations

Show how the electron configuration of magnesium can be assigned.

ANALYSIS Magnesium, $Z = 12$, has 12 electrons to be placed in specific orbitals. Assignments are made by putting 2 electrons in each orbital, according to the order shown in Figure 2.6.

- The first 2 electrons are placed in the 1s orbital $(1s^2)$.
- The next 2 electrons are placed in the 2s orbital $(2s^2)$.
- The next 6 electrons are placed in the three available 2p orbitals $(2p^6)$.
- The remaining 2 electrons are both put in the 3s orbital $(3s^2)$.

SOLUTION
Magnesium has the configuration $1s^2 2s^2 2p^6 3s^2$ or $[Ne]3s^2$.

Worked Example **2.8** Electron Configurations: Orbital-Filling Diagrams

Write the electron configuration of phosphorus, $Z = 15$, using up and down arrows to show how the electrons in each orbital are paired.

ANALYSIS Phosphorus has 15 electrons, which occupy orbitals according to the order shown in Figure 2.6.

- The first 2 are paired and fill the first shell $(1s^2)$.
- The next 8 fill the second shell $(2s^2 2p^6)$. All electrons are paired.
- The remaining 5 electrons enter the third shell, where 2 fill the 3s orbital $(3s^2)$ and 3 occupy the 3p subshell, one in each of the three p orbitals.

SOLUTION

$$\text{P} \quad \underset{1s^2}{\uparrow\downarrow} \quad \underset{2s^2}{\uparrow\downarrow} \quad \underset{2p^6}{\underbrace{\uparrow\downarrow \; \uparrow\downarrow \; \uparrow\downarrow}} \quad \underset{3s^2}{\uparrow\downarrow} \quad \underset{3p^3}{\underbrace{\uparrow \; \uparrow \; \uparrow}}$$

PROBLEM 2.19
Write electron configurations for the following elements. (You can check your answers in Table 2.3.)
(a) C   (b) P   (c) Cl   (d) K

PROBLEM 2.20
For an atom containing 33 electrons, identify the incompletely filled subshell, and show the paired and/or unpaired electrons in this subshell using up and down arrows.

🔑 KEY CONCEPT PROBLEM 2.21

Identify the atom with the following orbital-filling diagram.

$$1s^2 2s^2 2p^6 3s^2 3p^6 \quad \underset{4s}{\uparrow\downarrow} \qquad \underset{3d}{\underbrace{\uparrow\downarrow \quad \uparrow\downarrow \quad \uparrow\downarrow \quad \uparrow\downarrow \quad \uparrow\downarrow}} \qquad \underset{4p}{\underbrace{\uparrow \quad \underline{} \quad \underline{}}}$$

2.8 Electron Configurations and the Periodic Table

How is an atom's electron configuration related to its chemical behavior, and why do elements with similar behavior occur in the same group of the periodic table? As shown in Figure 2.7, the periodic table can be divided into four regions, or *blocks*, of elements according to the electron shells and subshells occupied by *the subshell filled last*.

- The main group 1A and 2A elements on the left side of the table (plus He) are called the *s*-**block elements** because an *s* subshell is filled last in these elements.
- The main group 3A–8A elements on the right side of the table (except He) are the *p*-**block elements** because a *p* subshell is filled last in these elements.
- The transition metals in the middle of the table are the *d*-**block elements** because a *d* subshell is filled last in these elements.
- The inner transition metals detached at the bottom of the table are the *f*-**block elements** because an *f* subshell is filled last in these elements.

s-Block element A main group element that results from the filling of an *s* orbital.

p-Block element A main group element that results from the filling of *p* orbitals.

d-Block element A transition metal element that results from the filling of *d* orbitals.

f-Block element An inner transition metal element that results from the filling of *f* orbitals.

Thinking of the periodic table as outlined in Figure 2.7 provides a simple way to remember the order of orbital filling shown previously in Figure 2.6. Beginning at the top left corner of the periodic table, the first row contains only two elements (H and He) because only two electrons are required to fill the *s* orbital in the first shell, $1s^2$. The second row begins with two *s*-block elements (Li and Be) and continues with six *p*-block elements (B through Ne), so electrons fill the next available *s* orbital (2*s*) and then the first available *p* orbitals (2*p*). The third row is similar to the second row, so the 3*s* and 3*p* orbitals are filled next. The fourth row again starts with 2 *s*-block elements (K and Ca) but is then followed by 10 *d*-block elements (Sc through Zn) and 6 *p*-block elements (Ga through Kr). Thus, the order of orbital filling is 4*s* followed by the first available *d* orbitals (3*d*) followed by 4*p*. Continuing through successive rows of the periodic table gives the entire filling order, identical to that shown in Figure 2.6.

$$1s \rightarrow 2s \rightarrow 2p \rightarrow 3s \rightarrow 3p \rightarrow 4s \rightarrow 3d \rightarrow 4p \rightarrow 5s \rightarrow$$
$$4d \rightarrow 5p \rightarrow 6s \rightarrow 4f \rightarrow 5d \rightarrow 6p \rightarrow 7s \rightarrow 5f \rightarrow 6d \rightarrow 7p$$

But why do the elements in a given group of the periodic table have similar properties? The answer emerges when you look at Table 2.4, which gives electron configurations for elements in the main groups 1A, 2A, 7A, and 8A. Focusing only on the

▶ **Figure 2.7**
The blocks of elements in the periodic table correspond to filling the different types of subshells.
Beginning at the top left and going across successive rows of the periodic table provides a method for remembering the order of orbital filling: $1s \rightarrow 2s \rightarrow 2p \rightarrow 3s \rightarrow 3p \rightarrow 4s \rightarrow 3d \rightarrow 4p$, and so on.

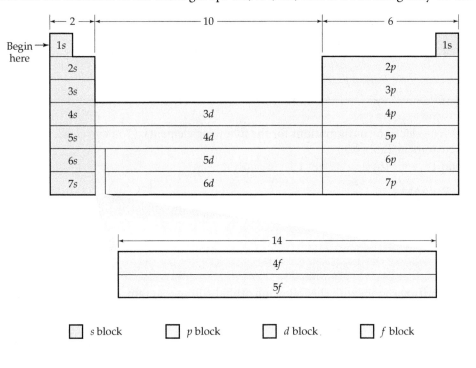

Table 2.4 Valence-Shell Electron Configurations for Group 1A, 2A, 7A, and 8A Elements

Group	Element	Atomic Number	Valence-Shell Electron Configuration
1A	Li (lithium)	3	$2s^1$
	Na (sodium)	11	$3s^1$
	K (potassium)	19	$4s^1$
	Rb (rubidium)	37	$5s^1$
	Cs (cesium)	55	$6s^1$
2A	Be (beryllium)	4	$2s^2$
	Mg (magnesium)	12	$3s^2$
	Ca (calcium)	20	$4s^2$
	Sr (strontium)	38	$5s^2$
	Ba (barium)	56	$6s^2$
7A	F (fluorine)	9	$2s^2\, 2p^5$
	Cl (chlorine)	17	$3s^2\, 3p^5$
	Br (bromine)	35	$4s^2\, 4p^5$
	I (iodine)	53	$5s^2\, 5p^5$
8A	He (helium)	2	$1s^2$
	Ne (neon)	10	$2s^2\, 2p^6$
	Ar (argon)	18	$3s^2\, 3p^6$
	Kr (krypton)	36	$4s^2\, 4p^6$
	Xe (xenon)	54	$5s^2\, 5p^6$

electrons in the outermost shell, or **valence shell**, *elements in the same group of the periodic table have similar electron configurations in their valence shells.* The group 1A elements, for example, all have one **valence electron**, ns^1 (where n represents the number of the valence shell: $n = 2$ for Li; $n = 3$ for Na; $n = 4$ for K; and so on). The group 2A elements have two valence electrons (ns^2); the group 7A elements have seven valence electrons ($ns^2\, np^5$); and the group 8A elements (except He) have eight valence electrons ($ns^2\, np^6$). You might also notice that the group numbers from 1A through 8A give the numbers of valence electrons for the elements in each main group. It is worth noting that the valence electrons are those in the outermost shell—not necessarily in the orbitals that were filled last!

What is true for the main group elements is also true for the other groups in the periodic table: atoms within a given group have the same number of valence electrons and have similar electron configurations. *Because the valence electrons are the most loosely held, they are the most important in determining an element's properties.* Similar electron configurations thus explain why the elements in a given group of the periodic table have similar chemical behavior.

Valence shell The outermost electron shell of an atom.

Valence electron An electron in the valence shell of an atom.

LOOKING AHEAD ▶▶▶ We have seen that elements in a given group have similar chemical behavior because they have similar valence electron configurations, and that many chemical properties exhibit periodic trends across the periodic table. The *chemical* behavior of nearly all the elements can be predicted based on their position in the periodic table, and this will be examined in more detail in Chapters 3 and 4. Similarly, the *nuclear* behavior of the different isotopes of a given element is related to the configuration of the nucleus (that is, the number of neutrons and protons) and will be examined in Chapter 11.

Worked Example 2.9 Electron Configurations: Valence Electrons

Write the electron configuration for the following elements, using both the complete and the shorthand notations. Indicate which electrons are the valence electrons.

(a) Na   **(b)** Cl   **(c)** Zr

ANALYSIS Locate the row and the block in which each of the elements is found in Figure 2.7. The location can be used to determine the complete electron configuration and to identify the valence electrons.

SOLUTION

(a) Na (sodium) is located in the third row and in the first column of the s-block. Therefore, all orbitals up to the $3s$ are completely filled, and there is one electron in the $3s$ orbital.

$$\text{Na: } 1s^2\, 2s^2\, 2p^6\, \underline{3s^1} \quad \text{or} \quad [\text{Ne}]\, \underline{3s^1} \quad (\text{valence electrons are underlined})$$

(b) Cl (chlorine) is located in the third row and in the fifth column of the p-block.

$$\text{Cl: } 1s^2\, 2s^2\, 2p^6\, \underline{3s^2\, 3p^5} \quad \text{or} \quad [\text{Ne}]\, \underline{3s^2\, 3p^5}$$

(c) Zr (zirconium) is located in the fifth row and in the second column of the d-block. All orbitals up to the $4d$ are completely filled, and there are 2 electrons in the $4d$ orbitals. Note that the $4d$ orbitals are filled after the $5s$ orbitals in both Figures 2.6 and 2.7.

$$\text{Zr: } 1s^2\, 2s^2\, 2p^6\, 3s^1\, 3p^6\, 4s^2\, 3d^{10}\, 4p^6\, \underline{5s^2\, 4d^2} \quad \text{or} \quad [\text{Kr}]\, \underline{5s^2\, 4d^2}$$

Worked Example 2.10 Electron Configurations: Valence-Shell Configurations

Using n to represent the number of the valence shell, write a general valence-shell configuration for the elements in group 6A.

ANALYSIS The elements in group 6A have 6 valence electrons. In each element, the first two of these electrons are in the valence s subshell, giving ns^2, and the next four electrons are in the valence p subshell, giving np^4.

SOLUTION
For group 6A, the general valence-shell configuration is $ns^2\, np^4$.

Worked Example 2.11 Electron Configurations: Inner Shells versus Valence Shell

How many electrons are in a tin atom? Give the number of electrons in each shell. How many valence electrons are there in a tin atom? Write the valence-shell configuration for tin.

ANALYSIS The total number of electrons will be the same as the atomic number for tin $(Z = 50)$. The number of valence electrons will equal the number of electrons in the valence shell.

SOLUTION
Checking the periodic table shows that tin has atomic number 50 and is in group 4A. The number of electrons in each shell is

Shell number:	1	2	3	4	5
Number of electrons:	2	8	18	18	4

As expected from the group number, tin has 4 valence electrons. They are in the $5s$ and $5p$ subshells and have the configuration $5s^2\, 5p^2$.

PROBLEM 2.22

Write the electron configuration for the following elements, using both the complete and the shorthand notations. Indicate which electrons are the valence electrons.

(a) F   **(b)** Al   **(c)** As

PROBLEM 2.23

Identify the group in which all the elements have the valence-shell configuration ns^2.

PROBLEM 2.24

For chlorine, identify the group number, give the number of electrons in each occupied shell, and write its valence-shell configuration.

🔑 KEY CONCEPT PROBLEM 2.25

Identify the group number, and write the general valence-shell configuration (for example, ns^1 for group 1A elements) for the elements indicated in red in the following periodic table.

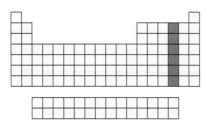

2.9 Electron-Dot Symbols

Valence electrons play such an important role in the behavior of atoms that it is useful to have a method for including them with atomic symbols. In an **electron-dot symbol**, dots are placed around the atomic symbol to indicate the number of valence electrons present. A group 1A atom, such as sodium, has a single dot; a group 2A atom, such as magnesium, has two dots; a group 3A atom, such as boron, has three dots; and so on.

Table 2.5 gives electron-dot symbols for atoms of the first few elements in each main group. As shown, the dots are distributed around the four sides of the element symbol, singly at first until each of the four sides has one dot. As more electron dots are added they will form pairs, with no more than two dots on a side. Note that helium differs from other noble gases in having only two valence electrons rather than eight. Nevertheless, helium is considered a member of group 8A because its properties resemble those of the other noble gases and because its highest occupied subshell is filled $(1s^2)$.

Electron-dot symbol An atomic symbol with dots placed around it to indicate the number of valence electrons.

TABLE 2.5 Electron-Dot Symbols for Some Main Group Elements							
1A	**2A**	**3A**	**4A**	**5A**	**6A**	**7A**	**NOBLE GASES**
H·							He:
Li·	·Be·	·Ḃ·	·Ċ·	·Ṅ:	·Ö:	·F̈:	:Ṅe:
Na·	·Mg·	·Äl·	·Ṡi·	·P̈·	·S̈:	·C̈l:	:Är:
K·	·Ca·	·Ga·	·Ge·	·As:	·Se:	·Br:	:Kr:

CHEMISTRY IN ACTION

Atoms and Light

What we see as *light* is really a wave of energy moving through space. The shorter the length of the wave (the *wavelength*), the higher the energy; the longer the wavelength, the lower the energy.

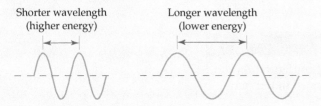

Shorter wavelength (higher energy)   Longer wavelength (lower energy)

▲ **The brilliant colors of fireworks are due to the release of the energy from excited atoms as electrons fall from higher to lower energy levels.**

Visible light has wavelengths in the range 400–800 nm, but that is just one small part of the overall *electromagnetic spectrum*, shown in the accompanying figure. Although we cannot see the other wavelengths of electromagnetic energy, we use them for many purposes and their names may be familiar to you: gamma rays, X rays, ultraviolet (UV) rays, infrared (IR) rays, microwaves, and radio waves.

What happens when a beam of electromagnetic energy collides with an atom? Remember that electrons are located in orbitals based on their energy levels. An atom with its electrons in their usual, lowest-energy locations is said to be in its *ground state*. If the amount of electromagnetic energy is just right, an electron can be kicked up from its usual energy level to a higher one. Energy from an electrical discharge or in the form of heat can also boost electrons to higher energy levels. With one of its electrons promoted to a higher energy, an atom is said to be *excited*. The excited state does not last long, though, because the electron quickly drops back to its more stable, ground-state energy level, releasing its extra energy in the process. If the released energy falls in the range of visible

light, we can see the result. Many practical applications, from neon lights to fireworks, are the result of this phenomenon.

In "neon" lights, noble gas atoms are excited by an electric discharge, giving rise to a variety of colors that depend on the gas—red from neon, white from krypton, and blue from argon—as electrons release energy and return to their ground states. Similarly, mercury or sodium atoms excited by electrical energy are responsible for the intense bluish or yellowish light, respectively, provided by some street lamps. In the same manner, metal atoms excited by heat are responsible for the spectacular colors of fireworks—red from strontium, green from barium, and blue from copper, for example.

The concentration of certain biologically important metals in body fluids, such as blood or urine, is measured by sensitive instruments relying on the same principle of electron excitation that we see in fireworks. These instruments measure the intensity of color produced in a flame by lithium (red), sodium (yellow), and potassium (violet), to determine the concentrations of these metals, which are included in most clinical lab reports.

See Chemistry in Action Problems 2.88 and 2.89 at the end of the chapter.

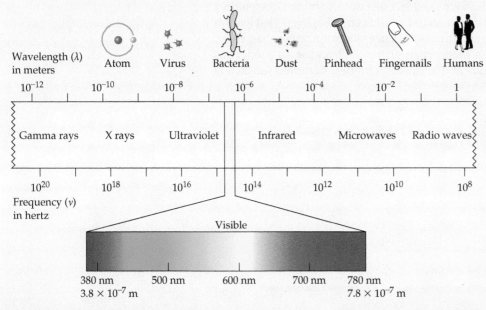

Wavelength (λ) in meters

| Atom | Virus | Bacteria | Dust | Pinhead | Fingernails | Humans |

10^{-12} 10^{-10} 10^{-8} 10^{-6} 10^{-4} 10^{-2} 1

Gamma rays   X rays   Ultraviolet   Infrared   Microwaves   Radio waves

10^{20} 10^{18} 10^{16} 10^{14} 10^{12} 10^{10} 10^{8}

Frequency (*v*) in hertz

Visible

380 nm   500 nm   600 nm   700 nm   780 nm
3.8×10^{-7} m 7.8×10^{-7} m

◄ **The electromagnetic spectrum consists of a continuous range of wavelengths, with the familiar visible region accounting for only a small portion near the middle of the range.**

Worked Example **2.12** Electron Configurations: Electron-Dot Symbols

Write the electron-dot symbol for any element X in group 5A.

ANALYSIS The group number, 5A, indicates 5 valence electrons. The first four are distributed singly around the four sides of the element symbol, and any additional are placed to form electron pairs.

SOLUTION

$\cdot\ddot{X}:$ (5 electrons)

PROBLEM 2.26

Write the electron-dot symbol for any element X in group 3A.

PROBLEM 2.27

Write electron-dot symbols for radon, lead, xenon, and radium.

PROBLEM 2.28

When an electron in a strontium atom drops from the excited state to the ground state, it emits red light, as explained in the Chemistry in Action on p. 66. When an electron in a copper atom drops from the excited state to the ground state, it emits blue light. What are the approximate wavelengths of the red light and the blue light? Which color is associated with higher energy?

SUMMARY: REVISITING THE CHAPTER GOALS

1. What is the modern theory of atomic structure? All matter is composed of *atoms*. An atom is the smallest and simplest unit into which a sample of an element can be divided while maintaining the properties of the element. Atoms are made up of subatomic particles called *protons, neutrons*, and *electrons*. Protons have a positive electrical charge, neutrons are electrically neutral, and electrons have a negative electrical charge. The protons and neutrons in an atom are present in a dense, positively charged central region called the *nucleus*. Electrons are situated a relatively large distance away from the nucleus, leaving most of the atom as empty space (*see Problems 34, 42, 43*).

2. How do atoms of different elements differ? Elements differ according to the number of protons their atoms contain, a value called the element's *atomic number* (Z). All atoms of a given element have the same number of protons and an equal number of electrons. The number of neutrons in an atom is not predictable but is generally as great or greater than the number of protons. The total number of protons plus neutrons in an atom is called the atom's *mass number* (A) (*see Problems 35, 44, 46, 86, 87, 92*).

3. What are isotopes, and what is atomic weight? Atoms with identical numbers of protons and electrons but different numbers of neutrons are called *isotopes*. The atomic weight of an element is the weighted average mass of atoms of the element's naturally occurring isotopes measured in *atomic mass units* (amu) (*see Problems 36–41, 45–53, 92, 96, 97*).

4. How is the periodic table arranged? Elements are organized into the *periodic table*, consisting of 7 rows, or *periods*, and 18 columns, or *groups*. The 2 groups on the left side of the table and the 6 groups on the right are called the *main group elements*. The 10 groups in the middle are the *transition metal groups*, and the 14 groups pulled out and displayed below the main part of the table are called the *inner transition metal groups*. Within a given group in the table, elements have the same number of valence electrons in their valence shell and similar electron configurations (*see Problems 29, 30, 54–65, 90, 91, 93*).

5. How are electrons arranged in atoms? The electrons surrounding an atom are grouped into layers, or *shells*. Within each shell, electrons are grouped into *subshells*, and within each subshell into *orbitals*—regions of space in which electrons are most likely to be found. The s orbitals are spherical, and the p orbitals are dumbbell-shaped.

Each shell can hold a specific number of electrons. The first shell can hold 2 electrons in an s orbital ($1s^2$); the second shell can hold 8 electrons in one s and three p orbitals ($2s^2\ 2p^6$); the third shell can hold 18 electrons in one s, three p, and five d orbitals ($3s^2\ 3p^6\ 3d^{10}$); and so on. The *electron configuration* of an element is predicted by assigning the element's electrons into orbitals, beginning with the lowest-energy orbital. The electrons in the outermost shell, or *valence shell*, can be represented using electron-dot symbols (*see Problems 31–33, 54, 55, 57, 66–83, 91, 94, 95, 98–100, 102–106*).

KEY WORDS

Alkali metal, *p. 54*

Alkaline earth metal, *p. 55*

Atom, *p. 45*

Atomic mass unit (amu), *p. 46*

Atomic number (Z), *p. 48*

Atomic theory, *p. 45*

Atomic weight, *p. 50*

d-Block element, *p. 62*

Electron, *p. 46*

Electron configuration, *p. 59*

Electron-dot symbol, *p. 65*

f-Block element, *p. 62*

Group, *p. 52*

Halogen, *p. 55*

Inner transition metal element, *p. 52*

Isotopes, *p. 50*

Main group element, *p. 52*

Mass number (*A*), *p. 49*

Neutron, *p. 46*

Noble gas, *p. 55*

Nucleus, *p. 46*

Orbital, *p. 57*

p-Block element, *p. 62*

Period, *p. 52*

Proton, *p. 46*

s-Block element, *p. 62*

Shell (electron), *p. 57*

Subatomic particles, *p. 46*

Subshell (electron), *p. 57*

Transition metal element, *p. 52*

Valence electron, *p. 63*

Valence shell, *p. 63*

UNDERSTANDING KEY CONCEPTS

2.29 Where on the following outline of a periodic table do the indicated elements or groups of elements appear?

   (a) Alkali metals   **(b)** Halogens

   (c) Alkaline earth metals   **(d)** Transition metals

   (e) Hydrogen   **(f)** Helium

   (g) Metalloids

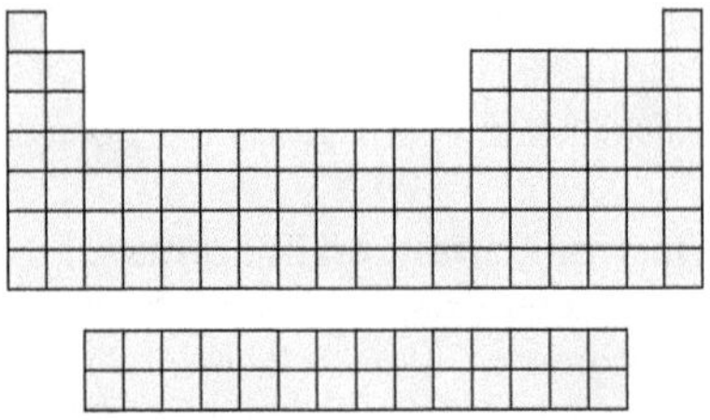

2.30 Is the element marked in red on the following periodic table likely to be a gas, a liquid, or a solid? What is the atomic number of the element in blue? Name at least one other element that is likely to be similar to the element in green.

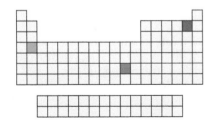

2.31 Use the blank periodic table below to show where the elements matching the following descriptions appear.

   (a) Elements with the valence-shell electron configuration $ns^2\,np^5$

   (b) An element whose third shell contains two *p* electrons

   (c) Elements with a completely filled valence shell

2.32 What atom has the following orbitial-filling diagram?

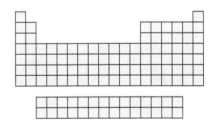

$1s^2\,2s^2\,2p^6\,3s^2\,3p^6$

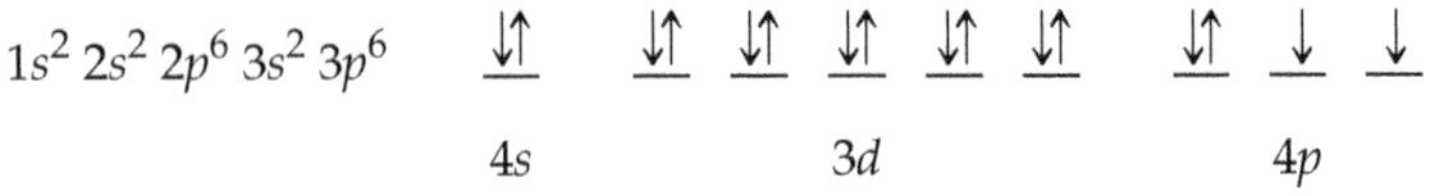

2.33 Use the orbitial-filling diagram below to show the electron configuration for As:

$1s^2\,2s^2\,2p^6\,3s^2\,3p^6$ —   — — —   — — —

                                     4s   3d   4p

ADDITIONAL PROBLEMS

ATOMIC THEORY AND THE COMPOSITION OF ATOMS

2.34   What four fundamental assumptions about atoms and matter make up modern atomic theory?

2.35   How do atoms of different elements differ?

2.36   Find the mass in grams of one atom of the following elements:

(a) Bi, atomic weight 208.9804 amu

(b) Xe, atomic weight 131.29 amu

(c) He, atomic weight 4.0026 amu

2.37   Find the mass in atomic mass units of the following:

(a) 1 O atom, with a mass of 2.66×10^{-23} g

(b) 1 Br atom, with a mass of 1.31×10^{-22} g

2.38   What is the mass in grams of 6.022×10^{23} N atoms of mass 14.01 amu?

2.39   What is the mass in grams of 6.022×10^{23} O atoms of mass 16.00 amu?

2.40   How many O atoms of mass 15.99 amu are in 15.99 g of oxygen?

2.41   How many C atoms of mass 12.00 amu are in 12.00 g of carbon?

2.42   What are the names of the three subatomic particles? What are their approximate masses in atomic mass units, and what electrical charge does each have?

2.43   Where within an atom are the three types of subatomic particles located?

2.44   Give the number of neutrons in each naturally occurring isotope of argon: argon-36, argon-38, argon-40.

2.45   Give the number of protons, neutrons, and electrons in the following isotopes:

(a) Al-27   (b) $^{28}_{14}\text{Si}$

(c) B-11   (d) $^{115}_{47}\text{Ag}$

2.46   Which of the following symbols represent isotopes of the same element?

(a) $^{19}_{9}X$ (b) $^{19}_{10}X$

(c) $^{21}_{9}X$ (d) $^{21}_{12}X$

2.47   Give the name and the number of neutrons in each isotope listed in Problem 2.46.

2.48   Write the symbols for the following isotopes:

(a) Its atoms contain 6 protons and 8 neutrons.

(b) Its atoms have mass number 39 and contain 19 protons.

(c) Its atoms have mass number 20 and contain 10 electrons.

2.49   Write the symbols for the following isotopes:

(a) Its atoms contain 50 electrons and 70 neutrons.

(b) Its atoms have $A = 56$ and $Z = 26$.

(c) Its atoms have $A = 226$ and contain 88 electrons.

2.50   There are three naturally occurring isotopes of carbon, with mass numbers of 12, 13, and 14. How many neutrons does each have? Write the symbol for each isotope, indicating its atomic number and mass number.

2.51   One of the most widely used isotopes in medical diagnostics is technicium-99*m* (the *m* indicates that it is a *metastable* isotope). Write the symbol for this isotope, indicating both mass number and atomic number.

2.52   Naturally occurring copper is a mixture of 69.17% Cu-63 with a mass of 62.93 amu and 30.83% Cu-65 with a mass of 64.93 amu. What is the atomic weight of copper?

2.53   Naturally occurring lithium is a mixture of 92.58% Li-7 with a mass of 7.016 amu and 7.42% Li-6 with a mass of 6.015 amu. What is the atomic weight of lithium?

THE PERIODIC TABLE

2.54   Why does the third period in the periodic table contain eight elements?

2.55   Why does the fourth period in the periodic table contain 18 elements?

2.56   Americium, atomic number 95, is used in household smoke detectors. What is the symbol for americium? Is americium a metal, a nonmetal, or a metalloid?

2.57   What subshell is being filled for the metalloid elements?

2.58   Answer the following questions for the elements from scandium through zinc:

(a) Are they metals or nonmetals?

(b) To what general class of elements do they belong?

(c) What subshell is being filled by electrons in these elements?

2.59   Answer the following questions for the elements from cerium through lutetium:

(a) Are they metals or nonmetals?

(b) To what general class of elements do they belong?

(c) What subshell is being filled by electrons in these elements?

2.60   For (a) rubidium (b) tungsten, (c) germanium, and (d) krypton, which of the following terms apply? (i) metal, (ii) nonmetal, (iii) metalloid (iv) transition element, (v) main group element, (vi) noble gas, (vii) alkali metal, (viii) alkaline earth metal.

2.61   For (a) calcium, (b) palladium, (c) carbon, and (d) radon, which of the following terms apply? (i) metal, (ii) nonmetal, (iii) metalloid (iv) transition element, (v) main group element, (vi) noble gas, (vii) alkali metal, (viii) alkaline earth metal.

2.62   Name an element in the periodic table that you would expect to be chemically similar to sulfur.

2.63   Name an element in the periodic table that you would expect to be chemically similar to potassium.

2.64 What elements in addition to lithium make up the alkali metal family?

2.65 What elements in addition to fluorine make up the halogen family?

ELECTRON CONFIGURATIONS

2.66 What is the maximum number of electrons that can go into an orbital?

2.67 What are the shapes and locations within an atom of s and p orbitals?

2.68 What is the maximum number of electrons that can go into the first shell? The second shell? The third shell?

2.69 What is the total number of orbitals in the third shell? The fourth shell?

2.70 How many subshells are there in the third shell? The fourth shell? The fifth shell?

2.71 How many orbitals would you expect to find in the last subshell of the fifth shell? How many electrons would you need to fill this subshell?

2.72 How many electrons are present in an atom with its $1s$, $2s$, and $2p$ subshells filled? What is this element?

2.73 How many electrons are present in an atom with its $1s$, $2s$, $2p$, $3s$, $3p$, and $4s$ subshells filled and with two electrons in the $3d$ subshell? What is this element?

2.74 Use arrows to show electron pairing in the valence p subshell of

(a) Sulfur

(b) Bromine

(c) Silicon

2.75 Use arrows to show electron pairing in the $5s$ and $4d$ orbitals of

(a) Rubidum

(b) Niobium

(c) Rhodium

2.76 Determine the number of unpaired electrons for each of the atoms in Problems 2.74 and 2.75.

2.77 Without looking back in the text, write the electron configurations for the following:

(a) Titanium $Z = 22$ (b) Phosphorus, $Z = 15$

(c) Argon, $Z = 18$ (d) Lanthanum, $Z = 57$

2.78 How many electrons does the element with $Z = 12$ have in its valence shell? Write the electron-dot symbol for this element.

2.79 How many valence electrons do group 4A elements have? Explain. Write a generic electron-dot symbol for elements in this group.

2.80 Identify the valence subshell occupied by electrons in beryllium and arsenic atoms.

2.81 What group in the periodic table has the valence-shell configuration $ns^2\ np^3$?

2.82 Give the number of valence electrons and draw electron-dot symbols for atoms of the following elements:

(a) Kr (b) C

(c) Ca (d) K

(e) B (f) Cl

2.83 Using n for the number of the valence shell, write a general valence-shell configuration for the elements in group 6A and in group 2A.

CHEMISTRY IN ACTION

2.84 What is the advantage of using a scanning tunneling microscope rather than a normal light microscope? [*Are Atoms Real? p. 48*]

2.85 For the Kanji character in the lower portion of the figure on p. 48: (a) How wide is the character in terms of iron atoms? (b) Given the radius of an iron atom is 126 pm, calculate the width of this character in centimeters. [*Are Atoms Real? p. 48*]

2.86 What are the first two elements that are made in stars? [*The Origin of Chemical Elements, p. 56*]

2.87 How are elements heavier than iron made? [*The Origin of Chemical Elements, p. 56*]

2.88 Which type of electromagnetic energy in the following pairs is of higher energy? [*Atoms and Light, p. 66*]

(a) Infrared, ultraviolet

(b) Gamma waves, microwaves

(c) Visible light, X rays

2.89 Why do you suppose ultraviolet rays from the sun are more damaging to the skin than visible light? [*Atoms and Light, p. 66*]

GENERAL QUESTIONS AND PROBLEMS

2.90 What elements in addition to helium make up the noble gas family?

2.91 Hydrogen is placed in group 1A on many periodic charts, even though it is not an alkali metal. On other periodic charts, however, hydrogen is included with group 7A even though it is not a halogen. Explain. (Hint: draw electron-dot symbols for H and for the 1A and 7A elements.)

2.92 Tellurium ($Z = 52$) has a *lower* atomic number than iodine ($Z = 53$), yet it has a *higher* atomic weight (127.60 amu for Te versus 126.90 amu for I). How is this possible?

2.93 What is the atomic number of the yet-undiscovered element directly below francium (Fr) in the periodic table?

2.94 Give the number of electrons in each shell for lead.

2.95 Identify the highest-energy occupied subshell in atoms of the following elements:

(a) Iodine (b) Scandium

(c) Arsenic (d) Aluminum

2.96 What is the atomic weight of naturally occurring bromine, which contains 50.69% Br-79 of mass 78.92 amu and 49.31% Br-81 of mass 80.91 amu?

2.97 **(a)** What is the mass (in amu and in grams) of a single atom of Carbon-12?

   (b) What is the mass (in grams) of 6.02×10^{23} atoms of Carbon-12?

   (c) Based on your answer to part (b), what would be the mass of 6.02×10^{23} atoms of Sodium-23?

2.98 An unidentified element is found to have an electron configuration by shell of 2 8 18 8 2. To what group and period does this element belong? Is the element a metal or a nonmetal? How many protons does an atom of the element have? What is the name of the element? Write its electron-dot symbol.

2.99 Germanium, atomic number 32, is used in building semiconductors for microelectronic devices, and has an electron configuration by shell of 2 8 18 4.

   (a) Write the electronic configuration for germanium.

   (b) In what shell and orbitals are the valence electrons?

2.100 Tin, atomic number 50, is directly beneath germanium (Problem 2.99) in the periodic table. What electron configuration by shell would you expect tin to have? Is tin a metal or a nonmetal?

2.101 A blood sample is found to contain 8.6 mg/dL of Ca. How many atoms of Ca are present in 8.6 mg? The atomic weight of Ca is 40.08 amu.

2.102 What is wrong with the following electron configurations?

   (a) Ni $1s^2\, 2s^2\, 2p^6\, 3s^2\, 3p^6\, 3d^{10}$

   (b) N $1s^2\, 2p^5$

   (c) Si $1s^2\, 2s^2\, 2p$ $\underline{\uparrow\downarrow}\ \underline{\quad}\ \underline{\quad}$

   (d) Mg $1s^2\, 2s^2\, 2p^6\, 3s$ $\underline{\uparrow\uparrow}$

2.103 Not all elements follow exactly the electron-filling order described in Figure 2.7. Atoms of which elements are represented by the following electron configurations?

   (a) $1s^2\, 2s^2\, 2p^6\, 3s^2\, 3p^6\, 3d^5\, 4s^1$

   (b) $1s^2\, 2s^2\, 2p^6\, 3s^2\, 3p^6\, 3d^{10}\, 4s^1$

   (c) $1s^2\, 2s^2\, 2p^6\, 3s^2\, 3p^6\, 3d^{10}\, 4s^2\, 4p^6\, 4d^5\, 5s^1$

   (d) $1s^2\, 2s^2\, 2p^6\, 3s^2\, 3p^6\, 3d^{10}\, 4s^2\, 4p^6\, 4d^{10}\, 5s^1$

2.104 What similarities do you see in the electron configurations for the atoms in Problem 2.103? How might these similarities explain their anomalous electron configurations?

2.105 Based on the identity of the elements whose electron configurations are given in Problem 2.103, write the electron configurations for the element with atomic number $Z = 79$.

2.106 What orbital is filled last in the most recently discovered element 117?

Ionic Compounds

CONTENTS

◄ Stalagmites and stalactites, such as these in a cave in the Nangu Stone Forest in China, are composed of the ionic compounds calcium carbonate, $CaCO_3$, and magnesium carbonate, $MgCO_3$.

CONCEPTS
TO REVIEW

A. The Periodic Table
(Sections 2.4 and 2.5)

B. Electron Configurations
(Sections 2.7 and 2.8)

CHAPTER GOALS

1. **What is an ion, what is an ionic bond, and what are the general characteristics of ionic compounds?**
   THE GOAL: Be able to describe ions and ionic bonds, and give the general properties of compounds that contain ionic bonds.

2. **What is the octet rule, and how does it apply to ions?**
   THE GOAL: Be able to state the octet rule, and use it to predict the electron configurations of ions of main group elements. (◀◀ B.)

3. **What is the relationship between an element's position in the periodic table and the formation of its ion?**
   THE GOAL: Be able to predict what ions are likely to be formed by atoms of a given element. (◀◀ A, B.)

4. **What determines the chemical formula of an ionic compound?**
   THE GOAL: Be able to write formulas for ionic compounds, given the identities of the ions.

5. **How are ionic compounds named?**
   THE GOAL: Be able to name an ionic compound from its formula or give the formula of a compound from its name.

6. **What are acids and bases?**
   THE GOAL: Be able to recognize common acids and bases.

There are more than 19 million known chemical compounds, ranging in size from small *diatomic* (two-atom) substances like carbon monoxide, CO, to deoxyribonucleic acid (DNA), which can contain several *billion* atoms linked together in a precise way. Clearly, there must be some force that holds atoms together in compounds; otherwise, the atoms would simply drift apart and no compounds could exist. The forces that hold atoms together in compounds are called *chemical bonds* and are of two major types: *ionic bonds* and *covalent bonds*. In this chapter, we look at ionic bonds and at the substances formed by them. In the next chapter, we will look at covalent bonds.

All chemical bonds result from the electrical attraction between opposite charges—between positively charged nuclei and negatively charged electrons. As a result, the way that different elements form bonds is related to their different electron configurations and the changes that take place as each atom tries to achieve a more stable electron configuration.

3.1 Ions

A general rule noted by early chemists is that metals, on the left side of the periodic table, tend to form compounds with nonmetals, on the right side of the table. The alkali metals of group 1A, for instance, react with the halogens of group 7A to form a variety of compounds. Sodium chloride (table salt), formed by the reaction of sodium with chlorine, is a familiar example. The names and chemical formulas of some other compounds containing elements from groups 1A and 7A include:

Potassium iodide, KI   Added to table salt to provide the iodide ion that is needed by the thyroid gland

Sodium fluoride, NaF   Added to many municipal water supplies to provide fluoride ion for the prevention of tooth decay

Sodium iodide, NaI   Used in laboratory scintillation counters to detect radiation (See Section 11.8)

The compositions and the properties of these alkali metal–halogen compounds are similar. For instance, the two elements always combine in a 1:1 ratio: one alkali metal atom for every halogen atom. Each compound has a high melting point (all are over 500 °C); each is a stable, white, crystalline solid; and each is soluble in water.

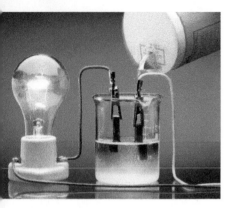

▲ **A solution of sodium chloride in water conducts electricity, allowing the bulb to light.**

Ion   An electrically charged atom or group of atoms.

Cation   A positively charged ion.

Anion   A negatively charged ion.

Furthermore, a water solution containing each compound conducts electricity, a property that gives a clue to the kind of chemical bond holding the atoms together.

Electricity can only flow through a medium containing charged particles that are free to move. The electrical conductivity of metals, for example, results from the movement of negatively charged electrons through the metal. But what charged particles might be present in the water solutions of alkali metal–halogen compounds? To answer this question, think about the composition of atoms. Atoms are electrically neutral because they contain equal numbers of protons and electrons. By gaining or losing one or more electrons, however, an atom can be converted into a charged particle called an **ion**.

The *loss* of one or more electrons from a neutral atom gives a *positively* charged ion called a **cation** (cat-ion). As we saw in Section 2.8, sodium and other alkali metal atoms have a single electron in their valence shell and an electron configuration symbolized as ns^1, where n represents the shell number. By losing this electron, an alkali metal is converted to a positively charged cation.

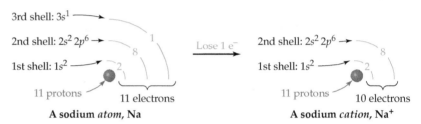

A sodium *atom*, Na   **A sodium *cation*, Na$^+$**

Conversely, the *gain* of one or more electrons by a neutral atom gives a *negatively* charged ion called an **anion** (an-ion). Chlorine and other halogen atoms have ns^2np^5 valence electrons and can easily gain an additional electron to fill out their valence subshell, thereby forming negatively charged anions.

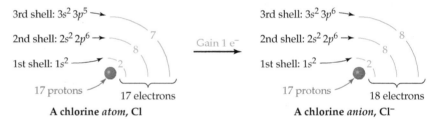

A chlorine *atom*, Cl   **A chlorine *anion*, Cl$^-$**

The symbol for a cation is written by adding the positive charge as a superscript to the symbol for the element; an anion symbol is written by adding the negative charge as a superscript. If one electron is lost or gained, the charge is +1 or −1 but the number 1 is omitted in the notation, as in Na$^+$ and Cl$^-$. If two or more electrons are lost or gained, however, the charge is ± 2 or greater and the number *is* used, as in Ca^{2+} and N^{3-}.

PROBLEM 3.1

Magnesium atoms lose two electrons when they react. Write the symbol of the ion that is formed. Is it a cation or an anion?

PROBLEM 3.2

Sulfur atoms gain two electrons when they react. Write the symbol of the ion that is formed. Is it a cation or an anion?

🔑 KEY CONCEPT PROBLEM 3.3

Write the symbol for the ion depicted here. Is it a cation or an anion?

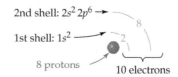

3.2 Periodic Properties and Ion Formation

The ease with which an atom loses an electron to form a positively charged cation is measured by a property called the atom's **ionization energy**, defined as the energy required to remove one electron from a single atom in the gaseous state. Conversely, the ease with which an atom *gains* an electron to form a negatively charged anion is measured by a property called **electron affinity**, defined as the energy released on adding an electron to a single atom in the gaseous state.

Ionization energy The energy required to remove one electron from a single atom in the gaseous state.

Electron affinity The energy released on adding an electron to a single atom in the gaseous state.

Ionization energy
(energy is added)   Atom + Energy $\xrightarrow{\text{Gain } e^-}$ Cation + Electron

Electron affinity
(energy is relased)   Atom + Electron $\xrightarrow{\text{Lose } e^-}$ Anion + Energy

The relative magnitudes of ionization energies and electron affinities for elements in the first four rows of the periodic table are shown in Figure 3.1. Because ionization energy measures the amount of energy that must be *added* to pull an electron away from a neutral atom, the small values shown in Figure 3.1 for alkali metals (Li, Na, K) and other elements on the left side of the periodic table mean that these elements lose an electron easily. Conversely, the large values shown for halogens (F, Cl, Br) and noble gases (He, Ne, Ar, Kr) on the right side of the periodic table mean that these elements do not lose an electron easily. Electron affinities, however, measure the amount of energy *released* when an atom gains an electron. Although electron affinities are small compared to ionization energies, the halogens nevertheless have the largest values and therefore gain an electron most easily, whereas metals have the smallest values and do not gain an electron easily:

Alkali metal {
Small ionization energy—electron easily lost
Small electron affinity—electron not easily gained
Net result: Cation formation is favored

Halogen {
Large ionization energy—electron not easily lost
Large electron affinity—electron easily gained
Net result: Anion formation is favored

You might also note in Figure 3.1 that main group elements near the *middle* of the periodic table—boron ($Z = 5$, group 3A) carbon ($Z = 6$, group 4A), and nitrogen ($Z = 7$, group 5A)—neither lose nor gain electrons easily and thus do not form ions easily. In the next chapter, we will see that these elements tend not to form ionic bonds but form covalent bonds instead.

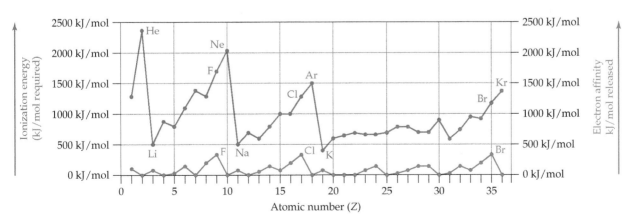

▲ **Figure 3.1**
Relative ionization energies (red) and electron affinities (blue) for elements in the first four rows of the periodic table.
Those elements having a value of zero for electron affinity do not accept an electron. Note that the alkali metals (Li, Na, K) have the lowest ionization energies and lose an electron most easily, whereas the halogens (F, Cl, Br) have the highest electron affinities and gain an electron most easily. The noble gases (He, Ne, Ar, Kr) neither gain nor lose an electron easily.

Because alkali metals such as sodium tend to lose an electron, and halogens such as chlorine tend to gain an electron, these two elements (sodium and chlorine) will react with each other by transfer of an electron from the metal to the halogen (Figure 3.2). The product that results—sodium chloride (NaCl)—is electrically neutral because the positive charge of each Na^+ ion is balanced by the negative charge of each Cl^- ion.

▶**Figure 3.2**
(a) Chlorine is a toxic green gas, sodium is a reactive metal, and sodium chloride is a harmless white solid. (b) Sodium metal burns with an intense yellow flame when immersed in chlorine gas, yielding white sodium chloride "smoke."

(a)   (b)

Worked Example 3.1 Periodic Trends: Ionization Energy

Look at the periodic trends in Figure 3.1, and predict where the ionization energy of rubidium is likely to fall on the chart.

ANALYSIS Identify the group number of rubidium (group 1A), and find where other members of the group appear in Figure 3.1.

SOLUTION
Rubidium (Rb) is the alkali metal below potassium (K) in the periodic table. Since the alkali metals Li, Na, and K all have ionization energies near the bottom of the chart, the ionization energy of rubidium is probably similar.

Worked Example 3.2 Periodic Trends: Formation of Anions and Cations

Which element is likely to lose an electron more easily, Mg or S?

ANALYSIS Identify the group numbers of the elements, and find where members of those groups appear in Figure 3.1.

SOLUTION
Magnesium, a group 2A element on the left side of the periodic table, has a relatively low ionization energy, and loses an electron easily. Sulfur, a group 6A element on the right side of the table, has a higher ionization energy, and loses an electron less easily.

PROBLEM 3.4
Look at the periodic trends in Figure 3.1, and predict approximately where the ionization energy of xenon is likely to fall.

PROBLEM 3.5
Which element in the following pairs is likely to lose an electron more easily?
(a) Be or B   **(b)** Ca or Co   **(c)** Sc or Se

PROBLEM 3.6
Which element in the following pairs is likely to gain an electron more easily?
(a) H or He   **(b)** S or Si   **(c)** Cr or Mn

3.3 Ionic Bonds

When sodium reacts with chlorine, the product is sodium chloride, a compound completely unlike either of the elements from which it is formed. Sodium is a soft, silvery metal that reacts violently with water, and chlorine is a corrosive, poisonous, green gas (Figure 3.2a). When chemically combined, however, they produce our familiar table salt containing Na$^+$ ions and Cl$^-$ ions. Because opposite electrical charges attract each other, the positive Na$^+$ ion and negative Cl$^-$ ion are said to be held together by an **ionic bond**.

When a vast number of sodium atoms transfer electrons to an equally vast number of chlorine atoms, a visible crystal of sodium chloride results. In this crystal, equal numbers of Na$^+$ and Cl$^-$ ions are packed together in a regular arrangement. Each positively charged Na$^+$ ion is surrounded by six negatively charged Cl$^-$ ions, and each Cl$^-$ ion is surrounded by six Na$^+$ ions (Figure 3.3). This packing arrangement allows each ion to be stabilized by the attraction of unlike charges on its six nearest-neighbor ions, while being as far as possible from ions of like charge.

Ionic bond The electrical attractions between ions of opposite charge in a crystal.

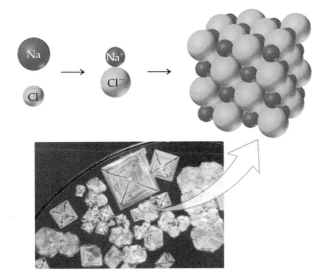

◄ **Figure 3.3**
The arrangement of Na$^+$ and Cl$^-$ ions in a sodium chloride crystal. Each positively charged Na$^+$ ion is surrounded by six negatively charged Cl$^-$ ions, and each Cl$^-$ ion is surrounded by six Na$^+$ ions. The crystal is held together by ionic bonds—the attraction between oppositely charged ions.

Because of the three-dimensional arrangement of ions in a sodium chloride crystal, we cannot speak of specific ionic bonds between specific pairs of ions. Rather, there are many ions attracted by ionic bonds to their nearest neighbors. We therefore speak of the whole NaCl crystal as being an **ionic solid** and of such compounds as being **ionic compounds**. The same is true of all compounds composed of ions.

Ionic solid A crystalline solid held together by ionic bonds.

Ionic compound A compound that contains ionic bonds.

3.4 Some Properties of Ionic Compounds

Like sodium chloride, ionic compounds are usually crystalline solids. Different ions vary in size and charge, therefore, they are packed together in crystals in different ways. The ions in each compound settle into a pattern that efficiently fills space and maximizes ionic bonding.

Because the ions in an ionic solid are held rigidly in place by attraction to their neighbors, they cannot move about. Once an ionic solid is dissolved in water, however, the ions can move freely, thereby accounting for the electrical conductivity of these compounds in solution.

The high melting points and boiling points observed for ionic compounds are also accounted for by ionic bonding. The attractive force between oppositely charged particles is extremely strong, and the ions need to gain a large amount of energy by being heated to high temperatures for them to loosen their grip on one another. Sodium chloride, for example, melts at 801 °C and boils at 1413 °C; potassium iodide melts at 681 °C and boils at 1330 °C.

▲ **The melting point of sodium chloride is 801 °C.**

Despite the strength of ionic bonds, ionic solids shatter if struck sharply. A blow disrupts the orderly arrangement of cations and anions, forcing particles of like electrical charge closer together. The close proximity of like charges creates repulsive energies that split the crystal apart.

Ionic compounds dissolve in water if the attraction between water and the ions overcomes the attraction of the ions for one another. Compounds like sodium chloride are very soluble in water and can be dissolved to make solutions of high concentration. Do not be misled, however, by the ease with which sodium chloride and other familiar ionic compounds dissolve in water. Many other ionic compounds, such as magnesium hydroxide or barium sulfate, are not water-soluble, because the attractive forces between these ions and water is not sufficient to overcome the ionic attractions in the crystals.

PROBLEM 3.7
Consider the ionic liquids described in the Chemistry in Action below. How are the properties of these ionic liquids different from other common ionic substances?

CHEMISTRY IN ACTION

Ionic Liquids

Imagine a substance that could help solve the problems of nuclear waste, make solar energy more efficient, revolutionize the development of biomass-based renewable energies, serve as a solvent for enzyme-based biochemical transformations, and act as a major component in a spinning-liquid mirror telescope stationed on the moon. Ionic liquids can do all that—and more! When discussing ionic substances, most of us think of hard, crystalline materials like common table salt (see Chemistry in Action, p. 83), with high melting points. But ionic liquids have very different properties, including low melting points, high viscosity, low-to-moderate electrical conductivity, and low volatility, which make them suitable for the widely varied uses described previously.

Although the details of the discovery of ionic liquids are in dispute, one of the first *room temperature ionic liquids* (or RTILs), ethylammonium nitrate, was synthesized in 1914 by Paul Walden. Most RTILs developed since then consist of a bulky, asymmetric organic cation (see Organic Chemistry in Chapters 12–19), combined with a variety of anions. The bulky cations cannot pack together in an ordered fashion, and so these substances do not condense into a solid at ambient temperatures. Rather, they tend to form highly viscous liquids that exhibit low volatility, ideal properties for a large-diameter spinning liquid mirror in a low-pressure environment like the moon. The viscous liquid can be covered with a thin metallic film that will form a parabolic reflective surface to collect long-wavelength infrared light. And the cost of the spinning-liquid mirror is about 1% of a conventional lens, which must be ground and polished.

The bulky cations also provide unique solvent properties, enabling them to dissolve substances that are not very soluble in more conventional solvents. Their low volatility also makes them attractive as "green," or environmentally friendly, solvents. Consider the practice of using biomass as a fuel source. One common approach is to convert sugar or starch (from corn, beets, or cane sugar) into ethanol by the process of fermentation. But the major component of these and most other plants is cellulose. Cellulose is a polymer (see Chemistry in Action on pp. 118 and 538) composed of many sugars joined together in a long chain. Cellulose is chemically similar to starch but is neither highly soluble in most solvents nor subject to fermentation. RTILs, however, such as that illustrated in the figure below, can be used to dissolve cellulose at moderate temperatures and facilitate its breakdown into simple fermentable sugars. At a volume of nearly 700 billion tons of the earth's biomass, cellulose represents an important renewable energy source. The ability to convert cellulose into fuel will certainly help meet our expanding energy needs.

See Chemistry in Action Problems 3.80 and 3.81 at the end of the chapter.

Benzylmethylimidazolium chloride

◀ **Pine wood fibers dissolving in an ionic liquid solvent consisting of benzyl methyl imidazolium chloride, whose structural formula is shown.**

3.5 Ions and the Octet Rule

We have seen that alkali metal atoms have a single valence-shell electron, ns^1. The electron-dot symbol X· is consistent with this valence electron configuration. Halogens, having seven valence electrons, ns^2np^5, can be represented using $:\overset{\cdot\cdot}{\underset{\cdot}{X}}\cdot$ as the electron-dot symbol. Noble gases can be represented as $:\overset{\cdot\cdot}{\underset{\cdot\cdot}{X}}:$, since they have eight valence electrons, ns^2np^6. Both the alkali metals and the halogens are extremely reactive, undergoing many chemical reactions and forming many compounds. The noble gases, however, are quite different. They are the least reactive of all elements.

Now look at sodium chloride and similar ionic compounds. When sodium or any other alkali metal reacts with chlorine or any other halogen, the metal transfers an electron from its valence shell to the valence shell of the halogen. Sodium thereby changes its valence-shell electron configuration from $2s^22p^63s^1$ in the atom to $2s^22p^6(3s^0)$ in the Na^+ ion, and chlorine changes from $3s^23p^5$ in the atom to $3s^23p^6$ in the Cl^- ion. *As a result, both sodium and chlorine gain noble gas electron configurations, with 8 valence electrons.* The Na^+ ion has 8 electrons in the $n = 2$ shell, matching the electron configuration of neon. The Cl^- ion has 8 electrons in the $n = 3$ shell, matching the electron configuration of argon.

$$\underset{1s^2\,2s^2\,2p^6\,3s^1}{Na} \quad + \quad \underset{1s^2\,2s^2\,2p^6\,3s^2\,3p^5}{Cl} \quad \longrightarrow \quad \underset{\underbrace{1s^2\,2s^2\,2p^63s^0}_{\substack{Neon\\configuration}}}{Na^+} \quad + \quad \underset{\underbrace{1s^2\,2s^2\,2p^6\,3s^2\,3p^6}_{\substack{Argon\\configuration}}}{Cl^-}$$

$$Na\cdot \quad + \quad \cdot\overset{\cdot\cdot}{\underset{\cdot\cdot}{Cl}}: \quad \longrightarrow \quad Na^+ \quad + \quad :\overset{\cdot\cdot}{\underset{\cdot\cdot}{Cl}}:^-$$

Evidently there is something special about having 8 valence electrons (filled s and p subshells) that leads to stability and lack of chemical reactivity. In fact, observations of many chemical compounds have shown that main group elements frequently combine in such a way that each winds up with 8 valence electrons, a so-called *electron octet*. This conclusion is summarized in a statement called the **octet rule**:

Octet rule Main group elements tend to undergo reactions that leave them with 8 valence electrons.

Put another way, main group *metals* tend to lose electrons when they react so that they attain an electron configuration like that of the noble gas just *before* them in the periodic table, and reactive main group *nonmetals* tend to gain electrons when they react so that they attain an electron configuration like that of the noble gas just *after* them in the periodic table. In both cases, the product ions have filled s and p subshells in their valence electron shell.

Worked Example 3.3 Electron Configurations: Octet Rule for Cations

Write the electron configuration of magnesium $(Z = 12)$. Show how many electrons a magnesium atom must lose to form an ion with a filled shell (8 electrons), and write the configuration of the ion. Explain the reason for the ion's charge, and write the ion's symbol.

ANALYSIS Write the electron configuration of magnesium as described in Section 2.7 and count the number of electrons in the valence shell.

SOLUTION

Magnesium has the electron configuration $1s^22s^22p^63s^2$. Since the second shell contains an octet of electrons $(2s^22p^6)$ and the third shell is only partially filled $(3s^2)$, magnesium can achieve a valence-shell octet by losing the 2 electrons in the

$3s$ subshell. The result is formation of a doubly charged cation, Mg^{2+}, with the neon configuration:

$$Mg^{2+} \qquad 1s^2 2s^2 2p^6 \text{ (Neon configuration, or } [\,Ne\,])$$

A neutral magnesium atom has 12 protons and 12 electrons. With the loss of 2 electrons, there is an excess of 2 protons, accounting for the +2 charge of the ion, Mg^{2+}.

Worked Example 3.4 Electron Configurations: Octet Rule for Anions

How many electrons must a nitrogen atom, $Z = 7$, gain to attain a noble gas configuration? Write the electron-dot and ion symbols for the ion formed.

ANALYSIS Write the electron configuration of nitrogen, and identify how many more electrons are needed to reach a noble gas configuration.

SOLUTION
Nitrogen, a group 5A element, has the electron configuration $1s^2 2s^2 2p^3$. The second shell contains 5 electrons $(2s^2 2p^3)$ and needs 3 more to reach an octet. The result is formation of a triply charged anion, N^{3-}, with 8 valence electrons, matching the neon configuration:

$$N^{3-} \qquad 1s^2 2s^2 2p^6 \quad \text{(Neon configuration)} \quad \ddot{\underset{\cdot\cdot}{:N}} :^{3-}$$

PROBLEM 3.8
Write the electron configuration of potassium, $Z = 19$, and show how a potassium atom can attain a noble gas configuration.

PROBLEM 3.9
How many electrons must an aluminum atom, $Z = 13$, lose to attain a noble gas configuration? Write the symbol for the ion formed.

 KEY CONCEPT PROBLEM 3.10

Which atom in the reaction depicted here gains electrons, and which loses electrons? Draw the electron-dot symbols for the resulting ions.

$$X: + \cdot \ddot{Y} \cdot \longrightarrow ?$$

3.6 Ions of Some Common Elements

The periodic table is the key to understanding and remembering which elements form ions and which do not. As shown in Figure 3.4, atoms of elements in the same group tend to form ions of the same charge. The metals of groups 1A and 2A, for example, form only +1 and +2 ions, respectively. The ions of these elements

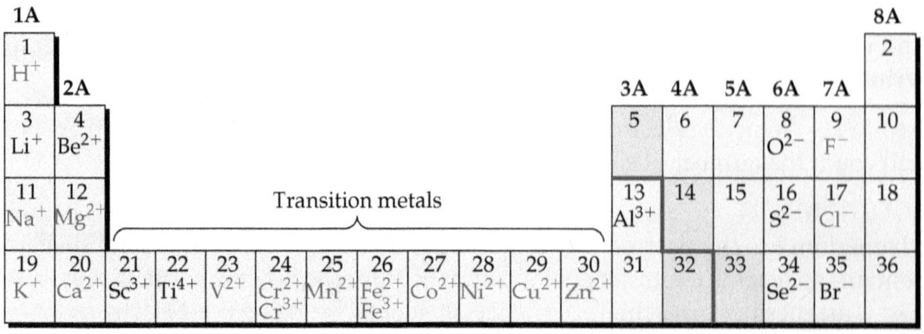

▶ **Figure 3.4**
Common ions formed by elements in the first four periods.
Ions important in biological chemistry are shown in red.

all have noble gas configurations as a result of electron loss from their valence s subshells. (Note in the following equations that the electrons being lost are shown as products.)

Group 1A: $M \cdot \rightarrow M^+ + e^-$
$(M = Li, Na, K, Rb, or Cs)$

Group 2A: $M: \rightarrow M^{2+} + 2e^-$
$(M = Be, Mg, Ca, Sr, Ba, or Ra)$

Four of these ions, Na^+, K^+, Mg^{2+}, and Ca^{2+}, are present in body fluids, where they play extremely important roles in biochemical processes.

The only group 3A element commonly encountered in ionic compounds is aluminum, which forms Al^{3+} by loss of three electrons from its valence s and p subshells. Aluminum is not thought to be an essential element in the human diet, although it is known to be present in some organisms.

The first three elements in groups 4A (C, Si, Ge) and 5A (N, P, As) do not ordinarily form cations or anions, because either too much energy is required to remove an electron or not enough energy is released by adding an electron to make the process energetically favorable. The bonding of these elements is largely covalent and will be described in the next chapter. Carbon, in particular, is the key element on which life is based. Together with hydrogen, nitrogen, phosphorus, and oxygen, carbon is present in all the essential biological compounds that we will be describing throughout the latter half of this book.

The group 6A elements, oxygen and sulfur, form large numbers of compounds, some of which are ionic and some of which are covalent. Their ions have noble gas configurations, achieved by gaining two electrons:

Group 6A: $\cdot \ddot{O} \cdot + 2e^- \longrightarrow : \ddot{O} :^{2-}$

$\cdot \ddot{S} \cdot + 2e^- \longrightarrow : \ddot{S} :^{2-}$

The halogens are present in many compounds as ions formed by gaining one electron:

Group 7A: $\cdot \ddot{X} : + e^- \longrightarrow : \ddot{X} :^-$
$(X = F, Cl, Br, I)$

Transition metals lose electrons to form cations, some of which are present in the human body. The charges of transition metal cations are not as predictable as those of main group elements, however, because many transition metal atoms can lose one or more d electrons in addition to losing valence s electrons. For example, iron $(\ldots 3s^2 3p^6 3d^6 4s^2)$ forms Fe^{2+} by losing two electrons from the $4s$ subshell and also forms Fe^{3+} by losing an additional electron from the $3d$ subshell. Looking at the electron configuration for iron shows why the octet rule is limited to main group elements: transition metal cations generally do not have noble gas configurations because they would have to lose *all* their d electrons.

Important Points about Ion Formation and the Periodic Table:

- **Metals form cations by losing one or more electrons.**
  - Group 1A and 2A metals form +1 and +2 ions, respectively (for example, Li^+ and Mg^{2+}) to achieve a noble gas configuration.
  - Transition metals can form cations of more than one charge (for example, Fe^{2+} and Fe^{3+}) by losing a combination of valence-shell s electrons and inner-shell d electrons.

- **Reactive nonmetals form anions by gaining one or more electrons to achieve a noble gas configuration.**
  - Group 6A nonmetals oxygen and sulfur form the anions O^{2-} and S^{2-}.
  - Group 7A elements (the halogens) form −1 ions; for example, F^- and Cl^-.

- **Group 8A elements (the noble gases) are unreactive.**
- **Ionic charges of main group elements can be predicted using the group number and the octet rule.**
  - For 1A and 2A metals: cation charge = group number
  - For nonmetals in groups 5A, 6A, and 7A: anion charge = 8 − (group number)

Worked Example 3.5 Formation of Ions: Gain/Loss of Valence Electrons

Which of the following ions is likely to form?

(a) S^{3-} (b) Si^{2+} (c) Sr^{2+}

ANALYSIS Count the number of valence electrons in each ion. For main group elements, only ions with a valence octet of electrons are likely to form.

SOLUTION

(a) Sulfur is in group 6A, has 6 valence electrons, and needs only 2 more to reach an octet. Gaining 2 electrons gives an S^{2-} ion with a noble gas configuration, but gaining 3 electrons does not. The S^{3-} ion is, therefore, unlikely to form.

(b) Silicon is a nonmetal in group 4A. Like carbon, it does not form ions because it would have to gain or lose too many electrons (4) to reach a noble gas electron configuration. The Si^{2+} ion does not have an octet and will not form.

(c) Strontium, a metal in group 2A, has only 2 outer-shell electrons and can lose both to reach a noble gas configuration. The Sr^{2+} ion has an octet and, therefore, forms easily.

PROBLEM 3.11
Is molybdenum more likely to form a cation or an anion? Why?

PROBLEM 3.12
Write symbols, both with and without electron dots, for the ions formed by the following processes:

(a) Gain of 2 electrons by selenium   (b) Loss of 2 electrons by barium
(c) Gain of 1 electron by bromine

PROBLEM 3.13
By mass, seawater contains 3.5% NaCl, or table salt (see Chemistry in Action, p. 83). If one liter of seawater contains 35 g of NaCl, how many gallons of water must be evaporated to produce one pound of NaCl?

3.7 Naming Ions

Main group metal cations in groups 1A, 2A, and 3A are named by identifying the metal, followed by the word "ion," as in the following examples:

$$K^+ \qquad Mg^{2+} \qquad Al^{3+}$$
Potassium ion   Magnesium ion   Aluminum ion

It is sometimes a little confusing to use the same name for both a metal and its ion, and you may occasionally have to stop and think about what is meant. For example, it is common practice in nutrition and health-related fields to talk about sodium or potassium in the bloodstream. Because both sodium and potassium *metals* react violently with water, however, they cannot possibly be present in blood. The references are to dissolved sodium and potassium *ions*.

Transition metals, such as iron or chromium, and many metals found in the *p*-block, such as tin and lead, can form more than one type of cation. To avoid confusion, a method is needed to differentiate between ions of these metals. Two systems are used. The first is an old system that gives the ion with the smaller charge the word ending *-ous* and the ion with the larger charge the ending *-ic*.

CHEMISTRY IN ACTION

Salt

If you are like most people, you feel a little guilty about reaching for the salt shaker at mealtime. The notion that high salt intake and high blood pressure go hand in hand is surely among the most highly publicized pieces of nutritional lore ever to appear.

Salt has not always been held in such disrepute. Historically, salt has been prized since the earliest recorded times as a seasoning and a food preservative. Words and phrases in many languages reflect the importance of salt as a life-giving and life-sustaining substance. We refer to a kind and generous person as "the salt of the earth," for instance, and we speak of being "worth one's salt." In Roman times, soldiers were paid in salt; the English word "salary" is derived from the Latin word for paying salt wages (*salarium*).

Salt is perhaps the easiest of all minerals to obtain and purify. The simplest method, used for thousands of years throughout the world in coastal climates where sunshine is abundant and rainfall is scarce, is to evaporate seawater. Though the exact amount varies depending on the source, seawater contains an average of about 3.5% by mass of dissolved substances, most of which is sodium chloride. It has been estimated that evaporation of all the world's oceans would yield approximately *4.5 million cubic miles* of NaCl.

Only about 10% of current world salt production comes from evaporation of seawater. Most salt is obtained by mining the vast deposits of *halite*, or *rock salt*, formed by evaporation of ancient inland seas. These salt beds vary in thickness up to hundreds of meters and vary in depth from a few meters to thousands of meters below the earth's surface. Salt mining has gone on for at least 3400 years, and the Wieliczka mine in Galicia, Poland, has been worked continuously from A.D. 1000 to the present.

What about the link between dietary salt intake and high blood pressure? Although sodium is a macronutrient that we need—it plays a critical role in charge balance and ion transport in cell membranes—too much sodium has been linked to both hypertension and kidney ailments. The recommended daily intake (RDI) for sodium is 2300 mg, which translates to roughly 4 g of salt. However, the average adult in most industrialized countries consumes over twice this amount, with most of it coming from processed foods.

What should an individual do? The best answer, as in so many things, is to use moderation and common sense. People with hypertension should make a strong effort to lower their

▲ **In many areas of the world, salt is still harvested by evaporation of ocean or tidal waters.**

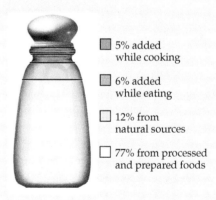

- ■ 5% added while cooking
- ■ 6% added while eating
- □ 12% from natural sources
- □ 77% from processed and prepared foods

sodium intake; others might be well advised to choose unsalted snacks, monitor their consumption of processed food, and read nutrition labels for sodium content.

See Chemistry in Action Problem 3.82 at the end of the chapter.

The second is a newer system in which the charge on the ion is given as a Roman numeral in parentheses right after the metal name. For example:

	Cr^{2+}	Cr^{3+}
Old name:	Chrom*ous* ion	Chrom*ic* ion
New name:	Chromium(II) ion	Chromium(III) ion

We will generally emphasize the new system in this book, but it is important to understand both systems because the old system is often found on labels of commercially supplied chemicals. The small differences between the names in either system illustrate the importance of reading a name very carefully before using a chemical. There are significant differences between compounds consisting of the same two elements but having different charges on the cation. In treating iron-deficiency anemia, for example, iron(II) compounds are preferable because the body absorbs them considerably better than iron(III) compounds.

The names of some common transition metal cations are listed in Table 3.1. Notice that the old names of the copper, iron, and tin ions are derived from their Latin names (*cuprum, ferrum,* and *stannum*).

TABLE 3.1 Names of Some Transition Metal Cations

Element	Symbol	Old Name	New Name
Chromium	Cr^{2+}	Chromous	Chromium(II)
	Cr^{3+}	Chromic	Chromium(III)
Copper	Cu^{+}	Cuprous	Copper(I)
	Cu^{2+}	Cupric	Copper(II)
Iron	Fe^{2+}	Ferrous	Iron(II)
	Fe^{3+}	Ferric	Iron(III)
Mercury	$*Hg_2^{2+}$	Mercurous	Mercury(I)
	Hg^{2+}	Mercuric	Mercury(II)
Tin	Sn^{2+}	Stannous	Tin(II)
	Sn^{4+}	Stannic	Tin(IV)

*This cation is composed of two mercury atoms, each of which has an average charge of +1.

Anions are named by replacing the ending of the element name with *-ide*, followed by the word "ion" (Table 3.2). For example, the anion formed by fluor*ine* is the fluor*ide* ion, and the anion formed by sulf*ur* is the sulf*ide* ion.

TABLE 3.2 Names of Some Common Anions

Element	Symbol	Name
Bromine	Br^-	Bromide ion
Chlorine	Cl^-	Chloride ion
Fluorine	F^-	Fluoride ion
Iodine	I^-	Iodide ion
Oxygen	O^{2-}	Oxide ion
Sulfur	S^{2-}	Sulfide ion

PROBLEM 3.14

Name the following ions:

(a) Cu^{2+} (b) F^- (c) Mg^{2+} (d) S^{2-}

PROBLEM 3.15

Write the symbols for the following ions:

(a) Silver(I) ion   (b) Iron(II) ion   (c) Cuprous ion   (d) Telluride ion

PROBLEM 3.16

Ringer's solution, which is used intravenously to adjust ion concentrations in body fluids, contains the ions of sodium, potassium, calcium, and chlorine. Give the names and symbols of these ions.

PERIODIC TABLE OF THE ELEMENTS

Main groups

Transition metals

Period	1A / 1	2A / 2	3B / 3	4B / 4	5B / 5	6B / 6	7B / 7	8B / 8	8B / 9	8B / 10	1B / 11	2B / 12	3A / 13	4A / 14	5A / 15	6A / 16	7A / 17	8A / 18
1	1 H 1.00794																	2 He 4.002602
2	3 Li 6.941	4 Be 9.012182											5 B 10.811	6 C 12.0107	7 N 14.0067	8 O 15.9994	9 F 18.998403	10 Ne 20.1797
3	11 Na 22.989770	12 Mg 24.3050											13 Al 26.981538	14 Si 28.0855	15 P 30.973761	16 S 32.065	17 Cl 35.453	18 Ar 39.948
4	19 K 39.0983	20 Ca 40.078	21 Sc 44.955910	22 Ti 47.867	23 V 50.9415	24 Cr 51.9961	25 Mn 54.938049	26 Fe 55.845	27 Co 58.933200	28 Ni 58.6934	29 Cu 63.546	30 Zn 65.39	31 Ga 69.723	32 Ge 72.64	33 As 74.92160	34 Se 78.96	35 Br 79.904	36 Kr 83.80
5	37 Rb 85.4678	38 Sr 87.62	39 Y 88.90585	40 Zr 91.224	41 Nb 92.90638	42 Mo 95.94	43 Tc [98]	44 Ru 101.07	45 Rh 102.90550	46 Pd 106.42	47 Ag 107.8682	48 Cd 112.411	49 In 114.818	50 Sn 118.710	51 Sb 121.760	52 Te 127.60	53 I 126.90447	54 Xe 131.293
6	55 Cs 132.90545	56 Ba 137.327	71 Lu 174.967	72 Hf 178.49	73 Ta 180.9479	74 W 183.84	75 Re 186.207	76 Os 190.23	77 Ir 192.217	78 Pt 195.078	79 Au 196.96655	80 Hg 200.59	81 Tl 204.3833	82 Pb 207.2	83 Bi 208.98038	84 Po [208.98]	85 At [209.99]	86 Rn [222.02]
7	87 Fr [223.02]	88 Ra [226.03]	103 Lr [262.11]	104 Rf [261.11]	105 Db [262.11]	106 Sg [266.12]	107 Bh [264.12]	108 Hs [269.13]	109 Mt [268.14]	110 Ds [271.15]	111 Rg [272.15]	112 Cn [285]	113	114 Fl [289]	115	116 Lv [292]	117*	118

*Lanthanide series

57 *La 138.9055	58 Ce 140.116	59 Pr 140.90765	60 Nd 144.24	61 Pm [145]	62 Sm 150.36	63 Eu 151.964	64 Gd 157.25	65 Tb 158.92534	66 Dy 162.50	67 Ho 164.93032	68 Er 167.259	69 Tm 168.93421	70 Yb 173.04

†Actinide series

89 †Ac [227.03]	90 Th 232.0381	91 Pa 231.03588	92 U 238.02891	93 Np [237.05]	94 Pu [244.06]	95 Am [243.06]	96 Cm [247.07]	97 Bk [247.07]	98 Cf [251.08]	99 Es [252.08]	100 Fm [257.10]	101 Md [258.10]	102 No [259.10]

a The labels on top (1A, 2A, etc.) are common American usage. The labels below these (1, 2, etc.) are those recommended by the International Union of Pure and Applied Chemistry.

Atomic weights in brackets are the masses of the longest-lived or most important isotope of radioactive elements.

Further information is available at http://www.shef.ac.uk/chemistry/web-elements/

*Element 117 is currently under review by IUPAC

USEFUL CONVERSION FACTORS AND RELATIONSHIPS

Length

SI unit: meter (m)

$1 \text{ km} = 0.62137 \text{ mi}$
$1 \text{ mi} = 5280 \text{ ft}$
$\quad\quad = 1.6093 \text{ km}$
$1 \text{ m} = 1.0936 \text{ yd}$
$1 \text{ in.} = 2.54 \text{ cm (exactly)}$
$1 \text{ cm} = 0.39370 \text{ in.}$
$1 \text{ Å} = 10^{-10} \text{ m}$

Mass

SI unit: kilogram (kg)

$1 \text{ kg} = 2.2046 \text{ lb}$
$1 \text{ lb} = 453.59 \text{ g}$
$\quad\quad = 16 \text{ oz}$
$1 \text{ amu} = 1.66053873 \times 10^{-24} \text{ g}$

Temperature

SI unit: Kelvin (K)

$0 \text{ K} = -273.15°C$
$\quad\quad = -459.67°F$
$\text{K} = °C + 273.15$
$°C = \frac{5}{9} (°F - 32°)$
$°F = \frac{9}{5} °C + 32°$

Energy (derived)

SI unit: Joule (J)

$1 \text{ J} = 1 \text{ kg-m}^2/\text{s}^2$
$1 \text{ J} = 0.2390 \text{ cal}$
$\quad\quad = 1 \text{ C} \times 1 \text{ V}$
$1 \text{ cal} = 4.184 \text{ J}$
$1 \text{ eV} = 1.602 \times 10^{-19} \text{ J}$

Pressure (derived)

SI unit: Pascal (Pa)

$1 \text{ Pa} = 1 \text{ N}/\text{m}^2$
$\quad\quad = 1 \text{ kg}/\text{m-s}^2$
$1 \text{ atm} = 101,325 \text{ Pa}$
$\quad\quad = 760 \text{ torr}$
$\quad\quad = 14.70 \text{ lb}/\text{in}^2$
$1 \text{ bar} = 10^5 \text{ Pa}$

Volume (derived)

SI unit: cubic meter (m^3)

$1 \text{ L} = 10^{-3} \text{ m}^3$
$\quad\quad = 1 \text{ dm}^3$
$\quad\quad = 10^3 \text{ cm}^3$
$\quad\quad = 1.0567 \text{ qt}$
$1 \text{ gal} = 4 \text{ qt}$
$\quad\quad = 3.7854 \text{ L}$
$1 \text{ cm}^3 = 1 \text{ mL}$
$1 \text{ in}^3 = 16.4 \text{ cm}^3$

FUNDAMENTAL CONSTANTS*

Atomic mass unit	1 amu	$= 1.66053873 \times 10^{-24} \text{ g}$
	1 g	$= 6.02214199 \times 10^{23} \text{ amu}$
Avogadro's number	N	$= 6.02214199 \times 10^{23}/\text{mol}$
Boltzmann's constant	k	$= 1.3806503 \times 10^{-23} \text{ J}/\text{K}$
Electron charge	e	$= 1.602176462 \times 10^{-19} \text{ C}$
Faraday's constant	F	$= 9.6485415 \times 10^4 \text{ C}/\text{mol}$
Gas constant	R	$= 0.082058205 \text{ L-atm}/\text{mol-K}$
Mass of electron	m_e	$= 5.485799 \times 10^{-4} \text{ amu}$
		$= 9.10938188 \times 10^{-28} \text{ g}$
Mass of neutron	m_n	$= 1.0086649 \text{ amu}$
		$= 1.67492716 \times 10^{-24} \text{ g}$
Mass of proton	m_p	$= 1.0072765 \text{ amu}$
		$= 1.67262158 \times 10^{-24} \text{ g}$
Pi	π	$= 3.1415927$
Planck's constant	h	$= 6.62606876 \times 10^{-34} \text{ J-s}$
Speed of light	c	$= 2.99792458 \times 10^8 \text{ m}/\text{s}$

*Fundamental constants are listed at the National Institute of Standards and Technology website:
http://physics.nist.gov/PhysRefData/contents.html

ISBN-13: 978-0-13-142913-0
ISBN-10: 0-13-142913-2

EAN

3.8 Polyatomic Ions

Ions that are composed of more than one atom are called **polyatomic ions**. Most polyatomic ions contain oxygen and another element, and their chemical formulas include subscripts to show how many of each type of atom are present. Sulfate ion, for example, is composed of 1 sulfur atom and 4 oxygen atoms and has a -2 charge: $SO_4{}^{2-}$. The atoms in a polyatomic ion are held together by covalent bonds of the sort discussed in the next chapter, and the entire group of atoms acts as a single unit. A polyatomic ion is charged because it contains a total number of electrons different from the total number of protons in the combined atoms.

The most common polyatomic ions are listed in Table 3.3. Note that the ammonium ion, NH_4^+, and the hydronium ion, H_3O^+, are the only cations; all the others are anions. These ions are encountered so frequently in chemistry, biology, and medicine that there is no alternative but to memorize their names and formulas. Fortunately, there are only a few of them.

Polyatomic ion An ion that is composed of more than one atom.

TABLE 3.3 Some Common Polyatomic Ions

Name	Formula	Name	Formula
Hydronium ion	H_3O^+	Nitrate ion	NO_3^-
Ammonium ion	NH_4^+	Nitrite ion	NO_2^-
Acetate ion	$CH_3CO_2^-$	Oxalate ion	$C_2O_4{}^{2-}$
Carbonate ion	$CO_3{}^{2-}$	Permanganate ion	MnO_4^-
Hydrogen carbonate ion (bicarbonate ion)	HCO_3^-	Phosphate ion	$PO_4{}^{3-}$
Chromate ion	$CrO_4{}^{2-}$	Hydrogen phosphate ion (biphosphate ion)	$HPO_4{}^{2-}$
Dichromate ion	$Cr_2O_7{}^{2-}$	Dihydrogen phosphate ion	$H_2PO_4^-$
Cyanide ion	CN^-	Sulfate ion	$SO_4{}^{2-}$
Hydroxide ion	OH^-	Hydrogen sulfate ion (bisulfate ion)	HSO_4^-
Hypochlorite ion	OCl^-	Sulfite ion	$SO_3{}^{2-}$

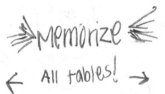

Note [...] ions—$CO_3{}^{2-}$ and HCO_3^-, for example—are related [...] ydrogen ion, H^+. In such instances, the ion with the [...] sing the prefix *bi-*. Thus, $CO_3{}^{2-}$ is the carbonate [...] e ion; similarly, $SO_4{}^{2-}$ is the sulfate ion, and HSO_4 [...]

PROBLEM 3.17

Name the following ions:

(a) NO_3^-

(b) CN^-

(c) OH^-

(d) $HPO_4{}^{2-}$

PROBLEM 3.18

Which of the biologically important ions (see Chemistry in Action, p. 86) belong to Group 1A? To Group 2A? To the transition metals? To the halogens?

CHEMISTRY IN ACTION

Biologically Important Ions

The human body requires many different ions for proper functioning. Several of these ions, such as Ca^{2+}, Mg^{2+}, and HPO_4^{2-}, are used as structural materials in bones and teeth in addition to having other essential functions. Although 99% of Ca^{2+} is contained in bones and teeth, small amounts in body fluids play a vital role in transmission of nerve impulses. Other ions, including essential transition metal ions such as Fe^{2+}, are required for specific chemical reactions in the body. And still others, such as K^+, Na^+, and Cl^-, are present in fluids throughout the body.

In order to maintain charge neutrality in solution, the total negative charge (from anions) must balance the total positive charge (from cations). Several monatomic anions, and several polyatomic anions, especially HCO_3^- and HPO_4^{2-}, are present in body fluids where they help balance the cation charges. Some of the most important ions and their functions are shown in the accompanying table.

See Chemistry in Action Problems 3.83, 3.84, and 3.85 at the end of the chapter.

Some Biologically Important Ions

Ion	Location	Function	Dietary source
Ca^{2+}	Outside cell; 99% of Ca^{2+} is in bones and teeth as $Ca_3(PO_4)_2$ and $CaCO_3$	Bone and tooth structure; necessary for blood clotting, muscle contraction, and transmission of nerve impulses	Milk, whole grains, leafy vegetables
Fe^{2+}	Blood hemoglobin	Transports oxygen from lungs to cells	Liver, red meat, leafy green vegetables
K^+	Fluids inside cells	Maintain ion concentrations in cells; regulate insulin release and heartbeat	Milk, oranges, bananas, meat
Na^+	Fluids outside cells	Protect against fluid loss; necessary for muscle contraction and transmission of nerve impulses	Table salt, seafood
Mg^{2+}	Fluids inside cells; bone	Present in many enzymes; needed for energy generation and muscle contraction	Leafy green plants, seafood, nuts
Cl^-	Fluids outside cells; gastric juice	Maintain fluid balance in cells; help transfer CO_2 from blood to lungs	Table salt, seafood
HCO_3^-	Fluids outside cells	Control acid–base balance in blood	By-product of food metabolism
HPO_4^{2-}	Fluids inside cells; bones and teeth	Control acid–base balance in cells	Fish, poultry, milk

3.9 Formulas of Ionic Compounds

Since all chemical compounds are neutral, it is relatively easy to figure out the formulas of ionic compounds. Once the ions are identified, all we need to do is decide how many ions of each type give a total charge of zero. Thus, the chemical formula of an ionic compound tells the ratio of anions and cations.

If the ions have the same charge, only one of each ion is needed:

$$K^+ \text{ and } F^- \text{ form } KF$$
$$Ca^{2+} \text{ and } O^{2-} \text{ form } CaO$$

This makes sense when we look at how many electrons must be gained or lost by each atom in order to satisfy the octet rule:

$$K\cdot + \cdot \ddot{\underset{..}{F}}: \longrightarrow K^+ + :\ddot{\underset{..}{F}}:^-$$
$$\cdot Ca \cdot + \cdot \ddot{\underset{..}{O}} \cdot \longrightarrow Ca^{2+} + :\ddot{\underset{..}{O}}:^{2-}$$

If the ions have different charges, however, unequal numbers of anions and cations must combine in order to have a net charge of zero. When potassium and oxygen combine, for example, it takes two K^+ ions to balance the -2 charge of the O^{2-} ion. Put another way, it takes two K atoms to provide the two electrons needed in order to complete the octet for the O atom:

$$2 \text{ K} \cdot \; + \; \cdot \overset{\cdot\cdot}{\underset{\cdot\cdot}{\text{O}}} \cdot \; \longrightarrow \; 2 \text{ K}^+ \; + \; : \overset{\cdot\cdot}{\underset{\cdot\cdot}{\text{O}}} : ^{2-}$$

$$2 \text{ K}^+ \quad \text{and} \quad \text{O}^{2-} \quad \text{form} \quad \text{K}_2\text{O}$$

The situation is reversed when a Ca^{2+} ion reacts with a Cl^- ion. One Ca atom can provide two electrons; each Cl atom requires only one electron to achieve a complete octet. Thus, there is one Ca^{2+} cation for every two Cl^- anions:

$$\cdot \text{Ca} \cdot \; + \; 2 \cdot \overset{\cdot\cdot}{\underset{\cdot\cdot}{\text{Cl}}} : \; \longrightarrow \; \text{Ca}^{2+} \; + \; 2 : \overset{\cdot\cdot}{\underset{\cdot\cdot}{\text{Cl}}} : ^-$$

$$\text{Ca}^{2+} \quad \text{and} \quad 2\text{Cl}^- \quad \text{form} \quad \text{CaCl}_2$$

It sometimes helps when writing the formulas for an ionic compound to remember that, when the two ions have different charges, the number of one ion is equal to the charge on the other ion. In magnesium phosphate, for example, the charge on the magnesium ion is +2 and the charge on the polyatomic phosphate ion is −3. Thus, there must be 3 magnesium ions with a total charge of $3 \times (+2) = +6$, and 2 phosphate ions with a total charge of $2 \times (-3) = -6$ for overall neutrality:

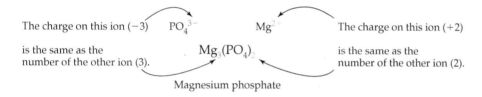

The charge on this ion (−3) $\text{PO}_4{}^{3-}$ Mg^{2+} The charge on this ion (+2)

is the same as the number of the other ion (3). $\text{Mg}_3(\text{PO}_4)_2$ is the same as the number of the other ion (2).

Magnesium phosphate

The formula of an ionic compound shows the lowest possible ratio of atoms in the compound and is thus known as a *simplest formula*. Because there is no such thing as a single neutral *particle* of an ionic compound, however, we use the term **formula unit** to identify the smallest possible neutral *unit* (Figure 3.5). For NaCl, the formula unit is 1 Na^+ ion and 1 Cl^- ion; for K_2SO_4, the formula unit is 2 K^+ ions and 1 $\text{SO}_4{}^{2-}$ ion; for CaF_2, the formula unit is 1 Ca^{2+} ion and 2 F^- ions; and so on.

Formula unit The formula that identifies the smallest neutral unit of an ionic compound.

One formula unit = (+1) + (−1) = 0   One formula unit = (+2) + (2)(−1) = 0

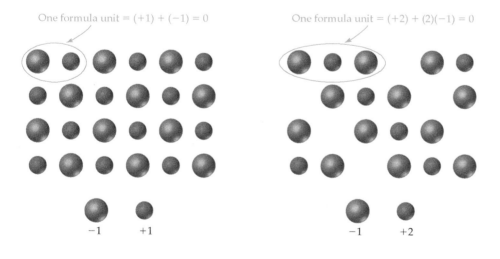

−1   +1   −1   +2

Figure 3.5
Formula units of ionic compounds. The sum of charges on the ions in a formula unit equals zero.

Once the numbers and kinds of ions in a compound are known, the formula is written using the following rules:

- List the cation first and the anion second; for example, NaCl rather than ClNa.
- Do not write the charges of the ions; for example, KF rather than K^+F^-.
- Use parentheses around a polyatomic ion formula if it has a subscript; for example, $\text{Al}_2(\text{SO}_4)_3$ rather than $\text{Al}_2\text{SO}_{43}$.

Worked Example 3.6 Ionic Compounds: Writing Formulas

Write the formula for the compound formed by calcium ions and nitrate ions.

ANALYSIS   Knowing the formula and charges on the cation and anion (Figure 3.4), we determine how many of each are needed to yield a neutral formula for the ionic compound.

SOLUTION
The two ions are Ca^{2+} and NO_3^-. Two nitrate ions, each with a -1 charge, will balance the $+2$ charge of the calcium ion.

$$Ca^{2+} \qquad \text{Charge} = 1 \times (+2) = +2$$
$$2NO_3^- \qquad \text{Charge} = 2 \times (-1) = -2$$

Since there are 2 ions, the nitrate formula must be enclosed in parentheses:

$$Ca(NO_3)_2 \qquad \text{Calcium nitrate}$$

PROBLEM 3.19
Write the formulas for the ionic compounds that silver(I) forms with each of the following:
(a) Iodide ion   **(b)** Oxide ion   **(c)** Phosphate ion

PROBLEM 3.20
Write the formulas for the ionic compounds that sulfate ion forms with the following:
(a) Sodium ion   **(b)** Iron(II) ion   **(c)** Chromium(III) ion

PROBLEM 3.21
The ionic compound containing ammonium ion and carbonate ion gives off the odor of ammonia, a property put to use in smelling salts for reviving someone who has fainted. Write the formula for this compound.

PROBLEM 3.22
An *astringent* is a compound that causes proteins in blood, sweat, and other body fluids to coagulate, a property put to use in antiperspirants. Two safe and effective astringents are the ionic compounds of aluminum with sulfate ion and with acetate ion. Write the formulas of both.

⊃══ KEY CONCEPT PROBLEM 3.23

Three ionic compounds are represented on this periodic table—red cation with red anion, blue cation with blue anion, and green cation with green anion. Give a likely formula for each compound.

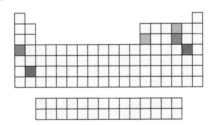

The ionic compound calcium nitride is represented here. What is the formula for calcium nitride, and what are the charges on the calcium and nitride ions?

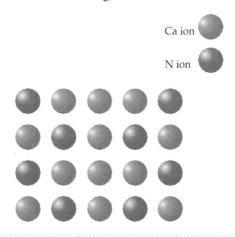

Ca ion

N ion

3.10 Naming Ionic Compounds

Just as in writing formulas for ionic compounds, these compounds are named by citing first the cation and then the anion, with a space between words. There are two kinds of ionic compounds, and the rules for naming them are slightly different.

Type I: Ionic compounds containing cations of main group elements (1A, 2A, aluminum). Since the charges on these cations do not vary, we do not need to specify the charge on the cation as discussed in Section 3.7. For example, NaCl is sodium chloride and $MgCO_3$ is magnesium carbonate.

Type II: Ionic compounds containing metals that can exhibit more than one charge. Since some metals, including the transition metals, often form more than one ion, we need to specify the charge on the cation in these compounds. Either the old (-ous, -ic) or the new (Roman numerals) system described in Section 3.7 can be used. Thus, $FeCl_2$ is called iron(II) chloride (or ferrous chloride), and $FeCl_3$ is called iron(III) chloride (or ferric chloride). Note that we do *not* name these compounds iron *di*chloride or iron *tri*chloride—once the charge on the metal is known, the number of anions needed to yield a neutral compound is also known and does not need to be included as part of the compound name. Table 3.4 lists some common ionic compounds and their uses.

TABLE 3.4 Some Common Ionic Compounds and Their Applications

Chemical Name (Common Name)	Formula	Applications
Ammonium carbonate	$(NH_4)_2CO_3$	Smelling salts
Calcium hydroxide (hydrated lime)	$Ca(OH)_2$	Mortar, plaster, whitewash
Calcium oxide (lime)	CaO	Lawn treatment, industrial chemical
Lithium carbonate ("lithium")	Li_2CO_3	Treatment of bipolar disorder
Magnesium hydroxide (milk of magnesia)	$Mg(OH)_2$	Antacid
Magnesium sulfate (Epsom salts)	$MgSO_4$	Laxative, anticonvulsant
Potassium permanganate	$KMnO_4$	Antiseptic, disinfectant*
Potassium nitrate (saltpeter)	KNO_3	Fireworks, matches, and desensitizer for teeth
Silver nitrate	$AgNO_3$	Antiseptic, germicide
Sodium bicarbonate (baking soda)	$NaHCO_3$	Baking powder, antacid, mouthwash, deodorizer
Sodium hypochlorite	$NaOCl$	Disinfectant; active ingredient in household bleach
Zinc oxide	ZnO	Skin protection, in calamine lotion

*Antiseptics and disinfectants can also be harmful/toxic to non-harmful microorganisms, but are used specifically to prevent infection from harmful microorganisms.

LOOKING AHEAD ▶▶▶ Because the formula unit for an ionic compound must be neutral, we can unambiguously write the formula from the name of the compound, and vice versa. As we shall see in Chapter 4, covalent bonding between atoms can produce a much greater variety of compounds. The rules for naming covalent compounds must be able to accommodate multiple combinations of elements (for example, CO and CO_2).

Worked Example 3.7 Ionic Compounds: Formulas Involving Polyatomic Ions

Magnesium carbonate is used as an ingredient in Bufferin (buffered aspirin) tablets. Write its formula.

ANALYSIS Since magnesium is a main group metal, we can determine its ionic compound formula by identifying the charges and formulas for the anion and the cation, remembering that the overall formula must be neutral.

SOLUTION
Look at the cation and the anion parts of the name separately. Magnesium, a group 2A element, forms the doubly positive Mg^{2+} cation; carbonate anion is doubly negative, CO_3^{2-} Because the charges on the anion and cation are equal, a formula of $MgCO_3$ will be neutral.

Worked Example 3.8 Ionic Compounds: Formulas and Ionic Charges

Sodium and calcium both form a wide variety of ionic compounds. Write formulas for the following compounds:

(a) Sodium bromide and calcium bromide
(b) Sodium sulfide and calcium sulfide
(c) Sodium phosphate and calcium phosphate

ANALYSIS Using the formulas and charges for the cations and the anions (from Tables 3.2 and 3.3), we determine how many of each cation and anion are needed to yield a formula that is neutral.

SOLUTION
(a) Cations $= Na^+$ and Ca^{2+}; anion $= Br^-$: NaBr and $CaBr_2$
(b) Cations $= Na^+$ and Ca^{2+}; anion $= S^{2-}$: Na_2S and CaS
(c) Cations $= Na^+$ and Ca^{2+}; anion $= PO_4^{3-}$: Na_3PO_4 and $Ca_2(PO_4)_2$

Worked Example 3.9 Naming Ionic Compounds

Name the following compounds, using Roman numerals to indicate the charges on the cations where necessary:

(a) KF   **(b)** $MgCl_2$ **(c)** $AuCl_3$ **(d)** Fe_2O_3

ANALYSIS For main group metals, the charge is determined from the group number, and no Roman numerals are necessary. For transition metals, the charge on the metal can be determined from the total charge(s) on the anion(s).

SOLUTION
(a) Potassium fluoride. No Roman numeral is necessary because a group 1A metal forms only one cation.
(b) Magnesium chloride. No Roman numeral is necessary because magnesium (group 2A) forms only Mg^{2+}.

(c) Gold(III) chloride. The 3 Cl^- ions require a +3 charge on the gold for a neutral formula. Since gold is a transition metal that can form other ions, the Roman numeral is necessary to specify the +3 charge.

(d) Iron(III) oxide. Because the 3 oxide anions (O^{2-}) have a total negative charge of −6, the 2 iron cations must have a total charge of +6. Thus, each is Fe^{3+}, and the charge on each is indicated by the Roman numeral (III).

PROBLEM 3.25

The compound Ag_2S is responsible for much of the tarnish found on silverware. Name this compound, and give the charge on the silver ion.

PROBLEM 3.26

Name the following compounds:

(a) SnO_2 (b) $Ca(CN)_2$ (c) Na_2CO_3
(d) Cu_2SO_4 (e) $Ba(OH)_2$ (f) $Fe(NO_3)_2$

PROBLEM 3.27

Write formulas for the following compounds:

(a) Lithium phosphate   (b) Copper(II) carbonate
(c) Aluminum sulfite   (d) Cuprous fluoride
(e) Ferric sulfate   (f) Ammonium chloride

KEY CONCEPT PROBLEM 3.28

The ionic compound, formed between chromium and oxygen is shown here. Name the compound, and write its formula.

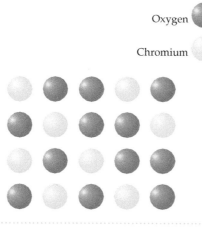

Oxygen

Chromium

3.11 H⁺ and OH⁻ Ions: An Introduction to Acids and Bases

Two of the most important ions we will be discussing in the remainder of this book are the hydrogen cation (H^+) and the hydroxide anion (OH^-). Since a hydrogen *atom* contains one proton and one electron, a hydrogen *cation* is simply a proton. When an acid dissolves in water, the proton typically attaches to a molecule of water to form the hydronium ion (H_3O^+), but chemists routinely use the H^+ and H_3O^+ ions interchangeably. A hydroxide anion, by contrast, is a polyatomic ion in which an oxygen atom is covalently bonded to a hydrogen atom. Although much of Chapter 10 is devoted to the chemistry of H^+ and OH^- ions, it is worth taking a preliminary look now.

◀◀ In Chapter 10 we will look at the chemical behavior of acids and bases and their importance in many areas of chemistry.

Acid A substance that provides H^+ ions in water;

Base A substance that provides OH^- ions in water

The importance of the H^+ cation and the OH^- anion is that they are fundamental to the concepts of *acids* and *bases*. In fact, one definition of an **acid** is a substance that provides H^+ ions when dissolved in water; for example, HCl, HNO_3, H_2SO_4, H_3PO_4. One definition of a **base** is a substance that provides OH^- ions when dissolved in water; for example, NaOH, KOH, $Ba(OH)_2$.

Hydrochloric acid (HCl), nitric acid (HNO_3) sulfuric acid (H_2SO_4), and phosphoric acid (H_3PO_4) are among the most common acids. When any of these substances is dissolved in water, H^+ ions are formed along with the corresponding anion (Table 3.5).

TABLE 3.5 Some Common Acids and the Anions Derived from Them

Acids		Anions	
Acetic acid	CH_3COOH	Acetate ion	*CH_3COO^-
Carbonic acid	H_2CO_3	Hydrogen carbonate ion (bicarbonate ion) Carbonate ion	CO_3^{2-}
Hydrochloric acid	HCl	Chloride ion	Cl^-
Nitric acid	HNO_3	Nitrate ion	NO_3^-
Nitrous acid	HNO_2	Nitrite ion	NO_2^-
Phosphoric acid	H_3PO_4	Dihydrogen phosphate ion Hydrogen phosphate ion Phosphate ion	$H_2PO_4^-$ HPO_4^{2-} PO_4^{3-}
Sulfuric acid	H_2SO_4	Hydrogen sulfate ion Sulfate ion	HSO_4^- SO_4^{2-}

*Sometimes written $C_2H_3O_2^-$ or as $CH_3CO_2^-$.

Different acids can provide different numbers of H^+ ions per acid molecule. Hydrochloric acid, for instance, provides one H^+ ion per acid molecule; sulfuric acid can provide two H^+ ions per acid molecule; and phosphoric acid can provide three H^+ ions per acid molecule.

▶▶▶ The behavior of polyprotic acids, or acids that provide more than one H^+ ion per acid molecule, will be discussed in more detail in Chapter 10.

Sodium hydroxide (NaOH; also known as *lye* or *caustic soda*), potassium hydroxide (KOH; also known as *caustic potash*), and barium hydroxide $[Ba(OH)_2]$ are examples of bases. When any of these compounds dissolves in water, OH^- anions go into solution along with the corresponding metal cation. Sodium hydroxide and potassium hydroxide provide one OH^- ion per formula unit; barium hydroxide provides two OH^- ions per formula unit, as indicated by its formula, $Ba(OH)_2$.

PROBLEM 3.29
Which of the following compounds are acids, and which are bases? Explain.
(a) HF   (b) $Ca(OH)_2$ (c) LiOH   (d) HCN

KEY CONCEPT PROBLEM 3.30

One of these pictures represents a solution of HCl, and one represents a solution of H_2SO_4. Which is which?

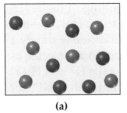
(a)

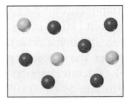
(b)

CHEMISTRY IN ACTION

Osteoporosis

Bone consists primarily of two components, one mineral and one organic. About 70% of bone is the ionic compound *hydroxyapatite*, $Ca_{10}(PO_4)_6(OH)_2$, called the *trabecular*, or spongy, bone. This mineral component is intermingled in a complex matrix with about 30% by mass of fibers of the protein *collagen*, called the *cortical*, or compact, bone. Hydroxyapatite gives bone its hardness and strength, whereas collagen fibers add flexibility and resistance to breaking.

Total bone mass in the body increases from birth until reaching a maximum in the mid-30s. By the early 40s, however, an age-related decline in bone mass begins to occur in both sexes. Bone density decreases, and the microarchitecture of bones is disrupted, resulting in weakening of bone structure, particularly in the wrists, hips, and spine. Should this thinning of bones become too great and the bones become too porous and brittle, a clinical condition called *osteoporosis* can result. Osteoporosis is, in fact, the most common of all bone diseases, affecting approximately 25 million people in the United States. Approximately 1.5 million bone fractures each year are caused by osteoporosis, at an estimated healthcare cost of $14 billion.

Although both sexes are affected by osteoporosis, the condition is particularly common in postmenopausal women, who undergo bone loss at a rate of 2–3% per year over and above that of the normal age-related loss. The cumulative lifetime bone loss, in fact, may approach 40–50% in women versus 20–30% in men. It has been estimated that half of all women over age 50 will have an osteoporosis-related bone fracture at some point in their life. Other risk factors, in addition to sex,

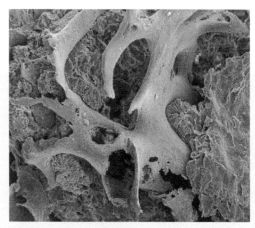

▲ **Normal bone is strong and dense; a bone affected by osteoporosis, shown here, is weak and spongy in appearance.**

include being thin, being sedentary, having a family history of osteoporosis, smoking, and having a diet low in calcium.

No cure exists for osteoporosis, but treatment for its prevention and management includes estrogen-replacement therapy for postmenopausal women as well as several approved medications called *bisphosphonates* that bind to the calcium in bone, slowing down bone loss by inhibiting the action of *osteoclasts*, or cells that break down bone tissue. Calcium supplements are also recommended, as is appropriate weight-bearing exercise. In addition, treatment with sodium fluoride is under active investigation and shows considerable promise. Fluoride ion reacts with hydroxyapatite to give *fluorapatite*, in which OH^- ions are replaced by F^-, increasing both bone strength and density.

$$Ca_{10}(PO_4)_6(OH)_2 + 2\ F^- \longrightarrow Ca_{10}(PO_4)_6F_2$$
$$\text{Hydroxyapatite} \qquad\qquad\qquad \text{Fluorapatite}$$

See Chemistry in Action Problems 3.86 and 3.87 at the end of the chapter.

SUMMARY: REVISITING THE CHAPTER GOALS

1. What is an ion, what is an ionic bond, and what are the general characteristics of ionic compounds? Atoms are converted into *cations* by the loss of one or more electrons and into *anions* by the gain of one or more electrons. Ionic compounds are composed of cations and anions held together by *ionic bonds*, which result from the attraction between opposite electrical charges. Ionic compounds conduct electricity when dissolved in water, and they are generally crystalline solids with high melting points and high boiling points (*see Problems 33, 35, 38–41, 80, 81, 95–97*).

2. What is the octet rule, and how does it apply to ions? A valence-shell electron configuration of 8 electrons in filled *s* and *p* subshells leads to stability and lack of reactivity, as typified by the noble gases in group 8A. According to the *octet rule,*

atoms of main group elements tend to form ions in which they have gained or lost the appropriate number of electrons to reach a noble gas configuration (*see Problems 42–49, 88, 89*).

3. What is the relationship between an element's position in the periodic table and the formation of its ion? Periodic variations in *ionization energy,* the amount of energy that must be supplied to remove an electron from an atom, show that metals lose electrons more easily than nonmetals. As a result, metals usually form cations. Similar periodic variations in *electron affinity,* the amount of energy released on adding an electron to an atom, show that reactive nonmetals gain electrons more easily than metals. As a result, reactive nonmetals usually form anions. The ionic charge can be predicted from the group number and the octet rule. For main group metals, the charge on the cation is equal to the group number. For nonmetals, the charge on the anion is equal to 8 − (group number) (*see Problems 31, 32, 36, 40, 41, 50–57, 88, 89, 96*).

4. What determines the chemical formula of an ionic compound? Ionic compounds contain appropriate numbers of anions and cations to maintain overall neutrality, thereby providing a means of determining their chemical formulas (*see Problems 36, 37, 64, 65, 68, 69, 86, 87, 90, 92, 94*).

5. How are ionic compounds named? Cations have the same name as the metal from which they are derived. Monatomic anions have the name ending -*ide*. For metals that form more than one ion, a Roman numeral equal to the charge on the ion is added to the name of the cation. Alternatively, the

ending -*ous* is added to the name of the cation with the lesser charge and the ending -*ic* is added to the name of the cation with the greater charge. To name an ionic compound, the cation name is given first, with the charge of the metal ion indicated if necessary, and the anion name is given second (*see Problems 36, 58-63, 66, 68, 70–75, 93, 94*).

6. What are acids and bases? The hydrogen ion (H^+) and the hydroxide ion (OH^-) are among the most important ions in chemistry because they are fundamental to the idea of acids and bases. According to one common definition, an *acid* is a substance that yields H^+ ions when dissolved in water, and a *base* is a substance that yields OH^- ions when dissolved in water (*see Problems 76–79, 91*).

KEY WORDS

Acid, *p. 92*

Anion, *p. 74*

Base, *p. 92*

Cation, *p. 74*

Electron affinity, *p. 75*

Formula unit, *p. 87*

Ion, *p. 74*

Ionic bond, *p. 77*

Ionic compound, *p. 77*

Ionic solid, *p. 77*

Ionization energy, *p. 75*

Octet rule, *p. 79*

Polyatomic ion, *p. 85*

UNDERSTANDING KEY CONCEPTS

3.31 Where on the blank outline of the periodic table are the following elements found?

(a) Elements that commonly form only one type of cation

(b) Elements that commonly form anions

(c) Elements that can form more than one type of cation

(d) Elements that do not readily form either anions or cations

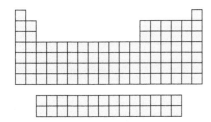

3.32 Where on the blank outline of the periodic table are the following elements found?

(a) Elements that commonly form +2 ions

(b) Elements that commonly form −2 ions

(c) An element that forms a +3 ion

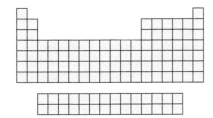

3.33 Write the symbols for the ions represented in the following drawings.

| (a) | (b) | (c) | (d) |

3.34 One of these drawings represents an Na atom, and one represents an Na^+ ion. Tell which is which, and explain why there is a difference in size.

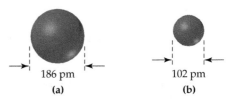

3.35 One of these drawings represents a Cl atom, and one represents a Cl^- ion. Tell which is which, and explain why there is a difference in size.

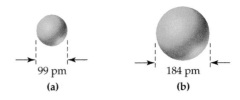

3.36 The elements in red in the periodic table can form cations having more than one charge. Write the formulas and names of the compounds that are formed between the red cations and the blue anions depicted in the periodic table.

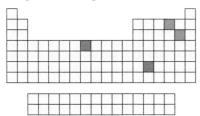

3.37 Each of these drawings (a)–(d) represents one of the following ionic compounds: $PbBr_2$, ZnS, CrF_3, Al_2O_3. Which is which?

(a) (b) (c)

(d)

ADDITIONAL PROBLEMS

IONS AND IONIC BONDING

3.38 Write equations for loss or gain of electrons by atoms that result in formation of the following ions:

(a) Ca^{2+} (b) Au^+

(c) F^- (d) Cr^{3+}

3.39 Write electronic configurations and symbols for the ions formed by the following:

(a) Gain of 3 electrons by phosphorus

(b) Loss of 1 electron by lithium

(c) Loss of 2 electrons by cobalt

(d) Loss of 3 electrons by thallium

3.40 Tell whether each statement about ions is true or false. If a statement is false, explain why.

(a) A cation is formed by addition of one or more electrons to an atom.

(b) Group 4A elements tend to lose 4 electrons to yield ions with a +4 charge.

(c) Group 4A elements tend to gain 4 electrons to yield ions with a −4 charge.

(d) The individual atoms in a polyatomic ion are held together by covalent bonds.

3.41 Tell whether each statement about ionic solids is true or false. If a statement is false, explain why.

(a) Ions are randomly arranged in ionic solids.

(b) All ions are the same size in ionic solids.

(c) Ionic solids can often be shattered by a sharp blow.

(d) Ionic solids have low boiling points.

IONS AND THE OCTET RULE

3.42 What is the *octet rule*?

3.43 Why do H and He not obey the octet rule?

3.44 Write the symbol for an ion that contains 34 protons and 36 electrons.

3.45 What is the charge of an ion that contains 21 protons and 19 electrons?

3.46 Identify the element X in the following ions, and tell which noble gas has the same electron configuration.

(a) X^{2+}, a cation with 36 electrons

(b) X^-, an anion with 36 electrons

3.47 Element Z forms an ion Z^{3+}, which contains 31 protons. What is the identity of Z, and how many electrons does Z^{3+} have?

3.48 Write the electron configuration for the following ions:

(a) Rb^+ (b) Br^-

(c) S^{2-} (d) Ba^{2+}

(e) Al^{3+}

3.49 Based on the following atomic numbers and electronic configurations, write the symbols for the following ions:

(a) $Z = 20$; $1s^2\, 2s^2\, 2p^6\, 3s^2\, 3p^6$

(b) $Z = 8$; $1s^2\, 2s^2\, 2p^6$

(c) $Z = 22$; $1s^2\, 2s^2\, 2p^6\, 3s^2\, 3p^6\, 3d^2$

(d) $Z = 19$; $1s^2\, 2s^2\, 2p^6\, 3s^2\, 3p^6$

(e) $Z = 13$; $1s^2\, 2s^2\, 2p^6$

PERIODIC PROPERTIES AND ION FORMATION

3.50 Looking only at the periodic table, tell which member of each pair of atoms has the larger ionization energy and thus loses an electron less easily:

(a) Li and O (b) Li and Cs

(c) K and Zn (d) Mg and N

3.51 Looking only at the periodic table, tell which member of each pair of atoms has the larger electron affinity and thus gains an electron more easily:

(a) Li and S

(b) Ba and I

(c) Ca and Br

3.52 Which of the following ions are likely to form? Explain.

(a) Li^{2+} (b) K^-

(c) Mn^{3+} (d) Zn^{4+}

(e) Ne^+

3.53 What is the charge on the cation formed from the following elements? For those elements that form more than one cation, indicate the ionic charges most commonly observed.

(a) Magnesium   (b) Tin

(c) Mercury   (d) Aluminum

3.54 Write the electron configurations of Cr^{2+} and Cr^{3+}.

3.55 Write the electron configurations of Co, Co^{2+} and Co^{3+}.

3.56 Would you expect the ionization energy of Li^+ to be less than, greater than, or the same as the ionization energy of Li? Explain.

3.57 (a) Write equations for the loss of an electron by a K atom and the gain of an electron by a K^+ ion.

(b) What is the relationship between the equations?

(c) What is the relationship between the ionization energy of a K atom and the electron affinity of a K^+ ion?

SYMBOLS, FORMULAS, AND NAMES FOR IONS

3.58 Name the following ions:

(a) S^{2-} (b) Sn^{2+} (c) Sr^{2+}

(d) Mg^{2+} (e) Au^+

3.59 Name the following ions in both the old and the new systems:

(a) Cr^{2+} (b) Fe^{3+} (c) Hg^{2+}

3.60 Write symbols for the following ions:

(a) Selenide ion   (b) Oxide ion

(c) Silver(I) ion

3.61 Write symbols for the following ions:

(a) Ferrous ion   (b) Tin(IV) ion

(c) Lead(II) ion   (d) Chromic ion

3.62 Write formulas for the following ions:

(a) Hydroxide ion   (b) Bisulfate ion

(c) Acetate ion   (d) Permanganate ion

(e) Hypochlorite ion   (f) Nitrate ion

(g) Carbonate ion   (h) Dichromate ion

3.63 Name the following ions:

(a) NO_2^- (b) CrO_4^{2-} (c) NH_4^+ (d) HPO_4^{2-}

NAMES AND FORMULAS FOR IONIC COMPOUNDS

3.64 Write formulas for the compounds formed by the sulfate ion with the following cations:

(a) Aluminum   (b) Silver(I)

(c) Zinc   (d) Barium

3.65 Write formulas for the compounds formed by the carbonate ion with the following cations:

(a) Strontium   (b) Fe(III)

(c) Ammonium   (d) Sn(IV)

3.66 Write the formula for the following substances:

(a) Sodium bicarbonate (baking soda)

(b) Potassium nitrate (a backache remedy)

(c) Calcium carbonate (an antacid)

(d) Ammonium nitrate (first aid cold packs)

3.67 Write the formula for the following compounds:

(a) Calcium hypochlorite, used as a swimming pool disinfectant

(b) Copper(II) sulfate, used to kill algae in swimming pools

(c) Sodium phosphate, used in detergents to enhance cleaning action

3.68 Complete the table by writing in the formula of the compound formed by each pair of ions:

	S^{2-}	Cl^-	PO_4^{3-}	CO_3^{2-}
Copper(II)	CuS			
Ca^{2+}				
NH_4^+				
Ferric ion				

3.69 Complete the table by writing in the formula of the compound formed by each pair of ions:

	O^{2-}	HSO_4^-	HPO_4^{2-}	$C_2O_4^{2-}$
K^+	K_2O			
Ni^{2+}				
NH_4^+				
Chromous				

3.70 Write the name of each compound in the table for Problem 3.68.

3.71 Write the name of each compound in the table for Problem 3.69.

3.72 Name the following substances:

(a) $MgCO_3$ (b) $Ca(CH_3CO_2)_2$

(c) $AgCN$ (d) $Na_2Cr_2O_7$

3.73 Name the following substances:

(a) $Fe(OH)_2$ (b) $KMnO_4$

(c) Na_2CrO_4 (d) $Ba_3(PO_4)_2$

3.74 Which of the following formulas is most likely to be correct for calcium phosphate?

(a) Ca_2PO_4 (b) $CaPO_4$

(c) $Ca_2(PO_4)_3$ (d) $Ca_2(PO_4)_2$

3.75 Fill in the missing information to give the correct formula for each compound:

(a) $Al_?(SO_4)_?$ (b) $(NH_4)_?(PO_4)_?$
(c) $Rb_?(SO_4)_?$

ACIDS AND BASES

3.76 What is the difference between an acid and a base?

3.77 Identify the following substances as either an acid or a base:

(a) H_2CO_3 (b) HCN
(c) $Mg(OH)_2$ (d) KOH

3.78 Write equations to show how the substances listed in Problem 3.77 give ions when dissolved in water.

3.79 Name the anions that result when the acids in Problem 3.77 are dissolved in water.

CHEMISTRY IN ACTION

3.80 Most ionic substances are solids at room temperature. Explain why the RTILs discussed in this application are liquids rather than solids. [*Ionic Liquids, p. 78*]

3.81 Ionic liquids are being evaluated for use in a moon-based spinning-liquid telescope. Which properties of ionic liquids make them particularly well-suited for this application? [*Ionic Liquids, p. 78*]

3.82 What is the RDI for sodium for adults, and what amount of table salt (in grams) contains this quantity of sodium? [*Salt, p. 83*]

3.83 Where are most of the calcium ions found in the body? [*Biologically Important Ions, p. 86*]

3.84 Excess sodium ion is considered hazardous, but a certain amount is necessary for normal body functions. What is the purpose of sodium in the body? [*Biologically Important Ions, p. 86*]

3.85 Before a person is allowed to donate blood, a drop of the blood is tested to be sure that it contains a sufficient amount of iron (men, 41 μg/dL; women, 38 μg/dL). What is the biological role of iron, and which ion of iron is involved? [*Biologically Important Ions, p. 86*]

3.86 Name each ion in hydroxyapatite, $Ca_{10}(PO_4)_6(OH)_2$; give its charge; and show that the formula represents a neutral compound. [*Osteoporosis, p. 93*]

3.87 Sodium fluoride reacts with hydroxyapatite to give fluorapatite. What is the formula of fluorapatite? [*Osteoporosis, p. 93*]

GENERAL QUESTIONS AND PROBLEMS

3.88 Explain why the hydride ion, H^-, has a noble gas configuration.

3.89 The H^- ion (Problem 3.88) is stable, but the Li^- ion is not. Explain.

3.90 Many compounds containing a metal and a nonmetal are not ionic, yet they are named using the Roman numeral system for ionic compounds described in Section 3.7. Write the chemical formulas for the following such compounds.

(a) Chromium(VI) oxide
(b) Vanadium(V) chloride
(c) Manganese(IV) oxide
(d) Molybdenum(IV) sulfide

3.91 The arsenate ion has the formula AsO_4^{3-}. Write the formula of the corresponding acid that contains this anion.

3.92 One commercially available calcium supplement contains calcium gluconate, a compound that is also used as an anticaking agent in instant coffee.

(a) If this compound contains 1 calcium ion for every 2 gluconate ions, what is the charge on a gluconate ion?

(b) What is the ratio of iron ions to gluconate ions in iron(III) gluconate, a commercial iron supplement?

3.93 The names given for the following compounds are incorrect. Write the correct name for each compound.

(a) Cu_3PO_4, copper(III) phosphate
(b) Na_2SO_4, sodium sulfide
(c) MnO_2, manganese(II) oxide
(d) $AuCl_3$, gold chloride
(e) $Pb(CO_3)_2$, lead(II) acetate
(f) Ni_2S_3, nickel(II) sulfide

3.94 The formulas given for the following compounds are incorrect. Write the correct formula for each compound.

(a) Cobalt(II) cyanide, $CoCN_2$
(b) Uranium(VI) oxide, UO_6
(c) Tin(II) sulfate, $Ti(SO_4)_2$
(d) Manganese(IV) oxide; MnO_4
(e) Potassium phosphate, K_2PO_4
(f) Calcium phosphide, CaP
(g) Lithium bisulfate, $Li(SO_4)_2$
(h) Aluminum hydroxide; $Al_2(OH)_3$

3.95 How many protons, electrons, and neutrons are in each of these ions?

(a) $^{16}O^{2-}$ (b) $^{89}Y^{3+}$ (c) $^{133}Cs^+$ (d) $^{81}Br^-$

3.96 Element X reacts with element Y to give a product containing X^{3+} ions and Y^{2-} ions.

(a) Is element X likely to be a metal or a nonmetal?
(b) Is element Y likely to be a metal or a nonmetal?
(c) What is the formula of the product?
(d) What groups of the periodic table are elements X and Y likely to be in?

3.97 Identify each of the ions having the following charges and electron configurations:

(a) X^{4+}; $[Ar] \, 4s^0 3d^3$ (b) X^+; $[Ar] \, 4s^0 3d^{10}$
(c) X^{4+}; $[Ar] \, 4s^0 3d^0$

Molecular Compounds

CONTENTS

◄ The Atomium monument in Brussels, Belgium, provides an artistic image of the binding forces between atoms.

1. **What is a covalent bond?**
   THE GOAL: Be able to describe the nature of covalent bonds and how they are formed. (◀◀ A, B, C.)

2. **How does the octet rule apply to covalent bond formation?**
   THE GOAL: Be able to use the octet rule to predict the numbers of covalent bonds formed by common main group elements. (◀◀ B, C.)

3. **What are the major differences between ionic and molecular compounds?**
   THE GOAL: Be able to compare the structures, compositions, and properties of ionic and molecular compounds.

4. **How are molecular compounds represented?**
   THE GOAL: Be able to interpret molecular formulas and draw Lewis structures for molecules. (◀◀ D.)

5. **What is the influence of valence-shell electrons on molecular shape?**
   THE GOAL: Be able to use Lewis structures to predict molecular geometry. (◀◀ D.)

6. **When are bonds and molecules polar?**
   THE GOAL: Be able to use electronegativity and molecular geometry to predict bond and molecular polarity. (◀◀ A, D.)

CONCEPTS TO REVIEW

A. The Periodic Table
(Sections 2.4 and 2.5)

B. Electron Configurations
(Sections 2.7 and 2.8)

C. The Octet Rule
(Section 3.5)

D. Electron-Dot Symbols
(Section 2.9)

We saw in the preceding chapter that ionic compounds are crystalline solids composed of positively and negatively charged ions. Not all substances, however, are ionic. In fact, with the exception of table salt (NaCl), baking soda ($NaHCO_3$), lime for the garden (CaO), and a few others, most of the compounds around us are *not* crystalline, brittle, high-melting ionic solids. We are much more likely to encounter gases (like those in air), liquids (such as water), low-melting solids (such as butter), and flexible solids (like plastics). All these materials are composed of *molecules* rather than ions, all contain *covalent* bonds rather than ionic bonds, and all consist primarily of nonmetal atoms rather than metals.

4.1 Covalent Bonds

How do we describe the bonding in carbon dioxide, water, polyethylene, and the many millions of nonionic compounds that make up our bodies and much of the world around us? Simply put, the bonds in such compounds are formed by the *sharing* of electrons between atoms (in contrast to ionic bonds, which involve the complete transfer of electrons from one atom to another). The bond formed when atoms share electrons is called a **covalent bond**, and the group of atoms held together by covalent bonds is called a **molecule**. A single molecule of water, for example, contains 2 hydrogen atoms and 1 oxygen atom covalently bonded to one another. We might visualize a water molecule using a space-filling model as shown here:

Covalent bond A bond formed by sharing electrons between atoms.

Molecule A group of atoms held together by covalent bonds.

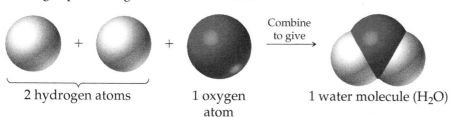

2 hydrogen atoms   1 oxygen atom   1 water molecule (H_2O)

Recall that according to the *octet rule* (Section 3.5), main group elements tend to undergo reactions that leave them with completed outer subshells with 8 valence electrons (or 2 for hydrogen), so that they have a noble gas electron configuration. Although metals and reactive nonmetals can achieve an electron octet by gaining or losing an appropriate number of electrons to form ions, the nonmetals can also achieve an electron octet by *sharing* an appropriate number of electrons in covalent bonds.

As an example of how covalent bond formation occurs, let us look first at the bond between 2 hydrogen atoms in a hydrogen molecule, H_2. Recall that a hydrogen *atom* consists of a positively charged nucleus and a single, negatively charged 1*s* valence electron, which we represent as H · using the electron-dot symbol. When 2 hydrogen atoms come together, electrical interactions occur. Some of these interactions are repulsive—the 2 positively charged nuclei repel each other, and the 2 negatively charged electrons repel each other. Other interactions, however, are attractive—each nucleus attracts both electrons, and each electron attracts both nuclei (Figure 4.1). Because the attractive forces are stronger than the repulsive forces, a covalent bond is formed, and the hydrogen atoms stay together.

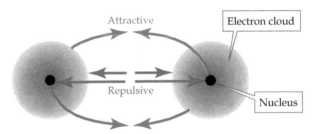

▲ **Figure 4.1**
A covalent H — H bond is the net result of attractive and repulsive forces.
The nucleus–electron attractions (blue arrows) are greater than the nucleus–nucleus and electron-electron repulsions (red arrows), resulting in a net attractive force that holds the atoms together to form an H_2 molecule.

In essence, the electrons act as a kind of "glue" to bind the 2 nuclei together into an H_2 molecule. Both nuclei are simultaneously attracted to the same electrons and are held together, much as two tug-of-war teams pulling on the same rope are held together.

Covalent bond formation in the H — H molecule can be visualized by imagining that the spherical 1*s* orbitals from the two individual atoms blend together and *overlap* to give an egg-shaped region in the H_2 molecule. The 2 electrons in the H — H covalent bond occupy the central region between the nuclei, giving both atoms a share in 2 valence electrons and the $1s^2$ electron configuration of the noble gas helium. For simplicity, the shared pair of electrons in a covalent bond is often represented as a line between atoms. Thus, the symbols H — H, H:H, and H_2 all represent a hydrogen molecule.

▲ **The two teams are joined together because both are holding onto the same rope. In a similar way, two atoms are bonded together when both hold onto the same electrons.**

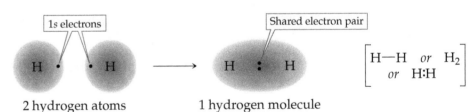

As you might imagine, the magnitudes of the various attractive and repulsive forces between nuclei and electrons in a covalent bond depend on how close the atoms are to each other. If the atoms are too far apart, the attractive forces are small and no bond exists. If the atoms are too close, the repulsive interaction between nuclei is so strong that it pushes the atoms apart. Thus, there is an optimum point where net attractive forces are maximized and where the H_2 molecule is most stable. This optimum distance between nuclei is called the **bond length** and is 74 pm (7.4×10^{-11} m) in the H_2 molecule.

Bond length The optimum distance between nuclei in a covalent bond.

As another example of covalent bond formation, look at the chlorine molecule, Cl_2. An individual chlorine atom has 7 valence electrons and the valence-shell electron configuration $3s^2 3p^5$. Using the electron-dot symbols for the valence electrons, each Cl atom can be represented as :C̈l·. The 3*s* orbital and 2 of the three 3*p* orbitals are filled by 2 electrons each, but the third 3p orbital holds only 1 electron. When 2 chlorine atoms approach each other, the unpaired 3p electrons are shared by both atoms in a covalent bond. Each chlorine atom in the resultant Cl_2 molecule now "owns" 6 outer-shell electrons and "shares" 2 more, giving each a valence-shell octet like that of the noble gas argon. We can represent the formation of a covalent bond between chlorine atoms as

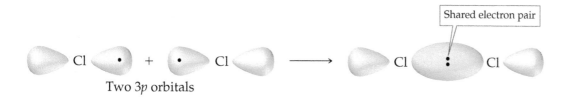

Such bond formation can also be pictured as the overlap of the 3p orbitals containing the single electrons, with resultant formation of a region of high electron density between the nuclei:

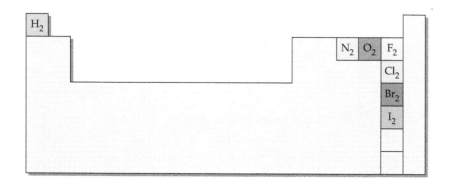

Two 3p orbitals

In addition to H_2 and Cl_2, five other elements always exist as *diatomic* (2-atom) molecules (Figure 4.2): nitrogen (N_2) and oxygen (O_2) are colorless, odorless, non-toxic gases present in air; fluorine (F_2) is a pale yellow, highly reactive gas; bromine (Br_2) is a dark red, toxic liquid; and iodine (I_2) is a violet crystalline solid.

◀ **Figure 4.2**
Diatomic elements in the periodic table.

PROBLEM 4.1
Draw the iodine molecule using electron-dot symbols, and indicate the shared electron pair. What noble gas configuration do the iodine atoms have in an (I_2) molecule?

4.2 Covalent Bonds and the Periodic Table

Covalent bonds can form between unlike atoms as well as between like atoms, making possible a vast number of **molecular compounds**. Water molecules, for example, consist of 2 hydrogen atoms joined by covalent bonds to an oxygen atom, H_2O; ammonia molecules consist of 3 hydrogen atoms covalently bonded to a nitrogen atom, NH_3; and methane molecules consist of 4 hydrogen atoms covalently bonded to a carbon atom, CH_4.

Molecular compound A compound that consists of molecules rather than ions.

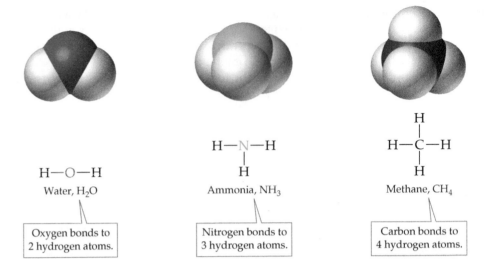

H—O—H
Water, H_2O

Oxygen bonds to 2 hydrogen atoms.

H—N—H
|
H
Ammonia, NH_3

Nitrogen bonds to 3 hydrogen atoms.

H
|
H—C—H
|
H
Methane, CH_4

Carbon bonds to 4 hydrogen atoms.

Note that in all these examples, each atom shares enough electrons to achieve a noble gas configuration: 2 electrons for hydrogen and octets for oxygen, nitrogen, and carbon. Hydrogen, with 1 valence electron ($H \cdot$), needs one more electron to achieve a noble gas configuration (that of helium, $1s^2$) and thus forms 1 covalent bond. Oxygen, with 6 valence electrons ($\cdot \ddot{O} \cdot$), needs two more electrons to have an octet; this happens when oxygen forms 2 covalent bonds. Nitrogen, with 5 valence electrons ($\cdot \ddot{N} \cdot$), needs three more electrons to achieve an octet and thus forms 3 covalent bonds. Carbon, with 4 valence electrons ($\cdot \dot{C} \cdot$), needs four more electrons and thus forms 4 covalent bonds. Figure 4.3 summarizes the number of covalent bonds typically formed by common main group elements.

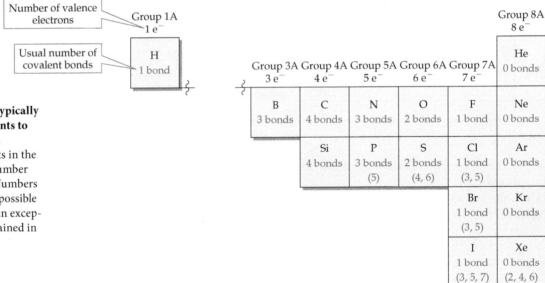

▶ **Figure 4.3**
Numbers of covalent bonds typically formed by main group elements to achieve octet configurations.
For P, S, Cl, and other elements in the third period and below, the number of covalent bonds may vary. Numbers in parentheses indicate other possible numbers of bonds that result in exceptions to the octet rule, as explained in the text.

The octet rule is a useful guideline, but it has numerous exceptions. Boron, for example, has only 3 valence electrons it can share ($\cdot \dot{B} \cdot$) and thus forms compounds in which it has only 3 covalent bonds and 6 electrons, such as BF_3. Exceptions to the octet rule are also seen with elements in the third row of the periodic table and below because these elements have vacant d orbitals that can be used for bonding. Phosphorus sometimes forms 5 covalent bonds (using 10 bonding electrons); sulfur sometimes forms 4 or 6 covalent bonds (using 8 and 12 bonding electrons, respectively); and chlorine, bromine, and iodine sometimes form 3, 5, or 7 covalent bonds. Phosphorus and sulfur, for example, form molecules such as PCl_5, SF_4, and SF_6.

BF$_3$
Boron trifluoride
(6 valence electrons on B)

PCl$_5$
Phosphorus pentachloride
(10 valence electrons on P)

SF$_6$
Sulfur hexafluoride
(12 valence electrons on S)

Worked Example 4.1 Molecular Compounds: Octet Rule and Covalent Bonds

Look at Figure 4.3 and tell whether the following molecules are likely to exist.

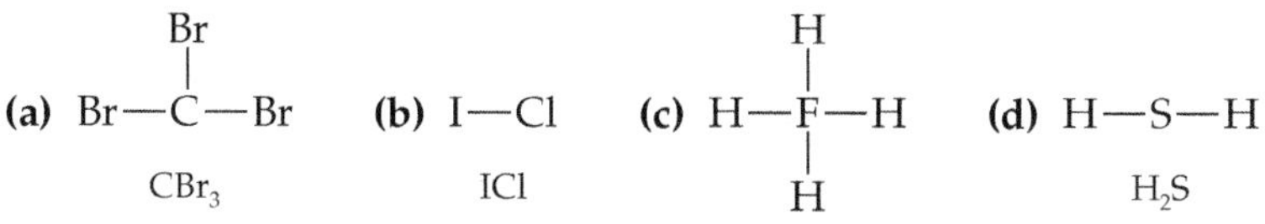

(a)
$$\begin{array}{c} Br \\ | \\ Br-C-Br \\ | \\ CBr_3 \end{array}$$

(b) I—Cl

ICl

(c)
$$\begin{array}{c} H \\ | \\ H-F-H \\ | \\ H \\ FH_4 \end{array}$$

(d) H—S—H

H$_2$S

ANALYSIS Count the number of covalent bonds formed by each element and see if the numbers correspond to those shown in Figure 4.3.

SOLUTION

(a) No. Carbon needs 4 covalent bonds but has only 3 in CBr_3.

(b) Yes. Both iodine and chlorine have 1 covalent bond in ICl.

(c) No. Fluorine only needs 1 covalent bond to achieve an octet. It cannot form more than 1 covalent bond because it is in the second period and does not have valence *d* orbitals to use for bonding.

(d) Yes. Sulfur, which is in group 6A like oxygen, often forms 2 covalent bonds.

Worked Example 4.2 Molecular Compounds: Electron-Dot Symbols

Using electron-dot symbols, show the reaction between a hydrogen atom and a fluorine atom.

ANALYSIS The electron-dot symbols show the valence electrons for the hydrogen and fluorine atoms. A covalent bond is formed by the sharing of unpaired valence electrons between the 2 atoms.

SOLUTION
Draw the electron-dot symbols for the H and F atoms, showing the covalent bond as a shared electron pair.

$$H\cdot + \cdot \ddot{\underset{\cdot\cdot}{F}}: \longrightarrow H\!:\!\ddot{\underset{\cdot\cdot}{F}}:$$

Worked Example 4.3 Molecular Compounds: Predicting Number of Bonds

What are likely formulas for the following molecules?

(a) $SiH_2Cl_?$ **(b)** $HBr_?$ **(c)** $PBr_?$

ANALYSIS The numbers of covalent bonds formed by each element should be those shown in Figure 4.3.

SOLUTION

(a) Silicon typically forms 4 bonds: SiH_2Cl_2
(b) Hydrogen forms only 1 bond: HBr
(c) Phosphorus typically forms 3 bonds: PBr_3

PROBLEM 4.2
How many covalent bonds are formed by each atom in the following molecules? Draw molecules using the electron-dot symbols and lines to show the covalent bonds.

(a) PH_3 **(b)** H_2Se **(c)** HCl   **(d)** SiF_4

PROBLEM 4.3
Lead forms both ionic and molecular compounds. Using Figure 4.3, the periodic table, and electronic configurations, predict which of the following lead compounds is more likely to be ionic and which is more likely to be molecular: $PbCl_2$, $PbCl_4$.

PROBLEM 4.4
What are likely formulas for the following molecules?

(a) $CH_2Cl_?$ **(b)** $BH_?$ **(c)** $NI_?$ **(d)** $SiCl_?$

4.3 Multiple Covalent Bonds

The bonding in some molecules cannot be explained by the sharing of only 2 electrons between atoms. For example, the carbon and oxygen atoms in carbon dioxide (CO_2) and the nitrogen atoms in the N_2 molecule cannot have electron octets if only 2 electrons are shared:

$$\ddot{\text{O}}\cdot + \cdot\dot{\text{C}}\cdot + \cdot\ddot{\text{O}}\cdot$$

$$\ddot{\text{O}}:\dot{\text{C}}:\ddot{\text{O}}\cdot$$

UNSTABLE—Carbon has only
6 electrons; each oxygen has only 7.

$$\cdot\dot{\text{N}}\cdot + \cdot\dot{\text{N}}\cdot$$

$$\cdot\ddot{\text{N}}:\ddot{\text{N}}\cdot$$

UNSTABLE—Each nitrogen
has only 6 electrons.

The only way the atoms in CO_2 and N_2 can have outer-shell electron octets is by sharing *more* than 2 electrons, resulting in the formation of *multiple* covalent bonds. Only if the carbon atom shares 4 electrons with each oxygen atom do all atoms in CO_2 have electron octets, and only if the 2 nitrogen atoms share 6 electrons do both have electron octets. A bond formed by sharing 2 electrons (one pair) is a **single bond**, a bond formed by sharing 4 electrons (two pairs) is a **double bond**, and a bond formed by sharing 6 electrons (three pairs) is a **triple bond**. Just as a single bond is represented by a single line between atoms, a double bond is represented by two lines between atoms and a triple bond by three lines:

Single bond A covalent bond formed by sharing one electron pair.

Double bond A covalent bond formed by sharing two electron pairs.

Triple bond A covalent bond formed by sharing three electron pairs.

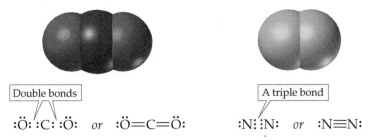

Double bonds

A triple bond

$$:\ddot{\text{O}}::\text{C}::\ddot{\text{O}}: \quad or \quad :\ddot{\text{O}}=\text{C}=\ddot{\text{O}}:$$

$$:\text{N}:\text{:N}: \quad or \quad :\text{N}\equiv\text{N}:$$

The carbon atom in CO_2 has 2 double bonds ($4e^-$ each) for a total of 8 electrons. Each oxygen atom also has a complete octet: a double bond ($4e^-$) plus two sets of lone pairs. Similarly, formation of a triple bond in N_2 allows each nitrogen to obtain a complete octet: 6 electrons from the triple bond plus a lone pair.

Carbon, nitrogen, and oxygen are the elements most often present in multiple bonds. Carbon and nitrogen form both double and triple bonds; oxygen forms double bonds. Multiple covalent bonding is particularly common in *organic* molecules, which consist predominantly of the element carbon. For example, ethylene, a simple compound used commercially to induce ripening in fruit, has the formula C_2H_4. The only way for the 2 carbon atoms to have octets is for them to share 4 electrons in a carbon-carbon double bond:

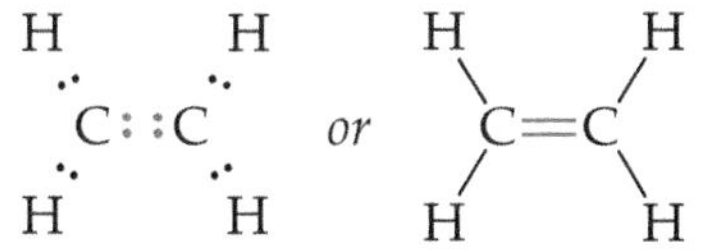

Ethylene—the carbon atoms share
4 electrons in a double bond.

As another example, acetylene, the gas used in welding, has the formula C_2H_2. To achieve octets, the 2 acetylene carbons share 6 electrons in a carbon-carbon triple bond:

H : C ⋮⋮ C : H *or* H—C≡C—H

Acetylene—the carbon atoms share
6 electrons in a triple bond.

Note that in compounds with multiple bonds like ethylene and acetylene, each carbon atom still forms a total of 4 covalent bonds.

Worked Example **4.4** Molecular Compounds: Multiple Bonds

The compound 1-butene contains a multiple bond. In the following representation, however, only the connections between atoms are shown; the multiple bond is not specifically indicated. Identify the position of the multiple bond.

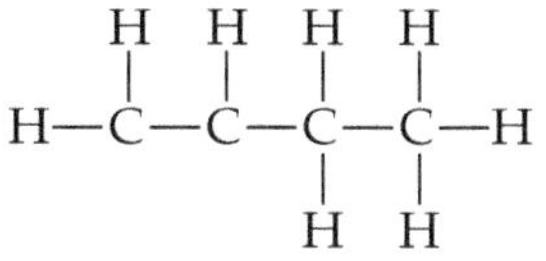

1-Butene

ANALYSIS Look for 2 adjacent atoms that appear to have fewer than the typical number of covalent bonds, and connect those atoms by a double or triple bond. Refer to Figure 4.3 to see how many bonds will typically be formed by hydrogen and carbon atoms.

SOLUTION

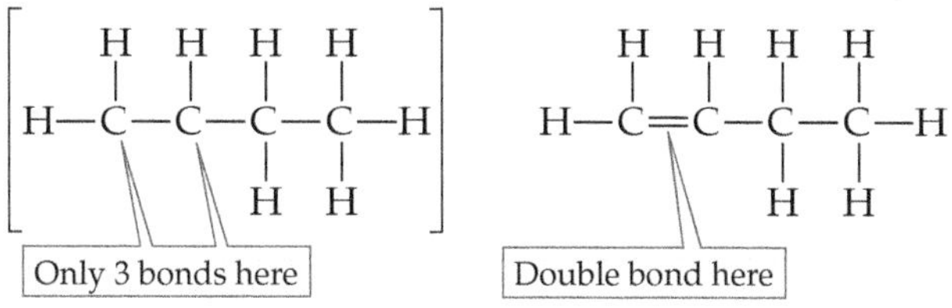

Worked Example **4.5** Multiple Bonds: Electron-Dot and Line Structures

Draw the oxygen molecule (a) using the electron-dot symbols, and (b) using lines rather than dots to indicate covalent bonds.

ANALYSIS   Each oxygen atom has 6 valence electrons and will tend to form 2 covalent bonds to reach an octet. Thus, each oxygen will need to share 4 electrons to form a double bond.

SOLUTION

$$:\overset{..}{O}::\overset{..}{O}:\quad \text{or}\quad :\overset{..}{O}=\overset{..}{O}:$$

PROBLEM 4.5

Acetic acid, the organic constituent of vinegar, can be drawn using electron-dot symbols as shown below. How many outer-shell electrons are associated with each atom? Draw the structure using lines rather than dots to indicate covalent bonds.

$$\begin{array}{c} \text{H} \overset{..}{\underset{..}{O}} : \\ \text{H}:\overset{..}{\underset{\overset{|}{H}}{C}}:\overset{..}{C}:\overset{..}{\underset{..}{O}}:\text{H} \\ \text{H} \end{array}$$

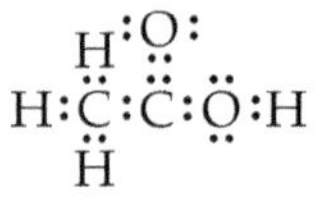

PROBLEM 4.6

Identify the positions of all double bonds in caffeine, a stimulant found in coffee and many soft drinks and as an additive in several over-the-counter drugs, such as aspirin.

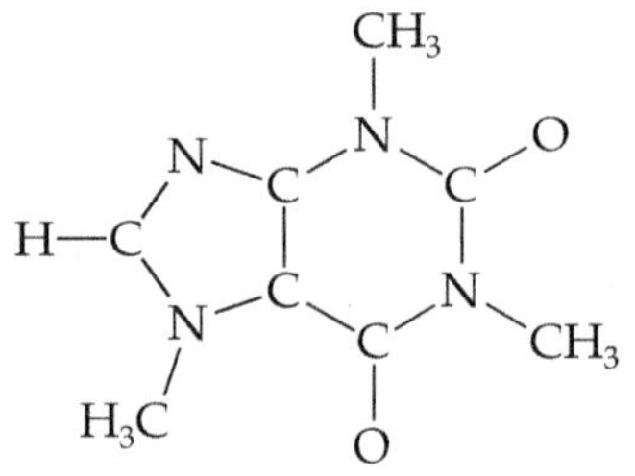

4.4 Coordinate Covalent Bonds

Coordinate covalent bond The covalent bond that forms when both electrons are donated by the same atom.

In the covalent bonds we have seen thus far, the shared electrons have come from different atoms. That is, the bonds result from the overlap of 2 singly occupied valence orbitals, 1 from each atom. Sometimes, though, a bond is formed by the overlap of a filled orbital on 1 atom with a vacant orbital on another atom so that both electrons come from the *same* atom. The bond that results in this case is called a **coordinate covalent bond**.

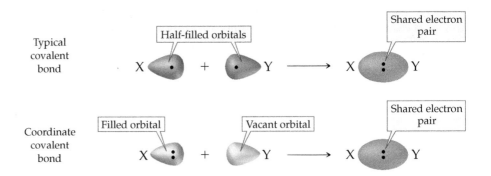

The ammonium ion, NH_4^+, is an example of a species with a coordinate covalent bond. When ammonia reacts in water solution with a hydrogen ion, H^+, the nitrogen atom donates 2 electrons from a filled valence orbital to form a coordinate covalent bond to the hydrogen ion, which has a vacant $1s$ orbital.

$$H^+ \ + \ H-\underset{\displaystyle \cdot\cdot}{\overset{\displaystyle |}{N}}-H \ \longrightarrow \ \left[H-\underset{\displaystyle \underset{\displaystyle H}{|}}{\overset{\displaystyle \overset{\displaystyle H}{|}}{N}}-H \right]^+$$

Once formed, a coordinate covalent bond contains two shared electrons and is no different from any other covalent bond. All four covalent bonds in NH_4^+ are identical, for example. Note, however, that formation of a coordinate covalent bond often results in unusual bonding patterns, such as an N atom with four covalent bonds rather than the usual three, or an oxygen atom with three bonds rather than the usual two (H_3O^+). An entire class of substances is based on the ability of transition metals to form coordinate covalent bonds with nonmetals. Called *coordination compounds*, many of these substances have important roles in living organisms. For example, toxic metals can be removed from the bloodstream by the formation of water-soluble coordination compounds.

▶▶▶ As another example, we will see in Chapter 19 that essential metal ions are held in enzyme molecules by coordinate covalent bonds.

4.5 Characteristics of Molecular Compounds

We saw in Section 3.4 that ionic compounds have high melting and boiling points because the attractive forces between oppositely charged ions are so strong that the ions are held tightly together. But *molecules* are neutral, so there is no strong electrostatic attraction between molecules. There are, however, several weaker forces between molecules, called *intermolecular forces*, which we will look at in more detail in Chapter 8.

When intermolecular forces are very weak, molecules of a substance are so weakly attracted to one another that the substance is a gas at ordinary temperatures. If the forces are somewhat stronger, the molecules are pulled together into a liquid; and if the forces are still stronger, the substance becomes a molecular solid. Even so, the melting points and boiling points of molecular solids are usually lower than those of ionic solids.

In addition to having lower melting points and boiling points, molecular compounds differ from ionic compounds in other ways. Most molecular compounds are insoluble in water, for instance, because they have little attraction to the strongly polar water molecules. In addition, they do not conduct electricity when melted because they have no charged particles. Table 4.1 provides a comparison of the properties of ionic and molecular compounds.

TABLE 4.1 A Comparison of Ionic and Molecular Compounds

Ionic Compounds	Molecular Compounds
Smallest components are ions (e.g., Na^+, Cl^-)	Smallest components are molecules (e.g., CO_2, H_2O)
Usually composed of metals combined with nonmetals	Usually composed of nonmetals with nonmetals
Crystalline solids	Gases, liquids, or low-melting-point solids
High melting points (e.g., NaCl = 801 °C)	Low melting points (H_2O = 0.0 °C)
High boiling points (above 700 °C) (e.g., NaCl = 1413 °C)	Low boiling points (e.g., H_2O = 100 °C; CH_3CH_2OH = 76 °C)
Conduct electricity when molten or dissolved in water	Do not conduct electricity
Many are water-soluble	Relatively few are water-soluble
Not soluble in organic liquids	Many are soluble in organic liquids

4.6 Molecular Formulas and Lewis Structures

Molecular formula A formula that shows the numbers and kinds of atoms in 1 molecule of a compound.

Structural formula A molecular representation that shows the connections among atoms by using lines to represent covalent bonds.

Lewis structure A molecular representation that shows both the connections among atoms and the locations of lone-pair valence electrons.

Lone pair A pair of electrons that is not used for bonding.

Formulas such as H_2O, NH_3, and CH_4, which show the numbers and kinds of atoms in one molecule of a compound, are called **molecular formulas**. Though important, molecular formulas are limited in their use because they do not provide information about how the atoms in a given molecule are connected.

Much more useful are **structural formulas**, which use lines to show how atoms are connected, and **Lewis structures**, which show both the connections among atoms and the placement of unshared valence electrons. In a water molecule, for instance, the oxygen atom shares two electron pairs in covalent bonds with 2 hydrogen atoms and has two other pairs of valence electrons that are not shared in bonds. Such unshared pairs of valence electrons are called **lone pairs**. In an ammonia molecule, three electron pairs are used in bonding, and there is one lone pair. In methane, all four electron pairs are bonding.

Note how a molecular formula differs from an ionic formula, described previously in Section 3.9. A *molecular* formula gives the number of atoms that are combined in one molecule of a compound, whereas an *ionic* formula gives only a ratio of ions (Figure 4.4). The formula C_2H_4 for ethylene, for example, says that every ethylene molecule consists of 2 carbon atoms and 4 hydrogen atoms. The formula NaCl for sodium chloride, however, says only that there are equal numbers of Na^+ and Cl^- ions in the crystal; the formula says nothing about how the ions interact with one another.

► **Figure 4.4**
The distinction between ionic and molecular compounds.
In ionic compounds, the smallest particle is an ion. In molecular compounds, the smallest particle is a molecule.

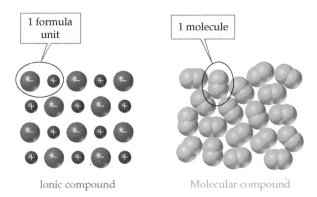

4.7 Drawing Lewis Structures

To draw a Lewis structure, you first need to know the connections among atoms. Sometimes the connections are obvious. Water, for example, can only be H—O—H because only oxygen can be in the middle and form 2 covalent bonds. Other times, you will have to be told how the atoms are connected.

Two approaches are used for drawing Lewis structures once the connections are known. The first is particularly useful for organic molecules like those found in living organisms because the atoms follow common bonding patterns. The second approach is a more general, stepwise procedure that works for all molecules.

Lewis Structures for Molecules Containing C, N, O, X (Halogen), and H

As summarized in Figure 4.3, carbon, nitrogen, oxygen, halogen, and hydrogen atoms usually maintain consistent bonding patterns:

- C forms 4 covalent bonds and often bonds to other carbon atoms.
- N forms 3 covalent bonds and has one lone pair of electrons.
- O forms 2 covalent bonds and has two lone pairs of electrons.
- Halogens $(X = F, Cl, Br, I)$ form 1 covalent bond and have three lone pairs of electrons.
- H forms 1 covalent bond.

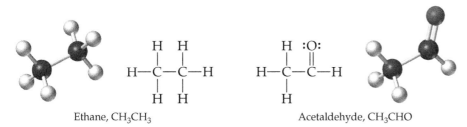

| Carbon 4 bonds | Nitrogen 3 bonds | Oxygen 2 bonds | Halogen 1 bond | Hydrogen 1 bond |

Relying on these common bonding patterns simplifies the writing of Lewis structures. In ethane (C_2H_6), a constituent of natural gas, for example, 3 of the 4 covalent bonds of each carbon atom are used in bonds to hydrogen, and the fourth is a carbon–carbon bond. There is no other arrangement in which all 8 atoms can have their usual bonding patterns. In acetaldehyde (C_2H_4O), a substance used in manufacturing perfumes, dyes, and plastics, 1 carbon has 3 bonds to hydrogen, while the other has 1 bond to hydrogen and a double bond to oxygen.

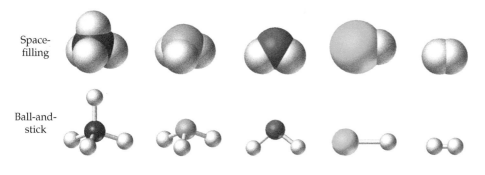

Ethane, CH_3CH_3 Acetaldehyde, CH_3CHO

Because Lewis structures are awkward for larger organic molecules, ethane is more frequently written as a **condensed structure** in which the bonds are not specifically shown. In its condensed form, ethane is CH_3CH_3, meaning that each carbon atom has 3 hydrogen atoms bonded to it (CH_3) and the 2 (CH_3) units are bonded to each other. In the same way, acetaldehyde can be written as CH_3CHO. Note that neither the lone-pair electrons nor the $C=O$ double bond in acetaldehyde is shown explicitly. You will get a lot more practice with such condensed structures in later chapters.

Many of the computer-generated pictures we will be using from now on will be *ball-and-stick models* rather than the space-filling models used previously. Space-filling models are more realistic, but ball-and-stick models do a better job of showing connections and molecular geometry. All models, regardless of type, use a consistent color code in which C is dark gray or black, H is white or ivory, O is red, N is blue, S is yellow, P is dark blue, F is light green, Cl is green, Br is brownish red, and I is purple.

Condensed structure A molecular representation in which bonds are not specifically shown but rather are understood by the order in which atoms are written.

▶▶ Condensed structures are used extensively to represent molecular structures in organic chemistry (Chapters 12–17).

Space-filling

Ball-and-stick

A General Method for Drawing Lewis Structures

A Lewis structure can be drawn for any molecule or polyatomic ion by following a five-step procedure. Take PCl_3, for example, a substance in which 3 chlorine atoms surround the central phosphorus atom.

STEP 1: **Find the total number of valence electrons of all atoms in the molecule or ion.** In PCl_3, for example, phosphorus (group 5A) has 5 valence electrons and chlorine (group 7A) has 7 valence electrons, giving a total of 26:

$$P + (3 \times Cl) = PCl_3$$
$$5e^- + (3 \times 7e^-) = 26e^-$$

For a polyatomic ion, add 1 electron for each negative charge or subtract 1 for each positive charge. In OH^-, the total is 8 electrons (6 from oxygen, 1 from hydrogen, plus 1 for the negative charge). In NH_4^+, the total is 8 (5 from nitrogen, 1 from each of 4 hydrogens, minus 1 for the positive charge).

STEP 2: **Draw a line between each pair of connected atoms to represent the two electrons in a covalent bond.** Remember that elements in the second row of the periodic table form the number of bonds discussed earlier in this section, whereas elements in the third row and beyond can use more than 8 electrons and form more than the "usual" number of bonds (Figure 4.3). A particularly common pattern is that an atom in the third row (or beyond) occurs as the central atom in a cluster. In PCl_3, for example, the phosphorus atom is in the center with the 3 chlorine atoms bonded to it:

$$\begin{array}{c} Cl \\ | \\ Cl-P-Cl \end{array}$$

STEP 3: **Using the remaining electrons, add lone pairs so that each atom connected to the central atom (except H) gets an octet.** In PCl_3, 6 of the 26 valence electrons were used to make the covalent bonds. From the remaining 20 electrons, each Cl atom needs three lone pairs to complete the octet:

$$\begin{array}{c} :\ddot{C}l: \\ | \\ :\ddot{C}l-P-\ddot{C}l: \end{array}$$

STEP 4: **Place any remaining electrons in lone pairs on the central atom.** In PCl_3, we have used 24 of the 26 available electrons—6 in three single bonds and 18 in the three lone pairs on each chlorine atom. This leaves 2 electrons for one lone pair on phosphorus:

$$\begin{array}{c} :\ddot{C}l: \\ | \\ :\ddot{C}l-\ddot{P}-\ddot{C}l: \end{array}$$

STEP 5: **If the central atom does not yet have an octet after all electrons have been assigned, take a lone pair from a neighboring atom, and form a multiple bond to the central atom.** In PCl_3, each atom has an octet, all 26 available electrons have been used, and the Lewis structure is finished.

Worked Examples 4.6–4.8 shows how to deal with cases where this fifth step is needed.

Worked Example 4.6 Multiple Bonds: Electron Dots and Valence Electrons

Draw a Lewis structure for the toxic gas hydrogen cyanide, HCN. The atoms are connected in the order shown in the preceding sentence.

ANALYSIS Follow the procedure outlined in the text.

SOLUTION

STEP 1: Find the total number of valence electrons:

$$H = 1, C = 4, N = 5 \text{ Total number of valence electrons} = 10$$

STEP 2: Draw a line between each pair of connected atoms to represent bonding electron pairs:

$$H-C-N \quad 2 \text{ bonds} = 4 \text{ electrons; 6 electrons remaining}$$

STEP 3: Add lone pairs so that each atom (except H) has a complete octet:

$$H-C-\ddot{N}:$$

STEP 4: All valence electrons have been used, and so step 4 is not needed. H and N have filled valence shells, but C does not.

STEP 5: If the central atom (C in this case) does not yet have an octet, use lone pairs from a neighboring atom (N) to form multiple bonds. This results in a triple bond between the C and N atoms, as shown in the electron dot and ball-and-stick representations below:

$$H-C\equiv N:$$

We can check the structure by noting that all 10 valence electrons have been used (in 4 covalent bonds and one lone pair) and that each atom has the expected number of bonds (1 bond for H, 3 for N, and 4 for C).

Worked Example 4.7 Lewis Structures: Location of Multiple Bonds

Draw a Lewis structure for vinyl chloride, C_2H_3Cl, a substance used in making polyvinyl chloride, or PVC, plastic.

ANALYSIS Since H and Cl form only 1 bond each, the carbon atoms must be bonded to each other, with the remaining atoms bonded to the carbons. With only 4 atoms available to bond with them, the carbon atoms cannot have 4 covalent bonds each unless they are joined by a double bond.

SOLUTION

STEP 1: The total number of valence electrons is 18; 4 from each of the 2 C atoms, 1 from each of the 3 H atoms, and 7 from the Cl atom.

STEP 2: Place the 2 C atoms in the center, and divide the 4 other atoms between them:

$$\begin{array}{ccc} H & & Cl \\ \diagdown & & \diagup \\ & C-C \\ \diagup & & \diagdown \\ H & & H \end{array}$$

The 5 bonds account for 10 valence electrons, with 8 remaining.

STEP 3: Place 6 of the remaining valence electrons around the Cl atom so that it has a complete octet, and place the remaining 2 valence electrons on one of the C atoms (either C, it does not matter):

$$\begin{array}{ccc} H & & :\ddot{C}l: \\ \diagdown & & \diagup \\ & C-\ddot{C}: \\ \diagup & & \diagdown \\ H & & H \end{array}$$

When all the valence electrons are distributed, the C atoms still do not have a complete octet; they each need 4 bonds but have only 3.

STEP 5: The lone pair of electrons on the C atom can be used to form a double bond between the C atoms, giving each a total of 4 bonds (8 electrons). Placement of the double bond yields the Lewis structure and ball-and-stick model for vinyl chloride shown below:

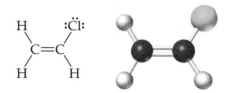

All 18 valence electrons are accounted for in 6 covalent bonds and three lone pairs, and each atom has the expected number of bonds.

Worked Example 4.8 Lewis Structures: Octet Rule and Multiple Bonds

Draw a Lewis structure for sulfur dioxide, SO_2. The connections are O—S—O.

ANALYSIS Follow the procedure outlined in the text.

SOLUTION

STEP 1: The total number of valence electrons is 18, 6 from each atom:

$$S + (2 \times O) = SO_2$$
$$6e^- + (2 + 6e^-) = 18e^-$$

STEP 2: O—S—O Two covalent bonds use 4 valence electrons.

STEP 3: :Ö—S—Ö: Adding three lone pairs to each oxygen to give each an octet uses 12 additional valence electrons.

STEP 4: :Ö—S—Ö: The remaining 2 valence electrons are placed on sulfur, but sulfur still does not have an octet.

STEP 5: Moving one lone pair from a neighboring oxygen to form a double bond with the central sulfur gives sulfur an octet (it does not matter on which side the S=O bond is written):

$$:\ddot{O}—\ddot{S}=\ddot{O}:$$

NOTE: The Lewis structure for SO_2 includes a single bond to one O and a double bond to the other O. It doesn't matter which O has the double bond—both structures are equally acceptable. In reality, however, the S—O bonds in this molecule are actually closer to 1.5, an average between the two possible structures we could draw. This is an example of *resonance structures*, or different Lewis structures that could be used to represent the same molecule.

▶▶▶ Aromatic compounds, a class of organic compounds discussed in Section 13.9, are an important example of resonance structures.

PROBLEM 4.8
Methylamine, CH_5N, is responsible for the characteristic odor of decaying fish. Draw a Lewis structure of methylamine.

PROBLEM 4.9
Add lone pairs where appropriate to the following structures:

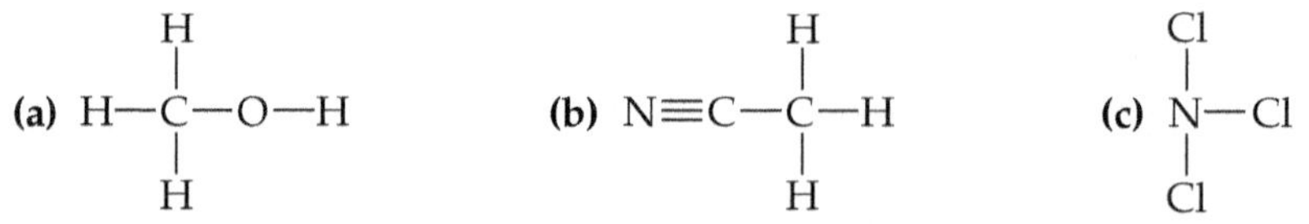

(a)
$$\begin{array}{c} H \\ | \\ H—C—O—H \\ | \\ H \end{array}$$

(b)
$$\begin{array}{c} H \\ | \\ N\equiv C—C—H \\ | \\ H \end{array}$$

(c)
$$\begin{array}{c} Cl \\ | \\ N—Cl \\ | \\ Cl \end{array}$$

PROBLEM 4.10

Draw Lewis structures for the following:

(a) Phosgene, $COCl_2$, a poisonous gas

(b) Hypochlorite ion, OCl^-, present in many swimming pool chemicals

(c) Hydrogen peroxide, H_2O_2

(d) Sulfur dichloride, SCl_2

PROBLEM 4.11

Draw a Lewis structure for nitric acid, HNO_3. The nitrogen atom is in the center, and the hydrogen atom is bonded to an oxygen atom.

CHEMISTRY IN ACTION

CO and NO: Pollutants or Miracle Molecules?

Carbon monoxide (CO) is a killer; everyone knows that. It is to blame for an estimated 3500 accidental deaths and suicides each year in the United States and is the number one cause of all deaths by poisoning. Nitric oxide (NO) is formed in combustion engines and reacts with oxygen to form nitrogen dioxide (NO_2), the reddish-brown gas associated with urban smog. What most people do not know, however, is that our bodies cannot function without these molecules. A startling discovery made in 1992 showed that CO and NO are key chemical messengers in the body, used by cells to regulate critical metabolic processes.

The toxicity of CO in moderate concentration is due to its ability to bind to hemoglobin molecules in the blood, thereby preventing the hemoglobin from carrying oxygen to tissues. The high reactivity of NO leads to the formation of compounds that are toxic irritants. However, low concentrations of CO and NO are produced in cells throughout the body. Both CO and NO are highly soluble in water and can diffuse from one cell to another, where they stimulate production of a substance called *guanylyl cyclase*. Guanylyl cyclase, in turn, controls the production of another substance called *cyclic GMP*, which regulates many cellular functions.

Levels of CO production are particularly high in certain regions of the brain, including those associated with long-term memory. Evidence from experiments with rat brains suggests that a special kind of cell in the brain's hippocampus is signaled by transfer of a molecular messenger from a neighboring cell. The receiving cell responds back to the signaling cell by releasing CO, which causes still more messenger molecules to be sent. After several rounds of this back-and-forth communication, the receiving cell undergoes some sort of change that becomes a memory. When CO production is blocked, possibly in response to a medical condition or exposure to certain toxic metals, long-term memories are no longer stored, and those memories that previously existed are erased. When CO production is stimulated, however, memories are again laid down.

▲ **Los Angeles at sunset. Carbon monoxide is a major component of photochemical smog, but it also functions as an essential chemical messenger in our bodies.**

NO controls a seemingly limitless range of functions in the body. The immune system uses NO to fight infections and tumors. It is also used to transmit messages between nerve cells and is associated with the processes involved in learning and memory, sleeping, and depression. Its most advertised role, however, is as a *vasodilator*, a substance that allows blood vessels to relax and dilate. This discovery led to the development of a new class of drugs that stimulate production of enzymes called nitric oxide synthases (NOS). These drugs can be used to treat conditions from erectile dysfunction (Viagra) to hypertension. Given the importance of NO in the fields of neuroscience, physiology, and immunology, it is not surprising that it was named "Molecule of the Year" in 1992.

See Chemistry in Action Problems 4.89 and 4.90 at the end of the chapter.

The molecular model shown here is a representation of methyl methacrylate, a starting material used to prepare Lucite plastic. Only the connections between atoms are shown; multiple bonds are not indicated.

(a) What is the molecular formula of methyl methacrylate?

(b) Indicate the positions of the multiple bonds and lone pairs in methyl methacrylate.

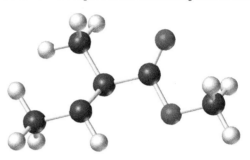

PROBLEM 4.13
Draw the Lewis dot structures for the molecules CO and NO discussed in the Chemistry in Action box on page 113. How do the Lewis structures provide insight into the reactivity of these molecules?

4.8 The Shapes of Molecules

Look back at the computer-generated drawings of molecules in the preceding section, and you will find that the molecules are shown with specific shapes. Acetylene is *linear*, water is *bent*, ammonia is *pyramid-shaped*, methane is *tetrahedral*, and ethylene is flat, or *planar*. What determines such shapes? Why, for example, are the 3 atoms in water connected at an angle of (104.5°) rather than in a straight line? Like so many properties, molecular shapes are related to the numbers and locations of the valence electrons around atoms.

Molecular shapes can be predicted by noting how many bonds and electron pairs surround individual atoms and applying what is called the **valence-shell electron-pair repulsion (VSEPR) model**. The basic idea of the VSEPR model is that the constantly moving valence electrons in bonds and lone pairs make up negatively charged clouds of electrons, which electrically repel one another. The clouds therefore tend to keep as far apart as possible, causing molecules to assume specific shapes. There are three steps to applying the VSEPR model:

STEP 1: Draw a Lewis structure of the molecule, and identify the atom whose geometry is of interest. In a simple molecule like PCl_3 or CO_2, this is usually the central atom.

STEP 2: Count the number of electron charge clouds surrounding the atom of interest. The number of charge clouds is simply the total number of lone pairs plus connections to other atoms. It does not matter whether a connection is a single bond or a multiple bond because we are interested only in the *number* of charge clouds, not in how many electrons each cloud contains. The carbon atom in carbon dioxide, for instance, has 2 double bonds to oxygen ($O{=}C{=}O$), and thus has two charge clouds.

STEP 3: Predict molecular shape by assuming that the charge clouds orient in space so that they are as far away from one another as possible. How they achieve this favorable orientation depends on their number, as summarized in Table 4.2.

If there are only two charge clouds, as occurs on the central atom of CO_2 (2 double bonds) and HCN (1 single bond and 1 triple bond), the clouds are farthest apart when

Valence-shell electron-pair repulsion (VSEPR) model A method for predicting molecular shape by noting how many electron charge clouds surround atoms and assuming that the clouds orient as far away from one another as possible.

TABLE 4.2 Molecular Geometry Around Atoms with 2, 3, and 4 Charge Clouds

NUMBER OF BONDS	NUMBER OF LONE PAIRS	TOTAL NUMBER OF CHARGE CLOUDS	MOLECULAR GEOMETRY		EXAMPLE
2	0	2	●—●—●	 Linear	O=C=O
3	0	3		 Trigonal planar	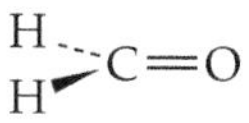 $\underset{H}{\overset{H}{>}}C=O$
2	1			Bent	$\underset{O}{\overset{O}{>}}S$
4	0	4		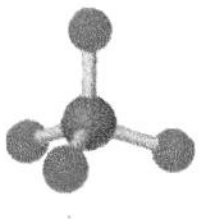 Tetrahedral	$H\overset{\overset{H}{|}}{\underset{H}{-}}{\overset{}{C}}-H$
3	1			Pyramidal	$H-\underset{H}{\overset{..}{N}}-H$
2	2			Bent	$H-\underset{H}{\overset{..}{O}}:$

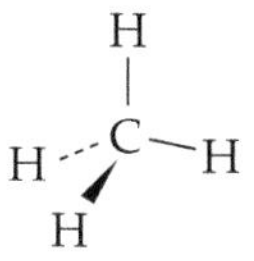

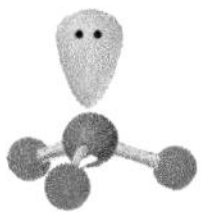

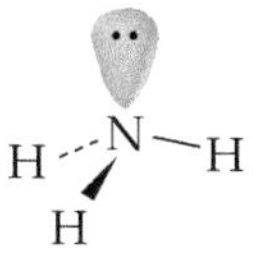

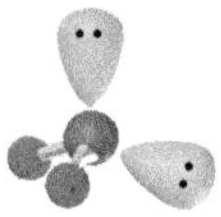

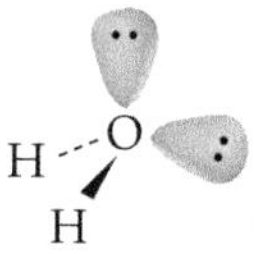

they point in opposite directions. Thus, both HCN and CO_2 are linear molecules, with **bond angles** of 180°:

> **Bond angle** The angle formed by 3 adjacent atoms in a molecule.

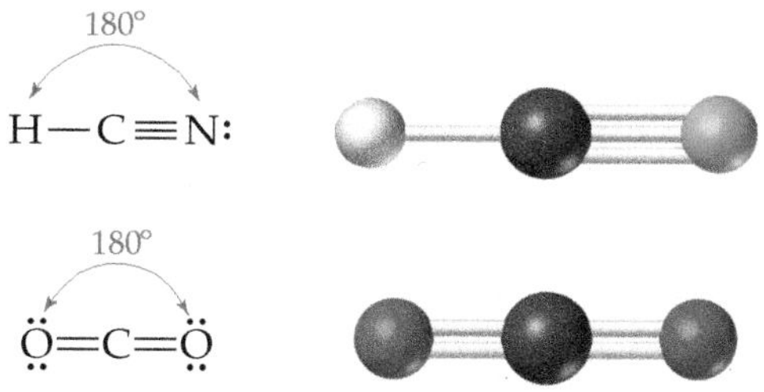

These molecules are linear, with bond angles of 180°.

$$\overset{180°}{H-C\equiv N:}$$

$$\overset{180°}{\ddot{O}=C=\ddot{O}}$$

When there are three charge clouds, as occurs on the central atom in formaldehyde (1 single bond and 1 double bond) and SO_2 (1 single bond, 1 double bond, and one lone pair), the clouds will be farthest apart if they lie in a plane and point to the corners of an equilateral triangle. Thus, a formaldehyde molecule is trigonal planar, with all bond angles near 120°. In the same way, an SO_2 molecule has a trigonal planar arrangement of its three electron clouds, but one point of the triangle is occupied by a lone pair. The connection between the 3 atoms is therefore bent rather than linear, with an O—S—O bond angle of approximately 120°:

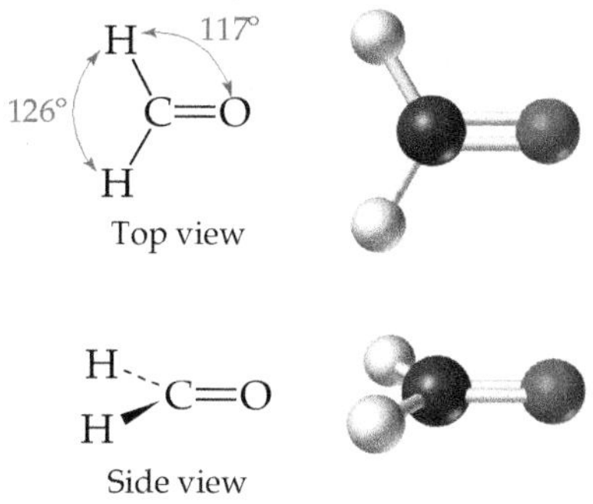

A formaldehyde molecule is planar triangular, with bond angles of roughly 120°.

$$\overset{126°}{}\underset{H}{\overset{H\overset{117°}{\frown}}{C}}=O$$

Top view

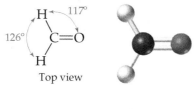

An SO_2 molecule is bent, with a bond angle of approximately 120°.

$$\underset{:\ddot{O}:}{\overset{:\ddot{O}:}{S}}\overset{120°}{}$$

Top view

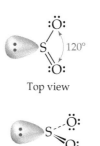

$$\underset{H}{\overset{H}{>}}C=O$$

Side view

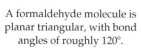

$$\underset{\ddot{O}:}{\overset{\ddot{O}:}{S}}$$

Side view

Note how the three-dimensional shapes of molecules like formaldehyde and SO_2 are shown. Solid lines are assumed to be in the plane of the paper; a dashed line recedes behind the plane of the paper away from the viewer; and a dark wedged line protrudes out of the paper toward the viewer. This standard method for showing three-dimensionality will be used throughout the rest of the book.

When there are four charge clouds, as occurs on the central atom in CH_4 (4 single bonds), NH_3 (3 single bonds and one lone pair), and H_2O (2 single bonds and two lone pairs), the clouds can be farthest apart when they extend to the corners of a *regular tetrahedron*. As illustrated in Figure 4.5, a **regular tetrahedron** is a geometric solid whose four identical faces are equilateral triangles. The central atom is at the center of the tetrahedron, the charge clouds point to the corners, and the angle between lines drawn from the center to any two corners is 109.5°.

Regular tetrahedron A geometric figure with four identical triangular faces.

▶**Figure 4.5**
The tetrahedral geometry of an atom surrounded by four charge clouds. The atom is located at the center of the regular tetrahedron, and the four charge clouds point toward the corners. The bond angle between the center and any two corners is 109.5°.

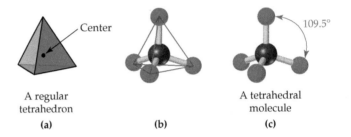

Center

A regular tetrahedron
(a)

A tetrahedral molecule
(c)

109.5°

(b)

Because valence-shell electron octets are so common, a great many molecules have geometries based on the tetrahedron. In methane (CH_4), for example, the carbon atom has tetrahedral geometry with H—C—H bond angles of exactly 109.5°. In ammonia (NH_3), the nitrogen atom has a tetrahedral arrangement of its four charge clouds, but one corner of the tetrahedron is occupied by a lone pair, resulting in an overall pyramidal shape for the molecule. Similarly, water, which has two corners of the tetrahedron occupied by lone pairs, has an overall bent shape.

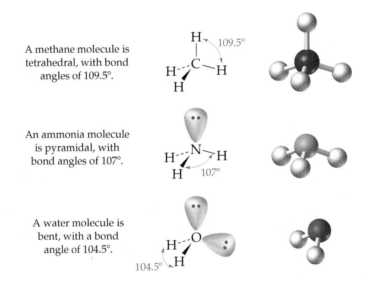

A methane molecule is tetrahedral, with bond angles of 109.5°.

An ammonia molecule is pyramidal, with bond angles of 107°.

A water molecule is bent, with a bond angle of 104.5°.

Note that the H—N—H bond angle in ammonia (107°) and the H—O—H bond angle in water (104.5°) are close to, but not exactly equal to, the ideal 109.5° tetrahedral value. The angles are diminished somewhat from their ideal value because the lone-pair charge clouds repel other electron clouds strongly and compress the rest of the molecule.

The geometry around atoms in larger molecules also derives from the shapes shown in Table 4.2. For example, each of the 2 carbon atoms in ethylene ($H_2C{=}CH_2$) has three charge clouds, giving rise to trigonal planar geometry. It turns out that the molecule as a whole is also planar, with H—C—C and H—C—H bond angles of approximately 120°:

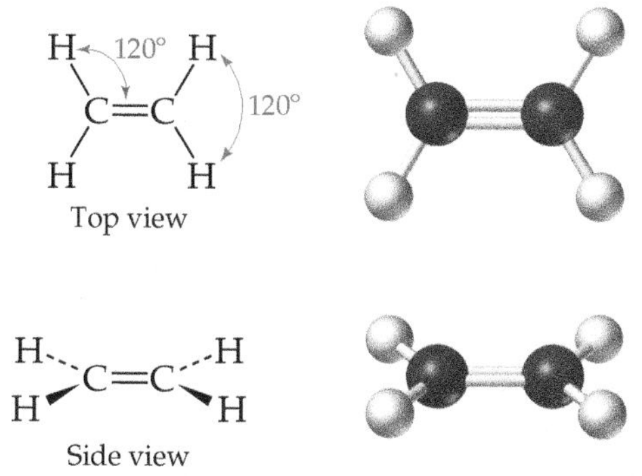

The ethylene molecule is planar, with bond angles of 120°.

H—120° H
\\   /
C=C   )120°
/   \\
H   H

Top view

H⋯ ⋯H
>C=C<
H   H

Side view

Carbon atoms bonded to 4 other atoms are each at the center of a tetrahedron, as shown here for ethane, H_3C—CH_3:

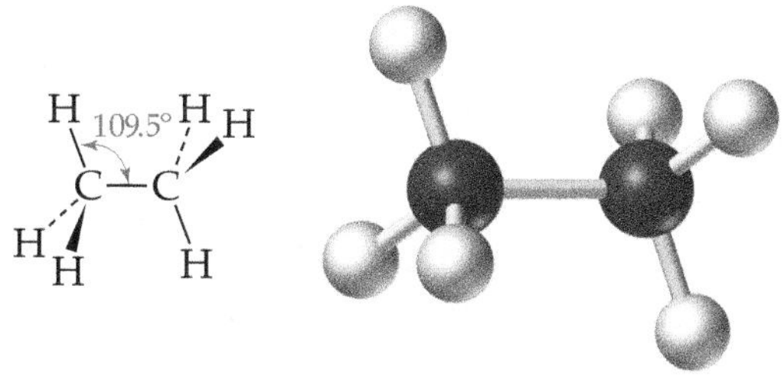

The ethane molecule has tetrahedral carbon atoms, with bond angles of 109.5°.

H 109.5° H H
\\   / /
C—C
/   \\
H   H
H   H

Worked Example 4.9 Lewis Structures: Molecular Shape

What shape would you expect for the hydronium ion, H_3O^+?

ANALYSIS Draw the Lewis structure for the molecular ion, and count the number of charge clouds around the central oxygen atom; imagine the clouds orienting as far away from one another as possible.

SOLUTION 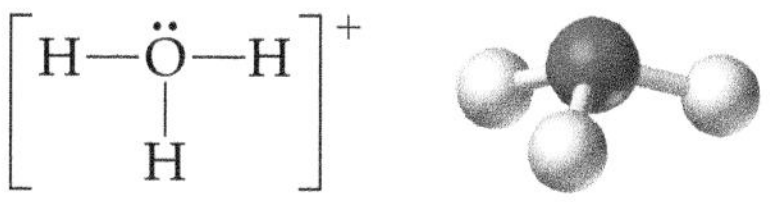
The Lewis structure for the hydronium ion shows that the oxygen atom has four charge clouds (3 single bonds and one lone pair). The hydronium ion is therefore pyramidal with bond angles of approximately 109.5°.

$$\left[H-\ddot{O}-H \atop \quad\ \ H \right]^+$$

Worked Example 4.10 Lewis Structures: Charge Cloud Geometry

Predict the geometry around each of the carbon atoms in an acetaldehyde molecule, CH_3CHO.

ANALYSIS Draw the Lewis structure and identify the number of charge clouds around each of the central carbon atoms.

SOLUTION
The Lewis structure of acetaldehyde shows that the CH_3 carbon has four charge clouds (4 single bonds) and the CHO carbon atom has three charge clouds (2 single bonds, 1 double bond). Table 4.2 indicates that the CH_3 carbon is tetrahedral, but the CHO carbon is trigonal planar.

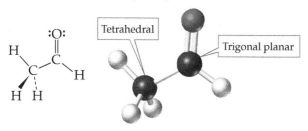

CHEMISTRY IN ACTION

VERY Big Molecules

How big can a molecule be? The answer is very, *very* big. The really big molecules in our bodies and in many items we buy are all *polymers*. Like a string of beads, a polymer is formed of many repeating units connected in a long chain. Each "bead" in the chain comes from a simple molecule that has formed chemical bonds at both ends, linking it to other molecules. The repeating units can be the same:

–a–a–a–a–a–a–a–a–a–a–a–a–

or they can be different. If different, they can be connected in an ordered pattern:

–a–b–a–b–a–b–a–b–a–b–a–b–

or in a random pattern:

–a–b–b–a–b–a–a–a–b–a–b–b–

Furthermore, the polymer chains can have branches, and the branches can have either the same repeating unit as the main chain or a different one:

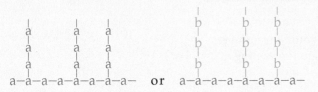

Still other possible variations include complex, three-dimensional networks of "cross-linked" chains. The rubber used in tires, for example, contains polymer chains connected by cross-linking atoms of sulfur to impart greater rigidity.

We all use synthetic polymers every day—we usually call them "plastics." Common synthetic polymers are made by connecting up to several hundred thousand smaller molecules together, producing giant polymer molecules with masses up to several million atomic mass units. Polyethylene, for example, is made by

▲ **The protective gear worn by motor-cyclists (shown above), firefighters, and security forces are composed of advanced composite materials based on polymers.**

combining as many as 50,000 ethylene molecules ($H_2C{=}CH_2$) to give a polymer with repeating $-CH_2CH-$ units:

Many $H_2C{=}CH_2$ $\longrightarrow$ $-CH_2CH_2CH_2CH_2CH_2CH_2-$
Ethylene   Polyethlene

The product is used in such items as chairs, toys, drain pipes, milk bottles, and packaging films. Other examples of polymers include the nylon used in clothing and pantyhose, molded hardware (nuts and bolts), and the Kevlar used in bulletproof vests (see Chemistry in Action on p. 538).

Nature began to exploit the extraordinary variety of polymer properties long before humans did. In fact, despite great progress in recent years, there is still much to be learned about the polymers in living things. Carbohydrates and proteins are polymers, as are the giant molecules of deoxyribonucleic acid (DNA) that govern many cellular processes, including reproduction, in all organisms. Nature's polymer molecules, though, are more complex than any that chemists have yet created.

▶▶ Carbohydrates are polymers composed of sugar molecules linked together in long chains (Chapter 21), while proteins are polymers of smaller molecules called amino acids (Chapter 18). DNA, a polymer of repeating nucleotide subunits, is discussed in Chapter 25.

See Chemistry in Action Problems 4.91 and 4.92 at the end of the chapter.

PROBLEM 4.14
Boron typically only forms 3 covalent bonds because it only has 3 valence electrons, but can form coordinate covalent bonds. Draw the Lewis structure for BF_4^- and predict the molecular shape of the ion.

PROBLEM 4.15
Predict shapes for the organic molecules chloroform, $CHCl_3$, and 1,1-dichloroethylene, $Cl_2C{=}CH_2$.

PROBLEM 4.16
Polycarbonate, also known as plexiglass, has the basic repeating unit shown below. What is the geometry of the electron clouds for the carbon atoms labeled "a" and "b" in this structure?

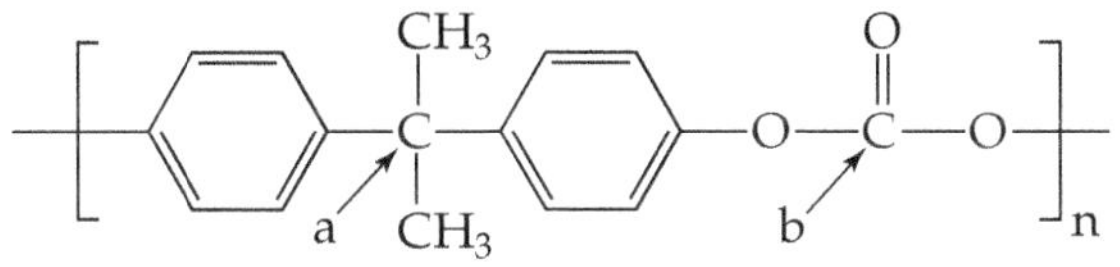

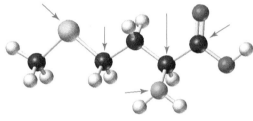

PROBLEM 4.17
Hydrogen selenide (H_2Se) resembles hydrogen sulfide (H_2S) in that both compounds have terrible odors and are poisonous. What are their shapes?

KEY CONCEPT PROBLEM 4.18

Draw a structure corresponding to the molecular model of the amino acid methionine shown here, and describe the geometry around the indicated atoms. (Remember the color key discussed in Section 4.7: black = carbon; white = hydrogen; red = oxygen; blue = nitrogen; yellow = sulfur.)

Methionine

4.9 Polar Covalent Bonds and Electronegativity

Electrons in a covalent bond occupy the region between the bonded atoms. If the atoms are identical, as in H_2 and Cl_2, the electrons are attracted equally to both atoms and are shared equally. If the atoms are *not* identical, however, as in HCl, the bonding electrons may be attracted more strongly by one atom than by the other and may be shared unequally. Such bonds are said to be **polar covalent bonds**. In hydrogen chloride, for example, electrons spend more time near the chlorine atom than near the hydrogen atom. Although the molecule as a whole is neutral, the chlorine is more negative than the hydrogen, resulting in *partial* charges on the atoms. These partial charges are represented by placing a $\delta-$ (Greek lowercase *delta*) on the more negative atom and a $\delta+$ on the more positive atom.

A particularly helpful way of visualizing this unequal distribution of bonding electrons is to look at what is called an *electrostatic potential map*, which uses color to portray the calculated electron distribution in a molecule. In HCl, for example, the electron-poor hydrogen is blue, and the electron-rich chlorine is reddish-yellow:

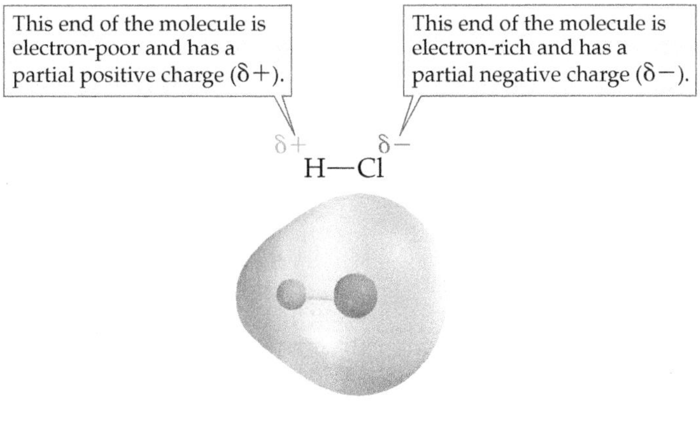

Polar covalent bond A bond in which the electrons are attracted more strongly by one atom than by the other.

This end of the molecule is electron-poor and has a partial positive charge ($\delta+$).

This end of the molecule is electron-rich and has a partial negative charge ($\delta-$).

$$\overset{\delta+}{H}-\overset{\delta-}{Cl}$$

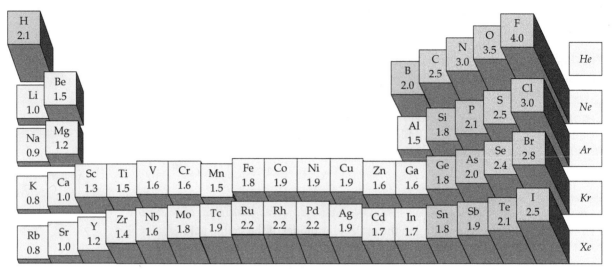

▲ **Figure 4.6**
Electronegativities of several main group and transition metal elements.
Reactive nonmetals at the top right of the periodic table are the most electronegative, and metals at the lower left are the least electronegative. The noble gases are not assigned values.

Electronegativity The ability of an atom to attract electrons in a covalent bond.

The ability of an atom to attract electrons in a covalent bond is called the atom's **electronegativity**. Fluorine, the most electronegative element, is assigned a value of 4, and less electronegative atoms are assigned lower values, as shown in Figure 4.6. Metallic elements on the left side of the periodic table attract electrons only weakly and have lower electronegativities, whereas the halogens and other reactive nonmetal elements on the upper right side of the table attract electrons strongly and have higher electronegativities. Note in Figure 4.6 that electronegativity generally decreases going down the periodic table within a group.

Comparing the electronegativities of bonded atoms makes it possible to compare the polarities of bonds and to predict the occurrence of ionic bonding. Both oxygen (electronegativity 3.5) and nitrogen (3.0), for instance, are more electronegative than carbon (2.5). As a result, both C—O and C—N bonds are polar, with carbon at the positive end. The larger difference in electronegativity values shows that the C—O bond is the more polar of the two:

Less polar —
$^{\delta+}C{-}N^{\delta-}$
Electronegativity difference:
$3.0 - 2.5 = 0.5$

— More polar
$^{\delta+}C{-}O^{\delta-}$
Electronegativity difference:
$3.5 - 2.5 = 1.0$

As a rule of thumb, electronegativity differences of less than 0.5 result in nonpolar covalent bonds, differences up to 1.9 indicate increasingly polar covalent bonds, and differences of 2 or more indicate ionic bonds. The electronegativity differences show, for example, that the bond between carbon and fluorine is highly polar covalent, the bond between sodium and chlorine is largely ionic, and the bond between rubidium and fluorine is almost completely ionic:

E.N difference		Type of bond
0 — 0.4	~	Covalent
0.5 — 1.9	~	Polar covalent
2.0 and above	~	Ionic

$^{\delta+}C{-}F^{\delta-}$ Na^+Cl^- Rb^+F^-

Electronegativity difference: 1.5   2.1   3.2

Note, though, that there is no sharp dividing line between covalent and ionic bonds; most bonds fall somewhere between two extremes.

LOOKING AHEAD ▶▶▶ The values given in Figure 4.6 indicate that carbon and hydrogen have similar electronegativities. As a result, C—H bonds are nonpolar. We will see in Chapters 12–25 how this fact helps explain the properties of organic and biological compounds, all of which have carbon and hydrogen as their principal constituents.

Worked Example **4.11** Electronegativity: Ionic, Nonpolar, and Polar Covalent Bonds

Predict whether each of the bonds between the following atoms would be ionic, polar covalent, or nonpolar covalent. If polar covalent, which atom would carry the partial positive and negative charges?

(a) C and Br   (b) Li and Cl

(c) N and H   (d) Si and I

ANALYSIS Compare the electronegativity values for the atoms and classify the nature of the bonding based on the electronegativity difference.

SOLUTION

(a) The electronegativity for C is 2.5, and for Br is 2.8; the difference is 0.3, indicating nonpolar covalent bonding would occur between these atoms.

(b) The electronegativity for Li is 1.0, and for Cl is 3.0; the difference is 2.0, indicating that ionic bonding would occur between these atoms.

(c) The electronegativity for N is 3.0, and for H is 2.5; the difference is 0.5. Bonding would be polar covalent, with $N = \delta-$ and $H = \delta+$.

(d) The electronegativity for Si is 1.8, and for I is 2.5; the difference is 0.7. Bonding would be polar covalent, with $I = \delta-$, and $Si = \delta+$.

PROBLEM 4.19
The elements H, N, O, P, and S are commonly bonded to carbon in organic compounds. Arrange these elements in order of increasing electronegativity.

PROBLEM 4.20
Use electronegativity differences to classify bonds between the following pairs of atoms as ionic, nonpolar covalent, or polar covalent. For those that are polar, use the symbols $\delta+$ and $\delta-$ to identify the location of the partial charges on the polar covalent bond.

(a) I and Cl   (b) Li and O

(c) Br and Br   (d) P and Br

4.10 Polar Molecules

Just as individual bonds can be polar, entire *molecules* can be polar if electrons are attracted more strongly to one part of the molecule than to another. Molecular polarity is due to the sum of all individual bond polarities and lone-pair contributions in the molecule and is often represented by an arrow pointing in the direction that electrons are displaced. The arrow is pointed at the negative end and is crossed at the positive end to resemble a plus sign, $(\delta+) \longmapsto (\delta-)$.

Molecular polarity depends on the shape of the molecule as well as the presence of polar covalent bonds and lone pairs. In water, for example, electrons are displaced away from the less electronegative hydrogen atoms toward the more electronegative oxygen atom so that the net polarity points between the two O—H bonds. In chloromethane, CH_3Cl, electrons are attracted from the carbon/hydrogen part of the molecule toward the electronegative chlorine atom so that the net polarity points along the C—Cl bond. Electrostatic potential maps show these polarities clearly, with electron-poor regions in blue and electron-rich regions in red.

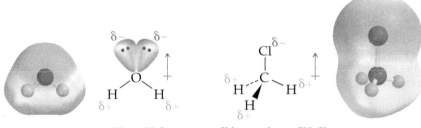

Water, H₂O   Chloromethane, CH₃Cl

Furthermore, just because a molecule has polar covalent bonds, it does not mean that the molecule is necessarily polar overall. Carbon dioxide (CO_2) and tetrachloromethane (CCl_4) molecules, for instance, have no net polarity because their symmetrical shapes cause the individual C=O and C—Cl bond polarities to cancel.

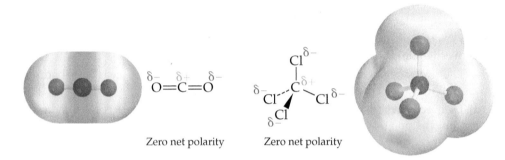

Zero net polarity   Zero net polarity

Polarity has a dramatic effect on the physical properties of molecules, particularly on melting points, boiling points, and solubilities. We will see numerous examples of such effects in subsequent chapters.

Worked Example 4.12 Electronegativity: Polar Bonds and Polar Molecules

Look at the structures of (a) hydrogen cyanide (HCN) and (b) vinyl chloride $(H_2C=CHCl)$, described in Worked Examples 4.6 and 4.7, decide whether or not the molecules are polar, and show the direction of net polarity in each.

ANALYSIS Draw a Lewis structure for each molecule to find its shape, and identify any polar bonds using the electronegativity values in Figure 4.6. Then, decide on net polarity by adding the individual contributions.

SOLUTION

(a) The carbon atom in hydrogen cyanide has two charge clouds, making HCN a linear molecule. The C—H bond is relatively nonpolar, but the C≡N bonding electrons are pulled toward the electronegative nitrogen atom. In addition, a lone pair protrudes from nitrogen. Thus, the molecule has a net polarity:

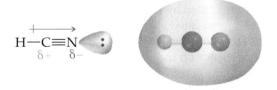

(b) Vinyl chloride, like ethylene, is a planar molecule. The C—H and C=C bonds are nonpolar, but the C—Cl bonding electrons are displaced toward the electronegative chlorine. Thus, the molecule has a net polarity:

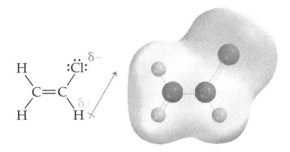

PROBLEM 4.21

Look at the molecular shape of formaldehyde (CH_2O) described on page 115, decide whether or not the molecule is polar, and show the direction of net polarity.

PROBLEM 4.22

Draw a Lewis structure for dimethyl ether (CH_3OCH_3), predict its shape, and tell whether or not the molecule is polar.

KEY CONCEPT PROBLEM 4.23

From this electrostatic potential map of methyllithium, identify the direction of net polarity in the molecule. Explain this polarity based on electronegativity values.

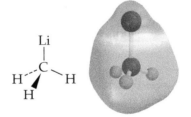

Methyllithium

4.11 Naming Binary Molecular Compounds

When two different elements combine, they form what is called a **binary compound**. The formulas of binary molecular compounds are usually written with the less electronegative element first. Thus, metals are always written before nonmetals, and a nonmetal farther left on the periodic table generally comes before a nonmetal farther right. For example,

Binary compound A compound formed by combination of two different elements.

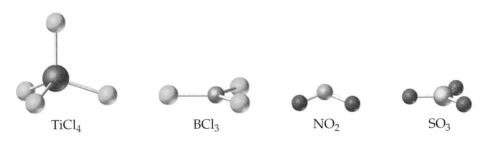

$TiCl_4$ BCl_3 NO_2 SO_3

As we learned in Section 3.9, the formulas of ionic compounds indicate the number of anions and cations necessary for a neutral formula unit, which depends on the charge on each of the ions. With molecular compounds, however, many combinations of atoms are possible, since nonmetals are capable of forming multiple covalent bonds.

TABLE 4.3 Numerical Prefixes Used in Chemical Names

Number	Prefix
1	mono-
2	di-
3	tri-
4	tetra-
5	penta-
6	hexa-
7	hepta-
8	octa-
9	nona-
10	deca-

When naming binary molecular compounds, therefore, we must identify exactly how many atoms of each element are included in the molecular formula. The names of binary molecular compounds are assigned in two steps, using the prefixes listed in Table 4.3 to indicate the number of atoms of each element combined.

STEP 1: Name the first element in the formula, using a prefix if needed to indicate the number of atoms.

STEP 2: Name the second element in the formula, using an *-ide* ending like for anions (Section 3.7), along with a prefix if needed.

The prefix *mono-*, meaning one, is omitted except where needed to distinguish between two different compounds with the same elements. For example, the two oxides of carbon are named carbon *mon*oxide for CO and carbon *di*oxide for CO_2. (Note that we say *mon*oxide rather than *mono*oxide.) Some other examples are:

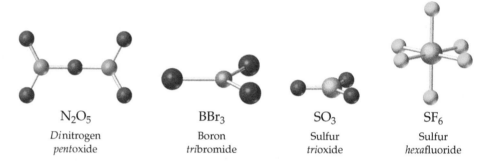

N_2O_5	BBr_3	SO_3	SF_6
*Di*nitrogen *pent*oxide	Boron *tri*bromide	Sulfur *tri*oxide	Sulfur *hexa*fluoride

Naming of molecular compounds can get complicated when more than two elements are present. This is particularly true for *organic compounds*, a class of molecular compounds composed largely of carbon (see examples in the Chemistry in Action on p. 125). The rules for naming these compounds will be discussed in later chapters.

Worked Example 4.13 Naming Molecular Compounds

Name the following compounds:

(a) N_2O_3 (b) $GeCl_4$ (c) PCl_5

SOLUTION

(a) Dinitrogen trioxide   (b) Germanium tetrachloride
(c) Phosphorus pentachloride

Worked Example 4.14 Writing Formulas for Molecular Compounds

Write molecular formulas for the following compounds:

(a) Nitrogen triiodide   (b) Silicon tetrachloride
(c) Carbon disulfide

SOLUTION

(a) NI_3 (b) $SiCl_4$ (c) CS_2

PROBLEM 4.24
Name the following compounds:

(a) S_2Cl_2 (b) ICl   (c) ICl_3

PROBLEM 4.25
Write formulas for the following compounds:
(a) Selenium tetrafluoride   (b) Diphosphorus pentoxide   (c) Bromine trifluoride

PROBLEM 4.26

Geraniol, one of the components of rose oil (see the following Chemistry in Action). has the basic structure represented below. Draw the structural formula for geraniol to include any multiple bonds, and then write the condensed structure for geraniol.

$$CH_3-\underset{\underset{H}{|}}{\overset{\overset{CH_3}{|}}{C}}-\underset{\underset{H}{|}}{\overset{\overset{H}{|}}{C}}-\underset{\underset{H}{|}}{\overset{\overset{H}{|}}{C}}-\underset{\underset{H}{|}}{\overset{\overset{CH_3}{|}}{C}}-\underset{\underset{H}{|}}{\overset{\overset{H}{|}}{C}}-OH$$

CHEMISTRY IN ACTION

Damascenone by Any Other Name Would Smell as Sweet

What's in a name? According to Shakespeare's *Romeo and Juliet,* a rose by any other name would smell as sweet. Chemical names, however, often provoke less favorable responses: "It's unpronounceable." "It's too complicated." "It must be something bad."

But why are chemical names so complicated? The reason is obvious once you realize that there are more than 19 *million* known chemical compounds. The full name of a chemical compound has to include enough information to tell chemists the composition and structure of the compound. It is as if every person on earth had to have his or her own unique name that described height, hair color, and other identifying characteristics in sufficient detail to distinguish him or her from every other person. Consider, also, that subtle differences in structure can result in significant differences in chemical or physical properties. Geraniol, for example, is used as a flavor additive in the food industry, while citronellol is used in perfumes and insect repellants, such as citronella candles. The common names for these substances are easier to remember, but their *chemical* names give us precise information about their structural differences and similarities. Geraniol ($C_{10}H_{18}O$), also known as *3,7-dimethylocta-2, 6-dien-1-ol* differs from citronellol ($C_{10}H_{20}O$ or *3,7-dimethyloct-6-en-1-ol*) by only one C — C double bond.

Unfortunately, people sometimes conclude that everything with a chemical name is unnatural and dangerous. Neither is true, of course. Acetaldehyde, for instance, is present naturally in most tart, ripe fruits and is often added in small amounts to artificial flavorings. When *pure*, however, acetaldehyde

▲ **The scent of these roses contains β-damascenone, β-ionone, citronellol, geraniol, nerol, eugenol, methyl eugenol, β-phenylethyl, alcohol, farnesol, linalool, terpineol, rose oxide, carvone, and many other natural substances.**

is also a flammable gas that is toxic and explosive in high concentrations.

Similar comparisons of desirable and harmful properties can be made for almost all chemicals, including water, sugar, and salt. The properties of a substance and the conditions surrounding its use must be evaluated before judgments are made. Damascenone, geraniol, and citronellol, by the way, are chemicals that contribute to the wonderful aroma of roses.

See Chemistry in Action Problems 4.93 and 4.94 at the end of the chapter.

SUMMARY: REVISITING THE CHAPTER GOALS

1. What is a covalent bond? A *covalent bond* is formed by the sharing of electrons between atoms rather than by the complete transfer of electrons from one atom to another. Atoms that share 2 electrons are joined by a *single bond* (such as C — C), atoms that share 4 electrons are joined by a *double bond* (such as C = C), and atoms that share 6 electrons are joined by a *triple*

bond (such as C ≡ C). The group of atoms held together by covalent bonds is called a *molecule*.

Electron sharing typically occurs when a singly occupied valence orbital on one atom *overlaps* a singly occupied valence orbital on another atom. The 2 electrons occupy both overlapping orbitals and belong to both atoms, thereby bonding the atoms together. Alternatively, electron sharing can occur when a filled orbital containing an unshared, *lone pair* of electrons on one atom overlaps a vacant orbital on another atom to form a *coordinate covalent bond* (see Problems 33–35, 40, 41, 44, 45, 89, 92).

2. How does the octet rule apply to covalent bond formation? Depending on the number of valence electrons, different atoms form different numbers of covalent bonds. In general, an atom shares enough electrons to reach a noble gas configuration. Hydrogen, for instance, forms 1 covalent bond because it needs to share 1 more electron to achieve the helium configuration ($1s^2$). Carbon and other group 4A elements form 4 covalent bonds because they need to share 4 more electrons to reach an octet. In the same way, nitrogen and other group 5A elements form 3 covalent bonds, oxygen and other group 6A elements form 2 covalent bonds, and halogens (group 7A elements) form 1 covalent bond (see Problems 38, 39, 50, 51, 95).

3. What are the major differences between ionic and molecular compounds? *Molecular compounds* can be gases, liquids, or low-melting solids. They usually have lower melting points and boiling points than ionic compounds, many are water insoluble, and they do not conduct electricity when melted or dissolved (see Problems 33, 35–37, 42, 43, 47, 99, 102, 103).

4. How are molecular compounds represented? Formulas such as H_2O, NH_3, and CH_4, which show the numbers and kinds of atoms in a molecule, are called *molecular formulas*. More useful are *Lewis structures*, which show how atoms are connected in molecules. Covalent bonds are indicated as lines between atoms, and valence electron lone pairs are shown as dots. Lewis struc-

tures are drawn by counting the total number of valence electrons in a molecule or polyatomic ion and then placing shared pairs (bonding) and lone pairs (nonbonding) so that all electrons are accounted for (see Problems 30, 46–66, 94–100, 104–109).

5. What is the influence of valence-shell electrons on molecular shape? Molecules have specific shapes that depend on the number of electron charge clouds (bonds and lone pairs) surrounding the various atoms. These shapes can often be predicted using the *valence-shell electron-pair repulsion (VSEPR)* model. Atoms with two electron charge clouds adopt linear geometry, atoms with three charge clouds adopt trigonal planar geometry, and atoms with four charge clouds adopt tetrahedral geometry (see Problems 27, 28–31, 67–72, 81, 96, 100, 109).

6. When are bonds and molecules polar? Bonds between atoms are *polar covalent* if the bonding electrons are not shared equally between the atoms. The ability of an atom to attract electrons in a covalent bond is the atom's *electronegativity* and is highest for reactive nonmetal elements on the upper right of the periodic table and lowest for metals on the lower left. Comparing electronegativities allows prediction of whether a given bond is covalent, polar covalent, or ionic. Just as individual bonds can be polar, entire molecules can be polar if electrons are attracted more strongly to one part of the molecule than to another. Molecular polarity is due to the sum of all individual bond polarities and lone-pair contributions in the molecule (see Problems 32, 73–84, 96, 97, 101).

CONCEPT MAP: ELECTROSTATIC FORCES

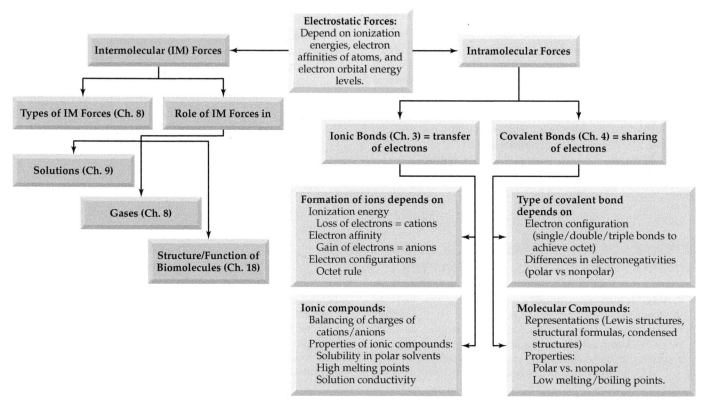

▲ Figure 4.7

Concept Maps. Chemistry, like most subjects, makes more sense when presented in context. When we understand the connections between concepts, or how one idea leads to another, it becomes easier to see the "big picture" and to appreciate why a certain concept is important. A concept map is one way of illustrating those connections and providing a context for what we have learned and what we will be learning in later chapters.

As you can see from the concept map in Figure 4.7, the electronic structure of atoms discussed in Chapter 2 plays a critical role in the chemical behavior of an element, specifically in terms of its tendency to form ionic compounds (Chapter 3) or molecular compounds (Chapter 4). Furthermore, the nature of the attractive forces between particles (intermolecular versus intramolecular) plays a role in the physical and chemical behavior of substances discussed in later chapters.

As we continue exploring new topics, we will expand certain areas of this concept map or add new branches as needed.

KEY WORDS

Binary compound, *p. 123*

Bond angle, *p. 115*

Bond length, *p. 100*

Condensed structure, *p. 109*

Coordinate covalent bond, *p. 106*

Covalent bond, *p. 99*

Double bond, *p. 104*

Electronegativity, *p. 120*

Lewis structure, *p. 108*

Lone pair, *p. 108*

Molecular compound, *p. 101*

Molecular formula, *p. 108*

Molecule, *p. 99*

Polar covalent bond, *p. 119*

Regular tetrahedron, *p. 116*

Single bond, *p. 104*

Structural formula, *p. 108*

Triple bond, *p. 104*

Valence-shell electron-pair repulsion (VSEPR) model, *p. 114*

UNDERSTANDING KEY CONCEPTS

4.27   What is the geometry around the central atom in the following molecular models? (There are no "hidden" atoms; all atoms in each model are visible.)

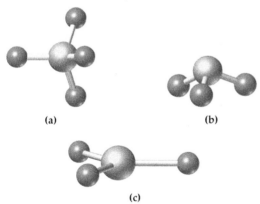

(a)   (b)

(c)

4.28   Three of the following molecular models have a tetrahedral central atom, and one does not. Which is the odd one?

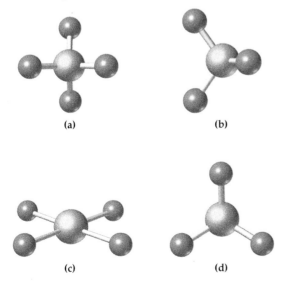

(a)   (b)

(c)   (d)

4.29   The ball-and-stick molecular model shown here is a representation of acetaminophen, the active ingredient in over-the-counter headache remedies such as Tylenol. The lines indicate only the connections between atoms, not whether the bonds are single, double, or triple (red = O, gray = C, blue = N, ivory = H).

(a) What is the molecular formula of acetaminophen?

(b) Indicate the positions of the multiple bonds in acetaminophen.

(c) What is the geometry around each carbon and each nitrogen?

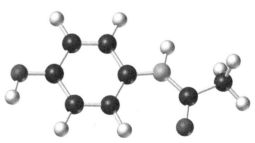

Acetaminophen

4.30   The atom-to-atom connections in vitamin C (ascorbic acid) are as shown here. Convert this skeletal drawing to a Lewis electron-dot structure for vitamin C by showing the positions of any multiple bonds and lone pairs of electrons.

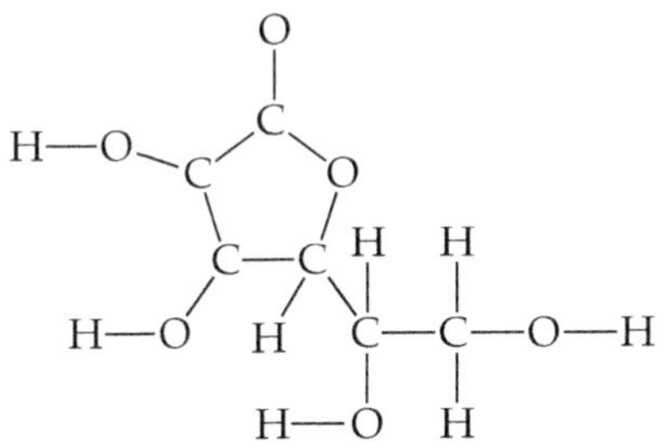

Vitamin C

4.31 The ball-and-stick molecular model shown here is a representation of thalidomide, a drug that has been approved for treating leprosy, but causes severe birth defects when taken by expectant mothers. The lines indicate only the connections between atoms, not whether the bonds are single, double, or triple (red = O, gray = C, blue = N, ivory = H).

(a) What is the molecular formula of thalidomide?

(b) Indicate the positions of the multiple bonds in thalidomide.

(c) What is the geometry around each carbon and each nitrogen?

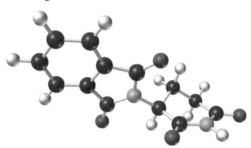

Thalidomide

4.32 Show the position of any electron lone pairs in this structure of acetamide, and indicate the electron-rich and electron-poor regions.

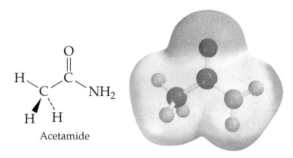

Acetamide

ADDITIONAL PROBLEMS

COVALENT BONDS

4.33 What is a covalent bond, and how does it differ from an ionic bond?

4.34 What is a coordinate covalent bond, and how does it differ from a covalent bond?

4.35 Which of the following elements would you expect to form (i) diatomic molecules, (ii) mainly covalent bonds, (iii) mainly ionic bonds, (iv) both covalent and ionic bonds? (More than one answer may apply; remember that some nonmetals can form ionic bonds with metals.)

(a) Oxygen   (b) Potassium   (c) Phosphorus

(d) Iodine   (e) Hydrogen   (f) Cesium

4.36 Identify the bonds formed between the following pairs of atoms as either covalent or ionic.

(a) Aluminum and bromine   (b) Carbon and fluorine

(c) Cesium and iodine   (d) Zinc and fluorine

(e) Lithium and chlorine

4.37 Write electron-dot symbols to show the number of covalent bonds and the lone pairs of electrons in the molecules that are formed by reactions between the atoms in Problem 4.36.

4.38 Look up tellurium ($Z = 52$) in the periodic table and predict how many covalent bonds it is likely to form. Explain.

4.39 Look up antimony in the periodic table ($Z = 51$). How many covalent bonds would you expect it to form? Based on this information, which of the following antimony compounds is covalent and which is ionic: $SbCl_3$ or $SbCl_5$?

4.40 Which of the following contains a coordinate covalent bond? (Hint: how many covalent bonds would you expect the central atom (underlined) to form?)

(a) $\underline{Pb}Cl_2$ (b) $\underline{Cu}(NH_3)_4{}^{2+}$ (c) $\underline{N}H_4{}^+$

4.41 Which of the following contains a coordinate covalent bond? (Hint: how many covalent bonds would you expect the central atom (underlined) to form?)

(a) $H_2\underline{O}$ (b) $\underline{B}F_4{}^-$ (c) $H_3\underline{O}^+$

4.42 Tin forms both an ionic compound and a covalent compound with chlorine. The ionic compound is $SnCl_2$. Is the covalent compound more likely to be $SnCl_3$, $SnCl_4$, or $SnCl_5$? Explain.

4.43 A compound of gallium with chlorine has a melting point of 77 °C and a boiling point of 201 °C. Is the compound ionic or covalent? What is a likely formula?

4.44 Nitrous oxide, N_2O, has the following structure. Which bond in N_2O is a coordinate covalent bond?

:N≡N—Ö:

Nitrous oxide

4.45 Thionyl chloride, $SOCl_2$ has the following structure. Which bond in $SOCl_2$ is a coordinate covalent bond?

:Ö:
|
S
:Cl̈   C̈l:

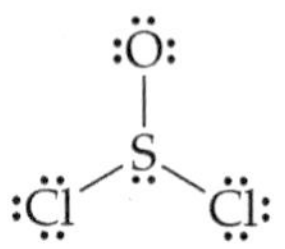

Thionyl chloride

STRUCTURAL FORMULAS

4.46 Distinguish between the following:

(a) A molecular formula and a structural formula

(b) A structural formula and a condensed structure

(c) A lone pair and a shared pair of electrons

4.47 Assume that you are given samples of two white crystalline compounds, one of them ionic and one covalent. Describe how you might tell which is which.

4.48 Determine the total number of valence electrons in the following molecules. If the molecule contains multiple bonds, indicate where the multiple bonds are located and whether they are double or triple bonds.

(a) N_2 (b) NOCl
(c) CH_3CH_2CHO (d) OF_2

4.49 Add lone pairs where appropriate to the following structures:

(a) $C\equiv O$ (b) CH_3SH

(c) $\left[H-\overset{H}{\underset{}{O}}-H \right]^+$ (d) $H_3C-\overset{H}{\underset{}{N}}-CH_3$

4.50 If a research paper appeared reporting the structure of a new molecule with formula C_2H_8 most chemists would be highly skeptical. Why?

4.51 Consider the following possible structural formulas for $C_3H_6O_2$. If a structure is not reasonable, explain what changes could be made to convert it to a reasonable structure.

(a) $H-\overset{\overset{H}{|}}{\underset{\underset{H}{|}}{C}}-\overset{\overset{H}{|}}{\underset{\underset{H}{|}}{C}}-\overset{\overset{O}{||}}{C}-OH$

(b) $H-\overset{\overset{H}{|}}{\underset{\underset{H}{|}}{C}}-\overset{\overset{OH}{|}}{\underset{\underset{OH}{|}}{C}}-C-H$ (c) $H-\overset{\overset{H}{|}}{\underset{\underset{H}{|}}{C}}-O-\overset{\overset{H}{|}}{\underset{\underset{H}{|}}{C}}-C=O$

4.52 Convert the following Lewis structures into structural formulas in which lines replace the bonding electrons. Include the lone pairs.

(a) $H:\ddot{O}:\ddot{N}::\ddot{O}:$ (b) $H:\overset{\overset{H}{\cdot\cdot}}{\underset{\underset{H}{\cdot\cdot}}{C}}:C:::N:$ (c) $H:\ddot{F}:$

4.53 Convert the following Lewis structure for the nitrate ion into a line structure that includes the lone pairs. Why does the nitrate ion have a −1 charge? $\left[\overset{:O:}{\underset{}{:\ddot{O}:\ddot{N}:\ddot{O}:}} \right]^-$

4.54 Convert the following structural formulas into condensed structures.

(a) $H-\overset{\overset{H}{|}}{\underset{\underset{H}{|}}{C}}-\overset{\overset{H}{|}}{\underset{\underset{H}{|}}{C}}-\overset{\overset{H}{|}}{\underset{\underset{H}{|}}{C}}-H$ (b) $\overset{H}{\underset{H}{>}}C=C\overset{H}{\underset{H}{<}}$

(c) $H-\overset{\overset{H}{|}}{\underset{\underset{H}{|}}{C}}-\overset{\overset{H}{|}}{\underset{\underset{H}{|}}{C}}-Cl$

4.55 Expand the following condensed structures into the correct structural formulas.

(a) $CH_3CH_2COCH(CH_3)_2$ (b) $CH_3CH_2COOCH_3$
(c) $CH_3CH_2OCH_2Cl$

4.56 Acetic acid is the major organic constituent of vinegar. Convert the following structural formula of acetic acid into a condensed structure similar to those shown in Problem 4.55.

$$H-\overset{\overset{H}{|}}{\underset{\underset{H}{|}}{C}}-\overset{\overset{O}{||}}{C}-O-H$$

DRAWING LEWIS STRUCTURES

4.57 Draw a Lewis structure for the following molecules:

(a) SF_6 (b) $AlCl_3$ (c) CS_2 (d) SeF_4
(e) $BeCl_2$ (Note: this molecule does not follow the octet rule.)
(f) N_2O_4

4.58 Draw a Lewis structure for the following molecules:

(a) Nitrous acid, HNO_2 (H is bonded to an O atom)
(b) Ozone, O_3
(c) Acetaldehyde, CH_3CHO

4.59 Ethanol, or "grain alcohol," has the formula C_2H_6O and contains an O—H bond. Propose a structure for ethanol that is consistent with common bonding patterns.

4.60 Dimethyl ether has the same molecular formula as ethanol (Problem 4.59) but very different properties. Propose a structure for dimethyl ether in which the oxygen is bonded to two carbons.

4.61 Hydrazine, a substance used to make rocket fuel, has the formula N_2H_4. Propose a structure for hydrazine.

4.62 Tetrachloroethylene, C_2Cl_4, is used commercially as a dry-cleaning solvent. Propose a structure for tetrachloroethylene based on the common bonding patterns expected in organic molecules. What kind of carbon-carbon bond is present?

4.63 Dimethyl sulfoxide, also known as DMSO, is an important organic solvent often used for drug delivery since it readily penetrates the skin. The formula for DMSO is $(CH_3)_2SO$. Draw a Lewis structure of DMSO; both C atoms are attached to the S atom.

4.64 Draw a Lewis structure for hydroxylamine, NH_2OH.

4.65 The carbonate ion, CO_3^{2-}, contains a double bond. Draw a Lewis structure for the ion and show why it has a charge of −2.

4.66 Draw a Lewis structure for the following polyatomic ions:

(a) Formate, HCO_2^- (b) Sulfite, SO_3^{2-}
(c) Thiocyanate, SCN^- (d) Phosphate, PO_4^{3+}
(e) Chlorite, ClO_2^- (chlorine is the central atom)

MOLECULAR GEOMETRY

4.67   Predict the geometry and bond angles around atom A for molecules with the general formulas AB_3 and AB_2E, where B represents another atom and E represents an electron pair.

4.68   Predict the geometry and bond angles around atom A for molecules with the general formulas AB_4, AB_3E, and AB_2E_2, where B represents another atom and E represents an electron pair.

4.69   Sketch the three-dimensional shape of the following molecules:

(a) Methylamine, CH_3NH_2 (b) Iodoform, CHI_3

(c) Ozone, O_3

(d) Phosphorus pentachloride, PCl_5

(e) Chloric acid, $HClO_3$

4.70   Predict the three-dimensional shape of the following molecules:

(a) SiF_4 (b) CF_2Cl_2 (c) SO_3

(d) BBr_3 (e) NF_3

4.71   Predict the geometry around each carbon atom in the amino acid alanine.

Alanine

4.72   Predict the geometry around each carbon atom in vinyl acetate, a precursor of the polyvinyl alcohol polymer used in automobile safety glass.

$$H_2C=CH-O-\overset{\overset{O}{\parallel}}{C}-CH_3$$
Vinyl acetate

POLARITY OF BONDS AND MOLECULES

4.73   Where in the periodic table are the most electronegative elements found, and where are the least electronegative elements found?

4.74   Predict the electronegativity of the yet-undiscovered element with $Z = 119$.

4.75   Look at the periodic table, and then order the following elements according to increasing electronegativity: K, Si, Be, O, B.

4.76   Look at the periodic table, and then order the following elements according to decreasing electronegativity: C, Ca, Cs, Cl, Cu.

4.77   Which of the following bonds are polar? If a bond is polar, identify the negative and positive ends of each bond by using $\delta+$ and $\delta-$.

(a) $I-Br$ (b) $O-H$

(c) $C-F$ (d) $N-C$

(e) $C-C$

4.78   Which of the following bonds are polar? If a bond is polar, identify the negative and positive ends of each bond by using $\delta+$ and $\delta-$.

(a) $O-Cl$ (b) $N-Cl$

(c) $P-H$ (d) $C-I$

(e) $C-O$

4.79   Based on electronegativity differences, would you expect bonds between the following pairs of atoms to be largely ionic or largely covalent?

(a) Be and F   (b) Ca and Cl

(c) O and H   (d) Be and Br

4.80   Arrange the following molecules in order of the increasing polarity of their bonds:

(a) HCl   (b) PH_3

(c) H_2O (d) CF_4

4.81   Ammonia, NH_3, and phosphorus trihydride, PH_3, both have a trigonal pyramid geometry. Which one is more polar? Explain.

4.82   Decide whether each of the compounds listed in Problem 4.80 is polar, and show the direction of polarity.

4.83   Carbon dioxide is a nonpolar molecule, whereas sulfur dioxide is polar. Draw Lewis structures for each of these molecules to explain this observation.

4.84   Water (H_2O) is more polar than hydrogen sulfide (H_2S). Explain.

NAMES AND FORMULAS OF MOLECULAR COMPOUNDS

4.85   Name the following binary compounds:

(a) PI_3 (b) $AsCl_3$ (c) P_4S_3

(d) Al_2F_6 (e) N_2O_5 (f) $AsCl_5$

4.86   Name the following compounds:

(a) SeO_2 (b) XeO_4

(c) N_2S_5 (d) P_3Se_4

4.87   Write formulas for the following compounds:

(a) Nitrogen dioxide   (b) Sulfur hexafluoride

(c) Bromine triiodide   (d) Dinitrogen trioxide

(e) Nitrogen triiodide   (f) Iodine heptafluoride

4.88   Write formulas for the following compounds:

(a) Silicon tetrachloride   (b) Sodium hydride

(c) Antimony pentafluoride (d) Osmium tetroxide

CHEMISTRY IN ACTION

4.89   The CO molecule is highly reactive and will bind to the Fe^{2+} ion in hemoglobin and interfere with O_2 transport. What type of bond is formed between the CO molecule and the Fe^{2+} ion? [*CO and NO: Pollutants or Miracle Molecules?, p. 113*]

4.90 What is a vasodilator, and why would it be useful in treating hypertension (high blood pressure)? [*CO and NO: Pollutants or Miracle Molecules?, p. 113*]

4.91 How is a polymer formed? [*VERY Big Molecules, p. 118*]

4.92 Do any polymers exist in nature? Explain. [*VERY Big Molecules, p. 118*]

4.93 Why are many chemical names so complex? [*Damascenone by Any Other Name, p. 125*]

4.94 Citronellol, one of the compounds found in the scent of roses, is also used in perfumes and in insect repellent products. Write the condensed formula from the structural formula of citronellol shown below. [*Damascenone by Any Other Name, p. 125*]

$$CH_3-\underset{\underset{H}{|}}{\overset{\overset{CH_3}{|}}{C}}=\underset{\underset{H}{|}}{\overset{\overset{H}{|}}{C}}-\underset{\underset{H}{|}}{\overset{\overset{H}{|}}{C}}-\underset{\underset{H}{|}}{\overset{\overset{CH_3}{|}}{C}}-\underset{\underset{H}{|}}{\overset{\overset{H}{|}}{C}}-\underset{\underset{H}{|}}{\overset{\overset{H}{|}}{C}}-OH$$

GENERAL QUESTIONS AND PROBLEMS

4.95 The discovery in the 1960s that xenon and fluorine react to form a molecular compound was a surprise to most chemists, because it had been thought that noble gases could not form bonds.

(a) Why was it thought that noble gases could not form bonds?

(b) Draw a Lewis structure of XeF_4 in which Xe is the central atom. How many electron clouds are there on the central atom?

(c) What type of bonds are the Xe—F bonds? Explain.

4.96 Acetone, a common solvent used in some nail polish removers, has the molecular formula C_3H_6O and contains a carbon-oxygen double bond.

(a) Propose two Lewis structures for acetone.

(b) What is the geometry around the carbon atoms in each of the structures?

(c) Which of the bonds in each structure are polar?

4.97 Draw the structural formulas for two compounds having the molecular formula C_2H_4O. What is the molecular geometry around the carbon atoms in each of these molecules? Would these molecules be polar or nonpolar? (Hint: there is one double bond.)

4.98 The following formulas are unlikely to be correct. What is wrong with each?

(a) CCl_3 (b) N_2H_5

(c) H_3S (d) C_2OS

4.99 Which of the compounds (a) through (d) contain ionic bonds? Which contain covalent bonds? Which contain coordinate covalent bonds? (A compound may contain more than one type of bond.)

(a) $BaCl_2$ (b) $Ca(NO_3)_2$

(c) BCl_4^- (d) $TiBr_4$

4.100 The phosphonium ion, PH_4^+, is formed by reaction of phosphine, PH_3, with an acid.

(a) Draw the Lewis structure of the phosphonium ion.

(b) Predict its molecular geometry.

(c) Describe how a fourth hydrogen can be added to PH_3.

(d) Explain why the ion has a +1 charge.

4.101 Compare the trend in electronegativity seen in Figure 4.6 (p. 120) with the trend in electron affinity shown in Figure 3.1 (p. 75). What similarities do you see? What differences? Explain.

4.102 Name the following compounds. Be sure to determine whether the compound is ionic or covalent so that you use the proper rules.

(a) $CaCl_2$ (b) $TeCl_2$ (c) BF_3

(d) $MgSO_4$ (e) K_2O (f) FeF_3

(g) PF_3

4.103 Titanium forms both molecular and ionic compounds with nonmetals, as, for example, $TiBr_4$ and TiO_2. One of these compounds has a melting point of 39 °C, and the other has a melting point of 1825 °C. Which is ionic and which is molecular? Explain your answer in terms of electronegativities of the atoms involved in each compound.

4.104 Draw a Lewis structure for chloral hydrate, known in detective novels as "knockout drops." Indicate all lone pairs.

$$Cl-\underset{\underset{Cl}{|}}{\overset{\overset{Cl}{|}}{C}}-\underset{\underset{H}{|}}{\overset{\overset{O-H}{|}}{C}}-O-H \qquad \text{Chloral hydrate}$$

4.105 The dichromate ion, $Cr_2O_7^{2-}$, has neither Cr—Cr nor O—O bonds. Draw a Lewis structure.

4.106 Oxalic acid, $H_2C_2O_4$, is a substance found in uncooked spinach leaves and other greens that can be poisonous at high concentrations (for example, in raw rhubarb leaves). If oxalic acid has a C—C single bond and the H atoms are both connected to O atoms, draw its Lewis structure.

4.107 Identify the fourth row elements represented by "X" in the following compounds.

(a) $\ddot{\text{O}}=\ddot{\text{X}}=\ddot{\text{O}}$ (b) structure with two F atoms bonded to X

4.108 Write Lewis structures for molecules with the following connections, showing the positions of any multiple bonds and lone pairs of electrons.

(a) $Cl-\underset{}{\overset{\overset{O}{|}}{C}}-O-\underset{\underset{H}{|}}{\overset{\overset{H}{|}}{C}}-H$ (b) $H-\underset{\underset{H}{|}}{\overset{\overset{H}{|}}{C}}-C-C-H$

4.109 Electron-pair repulsion influences the shapes of polyatomic ions in the same way it influences neutral molecules. Draw electron-dot symbols and predict the shape of the ammonium ion, NH_4^+, the sulfate ion, SO_4^{2-}, and the phosphite ion, PO_3^{3-}.

CHAPTER 5

Classification and Balancing of Chemical Reactions

CONTENTS

◀ Water reclamation and purification plants utilize the many different types of chemical reactions discussed in this chapter.

1. **How are chemical reactions written?**
    THE GOAL: Given the identities of reactants and products, be able to write a balanced chemical equation or net ionic equation.

2. **How are chemical reactions of ionic compounds classified?**
    THE GOAL: Be able to recognize precipitation, acid–base neutralization, and redox reactions.

3. **What are oxidation numbers, and how are they used?**
    THE GOAL: Be able to assign oxidation numbers to atoms in compounds and identify the substances oxidized and reduced in a given reaction. (◀◀ A.)

4. **What is a net ionic equation?**
    THE GOAL: Be able to recognize spectator ions and write the net ionic equation for reactions involving ionic compounds. (◀◀ A, B.)

CONCEPTS TO REVIEW

A. Periodic Properties and Ion Formation
(Section 3.2)

B. H⁺ and OH⁻ Ions: An Introduction to Acids and Bases
(Section 3.11)

A log burns in the fireplace, an oyster makes a pearl, a seed grows into a plant—these and almost all the other changes you see taking place around you are the result of chemical reactions. The study of how and why chemical reactions happen is a major part of chemistry, providing information that is both fascinating and practical. In this chapter, we will begin to look at chemical reactions, starting with a discussion of how to represent them in writing. We will then examine how to balance reactions and how to recognize different types or classes of chemical reactions.

5.1 Chemical Equations

One way to view chemical reactions is to think of them as "recipes." Like recipes, all the "ingredients" in a chemical equation and their relative amounts are given, as well as the amount of product that would be obtained. Take, for example, a recipe for making S'mores, a concoction of chocolate, marshmallows, and graham crackers, which could be written as:

Graham crackers + Roasted marshmallows + Chocolate bars ⟶ S'mores

This recipe, however, is simply a list of ingredients and gives no indication of the relative amounts of each ingredient, or how many s'mores we would obtain. A more detailed recipe would be:

2 Graham crackers + 1 Roasted marshmallow + $\frac{1}{4}$ Chocolate bar ⟶ 1 S'more

In this case, the relative amounts of each ingredient are given, as well as the amount of the final product.

Let us extend this analogy to a typical chemical reaction. When sodium bicarbonate is heated in the range 50–100 °C, sodium carbonate, water, and carbon dioxide are produced. In words, we might write the reaction as:

Sodium bicarbonate $\xrightarrow{\text{Heat}}$ Sodium carbonate + Water + Carbon dioxide

Just as in the recipe, the starting materials and final products are listed. Replacing the chemical names with formulas converts the word description of this reaction into a **chemical equation:**

$$\underbrace{2\,NaHCO_3}_{\text{Reactant}} \xrightarrow{\text{Heat}} \underbrace{Na_2CO_3 + H_2O + CO_2}_{\text{Products}}$$

Look at how this equation is written. The **reactants** are written on the left, the **products** are written on the right, and an arrow is placed between them to indicate a chemical change. Conditions necessary for the reaction to occur—heat in this particular instance—are often specified above the arrow.

Why is the number 2 placed before NaHCO₃ in the equation? The 2 is necessary because of a fundamental law of nature called the **law of conservation of mass**, which states that matter can neither be created nor destroyed in a chemical reaction.

Chemical equation An expression in which symbols and formulas are used to represent a chemical reaction.

Reactant A substance that undergoes change in a chemical reaction and is written on the left side of the reaction arrow in a chemical equation.

Product A substance that is formed in a chemical reaction and is written on the right side of the reaction arrow in a chemical equation.

Balanced equation A chemical equation in which the numbers and kinds of atoms are the same on both sides of the reaction arrow.

Coefficient A number placed in front of a formula to balance a chemical equation.

The bonds between atoms in the reactants are rearranged to form new compounds in chemical reactions, but none of the atoms disappear and no new ones are formed. As a consequence, chemical equations must be **balanced**, meaning that *the numbers and kinds of atoms must be the same on both sides of the reaction arrow.*

Law of conservation of mass   Matter is neither created nor destroyed in chemical reactions.

The numbers placed in front of formulas to balance equations are called **coefficients**, and they multiply all the atoms in a formula. Thus, the symbol "2 $NaHCO_3$" indicates two units of sodium bicarbonate, which contain 2 Na atoms, 2 H atoms, 2 C atoms, and 6 O atoms ($2 \times 3 = 6$, the coefficient times the subscript for O). Count the numbers of atoms on the right side of the equation to convince yourself that it is indeed balanced.

The substances that take part in chemical reactions may be solids, liquids, or gases, or they may be dissolved in a solvent. Ionic compounds, in particular, frequently undergo reactions in *aqueous solution*—that is, when they are dissolved in water. Sometimes this information is added to an equation by placing the appropriate abbreviations after the formulas:

$$(s) \qquad (l) \qquad (g) \qquad (aq)$$
$$\text{Solid} \quad \text{Liquid} \quad \text{Gas} \quad \text{Aqueous solution}$$

Thus, the decomposition of solid sodium bicarbonate can be written as

$$2\,NaHCO_3(s) \xrightarrow[\text{Heat}]{} Na_2CO_3(s) + H_2O(l) + CO_2(g)$$

Worked Example 5.1 Balancing Chemical Reactions

Use words to explain the following equation for the reaction used in extracting lead metal from its ores. Show that the equation is balanced.

$$2\,PbS(s) + 3\,O_2(g) \longrightarrow 2\,PbO(s) + 2\,SO_2(g)$$

SOLUTION

The equation can be read as, "Solid lead(II) sulfide plus gaseous oxygen yields solid lead(II) oxide plus gaseous sulfur dioxide."

To show that the equation is balanced, count the atoms of each element on each side of the arrow:

On the left:	2 Pb	2 S	$(3 \times 2)\,O = 6\,O$
On the right:	2 Pb	2 S	$2\,O + (2 \times 2)\,O = 6\,O$

From 2 PbO   From 2 SO₂

The numbers of atoms of each element are the same in the reactants and products, so the equation is balanced.

PROBLEM 5.1

Interpret the following equations using words:

(a) $CoCl_2(s) + 2\,HF(g) \longrightarrow CoF_2(s) + 2\,HCl(g)$

(b) $Pb(NO_3)_2(aq) + 2\,KI(aq) \longrightarrow PbI_2(s) + 2\,KNO_3(aq)$

PROBLEM 5.2

Which of the following equations are balanced?

(a) $HCl + KOH \longrightarrow H_2O + KCl$

(b) $CH_4 + Cl_2 \longrightarrow CH_2Cl_2 + HCl$

(c) $H_2O + MgO \longrightarrow Mg(OH)_2$

(d) $Al(OH)_3 + H_3PO_4 \longrightarrow AlPO_4 + 2\,H_2O$

5.2 Balancing Chemical Equations

Just as a recipe indicates the appropriate amounts of each ingredient needed to make a given dish, a balanced chemical equation indicates the appropriate amounts of reactants needed to generate a given amount of product. Although balancing chemical equations often involves some trial and error, most reactions can be balanced by the following four-step approach:

STEP 1: **Write an unbalanced equation, using the correct formulas for all given reactants and products.** For example, hydrogen and oxygen must be written as H_2 and O_2, rather than as H and O, since we know that both elements exist as diatomic molecules. Remember that *the subscripts in chemical formulas cannot be changed in balancing an equation because doing so would change the identity of the substances in the reaction.*

STEP 2: **Add appropriate coefficients to balance the numbers of atoms of each element.** It helps to begin with elements that appear in only one compound or formula on each side of the equation, leaving elements that exist in elemental forms, such as oxygen and hydrogen, until last. For example, in the reaction of sulfuric acid with sodium hydroxide to give sodium sulfate and water, we might balance first for sodium. We could do this by adding a coefficient of 2 for NaOH:

$$H_2SO_4 + NaOH \longrightarrow Na_2SO_4 + H_2O \quad \text{(Unbalanced)}$$
$$H_2SO_4 + 2\,NaOH \longrightarrow Na_2SO_4 + H_2O \quad \text{(Balanced for Na)}$$

Add this coefficient . . .   . . . to balance these 2 Na.

If a polyatomic ion appears on both sides of an equation, it is treated as a single unit. For example, the sulfate ion $(SO_4{}^{2-})$ in our example is balanced because there is one on the left and one on the right:

$$H_2SO_4 + 2\,NaOH \longrightarrow Na_2SO_4 + H_2O \quad \text{(Balanced for Na and sulfate)}$$

One sulfate here . . .   . . . and one here.

At this point, the equation can be balanced for H and O by adding a coefficient of 2 for H_2O:

$$H_2SO_4 + 2\,NaOH \longrightarrow Na_2SO_4 + 2\,H_2O \quad \text{(Completely balanced)}$$

4 H and 2 O here.   4 H and 2 O here.

STEP 3: **Check the equation to make sure the numbers and kinds of atoms on both sides of the equation are the same.**

STEP 4: **Make sure the coefficients are reduced to their lowest whole-number values.** For example, the equation:

$$2\,H_2SO_4 + 4\,NaOH \longrightarrow 2\,Na_2SO_4 + 4\,H_2O$$

is balanced but can be simplified by dividing all coefficients by 2:

$$H_2SO_4 + 2\,NaOH \longrightarrow Na_2SO_4 + 2\,H_2O$$

Worked Example 5.2 Balancing Chemical Equations

Write a balanced chemical equation for the Haber process, an important industrial reaction in which elemental nitrogen and hydrogen combine to form ammonia.

SOLUTION

STEP 1: Write an unbalanced equation, using the correct formulas for all reactants and products.

$$N_2(g) + H_2(g) \longrightarrow NH_3(g)$$

By examination, we see that only two elements, N and H, need to be balanced. Both these elements exist in nature as diatomic gases, as indicated on the reactant side of the unbalanced equation.

STEP 2: Add appropriate coefficients to balance the numbers of atoms of each element. Remember that the subscript 2 in N_2 and H_2 indicates that these are diatomic molecules (that is, 2 N atoms or 2 H atoms per molecule). Since there are 2 nitrogen atoms on the left, we must add a coefficient of 2 in front of the NH_3 on the right side of the equation to balance the equation with respect to N:

$$N_2(g) + H_2(g) \longrightarrow 2\,NH_3(g)$$

Now we see that there are 2 H atoms on the left, but 6 H atoms on the right. We can balance the equation with respect to hydrogen by adding a coefficient of 3 in front of the $H_2(g)$ on the left side:

$$N_2(g) + 3\,H_2(g) \longrightarrow 2\,NH_3(g)$$

STEP 3: Check the equation to make sure the numbers and kinds of atoms on both sides of the equation are the same.

On the left: $(1 \times 2)\,N = 2\,N$ $(3 \times 2)\,H = 6\,H$

On the right: $(2 \times 1)\,N = 2\,N$ $(2 \times 3)\,H = 6\,H$

STEP 4: Make sure the coefficients are reduced to their lowest whole-number values. In this case, the coefficients already represent the lowest whole-number values.

Worked Example 5.3 Balancing Chemical Equations

Natural gas (methane, CH_4) burns in oxygen to yield water and carbon dioxide (CO_2). Write a balanced equation for the reaction.

SOLUTION

STEP 1: Write the unbalanced equation, using correct formulas for all substances:

$$CH_4 + O_2 \longrightarrow CO_2 + H_2O \quad \text{(Unbalanced)}$$

STEP 2: Since carbon appears in one formula on each side of the arrow, let us begin with that element. In fact, there is only 1 carbon atom in each formula, so the equation is already balanced for that element. Next, note that there are 4 hydrogen atoms on the left (in CH_4) and only 2 on the right (in H_2O). Placing a coefficient of 2 before H_2O gives the same number of hydrogen atoms on both sides:

$$CH_4 + O_2 \longrightarrow CO_2 + 2\,H_2O \quad \text{(Balanced for C and H)}$$

Finally, look at the number of oxygen atoms. There are 2 on the left (in O_2) but 4 on the right (2 in CO_2 and 1 in each H_2O). If we place a 2 before the O_2, the number of oxygen atoms will be the same on both sides, but the numbers of other elements will not change:

$$CH_4 + 2\,O_2 \longrightarrow CO_2 + 2\,H_2O \quad \text{(Balanced for C, H, and O)}$$

STEP 3: Check to be sure the numbers of atoms on both sides are the same.

On the left: 1 C   4 H $(2 \times 2)\,O = 4\,O$

On the right: 1 C $(2 \times 2)\,H = 4\,H$ $2\,O + 2\,O = 4\,O$

From CO_2 From 2 H_2O

STEP 4: Make sure the coefficients are reduced to their lowest whole-number values. In this case, the answer is already correct.

Worked Example 5.4 Balancing Chemical Equations

Sodium chlorate ($NaClO_3$) decomposes when heated to yield sodium chloride and oxygen, a reaction used to provide oxygen for the emergency breathing masks in airliners. Write a balanced equation for this reaction.

SOLUTION

STEP 1: The unbalanced equation is:

$$NaClO_3 \longrightarrow NaCl + O_2$$

STEP 2: Both the Na and the Cl are already balanced, with only one atom of each on the left and right sides of the equation. There are 3 O atoms on the left, but only 2 on the right. The O atoms can be balanced by placing a coefficient of 1½ in front of O_2 on the right side of the equation:

$$NaClO_3 \longrightarrow NaCl + 1½\ O_2$$

STEP 3: Checking to make sure the same number of atoms of each type occurs on both sides of the equation, we see 1 atom of Na and Cl on both sides, and 3 O atoms on both sides.

STEP 4: In this case, obtaining all coefficients in their smallest whole-number values requires that we multiply all coefficients by 2 to obtain:

$$2\ NaClO_3 \longrightarrow 2\ NaCl + 3\ O_2$$

Checking gives

On the left:	$2\ Na\ 2\ Cl\ (2 \times 3)\ O = 6\ O$
On the right:	$2\ Na\ 2\ Cl\ (3 \times 2)\ O = 6\ O$

The oxygen in emergency breathing masks comes from heating sodium chlorate.

PROBLEM 5.3
Ozone (O_3) is formed in the earth's upper atmosphere by the action of solar radiation on oxygen molecules (O_2). Write a balanced equation for the formation of ozone from oxygen.

PROBLEM 5.4
Balance the following equations:
(a) $Ca(OH)_2 + HCl \longrightarrow CaCl_2 + H_2O$
(b) $Al + O_2 \longrightarrow Al_2O_3$
(c) $CH_3CH_3 + O_2 \longrightarrow CO_2 + H_2O$
(d) $AgNO_3 + MgCl_2 \longrightarrow AgCl + Mg(NO_3)_2$

🔑 KEY CONCEPT PROBLEM 5.5

The following diagram represents the reaction of A (red spheres) with B_2 (blue spheres). Write a balanced equation for the reaction.

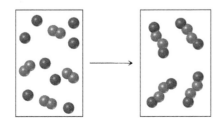

5.3 Classes of Chemical Reactions

One of the best ways to understand any subject is to look for patterns that help us categorize large amounts of information. When learning about chemical reactions, for instance, it is helpful to group the reactions of ionic compounds into three general classes: *precipitation reactions, acid–base neutralization reactions,* and *oxidation–reduction reactions.* This is not the only possible way of categorizing reactions but it is useful nonetheless. Let us look briefly at examples of each of these three reaction classes before studying them in more detail in subsequent sections.

Precipitate An insoluble solid that forms in solution during a chemical reaction.

- **Precipitation reactions** are processes in which an insoluble solid called a **precipitate** forms when reactants are combined in aqueous solution. Most precipitations take place when the anions and cations of two ionic compounds change partners. For example, an aqueous solution of lead(II) nitrate reacts with an aqueous solution of potassium iodide to yield an aqueous solution of potassium nitrate plus an insoluble yellow precipitate of lead iodide:

$$Pb(NO_3)_2\,(aq) + 2\,KI(aq) \longrightarrow 2\,KNO_3(aq) + PbI_2(s)$$

Salt An ionic compound formed from reaction of an acid with a base.

- **Acid–base neutralization reactions** are processes in which an acid reacts with a base to yield water plus an ionic compound called a **salt**. We will look at both acids and bases in more detail in Chapter 10, but you might recall for the moment that we previously defined acids as compounds that produce H^+ ions and bases as compounds that produce OH^- ions when dissolved in water. Thus, a neutralization reaction removes H^+ and OH^- ions from solution and yields neutral H_2O. The reaction between hydrochloric acid and sodium hydroxide is a typical example:

▶▶▶ See Section 3.11 for more discussion of acids and bases.

$$HCl(aq) + NaOH(aq) \longrightarrow H_2O(l) + NaCl(aq)$$

Note that in this reaction, the "salt" produced is sodium chloride, or common table salt. In a general sense, however, *any* ionic compound produced in an acid–base reaction is also called a salt. Other examples include potassium nitrate (KNO_3), magnesium bromide $(MgBr_2)$, and sodium sulfate (Na_2SO_4).

Oxidation–reduction (redox) reaction A reaction in which electrons are transferred from one atom to another.

- **Oxidation–reduction reactions**, or **redox reactions**, are processes in which one or more electrons are transferred between reaction partners (atoms, molecules, or ions). As a result of this transfer, the number of electrons assigned to individual atoms in the various reactants change. When metallic magnesium reacts with iodine vapor, for instance, a magnesium atom gives an electron to each of 2 iodine atoms, forming a Mg^{2+} ion and 2 I^- ions. The charge on the magnesium changes from 0 to +2, and the charge on each iodine changes from 0 to −1:

$$Mg(s) + I_2(g) \longrightarrow MgI_2(s)$$

Fundamentally, all reactions involving covalent compounds are classified as redox reactions, because electrons are rearranged as bonds are broken and new bonds are formed. The discussion here, however, will focus mainly on reactions involving ionic substances.

▲ Reaction of aqueous $Pb(NO_3)_2$ with aqueous KI gives a yellow precipitate of PbI_2.

Worked Example **5.5** Classifying Chemical Reactions

Classify the following as a precipitation, an acid–base neutralization, or a redox reaction.

(a) $Ca(OH)_2(aq) + 2\,HBr(aq) \longrightarrow 2\,H_2O(l) + CaBr_2(aq)$
(b) $Pb(ClO_4)_2(aq) + 2\,NaCl(aq) \longrightarrow PbCl_2(s) + 2\,NaClO_4(aq)$
(c) $2\,AgNO_3(aq) + Cu(s) \longrightarrow 2\,Ag(s) + Cu(NO_3)_2(aq)$

ANALYSIS One way to identify the class of reaction is to examine the products that form and match them with the descriptions for the types of reactions provided in this section. By a process of elimination, we can readily identify the appropriate reaction classification.

SOLUTION

(a) The products of this reaction are water and an ionic compound, or salt ($CaBr_2$). This is consistent with the description of an acid–base neutralization reaction.

(b) This reaction involves two aqueous reactants, $Pb(ClO_4)_2$ and $NaCl$, which combine to form a solid product, $PbCl_2$. This is consistent with a precipitation reaction.

(c) The products of this reaction are a solid, $Ag(s)$, and an aqueous ionic compound, $Cu(NO_3)_2$. This does not match the description of a neutralization reaction, which would form *water* and an ionic compound. One of the products *is* a solid, but the reactants are not both aqueous compound; one of the reactants is *also* a solid (Cu). Therefore, this reaction would not be classified as a precipitation reaction. By the process of elimination, then, it must be a redox reaction.

PROBLEM 5.6

Classify each of the following as a precipitation, an acid–base neutralization, or a redox reaction.

(a) $AgNO_3(aq) + KCl(aq) \longrightarrow AgCl(s) + KNO_3(aq)$

(b) $2\, Al(s) + 3\, Br_2(l) \longrightarrow 2\, AlBr_3(s)$

(c) $Ca(OH)_2(aq) + 2\, HNO_3(aq) \longrightarrow 2\, H_2O(l) + Ca(NO_3)_2(aq)$

PROBLEM 5.7

The reaction involved in photosynthesis combines carbon dioxide and water to create simple sugars:

$$CO_2(g) + H_2O(l) \xrightarrow{\text{Sunlight}} C_6H_{12}O_6(s)$$

Balance the equation and classify the reaction.

5.4 Precipitation Reactions and Solubility Guidelines

Now let us look at precipitation reactions in more detail. To predict whether a precipitation reaction will occur upon mixing aqueous solutions of two ionic compounds, you must know the **solubilities** of the potential products—how much of each compound will dissolve in a given amount of solvent at a given temperature. If a substance has a low solubility in water, then it is likely to precipitate from an aqueous solution. If a substance has a high solubility in water, then no precipitate will form.

Solubility is a complex matter, and it is not always possible to make correct predictions. As a rule of thumb, though, the following solubility guidelines for ionic compounds are useful.

Solubility The amount of a compound that will dissolve in a given amount of solvent at a given temperature.

General Rules on Solubility

RULE 1: **A compound is probably soluble if it contains one of the following cations:**
- Group 1A cation: Li^+, Na^+, K^+, Rb^+, Cs^+
- Ammonium ion: NH_4^+

RULE 2: **A compound is probably soluble if it contains one of the following anions:**
- Halide: Cl^-, Br^-, I^- except Ag^+, Hg_2^{2+}, and Pb^{2+} compounds
- Nitrate (NO_3^-), perchlorate (ClO_4^-), acetate ($CH_3CO_2^-$), sulfate (SO_4^{2-}) except Ba^{2+}, Hg_2^{2+}, and Pb^{2+} sulfates

If a compound does *not* contain at least one of the ions listed above, it is probably *not* soluble. Thus, Na_2CO_3 is soluble because it contains a group 1A cation, and $CaCl_2$ is soluble because it contains a halide anion. The compound $CaCO_3$, however, is probably *insoluble* because it contains none of the ions listed above. These same guidelines are presented in table form in Table 5.1.

Anything NOT on this table ⟶

NOT soluable

TABLE 5.1 General Solubility Guidelines for Ionic Compounds in Water

Soluble	Exceptions
Ammonium compounds (NH_4^+)	None
Lithium compounds (Li^+)	None
Sodium compounds (Na^+)	None
Potassium compounds (K^+)	None
Nitrates (NO_3^-)	None
Perchlorates (ClO_4^-)	None
Acetates ($CH_3CO_2^-$)	None
Chlorides (Cl^-)	
Bromides (Br^-)	Ag^+, Hg_2^{2+}, and Pb^{2+} compounds
Iodides (I^-)	
Sulfates (SO_4^{2-})	Ba^{2+}, Hg_2^{2+}, and Pb^{2+} compounds

CHEMISTRY IN ACTION

Gout and Kidney Stones: Problems in Solubility

One of the major pathways in the body for the breakdown of the nucleic acids DNA and RNA is by conversion to a substance called *uric acid*, $C_5H_4N_4O_3$, so named because it was first isolated from urine in 1776. Most people excrete about 0.5 g of uric acid every day in the form of sodium urate, the salt that results from an acid–base reaction of uric acid. Unfortunately, the amount of sodium urate that dissolves in water (or urine) is fairly low—only about 0.07 mg/mL at the normal body temperature of 37 °C. When too much sodium urate is produced or mechanisms for its elimination fail, its concentration in blood and urine rises, and the excess sometimes precipitates in the joints and kidneys.

Gout is a disorder of nucleic acid metabolism that primarily affects middle-aged men (only 5% of gout patients are women). It is characterized by an increased sodium urate concentration in blood, leading to the deposit of sodium urate crystals in soft tissue around the joints, particularly in the hands and at the base of the big toe. Deposits of the sharp, needlelike crystals cause an extremely painful inflammation that can lead ultimately to arthritis and even to bone destruction.

Just as increased sodium urate concentration in blood can lead to gout, increased concentration in urine can result in the formation of one kind of *kidney stones*, small crystals that precipitate in the kidney. Although often quite small, kidney stones cause excruciating pain when they pass through the ureter, the duct that carries urine from the kidney to the bladder. In some cases, complete blockage of the ureter occurs.

Treatment of excessive sodium urate production involves both dietary modification and drug therapy. Foods such as liver, sardines, and asparagus should be avoided, and drugs such as allopurinol can be taken to lower production of sodium urate. Allopurinol functions by inhibiting the action of an enzyme called *xanthine oxidase*, thereby blocking a step in nucleic acid metabolism.

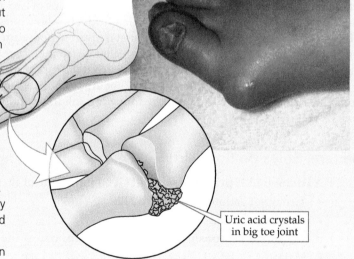

Uric acid crystals in big toe joint

▲ **Excess production of uric acid can cause gout, a painful condition characterized by the accumulation of sodium urate crystals in joints.**

See Chemistry in Action Problems 5.63 and 5.64 at the end of the chapter.

Let us try a problem. What will happen if aqueous solutions of sodium nitrate ($NaNO_3$) and potassium sulfate (K_2SO_4) are mixed? To answer this question, look at the guidelines to find the solubilities of the two possible products, Na_2SO_4 and KNO_3. Because both have group 1A cations (Na^+ and K^+), both are water-soluble and no precipitation will occur. If aqueous solutions of silver nitrate ($AgNO_3$) and sodium carbonate (Na_2CO_3) are mixed, however, the guidelines predict that a precipitate of insoluble silver carbonate (Ag_2CO_3) will form.

$$2\,AgNO_3(aq) + Na_2CO_3(aq) \longrightarrow Ag_2CO_3(s) + 2\,NaNO_3(aq)$$

Worked Example **5.6** Chemical Reactions: Solubility Rules

Will a precipitation reaction occur when aqueous solutions of $CdCl_2$ and $(NH_4)_2S$ are mixed?

SOLUTION

Identify the two potential products, and predict the solubility of each using the guidelines in the text. In this instance, $CdCl_2$ and $(NH_4)_2S$ might give CdS and NH_4Cl. Since the guidelines predict that CdS is insoluble, a precipitation reaction will occur:

$$CdCl_2(aq) + (NH_4)_2S(aq) \longrightarrow CdS(s) + 2\,NH_4Cl(aq)$$

PROBLEM 5.8

Predict the solubility of the following compounds:

(a) $CdCO_3$ (b) Na_2S

(c) $PbSO_4$ (d) $(NH_4)_3PO_4$

(e) Hg_2Cl_2

PROBLEM 5.9

Predict whether a precipitation reaction will occur in the following situations. If a precipitation reaction occurs, write the balanced chemical equation for the reaction.

(a) $NiCl_2(aq) + (NH_4)_2S(aq) \longrightarrow$
(b) $AgNO_3(aq) + CaBr_2(aq) \longrightarrow$

PROBLEM 5.10

In addition to kidney stone formation by sodium urate (See Chemistry in Action on p. 140), many kidney stones are formed by precipitation of oxalate by calcium. Oxalates are found in many foods, including spinach, blueberries, and chocolate. Show the balanced chemical equation for the precipitation of calcium oxalate, starting with calcium chloride ($CaCl_2$) and sodium oxalate ($Na_2C_2O_4$).

5.5 Acids, Bases, and Neutralization Reactions

When acids and bases are mixed in the correct proportion, both acidic and basic properties disappear because of a **neutralization reaction**. The most common kind of neutralization reaction occurs between an acid (generalized as HA), and a metal hydroxide (generalized as MOH), to yield water and a salt. The H^+ ion from the acid combines with the OH^- ion from the base to give neutral H_2O, whereas the anion from the acid (A^-) combines with the cation from the base (M^+) to give the salt:

Neutralization reaction The reaction of an acid with a base.

A neutralization reaction: $HA(aq) + MOH(aq) \longrightarrow H_2O(l) + MA(aq)$
                                  Acid   Base   Water   A salt

The reaction of hydrochloric acid with potassium hydroxide to produce potassium chloride is an example:

$$HCl(aq) + KOH(aq) \longrightarrow H_2O(l) + KCl(aq)$$

Another kind of neutralization reaction occurs between an acid and a carbonate (or bicarbonate) to yield water, a salt, and carbon dioxide. Hydrochloric acid reacts with potassium carbonate, for example, to give H_2O, KCl, and CO_2:

$$2\,HCl(aq) + K_2CO_3(aq) \longrightarrow H_2O(l) + 2\,KCl(aq) + CO_2(g)$$

The reaction occurs because the carbonate ion $(CO_3{}^{2-})$ reacts initially with H^+ to yield H_2CO_3, which is unstable and immediately decomposes to give CO_2 plus H_2O.

We will defer a more complete discussion of carbonates as bases until Chapter 10, but note for now that they yield OH^- ions when dissolved in water just as KOH and other bases do.

$$K_2CO_3(s) + H_2O(l) \xrightarrow{\text{Dissolve in water}} 2K^+(aq) + HCO_3{}^-(aq) + OH^-(aq)$$

LOOKING AHEAD ▶▶▶ Acids and bases are enormously important in biological chemistry. We will see in Chapter 18, for instance, how acids and bases affect the structure and properties of proteins.

Worked Example 5.7 Chemical Reactions: Acid–Base Neutralization

Write an equation for the neutralization reaction of aqueous HBr and aqueous $Ba(OH)_2$.

SOLUTION

The reaction of HBr with $Ba(OH)_2$ involves the combination of a proton (H^+) from the acid with OH^- from the base to yield water and a salt $(BaBr_2)$.

$$2\,HBr(aq) + Ba(OH)_2(aq) \longrightarrow 2\,H_2O(l) + BaBr_2(aq)$$

PROBLEM 5.11

Write and balance equations for the following acid–base neutralization reactions:
(a) $CsOH(aq) + H_2SO_4(aq) \longrightarrow$
(b) $Ca(OH)_2(aq) + CH_3CO_2H(aq) \longrightarrow$
(c) $NaHCO_3(aq) + HBr(aq) \longrightarrow$

5.6 Redox Reactions

Oxidation–reduction (redox) reactions, the third and final category of reactions that we will discuss here, are more complex than precipitation and neutralization reactions. Look, for instance, at the following examples and see if you can tell what they have in common. Copper metal reacts with aqueous silver nitrate to form silver metal and aqueous copper(II) nitrate; iron rusts in air to form iron(III) oxide; the zinc metal container on the outside of a battery reacts with manganese dioxide and ammonium chloride inside the battery to generate electricity and give aqueous zinc chloride plus manganese(III) oxide. Although these and many thousands of other reactions appear unrelated, all are examples of redox reactions.

$$Cu(s) + 2\,AgNO_3(aq) \longrightarrow 2\,Ag(s) + Cu(NO_3)_2(aq)$$
$$2\,Fe(s) + 3\,O_2(g) \longrightarrow Fe_2O_3(s)$$
$$Zn(s) + 2\,MnO_2(s) + 2\,NH_4Cl(s) \longrightarrow$$
$$ZnCl_2(aq) + Mn_2O_3(s) + 2\,NH_3(aq) + H_2O(l)$$

Historically, the word *oxidation* referred to the combination of an element with oxygen to yield an oxide, and the word *reduction* referred to the removal of oxygen from an oxide to yield the element. Today, though, the words have taken on a much broader meaning. An **oxidation** is now defined as the loss of one or more electrons by an atom,

Oxidation The loss of one or more electrons by an atom.

and a **reduction** is the gain of one or more electrons. Thus, an oxidation–reduction reaction, or redox reaction, is one in which *electrons are transferred from one atom to another.*

Reduction The gain of one or more electrons by an atom.

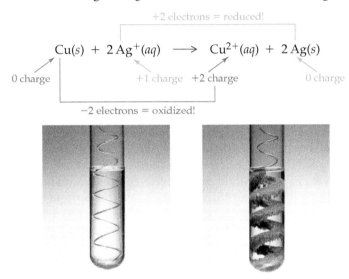

$$A^{2-} \longleftrightarrow A^- + \text{electron}$$
$$A^- \longleftrightarrow A + \text{electron}$$
$$A \longleftrightarrow A^+ + \text{electron}$$
$$A^+ \longleftrightarrow A^{2+} + \text{electron}$$

Oxidation

Reduction

Reactant A might be anything: a neutral atom, a monatomic ion, a polyatomic ion, or a molecule.

Take the reaction of copper with aqueous Ag^+ as an example, as shown in Figure 5.1. Copper metal gives an electron to each of 2 Ag^+ ions, forming Cu^{2+} and silver metal. Copper is oxidized in the process, and Ag^+ is reduced. You can follow the transfer of the electrons by noting that the charge on the copper increases from 0 to +2 when it loses 2 electrons, whereas the charge on Ag^+ decreases from +1 to 0 when it gains an electron.

+2 electrons = reduced!

$$Cu(s) + 2\,Ag^+(aq) \longrightarrow Cu^{2+}(aq) + 2\,Ag(s)$$

0 charge   +1 charge   +2 charge   0 charge

−2 electrons = oxidized!

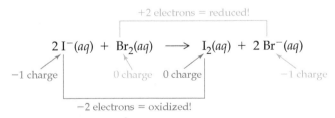

◄**Figure 5.1**
The copper wire reacts with aqueous Ag^+ ion and becomes coated with metallic silver. At the same time, copper(II) ions go into solution, producing the blue color.

Similarly, in the reaction of aqueous iodide ion with bromine, iodide ion gives an electron to bromine, forming iodine and bromide ion. Iodide ion is oxidized as its charge increases from −1 to 0, and bromine is reduced as its charge decreases from 0 to −1.

+2 electrons = reduced!

$$2\,I^-(aq) + Br_2(aq) \longrightarrow I_2(aq) + 2\,Br^-(aq)$$

−1 charge   0 charge   0 charge   −1 charge

−2 electrons = oxidized!

As these examples show, oxidation and reduction always occur together. Whenever one substance loses an electron (is oxidized), another substance must gain that electron (be reduced). The substance that gives up an electron and causes the reduction—the copper atom in the reaction of Cu with Ag^+ and the iodide ion in the reaction of I^- with Br_2—is called a **reducing agent**. The substance that gains an electron and causes the oxidation—the silver ion in the reaction of Cu with Ag^+ and the bromine molecule in the reaction of I^- with Br_2—is called an **oxidizing agent**. The charge on the reducing agent increases during the reaction, and the charge on the oxidizing agent decreases.

Reducing agent A reactant that causes a reduction in another reactant by giving up electron to it.

Oxidizing agent A reactant that causes an oxidation by taking electrons from another reactant.

Reducing agent	Loses one or more electrons
	Causes reduction
	Undergoes oxidation
	Becomes more positive (less negative)
	(May gain oxygen atoms)
Oxidizing agent	Gains one or more electrons
	Causes oxidation
	Undergoes reduction
	Becomes more negative (less positive)
	(May lose oxygen atoms)

Among the simplest of redox processes is the reaction of an element, usually a metal, with an aqueous cation to yield a different element and a different ion. Iron metal reacts with aqueous copper(II) ion, for example, to give iron(II) ion and copper metal. Similarly, magnesium metal reacts with aqueous acid to yield magnesium ion and hydrogen gas. In both cases, the reactant element (Fe or Mg) is oxidized, and the reactant ion (Cu^{2+} or H^+) is reduced.

$$Fe(s) + Cu^{2+}(aq) \longrightarrow Fe^{2+}(aq) + Cu(s)$$
$$Mg(s) + 2\,H^+(aq) \longrightarrow Mg^{2+}(aq) + H_2(g)$$

The reaction of a metal with water or aqueous acid (H^+) to release H_2 gas is a particularly important process. As you might expect based on the periodic properties discussed in Section 3.2, the alkali metals and alkaline earth metals (on the left side of the periodic table) are the most powerful reducing agents (electron donors), so powerful that they even react with pure water, in which the concentration of H^+ is very low. This is due in part to the fact that alkali metals and alkaline earth metals have low ionization energies. Ionization energy, which is a measure of how easily an element will lose an electron, tends to decrease as we move to the left and down in the periodic table. Thus, metals toward the middle of the periodic table, such as iron and chromium, have higher ionization energies and do not lose electrons as readily; they react only with aqueous acids but not with water. Those metals near the bottom right of the periodic table, such as platinum and gold, react with neither aqueous acid nor water. At the other extreme from the alkali metals, the reactive nonmetals at the top right of the periodic table have the highest ionization energies and are extremely weak reducing agents but powerful oxidizing agents (electron acceptors). This is, again, predictable based on the periodic property of electron affinity (Section 3.2), which becomes more energetically favored as we move up and to the right in the periodic table.

▶▶▶ The relationship between formation of ions and ionization energy/ electronegativity was discussed in Chapter 3.

We can make a few generalizations about the redox behavior of metals and nonmetals.

1. In reactions involving metals and nonmetals, metals tend to lose electrons while nonmetals tend to gain electrons. The number of electrons lost or gained can often be predicted based on the position of the element in the periodic table. (Section 3.5)
2. In reactions involving nonmetals, the "more metallic" element (farther down and/or to the left in the periodic table) tends to lose electrons, and the "less metallic" element (up and/or to the right) tends to gain electrons.

Redox reactions involve almost every element in the periodic table, and they occur in a vast number of processes throughout nature, biology, and industry. Here are just a few examples:

- **Corrosion** is the deterioration of a metal by oxidation, such as the rusting of iron in moist air. The economic consequences of rusting are enormous: it has been estimated that up to one-fourth of the iron produced in the United States is used to replace bridges, buildings, and other structures that have been destroyed by corrosion. (The raised dot in the formula $Fe_2O_3 \cdot H_2O$ for rust indicates that one water molecule is associated with each Fe_2O_3 in an undefined way.)

- **Combustion** is the burning of a fuel by rapid oxidation with oxygen in air. Gasoline, fuel oil, natural gas, wood, paper, and other organic substances of carbon and hydrogen are the most common fuels that burn in air. Even some metals, though, will burn in air. Magnesium and calcium are examples.

$$CH_4(g) + 2\,O_2(g) \longrightarrow CO_2(g) + 2\,H_2O(l)$$
  Methane
  (natural gas)

$$2\,Mg(s) + O_2(g) \longrightarrow 2\,MgO(s)$$

- **Respiration** is the process of breathing and using oxygen for the many biological redox reactions that provide the energy required by living organisms. We will see in Chapters 21–22 that in the respiration process, energy is released from food molecules slowly and in complex, multistep pathways, but that the overall result is similar to that of the simpler combustion reactions. For example, the simple sugar glucose $(C_6H_{12}O_6)$ reacts with O_2 to give CO_2 and H_2O according to the following equation:

$$C_6H_{12}O_6 + 6\,O_2 \longrightarrow 6\,CO_2 + 6\,H_2O + Energy$$
  Glucose
  (a carbohydrate)

- **Bleaching** makes use of redox reactions to decolorize or lighten colored materials. Dark hair is bleached to turn it blond, clothes are bleached to remove stains, wood pulp is bleached to make white paper, and so on. The oxidizing agent used depends on the situation: hydrogen peroxide (H_2O_2) is used for hair, sodium hypochlorite $(NaOCl)$ for clothes, and elemental chlorine for wood pulp, but the principle is always the same. In all cases, colored organic materials are destroyed by reaction with strong oxidizing agents.
- **Metallurgy,** the science of extracting and purifying metals from their ores, makes use of numerous redox processes. Worldwide, approximately 800 million tons of iron are produced each year by reduction of the mineral hematite, Fe_2O_3, with carbon monoxide.

$$Fe_2O_3(s) + 3\,CO(g) \longrightarrow 2\,Fe(s) + 3\,CO_2(g)$$

Worked Example 5.8 Chemical Reactions: Redox Reactions

For the following reactions, indicate which atom is oxidized and which is reduced, based on the definitions provided in this section. Identify the oxidizing and reducing agents.

(a) $Cu(s) + Pt^{2+}(aq) \longrightarrow Cu^{2+}(aq) + Pt(s)$

(b) $2\,Mg(s) + CO_2(g) \longrightarrow 2\,MgO(s) + C(s)$

ANALYSIS The definitions for oxidation include a loss of electrons, an increase in charge, and a gain of oxygen atoms; reduction is defined as a gain of electrons, a decrease in charge, and a loss of oxygen atoms.

SOLUTION

(a) In this reaction, the charge on the Cu atom increases from 0 to 2+. This corresponds to a loss of 2 electrons. The Cu is therefore oxidized and acts as the reducing agent. Conversely, the Pt^{2+} ion undergoes a decrease in charge from 2+ to 0, corresponding to a gain of 2 electrons for the Pt^{2+} ion. The Pt^{2+} is reduced, and acts as the oxidizing agent.

(b) In this case, the gain or loss of oxygen atoms is the easiest way to identify which atoms are oxidized and reduced. The Mg atom is gaining oxygen to form MgO; therefore, the Mg is being oxidized and acts as the reducing agent. The C atom in CO_2 is losing oxygen. Therefore, the C atom in CO_2 is being reduced, and so CO_2 acts as the oxidizing agent.

Worked Example 5.9 Chemical Reactions: Identifying Oxidizing/Reducing Agents

For the respiration and metallurgy examples discussed previously, identify the atoms being oxidized and reduced, and label the oxidizing and reducing agents.

ANALYSIS Again, using the definitions of oxidation and reduction provided in this section, we can determine which atom(s) are gaining/losing electrons or gaining/losing oxygen atoms.

SOLUTION

$$\textit{Respiration:} \quad C_6H_{12}O_6 + 6\,O_2 \longrightarrow 6\,CO_2 + 6\,H_2O$$

Because the charge associated with the individual atoms is not evident, we will use the definition of oxidation/reduction as the gaining/losing of oxygen atoms. In this reaction, there is only one reactant besides oxygen $(C_6H_{12}O_6)$, so we must determine *which* atom in the compound is changing. The ratio of carbon to oxygen in $C_6H_{12}O_4$ is 1:1, while the ratio in CO_2 is 1:2. Therefore, the C atoms are gaining oxygen and are oxidized; the $C_6H_{12}O_{16}$ is the reducing agent and O_2 is the oxidizing agent. Note that the ratio of hydrogen to oxygen in $C_6H_{12}O_6$ and in H_2O is 2:1. The H atoms are neither oxidized nor reduced.

$$\textit{Metallurgy:} \quad Fe_2O_3(s) + 3\,CO(g) \longrightarrow 2\,Fe(s) + 3\,CO_2(g)$$

The Fe_2O_3 is losing oxygen to form Fe(s); it is being reduced and acts as the oxidizing agent. In contrast, the CO is gaining oxygen to form CO_2; it is being oxidized and acts as the reducing agent.

Worked Example 5.10 Chemical Reactions: Identifying Redox Reactions

For the following reactions, identify the atom(s) being oxidized and reduced:

(a) $2\,Al(s) + 3\,Cl_2(g) \longrightarrow 2\,AlCl_3(s)$ **(b)** $C(s) + 2\,Cl_2(g) \longrightarrow CCl_4(l)$

ANALYSIS Again, there is no obvious increase or decrease in charge to indicate a gain or loss of electrons. Also, the reactions do not involve a gain or loss of oxygen. We can, however, evaluate the reactions in terms of the typical behavior of metals and nonmetals in reactions.

SOLUTION

(a) In this case, we have the reaction of a metal (Al) with a nonmetal (Cl_2). Because metals tend to lose electrons and nonmetals tend to gain electrons, we can assume that the Al atom is oxidized (loses electrons) and the Cl_2 is reduced (gains electrons).

(b) The carbon atom is the less electronegative element (farther to the left) and is less likely to gain an electron. The more electronegative element (Cl) will tend to gain electrons (be reduced).

PROBLEM 5.12
Identify the oxidized reactant, the reduced reactant, the oxidizing agent, and the reducing agent in the following reactions:
(a) $Fe(s) + Cu^{2+}(aq) \longrightarrow Fe^{2+}(aq) + Cu(s)$
(b) $Mg(s) + Cl_2(g) \longrightarrow MgCl_2(s)$
(c) $2\,Al(s) + Cr_2O_3(s) \longrightarrow 2\,Cr(s) + Al_2O_3(s)$

PROBLEM 5.13
Potassium, a silvery metal, reacts with bromine, a corrosive, reddish liquid, to yield potassium bromide, a white solid. Write the balanced equation, and identify the oxidizing and reducing agents.

PROBLEM 5.14
The redox reaction that provides energy for the lithium battery described in the Chemistry in Action on p. 147 is $2\,Li(s) + I_2(s) \rightarrow 2\,LiI(aq)$. Identify which reactant is being oxidized and which is being reduced in this reaction.

CHEMISTRY IN ACTION

Batteries

Imagine life without batteries: no cars (they do not start very easily without their batteries!), no heart pacemakers, no flashlights, no hearing aids, no laptops, no radios, no cell phones, nor thousands of other things. Modern society could not exist without batteries.

Although they come in many types and sizes, all batteries work using redox reactions. In a typical redox reaction carried out in the laboratory—say, the reaction of zinc metal with Ag^+ to yield Zn^{2+} and silver metal—the reactants are simply mixed in a flask and electrons are transferred by direct contact between the reactants. In a battery, however, the two reactants are kept in separate compartments and the electrons are transferred through a wire running between them.

The common household battery used for flashlights and radios is the *dry cell*, developed in 1866. One reactant is a can of zinc metal, and the other is a paste of solid manganese dioxide. A graphite rod sticks into the MnO_2 paste to provide electrical contact, and a moist paste of ammonium chloride separates the two reactants. If the zinc can and the graphite rod are connected by a wire, zinc sends electrons flowing through the wire toward the MnO_2 in a redox reaction. The resultant electrical current can then be used to power a lightbulb or a radio. The accompanying figure shows a cutaway view of a dry-cell battery.

$$Zn(s) + 2\,MnO_2(s) + 2\,NH_4Cl(s) \longrightarrow$$
$$ZnCl_2(aq) + Mn_2O_3(s) + 2\,NH_3(aq) + H_2O(l)$$

▲ **Think of all the devices we use every day—laptop computers, cell phones, iPods—that depend on batteries.**

Closely related to the dry-cell battery is the familiar *alkaline* battery, in which the ammonium chloride paste is replaced by an alkaline, or basic, paste of NaOH or KOH. The alkaline battery has a longer life than the standard dry-cell battery because the zinc container corrodes less easily under basic conditions. The redox reaction is:

$$Zn(s) + 2\,MnO_2(s) \longrightarrow ZnO(aq) + Mn_2O_3(s)$$

The batteries used in implanted medical devices such as pacemakers must be small, corrosion-resistant, reliable, and able to last up to 10 years. Nearly all pacemakers being implanted today—about 750,000 each year—use titanium-encased, lithium–iodine batteries, whose redox reaction is:

$$2\,Li(s) + I_2(s) \longrightarrow 2\,LiI(aq)$$

See Chemistry in Action Problems 5.65 and 5.66 at the end of the chapter.

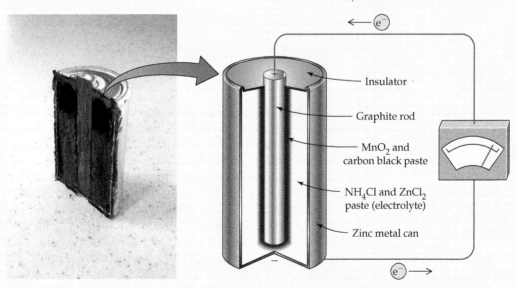

▲ **A dry-cell battery. The cutaway view shows the two reactants that make up the redox reaction.**

5.7 Recognizing Redox Reactions

How can you tell when a redox reaction is taking place? When ions are involved, it is simply a matter of determining whether there is a change in the charges. For reactions involving metals and nonmetals, we can predict the gain or loss of electrons as discussed previously. When molecular substances are involved, though, it is not as obvious. Is the combining of sulfur with oxygen a redox reaction? If so, which partner is the oxidizing agent and which is the reducing agent?

$$S(s) + O_2(g) \longrightarrow SO_2(g)$$

One way to evaluate this reaction is in terms of the oxygen gain by sulfur, indicating that S atoms are oxidized and O atoms are reduced. But can we also look at this reaction in terms of the gain or loss of electrons by the S and O atoms? Because oxygen is more electronegative than sulfur, the oxygen atoms in SO_2 attract the electrons in the S—O bonds more strongly than sulfur does, giving the oxygen atoms a larger share of the electrons than sulfur. By extending the ideas of oxidation and reduction to an increase or decrease in electron *sharing* instead of complete electron *transfer*, we can say that the sulfur atom is oxidized in its reaction with oxygen because it loses a share in some electrons, whereas the oxygen atoms are reduced because they gain a share in some electrons.

A formal system has been devised for keeping track of changes in electron sharing, and thus for determining whether atoms are oxidized or reduced in reactions. To each atom in a substance, we assign a value called an **oxidation number** (or *oxidation state*), which indicates whether the atom is neutral, electron-rich, or electron-poor. By comparing the oxidation number of an atom before and after a reaction, we can tell whether the atom has gained or lost shares in electrons. Note that *oxidation numbers do not necessarily imply ionic charges*. They are simply a convenient device for keeping track of electrons in redox reactions.

The rules for assigning oxidation numbers are straightforward:

- **An atom in its elemental state has an oxidation number of 0.**

- **A monatomic ion has an oxidation number equal to its charge.**

Oxidation number +1	Oxidation number +2	Oxidation number −1	Oxidation number −2
Na^+	Ca^{2+}	Cl^-	O^{2-}

- **In a molecular compound, an atom usually has the same oxidation number it would have if it were a monatomic ion.** Recall from Chapters 3 and 4 that the less electronegative elements (hydrogen and metals) on the left side of the periodic table tend to form cations, and the more electronegative elements (oxygen, nitrogen, and the halogens) near the top right of the periodic table tend to form anions. Hydrogen and metals therefore have positive oxidation numbers in most compounds, whereas reactive nonmetals generally have negative oxidation numbers. Hydrogen is usually +1, oxygen is usually −2, nitrogen is usually −3, and halogens are usually −1:

Electronegativity, or the propensity of an atom in a covalent bond to attract electrons, was introduced in Section 4.9.

Oxidation number A number that indicates whether an atom is neutral, electron-rich, or electron-poor.

Review the Important Points about Ion Formation and the Periodic Table listed in Section 3.6.

For compounds with more than one nonmetal element, such as SO_2, NO, or CO_2, the more electronegative element—oxygen in these examples—has a negative oxidation number and the less electronegative element has a positive oxidation number. Thus, in answer to the question posed at the beginning of this section, combining sulfur with oxygen to form SO_2 is a redox reaction because the oxidation number of sulfur increases from 0 to +4 and that of oxygen decreases from 0 to −2.

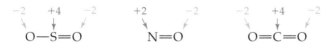

- **The sum of the oxidation numbers in a neutral compound is 0.** Using this rule, the oxidation number of any atom in a compound can be found if the oxidation numbers of the other atoms are known. In the SO_2 example just mentioned, each of the 2 O atoms has an oxidation number of −2, so the S atom must have an oxidation number of +4. In HNO_3, the H atom has an oxidation number of +1 and the strongly electronegative O atom has an oxidation number of −2, so the N atom must have an oxidation number of +5. In a polyatomic ion, the sum of the oxidation numbers equals the charge on the ion.

$$\overset{+1}{H}-\overset{-2}{O}-\overset{+5}{N}=\overset{-2}{O} \qquad \text{Total} = 1 + 5 + 3(-2) = 0$$
$$\underset{-2}{|}$$
$$O$$

Worked Examples 5.11 and 5.12 show further instances of assigning and using oxidation numbers.

Worked Example **5.11** Redox Reactions: Oxidation Numbers

What is the oxidation number of the titanium atom in $TiCl_4$? Name the compound using a Roman numeral (Section 3.10).

SOLUTION
Chlorine, a reactive nonmetal, is more electronegative than titanium and has an oxidation number of −1. Because there are 4 chlorine atoms in $TiCl_4$, the oxidation number of titanium must be +4. The compound is named titanium(IV) chloride. Note that the Roman numeral IV in the name of this molecular compound refers to the oxidation number +4 rather than to a true ionic charge.

Worked Example **5.12** Redox Reactions: Identifying Redox Reactions

Use oxidation numbers to show that the production of iron metal from its ore (Fe_2O_3) by reaction with charcoal (C) is a redox reaction. Which reactant has been oxidized, and which has been reduced? Which reactant is the oxidizing agent, and which is the reducing agent?

$$2\ Fe_2O_3(s) + 3\ C(s) \longrightarrow 4\ Fe(s) + 3\ CO_2(g)$$

SOLUTION
The idea is to assign oxidation numbers to both reactants and products and see if there has been a change. In the production of iron from Fe_2O_3, the oxidation number of Fe changes from +3 to 0, and the oxidation number of C changes from 0 to +4. Iron has thus been reduced (decrease in oxidation number), and carbon has been oxidized (increase in oxidation number). Oxygen is neither oxidized nor reduced because its oxidation number does not change. Carbon is the reducing agent, and Fe_2O_3 is the oxidizing agent.

$$2\ \overset{+3\ -2}{Fe_2O_3} + 3\ \overset{0}{C} \longrightarrow 4\ \overset{0}{Fe} + 3\ \overset{+4\ -2}{CO_2}$$

PROBLEM 5.15

What are the oxidation numbers of the metal atoms in the following compounds? Name each, using the oxidation number as a Roman numeral.

(a) VCl_3 (b) $SnCl_4$ (c) CrO_3 (d) $Cu(NO_3)_2$ (e) $NiSO_4$

PROBLEM 5.16

Assign an oxidation number to each atom in the reactants and products shown here to determine which of the following reactions are redox reactions:

(a) $Na_2S(aq) + NiCl_2(aq) \longrightarrow 2\,NaCl(aq) + NiS(s)$

(b) $2\,Na(s) + 2\,H_2O(l) \longrightarrow 2\,NaOH(aq) + H_2(g)$

(c) $C(s) + O_2(g) \longrightarrow CO_2(g)$

(d) $CuO(s) + 2\,HCl(aq) \longrightarrow CuCl_2(aq) + H_2O(l)$

(e) $2\,MnO_4^-(aq) + 5\,SO_2(g) + 2\,H_2O(l) \longrightarrow$
$2\,Mn^{2+}(aq) + 5\,SO_4^{2-}(aq) + 4\,H^+(aq)$

PROBLEM 5.17

For each of the reactions you identified as redox reactions in Problem 5.16, identify the oxidizing agent and the reducing agent.

5.8 Net Ionic Equations

In the equations we have been writing up to this point, all the substances involved in reactions have been written using their full formulas. In the precipitation reaction of lead(II) nitrate with potassium iodide mentioned in Section 5.3, for example, only the parenthetical *aq* indicated that the reaction actually takes place in aqueous solution, and nowhere was it explicitly indicated that ions are involved:

$$Pb(NO_3)_2(aq) + 2\,KI(aq) \longrightarrow 2\,KNO_3(aq) + PbI_2(s)$$

In fact, lead(II) nitrate, potassium iodide, and potassium nitrate dissolve in water to yield solutions of ions. Thus, it is more accurate to write the reaction as an **ionic equation**, in which all the ions are explicitly shown:

Ionic equation An equation in which ions are explicitly shown.

An ionic equation: $Pb^{2+}(aq) + 2\,NO_3^-(aq) + 2\,K^+(aq) + 2\,I^-(aq) \longrightarrow$
$2\,K^+(aq) + 2\,NO_3^-(aq) + PbI_2(s)$

A look at this ionic equation shows that the NO_3^- and K^+ ions undergo no change during the reaction. They appear on both sides of the reaction arrow and act merely as **spectator ions**, that is, they are present but play no role. The actual reaction, when stripped to its essentials, can be described more simply by writing a **net ionic equation**, which includes only the ions that undergo change and ignores all spectator ions:

Spectator ion An ion that appears unchanged on both sides of a reaction arrow.

Net ionic equation An equation that does not include spectator ions.

Ionic equation: $Pb^{2+}(aq) + 2\,\cancel{NO_3^-}(aq) + 2\,\cancel{K^+}(aq) + 2\,I^-(aq) \longrightarrow$
$2\,\cancel{K^+}(aq) + 2\,\cancel{NO_3^-}(aq) + PbI_2(s)$

Net ionic equation: $Pb^{2+}(aq) + 2\,I^-(aq) \longrightarrow PbI_2(s)$

Note that a net ionic equation, like all chemical equations, must be balanced both for atoms and for charge, with all coefficients reduced to their lowest whole numbers. Note also that all compounds that do *not* give ions in solution—all insoluble compounds and all molecular compounds—are represented by their full formulas.

We can apply the concept of ionic equations to acid–base neutralization reactions and redox reactions as well. Consider the neutralization reaction between KOH and HNO_3:

$$KOH(aq) + HNO_3(aq) \longrightarrow H_2O(l) + KNO_3(aq)$$

Since acids and bases are identified based on the ions they form when dissolved in aqueous solutions, we can write an ionic equation for this reaction:

Ionic equation: $\cancel{K^+}(aq) + OH^-(aq) + H^+(aq) + \cancel{NO_3^-}(aq) \longrightarrow$
$H_2O(l) + \cancel{K^+}(aq) + \cancel{NO_3^-}(aq)$

Eliminating the spectator ions (K^+ and NO_3^-), we obtain the net ionic equation for the neutralization reaction:

Net ionic equation: $\quad OH^-(aq) + H^+(aq) \longrightarrow H_2O(l)$

The net ionic equation confirms the basis of the acid–base neutralization; the OH^- from the base and the H^+ from the acid neutralize each other to form water.

Similarly, many redox reactions can be viewed in terms of ionic equations. Consider the reaction between $Cu(s)$ and $AgNO_3$ from Section 5.6:

$$Cu(s) + 2\,AgNO_3(aq) \longrightarrow 2\,Ag^+(aq) + Cu(NO_3)_2(aq)$$

The aqueous products and reactants can be written as dissolved ions:

Ionic equation: $\quad Cu(s) + 2\,Ag^+(aq) + 2\,\cancel{NO_3^-(aq)} \longrightarrow$
$$2\,Ag(s) + Cu^{2+}(aq) + 2\,\cancel{NO_3^-(aq)}$$

Again, eliminating the spectator ions (NO_3^-), we obtain the net ionic equation for this redox reaction:

Net ionic equation: $\quad Cu(s) + 2\,Ag^+(aq) \longrightarrow 2\,Ag(s) + Cu^{2+}(aq)$

It is now clear that the $Cu(s)$ loses 2 electrons and is oxidized, whereas each Ag^+ ion gains an electron and is reduced.

Worked Example 5.13 Chemical Reactions: Net Ionic Reactions

Write balanced net ionic equations for the following reactions:

(a) $AgNO_3(aq) + ZnCl_2(aq) \longrightarrow$
(b) $HCl(aq) + Ca(OH)_2(aq) \longrightarrow$
(c) $6\,HCl(aq) + 2\,Al(s) \longrightarrow 2\,AlCl_3(aq) + 3\,H_2(g)$

SOLUTION

(a) The solubility guidelines discussed in Section 5.4 predict that a precipitate of insoluble $AgCl$ forms when aqueous solutions of Ag^+ and Cl^- are mixed. Writing all the ions separately gives an ionic equation, and eliminating spectator ions Zn^{2+} and NO_3^- gives the net ionic equation.

Ionic equation: $\quad 2\,Ag^+(aq) + 2\,\cancel{NO_3^-(aq)} + \cancel{Zn^{2+}(aq)} + 2\,Cl^-(aq) \longrightarrow$
$$2\,AgCl(s) + \cancel{Zn^{2+}(aq)} + 2\,\cancel{NO_3^-(aq)}$$

Net ionic equation: $\quad 2\,Ag^+(aq) + 2\,Cl^-(aq) \longrightarrow 2\,AgCl(s)$

The coefficients can all be divided by 2 to give:

Net ionic equation: $\quad Ag^+(aq) + Cl^+(aq) \longrightarrow AgCl(s)$

A check shows that the equation is balanced for atoms and charge (zero on each side).

(b) Allowing the acid HCl to react with the base $Ca(OH)_2$ leads to a neutralization reaction. Writing the ions separately, and remembering to write a complete formula for water, gives an ionic equation. Then eliminating the spectator ions and dividing the coefficients by 2 gives the net ionic equation.

Ionic equation: $\quad 2\,H^+(aq) + 2\,\cancel{Cl^-(aq)} + \cancel{Ca^{2+}(aq)} + 2\,OH^-(aq) \longrightarrow$
$$2\,H_2O(l) + \cancel{Ca^{2+}(aq)} + 2\,\cancel{Cl^-(aq)}$$

Net ionic equation: $\quad H^+(aq) + OH^-(aq) \longrightarrow H_2O(l)$

A check shows that atoms and charges are the same on both sides of the equation.

(c) The reaction of Al metal with acid (HCl) is a redox reaction. The Al is oxidized, since the oxidation number increases from $0 \rightarrow +3$, whereas the H in HCl is reduced from $+1 \rightarrow 0$. We write the ionic equation by showing the ions that are formed for each aqueous ionic species. Eliminating the spectator ions yields the net ionic equation.

Ionic equation: $6\,H^+(aq) + 6\,\cancel{Cl^-(aq)} + 2\,Al(s) \longrightarrow$

$$2\,Al^{3+}(aq) + 6\,\cancel{Cl^-(aq)} + 3\,H_2(g)$$

Net ionic equation: $\quad 6\,H^+(aq) + 2\,Al(s) \longrightarrow 2\,Al^{3+}(aq) + 3\,H_2(g)$

A check shows that atoms and charges are the same on both sides of the equation.

PROBLEM 5.18

Write net ionic equations for the following reactions:

(a) $Zn(s) + Pb(NO_3)_2(aq) \longrightarrow Zn(NO_3)_2(aq) + Pb(s)$

(b) $2\,KOH(aq) + H_2SO_4(aq) \longrightarrow K_2SO_4(aq) + 2\,H_2O(l)$

(c) $2\,FeCl_3(aq) + SnCl_2(aq) \longrightarrow 2\,FeCl_2(aq) + SnCl_4(aq)$

PROBLEM 5.19

Identify each of the reactions in Problem 5.18 as an acid–base neutralization, a precipitation, or a redox reaction.

SUMMARY: REVISITING THE CHAPTER GOALS

1. How are chemical reactions written? Chemical equations must be *balanced*; that is, the numbers and kinds of atoms must be the same in both the reactants and the products. To balance an equation, *coefficients* are placed before formulas but the formulas themselves cannot be changed (*see Problems 21–23, 26–37, 59, 60, 64, 67, 68, 71, 72, 75, 76, 79, 80*).

2. How are chemical reactions of ionic compounds classified? There are three common types of reactions of ionic compounds (*see Problems 38–50, 65, 70, 79, 81*).

Precipitation reactions are processes in which an insoluble solid called a *precipitate* is formed. Most precipitations take place when the anions and cations of two ionic compounds change partners. Solubility guidelines for ionic compounds are used to predict when precipitation will occur (*see Problems 24, 25, 43–46, 49, 69, 76–78*).

Acid–base neutralization reactions are processes in which an acid reacts with a base to yield water plus an ionic compound called a *salt*. Since acids produce H^+ ions and bases produce OH^- ions when dissolved in water, a neutralization reaction removes H^+ and OH^- ions from solution and yields neutral H_2O (*see Problems 37, 39, 75, 81*).

Oxidation–reduction (redox) reactions are processes in which one or more electrons are transferred between reaction partners.

An *oxidation* is defined as the loss of one or more electrons by an atom, and a *reduction* is the gain of one or more electrons. An *oxidizing agent* causes the oxidation of another reactant by accepting electrons, and a *reducing agent* causes the reduction of another reactant by donating electrons (*see Problems 51–54, 57–62, 65, 66, 68, 82*).

3. What are oxidation numbers, and how are they used? *Oxidation numbers* are assigned to atoms in reactants and products to provide a measure of whether an atom is neutral, electron-rich, or electron-poor. By comparing the oxidation number of an atom before and after reaction, we can tell whether the atom has gained or lost shares in electrons and thus whether a redox reaction has occurred (*see Problems 51–62, 65, 66, 70–74, 82*).

4. What is a net ionic equation? The *net ionic equation* only includes those ions that are directly involved in the ionic reaction. These ions can be identified because they are found in different phases or compounds on the reactant and product sides of the chemical equation. The net ionic equation does not include *spectator ions*, which appear in the same state on both sides of the chemical equation (*see Problems 39, 47, 48, 50, 69, 76–78, 81*).

KEY WORDS

Balanced equation, *p. 134*

Chemical equation, *p. 133*

Coefficient, *p. 134*

Ionic equation, *p. 150*

Law of conservation of mass, *p. 133*

Net ionic equation, *p. 150*

Neutralization reaction, *p. 141*

Oxidation, *p. 143*

Oxidation number, *p. 148*

Oxidation–reduction (redox) reaction, *p. 138*

Oxidizing agent, *p. 143*

Precipitate, *p. 138*

Product, *p. 133*

Reactant, *p. 133*

Reducing agent, *p. 143*

Reduction, *p. 143*

Salt, *p. 138*

Solubility, *p. 139*

Spectator ion, *p. 150*

UNDERSTANDING KEY CONCEPTS

5.20   Assume that the mixture of substances in drawing (a) undergoes a reaction. Which of the drawings (b)–(d) represents a product mixture consistent with the law of conservation of mass?

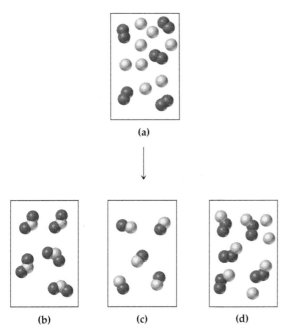

5.21   Reaction of A (green spheres) with B (blue spheres) is shown in the following diagram:

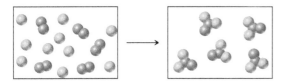

Which equation best describes the reaction?

(a) $A_2 + 2\,B \longrightarrow A_2B_2$

(b) $10\,A + 5\,B_2 \longrightarrow 5\,A_2B_2$

(c) $2\,A + B_2 \longrightarrow A_2B_2$

(d) $5\,A + 5\,B_2 \longrightarrow 5\,A_2B_2$

5.22   If blue spheres represent nitrogen atoms and red spheres represent oxygen atoms in the following diagrams, which box

represents reactants and which represents products for the reaction $2\,NO(g) + O_2(g) \longrightarrow 2\,NO_2(g)$?

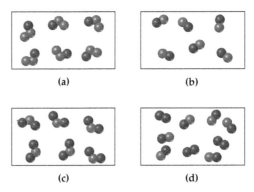

5.23   Assume that an aqueous solution of a cation (represented as red spheres in the diagram) is allowed to mix with a solution of an anion (represented as yellow spheres). Three possible outcomes are represented by boxes (1)–(3):

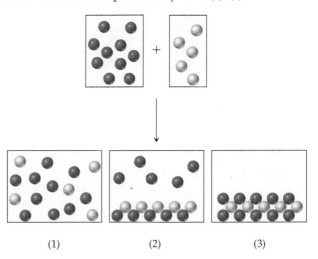

Which outcome corresponds to each of the following reactions?

(a) $2\,Na^+(aq) + CO_3^{2-}(aq) \longrightarrow$

(b) $Ba^{2+}(aq) + CrO_4^{2-}(aq) \longrightarrow$

(c) $2\,Ag^+(aq) + SO_3^{2-}(aq) \longrightarrow$

5.24   An aqueous solution of a cation (represented as blue spheres in the diagram) is allowed to mix with a solution of an anion (represented as green spheres) and the following result is obtained:

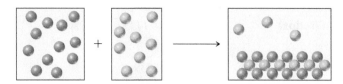

Which combinations of cation and anion, chosen from the following lists, are compatible with the observed results? Explain.

Cations: Na^+, Ca^{2+}, Ag^+, Ni^{2+}

Anions: Cl^-, CO_3^{2-}, CrO_4^{2-}, NO_3^-

5.25   A molecular view of two ionic solutions is presented right:

(a) Which compound is most likely dissolved in beaker A: KBr, $CaCl_2$, PbI_2, Na_2SO_4?

(b) Which compound is most likely dissolved in beaker B: Na_2CO_3, $BaSO_4$, $Cu(NO_3)_2$, $FeCl_3$?

(c) Identify the precipitate and spectator ions for any reaction that will result when beakers A and B are mixed.

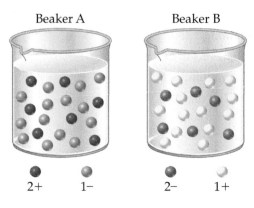

ADDITIONAL PROBLEMS

BALANCING CHEMICAL EQUATIONS

5.26   What is meant by the term "balanced equation"?

5.27   Why is it not possible to balance an equation by changing the subscript on a substance, say from H_2O to H_2O_2?

5.28   Write balanced equations for the following reactions:

(a) Gaseous sulfur dioxide reacts with water to form aqueous sulfurous acid (H_2SO_3).

(b) Liquid bromine reacts with solid potassium metal to form solid potassium bromide.

(c) Gaseous propane (C_3H_8) burns in oxygen to form gaseous carbon dioxide and water vapor.

5.29   Balance the following equation for the synthesis of hydrazine, N_2H_4, a substance used as rocket fuel.

$$NH_3(g) + Cl_2(g) \longrightarrow N_2H_4(l) + NH_4Cl(s)$$

5.30   Which of the following equations are balanced? Balance those that need it.

(a) $2\,C_2H_6(g) + 5\,O_2(g) \longrightarrow 2\,CO_2(g) + 6\,H_2O(l)$

(b) $3\,Ca(OH)_2(aq) + 2\,H_3PO_4(aq) \longrightarrow$
$$Ca_3(PO_4)_2(aq) + 6\,H_2O(l)$$

(c) $Mg(s) + O_2(g) \longrightarrow 2\,MgO(s)$

(d) $K(s) + H_2O(l) \longrightarrow KOH(aq) + H_2(g)$

5.31   Which of the following equations are balanced? Balance those that need it.

(a) $CaC_2 + 2\,H_2O \longrightarrow Ca(OH)_2 + C_2H_2$

(b) $C_2H_8N_2 + 2\,N_2O_4 \longrightarrow 2\,N_2 + 2\,CO_2 + 4\,H_2O$

(c) $3\,MgO + 2\,Fe \longrightarrow Fe_2O_3 + 3\,Mg$

(d) $N_2O \longrightarrow N_2 + O_2$

5.32   Balance the following equations:

(a) $Hg(NO_3)_2(aq) + LiI(aq) \longrightarrow$
$$LiNO_3(aq) + HgI_2(s)$$

(b) $I_2(s) + Cl_2(g) \longrightarrow ICl_5(s)$

(c) $Al(s) + O_2(g) \longrightarrow Al_2O_3(s)$

(d) $CuSO_4(aq) + AgNO_3(aq) \longrightarrow$
$$Ag_2SO_4(s) + Cu(NO_3)_2(aq)$$

(e) $Mn(NO_3)_3(aq) + Na_2S(aq) \longrightarrow$
$$Mn_2S_3(s) + NaNO_3(aq)$$

5.33   Balance the following equations:

(a) $NO_2(g) + O_2(g) \longrightarrow N_2O_5(g)$

(b) $P_4O_{10}(s) + H_2O(l) \longrightarrow H_3PO_4(aq)$

(c) $B_2H_6(l) + O_2(g) \longrightarrow B_2O_3(s) + H_2O(l)$

(d) $Cr_2O_3(s) + CCl_4(l) \longrightarrow CrCl_3(s) + COCl_2(aq)$

(e) $Fe_3O_4(s) + O_2(g) \longrightarrow Fe_2O_3(s)$.

5.34   When organic compounds are burned, they react with oxygen to form CO_2 and H_2O. Write balanced equations for the combustion of the following:

(a) C_4H_{10} (butane, used in lighters)

(b) C_2H_6O (ethyl alcohol, used in gasohol and as race car fuel)

(c) C_8H_{18} (octane, a component of gasoline)

5.35   When organic compounds are burned without enough oxygen, carbon monoxide is formed as a product instead of carbon dioxide. Write and balance the combustion reactions from Problem 5.34 using CO as a product instead of CO_2.

5.36 Hydrofluoric acid (HF) is used to etch glass (SiO_2). The products of the reaction are silicon tetrafluoride and water. Write the balanced chemical equation.

5.37 Write a balanced equation for the reaction of aqueous sodium carbonate (Na_2CO_3) with aqueous nitric acid (HNO_3) to yield CO_2, $NaNO_3$, and H_2O.

TYPES OF CHEMICAL REACTIONS

5.38 Identify each of the following reactions as a precipitation, neutralization, or redox reaction:

(a) $Mg(s) + 2\,HCl(aq) \longrightarrow MgCl_2(aq) + H_2(g)$

(b) $KOH(aq) + HNO_3(aq) \longrightarrow KNO_3(aq) + H_2O(l)$

(c) $Pb(NO_3)_2(aq) + 2\,HBr(aq) \longrightarrow$
$$PbBr_2(s) + 2\,HNO_3(aq)$$

(d) $Ca(OH)_2(aq) + 2\,HCl(aq) \longrightarrow$
$$2\,H_2O(l) + CaCl_2(aq)$$

5.39 Write balanced ionic equations and net ionic equations for the following reactions:

(a) Aqueous sulfuric acid is neutralized by aqueous potassium hydroxide.

(b) Aqueous magnesium hydroxide is neutralized by aqueous hydrochloric acid.

5.40 Write balanced ionic equations and net ionic equations for the following reactions:

(a) A precipitate of barium sulfate forms when aqueous solutions of barium nitrate and potassium sulfate are mixed.

(b) Zinc ion and hydrogen gas form when zinc metal reacts with aqueous sulfuric acid.

5.41 Identify each of the reactions in Problem 5.30 as a precipitation, neutralization, or redox reaction.

5.42 Identify each of the reactions in Problem 5.32 as a precipitation, neutralization, or redox reaction.

5.43 Which of the following substances are likely to be soluble in water?

(a) $ZnSO_4$ (b) $NiCO_3$

(c) $PbCl_2$ (d) $Ca_3(PO_4)_2$

5.44 Which of the following substances are likely to be soluble in water?

(a) Ag_2O (b) $Ba(NO_3)_2$

(c) $SnCO_3$ (d) Al_2S_3

5.45 Use the solubility guidelines in Section 5.4 to predict whether a precipitation reaction will occur when aqueous solutions of the following substances are mixed.

(a) $NaOH + HClO_4$

(b) $FeCl_2 + KOH$

(c) $(NH_4)_2SO_4 + NiCl_2$

5.46 Use the solubility guidelines in Section 5.4 to predict whether precipitation reactions will occur between the

listed pairs of reactants. Write balanced equations for those reactions that should occur.

(a) NaBr and $Hg_2(NO_3)_2$

(b) $CuCl_2$ and K_2SO_4

(c) $LiNO_3$ and $Ca(CH_3CO_2)_2$

(d) $(NH_4)_2CO_3$ and $CaCl_2$

(e) KOH and $MnBr_2$

(f) Na_2S and $Al(NO_3)_3$

5.47 Write net ionic equations for the following reactions:

(a) $Mg(s) + CuCl_2(aq) \longrightarrow MgCl_2(aq) + Cu(s)$

(b) $2\,KCl(aq) + Pb(NO_3)_2(aq) \longrightarrow$
$$PbCl_2(s) + 2\,KNO_3(aq)$$

(c) $2\,Cr(NO_3)_3(aq) + 3\,Na_2S(aq) \longrightarrow$
$$Cr_2S_3(s) + 6\,NaNO_3(aq)$$

5.48 Write net ionic equations for the following reactions:

(a) $2\,AuCl_3(aq) + 3\,Sn(s) \longrightarrow 3\,SnCl_2(aq) + 2\,Au(s)$

(b) $2\,NaI(aq) + Br_2(l) \longrightarrow 2\,NaBr(aq) + I_2(s)$

(c) $2\,AgNO_3(aq) + Fe(s) \longrightarrow Fe(NO_3)_2(aq) + 2\,Ag(s)$

5.49 Complete the following precipitation reactions using balanced chemical equations:

(a) $FeSO_4(aq) + Sr(OH)_2(aq) \longrightarrow$

(b) $Na_2S(aq) + ZnSO_4(aq) \longrightarrow$

5.50 Write net ionic equations for each of the reactions in Problem 5.49.

REDOX REACTIONS AND OXIDATION NUMBERS

5.51 Where in the periodic table are the best reducing agents found? The best oxidizing agents?

5.52 Where in the periodic table are the most easily reduced elements found? The most easily oxidized?

5.53 In each of the following, tell whether the substance gains electrons or loses electrons in a redox reaction:

(a) An oxidizing agent

(b) A reducing agent

(c) A substance undergoing oxidation

(d) A substance undergoing reduction

5.54 For the following substances, tell whether the oxidation number increases or decreases in a redox reaction:

(a) An oxidizing agent

(b) A reducing agent

(c) A substance undergoing oxidation

(d) A substance undergoing reduction

5.55 Assign an oxidation number to each element in the following compounds or ions:

(a) N_2O_5 (b) $SO_3{}^{2-}$

(c) CH_2O (d) $HClO_3$

5.56 Assign an oxidation number to the metal in the following compounds:

(a) $CoCl_3$

(b) $FeSO_4$

(c) UO_3

(d) CuF_2

(e) TiO_2

(f) SnS

5.57 Which element is oxidized and which is reduced in the following reactions?

(a) $Si(s) + 2\,Cl_2(g) \longrightarrow SiCl_4(l)$

(b) $Cl_2(g) + 2\,NaBr(aq) \longrightarrow Br_2(aq) + 2\,NaCl(aq)$

(c) $SbCl_3(s) + Cl_2(g) \longrightarrow SbCl_5(s)$

5.58 Which element is oxidized and which is reduced in the following reactions?

(a) $2\,SO_2(g) + O_2(g) \longrightarrow 2\,SO_3(g)$

(b) $2\,Na(s) + Cl_2(g) \longrightarrow 2\,NaCl(s)$

(c) $CuCl_2(aq) + Zn(s) \longrightarrow ZnCl_2(aq) + Cu(s)$

(d) $2\,NaCl(aq) + F_2(g) \longrightarrow 2\,NaF(aq) + Cl_2(g)$

5.59 Balance each of the following redox reactions:

(a) $Al(s) + H_2SO_4(aq) \longrightarrow Al_2(SO_4)_3(aq) + H_2(g)$

(b) $Fe(s) + Cl_2(g) \longrightarrow FeCl_3(s)$

(c) $CO(g) + I_2O_5(s) \longrightarrow I_2(s) + CO_2(g)$

5.60 Balance each of the following redox reactions:

(a) $N_2O_4(l) + N_2H_4(l) \longrightarrow N_2(g) + H_2O(g)$

(b) $CaH_2(s) + H_2O(l) \longrightarrow Ca(OH)_2(aq) + H_2(g)$

(c) $Al(s) + H_2O(l) \longrightarrow Al(OH)_3(s) + H_2(g)$

5.61 Identify the oxidizing agent and the reducing agent in Problem 5.59.

5.62 Identify the oxidizing agent and the reducing agent in Problem 5.60.

CHEMISTRY IN ACTION

5.63 Sodium urate, the principal constituent of some kidney stones and the substance responsible for gout, has the formula $NaC_5H_3N_4O_3$. In aqueous solution, the solubility of sodium urate is only 0.067 g/L. How many grams of sodium urate could be dissolved in the blood before precipitation might occur? (The average adult has a blood capacity of about 5 L.) [*Gout and Kidney Stones, p. 140*]

5.64 Uric acid is formed in the body by the metabolism of purines. The reaction can be represented as $C_5H_4N_4$ (purine) $+ O_2 \rightarrow C_5H_4N_4O_3$ (uric acid).

(a) Balance the reaction.

(b) What type of reaction is this? [*Gout and Kidney Stones, p. 140*]

5.65 The rechargeable NiCd battery uses the following reaction:

$2\,NiO(OH) + Cd + 2\,H_2O \longrightarrow 2\,Ni(OH)_2 + Cd(OH)_2.$

Which reactant is being oxidized and which is being reduced in this reaction? [*Batteries, p. 147*]

5.66 Identify the oxidizing and reducing agents in a typical dry-cell battery. [*Batteries, p. 147*]

GENERAL QUESTIONS AND PROBLEMS

5.67 Balance the following equations.

(a) The thermite reaction, used in welding:
$Al(s) + Fe_2O_3(s) \longrightarrow Al_2O_3(l) + Fe(l)$

(b) The explosion of ammonium nitrate:
$NH_4NO_3(s) \longrightarrow N_2(g) + O_2(g) + H_2O(g)$

5.68 Lithium oxide is used aboard the space shuttle to remove water from the atmosphere according to the equation:

$$Li_2O(s) + H_2O(g) \longrightarrow LiOH(s)$$

(a) Balance the chemical equation.

(b) Is this a redox reaction? Why or why not?

5.69 Look at the solubility guidelines in Section 5.4 and predict whether a precipitate forms when $CuCl_2(aq)$ and $Na_2CO_3(aq)$ are mixed. If so, write both the balanced equation and the net ionic equation for the process.

5.70 Balance the following equations and classify each as a precipitation, neutralization, or redox reaction:

(a) $Al(OH)_3(aq) + HNO_3(aq) \longrightarrow$
$\qquad\qquad\qquad\qquad Al(NO_3)_3(aq) + H_2O(l)$

(b) $AgNO_3(aq) + FeCl_3(aq) \longrightarrow$
$\qquad\qquad\qquad\qquad AgCl(s) + Fe(NO_3)_3(aq)$

(c) $(NH_4)_2Cr_2O_7(s) \longrightarrow Cr_2O_3(s) + H_2O(g) + N_2(g)$

(d) $Mn_2(CO_3)_3(s) \longrightarrow Mn_2O_3(s) + CO_2(g)$

5.71 White phosphorus (P_4) is a highly reactive form of elemental phosphorus that reacts with oxygen to form a variety of molecular compounds, including diphosphorus pentoxide.

(a) Write the balanced chemical equation for this reaction.

(b) Calculate the oxidation number for P and O on both sides of the reaction, and identify the oxidizing and reducing agents.

5.72 The combustion of fossil fuels containing sulfur contributes to the phenomenon known as acid rain. The combustion process releases sulfur in the form of sulfur dioxide, which is converted to sulfuric acid in a process involving two reactions.

(a) In the first reaction, sulfur dioxide reacts with molecular oxygen to form sulfur trioxide. Write the balanced chemical equation for this reaction.

(b) In the second reaction, sulfur trioxide reacts with water in the atmosphere to form sulfuric acid. Write the balanced chemical equation for this reaction.

(c) Calculate the oxidation number for the S atom in each compound in these reactions.

5.73 The transition metals form compounds with oxygen in which the metals have different oxidation states. Calculate the oxidation number for the transition metal in the following sets of compounds:

(a) Mn in MnO_2, Mn_2O_3, and $KMnO_4$

(b) Cr in CrO_2, CrO_3, and Cr_2O_3.

5.74 In the Breathalyzer test, blood alcohol is determined by reaction of the alcohol with potassium dichromate:

$$16H^+(aq) + 2Cr_2O_7^{2-}(aq) + C_2H_5OH(aq) \longrightarrow$$
$$4Cr^{3+}(aq) + 2CO_2(g) + 11H_2O(l)$$

(a) Calculate the oxidation number of Cr in $Cr_2O_7^{2-}$.

(b) Calculate the oxidation number of C in C_2H_5OH and in CO_2.

(c) Identify the oxidizing agent and the reducing agent in this reaction.

5.75 Milk of magnesia is a suspension of magnesium hydroxide in water that is used to neutralize excess stomach acid. Write the balanced chemical equation for this neutralization reaction.

5.76 Iron in drinking water is removed by precipitation of the Fe^{3+} ion by reaction with NaOH to produce iron(III) hydroxide. Write the balanced chemical equation and the net ionic equation for this reaction.

5.77 Hard water contains magnesium and calcium ions (Mg^{2+}, Ca^{2+}), which can precipitate out in hot water pipes and water heaters as carbonates. Write the net ionic equation for this reaction.

5.78 Pepto-Bismol™, an antacid and antidiarrheal, contains bismuth subsalicylate, $C_7H_5BiO_4$. Some users of this product can experience a condition known as "black tongue," which is caused by the reaction of bismuth(III) ions with trace amounts of S^{2-} in saliva to form a black precipitate. Write the balanced net ionic equation for this precipitation reaction.

5.79 Iron is produced from iron ore by reaction with carbon monoxide:

$$Fe_2O_3(s) + CO(g) \longrightarrow Fe(s) + CO_2(g)$$

(a) Balance the chemical equation.

(b) Classify the reaction as a precipitation, neutralization, or redox reaction.

5.80 Balance the reaction for the synthesis of urea, commonly used as a fertilizer:

$$CO_2(g) + NH_3(g) \longrightarrow NH_2CONH_2(s) + H_2O(l)$$

5.81 Geologists identify carbonate minerals by reaction with acids. Dolomite, for example, contains magnesium carbonate, which reacts with hydrochloric acid by the following reaction:

$$MgCO_3(s) + HCl(aq) \longrightarrow MgCl_2(aq) + CO_2(g) + H_2O(l)$$

(a) Balance the reaction and write the net ionic equation.

(b) Classify the reaction as a precipitation, neutralization, or redox reaction.

5.82 Iodine, used as an antiseptic agent, can be prepared in the laboratory by the following reaction:

$$2NaI(s) + 2H_2SO_4(aq) + MnO_2(s) \longrightarrow$$
$$Na_2SO_4(aq) + MnSO_4(aq) + I_2(g) + 2H_2O(l)$$

(a) Determine the oxidation number for the Mn and I on both sides of the equation.

(b) Identify the oxidizing and reducing agents.

CHAPTER 6

Chemical Reactions: Mole and Mass Relationships

◀ The amount of CO_2 and H_2O produced by the fuel combustion of airplanes and automobiles can be calculated using mole ratios and mole-to-mass conversions.

1. **What is the mole, and why is it useful in chemistry?**
   THE GOAL: Be able to explain the meaning and uses of the mole and Avogadro's number.

2. **How are molar quantities and mass quantities related?**
   THE GOAL: Be able to convert between molar and mass quantities of an element or compound. (◀◀ A.)

3. **What are the limiting reagent, theoretical yield, and percent yield of a reaction?**
   THE GOAL: Be able to take the amount of product actually formed in a reaction, calculate the amount that could form theoretically, and express the results as a percent yield. (◀◀ A, B.)

A. Problem Solving: Unit Conversions and Estimating Answers
(Section 1.12)

B. Balancing Chemical Equations
(Section 5.2)

W hen chefs prepare to cook a rice pudding, they don't count out individual grains of rice, or individual raisins, or individual sugar crystals. Rather, they measure out appropriate amounts of the necessary ingredients using more convenient units—such as cups, or tablespoons. When chemists prepare chemical reactions, they use the same approach. In this chapter we introduce the concept of the mole and how chemists use it when studying the quantitative relationships between reactants and products.

6.1 The Mole and Avogadro's Number

In the previous chapter, we learned how to use the balanced chemical equation to indicate what is happening at the molecular level during a reaction. Now, let us imagine a laboratory experiment: the reaction of ethylene (C_2H_4) with hydrogen chloride (HCl) to prepare ethyl chloride (C_2H_5Cl), a colorless, low-boiling liquid used by doctors and athletic trainers as a spray-on anesthetic. The reaction is represented as

$$C_2H_4(g) + HCl(g) \rightarrow C_2H_5Cl(g)$$

In this reaction, 1 molecule of ethylene reacts with 1 molecule of hydrogen chloride to produce 1 molecule of ethyl chloride.

How, though, can you be sure you have a 1 to 1 ratio of reactant molecules in your reaction flask? Since it is impossible to hand-count the number of molecules correctly, you must weigh them instead. (This is a common method for dealing with all kinds of small objects: Nails, nuts, and grains of rice are all weighed rather than counted.) But the weighing approach leads to another problem. How many molecules are there in 1 gram of ethylene, hydrogen chloride, or any other substance? The answer depends on the identity of the substance, because different molecules have different masses.

To determine how many molecules of a given substance are in a certain mass, it is helpful to define a quantity called *molecular weight*. Just as the *atomic weight* of an element is the average mass of the element's *atoms*, the **molecular weight (MW)** of a molecule is the average mass of a substance's *molecules*. Numerically, a substance's molecular weight (or **formula weight** for an ionic compound) is equal to the sum of the atomic weights for all the atoms in the molecule or formula unit.

For example, the molecular weight of ethylene (C_2H_4) is 28.0 amu, the molecular weight of HCl is 36.5 amu, and the molecular weight of ethyl chloride (C_2H_5Cl) is 64.5 amu. (The actual values are known more precisely but are rounded off here for convenience.)

Molecular weight The sum of atomic weights of all atoms in a molecule.

◀◀ See Section 2.3 for discussion of atomic weight.

Formula weight The sum of atomic weights of all atoms in one formula unit of any compound, whether molecular or ionic.

For ethylene, C_2H_4:

Atomic weight of 2 C = 2 × 12.0 amu = 24.0 amu

Atomic weight of 4 H = 4 × 1.0 amu = 4.0 amu

MW of C_2H_4 = 28.0 amu

▲ These samples of sulfur, copper, mercury, and helium each contain 1 mol. Do they all have the same mass?

For hydrogen chloride, **HCl:**

$$\text{Atomic weight of H} = 1.0 \text{ amu}$$
$$\underline{\text{Atomic weight of Cl} = 35.5 \text{ amu}}$$
$$\text{MW of HCl} \qquad = 36.5 \text{ amu}$$

For ethyl chloride, **C₂H₅Cl:**

$$\text{Atomic weight of 2 C} = 2 \times 12.0 \text{ amu} = 24.0 \text{ amu}$$
$$\text{Atomic weight of 5 H} = 5 \times 1.0 \text{ amu} = 5.0 \text{ amu}$$
$$\underline{\text{Atomic weight of Cl} \qquad\qquad = 35.5 \text{ amu}}$$
$$\text{MW of C}_2\text{H}_5\text{Cl} \qquad\qquad = 64.5 \text{ amu}$$

How are molecular weights used? Since the mass ratio of 1 ethylene molecule to 1 HCl molecule is 28.0 to 36.5, the mass ratio of *any* given number of ethylene molecules to the same number of HCl molecules is also 28.0 to 36.5. In other words, a 28.0 to 36.5 *mass* ratio of ethylene and HCl always guarantees a 1 to 1 *number* ratio. *Samples of different substances always contain the same number of molecules or formula units whenever their mass ratio is the same as their molecular or formula weight ratio* (Figure 6.1).

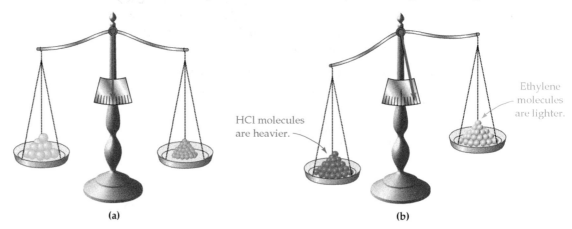

HCl molecules are heavier.

Ethylene molecules are lighter.

(a)　　　　　　　　　(b)

▲ **Figure 6.1**
(a) Because the yellow balls (left pan) are bigger than the green balls (right pan), you cannot get an equal number by taking equal weights. The same is true for atoms or molecules of different substances. (b) Equal numbers of ethylene and HCl molecules always have a mass ratio equal to the ratio of their molecular weights, 28.0 to 36.5.

A particularly convenient way to use this mass/number relationship for molecules is to measure amounts in grams that are numerically equal to molecular weights. If, for instance, you were to carry out your experiment with 28.0 g of ethylene and 36.5 g of HCl, you could be certain that you would have a 1 to 1 ratio of reactant molecules.

When referring to the vast numbers of molecules or formula units that take part in a visible chemical reaction, it is convenient to use a counting unit called a **mole**, abbreviated *mol*. One mole of any substance is the amount whose mass in grams—its **molar mass**—is numerically equal to its molecular or formula weight in amu. One mole of ethylene has a mass of 28.0 g, one mole of HCl has a mass of 36.5 g, and one mole of ethyl chloride has a mass of 64.5 g.

Just how many molecules are there in a mole? Think back to Chapter 2 where we learned to calculate the number of atoms in a sample of an element given its weight in grams, the atomic mass of the atom, and a gram/amu conversion factor. In Problem 2.2, you (hopefully!) found that a 1 gram sample of hydrogen (atomic mass 1 amu) and a 12 gram sample of carbon (atomic mass 12 amu) each contain 6.022×10^{23} atoms. One mole of any substance, therefore, contains 6.022×10^{23} formula units, a value called **Avogadro's number** (abbreviated N_A) after the Italian scientist who first recognized the importance of the mass/number relationship in molecules. Avogadro's

Mole The amount of a substance whose mass in grams is numerically equal to its molecular or formula weight.

Molar mass The mass in grams of 1 mole of a substance, numerically equal to molecular weight.

number of formula units of any substance—that is, one mole—has a mass in grams numerically equal to the molecular weight of the substance.

> **Avogadro's number (N_A)** The number of formula units in 1 mole of anything; 6.022×10^{23}.

$$1 \text{ mol HCl} = 6.022 \times 10^{23} \text{ HCl molecules} = 36.5 \text{ g HCl}$$

$$1 \text{ mol C}_2\text{H}_4 = 6.022 \times 10^{23} \text{ C}_2\text{H}_4 \text{ molecules} = 28.0 \text{ g C}_2\text{H}_4$$

$$1 \text{ mol C}_2\text{H}_5\text{Cl} = 6.022 \times 10^{23} \text{ C}_2\text{H}_5\text{Cl molecules} = 64.5 \text{ g C}_2\text{H}_5\text{Cl}$$

How big is Avogadro's number? Our minds cannot really conceive of the magnitude of a number like 6.022×10^{23}, but the following comparisons will give you a sense of the scale:

Amount of water in world's oceans (liters)   Age of earth in (seconds)

Population of earth

Avogadro's number: 602,200,000,000,000,000,000,000

Distance from earth to sun (centimeters)   Average college tuition (U.S. dollars)

Worked Example 6.1 Molar Mass and Avogadro's Number: Number of Molecules

Pseudoephedrine hydrochloride ($C_{10}H_{16}ClNO$) is a nasal decongestant commonly found in cold medication. (a) What is the molar mass of pseudoephedrine hydrochloride? (b) How many molecules of pseudoephedrine hydrochloride are in a tablet that contains 30.0 mg of this decongestant?

ANALYSIS We are given a mass and need to convert to a number of molecules. This is most easily accomplished by using the molar mass of pseudoephedrine hydrochloride calculated in part (a) as the conversion factor from mass to moles and realizing that this mass (in grams) contains Avogadro's number of molecules (6.022×10^{23}).

BALLPARK ESTIMATE The formula for pseudoephedrine contains 10 carbon atoms (each one of atomic weight 12.0 amu), so the molecular weight is greater than 120 amu, probably near 200 amu. Thus, the molecular weight should be near 200 g/mol. The mass of 30 mg of pseudoepinephrine HCl is less than the mass of 1 mol of this compound by a factor of roughly 10^4 (0.03 g versus 200 g), which means that the number of molecules should also be smaller by a factor of 10^4 (on the order of 10^{19} in the tablet versus 10^{23} in 1 mol).

SOLUTION

(a) The molecular weight of pseudoephedrine is found by summing the atomic weights of all atoms in the molecule:

Atomic Weight of 10 atoms of C:	10×12.011 amu =	120.11 amu
16 atoms of H:	16×1.00794 amu =	16.127 amu
1 atom of Cl:	1×35.4527 amu =	35.4527 amu
1 atom of N:	1×14.0067 amu =	14.0067 amu
1 atom of O:	1×15.9994 amu =	15.9994 amu
MW of $C_{10}H_{16}ClNO$		= 201.6958 amu $\longrightarrow$ 201.70 g/mol

Remember that atomic mass in amu converts directly to molar mass in g/mol. Also, following the rules for significant figures from Sections 1.9 and 1.11, our final answer is rounded to the second decimal place.

(b) Since this problem involves unit conversions, we can use the step-wise solution introduced in Chapter 1.

STEP 1: **Identify known information.** We are given the mass of pseudoephedrine hydrochloride (in mg).	30.0 mg pseudoephedrine hydrochloride
STEP 2: **Identify answer and units.** We are looking for the number of molecules of pseudoephedrine hydrochloride in a 30 mg tablet.	?? = molecules
STEP 3: **Identify conversion factors.** Since the molecular weight of pseudoephedrine hydrochloride is 201.70 amu, 201.70 g contains 6.022×10^{23} molecules. We can use this ratio as a conversion factor to convert from mass to molecules. We will also need to convert 30 mg to g.	$\dfrac{6.022 \times 10^{23} \text{ molecules}}{201.70 \text{ g}}$ $\dfrac{.001 \text{ g}}{1 \text{ mg}}$

| STEP 4: **Solve.** Set up an equation so that unwanted units cancel. | $(30.0 \text{ mg pseudoephedrine hydrochloride}) \times \left(\dfrac{.001 \text{ g}}{1 \text{ mg}}\right) \times \left(\dfrac{6.022 \times 10^{23} \text{ molecules}}{201.70 \text{ g}}\right)$ $= 8.96 \times 10^{19}$ molecules of pseudoephedrine hydrochloride |

BALLPARK CHECK Our estimate for the number of molecules was on the order of 10^{19}, which is consistent with the calculated answer.

Worked Example 6.2 Avogadro's Number: Atom to Mass Conversions

A tiny pencil mark just visible to the naked eye contains about 3×10^{17} atoms of carbon. What is the mass of this pencil mark in grams?

ANALYSIS We are given a number of atoms and need to convert to mass. The conversion factor can be obtained by realizing that the atomic weight of carbon in grams contains Avogadro's number of atoms (6.022×10^{23}).

BALLPARK ESTIMATE Since we are given a number of atoms that is six orders of magnitude less than Avogadro's number, we should get a corresponding mass that is six orders of magnitude less than the molar mass of carbon, which means a mass for the pencil mark of about 10^{-6} g.

SOLUTION

STEP 1: **Identify known information.** We know the number of carbon atoms in the pencil mark.	3×10^{17} atoms of carbon
STEP 2: **Identify answer and units.**	Mass of carbon $= \text{?? g}$
STEP 3: **Identify conversion factors.** The atomic weight of carbon is 12.01 amu, so 12.01 g of carbon contains 6.022×10^{23} atoms.	$\dfrac{12.01 \text{ g carbon}}{6.022 \times 10^{23} \text{ atoms}}$
STEP 4: **Solve.** Set up an equation using the conversion factors so that unwanted units cancel.	$(3 \times 10^{17} \text{ atoms})\left(\dfrac{12.01 \text{ g carbon}}{6.022 \times 10^{23} \text{ atoms}}\right) = 6 \times 10^{-6}$ g carbon

BALLPARK CHECK The answer is of the same magnitude as our estimate and makes physical sense.

PROBLEM 6.1
Calculate the molecular weight of the following substances:
(a) Ibuprofen, $C_{13}H_{18}O_2$ (b) Phenobarbital, $C_{12}H_{12}N_2O_3$

PROBLEM 6.2
How many molecules of ascorbic acid (vitamin C, $C_6H_8O_6$) are in a 500 mg tablet?

PROBLEM 6.3
What is the mass in grams of 5.0×10^{20} molecules of aspirin ($C_9H_8O_4$)?

KEY CONCEPT PROBLEM 6.4

What is the molecular weight of cytosine, a component of DNA (deoxyribonucleic acid)? (black = C, blue = N, red = O, white = H.)

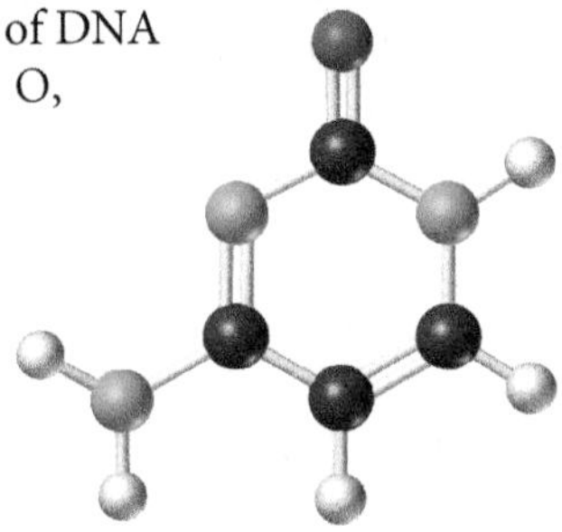

Cytosine

6.2 Gram–Mole Conversions

To ensure that we have the correct molecule to molecule (or mole to mole) relationship between reactants as specified by the balanced chemical equation, we can take advantage of the constant mass ratio between reactants. The mass in grams of 1 mol of any substance (that is, Avogadro's number of molecules or formula units) is called the molar mass of the substance.

Molar mass = Mass of 1 mol of substance

= Mass of 6.022×10^{23} molecules (formula units) of substance

= Molecular (formula) weight of substance in grams

In effect, molar mass serves as a conversion factor between numbers of moles and mass. If you know how many moles you have, you can calculate their mass; if you know the mass of a sample, you can calculate the number of moles. Suppose, for example, we need to know how much 0.25 mol of water weighs. The molecular weight of H_2O is $(2 \times 1.0 \text{ amu}) + 16.0 \text{ amu} = 18.0 \text{ amu}$, so the molar mass of water is 18.0 g/mol. Thus, the conversion factor between moles of water and mass of water is 18.0 g/mol:

$$\boxed{\text{Molar mass used as conversion factor}}$$

$$0.25 \text{ mol } H_2O \times \frac{18.0 \text{ g } H_2O}{1 \text{ mol } H_2O} = 4.5 \text{ g } H_2O$$

Alternatively, suppose we need to know how many moles of water are in 27 g of water. The conversion factor is 1 mol/18.0 g:

$$\boxed{\text{Molar mass used as conversion factor}}$$

$$27 \text{ g } H_2O \times \frac{1 \text{ mol } H_2O}{18.0 \text{ g } H_2O} = 1.5 \text{ mol } H_2O$$

Note that the 1 mol in the numerator is an exact number, so the number of significant figures in the final answer is based on the 27 g H_2O (2 sig figs.). Worked Examples 6.3 and 6.4 give more practice in gram–mole conversions.

Worked Example 6.3 Molar Mass: Mole to Gram Conversion

The nonprescription pain relievers Advil and Nuprin contain ibuprofen $(C_{13}H_{18}O_2)$, whose molecular weight is 206.3 amu (Problem 6.1a). If all the tablets in a bottle of pain reliever together contain 0.082 mol of ibuprofen, what is the number of grams of ibuprofen in the bottle?

ANALYSIS We are given a number of moles and asked to find the mass. Molar mass is the conversion factor between the two.

BALLPARK ESTIMATE Since 1 mol of ibuprofen has a mass of about 200 g, 0.08 mol has a mass of about $0.08 \times 200 \text{ g} = 16 \text{ g}$.

SOLUTION

STEP 1: **Identify known information.**	0.082 mol ibuprofen in bottle
STEP 2: **Identify answer and units.**	mass ibuprofen in bottle = ?? g
STEP 3: **Identify conversion factor.** We use the molecular weight of ibuprofen to convert from moles to grams.	1 mol ibuprofen = 206.3 g $\dfrac{206.3 \text{ g ibuprofen}}{1 \text{ mol ibuprofen}}$
STEP 4: **Solve.** Set up an equation using the known information and conversion factor so that unwanted units cancel.	$0.082 \text{ mol } C_{13}H_{18}O_2 \times \dfrac{206.3 \text{ g ibuprofen}}{1 \text{ mol ibuprofen}} = 17 \text{ g } C_{13}H_{18}O_2$

BALLPARK CHECK The calculated answer is consistent with our estimate of 16 g.

CHEMISTRY IN ACTION

Did Ben Franklin Have Avogadro's Number? A Ballpark Calculation

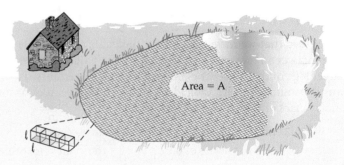
Area = A

"At" length being at Clapham, where there is on the common a large pond . . . I fetched out a cruet of oil and dropped a little of it on the water. I saw it spread itself with surprising swiftness upon the surface. The oil, though not more than a teaspoonful, produced an instant calm over a space several yards square which spread amazingly and extended itself gradually . . . making all that quarter of the pond, perhaps half an acre, as smooth as a looking glass. *Excerpt from a letter of Benjamin Franklin to William Brownrigg, 1773.*

▲ **What did these two have in common? [Benjamin Franklin (left), Amedeo Avogadro (right)]**

Benjamin Franklin, author and renowned statesman, was also an inventor and a scientist. Every school-child knows of Franklin's experiment with a kite and a key, demonstrating that lightning is electricity. Less well known is that his measurement of the extent to which oil spreads on water makes possible a simple estimate of molecular size and Avogadro's number.

The calculation goes like this: Avogadro's number is the number of molecules in 1 mole of any substance. So, if we can estimate both the number of molecules and the number of moles in Franklin's teaspoon of oil, we can calculate Avogadro's number. Let us start by calculating the number of molecules in the oil.

1. The volume (V) of oil Franklin used was 1 tsp = 4.9 cm^3, and the area (A) covered by the oil was 1/2 acre = $2.0 \times 10^7 \text{ cm}^2$. We will assume that the oil molecules are tiny cubes that pack closely together and form a layer only one molecule thick. As shown in the accompanying figure, the volume of the oil is equal to the surface area of the layer times the

length (l) of the side of one molecule: $V = A \times l$. Rearranging this equation to find the length then gives us an estimate of molecular size:

$$l = \frac{V}{A} = \frac{4.9 \text{ cm}^3}{2.0 \times 10^7 \text{ cm}^2} = 2.5 \times 10^{-7} \text{ cm}$$

2. The area of the oil layer is the area of the side of one molecule (l^2) times the number of molecules (N) of oil: $A = l^2 \times N$. Rearranging this equation gives us the number of molecules:

$$N = \frac{A}{l^2} = \frac{2 \times 10^7 \text{ cm}^2}{(2.5 \times 10^{-7} \text{ cm})^2} = 3.2 \times 10^{20} \text{ molecules}$$

3. To calculate the number of moles, we first need to know the mass (M) of the oil. This could have been determined by weighing the oil, but Franklin neglected to do so. Let us therefore estimate the mass by multiplying the volume (V) of the oil by the density (D) of a typical oil, 0.95 g/cm^3. (Since oil floats on water, it is not surprising that the density of oil is a bit less than the density of water, which is 1.00 g/cm^3.)

$$M = V \times D = 4.9 \text{ cm}^3 \times 0.95 \frac{\text{g}}{\text{cm}^3} = 4.7 \text{ g}$$

4. We now have to make one final assumption about the molecular weight of the oil before we complete the calculation. Assuming that a typical oil has MW = 200 amu, then the mass of 1 mol of oil is 200 g. Dividing the mass of the oil (M) by the mass of 1 mol gives the number of moles of oil:

$$\text{Moles of oil} = \frac{4.7 \text{ g}}{200 \text{ g/mol}} = 0.024 \text{ mol}$$

5. Finally, the number of molecules per mole—Avogadro's number—can be obtained by dividing the estimated number of molecules (step 2) by the estimated moles (step 4):

$$\text{Avogadro's number} = \frac{3.2 \times 10^{20} \text{ molecules}}{0.024 \text{ mol}} = 1.3 \times 10^{22}$$

The calculation is not very accurate, of course, but Ben was not really intending for us to calculate Avogadro's number when he made a rough estimate of how much his oil spread out. Nevertheless, the result is not too bad for such a simple experiment.

See Chemistry in Action Problem 6.58 at the end of the chapter.

Worked Example 6.4 Molar Mass: Gram to Mole Conversion

The maximum dose of sodium hydrogen phosphate (Na_2HPO_4, MW = 142.0 molar mass) that should be taken in one day for use as a laxative is 3.8 g. How many moles of sodium hydrogen phosphate, how many moles of Na^+ ions, and how many total moles of ions are in this dose?

ANALYSIS Molar mass is the conversion factor between mass and number of moles. The chemical formula Na_2HPO_4 shows that each formula unit contains 2 Na^+ ions and 1 HPO_4^{2-} ion.

BALLPARK ESTIMATE The maximum dose is about two orders of magnitude smaller than the molecular weight (approximately 4 g compared to 142 g). Thus, the number of moles of sodium hydrogen phosphate in 3.8 g should be about two orders of magnitude less than one mole. The number of moles of Na_2HPO_4 and total moles of ions, then, should be on the order of 10^{-2}.

SOLUTION

STEP 1: **Identify known information.** We are given the mass and molecular weight of Na_2HPO_4.	3.8 g Na_2HPO_4; MW = 142.0 amu
STEP 2: **Identify answer and units.** We need to find the number of moles of Na_2HPO_4, and the total number of moles of ions.	Moles of Na_2HPO_4 = ?? mol Moles of Na^+ ions = ?? mol Total moles of ions = ?? mol
STEP 3: **Identify conversion factor.** We can use the molecular weight of Na_2HPO_4 to convert from grams to moles.	$\dfrac{1 \text{ mol } Na_2HPO_4}{142.0 \text{ g } Na_2HPO_4}$
STEP 4: **Solve.** We use the known information and conversion factor to obtain moles of Na_2HPO_4; since 1 mol of Na_2HPO_4 contains 2 mol of Na^+ ions and 1 mol of HPO_4^{2-} ions, we multiply these values by the number of moles in the sample.	$3.8 \text{ g } Na_2HPO_4 \times \dfrac{1 \text{ mol } Na_2HPO_4}{142.0 \text{ g } Na_2HPO_4} = 0.027 \text{ mol } Na_2HPO_4$ $\dfrac{2 \text{ mol } Na^+}{1 \text{ mol } Na_2HPO_4} \times 0.027 \text{ mol } Na_2HPO_4 = 0.054 \text{ mol } Na^+$ $\dfrac{3 \text{ mol ions}}{1 \text{ mol } Na_2HPO_4} \times 0.027 \text{ mol } Na_2HPO_4 = 0.081 \text{ mol ions}$

BALLPARK CHECK: The calculated answers (0.027 mol Na_2HPO_4, 0.081 mol ions) are on the order of 10^{-2}, consistent with our estimate.

PROBLEM 6.5
How many moles of ethyl alcohol, C_2H_6O, are in a 10.0 g sample? How many grams are in a 0.10 mol sample of ethyl alcohol?

PROBLEM 6.6
Which weighs more, 5.00 g or 0.0225 mol of acetaminophen ($C_8H_9NO_2$)?

PROBLEM 6.7
How would our estimate of Avogadro's number be affected if we were to assume that Benjamin Franklin's oil molecules were spherical rather than cubes (see Chemistry in Action on p. 164)? If the density of the oil was 0.90 g/mL? If the molar mass was 150 g/mol rather than 200 g/mol?

6.3 Mole Relationships and Chemical Equations

In a typical recipe, the amounts of ingredients needed are specified using a variety of units: the amount of flour, for example, is usually specified in cups, whereas the amount of salt or vanilla flavoring might be indicated in teaspoons. In chemical reactions, the appropriate unit to specify the relationship between reactants and products is the mole.

The coefficients in a balanced chemical equation tell how many *molecules*, and thus, how many *moles*, of each reactant are needed and how many molecules, and thus, moles, of each product are formed. You can then use molar mass to calculate reactant and product masses. If, for example, you saw the following balanced equation for the industrial synthesis of ammonia, you would know that 3 mol of H_2 (3 mol $\times$ 2.0 g/mol = 6.0 g) are required for reaction with 1 mol of N_2 (28.0 g) to yield 2 mol of NH_3 (2 mol $\times$ 17.0 g/mol = 34.0 g).

This number of moles of hydrogen... ...reacts with this number of moles of nitrogen... to yield this number of moles of ammonia.

$$3\,H_2 \ + \ 1\,N_2 \ \longrightarrow \ 2\,NH_3$$

The coefficients can be put in the form of *mole ratios*, which act as conversion factors when setting up factor-label calculations. In the ammonia synthesis, for example, the mole ratio of H_2 to N_2 is 3:1, the mole ratio of H_2 to NH_3 is 3:2, and the mole ratio of N_2 to NH_3 is 1:2:

$$\frac{3\text{ mol }H_2}{1\text{ mol }N_2} \qquad \frac{3\text{ mol }H_2}{2\text{ mol }NH_3} \qquad \frac{1\text{ mol }N_2}{2\text{ mol }NH_3}$$

Worked Example 6.5 shows how to set up and use mole ratios.

Worked Example 6.5 Balanced Chemical Equations: Mole Ratios

Rusting involves the reaction of iron with oxygen to form iron(III) oxide, Fe_2O_3:

$$4\,Fe(s) \ + \ 3\,O_2(g) \ \longrightarrow \ 2\,Fe_2O_3(s)$$

(a) What are the mole ratios of the product to each reactant and of the reactants to each other?

(b) How many moles of iron(III) oxide are formed by the complete oxidation of 6.2 mol of iron?

ANALYSIS AND SOLUTION

(a) The coefficients of a balanced equation represent the mole ratios:

$$\frac{2\text{ mol }Fe_2O_3}{4\text{ mol }Fe} \qquad \frac{2\text{ mol }Fe_2O_3}{3\text{ mol }O_2} \qquad \frac{4\text{ mol }Fe}{3\text{ mol }O_2}$$

(b) To find how many moles of Fe_2O_3 are formed, write down the known information—6.2 mol of iron—and select the mole ratio that allows the quantities to cancel, leaving the desired quantity:

$$6.2\text{ mol Fe} \times \frac{2\text{ mol }Fe_2O_3}{4\text{ mol Fe}} = 3.1\text{ mol }Fe_2O_3$$

Note that mole ratios are exact numbers and therefore do not limit the number of significant figures in the result of a calculation.

PROBLEM 6.8

(a) Balance the following equation, and tell how many moles of nickel will react with 9.81 mol of hydrochloric acid.

$$Ni(s) \ + \ HCl(aq) \ \longrightarrow \ NiCl_2(aq) \ + \ H_2(g)$$

(b) How many moles of $NiCl_2$ can be formed in the reaction of 6.00 mol of Ni and 12.0 mol of HCl?

PROBLEM 6.9

Plants convert carbon dioxide and water to glucose $(C_6H_{12}O_6)$ and oxygen in the process of photosynthesis. Write a balanced equation for this reaction, and determine how many moles of CO_2 are required to produce 15.0 mol of glucose.

6.4 Mass Relationships and Chemical Equations

It is important to remember that the coefficients in a balanced chemical equation represent molecule to molecule (or mole to mole) relationships between reactants and products. Mole ratios make it possible to calculate the molar amounts of reactants and products, but actual amounts of substances used in the laboratory are weighed out in grams. Regardless of what units we use to specify the amount of reactants and/or products (mass, volume, number of molecules, and so on), the reaction always takes place on a mole to mole basis. Thus, we need to be able to carry out three kinds of conversions when doing chemical arithmetic:

- **Mole to mole conversions** are carried out using *mole ratios* as conversion factors. Worked Example 6.5 at the end of the preceding section is an example of this kind of calculation.

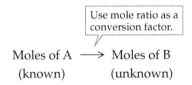

- **Mole to mass and mass to mole conversions** are carried out using *molar mass* as a conversion factor. Worked Examples 6.3 and 6.4 at the end of Section 6.2 are examples of this kind of calculation.

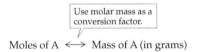

- **Mass to mass conversions** are frequently needed but cannot be carried out directly. If you know the mass of substance A and need to find the mass of substance B, you must first convert the mass of A into moles of A, then carry out a mole to mole conversion to find moles of B, and then convert moles of B into the mass of B (Figure 6.2).

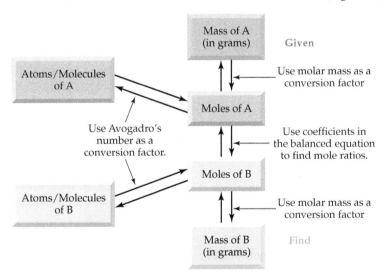

◄ **Figure 6.2**

A summary of conversions between moles, grams, and number of atoms or molecules for substances in a chemical reaction.
The numbers of moles tell how many molecules of each substance are needed, as given by the coefficients in the balanced equation; the numbers of grams tell what mass of each substance is needed.

Overall, there are four steps for determining mass relationships among reactants and products:

STEP 1: Write the balanced chemical equation.

STEP 2: Choose molar masses and mole ratios to convert the known information into the needed information.

STEP 3: Set up the factor-label expressions.

STEP 4: Calculate the answer and check the answer against the ballpark estimate you made before you began your calculations.

Worked Example 6.6 Mole Ratios: Mole to Mass Conversions

In the atmosphere, nitrogen dioxide reacts with water to produce NO and nitric acid, which contributes to pollution by acid rain:

$$3\,NO_2(g) + H_2O(l) \longrightarrow 2\,HNO_3(aq) + NO(g)$$

How many grams of HNO_3 are produced for every 1.0 mol of NO_2 that reacts? The molecular weight of HNO_3 is 63.0 amu.

ANALYSIS We are given the number of moles of a reactant and are asked to find the mass of a product. Problems of this sort always require working in moles and then converting to mass, as outlined in Figure 6.2.

BALLPARK ESTIMATE The molar mass of nitric acid is approximately 60 g/mol, and the coefficients in the balanced equation say that 2 mol of HNO_3 are formed for each 3 mol of NO_2 that undergo reaction. Thus, 1 mol of NO_2 should give about 2/3 mol HNO_3, or 2/3 mol $\times$ 60 g/mol = 40 g.

SOLUTION

STEP 1: **Write balanced equation.**

STEP 2: **Identify conversion factors.** We need a mole to mole conversion to find the number of moles of product, and then a mole to mass conversion to find the mass of product. For the first conversion we use the mole ratio of HNO_3 to NO_2 as a conversion factor, and for the mole to mass calculation, we use the molar mass of HNO_3 (63.0 g/mol) as a conversion factor.

STEP 3: **Set up factor labels.** Identify appropriate mole ratio factor labels to convert moles NO_2 to moles HNO_3, and moles HNO_3 to grams.

STEP 4: **Solve.**

$$3\,NO_2(g) + H_2O(l) \longrightarrow 2\,HNO_3(aq) + NO(g)$$

$$\frac{2\ \text{mol}\ HNO_3}{3\ \text{mol}\ NO_2}$$

$$\frac{63.0\ \text{g}\ HNO_3}{1\ \text{mol}\ HNO_3}$$

$$1.0\ \text{mol}\ NO_2 \times \frac{2\ \text{mol}\ HNO_3}{3\ \text{mol}\ NO_2} \times \frac{63.0\ \text{g}\ HNO_3}{1\ \text{mol}\ HNO_3} = 42\ \text{g}\ HNO_3$$

BALLPARK CHECK Our estimate was 40 g!

Worked Example 6.7 Mole Ratios: Mass to Mole/Mole to Mass Conversions

The following reaction produced 0.022 g of calcium oxalate (CaC_2O_4). What mass of calcium chloride was used as reactant? (The molar mass of CaC_2O_4 is 128.1 g/mol, and the molar mass of $CaCl_2$ is 111.0 g/mol.)

$$CaCl_2(aq) + Na_2C_2O_4(aq) \longrightarrow CaC_2O_4(s) + 2\,NaCl(aq)$$

ANALYSIS Both the known information and that to be found are masses, so this is a mass to mass conversion problem. The mass of CaC_2O_4 is first converted into moles, a mole ratio is used to find moles of $CaCl_2$, and the number of moles of $CaCl_2$ is converted into mass.

BALLPARK ESTIMATE The balanced equation says that 1 mol of CaC_2O_4 is formed for each mole of $CaCl_2$ that reacts. Because the formula weights of the two substances are similar, it should take about 0.02 g of $CaCl_2$ to form 0.02 g of CaC_2O_4.

SOLUTION

STEP 1: **Write the balanced equation.**

STEP 2: **Identify conversion factors.** Convert the mass of CaC_2O_4 into moles, use a mole ratio to find moles of $CaCl_2$, and convert the number of moles of $CaCl_2$ to mass. We will need three conversion factors.

STEP 3: **Set up factor-labels.** We will need to perform gram to mole and mole to mole conversions to get from grams CaC_2O_4 to grams $CaCl_2$.

STEP 4: **Solve.**

$$CaCl_2(aq) + Na_2C_2O_4(aq) \longrightarrow CaC_2O_4(s) + 2\,NaCl(aq)$$

mass CaC_2O_4 to moles: $\dfrac{1\ \text{mol}\ CaC_2O_4}{128.1\ \text{g}}$

moles CaC_2O_4 to moles $CaCl_2$: $\dfrac{1\ \text{mol}\ CaCl_2}{1\ \text{mol}\ CaC_2O_4}$

moles $CaCl_2$ to mass: $\dfrac{111.0\ \text{g}\ CaCl_2}{1\ \text{mol}\ CaCl_2}$

$$0.022\ \text{g}\ CaC_2O_4 \times \frac{1\ \text{mol}\ CaC_2O_4}{128.1\ \text{g}\ CaC_2O_4} \times$$

$$\frac{1\ \text{mol}\ CaCl_2}{1\ \text{mol}\ CaC_2O_4} \times \frac{111.0\ \text{g}\ CaCl_2}{1\ \text{mol}\ CaCl_2} = 0.019\ \text{g}\ CaCl_2$$

BALLPARK CHECK The calculated answer (0.019 g) is consistent with our estimate (0.02 g).

PROBLEM 6.10

Hydrogen fluoride is one of the few substances that react with glass (which is made of silicon dioxide, SiO_2).

$$4 HF(g) + SiO_2(s) \longrightarrow SiF_4(g) + 2 H_2O(l)$$

(a) How many moles of HF will react completely with 9.90 mol of SiO_2?

(b) What mass of water (in grams) is produced by the reaction of 23.0 g of SiO_2?

PROBLEM 6.11

The tungsten metal used for filaments in light bulbs is made by reaction of tungsten trioxide with hydrogen:

$$WO_3(s) + 3 H_2(g) \longrightarrow W(s) + 3 H_2O(g)$$

How many grams of tungsten trioxide, and how many grams of hydrogen must you start with to prepare 5.00 g of tungsten? (For WO_3, MW = 231.8 amu.)

6.5 Limiting Reagent and Percent Yield

All the calculations we have done in the last several sections have assumed that 100% of the reactants are converted to products. Only rarely is this the case in practice, though. Let us return to the recipe for s'mores presented in the previous chapter:

2 Graham crackers + 1 Roasted marshmallow + $\frac{1}{4}$ Chocolate bar $\longrightarrow$ 1 S'more

When you check your supplies, you find that you have 20 graham crackers, 8 marshmallows, and 3 chocolate bars. How many s'mores can you make? (Answer = 8!) You have enough graham crackers and chocolate bars to make more, but you will run out of marshmallows after you have made eight s'mores. In a similar way, when running a chemical reaction we don't always have the exact amounts of reagents to allow all of them to react completely. The reactant that is exhausted first in such a reaction is called the **limiting reagent**. The amount of product you obtain if the limiting reagent is completely consumed is called the **theoretical yield** of the reaction.

Suppose that, while you are making s'mores, one of your eight marshmallows gets burned to a crisp. If this happens, the actual number of s'mores produced will be less than what you predicted based on the amount of starting materials. Similarly, chemical reactions do not always yield the exact amount of product predicted by the initial amount of reactants. More frequently, a majority of the reactant molecules behave as written, but other processes, called *side reactions*, also occur. In addition, some of the product may be lost in handling. As a result, the amount of product actually formed—the reaction's **actual yield**—is somewhat less than the theoretical yield. The amount of product actually obtained in a reaction is usually expressed as a **percent yield**:

$$Percent\ yield = \frac{Actual\ yield}{Theoretical\ yield} \times 100\%$$

A reaction's actual yield is found by weighing the amount of product obtained. The theoretical yield is found by using the amount of limiting reagent in a mass to mass calculation like those illustrated in the preceding section (see Worked Example 6.7). Worked Examples 6.8–6.10 involve limiting reagent, percent yield, actual yield, and theoretical yield calculations.

Limiting reagent The reactant that runs out first in any given reaction.

Theoretical yield The amount of product formed, assuming complete reaction of the limiting reagent.

Actual yield The amount of product actually formed in a reaction.

Percent yield The percent of the theoretical yield actually obtained from a chemical reaction.

Worked Example 6.8 Percent Yield

The combustion of acetylene gas (C_2H_2) produces carbon dioxide and water, as indicated in the following reaction:

$$2\,C_2H_2(g)\ +\ 5\,O_2(g)\ \longrightarrow\ 4\,CO_2(g)\ +\ 2\,H_2O(g)$$

When 26.0 g of acetylene is burned in sufficient oxygen for complete reaction, the theoretical yield of CO_2 is 88.0 g. Calculate the percent yield for this reaction if the actual yield is only 72.4 g CO_2.

ANALYSIS The percent yield is calculated by dividing the actual yield by the theoretical yield and multiplying by 100.

BALLPARK ESTIMATE The theoretical yield (88.0 g) is close to 100 g. The actual yield (72.4 g) is about 15 g less than the theoretical yield. The actual yield is thus about 15% less than the theoretical yield, so the percent yield is about 85%.

SOLUTION

$$\text{Percent yield} = \frac{\text{Actual yield}}{\text{Theoretical yield}} \times 100 = \frac{72.4\text{ g } CO_2}{88.0\text{ g } CO_2} \times 100 = 82.3\%$$

BALLPARK CHECK The calculated percent yield agrees very well with our estimate of 85%.

Worked Example 6.9 Mass to Mole Conversions: Limiting Reagent and Theoretical Yield

The element boron is produced commercially by the reaction of boric oxide with magnesium at high temperature:

$$B_2O_3(l)\ +\ 3\,Mg(s)\ \longrightarrow\ 2\,B(s)\ +\ 3\,MgO(s)$$

What is the theoretical yield of boron when 2350 g of boric oxide is reacted with 3580 g of magnesium? The molar masses of boric oxide and magnesium are 69.6 g/mol and 24.3 g/mol, respectively.

ANALYSIS To calculate theoretical yield, we first have to identify the limiting reagent. The theoretical yield in grams is then calculated from the amount of limiting reagent used in the reaction. The calculation involves the mass to mole and mole to mass conversions discussed in the preceding section.

SOLUTION

STEP 1: **Identify known information.** We have the masses and molar masses of the reagents.

2350 g B_2O_3, molar mass 69.6 g/mol
3580 g Mg, molar mass 24.3 g/mol

STEP 2: **Identify answer and units.** We are solving for the theoretical yield of boron.

Theoretical mass of B = ?? g

STEP 3: **Identify conversion factors.** We can use the molar masses to convert from masses to moles of reactants (B_2O_3, Mg). From moles of reactants, we can use mole ratios from the balanced chemical equation to find the number of moles of B produced, assuming complete conversion of a given reactant. B_2O_3 is the limiting reagent, since complete conversion of this reagent yields less product (67.6 mol B formed) than does complete conversion of Mg (98.0 mol B formed).

$$(2350\text{ g } B_2O_3) \times \frac{1\text{ mol } B_2O_3}{69.6\text{ g } B_2O_3} = 33.8\text{ mol } B_2O_3$$

$$(3580\text{ g } Mg) \times \frac{1\text{ mol } Mg}{24.3\text{ g } Mg} = 147\text{ mol } Mg$$

$$33.8\text{ mol } B_2O_3 \times \frac{2\text{ mol } B}{1\text{ mol } B_2O_3} = 67.6\text{ mol } B^*$$

$$147\text{ mol } Mg \times \frac{2\text{ mol } B}{3\text{ mol } Mg} = 98.0\text{ mol } B$$

($^*B_2O_3$ is the limiting reagent because it yields fewer moles of B!)

STEP 4: **Solve.** Once the limiting reagent has been identified (B_2O_3), the theoretical amount of B that should be formed can be calculated using a mole to mass conversion.

$$67.6\text{ mol } B \times \frac{10.8\text{ g } B}{1\text{ mol } B} = 730\text{ g } B$$

Worked Example **6.10** Mass to Mole Conversion: Percent Yield

The reaction of ethylene with water to give ethyl alcohol (CH_3CH_2OH) occurs with 78.5% actual yield. How many grams of ethyl alcohol are formed by reaction of 25.0 g of ethylene? (For ethylene, MW = 28.0 amu; for ethyl alcohol, MW = 46.0 amu.)

$$H_2C=CH_2 + H_2O \longrightarrow CH_3CH_2OH$$

ANALYSIS Treat this as a typical mass relationship problem to find the amount of ethyl alcohol that can theoretically be formed from 25.0 g of ethylene, and then multiply the answer by 0.785 (the fraction of the theoretical yield actually obtained) to find the amount actually formed.

BALLPARK ESTIMATE The 25.0 g of ethylene is a bit less than 1 mol; since the percent yield is about 78%, a bit less than 0.78 mol of ethyl alcohol will form—perhaps about 3/4 mol, or $3/4 \times 46$ g = 34 g.

SOLUTION
The theoretical yield of ethyl alcohol is:

$$25.0 \text{ g ethylene} \times \frac{1 \text{ mol ethylene}}{28.0 \text{ g ethylene}} \times \frac{1 \text{ mol ethyl alc.}}{1 \text{ mol ethylene}} \times \frac{46.0 \text{ g ethyl alc.}}{1 \text{ mol ethyl alc.}}$$

$$= 41.1 \text{ g ethyl alcohol}$$

and so the actual yield is:

$$41.1 \text{ g ethyl alc.} \times 0.785 = 32.3 \text{ g ethyl alcohol}$$

BALLPARK CHECK The calculated result (32.3 g) is close to our estimate (34 g).

PROBLEM 6.12
What is the theoretical yield of ethyl chloride in the reaction of 19.4 g of ethylene with 50 g of hydrogen chloride? What is the percent yield if 25.5 g of ethyl chloride is actually formed? (For ethylene, MW = 28.0 amu; for hydrogen chloride, MW = 36.5 amu; for ethyl chloride, MW = 64.5 amu.)

$$H_2C=CH_2 + HCl \longrightarrow CH_3CH_2Cl$$

PROBLEM 6.13
The reaction of ethylene oxide with water to give ethylene glycol (automobile antifreeze) occurs in 96.0% actual yield. How many grams of ethylene glycol are formed by reaction of 35.0 g of ethylene oxide? (For ethylene oxide, MW = 44.0 amu; for ethylene glycol, MW = 62.0 amu.)

$$\underset{\text{Ethylene oxide}}{H_2C-CH_2} + H_2O \longrightarrow \underset{\text{Ethylene glycol}}{HOCH_2CH_2OH}$$

PROBLEM 6.14
The recommended daily intake of iron is 8 mg for adult men and 18 mg for premenopausal women (see Chemistry in Action on p. 172). Convert these masses of iron into moles.

Identify the limiting reagent in the reaction mixture shown below. The balanced reaction is:

$$A_2 + 2B_2 \longrightarrow 2AB_2$$

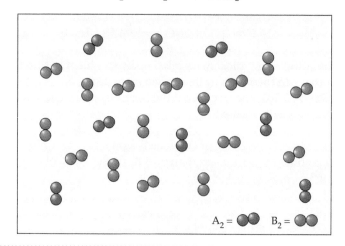

$A_2 =$ ⬤⬤ $B_2 =$ ⬤⬤

CHEMISTRY IN ACTION

Anemia – A Limiting Reagent Problem?

Anemia is the most commonly diagnosed blood disorder, with symptoms typically including lethargy, fatigue, poor concentration, and sensitivity to cold. Although anemia has many causes, including genetic factors, the most common cause is insufficient dietary intake or absorption of iron.

Hemoglobin (abbreviated Hb), the iron-containing protein found in red blood cells, is responsible for oxygen transport throughout the body. Low iron levels in the body result in decreased production and incorporation of Hb into red blood cells. In addition, blood loss due to injury or to menstruation in women increases the body's demand for iron in order to replace lost Hb. In the United States, nearly 20% of women of childbearing age suffer from iron-deficiency anemia compared to only 2% of adult men.

The recommended minimum daily iron intake is 8 mg for adult men and 18 mg for premenopausal women. One way to ensure sufficient iron intake is a well-balanced diet that includes iron-fortified grains and cereals, red meat, egg yolks, leafy green vegetables, tomatoes, and raisins. Vegetarians should pay extra attention to their diet, because the iron in fruits and vegetables is not as readily absorbed by the body as the iron

▲ **Can cooking in cast iron pots decrease anemia?**

in meat, poultry, and fish. Vitamin supplements containing folic acid and either ferrous sulfate or ferrous gluconate can decrease iron deficiencies, and vitamin C increases the absorption of iron by the body.

However, the simplest way to increase dietary iron may be to use cast iron cookware. Studies have demonstrated that the iron content of many foods increases when cooked in an iron pot. Other studies involving Ethiopian children showed that those who ate food cooked in iron cookware were less likely to suffer from iron-deficiency anemia than their playmates who ate similar foods prepared in aluminum cookware.

See Chemistry in Action Problems 6.59 and 6.60 at the end of the chapter.

▶▶▶ We'll explore the role of hemoglobin in oxygen transport in greater detail in Chapter 9.

CONCEPT MAP: CHEMICAL REACTIONS (CHAPTERS 5, 6)

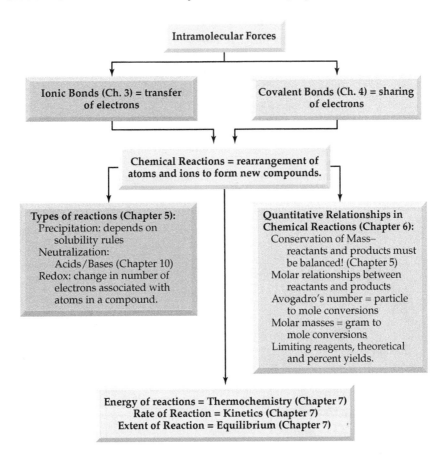

▶ **Figure 6.3**

Concept Maps. In Chapters 5 and 6, we examined chemical reactions. As shown in the concept map above, chemical reactions represent a rearrangement of the intermolecular forces within compounds as bonds in the reactants are broken and new bonds are formed to generate products. Ionic reactions can be classified as precipitation reactions, neutralization reactions, or redox reactions. One class of reactions (acid–base neutralization) will be examined in further detail in Chapter 10. Other characteristics of reactions will be examined in Chapter 7.

SUMMARY: REVISITING THE CHAPTER GOALS

1. What is the mole, and why is it useful in chemistry?
A *mole* refers to *Avogadro's number* (6.022×10^{23}) of formula units of a substance. One mole of any substance has a mass (*molar mass*) equal to the molecular or formula weight of the substance in grams. Because equal numbers of moles contain equal numbers of formula units, molar masses act as conversion factors between numbers of moles and masses in grams (*see Problems 16, 21–25, 27, 28, 32, 33, 38, 41, 62, 63*).

2. How are molar quantities and mass quantities related?
The coefficients in a balanced chemical equation represent the numbers of moles of reactants and products in a reaction. Thus, the ratios of coefficients act as *mole ratios* that relate amounts of reactants and/or products. By using molar masses and mole ratios in factor-label calculations, unknown masses or molar amounts can be found from known masses or molar amounts (*see Problems 17, 20, 25, 26, 29–31, 34–57, 59–61, 63–76*).

3. What are the limiting reagent, theoretical yield, and percent yield of a reaction? The *limiting reagent* is the reactant that runs out first. The *theoretical yield* is the amount of product that would be formed based on the amount of the limiting reagent. The *actual yield* of a reaction is the amount of product obtained. The *percent yield* is the amount of product obtained divided by the amount theoretically possible and multiplied by 100% (*see Problems 18, 19, 52–57, 71, 72*).

KEY WORDS

Actual yield, *p. 169*

Avogadro's number (N_A), *p. 161*

Formula weight, *p. 159*

Limiting reagent, *p. 169*

Molar mass, *p. 160*

Mole, *p. 160*

Molecular weight (MW), *p. 159*

Percent yield, *p. 169*

Theoretical yield, *p. 169*

UNDERSTANDING KEY CONCEPTS

6.16   Methionine, an amino acid used by organisms to make proteins, can be represented by the following ball-and-stick molecular model. Write the formula for methionine, and give its molecular weight (red = O, black = C, blue = N, yellow = S, white = H).

Methionine

6.17   The following diagram represents the reaction of A_2 (red spheres) with B_2 (blue spheres):

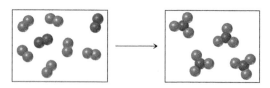

(a) Write a balanced equation for the reaction.

(b) How many moles of product can be made from 1.0 mol of A_2? From 1.0 mol of B_2?

6.18   Consider the balanced chemical equation: $2A + B_2 \rightarrow 2AB$. Given the reaction vessel below, determine the theoretical yield of product.

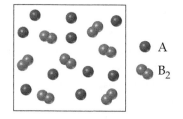

6.19   Consider the balanced chemical equation: $A_2 + 2 B_2 \rightarrow 2 AB_2$. A reaction is performed with the initial amounts of A_2 and B_2 shown in part (a). The amount of product obtained is shown in part (b). Calculate the percent yield.

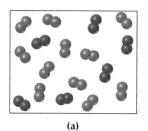

(a)

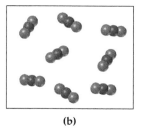

(b)

6.20   The following drawing represents the reaction of ethylene oxide with water to give ethylene glycol, a compound used as automobile antifreeze. What mass in grams of ethylene oxide is needed to react with 9.0 g of water, and what mass in grams of ethylene glycol is formed?

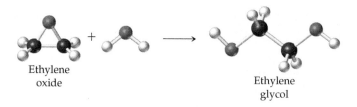

Ethylene
oxide

Ethylene
glycol

ADDITIONAL PROBLEMS

MOLAR MASSES AND MOLES

6.21   What is a mole of a substance? How many molecules are in 1 mol of a molecular compound?

6.22   What is the difference between molecular weight and formula weight? Between molecular weight and molar mass?

6.23   How many Na^+ ions are in a mole of Na_2SO_4? How many SO_4^{2-} ions?

6.24   How many moles of ions are in 1.75 mol of K_2SO_4?

6.25   How many calcium atoms are in 16.2 g of calcium?

6.26 What is the mass in grams of 2.68×10^{22} atoms of uranium?

6.27 Calculate the molar mass of each of the following compounds:

(a) Calcium carbonate, $CaCO_3$

(b) Urea, $CO(NH_2)_2$

(c) Ethylene glycol, $C_2H_6O_2$

6.28 How many moles of carbon atoms are there in 1 mol of each compound in Problem 6.27?

6.29 How many atoms of carbon, and how many grams of carbon are there in 1 mol of each compound in Problem 6.27?

6.30 Caffeine has the formula $C_8H_{10}N_4O_2$. If an average cup of coffee contains approximately 125 mg of caffeine, how many moles of caffeine are in one cup?

6.31 How many moles of aspirin, $C_9H_8O_4$, are in a 500 mg tablet?

6.32 What is the molar mass of diazepam (Valium), $C_{16}H_{13}ClN_2O$?

6.33 Calculate the molar masses of the following substances:

(a) Aluminum sulfate, $Al_2(SO_4)_3$

(b) Sodium bicarbonate, $NaHCO_3$

(c) Diethyl ether, $(C_2H_5)_2O$

(d) Penicillin V, $C_{16}H_{18}N_2O_5S$

6.34 How many moles are present in a 4.50 g sample of each compound listed in Problem 6.33?

6.35 The recommended daily dietary intake of calcium for adult men and premenopausal women is 1000 mg/day. Calcium citrate, $Ca_3(C_6H_5O_7)_2$ (MW = 498.5 amu), is a common dietary supplement. What mass of calcium citrate would be needed to provide the recommended daily intake of calcium?

6.36 What is the mass in grams of 0.0015 mol of aspirin, $C_9H_8O_4$? How many aspirin molecules are there in this 0.0015 mol sample?

6.37 How many grams are present in a 0.075 mol sample of each compound listed in Problem 6.33?

6.38 The principal component of many kidney stones is calcium oxalate, CaC_2O_4. A kidney stone recovered from a typical patient contains 8.5×10^{20} formula units of calcium oxalate. How many moles of CaC_2O_4 are present in this kidney stone? What is the mass of the kidney stone in grams?

MOLE AND MASS RELATIONSHIPS FROM CHEMICAL EQUATIONS

6.39 At elevated temperatures in an automobile engine, N_2 and O_2 can react to yield NO, an important cause of air pollution.

(a) Write a balanced equation for the reaction.

(b) How many moles of N_2 are needed to react with 7.50 mol of O_2?

(c) How many moles of NO can be formed when 3.81 mol of N_2 reacts?

(d) How many moles of O_2 must react to produce 0.250 mol of NO?

6.40 Ethyl acetate reacts with H_2 in the presence of a catalyst to yield ethyl alcohol:

$$C_4H_8O_2(l) + H_2(g) \longrightarrow C_2H_6O(l)$$

(a) Write a balanced equation for the reaction.

(b) How many moles of ethyl alcohol are produced by reaction of 1.5 mol of ethyl acetate?

(c) How many grams of ethyl alcohol are produced by reaction of 1.5 mol of ethyl acetate with H_2?

(d) How many grams of ethyl alcohol are produced by reaction of 12.0 g of ethyl acetate with H_2?

(e) How many grams of H_2 are needed to react with 12.0 g of ethyl acetate?

6.41 The active ingredient in Milk of Magnesia (an antacid) is magnesium hydroxide, $Mg(OH)_2$. A typical dose (one tablespoon) contains 1.2 g of $Mg(OH)_2$. Calculate (a) the molar mass of magnesium hydroxide, and (b) the amount of magnesium hydroxide (in moles) in one teaspoon.

6.42 Ammonia, NH_3, is prepared for use as a fertilizer by reacting N_2 with H_2.

(a) Write a balanced equation for the reaction.

(b) How many moles of N_2 are needed for reaction to make 16.0 g of NH_3?

(c) How many grams of H_2 are needed to react with 75.0 g of N_2?

6.43 Hydrazine, N_2H_4, a substance used as rocket fuel, reacts with oxygen as follows:

$$N_2H_4(l) + O_2(g) \longrightarrow NO_2(g) + H_2O(g)$$

(a) Balance the equation.

(b) How many moles of oxygen are needed to react with 165 g of hydrazine?

(c) How many grams of oxygen are needed to react with 165 g of hydrazine?

6.44 One method for preparing pure iron from Fe_2O_3 is by reaction with carbon monoxide:

$$Fe_2O_3(s) + CO(g) \longrightarrow Fe(s) + CO_2(g)$$

(a) Balance the equation.

(b) How many grams of CO are needed to react with 3.02 g of Fe_2O_3?

(c) How many grams of CO are needed to react with 1.68 mol of Fe_2O_3?

6.45 Magnesium metal burns in oxygen to form magnesium oxide, MgO.

(a) Write a balanced equation for the reaction.

(b) How many grams of oxygen are needed to react with 25.0 g of Mg? How many grams of MgO will result?

(c) How many grams of Mg are needed to react with 25.0 g of O_2? How many grams of MgO will result?

6.46 Titanium metal is obtained from the mineral rutile, TiO_2. How many kilograms of rutile are needed to produce 95 kg of Ti?

6.47 In the preparation of iron from hematite (Problem 6.44), how many moles of carbon monoxide are needed to react completely with 105 kg of Fe_2O_3?

6.48 The eruption of Mount St. Helens volcano in 1980 injected 4×10^8 kg of SO_2 into the atmosphere. If all this SO_2 was converted to sulfuric acid, how many moles of H_2SO_4 would be produced? How many kg?

6.49 The thermite reaction was used to produce molten iron for welding applications before arc welding was available. The thermite reaction is:

$$Fe_2O_3(s) + 2\,Al(s) \longrightarrow Al_2O_3(s) + 2\,Fe(l)$$

How many moles of molten iron can be produced from 1.5 kg of iron(III) oxide?

6.50 Pyrite, also known as fool's gold, is composed of iron disulfide, FeS_2. It is used commercially to produce SO_2 used in the production of paper products. How many moles of SO_2 can be produced from 1.0 kg of pyrite?

6.51 Diborane (B_2H_6) is a gas at room temperature that forms explosive mixtures with air. It reacts with oxygen according to the following equation:

$$B_2H_6(g) + 3\,O_2(g) \longrightarrow B_2O_3(s) + 3\,H_2O(l)$$

How many grams of diborane will react with 7.5 mol of O_2?

LIMITING REAGENT AND PERCENT YIELD

6.52 Once made by heating wood in the absence of air, methanol (CH_3OH) is now made by reacting carbon monoxide and hydrogen at high pressure:

$$CO(g) + 2\,H_2(g) \longrightarrow CH_3OH(l)$$

(a) If 25.0 g of CO is reacted with 6.00 g of H_2, which is the limiting reagent?

(b) How many grams of CH_3OH can be made from 10.0 g of CO if it all reacts?

(c) If 9.55 g of CH_3OH is recovered when the amounts in part (b) are used, what is the percent yield?

6.53 In Problem 6.43, hydrazine reacted with oxygen according to the (unbalanced) equation:

$$N_2H_4(l) + O_2(g) \longrightarrow NO_2(g) + H_2O(g)$$

(a) If 75.0 kg of hydrazine are reacted with 75.0 kg of oxygen, which is the limiting reagent?

(b) How many kilograms of NO_2 are produced from the reaction of 75.0 kg of the limiting reagent?

(c) If 59.3 kg of NO_2 are obtained from the reaction in part (a), what is the percent yield?

6.54 Dichloromethane, CH_2Cl_2, the solvent used to decaffeinate coffee beans, is prepared by reaction of CH_4 with Cl_2.

(a) Write the balanced equation. (HCl is also formed.)

(b) How many grams of Cl_2 are needed to react with 50.0 g of CH_4?

(c) How many grams of dichloromethane are formed from 50.0 g of CH_4 if the percent yield for the reaction is 76%?

6.55 Cisplatin $\left[Pt(NH_3)_2Cl_2 \right]$, a compound used in cancer treatment, is prepared by reaction of ammonia with potassium tetrachloroplatinate:

$$K_2PtCl_4 + 2\,NH_3 \longrightarrow 2\,KCl + Pt(NH_3)_2Cl_2$$

(a) How many grams of NH_3 are needed to react with 55.8 g of K_2PtCl_4?

(b) How many grams of cisplatin are formed from 55.8 g of K_2PtCl_4 if the percent yield for the reaction is 95%?

6.56 Nitrobenzene $(C_6H_5NO_2)$ is used in small quantities as a flavoring agent or in perfumes, but can be toxic in large amounts. It is produced by reaction of benzene (C_6H_6) with nitric acid:

$$C_6H_6(l) + HNO_3(aq) \longrightarrow C_6H_5NO_2(l) + H_2O(l).$$

(a) Identify the limiting reagent in the reaction of 27.5 g of nitric acid with 75 g of benzene.

(b) Calculate the theoretical yield for this reaction.

6.57 Calculate the percent yield if 48.2 g of nitrobenzene is obtained from the reaction described in Problem 6.56.

CHEMISTRY IN ACTION

6.58 What do you think might be some of the errors involved in calculating Avogadro's number by spreading oil on a pond? [*Did Ben Franklin Have Avogadro's Number? p. 164*]

6.59 Dietary iron forms a 1:1 complex with hemoglobin (Hb), which is responsible for O_2 transport in the body based on the following equation:

$$Hb + 4\,O_2 \longrightarrow Hb(O_2)_4$$

How many moles of oxygen could be transported by the hemoglobin complex formed from 8 mg of dietary iron? [*Anemia—A Limiting Reagent Problem? p. 172*]

6.60 Ferrous sulfate is one dietary supplement used to treat iron-deficiency anemia. What are the molecular formula and molecular weight of this compound? How many milligrams of iron are in 250 mg of ferrous sulfate?

GENERAL QUESTIONS AND PROBLEMS

6.61 Zinc metal reacts with hydrochloric acid (HCl) according to the equation:

$$Zn(s) + 2\,HCl(aq) \longrightarrow ZnCl_2(aq) + H_2(g)$$

(a) How many grams of hydrogen are produced if 15.0 g of zinc reacts?

(b) Is this a redox reaction? If so, tell what is reduced, what is oxidized, and identify the reducing and oxidizing agents.

6.62 Batrachotoxin, $C_{31}H_{42}N_2O_6$, an active component of South American arrow poison, is so toxic that $0.05\ \mu g$ can kill a person. How many molecules is this?

6.63 Lovastatin, a drug used to lower serum cholesterol, has the molecular formula of $C_{24}H_{36}O_5$.

(a) Calculate the molar mass of lovastatin.

(b) How many moles of lovastatin are present in a typical dose of one 10 mg tablet?

6.64 When table sugar $(\text{sucrose},\ C_{12}H_{22}O_{11})$ is heated, it decomposes to form C and H_2O.

(a) Write a balanced equation for the process.

(b) How many grams of carbon are formed by the breakdown of 60.0 g of sucrose?

(c) How many grams of water are formed when 6.50 g of carbon are formed?

6.65 Although Cu is not sufficiently active to react with acids, it can be dissolved by concentrated nitric acid, which functions as an oxidizing agent according to the following equation:

$$Cu(s) + 4\,HNO_3(aq) \longrightarrow$$
$$Cu(NO_3)_2(aq) + 2\,NO_2(g) + 2\,H_2O(l)$$

(a) Write the net ionic equation for this process.

(b) Is 35.0 g of HNO_3 sufficient to dissolve 5.00 g of copper?

6.66 The net ionic equation for the Breathalyzer test used to indicate alcohol concentration in the body is

$$16\,H^+(aq) + 2\,Cr_2O_7^{2-}(aq) + 3\,C_2H_6O(aq) \longrightarrow$$
$$3\,C_2H_4O_2(aq) + 4\,Cr^{3+}(aq) + 11\,H_2O(l)$$

(a) How many grams of $K_2Cr_2O_7$ must be used to consume 1.50 g of C_2H_6O?

(b) How many grams of $C_2H_4O_2$ can be produced from 80.0 g of C_2H_6O?

6.67 Ethyl alcohol is formed by enzyme action on sugars and starches during fermentation:

$$C_6H_{12}O_6 \longrightarrow 2\,CO_2 + 2\,C_2H_6O$$

If the density of ethyl alcohol is 0.789 g/mL, how many quarts can be produced by the fermentation of 100.0 lb of sugar?

6.68 Gaseous ammonia reacts with oxygen in the presence of a platinum catalyst to produce nitrogen monoxide and water vapor.

(a) Write a balanced chemical equation for this reaction.

(b) What mass of nitrogen monoxide would be produced by complete reaction of 17.0 g of ammonia?

6.69 Sodium hypochlorite, the primary component in commercial bleach, is prepared by bubbling chlorine gas through solutions of sodium hydroxide:

$$NaOH(aq) + Cl_2(g) \longrightarrow NaOCl(aq) + H_2O(l)$$

How many moles of sodium hypochlorite can be prepared from 32.5 g of NaOH?

6.70 Barium sulfate is an insoluble ionic compound swallowed by patients before having an X-ray of their gastrointestinal tract.

(a) Write the balanced chemical equation for the precipitation reaction between barium chloride and sodium sulfate.

(b) What mass of barium sulfate can be produced by complete reaction of 27.4 g of Na_2SO_4?

6.71 The last step in the production of nitric acid is the reaction of nitrogen dioxide with water:

$$NO_2(g) + H_2O(l) \longrightarrow HNO_3(aq) + NO(g)$$

(a) Balance the chemical equation.

(b) If 65.0 g of nitrogen dioxide is reacted with excess water, calculate the theoretical yield.

(c) If only 43.8 g of nitric acid is obtained, calculate the percent yield.

6.72 Acetylsalicylic acid, the active ingredient in aspirin, is prepared from salicylic acid by reaction with acetic anhydride:

$$C_7H_6O_3\quad +\quad C_4H_6O_3 \longrightarrow C_9H_8O_4\quad +\quad C_2H_4O_2$$
(salicylic acid) (acetic anhydride) (acetylsalicylic acid) (acetic acid)

(a) Calculate the theoretical yield if 47 g of salicylic acid is reacted with 25 g of acetic anhydride.

(b) What is the percent yield if only 35 g is obtained?

6.73 Jewelry and tableware can be silver-plated by reduction of silver ions from a solution of silver nitrate. The net ionic equation is $Ag^+(aq) + e^- \longrightarrow Ag(s)$. How many grams of silver nitrate would be needed to plate 15.2 g of silver on a piece of jewelry?

6.74 Elemental phosphorus exists as molecules of P_4. It reacts with $Cl_2(g)$ to produce phosphorus pentachloride.

(a) Write the balanced chemical equation for this reaction.

(b) What mass of phosphorus pentachloride would be produced by the complete reaction of 15.2 g of P_4?

6.75 Lithium oxide is used aboard the space shuttle to remove water from the atmosphere according to the equation

$$Li_2O(s) + H_2O(g) \longrightarrow 2\,LiOH(s)$$

How many grams of Li_2O must be carried on board to remove 80.0 kg of water?

6.76 One of the reactions used to provide thrust for space shuttle launch involves the reaction of ammonium perchlorate with aluminum to produce $AlCl_3(s)$, $H_2O(g)$, and $NO(g)$.

(a) Write the balanced chemical equation for this reaction.

(b) How many moles of gas are produced by the reaction of 14.5 kg of ammonium perchlorate?

CHAPTER 7

Chemical Reactions:
Energy, Rates, and Equilibrium

▲ Many spontaneous chemical reactions are accompanied
by the release of energy, in some cases explosively.

CONTENTS

CONCEPTS TO REVIEW

A. Energy and Heat
(Section 1.13)

B. Ionic Bonds
(Section 3.3)

C. Covalent Bonds
(Section 4.1)

D. Chemical Equations
(Section 5.1)

1. **What energy changes take place during reactions?**
    THE GOAL: Be able to explain the factors that influence energy changes in chemical reactions. (◀◀ A, B, and C)

2. **What is "free energy," and what is the criterion for spontaneity in chemistry?**
    THE GOAL: Be able to define enthalpy, entropy, and free-energy changes, and explain how the values of these quantities affect chemical reactions.

3. **What determines the rate of a chemical reaction?**
    THE GOAL: Be able to explain activation energy and other factors that determine reaction rate. (◀◀ D)

4. **What is chemical equilibrium?**
    THE GOAL: Be able to describe what occurs in a reaction at equilibrium, and write the equilibrium equation for a given reaction. (◀◀ D)

5. **What is Le Châtelier's principle?**
    THE GOAL: Be able to state Le Châtelier's principle, and use it to predict the effect of changes in temperature, pressure, and concentration on reactions.

We have yet to answer many questions about reactions. Why, for instance, do reactions occur? Just because a balanced equation can be written it does not mean it will take place. We can write a balanced equation for the reaction of gold with water, for example, but the reaction does not occur in practice—so your gold jewelry is safe in the shower.

Balanced, but does not occur $2 \, Au(s) + 3 \, H_2O(l) \longrightarrow Au_2O_3(s) + 3 \, H_2(g)$

To describe reactions more completely, several fundamental questions are commonly asked: Is energy released or absorbed when a reaction occurs? Is a given reaction fast or slow? Does a reaction continue until all reactants are converted to products, or is there a point beyond which no additional product forms?

7.1 Energy and Chemical Bonds

There are two fundamental and interconvertible kinds of energy: *potential* and *kinetic*. **Potential energy** is stored energy. The water in a reservoir behind a dam, an automobile poised to coast downhill, and a coiled spring have potential energy waiting to be released. **Kinetic energy**, by contrast, is the energy of motion. When the water falls over the dam and turns a turbine, when the car rolls downhill, or when the spring uncoils and makes the hands on a clock move, the potential energy in each is converted to kinetic energy. Of course, once all the potential energy is converted, nothing further occurs. The water at the bottom of the dam, the car at the bottom of the hill, and the uncoiled spring no longer have potential energy and thus, undergo no further change.

In chemical compounds, the attractive forces between ions or atoms are a form of potential energy, similar to the attractive forces between the poles of a magnet. When these attractive forces result in the formation of ionic or covalent bonds between ions or atoms, the potential energy is often converted into **heat**—a measure of the kinetic energy of the particles that make up the molecule. Breaking these bonds requires an input of energy.

In chemical reactions, some of the chemical bonds in the reactants must break (energy in) so that new bonds can form in the products (energy out). If the reaction products have less potential energy than the reactants, we say that the products are *more stable* than the reactants. The term "stable" is used in chemistry to describe a substance that has little remaining potential energy and consequently little tendency to undergo further change. Whether a reaction occurs, and how much energy or heat

Potential energy Stored energy.

Kinetic energy The energy of an object in motion.

Heat A measure of the transfer of thermal energy.

is associated with the reaction, depends on the difference in the amount of potential energy contained in the reactants and products.

7.2 Heat Changes during Chemical Reactions

Why does chlorine react so easily with many elements and compounds, but nitrogen does not? What difference between Cl_2 molecules and N_2 molecules accounts for their different reactivities? The answer is that the nitrogen–nitrogen triple bond is much *stronger* than the chlorine–chlorine single bond and cannot be broken as easily in chemical reactions.

Bond dissociation energy The amount of energy that must be supplied to break a bond and separate the atoms in an isolated gaseous molecule.

The strength of a covalent bond is measured by its **bond dissociation energy**, defined as the amount of energy that must be supplied to break the bond and separate the atoms in an isolated gaseous molecule. The greater the bond dissociation energy, the more stable the chemical bond between the atoms or ions. The triple bond in N_2, for example, has a bond dissociation energy of 226 kcal/mol (946 kJ/mol), whereas the single bond in chlorine has a bond dissociation energy of only 58 kcal/mol (243 kJ/mol):

$$:N:::N: \xrightarrow{\text{226 kcal/mol}} :\dot{N}\cdot + \cdot\dot{N}: \qquad N_2 \text{ bond dissociation energy} = 226 \text{ kcal/mol (946 kJ/mol)}$$

$$:\ddot{\underset{\cdot\cdot}{C}l}:\ddot{\underset{\cdot\cdot}{C}l}: \xrightarrow{\text{58 kcal/mol}} :\ddot{\underset{\cdot\cdot}{C}l}\cdot + \cdot\ddot{\underset{\cdot\cdot}{C}l}: \qquad Cl_2 \text{ bond dissociation energy} = 58 \text{ kcal/mol (243 kJ/mol)}$$

The greater stability of the triple bond in N_2 explains why nitrogen molecules are less reactive than Cl_2 molecules. Some typical bond dissociation energies are given in Table 7.1

TABLE 7.1 Average Bond Dissociation Energies

Bond	Bond Dissociation Energy (kcal/mol, kJ/mol)	Bond	Bond Dissociation Energy (kcal/mol, kJ/mol)	Bond	Bond Dissociation Energy (kcal/mol, kJ/mol)
C—H	99, 413	N—H	93, 391	C=C	147, 614
C—C	83, 347	N—N	38, 160	C≡C	201, 839
C—N	73, 305	N—Cl	48, 200	C=O*	178, 745
C—O	86, 358	N—O	48, 201	O=O	119, 498
C—Cl	81, 339	H—H	103, 432	N=O	145, 607
Cl—Cl	58, 243	O—H	112, 467	C≡N	213, 891
H—Cl	102, 427	O—Cl	49, 203	N≡N	226, 946

*The C=O bond dissociation energies in CO_2 are 191 kcal/mol (799 kJ/mol).

Endothermic A process or reaction that absorbs heat.

Exothermic A process or reaction that releases heat.

A chemical change that absorbs heat, like the breaking of bonds, is said to be **endothermic**, from the Greek words *endon* (within) and *therme* (heat), meaning that *heat is put in*. The reverse of bond breaking is bond formation, a process that *releases* heat and is described as **exothermic**, from the Greek *exo* (outside), meaning that heat goes *out*. The amount of energy released in forming a bond is numerically the same as that absorbed in breaking it. When nitrogen atoms combine to give N_2, 226 kcal/mol (946 kJ/mol) of heat is released. Similarly, when chlorine atoms combine to give Cl_2, 58 kcal/mol (243 kJ/mol) of heat is released. We indicate the direction of energy flow in a chemical change by the sign associated with the number. If heat is absorbed (endothermic) then the sign is positive to indicate energy is *gained* by the substance. If heat is released (exothermic) then the sign is negative to indicate energy is *lost* by the substance during the change.

$$\cdot\dot{N}\cdot + \cdot\dot{N}: \longrightarrow :N:::N: + 226 \text{ kcal/mol (946 kJ/mol) heat released}$$

$$:\ddot{\underset{\cdot\cdot}{C}l}\cdot + \cdot\ddot{\underset{\cdot\cdot}{C}l}: \longrightarrow :\ddot{\underset{\cdot\cdot}{C}l}:\ddot{\underset{\cdot\cdot}{C}l}: + 58 \text{ kcal/mol (243 kJ/mol) heat released}$$

The same energy relationships that govern bond breaking and bond formation apply to every physical or chemical change. That is, the amount of heat transferred during a change in one direction is numerically equal to the amount of heat transferred during the change in the opposite direction. Only the *direction* of the heat transfer is different. This relationship reflects a fundamental law of nature called the *law of conservation of energy*:

Law of conservation of energy Energy can be neither created nor destroyed in any physical or chemical change.

If more energy could be released by an exothermic reaction than was consumed in its reverse, the law would be violated, and we could "manufacture" energy out of nowhere by cycling back and forth between forward and reverse reactions—a clear impossibility.

In every chemical reaction, some bonds in the reactants are broken, and new bonds are formed in the products. The difference between the heat energy absorbed in breaking bonds and the heat energy released in forming bonds is called the **heat of reaction** and is a quantity that we can measure. Heats of reaction that are measured when a reaction is held at constant pressure are represented by the abbreviation ΔH, where Δ (the Greek capital letter delta) is a general symbol used to indicate "a change in," and H is a quantity called **enthalpy**. Thus, the value of ΔH represents the **enthalpy change** that occurs during a reaction. The terms *enthalpy change* and *heat of reaction* are often used interchangeably, but we will generally use the latter term in this book.

Heat of reaction, or **Enthalpy change** (ΔH) The difference between the energy of bonds broken in reactants and the energy of bonds formed in products.

Enthalpy (H) A measure of the amount of energy associated with substances involved in a reaction.

7.3 Exothermic and Endothermic Reactions

When the total strength of the bonds formed in the products is *greater* than the total strength of the bonds broken in the reactants, the net result is that energy is released and a reaction is exothermic. All combustion reactions are exothermic; for example, burning 1 mol of methane releases 213 kcal (891 kJ) of energy in the form of heat. The heat released in an exothermic reaction can be thought of as a reaction product, and the heat of reaction ΔH is assigned a *negative* value, because overall, heat is *lost* during the reaction.

An exothermic reaction—negative ΔH

Heat is a product.

$$CH_4(g) + 2\,O_2(g) \longrightarrow CO_2(g) + 2\,H_2O(l) + 213 \text{ kcal (891 kJ)}$$

or

$$CH_4(g) + 2\,O_2(g) \longrightarrow CO_2(g) + 2\,H_2O(l) \qquad \Delta H = -213 \text{ kcal/mol } (-891 \text{ kJ/mol})$$

The heat of reaction can be calculated as the difference between the bond dissociation energies in the products and the bond dissociation energies of the reactants:

$$\Delta H = \Sigma(\text{Bond dissociation energies})_{\text{reactants}} - \Sigma(\text{Bond dissociation energies})_{\text{products}}$$

Look again at the reaction involving the combustion of methane. By counting the number of bonds on each side of the chemical equation, we can use the average bond dissociation energies from Table 7.1 to estimate ΔH for the reaction.

Reactants	Bond Dissociation Energies (kcal/mol)	Products	Bond Dissociation Energies (kcal/mol)
(C—H) × 4	99 × 4 = 396 kcal	(C=O) × 2	191 × 2 = 382 kcal
(O=O) × 2	119 × 2 = 238 kcal	(H—O) × 4	112 × 4 = 448 kcal
Total:	= 634 kcal		= 830 kcal

$$\Delta H = (634 \text{ kcal})_{\text{reactants}} - (830 \text{ kcal})_{\text{products}} = -196 \text{ kcal}(-820 \text{ kJ})$$

▲ The reaction between aluminum metal and iron(III) oxide, called the *thermite reaction*, is so strongly exothermic that it melts iron.

In this reaction, the input of energy needed to break the bonds in the reactants is less than the amount of energy released when forming bonds in the products. The excess energy is released as heat, and the reaction is exothermic (ΔH = negative).

It should be noted that the bond energies in Table 7.1 are average values, and that actual bond energies may vary depending on the chemical environment in which the bond is found. The average $C\!=\!O$ bond energy, for example, is 178 kcal/mol, but the actual value for the $C\!=\!O$ bonds in the CO_2 molecule is 191 kcal/mol. The average $C\!-\!H$ bond energy is 99 kca/mol (413 kJ/mol), but in CH_3CH_3 the $C\!-\!H$ bond dissociation energy is actually 101 kcal/mol (423 kJ/mol). Thus, the calculated ΔH for a reaction using average bond energies may differ slightly from the value obtained by experiment. For the combustion of methane, for example, the ΔH estimated from bond energies is −196 kcal/mol (−820 kJ/mol), while the value measured experimentally is −213 kcal/mol (−891 kJ/mol), a difference of about 9%.

Note that ΔH is given in units of kilocalories or kilojoules per mole, where "per mole" means the reaction of *molar amounts of products and reactants as represented by the coefficients of the balanced equation*. Thus, the experimental value ΔH = −213 kcal/mol (−891 kJ/mol) refers to the amount of heat released when 1 mol (16.0 g) of methane reacts with 2 mol of O_2 to give 1 mol of CO_2 gas and 2 mol of liquid H_2O. If we were to double the amount of methane from 1 mol to 2 mol, the amount of heat released would also double.

The quantities of heat released in the combustion of several fuels, including natural gas (which is primarily methane), are compared in Table 7.2. The values are given in kilocalories and kilojoules per gram to make comparisons easier. You can see from the table why there is interest in the potential of hydrogen as a fuel.

TABLE 7.2 Energy Values of Some Common Fuels

Fuel	Energy Value (kcal/g, kJ/g)
Wood (pine)	4.3, 18.0
Ethyl alcohol	7.1, 29.7
Coal (anthracite)	7.4, 31.0
Crude oil (Texas)	10.5, 43.9
Gasoline	11.5, 48.1
Natural gas	11.7, 49.0
Hydrogen	34.0, 142

When the total energy released upon bond formation in the products is *less* than the total energy added to break the bonds in the reactants, the net result is that energy is absorbed and a reaction is endothermic. The combination of nitrogen and oxygen to give nitrogen oxide (also known as nitric oxide), a gas present in automobile exhaust, is such a reaction. The heat added in an endothermic reaction is like a reactant, and ΔH is assigned a *positive* value because heat is *added*.

An endothermic reaction—positive ΔH

Heat is a reactant.

$$N_2(g) \;+\; O_2(g) \;+\; 43 \text{ kcal (180 kJ)} \;\longrightarrow\; 2\, NO(g)$$

or

$$N_2(g) \;+\; O_2(g) \;\longrightarrow\; 2\, NO(g) \qquad \Delta H \;=\; +43 \text{ kcal/mol} \, (+180 \text{ kJ/mol})$$

Important Points about Heat Transfers and Chemical Reactions

- An exothermic reaction releases heat to the surroundings; ΔH is negative.
- An endothermic reaction absorbs heat from the surroundings; ΔH is positive.
- The reverse of an exothermic reaction is endothermic.
- The reverse of an endothermic reaction is exothermic.
- The amount of heat absorbed or released in the reverse of a reaction is equal to that released or absorbed in the forward reaction, but ΔH has the opposite sign.

Worked Examples 7.1–7.4 show how to calculate the amount of heat absorbed or released for reaction of a given amount of reactant. All that is needed is the balanced equation and its accompanying ΔH or the bond dissociation energies to permit calculation of ΔH. Mole ratios and molar masses are used to convert between masses and moles of reactants or products, as discussed in Sections 6.3 and 6.4.

Worked Example 7.1 Heat of Reaction from Bond Energies

Estimate the ΔH (in kcal/mol) for the reaction of hydrogen and oxygen to form water:

$$2\,H_2 + O_2 \longrightarrow 2\,H_2O \quad \Delta H = ?$$

ANALYSIS The individual bond energies from Table 7.1 can be used to calculate the total bond energies of reactants and products. ΔH can then be calculated as

$$\Delta H = \Sigma(\text{Bond dissociation energies})_{\text{reactants}} - \Sigma(\text{Bond dissociation energies})_{\text{products}}$$

BALLPARK ESTIMATE The average H—H bond energy is ~100 kcal/mol and the O=O bond energy is ~120 kcal/mol. Thus, the total energy needed to break reactant bonds is ~ $(200 + 120) = 320$ kcal/mol. The O—H bonds are ~110 kcal/mol, so the total energy released when product bonds are formed is ~440 kcal/mol. Based on these estimates, $\Delta H \sim -120$ kcal/mol.

SOLUTION

$$\Delta H = \Sigma(\text{Bond dissociation energies})_{\text{reactants}} - \Sigma(\text{Bond dissociation energies})_{\text{products}}$$
$$= (2(\text{H—H}) + (\text{O=O})) - (4(\text{O—H}))$$
$$= (2(103\,\text{kcal/mol}) + (119\,\text{kcal/mol})) - (4(112\,\text{kcal/mol})) = -123\,\text{kcal/mol}$$

BALLPARK CHECK Our estimate was -120 kcal/mol, within 3% of the calculated answer.

Worked Example 7.2 Heat of Reaction: Moles

Methane undergoes combustion with O_2 according to the following equation:

$$CH_4(g) + 2\,O_2(g) \longrightarrow CO_2(g) + 2\,H_2O(l) \quad \Delta H = -213\,\frac{\text{kcal}}{\text{mol CH}_4}$$

How much heat (in kcal and kJ) is released during the combustion of 0.35 mol of methane?

ANALYSIS Since the value of ΔH for the reaction (213 kcal/mol) is negative, it indicates the amount of heat released when 1 mol of methane reacts with O_2. We need to find the amount of heat released when an amount other than 1 mol reacts, using appropriate factor-label calculations to convert from our known or given units to kilocalories, and then to kilojoules.

BALLPARK ESTIMATE Since 213 kcal is released for each mole of methane that reacts, 0.35 mol of methane should release about one-third of 213 kcal, or about 70 kcal. There are about 4 kJ per kcal, so 70 kcal is about 280 kJ.

SOLUTION

To find the amount of heat released (in kilocalories) by combustion of 0.35 mol of methane, we use a conversion factor of kcal/mol, and then we can convert to kilojoules using a kJ/kcal conversion factor (see Section 1.13):

$$0.35 \text{ mol CH}_4 \times \frac{-213 \text{ kcal}}{1 \text{ mol CH}_4} = -75 \text{ kcal}$$

$$-75 \text{ kcal} \times \left(\frac{4.184 \text{ kJ}}{\text{kcal}}\right) = -314 \text{ kJ}$$

The negative sign indicates that the 75 kcal (314 kJ) of heat is released.

BALLPARK CHECK The calculated answer is consistent with our estimate (70 kcal or 280 kJ).

Worked Example 7.3 Heat of Reaction: Mass to Mole Conversion

How much heat is released during the combustion of 7.50 g of methane (molar mass = 16.0 g/mol)?

$$CH_4(g) + 2\,O_2(g) \longrightarrow CO_2(g) + 2\,H_2O(l) \quad \Delta H = -213\frac{\text{kcal}}{\text{mol CH}_4} = -891\frac{\text{kJ}}{\text{mol CH}_4}$$

ANALYSIS We can find the moles of methane involved in the reaction by using the molecular weight in a mass to mole conversion, and then use ΔH to find the heat released.

BALLPARK ESTIMATE Since 1 mol of methane (molar mass = 16.0 g/mol) has a mass of 16.0 g, 7.50 g of methane is a little less than 0.5 mol. Thus, less than half of 213 kcal, or about 100 kcal (418 kJ), is released from combustion of 7.50 g.

SOLUTION

Going from a given mass of methane to the amount of heat released in a reaction requires that we first find the number of moles of methane by including molar mass (in mol/g) in the calculation and then converting moles to kilocalories or kilojoules:

$$7.50 \text{ g CH}_4 \times \frac{1 \text{ mol CH}_4}{16.0 \text{ g CH}_4} \times \frac{-213 \text{ kcal}}{1 \text{ mol CH}_4} = -99.8 \text{ kcal}$$

or

$$7.50 \text{ g CH}_4 \times \frac{1 \text{ mol CH}_4}{16.0 \text{ g CH}_4} \times \frac{-891 \text{ kJ}}{1 \text{ mol CH}_4} = -418 \text{ kJ}$$

The negative sign indicates that the 99.8 kcal (418 kJ) of heat is released.

BALLPARK CHECK Our estimate was −100 kcal (−418 kJ)!

Worked Example 7.4 Heat of Reaction: Mole Ratio Calculations

How much heat is released in kcal and kJ when 2.50 mol of O_2 reacts completely with methane?

$$CH_4(g) + 2\,O_2(g) \longrightarrow CO_2(g) + 2\,H_2O(l) \quad \Delta H = -213\frac{\text{kcal}}{\text{mol CH}_4} = -891\frac{\text{kJ}}{\text{mol CH}_4}$$

ANALYSIS Since the ΔH for the reaction is based on the combustion of 1 mol of methane, we will need to perform a mole ratio calculation.

BALLPARK ESTIMATE The balanced equation shows that 213 kcal (891 kJ) is released for each 2 mol of oxygen that reacts. Thus, 2.50 mol of oxygen should release a bit more than 213 kcal, perhaps about 250 kcal (1050 kJ).

SOLUTION

To find the amount of heat released by combustion of 2.50 mol of oxygen, we include in our calculation a mole ratio based on the balanced chemical equation:

$$2.50 \text{ mol } O_2 \times \frac{1 \text{ mol } CH_4}{2 \text{ mol } O_2} \times \frac{-213 \text{ kcal}}{1 \text{ mol } CH_4} = -266 \text{ kcal}$$

or

$$2.50 \text{ mol } O_2 \times \frac{1 \text{ mol } CH_4}{2 \text{ mol } O_2} \times \frac{-891 \text{ kJ}}{1 \text{ mol } CH_4} = -1110 \text{ kJ}$$

The negative sign indicates that the 266 kcal (1110 kJ) of heat is released.

BALLPARK CHECK   The calculated answer is close to our estimate (-250 kcal or -1050 kJ).

CHEMISTRY IN ACTION

Energy from Food

Any serious effort to lose weight usually leads to studying the caloric values of foods. Have you ever wondered how the numbers quoted on food labels are obtained?

Food is "burned" in the body to yield H_2O, CO_2, and energy, just as natural gas is burned in furnaces to yield the same products. In fact, the "caloric value" of a food is just the heat of reaction for complete combustion of the food (minus a small correction factor). The value is the same whether the food is burned in the body or in the laboratory. One gram of protein releases 4 kcal, 1 g of table sugar (a carbohydrate) releases 4 kcal, and 1 g of fat releases 9 kcal (see Table).

▲ **This frosted donut provides your body with 330 Calories. Burning this donut in a calorimeter releases 330 kcal (1380 kJ) as heat.**

Caloric Values of Some Foods

Substance, Sample Size	Caloric Value (kcal, kJ)	
Protein, 1 g	4,	17
Carbohydrate, 1 g	4,	17
Fat, 1 g	9,	38
Alcohol, 1 g	7.1,	29.7
Cola drink, 12 fl oz (369 g)	160,	670
Apple, one medium (138 g)	80,	330
Iceberg lettuce, 1 cup shredded (55 g)	5,	21
White bread, 1 slice (25 g)	65,	270
Hamburger patty, 3 oz (85 g)	245,	1030
Pizza, 1 slice (120 g)	290,	1200
Vanilla ice cream, 1 cup (133 g)	270,	1130

The caloric value of a food is usually given in "Calories" (note the capital C), where 1 Cal = 1000 cal = 1 kcal = 4.184 kJ. To determine these values experimentally, a carefully dried and weighed food sample is placed together with oxygen in an instrument called a *calorimeter*, the food is ignited, the temperature change is measured, and the amount of heat given off is calculated from the temperature change. In the calorimeter, the heat from the food is released very quickly and the temperature rises dramatically. Clearly, though, something a bit different goes on when food is burned in the body, otherwise we would burst into flames after a meal!

It is a fundamental principle of chemistry that the total heat released or absorbed in going from reactants to products is the same, no matter how many reactions are involved. The body applies this principle by withdrawing energy from food a bit at a time in a long series of interconnected reactions rather than all at once in a single reaction. These and other reactions that are continually taking place in the body—called the body's *metabolism*—will be examined in later chapters.

See Chemistry in Action Problems 7.70 and 7.71 at the end of the chapter.

PROBLEM 7.1

In photosynthesis, green plants convert carbon dioxide and water into glucose ($C_6H_{12}O_6$) according to the following equation:

$$6\,CO_2(g) + 6\,H_2O(l) \longrightarrow C_6H_{12}O_6(aq) + 6\,O_2(g)$$

(a) Estimate ΔH for the reaction using bond dissociation energies from Table 7.1. Give your answer in kcal/mol and kJ/mol. $C_6H_{12}O_6$ has five C—C bonds, seven C—H bonds, seven C—O bonds, and five O—H bonds).

(b) Is the reaction endothermic or exothermic?

PROBLEM 7.2

The following equation shows the conversion of aluminum oxide (from the ore bauxite) to aluminum:

$$2\,Al_2O_3(s) \longrightarrow 4\,Al(s) + 3\,O_2(g) \quad \Delta H = +801\ \text{kcal/mol}\ (+3350\ \text{kJ/mol})$$

(a) Is the reaction exothermic or endothermic?

(b) How many kilocalories are required to produce 1.00 mol of aluminum? How many kilojoules?

(c) How many kilocalories are required to produce 10.0 g of aluminum? How many kilojoules?

PROBLEM 7.3

How much heat is absorbed (in kilocalories and kilojoules) during production of 127 g of NO by the combination of nitrogen and oxygen?

$$N_2(g) + O_2(g) \longrightarrow 2\,NO(g) \quad \Delta H = +43\ \text{kcal/mol}\ (+180\ \text{kJ/mol})$$

PROBLEM 7.4

Once consumed, the body metabolizes alcohol (ethanol, CH_3CH_2OH; MW $=$ 46 g/mol) to carbon dioxide and water. The balanced reaction is: $CH_3CH_2OH +$ $3\,O_2 \longrightarrow 2\,CO_2 + 3\,H_2O$. Using the bond energies in Table 7.1, estimate the ΔH for this reaction in kcal/mol. How does it compare to the caloric value of alcohol (in Cal/g) given in Chemistry in Action: Energy from Food on p. 185?

7.4 Why Do Chemical Reactions Occur? Free Energy

Events that lead to lower energy states tend to occur spontaneously. Water falls downhill, for instance, releasing its stored (potential) energy and reaching a lower-energy, more stable position. Similarly, a wound-up spring uncoils when set free. Applying this lesson to chemistry, the obvious conclusion is that exothermic processes—those that release heat energy—should be spontaneous. A log burning in a fireplace is just one example of a spontaneous reaction that releases heat. At the same time, endothermic processes, which absorb heat energy, should not be spontaneous. Often, these conclusions are correct, but not always. Many, but not all, exothermic processes take place spontaneously, and many, but not all, endothermic processes are nonspontaneous.

Before exploring the situation further, it is important to understand what the word "spontaneous" means in chemistry, which is not quite the same as in everyday language. A **spontaneous process** is one that, once started, proceeds on its own without any external influence. The change does not necessarily happen quickly, like a spring suddenly uncoiling or a car coasting downhill. It can also happen slowly, like the gradual rusting away of an abandoned bicycle. A *nonspontaneous process*, by contrast, takes place only in the presence of a continuous external influence. Energy must be continually expended to rewind a spring or push a car uphill. The reverse of a spontaneous process is always nonspontaneous.

As an example of a process that takes place spontaneously yet absorbs heat, think about what happens when you take an ice cube out of the freezer. The ice spontaneously

▲ Events that lead to lower energy tend to occur spontaneously. Thus, water always flows *down* a waterfall, not up.

Spontaneous process A process or reaction that, once started, proceeds on its own without any external influence.

melts to give liquid water above 0 °C, even though it *absorbs* heat energy from the surroundings. What this and other spontaneous endothermic processes have in common is *an increase in molecular disorder, or randomness.* When the solid ice melts, the H_2O molecules are no longer locked in position but are now free to move around randomly in the liquid water.

The amount of disorder in a system is called the system's **entropy**, symbolized by S and expressed in units of calories (or Joules) per mole-kelvin $[cal/(mol \cdot K)$ or $J/(mol \cdot K)]$. The greater the disorder, or randomness, of the particles in a substance or mixture, the larger the value of S (Figure 7.1). Gases have more disorder and therefore higher entropy than liquids because particles in the gas move around more freely than particles in the liquid. Similarly, liquids have higher entropy than solids. In chemical reactions, entropy increases when, for example, a gas is produced from a solid or when 2 mol of reactants split into 4 mol of products.

Entropy (S) A measure of the amount of molecular disorder in a system.

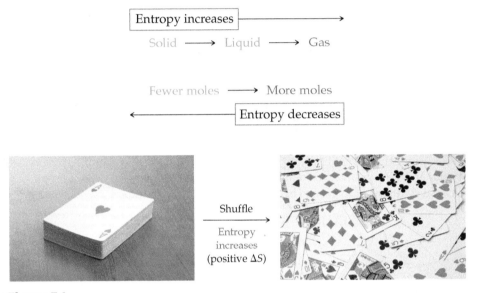

▲ **Figure 7.1**

Entropy and values of S.
A new deck of cards, neatly stacked, has more order and lower entropy than the randomly shuffled and strewn cards on the right. The value of the entropy change, ΔS, for converting the system on the left to that on the right is positive because entropy increases.

The **entropy change** for a process, ΔS, has a *positive* value if disorder increases because the process adds disorder to the system. The melting of ice to give water is an example. Conversely, ΔS has a *negative* value if the disorder of a system decreases. The freezing of water to give ice is an example.

It thus appears that two factors determine the spontaneity of a chemical or physical change: the release or absorption of heat, ΔH, and the increase or decrease in entropy, ΔS. *To decide whether a process is spontaneous, both the enthalpy change and the entropy change must be taken into account.* We have already seen that a negative ΔH favors spontaneity, but what about ΔS? The answer is that an increase in molecular disorder (ΔS positive) favors spontaneity. A good analogy is the bedroom or office that seems to spontaneously become more messy over time (an increase in disorder, ΔS positive); to clean it up (a decrease in disorder, ΔS negative) requires an input of energy, a nonspontaneous process. Using our chemical example, the combustion of a log spontaneously converts large, complex molecules like lignin and cellulose (high molecular order, low entropy) into CO_2 and H_2O (a large number of small molecules with higher entropy). For this process, the level of disorder increases, and so ΔS is positive. The reverse process—turning CO_2 and H_2O back into cellulose—does occur in photosynthesis, but it requires a significant input of energy in the form of sunlight.

When enthalpy and entropy are both favorable (ΔH negative, ΔS positive), a process is spontaneous; when both are unfavorable, a process is nonspontaneous. Clearly,

Entropy change ΔS A measure of the increase in disorder ($\Delta S = +$) or decrease in disorder ($\Delta S = -$) as a chemical reaction or physical change occurs.

Free-energy change ΔG A measure of the change in free energy as a chemical reaction or physical change occurs.

however, the two factors do not have to operate in the same direction. It is possible for a process to be *unfavored* by enthalpy (the process absorbs heat, and so, has a positive ΔH) and yet be *favored* by entropy (there is an increase in disorder, and so, ΔS is positive). The melting of an ice cube above 0 °C, for which $\Delta H = +1.44\,kcal/mol\,(+6.02\,kJ/mol)$ and $\Delta S = +5.26\,cal/(mol \cdot K)(+22.0\,J/(mol \cdot K))$ is such a process. To take both heat of reaction (ΔH) and change in disorder (ΔS) into account when determining the spontaneity of a process, a quantity called the **free-energy change** (ΔG) is needed:

Free-energy change

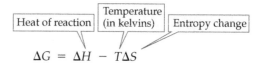

$$\Delta G = \Delta H - T\Delta S$$

Exergonic A spontaneous reaction or process that releases free energy and has a negative ΔG.

Endergonic A nonspontaneous reaction or process that absorbs free energy and has a positive ΔG.

The value of the free-energy change, ΔG, determines spontaneity. A negative value for ΔG means that free energy is released and the reaction or process is spontaneous. Such events are said to be **exergonic**. A positive value for ΔG means that free energy must be added and the process is nonspontaneous. Such events are said to be **endergonic**.

The equation for the free-energy change shows that spontaneity also depends on temperature (T). At low temperatures, the value of $T\,\Delta S$ is often small so that ΔH is the dominant factor. At a high enough temperature, however, the value of $T\,\Delta S$ can become larger than ΔH. Thus, an endothermic process that is nonspontaneous at a low temperature can become spontaneous at a higher temperature. An example is the industrial synthesis of hydrogen by reaction of carbon with water:

$$C(s) + H_2O(l) \longrightarrow CO(g) + H_2(g)$$
$$\Delta H = +31.3\,kcal/mol\,(+131.0\,kJ/mol) \qquad (Unfavorable)$$
$$\Delta S = +32\,cal/(mol \cdot K)(+134\,J/(mol \cdot K)) \quad (Favorable)$$

The reaction has an unfavorable (positive) ΔH term but a favorable (positive) ΔS term because disorder increases when a solid and a liquid are converted into two gases. No reaction occurs if carbon and water are mixed together at 25 °C (298 K) because the unfavorable ΔH is larger than the favorable $T\,\Delta S$. Above about 700 °C (973 K), however, the favorable $T\,\Delta S$ becomes larger than the unfavorable ΔH, so the reaction becomes spontaneous.

Important Points about Spontaneity and Free Energy

- A spontaneous process, once begun, proceeds without any external assistance and is exergonic; that is, free energy is released and it has a negative value of ΔG.
- A nonspontaneous process requires continuous external influence and is endergonic; that is, free energy is added and it has a positive value of ΔG.
- The value of ΔG for the reverse of a reaction is numerically equal to the value of ΔG for the forward reaction, but has the opposite sign.
- Some nonspontaneous processes become spontaneous with a change in temperature.

LOOKING AHEAD ▶▶▶ In later chapters, we will see that a knowledge of free-energy changes is especially important for understanding how metabolic reactions work. Living organisms cannot raise their temperatures to convert nonspontaneous reactions into spontaneous reactions, so they must resort to other strategies, which we will explore in Chapter 20.

Worked Example 7.5 Entropy Change of Processes

Does entropy increase or decrease in the following processes?

(a) Smoke from a cigarette disperses throughout a room rather than remaining in a cloud over the smoker's head.
(b) Water boils, changing from liquid to vapor.
(c) A chemical reaction occurs: $3 H_2(g) + N_2(g) \longrightarrow 2 NH_3(g)$

ANALYSIS Entropy is a measure of molecular disorder. Entropy increases when the products are more disordered than the reactants; entropy decreases when the products are less disordered than the reactants.

SOLUTION

(a) Entropy increases because smoke particles are more disordered when they are randomly distributed in the larger volume.
(b) Entropy increases because H_2O molecules have more freedom and disorder in the gas phase than in the liquid phase.
(c) Entropy decreases because 4 mol of reactant gas particles become 2 mol of product gas particles, with a consequent decrease in freedom and disorder.

Worked Example 7.6 Spontaneity of Reactions: Enthalpy, Entropy, and Free Energy

The industrial method for synthesizing hydrogen by reaction of carbon with water has $\Delta H = +31.3$ kcal/mol ($+131$ kJ/mol) and $\Delta S = +32$ cal/[mol·K]($+134$ J/[mol·K]). What is the value of ΔG (in kcal and kJ) for the reaction at 27 °C (300 K)? Is the reaction spontaneous or nonspontaneous at this temperature?

$$C(s) + H_2O(l) \longrightarrow CO(g) + H_2(g)$$

ANALYSIS The reaction is endothermic (ΔH positive) and does not favor spontaneity, whereas the ΔS indicates an increase in disorder (ΔS positive), which *does* favor spontaneity. Calculate ΔG to determine spontaneity.

BALLPARK ESTIMATE The unfavorable ΔH ($+31.3$ kcal/mol) is 1000 times greater than the favorable ΔS ($+32$ cal/mol·K), so the reaction will be spontaneous (ΔG negative) only when the temperature is high enough to make the $T \Delta S$ term in the equation for ΔG larger than the ΔH term. This happens at $T \geq 1000$ K. Since $T = 300$ K, expect ΔG to be positive and the reaction to be nonspontaneous.

SOLUTION
Use the free-energy equation to determine the value of ΔG at this temperature. (Remember that ΔS has units of *calories* per mole-kelvin or *joules* per mole-kelvin, not kilocalories per mole-kelvin or kilojoules per mole-kelvin.)

$$\Delta G = \Delta H - T \Delta S$$

$$\Delta G = +31.3 \frac{kcal}{mol} - (300\ K)\left(+32 \frac{cal}{mol \cdot K}\right)\left(\frac{1\ kcal}{1000\ cal}\right) = +21.7 \frac{kcal}{mol}$$

$$\Delta G = +131 \frac{kJ}{mol} - (300\ K)\left(+134 \frac{J}{mol \cdot K}\right)\left(\frac{1\ kJ}{1000\ J}\right) = +90.8 \frac{kJ}{mol}$$

BALLPARK CHECK Because ΔG is positive, the reaction is nonspontaneous at 300 K, consistent with our estimate.

PROBLEM 7.5
Does entropy increase or decrease in the following processes?

(a) Complex carbohydrates are metabolized by the body, converted into simple sugars.
(b) Steam condenses on a glass surface.
(c) $2 SO_2(g) + O_2(g) \longrightarrow 2 SO_3(g)$

PROBLEM 7.6

Lime (CaO) is prepared by the decomposition of limestone ($CaCO_3$).

$$CaCO_3(s) \longrightarrow CaO(s) + CO_2(g) \quad \Delta H = +42.6 \text{ kcal/mol} (+178.3 \text{ kJ/mol});$$
$$\Delta S = +38.0 \text{ cal}/(\text{mol} \cdot \text{K})(+159 \text{ J}/(\text{mol} \cdot \text{K})) \text{ at } 25 \text{ °C}$$

(a) Calculate ΔG at 25 °C. Give your answer in kcal/mol and kJ/mol. Does the reaction occur spontaneously?

(b) Would you expect the reaction to be spontaneous at higher or lower temperatures?

PROBLEM 7.7

The melting of solid ice to give liquid water has $\Delta H = +1.44 \text{ kcal/mol} (+6.02 \text{ kJ/mol})$ and $\Delta S = +5.26 \text{ cal}/(\text{mol} \cdot \text{K})(+22.0 \text{ J}/(\text{mol} \cdot \text{K}))$. What is the value of ΔG for the melting process at the following temperatures? Give your answer in kcal/mol and kJ/mol. Is the melting spontaneous or nonspontaneous at these temperatures?

(a) −10 °C (263 K)   **(b)** 0 °C (273 K)   **(c)** +10 °C (283 K)

KEY CONCEPT PROBLEM 7.8

The following diagram portrays a reaction of the type $A(s) \longrightarrow B(s) + C(g)$, where the different colored spheres represent different molecular structures. Assume that the reaction has $\Delta H = -23.5 \text{ kcal/mol} (-98.3 \text{ kJ/mol})$.

(a) What is the sign of ΔS for the reaction?

(b) Is the reaction likely to be spontaneous at all temperatures, nonspontaneous at all temperatures, or spontaneous at some but nonspontaneous at others?

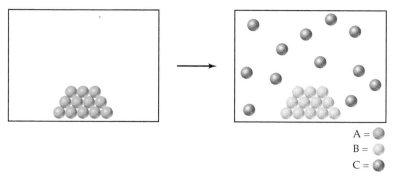

7.5 How Do Chemical Reactions Occur? Reaction Rates

Just because a chemical reaction has a favorable free-energy change does not mean that it occurs rapidly. The value of ΔG tells us only whether a reaction *can* occur; it says nothing about how *fast* the reaction will occur or about the details of the molecular changes that take place during the reaction. It is now time to look into these other matters.

For a chemical reaction to occur, reactant particles must collide, some chemical bonds have to break, and new bonds have to form. Not all collisions lead to products, however. One requirement for a productive collision is that the colliding molecules must approach with the correct orientation so that the atoms about to form new bonds can connect. In the reaction of ozone (O_3) with nitric oxide (NO) to give oxygen (O_2) and nitrogen dioxide (NO_2), for example, the two reactants must collide so that the nitrogen atom of NO strikes a terminal oxygen atom of O_3 (Figure 7.2).

Another requirement for a reaction to occur is that the collision must take place with enough energy to break the appropriate bonds in the reactant. If the reactant particles are moving slowly, collisions might be too gentle to overcome the repulsion between electrons in the different reactants, and the particles will simply bounce apart. A reaction will only occur if the collisions between reactant molecules are sufficiently energetic.

Effective collision:

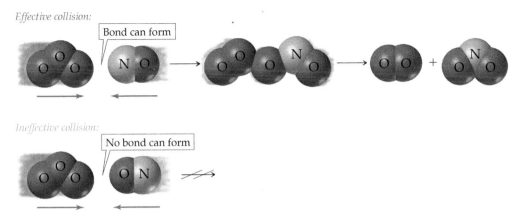

◄ **Figure 7.2**

How do chemical reactions occur?
For a collision between NO and O_3 molecules to give O_2 and NO_2, the molecules must collide so that the correct atoms come into contact. No bond forms if the molecules collide with the wrong orientation.

Ineffective collision:

For this reason, many reactions with a favorable free-energy change do not occur at room temperature. To get such a reaction started, energy (heat) must be added. The heat causes the reactant particles to move faster, thereby increasing both the frequency and the force of the collisions. We all know that matches burn, for instance, but we also know that they do not burst into flame until struck. The heat of friction provides enough energy for a few molecules to react. Once started, the reaction sustains itself as the energy released by reacting molecules gives other molecules enough energy to react.

The energy change that occurs during the course of a chemical reaction can be visualized in an energy diagram like that in Figure 7.3. At the beginning of the reaction (left side of the diagram), the reactants are at the energy level indicated. At the end of the reaction (right side of the diagram), the products are at a lower energy level than the reactants if the reaction is exergonic (Figure 7.3a) but higher than the reactants if the reaction is endergonic (Figure 7.3b).

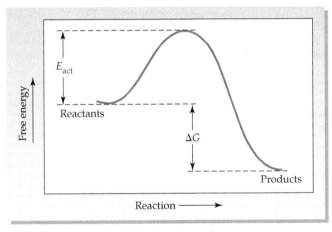

(a) An exergonic reaction

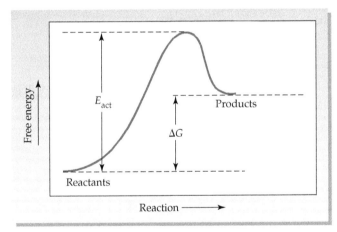

(b) An endergonic reaction

▲ **Figure 7.3**

Reaction energy diagrams show energy changes during a chemical reaction.
A reaction begins on the left and proceeds to the right. (a) In an exergonic reaction, the product energy level is lower than that of reactants. (b) In an endergonic reaction, the situation is reversed. The height of the barrier between reactant and product energy levels is the activation energy, E_{act}. The difference between reactant and product energy levels is the free-energy change, ΔG.

Lying between the reactants and the products is an energy "barrier" that must be surmounted. The height of this barrier represents the amount of energy the colliding particles must have for productive collisions to occur, an amount called the **activation energy (E_{act})** of the reaction. The size of the activation energy determines the **reaction rate**, or how fast the reaction occurs. The lower the activation energy, the greater the number of productive collisions in a given amount of time, and the faster the reaction. Conversely, the higher the activation energy, the lower the number of productive collisions, and the slower the reaction.

Activation energy (E_{act}) The amount of energy necessary for reactants to surmount the energy barrier to reaction; determines reaction rate.

Reaction rate A measure of how rapidly a reaction occurs; determined by E_{act}.

Note that the size of the activation energy and the size of the free-energy change are unrelated. A reaction with a large E_{act} takes place very slowly even if it has a large negative ΔG. Every reaction is different; each has its own characteristic activation energy and free-energy change.

Worked Example 7.7 Energy of Reactions: Energy Diagrams

Draw an energy diagram for a reaction that is very fast but has a small negative free-energy change.

ANALYSIS A very fast reaction has a small E_{act}. A reaction with a small negative free-energy change is a favorable reaction with a small energy difference between starting materials and products.

SOLUTION

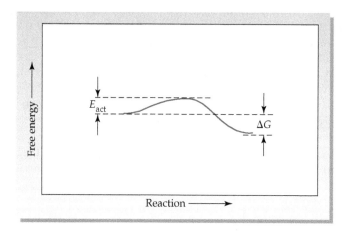

PROBLEM 7.9

Draw an energy diagram for a reaction that is very slow but highly favorable.

PROBLEM 7.10

Draw an energy diagram for a reaction that is slightly unfavorable.

7.6 Effects of Temperature, Concentration, and Catalysts on Reaction Rates

Several things can be done to help reactants over an activation energy barrier and thereby speed up a reaction. Let us look at some possibilities.

Temperature

One way to increase reaction rate is to add energy to the reactants by raising the temperature. With more energy in the system, the reactants move faster, so the frequency of collisions increases. Furthermore, the force with which collisions occur increases, making them more likely to overcome the activation barrier. As a rule of thumb, a 10 °C rise in temperature causes a reaction rate to double.

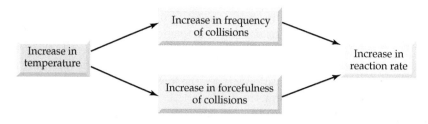

Concentration

A second way to speed up a reaction is to increase the **concentrations** of the reactants. As the concentration increases, reactants are crowded together, and collisions between reactant molecules become more frequent. As the frequency of collisions increases, reactions between molecules become more likely. Flammable materials burn more rapidly in pure oxygen than in air, for instance, because the concentration of O_2 molecules is higher (air is approximately 21% oxygen). Hospitals must therefore take extraordinary precautions to ensure that no flames are used near patients receiving oxygen. Although different reactions respond differently to concentration changes, doubling or tripling a reactant concentration often doubles or triples the reaction rate.

Concentration A measure of the amount of a given substance in a mixture.

Increase in concentration $\longrightarrow$ Increase in frequency of collisions $\longrightarrow$ Increase in reaction rate

Catalysts

A third way to speed up a reaction is to add a **catalyst**—a substance that accelerates a chemical reaction but is itself unchanged in the process. For example, metals such as nickel, palladium, and platinum catalyze the addition of hydrogen to the carbon–carbon double bonds in vegetable oils to yield semisolid margarine. Without the metal catalyst, the reaction does not occur.

Catalyst A substance that speeds up the rate of a chemical reaction but is itself unchanged.

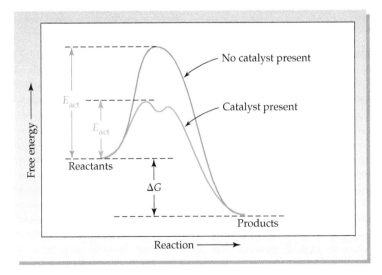

A catalyst does not affect the energy level of either reactants or products. Rather, it increases reaction rate either by letting a reaction take place through an alternative pathway with a lower energy barrier, or by orienting the reacting molecules appropriately. In a reaction energy diagram, the catalyzed reaction has a lower activation energy (Figure 7.4). It is worth noting that the free-energy change for a reaction depends *only* on the difference in the energy levels of the reactants and products, and *not* on the pathway of the reaction. Therefore, a catalyzed reaction releases (or absorbs) the same amount of energy as an uncatalyzed reaction. It simply occurs more rapidly.

◀ **Figure 7.4**
A reaction energy diagram for a reaction in the presence (green curve) and absence (blue curve) of a catalyst. The catalyzed reaction has a lower (E_{act}) because it uses an alternative pathway (represented by the multiple bumps in the green line) with a lower energy barrier. The free-energy change, ΔG, is unaffected by the presence of a catalyst.

In addition to their widespread use in industry, we also rely on catalysts to reduce the air pollution created by exhaust from automobile engines. The catalytic converters in most automobiles are tubes packed with catalysts of two types (Figure 7.5). One catalyst accelerates the complete combustion of hydrocarbons and CO in the exhaust to give CO_2 and H_2O, and the other decomposes NO to N_2 and O_2.

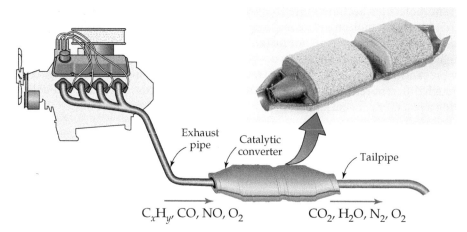

▶ **Figure 7.5**

A catalytic converter.
The exhaust gases from an automobile pass through a two-stage catalytic converter. In one stage, carbon monoxide and unburned hydrocarbons are converted to CO_2 and H_2O. In the second stage, NO is converted to N_2 and O_2.

Exhaust pipe

Catalytic converter

Tailpipe

C_xH_y, CO, NO, O_2 CO_2, H_2O, N_2, O_2

Table 7.3 summarizes the effects of changing conditions on reaction rates.

TABLE 7.3 Effects of Changes in Reaction Conditions on Reaction Rates

Change	Effect
Concentration	Increase in reactant concentration increases rate. Decrease in reactant concentration decreases rate.
Temperature	Increase in temperature increases rate. Decrease in temperature decreases rate.
Catalyst added	Increases reaction rate.

LOOKING AHEAD ▶▶▶ The thousands of biochemical reactions continually taking place in our bodies are catalyzed by large protein molecules called *enzymes*, which promote reactions by controlling the orientation of the reacting molecules. Since almost every reaction is catalyzed by its own specific enzyme, the study of enzyme structure, activity, and control is a central part of biochemistry. We will look more closely at enzymes and how they work in Chapter 19.

PROBLEM 7.11

Ammonia is synthesized industrially by reaction of nitrogen and hydrogen according to the equation $3 H_2(g) + N_2(g) \longrightarrow 2 NH_3(g)$. The free-energy change for this reaction is $\Delta G = -3.8$ kcal/mol (-16 kJ/mol), yet this reaction does not readily occur at room temperature.

(a) Draw a reaction energy diagram for this reaction, indicating E_{act} and ΔG.

(b) List three ways to increase the rate of this reaction.

PROBLEM 7.12

As we exercise, our bodies metabolize glucose, converting it to CO_2 and H_2O, to supply the energy necessary for physical activity. The simplified reaction is:

$$C_6H_{12}O_6(aq) + 6 O_2(g) \longrightarrow 6 CO_2(g) + 6 H_2O(l) + 678 \text{ kcal}(2840 \text{ kJ})$$

How many grams of water would have to be evaporated as sweat to remove the heat generated by the metabolism of 1 mol of glucose? (See Chemistry in Action: Regulation of Body Temperature on p. 195).

CHEMISTRY IN ACTION

Regulation of Body Temperature

Maintaining normal body temperature is crucial. If the body's thermostat is unable to maintain a temperature of 37 °C, the rates of the many thousands of chemical reactions that take place constantly in the body will change accordingly, with potentially disastrous consequences.

If, for example, a skater fell through the ice of a frozen lake, *hypothermia* could soon result. Hypothermia is a dangerous state that occurs when the body is unable to generate enough heat to maintain normal temperature. All chemical reactions in the body slow down because of the lower temperature, energy production drops, and death can result. Slowing the body's reactions can also be used to advantage, however. During open-heart surgery, the heart is stopped and maintained at about 15 °C, while the body, which receives oxygenated blood from an external pump, is cooled to 25–32 °C.

In this case, the body is receiving oxygenated blood from an external pump in an operating chamber under medical supervision. If hypothermia occurred due to some other environmental condition, the heart would slow down, respiration would decrease, and the body would not receive sufficient oxygen and death would result.

Conversely, a marathon runner on a hot, humid day might become overheated, and *hyperthermia* could result. Hyperthermia, also called *heat stroke*, is an uncontrolled rise in temperature as the result of the body's inability to lose sufficient heat. Chemical reactions in the body are accelerated at higher temperatures, the heart struggles to pump blood faster to supply increased oxygen, and brain damage can result if the body temperature rises above 41 °C.

Body temperature is maintained both by the thyroid gland and by the hypothalamus region of the brain, which act together to regulate metabolic rate. When the body's environment changes, temperature receptors in the skin, spinal cord, and abdomen send signals to the hypothalamus, which contains both heat-sensitive and cold-sensitive neurons.

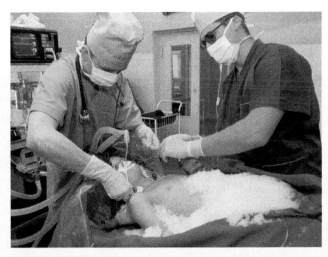

▲ **The body is cooled to 25–32°C by immersion in ice prior to open-heart surgery to slow down metabolism.**

Stimulation of the heat-sensitive neurons on a hot day causes a variety of effects: Impulses are sent to stimulate the sweat glands, dilate the blood vessels of the skin, decrease muscular activity, and reduce metabolic rate. Sweating cools the body through evaporation; approximately 540 cal (2260 J) is removed by evaporation of 1.0 g of sweat. Dilated blood vessels cool the body by allowing more blood to flow close to the surface of the skin, where heat is removed by contact with air. Decreased muscular activity and a reduced metabolic rate cool the body by lowering internal heat production.

Stimulation of the cold-sensitive neurons on a cold day also causes a variety of effects: The hormone epinephrine is released to stimulate metabolic rate; peripheral blood vessels contract to decrease blood flow to the skin and prevent heat loss; and muscular contractions increase to produce more heat, resulting in shivering and "goosebumps."

One further comment: Drinking alcohol to warm up on a cold day actually has the opposite effect. Alcohol causes blood vessels to dilate, resulting in a warm feeling as blood flow to the skin increases. Although the warmth feels good temporarily, body temperature ultimately drops as heat is lost through the skin at an increased rate.

See Chemistry in Action Problems 7.72 and 7.73 at the end of the chapter.

7.7 Reversible Reactions and Chemical Equilibrium

Many chemical reactions result in the virtually complete conversion of reactants into products. When sodium metal reacts with chlorine gas, for example, both are entirely consumed. The sodium chloride product is so much more stable than the reactants that, once started, the reaction keeps going until it is complete.

What happens, though, when the reactants and products are of approximately equal stability? This is the case, for example, in the reaction of acetic acid (the main organic constituent of vinegar) with ethyl alcohol to yield ethyl acetate, a solvent used in nail-polish remover and glue.

$$\underset{\text{Acetic acid}}{CH_3\overset{\overset{\displaystyle O}{\|}}{C}OH} + \underset{\text{Ethyl alcohol}}{HOCH_2CH_3} \underset{\text{Or this direction?}}{\overset{\text{This direction?}}{\rightleftharpoons}} \underset{\text{Ethyl acetate}}{CH_3\overset{\overset{\displaystyle O}{\|}}{C}OCH_2CH_3} + \underset{\text{Water}}{H_2O}$$

Reversible reaction A reaction that can go in either direction, from products to reactants or reactants to products.

Chemical equilibrium A state in which the rates of forward and reverse reactions are the same.

▶ **Figure 7.6**
Reaction rates in an equilibrium reaction.
The forward rate is large initially but decreases as the concentrations of reactants drop. The reverse rate is small initially but increases as the concentrations of products increase. At equilibrium, the forward and reverse reaction rates are equal.

▲ When the number of people moving up is the same as the number of people moving down, the number of people on each floor remains constant, and the two populations are in equilibrium.

Imagine the situation if you mix acetic acid and ethyl alcohol. The two begin to form ethyl acetate and water. But as soon as ethyl acetate and water form, they begin to go back to acetic acid and ethyl alcohol. Such a reaction, which easily goes in either direction, is said to be **reversible** and is indicated by a double arrow ($\rightleftharpoons$) in equations. The reaction read from left to right as written is referred to as the *forward reaction*, and the reaction from right to left is referred to as the *reverse reaction*.

Now suppose you mix some ethyl acetate and water. The same thing occurs: As soon as small quantities of acetic acid and ethyl alcohol form, the reaction in the other direction begins to take place. No matter which pair of reactants is mixed together, both reactions occur until ultimately the concentrations of reactants and products reach constant values and undergo no further change. At this point, the reaction vessel contains all four substances—acetic acid, ethyl acetate, ethyl alcohol, and water—and the reaction is said to be in a state of **chemical equilibrium**.

Since the reactant and product concentrations undergo no further change once equilibrium is reached, you might conclude that the forward and reverse reactions have stopped. That is not the case, however. The forward reaction takes place rapidly at the beginning of the reaction but then slows down as reactant concentrations decrease. At the same time, the reverse reaction takes place slowly at the beginning but then speeds up as product concentrations increase (Figure 7.6). Ultimately, the forward and reverse rates become equal and change no further.

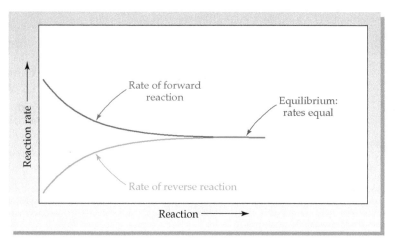

Chemical equilibrium is an active, dynamic condition. All substances present are continuously being made and unmade at the same rate, so their concentrations are constant at equilibrium. As an analogy, think of two floors of a building connected by up and down escalators. If the number of people moving up is the same as the number of people moving down, the numbers of people on each floor remain constant. *Individual people* are continuously changing from one floor to the other, but the *total populations* of the two floors are in equilibrium.

Note that it is not necessary for the concentrations of reactants and products at equilibrium to be equal (just as it is not necessary for the numbers of people on two floors connected by escalators to be equal). Equilibrium can be reached at any point between pure products and pure reactants. The extent to which the forward or reverse reaction is favored over the other is a characteristic property of a given reaction under given conditions.

7.8 Equilibrium Equations and Equilibrium Constants

Remember that the rate of a reaction depends on the number of collisions between molecules (Section 7.5), and that the number of collisions in turn depends on concentration, i.e., the number of molecules in a given volume (Section 7.6). For a reversible reaction, then, the rates of both the forward *and* the reverse reactions must depend on the concentration of reactants and products, respectively. When a reaction reaches equilibrium, the rates of the forward and reverse reactions are equal, and the concentrations of reactants and products remain constant. We can use this fact to obtain useful information about a reaction.

Let us look at the details of a specific equilibrium reaction. Suppose that you allow various mixtures of sulfur dioxide and oxygen to come to equilibrium with sulfur trioxide at a temperature of 727 °C and then measure the concentrations of all three gases in the mixtures.

$$2\,SO_2(g) + O_2(g) \rightleftharpoons 2\,SO_3(g)$$

In one experiment, we start with only 1.00 mol of SO_2 and 1.00 mol of O_2 in a 1.00 L container. In other words, the initial concentrations of reactants are 1.00 mol/L. When the reaction reaches equilibrium, we have 0.0620 mol/L of SO_2, 0.538 mol/L of O_2, and 0.938 mol/L of SO_3. In another experiment, we start with 1.00 mol/L of SO_3. When this reaction reaches equilibrium, we have 0.150 mol/L of SO_2, 0.0751 mol/L of O_2, and 0.850 mol/L of SO_3. In both cases, we see that there is substantially more product (SO_3) than reactants when the reaction reaches equilibrium, regardless of the starting conditions. Is it possible to predict what the equilibrium conditions will be for any given reaction?

As it turns out, the answer is YES! No matter what the original concentrations were, and no matter what concentrations remain at equilibrium, we find that a constant numerical value is obtained if the equilibrium concentrations are substituted into the expression

$$\frac{[SO_3]^2}{[SO_2]^2[O_2]} = \text{constant at a given T}$$

The square brackets in this expression indicate the concentration of each substance expressed as moles per liter. Using the equilibrium concentrations for each of the experiments described above, we can calculate the value and verify that it is constant:

Experiment 1. $\dfrac{[SO_3]^2}{[SO_2]^2[O_2]} = \dfrac{(0.938\ \text{mol/L})^2}{(0.0620\ \text{mol/L})^2(0.538\ \text{mol/L})} = 425$

Experiment 2. $\dfrac{[SO_3]^2}{[SO_2]^2[O_2]} = \dfrac{(0.850\ \text{mol/L})^2}{(0.150\ \text{mol/L})^2(0.0751\ \text{mol/L})} = 428$

At a temperature of 727 °C, the actual value of the constant is 429. Within experimental error, the ratios of product and reactant concentrations for the two experiments at equilibrium yield the same result. Numerous experiments like those just described have led to a general equation that is valid for any reaction. Consider a general reversible reaction:

$$a\text{A} + b\text{B} + \ldots \rightleftharpoons m\text{M} + n\text{N} + \ldots$$

where A, B, . . . are reactants; M, N, . . . are products; and $a, b, \ldots, m, n, \ldots$ are coefficients in the balanced equation. At equilibrium, the composition of the reaction mixture obeys the following *equilibrium equation*, where K is the **equilibrium constant**.

Equilibrium equation $K = \dfrac{[M]^m[N]^n \cdots}{[A]^a[B]^b \cdots}$ — Product concentrations

— Reactant concentrations

Equilibrium constant

Equilibrium constant (K) Value obtained at a given temperature from the ratio of the concentrations of products and reactants, each raised to a power equal to its coefficient in the balanced equation.

The equilibrium constant K is the number obtained by multiplying the equilibrium concentrations of the products and dividing by the equilibrium concentrations of the reactants, with the concentration of each substance raised to a power equal to its coefficient in the balanced equation. If we take another look at the reaction between sulfur dioxide and oxygen, we can now see how the equilibrium constant was obtained:

$$2\,SO_2\,(g)\,+\,O_2\,(g)\, \rightleftharpoons\,2\,SO_3\,(g)$$

$$K = \frac{[SO_3]^2}{[SO_2]^2\,[O_2]}$$

Note that if there is no coefficient for a reactant or product in the reaction equation, it is assumed to be 1. The value of K varies with temperature (25 °C) is assumed unless otherwise specified—and units are usually omitted.

For reactions that involve pure solids or liquids, these pure substances are omitted when writing the equilibrium constant expression. To explain why, consider the decomposition of limestone from Problem 7.6:

▶▶▶ The practice of omitting pure substances in the equilibrium constant expression will be utilized in Chapter 10 when we discuss equilibria involving acids and bases.

$$CaCO_3(s) \longrightarrow CaO(s) + CO_2(g)$$

Writing the equilibrium constant expression for this reaction as the concentration of products over the concentration of reactions would yield

$$K = \frac{[\,CaO\,][\,CO_2\,]}{[\,CaCO_3\,]}$$

Consider the solids CaO and $CaCO_3$. Their concentrations (in moles/L) can be calculated from their molar masses and densities at a given temperature. For example, the concentration of CaO at 25 °C can be calculated as

$$\frac{\left(3.25\,\frac{g\,CaO}{cm^3}\right) \cdot \left(\frac{1000\,cm^3}{L}\right)}{56.08\,\frac{g\,CaO}{mol\,CaO}} = 58.0\,\frac{mol\,CaO}{L}$$

The ratio of products over reactants would change if CO_2 was added to or removed from the reaction. The concentration of CaO, however, is the same whether we have 10 grams or 500 grams. Adding solid CaO will not change the ratio of products over reactants. Since the concentration of solids is independent of the amount of solid present, these concentrations are omitted and the expression for K becomes

$$K = \frac{[\,CaO\,][\,CO_2\,]}{[\,CaCO_3\,]} = [\,CO_2\,]$$

The value of the equilibrium constant indicates the position of a reaction at equilibrium. If the forward reaction is favored, the product term $[\,M\,]^m[\,N\,]^n$ is larger than the reactant term $[\,A\,]^a[\,B\,]^b$, and the value of K is larger than 1. If instead the reverse reaction is favored, $[\,M\,]^m[\,N\,]^n$ is smaller than $[\,A\,]^a[\,B\,]^b$ at equilibrium, and the value of K is smaller than 1.

For a reaction such as the combination of hydrogen and oxygen to form water vapor, the equilibrium constant is enormous (3.1×10^{81}), showing how greatly the formation of water is favored. Equilibrium is effectively nonexistent for such reactions, and the reaction is described as *going to completion*.

On the other hand, the equilibrium constant is very small for a reaction such as the combination of nitrogen and oxygen at 25 °C to give NO (4.7×10^{-31}), showing what we know from observation—that N_2 and O_2 in the air do not combine noticeably at room temperature:

$$N_2(g) + O_2(g) \rightleftharpoons 2\,NO(g) \quad K = \frac{[\,NO\,]^2}{[\,N_2\,][\,O_2\,]} = 4.7 \times 10^{-31}$$

When K is close to 1, say between 10^3 and 10^{-3}, significant amounts of both reactants and products are present at equilibrium. An example is the reaction of acetic acid with ethyl alcohol to give ethyl acetate (Section 7.7). For this reaction, $K = 3.4$.

$$CH_3CO_2H + CH_3CH_2OH \rightleftharpoons CH_3CO_2CH_2CH_3 + H_2O$$

$$K = \frac{[CH_3CO_2CH_2CH_3][H_2O]}{[CH_3CO_2H][CH_3CH_2OH]} = 3.4$$

We can summarize the meaning of equilibrium constants in the following way:

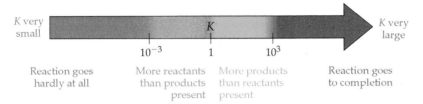

K very small			K very large
10^{-3}	1	10^3	
Reaction goes hardly at all	More reactants than products present	More products than reactants present	Reaction goes to completion

K much smaller than 0.001   Only reactants are present at equilibrium; essentially no reaction occurs.

K between 0.001 and 1   More reactants than products are present at equilibrium.

K between 1 and 1000   More products than reactants are present at equilibrium.

K much larger than 1000   Only products are present at equilibrium; reaction goes essentially to completion.

Worked Example 7.8 Writing Equilibrium Equations

The first step in the industrial synthesis of hydrogen is the reaction of steam with methane to give carbon monoxide and hydrogen. Write the equilibrium equation for the reaction.

$$H_2O(g) + CH_4(g) \rightleftharpoons CO(g) + 3 H_2(g)$$

ANALYSIS   The equilibrium constant K is the number obtained by multiplying the equilibrium concentrations of the products (CO and H_2) and dividing by the equilibrium concentrations of the reactants (H_2O and CH_4), with the concentration of each substance raised to the power of its coefficient in the balanced equation.

SOLUTION

$$K = \frac{[CO][H_2]^3}{[H_2O][CH_4]}$$

Worked Example 7.9 Equilibrium Equations: Calculating K

In the reaction of Cl_2 with PCl_3, the concentrations of reactants and products were determined experimentally at equilibrium and found to be 7.2 mol/L for PCl_3, 7.2 mol/L for Cl_2, and 0.050 mol/L for PCl_5.

$$PCl_3(g) + Cl_2(g) \rightleftharpoons PCl_5(g)$$

Write the equilibrium equation, and calculate the equilibrium constant for the reaction. Which reaction is favored, the forward one or the reverse one?

ANALYSIS   All the coefficients in the balanced equation are 1, so the equilibrium constant equals the concentration of the product, PCl_5, divided by the product of the concentrations of the two reactants, PCl_3 and Cl_2. Insert the values given for each concentration, and calculate the value of K.

BALLPARK ESTIMATE   At equilibrium, the concentration of the reactants (7.2 mol/L for each reactant) is higher than the concentration of the product (0.05 mol/L), so we expect a value of K less than 1.

SOLUTION

$$K = \frac{[PCl_5]}{[PCl_3][Cl_2]} = \frac{0.050 \text{ mol/L}}{(7.2 \text{ mol/L})(7.2 \text{ mol/L})} = 9.6 \times 10^{-4}$$

The value of K is less than 1, so the reverse reaction is favored. Note that units for K are omitted.

BALLPARK CHECK Our calculated value of K is just as we predicted: $K < 1$.

PROBLEM 7.13
Write equilibrium equations for the following reactions:
(a) $N_2O_4(g) \rightleftharpoons 2 NO_2(g)$
(b) $2 H_2S(g) + O_2(g) \rightleftharpoons 2 S(s) + 2 H_2O(g)$
(c) $2 BrF_5(g) \rightleftharpoons Br_2(g) + 5 F_2(g)$

PROBLEM 7.14
Do the following reactions favor reactants or products at equilibrium? Give relative concentrations at equilibrium.
(a) $Sucrose(aq) + H_2O(l) \rightleftharpoons Glucose(aq) + Fructose(aq)$ $K = 1.4 \times 10^5$
(b) $NH_3(aq) + H_2O(l) \rightleftharpoons NH_4^+(aq) + OH^-(aq)$ $K = 1.6 \times 10^{-5}$
(c) $Fe_2O_3(s) + 3 CO(g) \rightleftharpoons 2 Fe(s) + 3 CO_2(g)$ K (at 727 °C) $= 24.2$

PROBLEM 7.15
For the reaction $H_2(g) + I_2(g) \rightleftharpoons 2 HI(g)$, equilibrium concentrations at 25 °C are $[H_2] = 0.0510$ mol/L, $[I_2] = 0.174$ mol/L, and $[HI] = 0.507$ mol/L. What is the value of K at 25 °C?

🔑 **KEY CONCEPT PROBLEM 7.16**

The following diagrams represent two similar reactions that have achieved equilibrium:

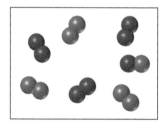

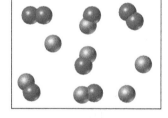

$A_2 + B_2 \longrightarrow 2 AB$ $A_2 + 2B \longrightarrow 2 AB$

(a) Write the expression for the equilibrium constant for each reaction.
(b) Calculate the value for the equilibrium constant for each reaction.

7.9 Le Châtelier's Principle: The Effect of Changing Conditions on Equilibria

The effect of a change in reaction conditions on chemical equilibrium is predicted by a general rule called *Le Châtelier's principle*:

Le Châtelier's principle When a stress is applied to a system at equilibrium, the equilibrium shifts to relieve the stress.

The word "stress" in this context means any change in concentration, pressure, volume, or temperature that disturbs the original equilibrium and causes the rates of the forward and reverse reactions to become temporarily unequal.

We saw in Section 7.6 that reaction rates are affected by changes in temperature and concentration, and by addition of a catalyst. But what about equilibria? Are they similarly affected? The answer is that changes in concentration, temperature, and pressure *do* affect equilibria, but that addition of a catalyst does not (except to reduce the time it takes to reach equilibrium). The change caused by a catalyst affects forward and reverse reactions equally so that equilibrium concentrations are the same in both the presence and the absence of the catalyst.

Effect of Changes in Concentration

Let us look at the effect of a concentration change by considering the reaction of CO with H_2 to form CH_3OH (methanol). Once equilibrium is reached, the concentrations of the reactants and product are constant, and the forward and reverse reaction rates are equal.

$$CO(g) + 2 H_2(g) \rightleftharpoons CH_3OH(g)$$

What happens if the concentration of CO is increased? To relieve the "stress" of added CO, according to Le Châtelier's principle, the extra CO must be used up. In other words, the rate of the forward reaction must increase to consume CO. Think of the CO added on the left as "pushing" the equilibrium to the right:

$$\underset{CO(g) + 2 H_2(g) \rightleftharpoons CH_3OH(g)}{[CO \longrightarrow]}$$

Of course, as soon as more CH_3OH forms, the reverse reaction also speeds up, some CH_3OH converts back to CO and H_2. Ultimately, the forward and reverse reaction rates adjust until they are again equal, and equilibrium is reestablished. At this new equilibrium state, the value of $[H_2]$ is lower because some of the H_2 reacted with the added CO and the value of $[CH_3OH]$ is higher because CH_3OH formed as the reaction was driven to the right by the addition of CO. The changes offset each other, however, so that the value of the equilibrium constant K remains constant.

$$CO(g) + 2 H_2(g) \rightleftharpoons CH_3OH(g)$$

If this increases . . .   . . . then this decreases . . .   . . . and this increases . . .

. . . but this remains constant. $K = \dfrac{[CH_3OH]}{[CO][H_2]^2}$

What happens if CH_3OH is added to the reaction at equilibrium? Some of the methanol reacts to yield CO and H_2, making the values of $[CO]$, $[H_2]$, and $[CH_3OH]$ higher when equilibrium is reestablished. As before, the value of K does not change.

If this increases . . .

$$CO(g) + 2 H_2(g) \rightleftharpoons CH_3OH(g)$$

. . . then this increases . . .   . . . and this increases . . .

. . . but this remains constant. $K = \dfrac{[CH_3OH]}{[CO][H_2]^2}$

Alternatively, we can view chemical equilibrium as a *balance* between the free energy of the reactants (on the left) and the free energy of the products (on the right). Adding more reactants tips the balance in favor of the reactants. In order to restore the balance, reactants must be converted to products, or the reaction must shift to the right. If, instead, we remove reactants, then the balance is too heavy on the product side and the reaction must shift left, generating more reactants to restore balance.

▶ Equilibrium represents a balance between the free energy of reactants and products. Adding reactants (or products) to one side upsets the balance, and the reaction will proceed in a direction to restore the balance.

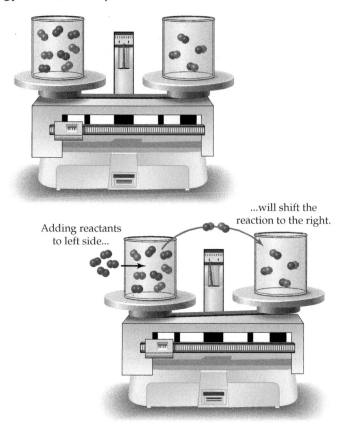

Adding reactants to left side...

...will shift the reaction to the right.

Finally, what happens if a reactant is continuously supplied or a product is continuously removed? Because the concentrations are continuously changing, equilibrium can never be reached. As a result, it is sometimes possible to force a reaction to produce large quantities of a desirable product even when the equilibrium constant is unfavorable. Take the reaction of acetic acid with ethanol to yield ethyl acetate, for example. As discussed in the preceding section, the equilibrium constant K for this reaction is 3.4, meaning that substantial amounts of reactants and products are both present at equilibrium. If, however, the ethyl acetate is removed as soon as it is formed, the production of more and more product is forced to occur, in accord with Le Châtelier's principle.

> Continuously removing this product from the reaction forces more of it to be produced.

$$\underset{\text{Acetic acid}}{CH_3\overset{\overset{\displaystyle O}{\|}}{C}OH} + \underset{\text{Ethyl alcohol}}{CH_3CH_2OH} \rightleftharpoons \underset{\text{Ethyl acetate}}{CH_3\overset{\overset{\displaystyle O}{\|}}{C}OCH_2CH_3} + H_2O$$

Metabolic reactions sometimes take advantage of this effect, with one reaction prevented from reaching equilibrium by the continuous consumption of its product in a further reaction.

Effect of Changes in Temperature and Pressure

We noted in Section 7.2 that the reverse of an exothermic reaction is always endothermic. Equilibrium reactions are therefore exothermic in one direction and endothermic in the other. Le Châtelier's principle predicts that an increase in temperature will cause an equilibrium to shift in favor of the endothermic reaction so the additional heat is absorbed. Conversely, a decrease in temperature will cause an equilibrium to shift in favor of the exothermic reaction so additional heat is released. In other words, you can think of heat as a reactant or product whose increase or decrease stresses an equilibrium just as a change in reactant or product concentration does.

Endothermic reaction   Favored by increase in temperature
(Heat is absorbed)

Exothermic reaction   Favored by decrease in temperature
(Heat is released)

In the exothermic reaction of N_2 with H_2 to form NH_3, for example, raising the temperature favors the reverse reaction, which absorbs the heat:

$$[\longleftarrow \text{Heat}]$$
$$N_2(g) \; + \; 3\,H_2(g) \; \rightleftharpoons \; 2\,NH_3(g) \; + \; \text{Heat}$$

We can also use the balance analogy to predict the effect of temperature on an equilibrium mixture; this time, we think of heat as a reactant or product. Increasing the temperature of the reaction is the same as adding heat to the left side (for an endothermic reaction) or to the right side (for an exothermic reaction). The reaction then proceeds in the appropriate direction to restore "balance" to the system.

What about changing the pressure? Pressure influences an equilibrium only if one or more of the substances involved is a gas. As predicted by Le Châtelier's principle, decreasing the volume to increase the pressure in such a reaction shifts the equilibrium in the direction that decreases the number of molecules in the gas phase and thus, decreases the pressure. For the ammonia synthesis, decreasing the volume *increases* the concentration of reactants and products, but has a greater effect on the reactant side of the equilibrium since there are more moles of gas phase reactants. Increasing the pressure, therefore, favors the forward reaction because 4 mol of gas is converted to 2 mol of gas.

$$[\text{Pressure} \longrightarrow]$$
$$\underbrace{N_2(g) \; + \; 3\,H_2(g)}_{\text{4 mol of gas}} \; \rightleftharpoons \; \underbrace{2\,NH_3(g)}_{\text{2 mol of gas}}$$

The effects of changing reaction conditions on equilibria are summarized in Table 7.4

TABLE **7.4** Effects of Changes in Reaction Conditions on Equilibria	
Change	**Effect**
Concentration	Increase in reactant concentration or decrease in product concentration favors forward reaction. Increase in product concentration or decrease in reactant concentration favors reverse reaction.
Temperature	Increase in temperature favors endothermic reaction. Decrease in temperature favors exothermic reaction.
Pressure	Increase in pressure favors side with fewer moles of gas. Decrease in pressure favors side with more moles of gas.
Catalyst added	Equilibrium reached more quickly; value of K unchanged.

LOOKING AHEAD ▶▶▶ In Chapter 20, we will see how Le Châtelier's principle is exploited to keep chemical "traffic" moving through the body's metabolic pathways. It often happens that one reaction in a series is prevented from reaching equilibrium because its product is continuously consumed in another reaction.

CHEMISTRY IN ACTION

Coupled Reactions

Living organisms are highly complex systems that use chemical reactions to produce the energy needed for daily activity. Many of these reactions occur very slowly—if at all—at normal body temperature, so organisms use several different strategies discussed in this chapter to obtain the energy they need and to function optimally. For example, the rates of slow reactions are increased by using biocatalysts, otherwise known as enzymes (Chapter 19). Le Châtelier's principle is used for regulation of critical processes, including oxygen transport (Chemistry in Action: Breathing and O_2 Transport, p. 263) and blood pH (Chemistry in Action: Buffers in the Body, p. 312). But what about reactions that do not occur spontaneously? One useful strategy is to "couple" a nonspontaneous reaction with a spontaneous one.

Coupling of reactions is a common strategy in both biochemical and industrial applications. Consider the following reaction for the recovery of copper metal from the smelting of ore containing Cu_2S:

$$Cu_2S(s) \longrightarrow 2\,Cu(s) + S(s) \quad \Delta G = +86.2\,kJ\,(+21.6\,kcal)$$

Since ΔG for this process is positive (endergonic), this reaction will not proceed spontaneously. But when the smelting process is performed at elevated temperatures in the presence of oxygen, this reaction can be "coupled" with another reaction:

$$Cu_2S(s) \longrightarrow 2\,Cu(s) + S(s) \quad \Delta G = +86.2\,kJ\,(+21.6\,kcal)$$
$$S(s) + O_2(g) \longrightarrow SO_2(g) \quad \Delta G = -300.1\,kJ\,(-71.7\,kcal)$$

Net Reaction: $Cu_2S(s) + O_2(g) \longrightarrow 2\,Cu(s) + SO_2(g)$
$$\Delta G = -213.9\,kJ\,(-51.1\,kcal)$$

The overall reaction has a negative ΔG (exergonic) to produce pure copper spontaneously.

Coupled Reactions in Biochemistry

An important example of coupled reactions in biochemistry is the endergonic phosphorylation of glucose (Section 22.6), which is the essential first step in the metabolism of glucose. It is combined with the hydrolysis of adenosine triphosphate (ATP) to form adenosine diphosphate (ADP), an exergonic process:

Glucose + $HOPO_3^{2-} \longrightarrow$ Glucose-6-phosphate + H_2O
$$\Delta G = +13.8\,kJ/mol$$

ATP + $H_2O \longrightarrow$ ADP + $HOPO_3^{2-}$ + H^+ $\quad \Delta G = -30.5\,kJ/mol$

Net Reaction: Glucose + ATP $\longrightarrow$ ADP + Glucose-6-phosphate
$$\Delta G = -16.7\,kJ/mol$$

In addition to the production of glucose-6-phosphate, which is critical for metabolic activity, any heat that is generated by the coupled reactions can be used to maintain body temperature.

See Chemistry in Action Problems 7.74 and 7.75 at the end of the chapter.

Worked Example 7.10 Le Châtelier's Principle and Equilibrium Mixtures

Nitrogen reacts with oxygen to give NO:

$$N_2(g) + O_2(g) \rightleftharpoons 2\,NO(g) \quad \Delta H = +43\,kcal/mol\,(+180\,kJ/mol)$$

Explain the effects of the following changes on reactant and product concentrations:

(a) Increasing temperature   **(b)** Increasing the concentration of NO

(c) Adding a catalyst

SOLUTION

(a) The reaction is endothermic (positive ΔH), so increasing the temperature favors the forward reaction. The concentration of NO will be higher at equilibrium.

(b) Increasing the concentration of NO, a product, favors the reverse reaction. At equilibrium, the concentrations of both N_2 and O_2, as well as that of NO, will be higher.

(c) A catalyst accelerates the rate at which equilibrium is reached, but the concentrations at equilibrium do not change.

PROBLEM 7.17

Is the yield of SO_3 at equilibrium favored by a higher or lower pressure? By a higher or lower temperature?

$$2\,SO_2(g) + O_2(g) \rightleftharpoons 2\,SO_3(g) \quad \Delta H = -47\,\text{kcal/mol}$$

PROBLEM 7.18

What effect do the listed changes have on the position of the equilibrium in the reaction of carbon with hydrogen?

$$C(s) + 2\,H_2(g) \rightleftharpoons CH_4(g) \quad \Delta H = -18\,\text{kcal/mol}\,(-75\,\text{kJ/mol})$$

(a) Increasing temperature

(b) Increasing pressure by decreasing volume

(c) Allowing CH_4 to escape continuously from the reaction vessel

PROBLEM 7.19

Another example of a coupled reaction used in the smelting of copper ore (Chemistry in Action: Coupled Reactions, p. 204) involves the following two reactions performed at 375 °C:

(1) $Cu_2O(s) \longrightarrow 2\,Cu(s) + \frac{1}{2}O_2(g) \quad \Delta G\,(\text{at } 375\,°C) = +140.0\,\text{kJ}\,(+33.5\,\text{kcal})$

(2) $C(s) + \frac{1}{2}O_2(g) \longrightarrow CO(g) \quad \Delta G\,(\text{at } 375\,°C) = -143.8\,\text{kJ}\,(-34.5\,\text{kcal})$

Derive the overall reaction and calculate the net free-energy change for the coupled reaction.

SUMMARY: REVISITING THE CHAPTER GOALS

1. What energy changes take place during reactions? The strength of a covalent bond is measured by its *bond dissociation energy*, the amount of energy that must be supplied to break the bond in an isolated gaseous molecule. For any reaction, the heat released or absorbed by changes in bonding is called the *heat of reaction*, or *enthalpy change* (ΔH). If the total strength of the bonds formed in a reaction is greater than the total strength of the bonds broken, then heat is released (negative ΔH) and the reaction is said to be *exothermic*. If the total strength of the bonds formed in a reaction is less than the total strength of the bonds broken, then heat is absorbed (positive ΔH) and the reaction is said to be *endothermic* (see Problems 26–33, 40, 62, 63, 70, 71, 76–78, 80, 81, 83, 85).

2. What is "free-energy," and what is the criterion for spontaneity in chemistry? *Spontaneous reactions* are those that, once started, continue without external influence; nonspontaneous reactions require a continuous external influence. Spontaneity depends on two factors, the amount of heat absorbed or released in a reaction (ΔH) and the *entropy change* (ΔS), which measures the change in molecular disorder in a reaction. Spontaneous reactions are favored by a release of heat (negative ΔH) and an increase in disorder (positive ΔS). The *free-energy change* (ΔG) takes both factors into account, according to the equation $\Delta G = \Delta H - T\,\Delta S$. A negative value for ΔG indicates spontaneity, and a positive value for ΔG indicates nonspontaneity (see Problems 20–22, 25, 34–43, 46, 50, 51, 73, 84).

3. What determines the rate of a chemical reaction? A chemical reaction occurs when reactant particles collide with proper orientation and sufficient energy. The exact amount of collision energy necessary is called the *activation energy* (E_{act}). A high activation energy results in a slow reaction because few collisions occur with sufficient force, whereas a low activation energy results in a fast reaction. Reaction rates can be increased by raising the temperature, by raising the concentrations of reactants, or by adding a *catalyst*, which accelerates a reaction without itself undergoing any change (see Problems 23, 24, 44–51, 75).

4. What is chemical equilibrium? A reaction that can occur in either the forward or reverse direction is *reversible* and will ultimately reach a state of *chemical equilibrium*. At equilibrium, the forward and reverse reactions occur at the same rate, and the concentrations of reactants and products are constant. Every reversible reaction has a characteristic *equilibrium constant* (K), given by an *equilibrium equation* (see Problems 52–63, 78, 82).

For the reaction: $aA + bB + \cdots \rightleftharpoons mM + nN + \cdots$

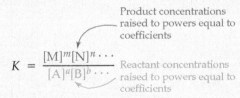

$$K = \frac{[M]^m[N]^n\cdots}{[A]^a[B]^b\cdots}$$

Product concentrations raised to powers equal to coefficients

Reactant concentrations raised to powers equal to coefficients

5. What is Le Châtelier's principle? *Le Châtelier's principle* states that when a stress is applied to a system in equilibrium, the equilibrium shifts so that the stress is relieved. Applying this principle allows prediction of the effects of changes in temperature, pressure, and concentration (see Problems 62–69, 79, 82).

CONCEPT MAP: CHEMICAL REACTIONS: ENERGY, RATES, AND EQUILIBRIUM

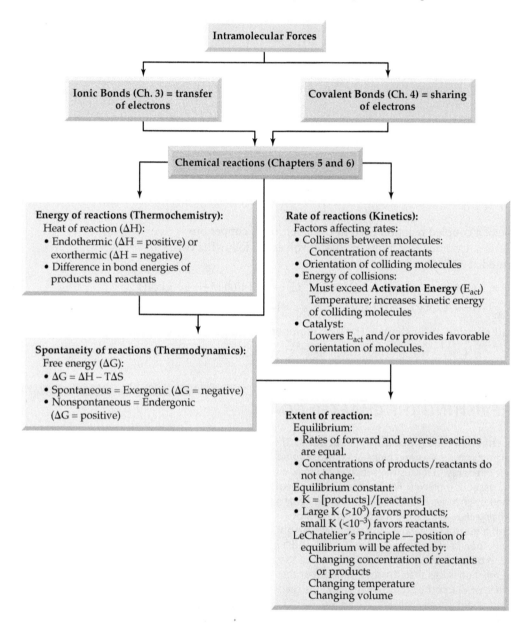

▶ **Figure 7.7**

Concept Map: We discussed the fundamentals of chemical reactions in Chapters 5 and 6. In Chapter 7 we looked at the heats of reaction, rates of reaction, spontaneity of reactions, and the extent of reaction as indicated by the equilibrium constant, K. These concepts, and the connections between them and previous concepts, are shown here in Figure 7.7.

KEY WORDS

Activation energy (E_{act}), *p. 191*

Bond dissociation energy, *p. 180*

Catalyst, *p. 193*

Chemical equilibrium, *p. 196*

Concentration, *p. 193*

Endergonic, *p. 188*

Endothermic, *p. 180*

Enthalpy (H), *p. 181*

Enthalpy change (ΔH), *p. 181*

Entropy (S), *p. 187*

Entropy change (ΔS), *p. 187*

Equilibrium constant (K), *p. 197*

Exergonic, *p. 188*

Exothermic, *p. 180*

Free-energy change (ΔG), *p. 188*

Heat, *p. 179*

Heat of reaction, *p. 181*

Kinetic energy, *p. 179*

Law of conservation of energy, *p. 181*

Le Châtelier's principle, *p. 200*

Potential energy, *p. 179*

Reaction rate, *p. 191*

Reversible reaction, *p. 196*

Spontaneous process, *p. 186*

UNDERSTANDING KEY CONCEPTS

7.20   What are the signs of ΔH, ΔS, and ΔG for the spontaneous conversion of a crystalline solid into a gas? Explain.

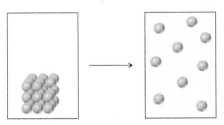

7.21   What are the signs of ΔH, ΔS, and ΔG for the spontaneous condensation of a vapor to a liquid? Explain.

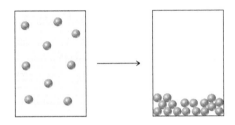

7.22   Consider the following spontaneous reaction of A_2 molecules (red) and B_2 molecules (blue):

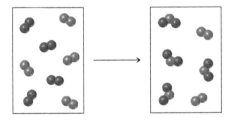

    (a) Write a balanced equation for the reaction.

    (b) What are the signs of ΔH, ΔS, and ΔG for the reaction? Explain.

7.23   Two curves are shown in the following energy diagram:

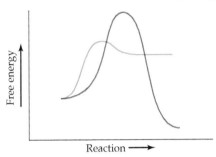

    (a) Which curve represents the faster reaction, and which the slower?

    (b) Which curve represents the spontaneous reaction, and which the nonspontaneous?

7.24   Draw energy diagrams for the following situations:

    (a) A slow reaction with a large negative ΔG

    (b) A fast reaction with a small positive ΔG

7.25   The following diagram portrays a reaction of the type $A(s) \longrightarrow B(g) + C(g)$, where the different colored spheres represent different molecular structures. Assume that the reaction has $\Delta H = +9.1$ kcal/mol ($+38.1$ kJ/mol).

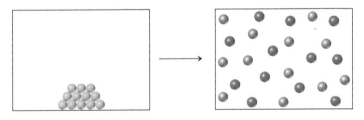

    (a) What is the sign of ΔS for the reaction?

    (b) Is the reaction likely to be spontaneous at all temperatures, nonspontaneous at all temperatures, or spontaneous at some but nonspontaneous at others?

ADDITIONAL PROBLEMS

ENTHALPY AND HEAT OF REACTION

7.26   Is the total enthalpy (H) of the reactants for an endothermic reaction greater than or less than the total enthalpy of the products?

7.27   What is meant by the term *heat of reaction*? What other name is a synonym for this term?

7.28   The vaporization of Br_2 from the liquid to the gas state requires 7.4 kcal/mol (31.0 kJ/mol).

    (a) What is the sign of ΔH for this process? Write a reaction showing heat as a product or reactant.

    (b) How many kilocalories are needed to vaporize 5.8 mol of Br_2?

    (c) How many kilojoules are needed to evaporate 82 g of Br_2?

7.29   Converting liquid water to solid ice releases 1.44 kcal/mol (6.02 kJ/mol).

    (a) What is the sign of ΔH for this process? Write a reaction showing heat as a product or reactant.

    (b) How many kilojoules are released by freezing 2.5 mol of H_2O?

(c) How many kilocalories are released by freezing 32 g of H_2O?

(d) How many kilocalories are absorbed by melting 1 mol of ice?

7.30 Acetylene $(H—C≡C—H)$ is the fuel used in welding torches.

(a) Write the balanced chemical equation for the combustion reaction of 1 mol of acetylene with $O_2(g)$ to produce $CO_2(g)$ and water vapor.

(b) Estimate ΔH for this reaction (in kJ/mol) using the bond energies listed in Table 7.1

(c) Calculate the energy value (in kJ/g) for acetylene. How does it compare to the energy values for other fuels in Table 7.2?

7.31 Nitrogen in air reacts at high temperatures to form NO_2 according to the following reaction: $N_2 + 2 O_2 \longrightarrow 2 NO_2$

(a) Draw structures for the reactant and product molecules indicating single, double, and triple bonds.

(b) Estimate ΔH for this reaction (in kcal and kJ) using the bond energies from Table 7.1.

7.32 Glucose, also known as "blood sugar" when measured in blood, has the formula $C_6H_{12}O_6$.

(a) Write the equation for the combustion of glucose with O_2 to give CO_2 and H_2O.

(b) If 3.8 kcal (16 kJ) is released by combustion of each gram of glucose, how many kilocalories are released by the combustion of 1.50 mol of glucose? How many kilojoules?

(c) What is the minimum amount of energy (in kJ) a plant must absorb to produce 15.0 g of glucose?

7.33 During the combustion of 5.00 g of octane, C_8H_{18}, 239.5 kcal (1002 kJ) is released.

(a) Write a balanced equation for the combustion reaction.

(b) What is the sign of ΔH for this reaction?

(c) How much energy (in kJ) is released by the combustion of 1.00 mol of C_8H_{18}?

(d) How many grams and how many moles of octane must be burned to release 450.0 kcal?

(e) How many kilojoules are released by the combustion of 17.0 g of C_8H_{18}?

ENTROPY AND FREE ENERGY

7.34 Which of the following processes results in an increase in entropy of the system?

(a) A drop of ink spreading out when it is placed in water

(b) Steam condensing into drops on windows

(c) Constructing a building from loose bricks

7.35 For each of the following processes, specify whether entropy increases or decreases. Explain each of your answers.

(a) Assembling a jigsaw puzzle

(b) $I_2(s) + 3 F_2(g) \longrightarrow 2 IF_3(g)$

(c) A precipitate forming when two solutions are mixed

(d) $C_6H_{12}O_6(aq) + 6 O_2(g) \longrightarrow 6 CO_2(g) + 6 H_2O(g)$

(e) $CaCO_3(s) \longrightarrow CaO(s) + CO_2(g)$

(f) $Pb(NO_3)_2(aq) + 2 NaCl(aq) \longrightarrow$
$$PbCl_2(s) + 2 NaNO_3(aq)$$

7.36 What two factors affect the spontaneity of a reaction?

7.37 What is the difference between an exothermic reaction and an exergonic reaction?

7.38 Why are most spontaneous reactions exothermic?

7.39 Under what conditions might a reaction be endothermic, but exergonic? Explain.

7.40 For the reaction
$$NaCl(s) \xrightarrow{Water} Na^+(aq) + Cl^-(aq),$$
$$\Delta H = +1.00 \text{ kcal/mol } (+4.184 \text{ kJ/mol})$$

(a) Is this process endothermic or exothermic?

(b) Does entropy increase or decrease in this process?

(c) Table salt (NaCl) readily dissolves in water. Explain, based on your answers to parts (a) and (b).

7.41 For the reaction $2 Hg(l) + O_2(g) \longrightarrow 2 HgO(s)$,
$$\Delta H = -43 \text{ kcal/mol } (-180 \text{ kJ/mol}).$$

(a) Does entropy increase or decrease in this process? Explain.

(b) Under what conditions would you expect this process to be spontaneous?

7.42 The reaction of gaseous H_2 and liquid Br_2 to give gaseous HBr has $\Delta H = -17.4 \text{ kcal/mol } (-72.8 \text{ kJ/mol})$ and $\Delta S = 27.2 \text{ cal/(mol·K)}(114 \text{ J/(mol·K)})$.

(a) Write the balanced equation for this reaction.

(b) Does entropy increase or decrease in this process?

(c) Is this process spontaneous at all temperatures? Explain.

(d) What is the value of ΔG (in kcal and kJ) for the reaction at 300 K?

7.43 The following reaction is used in the industrial synthesis of PVC polymer:
$$Cl_2(g) + H_2C=CH_2(g) \longrightarrow$$
$$ClCH_2CH_2Cl(l) \quad \Delta H = -52 \text{ kcal/mol } (-218 \text{ kJ/mol})$$

(a) Is ΔS positive or negative for this process?

(b) Is this process spontaneous at all temperatures? Explain.

RATES OF CHEMICAL REACTIONS

7.44 What is the activation energy of a reaction?

7.45 Which reaction is faster, one with $E_{act} = +10 \text{ kcal/mol } (+41.8 \text{ kJ/mol})$ or one with $E_{act} = +5 \text{ kcal/mol } (+20.9 \text{ kJ/mol})$? Explain.

7.46 Draw energy diagrams for exergonic reactions that meet the following descriptions:

(a) A slow reaction that has a small free-energy change

(b) A fast reaction that has a large free-energy change

7.47 Why does increasing concentration generally increase the rate of a reaction?

7.48 What is a catalyst, and what effect does it have on the activation energy of a reaction?

7.49 If a catalyst changes the activation energy of a forward reaction from 28.0 kcal/mol to 23.0 kcal/mol, what effect does it have on the reverse reaction?

7.50 For the reaction $C(s, \text{diamond}) \longrightarrow C(s, \text{graphite})$,

$$\Delta G = -0.693 \text{ kcal/mol} (-2.90 \text{ kJ/mol}) \text{ at } 25 \text{ °C}.$$

(a) According to this information, do diamonds spontaneously turn into graphite?

(b) In light of your answer to part (a), why can diamonds be kept unchanged for thousands of years?

7.51 The reaction between hydrogen gas and carbon to produce the gas known as ethylene is

$$2 H_2(g) + 2 C(s) \longrightarrow H_2C{=}CH_2(g),$$
$$\Delta G = +16.3 \text{ kcal/mol} (+68.2 \text{ kJ/mol}) \text{ at } 25 \text{ °C}.$$

(a) Is this reaction spontaneous at 25 °C?

(b) Would it be reasonable to try to develop a catalyst for the reaction run at 25 °C? Explain.

CHEMICAL EQUILIBRIA

7.52 What is meant by the term "chemical equilibrium"? Must amounts of reactants and products be equal at equilibrium?

7.53 Why do catalysts not alter the amounts of reactants and products present at equilibrium?

7.54 Write the equilibrium constant expressions for the following reactions:

(a) $2 CO(g) + O_2(g) \rightleftharpoons 2 CO_2(g)$

(b) $Mg(s) + HCl(aq) \rightleftharpoons MgCl_2(aq) + H_2(g)$

(c) $HF(aq) + H_2O(l) \rightleftharpoons H_3O^+(aq) + F^-(aq)$

(d) $S(s) + O_2(g) \rightleftharpoons SO_2(g)$

7.55 Write the equilibrium constant expressions for the following reactions.

(a) $S_2(g) + 2 H_2(g) \rightleftharpoons 2 H_2S(g)$

(b) $H_2S(aq) + Cl_2(aq) \rightleftharpoons S(s) + 2 HCl(aq)$

(c) $Br_2(g) + Cl_2(g) \rightleftharpoons 2 BrCl(g)$

(d) $C(s) + H_2O(g) \rightleftharpoons CO(g) + H_2(g)$

7.56 For the reaction $N_2O_4(g) \rightleftharpoons 2 NO_2(g)$, the equilibrium concentrations at 25 °C are $[NO_2] = 0.0325 \text{ mol/L}$ and $[N_2O_4] = 0.147 \text{ mol/L}$.

(a) What is the value of K at 25 °C? Are reactants or products favored?

7.57 For the reaction $2 CO(g) + O_2(g) \rightleftharpoons 2 CO_2(g)$, the equilibrium concentrations at a certain temperature are $[CO_2] = 0.11 \text{ mol/L}$, $[O_2] = 0.015 \text{ mol/L}$, $[CO] = 0.025 \text{ mol/L}$.

(a) Write the equilibrium constant expression for the reaction.

(b) What is the value of K at this temperature? Are reactants or products favored?

7.58 Use your answer from Problem 7.56 to calculate the following:

(a) $[N_2O_4]$ at equilibrium when $[NO_2] = 0.0250 \text{ mol/L}$

(b) $[NO_2]$ at equilibrium when $[N_2O_4] = 0.0750 \text{ mol/L}$

7.59 Use your answer from Problem 7.57 to calculate the following:

(a) $[O_2]$ at equilibrium when $[CO_2] = 0.18 \text{ mol/L}$ and $[CO] = 0.0200 \text{ mol/L}$

(b) $[CO_2]$ at equilibrium when $[CO] = 0.080 \text{ mol/L}$ and $[O_2] = 0.520 \text{ mol/L}$

7.60 Would you expect to find relatively more reactants or more products for the reaction in Problem 7.56 if the pressure is raised? Explain.

7.61 Would you expect to find relatively more reactants or more products for the reaction in Problem 7.57 if the pressure is lowered?

LE CHÂTELIER'S PRINCIPLE

7.62 Oxygen can be converted into ozone by the action of lightning or electric sparks:

$$3 O_2(g) \rightleftharpoons 2 O_3(g)$$

For this reaction, $\Delta H = +68 \text{ kcal/mol} (+285 \text{ kJ/mol})$ and $K = 2.68 \times 10^{-29}$ at 25 °C.

(a) Is the reaction exothermic or endothermic?

(b) Are the reactants or the products favored at equilibrium?

(c) Explain the effect on the equilibrium of

(1) increasing pressure by decreasing volume.

(2) increasing the concentration of $O_2(g)$.

(3) increasing the concentration of $O_3(g)$.

(4) adding a catalyst.

(5) increasing the temperature.

7.63 Hydrogen chloride can be made from the reaction of chlorine and hydrogen:

$$Cl_2(g) + H_2(g) \longrightarrow 2 HCl(g)$$

For this reaction, $K = 26 \times 10^{33}$ and $\Delta H = -44 \text{ kcal/mol} (-184 \text{ kJ/mol})$ at 25 °C.

(a) Is the reaction endothermic or exothermic?

(b) Are the reactants or the products favored at equilibrium?

(c) Explain the effect on the equilibrium of
   (1) Increasing pressure by decreasing volume
   (2) Increasing the concentration of $HCl(g)$
   (3) Decreasing the concentration of $Cl_2(g)$
   (4) Increasing the concentration of $H_2(g)$
   (5) Adding a catalyst

7.64 When the following equilibria are disturbed by increasing the pressure, does the concentration of reaction products increase, decrease, or remain the same?

(a) $2 CO_2(g) \rightleftharpoons 2 CO(g) + O_2(g)$

(b) $N_2(g) + O_2(g) \rightleftharpoons 2 NO(g)$

(c) $Si(s) + 2 Cl_2(g) \rightleftharpoons SiCl_4(g)$

7.65 For the following equilibria, use Le Châtelier's principle to predict the direction of the reaction when the pressure is increased by decreasing the volume of the equilibrium mixture.

(a) $C(s) + H_2O(g) \rightleftharpoons CO(g) + H_2(g)$

(b) $2 H_2(g) + O_2(g) \rightleftharpoons 2 H_2O(g)$

(c) $2 Fe(s) + 3 H_2O(g) \rightleftharpoons Fe_2O_3(s) + 3 H_2(g)$

7.66 The reaction $CO(g) + H_2O(g) \rightleftharpoons CO_2(g) + H_2(g)$ has $\Delta H = -9.8 \, kcal/mol \, (-41 \, kJ/mol)$. Does the amount of H_2 in an equilibrium mixture increase or decrease when the temperature is decreased?

7.67 The reaction $3 O_2(g) \rightleftharpoons 2 O_3(g)$ has $\Delta H = +68 \, kcal/mol \, (+285 \, kJ/mol)$. Does the equilibrium constant for the reaction increase or decrease when the temperature increases?

7.68 The reaction $H_2(g) + I_2(g) \rightleftharpoons 2 HI(g)$ has $\Delta H = -2.2 \, kcal/mol \, (-9.2 kJ/mol)$. Will the equilibrium concentration of HI increase or decrease when

(a) I_2 is added?

(b) H_2 is removed?

(c) a catalyst is added?

(d) the temperature is increased?

7.69 The reaction $Fe^{3+}(aq) + Cl^-(aq) \rightleftharpoons FeCl^{2+}(aq)$ is endothermic. How will the equilibrium concentration of $FeCl^{2+}$ change when

(a) $Fe(NO_3)_3$ is added?

(b) Cl^- is precipitated by addition of $AgNO_3$?

(c) the temperature is increased?

(d) a catalyst is added?

CHEMISTRY IN ACTION

7.70 Which provides more energy, 1 g of carbohydrate or 1 g of fat? [*Energy from Food, p. 185*]

7.71 How many Calories (that is, kilocalories) are in a 45.0 g serving of potato chips if we assume that they are essentially 50% carbohydrate and 50% fats? [*Energy from Food, p. 185*]

7.72 Which body organs help to regulate body temperature? [*Regulation of Body Temperature, p. 195*]

7.73 What is the purpose of blood vessel dilation? [*Regulation of Body Temperature, p. 195*]

7.74 The ATP required for the production of glucose-6-phosphate is regenerated by another coupled reaction:

$$ADP + HOPO_3{}^{2-} \longrightarrow ATP + H_2O \quad \Delta G = +30.5 \, kJ/mol$$

$$Phosphoenolpyruvate + H_2O \longrightarrow pyruvate + HOPO_3{}^{2-}$$
$$\Delta G = -61.9 \, kJ/mol$$

Derive the net reaction and calculate ΔG for the coupled reaction. [*Coupled Reactions, p. 204*]

7.75 The coupling of reactions in the smelting of copper at elevated temperatures yields an overall reaction that is energetically favorable. Why is the use of elevated temperature not feasible for most living organisms, and what other strategies do they use to make reactions occur at normal body temperatures? [*Coupled Reactions, p. 204*]

GENERAL QUESTIONS AND PROBLEMS

7.76 For the unbalanced combustion reaction shown below, 1 mol of ethanol, C_2H_5OH, releases 327 kcal (1370 kJ).

$$C_2H_5OH + O_2 \longrightarrow CO_2 + H_2O$$

(a) Write a balanced equation for the combustion reaction.

(b) What is the sign of ΔH for this reaction?

(c) How much heat (in kilocalories) is released from the combustion of 5.00 g of ethanol?

(d) How many grams of C_2H_5OH must be burned to raise the temperature of 500.0 mL of water from 20.0 °C to 100.0 °C? (The specific heat of water is 1.00 cal/g·°C or 4.184 J/g·°C. See Section 1.13.)

(e) If the density of ethanol is 0.789 g/mL, calculate the combustion energy of ethanol in kilocalories/milliliter and kilojoules/milliliter

7.77 For the production of ammonia from its elements, $\Delta H = -22 \, kcal/mol \, (-92 \, kJ/mol)$.

(a) Is this process endothermic or exothermic?

(b) How much energy (in kilocalories and kilojoules) is involved in the production of 0.700 mol of NH_3?

7.78 Magnetite, an iron ore with formula Fe_3O_4, can be reduced by treatment with hydrogen to yield iron metal and water vapor.

(a) Write the balanced equation.

(b) This process requires 36 kcal (151 kJ) for every 1.00 mol of Fe_3O_4 reduced. How much energy (in kilocalories and kilojoules) is required to produce 55 g of iron?

(c) How many grams of hydrogen are needed to produce 75 g of iron?

(d) This reaction has $K = 2.3 \times 10^{-18}$. Are the reactants or the products favored?

7.79 Hemoglobin (Hb) reacts reversibly with O_2 to form HbO_2, a substance that transfers oxygen to tissues:

$$Hb(aq) + O_2(aq) \rightleftharpoons HbO_2(aq)$$

Carbon monoxide (CO) is attracted to Hb 140 times more strongly than O_2 and establishes another equilibrium.

(a) Explain, using Le Châtelier's principle, why inhalation of CO can cause weakening and eventual death.

(b) Still another equilibrium is established when both O_2 and CO are present:

$$Hb(CO)(aq) + O_2(aq) \rightleftharpoons HbO_2(aq) + CO(aq)$$

Explain, using Le Châtelier's principle, why pure oxygen is often administered to victims of CO poisoning.

7.80 Urea is a metabolic waste product that decomposes to ammonia and water according to the following reaction:

$$NH_2CONH_2 + H_2O \longrightarrow 2\,NH_3 + CO_2.$$

(a) Draw the Lewis structure for urea.

(b) Estimate ΔH (in kcal and kJ) for this reaction using the bond energies from Table 7.1.

7.81 For the evaporation of water, $H_2O(l) \longrightarrow H_2O(g)$, at 100 °C, $\Delta H = +9.72$ kcal/mol ($+40.7$ kJ/mol).

(a) How many kilocalories are needed to vaporize 10.0 g of $H_2O(l)$?

(b) How many kilojoules are released when 10.0 g of $H_2O(g)$ is condensed?

7.82 Ammonia reacts slowly in air to produce nitrogen monoxide and water vapor:

$$NH_3(g) + O_2(g) \rightleftharpoons NO(g) + H_2O(g) + Heat$$

(a) Balance the equation.

(b) Write the equilibrium equation.

(c) Explain the effect on the equilibrium of

(1) raising the pressure.
(2) adding $NO(g)$.
(3) decreasing the concentration of NH_3.
(4) lowering the temperature.

7.83 Methanol, CH_3OH, is used as race car fuel.

(a) Write the balanced equation for the combustion reaction of methanol with O_2 to form CO_2 and H_2O.

(b) $\Delta H = -174$ kcal/mol (-728 kJ/mol) methanol for the process. How many kilocalories are released by burning 1.85 mol of methanol?

(c) How many kilojoules are released by burning 50.0 g of methanol?

7.84 Sketch an energy diagram for a system in which the forward reaction has $E_{act} = +25$ kcal/mol ($+105$ kJ/mol) and the reverse reaction has $E_{act} = +35$ kcal/mol ($+146$ kJ/mol).

(a) Is the forward process endergonic or exergonic?

(b) What is the value of ΔG for the reaction?

7.85 The thermite reaction (photograph, p. 181), in which aluminum metal reacts with iron(III) oxide to produce a spectacular display of sparks, is so exothermic that the product (iron) is in the molten state:

$$2\,Al(s) + Fe_2O_3(s) \longrightarrow 2\,Al_2O_3(s) + 2\,Fe(l)$$
$$\Delta H = -202.9 \text{ kcal/mol } (-848.9 \text{ kJ/mol})$$

(a) How much heat is released (in kilojoules) when 0.255 mol of Al is used in this reaction?

(b) How much heat (in kilocalories) is released when 5.00 g of Al is used in the reaction?

7.86 How much heat (in kilocalories) is evolved or absorbed in the reaction of 1.00 g of Na with H_2O? Is the reaction exothermic or endothermic?

$$2\,Na(s) + 2\,H_2O(l) \longrightarrow 2\,NaOH(aq) + H_2(g)$$
$$\Delta H = -88.0 \text{ kcal/mol } (-368 \text{ kJ/mol})$$

CHAPTER 8

Gases, Liquids, and Solids

CONTENTS

◄ This winter scene in Yellowstone National Park shows the three states of matter for water—solid (snow/ice), liquid (water), and gas (steam/water vapor)—all present at the same time.

CHAPTER GOALS

1. **What are the major intermolecular forces, and how do they affect the states of matter?**
   THE GOAL: Be able to explain dipole–dipole forces, London dispersion forces, and hydrogen bonding, recognize which of these forces affect a given molecule, and understand how these forces are related to the physical properties of a substance. (◀◀ B.)

2. **How do scientists explain the behavior of gases?**
   THE GOAL: Be able to state the assumptions of the kinetic–molecular theory and use these assumptions to explain the behavior of gases. (◀◀ B.)

3. **How do gases respond to changes in temperature, pressure, and volume?**
   THE GOAL: Be able to use Boyle's law, Charles's law, Gay-Lussac's law, and Avogadro's law to explain the effect on gases of a change in pressure, volume, or temperature.

4. **What is the ideal gas law?**
   THE GOAL: Be able to use the ideal gas law to find the pressure, volume, temperature, or molar amount of a gas sample.

5. **What is partial pressure?**
   THE GOAL: Be able to define partial pressure and use Dalton's law of partial pressures.

6. **What are the various kinds of solids, and how do they differ?**
   THE GOAL: Be able to recognize the different kinds of solids and describe their characteristics. (◀◀ A., B.)

7. **What factors affect a change of state?**
   THE GOAL: Be able to apply the concepts of heat change, equilibrium, vapor pressure, and intermolecular forces to changes of state. (◀◀ A., B., C.)

The previous seven chapters dealt with matter at the atomic level. We have seen that all matter is composed of atoms, ions, or molecules; that these particles are in constant motion; that atoms combine to make compounds using chemical bonds; and that physical and chemical changes are accompanied by the release or absorption of energy. Now it is time to look at a different aspect of matter, concentrating not on the properties and small-scale behavior of individual atoms but on the properties and large-scale behavior of visible amounts of matter and the factors that affect those properties.

8.1 States of Matter and Their Changes

Matter exists in any of three phases, or *states*—solid, liquid, or gas. The state in which a compound exists under a given set of conditions depends on the relative strength of the attractive forces between particles compared to the kinetic energy of the particles. Kinetic energy (Section 7.1) is energy associated with motion and is related to the temperature of the substance. In gases, the attractive forces between particles are very weak compared to their kinetic energy, so the particles move about freely, are far apart, and have almost no influence on one another. In liquids, the attractive forces between particles are stronger, pulling the particles close together but still allowing them considerable freedom to move about. In solids, the attractive forces are much stronger than the kinetic energy of the particles, so the atoms, molecules, or ions are held in a specific arrangement and can only wiggle around in place (Figure 8.1).

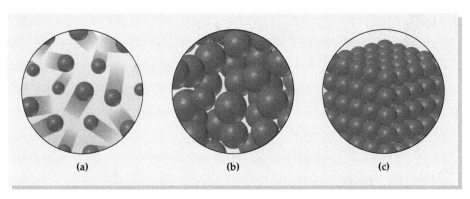

(a)　　　(b)　　　(c)

◀ Figure 8.1

A molecular comparison of gases, liquids, and solids.

(a) In gases, the particles feel little attraction for one another and are free to move about randomly. (b) In liquids, the particles are held close together by attractive forces but are free to slide over one another. (c) In solids, the particles are strongly attracted to one another. They can move slightly, but are held in a fairly rigid arrangement with respect to one another.

Change of state The change of a substance from one state of matter (gas, liquid, or solid) to another.

▶▶ You might want to reread Section 7.4 to brush up on these concepts.

The transformation of a substance from one state to another is called a *phase change*, or a **change of state**. Every change of state is reversible and, like all chemical and physical processes, is characterized by a free-energy change, ΔG. A change of state that is spontaneous in one direction (exergonic, negative ΔG) is nonspontaneous in the other direction (endergonic, positive ΔG). As always, the free-energy change ΔG has both an enthalpy term ΔH and a temperature-dependent entropy term ΔS, according to the equation $\Delta G = \Delta H - T\Delta S$.

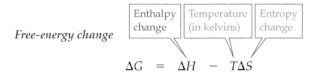

$$Free\text{-}energy\ change \qquad \Delta G \ = \ \Delta H \ - \ T\Delta S$$

The enthalpy change ΔH is a measure of the heat absorbed or released during a given change of state. In the melting of a solid to a liquid, for example, heat is absorbed and ΔH is positive (endothermic). In the reverse process—the freezing of a liquid to a solid—heat is released and ΔH is negative (exothermic). Look at the change between ice and water for instance:

Melting: $H_2O(s) \longrightarrow H_2O(l)$ $\Delta H = +1.44\ kcal/mol$ or $+6.02\ kJ/mol$

Freezing: $H_2O(l) \longrightarrow H_2O(s)$ $\Delta H = -1.44\ kcal/mol$ or $-6.02\ kJ/mol$

The entropy change ΔS is a measure of the change in molecular disorder or freedom that occurs during a process. In the melting of a solid to a liquid, for example, disorder increases because particles gain freedom of motion, so ΔS is positive. In the reverse process—the freezing of a liquid to a solid—disorder decreases as particles are locked into position, so ΔS is negative. Look at the change between ice and water:

Melting: $H_2O(s) \longrightarrow H_2O(l)$ $\Delta S = +5.26\ cal/(mol \cdot K)$ or $+22.0\ J/(mol \cdot K)$

Freezing: $H_2O(l) \longrightarrow H_2O(s)$ $\Delta S = -5.26\ cal/(mol \cdot K)$ or $-22.0\ J/(mol \cdot K)$

As with all processes that are unfavored by one term in the free-energy equation but favored by the other, the sign of ΔG depends on the temperature (Section 7.4). The melting of ice, for instance, is unfavored by a positive ΔH but favored by a positive ΔS. Thus, at a low temperature, the unfavorable ΔH is larger than the favorable $T\Delta S$, so ΔG is positive and no melting occurs. At a higher temperature, however, $T\Delta S$ becomes larger than ΔH, so ΔG is negative and melting *does* occur. The exact temperature at

▶ **Figure 8.2**
Changes of state.
The changes are endothermic from bottom to top and exothermic from top to bottom. Solid and liquid states are in equilibrium at the melting point; liquid and gas states are in equilibrium at the boiling point.

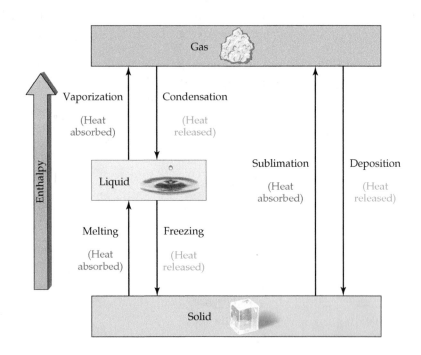

which the changeover in behavior occurs is called the **melting point (mp)** and represents the temperature at which solid and liquid coexist in equilibrium. In the corresponding change from a liquid to a gas, the two states are in equilibrium at the **boiling point (bp)**.

   The names and enthalpy changes associated with the different changes of state are summarized in Figure 8.2. Note that a solid can change directly to a gas without going through the liquid state—a process called *sublimation*. Dry ice (solid CO_2) at atmospheric pressure, for example, changes directly to a gas without melting.

Melting point (mp) The temperature at which solid and liquid are in equilibrium.

Boiling point (bp) The temperature at which liquid and gas are in equilibrium.

Worked Example **8.1** Change of State: Enthalpy, Entropy, and Free Energy

The change of state from liquid to gas for chloroform, formerly used as an anesthetic, has $\Delta H = +6.98$ kcal/mol $(+29.2$ kJ/mol$)$ and a $\Delta S = +20.9$ cal/(mol·K) $[+87.4$ J/(mol·K)$]$.

(a) Is the change of state from liquid to gas favored or unfavored by ΔH? by ΔS?

(b) Is the change of state from liquid to gas favored or unfavored at 35 °C?

(c) Is this change of state spontaneous at 65 °C?

ANALYSIS A process will be favored if energy is released $(\Delta H =$ negative$)$ and if there is a decrease in disorder $(\Delta S =$ positive$)$. In cases in which one factor is favorable and the other is unfavorable, then we can calculate the free-energy change to determine if the process is favored:

$$\Delta G = \Delta H - T\Delta S$$

When ΔG is negative, the process is favored.

SOLUTION

(a) The ΔH does NOT favor this change of state $(\Delta H =$ positive$)$, but the ΔS does favor the process. Since the two factors are not in agreement, we must use the equation for free-energy change to determine if the process is favored at a given temperature.

(b) Substituting the values for ΔH and ΔS into the equation for free-energy change we can determine if ΔG is positive or negative at 35 °C (308 K). Note that we must first convert degrees celsius to kelvins and convert the ΔS from cal to kcal so the units can be added together.

$$\Delta G = \Delta H - T\Delta S = \left(\frac{6.98 \text{ kcal}}{\text{mol}}\right) - (308 \text{ K})\left(\frac{20.9 \text{ cal}}{\text{mol} \cdot \text{K}}\right)\left(\frac{1 \text{ kcal}}{1000 \text{ cal}}\right)$$

$$= 6.98 \frac{\text{kcal}}{\text{mol}} - 6.44 \frac{\text{kcal}}{\text{mol}} = +0.54 \frac{\text{kcal}}{\text{mol}}$$

$$\left(+0.54 \frac{\text{kcal}}{\text{mol}}\right)\left(\frac{4.184 \text{ kJ}}{\text{kcal}}\right) = +2.26 \frac{\text{kJ}}{\text{mol}}$$

Since the $\Delta G =$ positive, this change of state is not favored at 35 °C.

(c) Repeating the calculation using the equation for free-energy change at 65 °C (338 K):

$$\Delta G = \Delta H - T\Delta S = \left(\frac{6.98 \text{ kcal}}{\text{mol}}\right) - (338 \text{ K})\left(\frac{20.9 \text{ cal}}{\text{mol} \cdot \text{K}}\right)\left(\frac{1 \text{ kcal}}{1000 \text{ cal}}\right)$$

$$= 6.98 \frac{\text{kcal}}{\text{mol}} - 7.06 \frac{\text{kcal}}{\text{mol}} = -0.08 \frac{\text{kcal}}{\text{mol}} \left(\text{or} -0.33 \frac{\text{kJ}}{\text{mol}}\right)$$

Because ΔG is negative in this case, the change of state is favored at this temperature.

PROBLEM 8.1

The change of state from liquid H_2O to gaseous H_2O has $\Delta H = +9.72$ kcal/mol ($+40.7$ kJ/mol) and $\Delta S = -26.1$ cal/(mol·K)[-109 J/(mol·K)].

(a) Is the change from liquid to gaseous H_2O favored or unfavored by ΔH? By ΔS?

(b) What is the value of ΔG (in kcal/mol and kJ/mol) for the change from liquid to gaseous H_2O at 373 K?

(c) What are the values of ΔH and ΔS (in kcal/mol and kJ/mol) for the change from gaseous to liquid H_2O?

8.2 Intermolecular Forces

What determines whether a substance is a gas, a liquid, or a solid at a given temperature? Why does rubbing alcohol evaporate much more readily than water? Why do molecular compounds have lower melting points than ionic compounds? To answer these and a great many other such questions, we need to look into the nature of **intermolecular forces**—the forces that act *between different molecules* rather than within an individual molecule.

In gases, the intermolecular forces are negligible, so the gas molecules act independently of one another. In liquids and solids, however, intermolecular forces are strong enough to hold the molecules in close contact. As a general rule, the stronger the intermolecular forces in a substance, the more difficult it is to separate the molecules, and the higher the melting and boiling points of the substance.

There are three major types of intermolecular forces: *dipole–dipole, London dispersion*, and *hydrogen bonding*. We will discuss each in turn.

Dipole–Dipole Forces

Many molecules contain polar covalent bonds and may therefore have a net molecular polarity. In such cases, the positive and negative ends of different molecules are attracted to one another by what is called a **dipole–dipole force** (Figure 8.3).

Dipole–dipole forces are weak, with strengths on the order of 1 kcal/mol (4 kJ/mol) compared to the 70–100 kcal/mol (300–400 kJ/mol) typically found for the strength of a covalent bond (see Table 7.1). Nevertheless, the effects of dipole–dipole forces are important, as can be seen by looking at the difference in boiling points between polar and nonpolar molecules. Butane, for instance, is a nonpolar molecule with a molecular weight of 58 amu and a boiling point of –0.5 °C, whereas acetone has the same molecular weight yet boils 57 °C higher because it is polar.

Intermolecular force A force that acts between molecules and holds molecules close to one another.

▶▶ Recall from Sections 4.9 and 4.10 that a polar covalent bond is one in which the electrons are attracted more strongly by one atom than by the other.

Dipole–dipole force The attractive force between positive and negative ends of polar molecules.

▶▶ Recall from Section 4.9 how molecular polarities can be visualized using electrostatic potential maps.

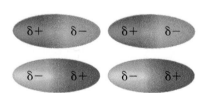

▲ **Figure 8.3**
Dipole–dipole forces.
The positive and negative ends of polar molecules are attracted to one another by dipole–dipole forces. As a result, polar molecules have higher boiling points than nonpolar molecules of similar size.

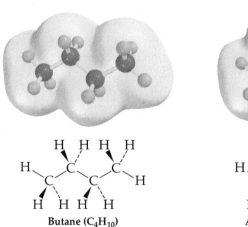

Butane (C_4H_{10})

Mol wt = 58 amu
bp = −0.5 °C

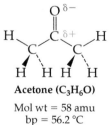

Acetone (C_3H_6O)

Mol wt = 58 amu
bp = 56.2 °C

London Dispersion Forces

Only polar molecules experience dipole–dipole forces, but all molecules, regardless of structure, experience *London dispersion forces*. **London dispersion forces** are caused by the constant motion of electrons within molecules. Take even a simple nonpolar molecule like Br_2, for example. Averaged over time, the distribution of electrons throughout the molecule is uniform, but at any given *instant* there may be more electrons at one end of the molecule than at the other (Figure 8.4). At that instant, the molecule has a short-lived polarity. Electrons in neighboring molecules are attracted to the positive end of the polarized molecule, resulting in a polarization of the neighbor and creation of an attractive London dispersion force that holds the molecules together. As a result, Br_2 is a liquid at room temperature rather than a gas.

London dispersion force The short-lived attractive force due to the constant motion of electrons within molecules.

$\delta-$ $\delta+$ $\delta-$ $\delta+$

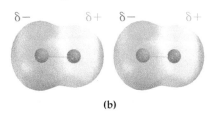

(a)   (b)

◀ **Figure 8.4**
(a) Averaged over time, the electron distribution in a Br_2 molecule is symmetrical. (b) At any given instant, however, the electron distribution may be unsymmetrical, resulting in a temporary polarity that induces a complementary polarity in neighboring molecules.

London dispersion forces are weak—in the range 0.5–2.5 kcal/mol (2–10 kJ/mol)—but they increase with molecular weight and amount of surface area available for interaction between molecules. The larger the molecular weight, the more electrons there are moving about and the greater the temporary polarization of a molecule. The larger the amount of surface contact, the greater the close interaction between different molecules.

The effect of surface area on the magnitude of London dispersion forces can be seen by comparing a roughly spherical molecule with a flatter, more linear one having the same molecular weight. Both 2,2-dimethylpropane and pentane, for instance, have the same formula (C_5H_{12}), but the nearly spherical shape of 2,2-dimethylpropane allows for less surface contact with neighboring molecules than does the more linear shape of pentane (Figure 8.5). As a result, London dispersion forces are smaller for 2,2-dimethylpropane, molecules are held together less tightly, and the boiling point is correspondingly lower: 9.5 °C for 2,2-dimethylpropane versus 36 °C for pentane.

◀ **Figure 8.5**
London dispersion forces.
More compact molecules like 2,2-dimethylpropane have smaller surface areas, weaker London dispersion forces, and lower boiling points. By comparison, flatter, less compact molecules like pentane have larger surface areas, stronger London dispersion forces, and higher boiling points.

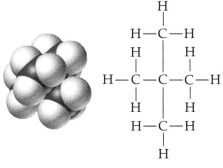

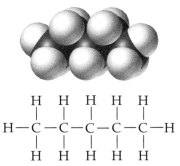

(a) 2,2-Dimethylpropane (bp = 9.5 °C)   **(b)** Pentane (bp = 36 °C)

Hydrogen Bonds

In many ways, hydrogen bonding is responsible for life on earth. It causes water to be a liquid rather than a gas at ordinary temperatures, and it is the primary intermolecular force that holds huge biomolecules in the shapes needed to play their essential roles in biochemistry. Deoxyribonucleic acid (DNA) and keratin (Figure 8.6), for instance, are long molecular chains that form a α-helix, held in place largely due to hydrogen bonding.

A **hydrogen bond** is an attractive interaction between an unshared electron pair on an electronegative O, N, or F atom and a positively polarized hydrogen atom bonded to

Hydrogen bond The attraction between a hydrogen atom bonded to an electronegative O, N, or F atom and another nearby electronegative O, N, or F atom.

▶ **Figure 8.6**
The α-helical structure of keratin results from hydrogen bonding along the amino acid backbone of the molecule. Hydrogen bonding is represented by gray dots in the ball and stick model on the left and red dots in the molecular structure on the right.

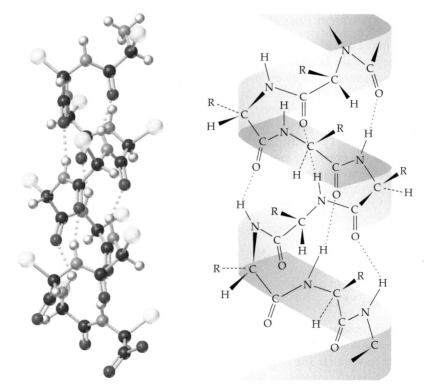

another electronegative O, N, or F. For example, hydrogen bonds occur in both water and ammonia:

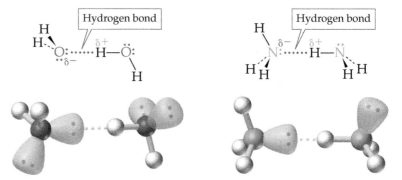

Hydrogen bonding is really just a special kind of dipole–dipole interaction. The O—H, N—H, and F—H bonds are highly polar, with a partial positive charge on the hydrogen and a partial negative charge on the electronegative atom. In addition, the hydrogen atom has no inner-shell electrons to act as a shield around its nucleus, and it is small, so it can be approached closely. As a result, the dipole–dipole attractions involving positively polarized hydrogens are unusually strong, and hydrogen bonds result. Water, in particular, is able to form a vast three-dimensional network of hydrogen bonds because each H_2O molecule has two hydrogens and two electron pairs (Figure 8.7).

▶ **Figure 8.7**
Hydrogen bonding in water.
The intermolecular attraction in water is especially strong because each oxygen atom has two lone pairs and two hydrogen atoms, allowing the formation of as many as four hydrogen bonds per molecule. Individual hydrogen bonds are constantly being formed and broken.

Hydrogen bonds can be quite strong, with energies up to 10 kcal/mol (40 kJ/mol). To see the effect of hydrogen bonding, look at Table 8.1, which compares the boiling points of binary hydrogen compounds of second-row elements with their third-row counterparts. Because NH_3, H_2O, and HF molecules are held tightly together by hydrogen bonds, an unusually large amount of energy must be added to separate them in the boiling process. As a result, the boiling points of NH_3, H_2O, and HF are much higher than the boiling points of their second-row neighbor CH_4 and of related third-row compounds.

TABLE 8.1 Boiling Points for Binary Hydrogen Compounds of Some Second-row and Third-row Elements

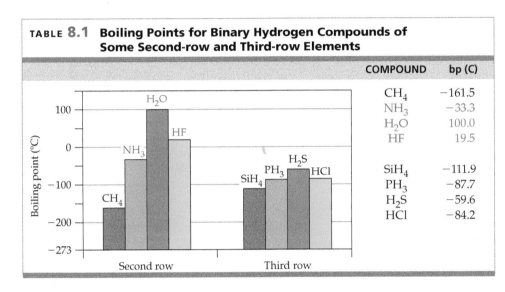

COMPOUND	bp (C)
CH_4	−161.5
NH_3	−33.3
H_2O	100.0
HF	19.5
SiH_4	−111.9
PH_3	−87.7
H_2S	−59.6
HCl	−84.2

A summary and comparison of the various kinds of intermolecular forces is shown in Table 8.2.

TABLE 8.2 A Comparison of Intermolecular Forces

Force	Strength	Characteristics
Dipole–dipole	Weak (1 kcal/mol, 4 kJ/mol))	Occurs between polar molecules
London dispersion	Weak (0.5–2.5 kcal/mol, 2–10 kJ/mol)	Occurs between all molecules; strength depends on size
Hydrogen bond	Moderate (2–10 kcal/mol, 8–40 kJ/mol)	Occurs between molecules with O—H, N—H, and F—H bonds

LOOKING AHEAD ▸▸▸ Dipole–dipole forces, London dispersion forces, and hydrogen bonds are traditionally called "intermolecular forces" because of their influence on the properties of molecular compounds. But these same forces can also operate between different parts of a very large molecule. In this context, they are often referred to as "noncovalent interactions." In later chapters, we will see how noncovalent interactions determine the shapes of biologically important molecules such as proteins and nucleic acids.

Worked Example 8.2 Identifying Intermolecular Forces: Polar versus Nonpolar

Identify the intermolecular forces that influence the properties of the following compounds:

(a) Methane, CH_4 **(b)** HCl   **(c)** CH_3COOH

ANALYSIS The intermolecular forces will depend on the molecular structure, what type of bonds are in the molecule (polar or non-polar), and how the bonds are arranged.

SOLUTION

(a) Since methane contains only C—H bonds, it is a nonpolar molecule; it has only London dispersion forces.

(b) The H—Cl bond is polar, so this is a polar molecule; it has both dipole–dipole forces and London dispersion forces.

(c) Acetic acid is a polar molecule with an O—H bond. Thus, it has dipole–dipole forces, London dispersion forces, and hydrogen bonds.

PROBLEM 8.2

Would you expect the boiling points to increase or decrease in the following series? Explain.

(a) Kr, Ar, Ne   (b) Cl_2, Br_2, I_2

PROBLEM 8.3

Which of the following compounds form hydrogen bonds?

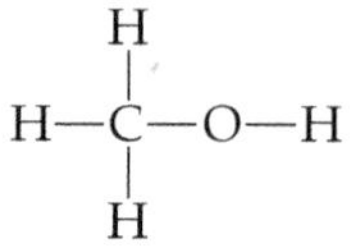

Methyl alcohol	Ethylene	Methylamine
(a)	(b)	(c)

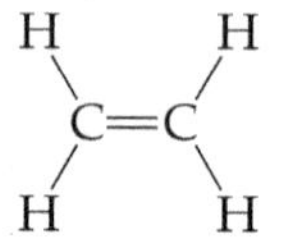

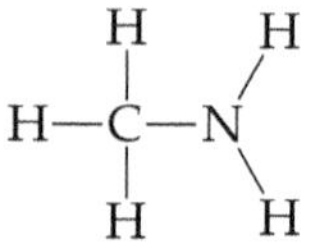

PROBLEM 8.4

Identify the intermolecular forces (dipole–dipole, London dispersion, hydrogen bonding) that influence the properties of the following compounds:

(a) Ethane, CH_3CH_3

(b) Ethyl alcohol, CH_3CH_2OH

(c) Ethyl chloride, CH_3CH_2Cl

8.3 Gases and the Kinetic–Molecular Theory

Gases behave quite differently from liquids and solids. Gases, for instance, have low densities and are easily compressed to a smaller volume when placed under pressure, a property that allows them to be stored in large tanks. Liquids and solids, by contrast, are much more dense and much less compressible. Furthermore, gases undergo a far larger expansion or contraction when their temperature is changed than do liquids and solids.

The behavior of gases can be explained by a group of assumptions known as the **kinetic–molecular theory of gases**. We will see in the next several sections how the following assumptions account for the observable properties of gases:

Kinetic–molecular theory of gases A group of assumptions that explain the behavior of gases.

- **A gas consists of many particles, either atoms or molecules, moving about at random with no attractive forces between them.** Because of this random motion, different gases mix together quickly.
- **The amount of space occupied by the gas particles themselves is much smaller than the amount of space between particles.** Most of the volume taken up by gases is empty space, accounting for the ease of compression and low densities of gases.
- **The average kinetic energy of gas particles is proportional to the Kelvin temperature.** Thus, gas particles have more kinetic energy and move faster as the temperature increases. (In fact, gas particles move much faster than you might suspect. The average speed of a helium atom at room temperature and atmospheric pressure is approximately 1.36 km/s, or 3000 mi/hr, nearly that of a rifle bullet.)

- **Collisions of gas particles, either with other particles or with the wall of their container, are elastic; that is, the total kinetic energy of the particles is constant.** The pressure of a gas against the walls of its container is the result of collisions of the gas particles with the walls. The more collisions and the more forceful each collision, the higher the pressure.

A gas that obeys all the assumptions of the kinetic–molecular theory is called an **ideal gas**. In practice, though, there is no such thing as a perfectly ideal gas. All gases behave somewhat differently than predicted when, at very high pressures or very low temperatures, their particles get closer together and interactions between particles become significant. As a rule, however, most real gases display nearly ideal behavior under normal conditions.

8.4 Pressure

We are all familiar with the effects of air pressure. When you fly in an airplane, the change in air pressure against your eardrums as the plane climbs or descends can cause a painful "popping." When you pump up a bicycle tire, you increase the pressure of air against the inside walls of the tire until the tire feels hard.

In scientific terms, **pressure** (P) is defined as a force (F) per unit area (A) pushing against a surface; that is, $P = F/A$. In the bicycle tire, for example, the pressure you feel is the force of air molecules colliding with the inside walls of the tire. The units you probably use for tire pressure are pounds per square inch (psi), where 1 psi is equal to the pressure exerted by a 1-pound object resting on a 1-square inch surface.

We on earth are under pressure from the atmosphere, the blanket of air pressing down on us (Figure 8.8). Atmospheric pressure is not constant, however; it varies slightly from day to day depending on the weather, and it also varies with altitude. Due to gravitational forces, the density of air is greatest at the earth's surface and decreases with increasing altitude. As a result, air pressure is greatest at the surface: it is about 14.7 psi at sea level but only about 4.7 psi on the summit of Mt. Everest.

One of the most commonly used units of pressure is the *millimeter of mercury*, abbreviated *mmHg* and often called a *torr* (after the Italian physicist Evangelista Torricelli). This unusual unit dates back to the early 1600s when Torricelli made the first mercury *barometer*. As shown in Figure 8.9, a barometer consists of a long, thin tube that is sealed at one end, filled with mercury, and then inverted into a dish of mercury. Some mercury runs from the tube into the dish until the downward pressure of the mercury in the column is exactly balanced by the outside atmospheric pressure, which presses down on the mercury in the dish and pushes it up into the column. The height of the mercury column varies depending on the altitude and weather conditions, but standard atmospheric pressure at sea level is defined to be exactly 760 mm.

Gas pressure inside a container is often measured using an open-ended *manometer*, a simple instrument similar in principle to the mercury barometer. As shown in Figure 8.10, an open-ended manometer consists of a U-tube filled with mercury, with one end connected to a gas-filled container and the other end open to the atmosphere. The difference between the heights of the mercury levels in the two arms of the U-tube indicates the difference between the pressure of the gas in the container and the pressure of the atmosphere. If the gas pressure inside the container is less than atmospheric, the mercury level is higher in the arm connected to the container (Figure 8.10a). If the gas pressure inside the container is greater than atmospheric, the mercury level is higher in the arm open to the atmosphere (Figure 8.10b).

Pressure is given in the SI system (Section 2.1) by a unit named the *pascal* (Pa), where 1 Pa = 0.007500 mmHg (or 1 mmHg = 133.32 Pa). Measurements in pascals are becoming more common, and many clinical laboratories have made the switchover. Higher pressures are often still given in *atmospheres* (atm), where 1 atm = 760 mmHg exactly.

$$\text{Pressure units: 1 atm} = 760\,\text{mmHg} = 14.7\,\text{psi} = 101{,}325\,\text{Pa}$$

$$1\,\text{mmHg} = 1\,\text{torr} = 133.32\,\text{Pa}$$

Ideal gas A gas that obeys all the assumptions of the kinetic–molecular theory.

Pressure (P) The force per unit area pushing against a surface.

▲ **Figure 8.8**

Atmospheric pressure.
A column of air weighing 14.7 lb presses down on each square inch of the earth's surface at sea level, resulting in what we call atmospheric pressure.

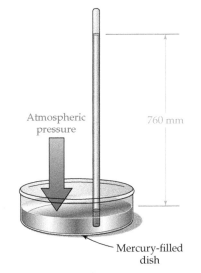

▲ **Figure 8.9**

Measuring atmospheric pressure.
A mercury barometer measures atmospheric pressure by determining the height of a mercury column in a sealed glass tube. The downward pressure of the mercury in the column is exactly balanced by the outside atmospheric pressure, which presses down on the mercury in the dish and pushes it up into the column.

▶ **Figure 8.10**

Open-ended manometers for measuring pressure in a gas-filled bulb.
(a) When the pressure in the gas-filled container is lower than atmospheric, the mercury level is higher in the arm open to the container. (b) When the pressure in the container is higher than atmospheric, the mercury level is higher in the arm open to the atmosphere.

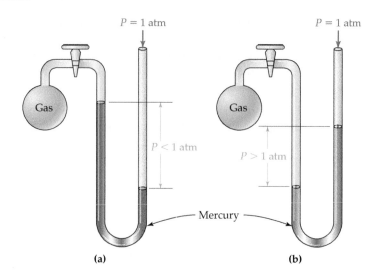

(a)   (b)

Worked Example 8.3 Unit Conversions (Pressure): psi, Atmospheres, and Pascals

A typical bicycle tire is inflated with air to a pressure of 55 psi. How many atmospheres is this? How many pascals?

ANALYSIS Using the starting pressure in psi, the pressure in atm and pascals can be calculated using the equivalent values in appropriate units as conversion factors.

SOLUTION

STEP 1: **Identify known information.**

Pressure = 55 psi

STEP 2: **Identify answer and units.**

Pressure = ?? atm = ?? pascals

STEP 3: **Identify conversion factors.** Using equivalent values in appropriate units, we can obtain conversion factors to convert to atm and pascals.

$$14.7 \text{ psi} = 1 \text{ atm} \rightarrow \frac{1 \text{ atm}}{14.7 \text{ psi}}$$

$$14.7 \text{ psi} = 101{,}325 \text{ Pa} \rightarrow \frac{101{,}325 \text{ Pa}}{14.7 \text{ psi}}$$

STEP 4: **Solve.** Use the appropriate conversion factors to set up an equation in which unwanted units cancel.

$$(55 \text{ psi}) \times \left(\frac{1 \text{ atm}}{14.7 \text{ psi}} \right) = 3.7 \text{ atm}$$

$$(55 \text{ psi}) \times \left(\frac{101{,}325 \text{ Pa}}{14.7 \text{ psi}} \right) = 3.8 \times 10^5 \text{ Pa}$$

Worked Example 8.4 Unit Conversions (Pressure): mmHg to Atmospheres

The pressure in a closed flask is measured using a manometer. If the mercury level in the arm open to the sealed vessel is 23.6 cm higher than the level of mercury in the arm open to the atmosphere, what is the gas pressure (in atm) in the closed flask?

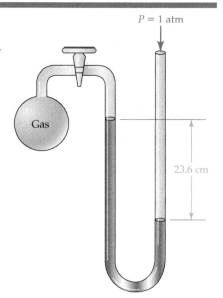

ANALYSIS Since the mercury level is higher in the arm open to the flask, the gas pressure in the flask is lower than atmospheric pressure (1 atm = 760 mmHg). We can convert the difference in the level of mercury in the two arms of the manometer from mmHg to atmospheres to determine the difference in pressure.

BALLPARK ESTIMATE The height difference (23.6 cm) is about one-third the height of a column of Hg that is equal to 1 atm (or 76 cm Hg). Therefore, the pressure in the flask should be about 0.33 atm lower than atmospheric pressure, or about 0.67 atm.

SOLUTION
Since the height difference is given in cm Hg, we must first convert to mmHg, and then to atm. The result is the difference in gas pressure between the flask and the open atmosphere (1 atm).

$$(23.6 \text{ cm Hg})\left(\frac{10 \text{ mmHg}}{\text{cm Hg}}\right)\left(\frac{1 \text{ atm}}{760 \text{ mmHg}}\right) = 0.311 \text{ atm}$$

The pressure in the flask is calculated by subtracting this difference from 1 atm:

$$1 \text{ atm} - 0.311 \text{ atm} = 0.689 \text{ atm}$$

BALLPARK CHECK This result agrees well with our estimate of 0.67 atm.

PROBLEM 8.5
The air pressure outside a jet airliner flying at 35,000 ft is about 0.289 atm. Convert this pressure to mmHg, psi, and pascals.

PROBLEM 8.6
The increase in atmospheric CO_2 levels has been correlated with the combustion of fossil fuels (see Chemistry in Action: Greenhouse Gases and Global Warming on p. 224). How would the atmospheric CO_2 levels be affected by a shift to corn-based ethanol or some other biomass-based fuel? Explain.

KEY CONCEPT PROBLEM 8.7

What is the pressure of the gas inside the following manometer (in mmHg) if outside pressure is 750 mmHg?

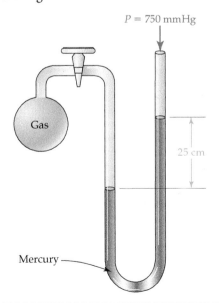

P = 750 mmHg

Gas

25 cm

Mercury

CHEMISTRY IN ACTION

Greenhouse Gases and Global Warming

The mantle of gases surrounding the earth is far from the uniform mixture you might expect, consisting of layers that vary in composition and properties at different altitudes. The ability of the gases in these layers to absorb radiation is responsible for life on earth as we know it.

The *stratosphere*—the layer extending from about 12 km up to 50 km altitude—contains the ozone layer that is responsible for absorbing harmful UV radiation. The *troposphere* is the layer extending from the surface up to about 12 km altitude. It should not surprise you to learn that the troposphere is the layer most easily disturbed by human activities and that this layer has the greatest impact on the earth's surface conditions. Among those impacts, a process called the *greenhouse effect* is much in the news today.

The greenhouse effect refers to the warming that occurs in the troposphere as gases absorb radiant energy. Much of the radiant energy reaching the Earth's surface from the sun is reflected back into space, but some is absorbed by atmospheric gases, particularly those referred to as *greenhouse gases* (GHGs)—water vapor, carbon dioxide, and methane. This absorbed radiation warms the atmosphere and acts to maintain a relatively stable temperature of 15 °C (59 °F) at the Earth's surface. Without the greenhouse effect, the average surface temperature would be about −18 °C (0 °F)—a temperature so low that Earth would be frozen and unable to sustain life.

The basis for concern about the greenhouse effect is the fear that human activities over the past century have disturbed the earth's delicate thermal balance. Should increasing amounts of radiation be absorbed, increased atmospheric heating will result, and global temperatures will continue to rise.

Measurements show that the concentration of atmospheric CO_2 has been rising in the last 150 years, from an estimated 290 parts per million (ppm) in 1850 to current levels approaching 400 ppm. The increase in CO_2 levels is largely because of the increased burning of fossil fuels and correlates with a concurrent increase in average global temperatures. The latest Assessment Report of the Intergovernmental Panel on Climate Change published in November 2007 concluded that "[W]arming of the climate system is unequivocal, as is now evident from observations of increases in global average air and ocean temperatures, widespread melting of snow and ice and rising global average sea level. . . . Continued GHG emissions at or above current rates would cause further warming and induce many changes in the global climate system during the 21st century that would *very likely* be larger than those observed during the 20th century."

Increased international concerns about the political and economic impacts of global climate change prompted development of the Kyoto Protocol to the United Nations Framework Convention on Climate Change (UNFCCC). Under the protocol, countries commit to a reduction in the production and emission of greenhouse gases, including CO_2, methane, and chlorofluorocarbons (CFCs). As of April 2010, 191 countries have signed and ratified the protocol. These concerns have also resulted in market pressures to develop sustainable and renewable energy sources, as well as more efficient technologies, such as hybrid electric vehicles.

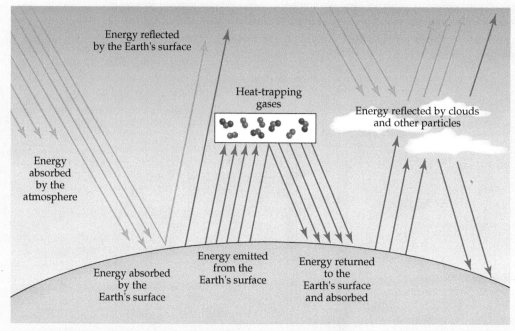

▲ Greenhouse gases (GHG) trap heat reflected from the earth's surface, resulting in the increase in surface temperatures known as global warming.

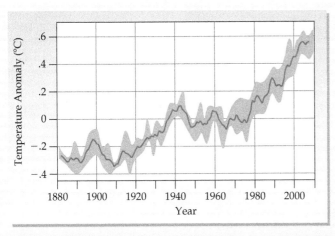

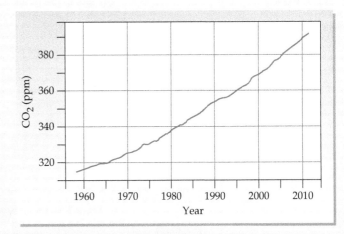

▲ **Concentrations of atmospheric CO₂ and global average temperatures have increased dramatically in the last 150 years because of increased fossil fuel use, causing serious changes in earth's climate system.**
© NASA, GISS Surface Temperature Analysis.

See Chemistry in Action Problems 8.100 and 8.101 at the end of the chapter.

8.5 Boyle's Law: The Relation between Volume and Pressure

The physical behavior of all gases is much the same, regardless of identity. Helium and chlorine, for example, are completely different in their *chemical* behavior, but are very similar in many of their physical properties. Observations of many different gases by scientists in the 1700s led to the formulation of what are now called the **gas laws**, which make it possible to predict the influence of pressure (P), volume (V), temperature (T), and molar amount (n) on any gas or mixture of gases. We will begin by looking at *Boyle's law*, which describes the relation between volume and pressure.

Imagine that you have a sample of gas inside a cylinder that has a movable plunger at one end (Figure 8.11). What happens if you double the pressure on the gas by pushing the plunger down, while keeping the temperature constant? Since the gas particles are forced closer together, the volume of the sample decreases.

Gas laws A series of laws that predict the influence of pressure (P), volume (V), and temperature (T) on any gas or mixture of gases.

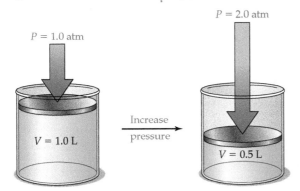

◄ **Figure 8.11**
Boyle's law.
The volume of a gas decreases proportionately as its pressure increases. For example, if the pressure of a gas sample is doubled, the volume is halved.

According to **Boyle's law**, the volume of a fixed amount of gas at a constant temperature is inversely proportional to its pressure, meaning that volume and pressure change in opposite directions. As pressure goes up, volume goes down; as pressure goes down, volume goes up (Figure 8.12). This observation is consistent with the kinetic–molecular theory. Since most of the volume occupied by gases is empty space, gases are easily compressed into smaller volumes. Since the average kinetic energy remains constant, the number of collisions must increase as the interior surface area of the container decreases, leading to an increase in pressure.

▶ **Figure 8.12**
Boyle's law.
Pressure and volume are inversely related. Graph (a) demonstrates the decrease in volume as pressure increases, whereas graph (b) shows the linear relationship between V and $1/P$.

▶ **Figure 8.12**
Boyle's law.
Pressure and volume are inversely related. Graph (a) demonstrates the decrease in volume as pressure increases, whereas graph (b) shows the linear relationship between V and $1/P$.

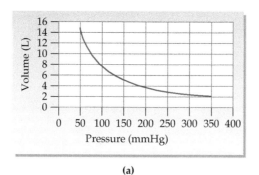

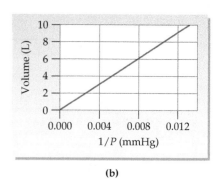

(a) (b)

Boyle's law The volume of a gas is inversely proportional to its pressure for a fixed amount of gas at a constant temperature. That is, P times V is constant when the amount of gas n and the temperature T are kept constant. (The symbol $\propto$ means "is proportional to," and k denotes a constant value.)

$$\text{Volume } (V) \propto \frac{1}{\text{Pressure } (P)}$$

$$\text{or} \quad PV = k \quad (\text{A constant value})$$

Because $P \times V$ is a constant value for a fixed amount of gas at a constant temperature, the starting pressure (P_1) times the starting volume (V_1) must equal the final pressure (P_2) times the final volume (V_2). Thus, Boyle's law can be used to find the final pressure or volume when the starting pressure or volume is changed.

$$\text{Since} \quad P_1 V_1 = k \quad \text{and} \quad P_2 V_2 = k$$

$$\text{then} \quad P_1 V_1 = P_2 V_2$$

$$\text{so} \quad P_2 = \frac{P_1 V_1}{V_2} \quad \text{and} \quad V_2 = \frac{P_1 V_1}{P_2}$$

As an example of Boyle's law behavior, think about what happens every time you breathe. Between breaths, the pressure inside your lungs is equal to atmospheric pressure. When inhalation takes place, your diaphragm lowers and the rib cage expands, increasing the volume of the lungs and thereby decreasing the pressure inside them (Figure 8.13). Air

▶ **Figure 8.13**
Boyle's law in breathing.
During inhalation, the diaphragm moves down and the rib cage moves up and out, thus increasing lung volume, decreasing pressure, and drawing in air. During exhalation, the diaphragm moves back up, lung volume decreases, pressure increases, and air moves out.

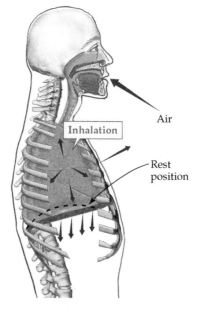

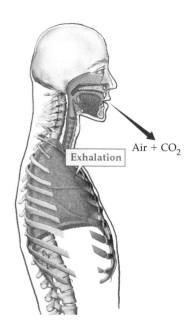

Lung volume increases, causing pressure in lungs to *decrease*. Air flows *in*.

Lung volume decreases, causing pressure in lungs to *increase*. Air flows *out*.

must then move into the lungs to equalize their pressure with that of the atmosphere. When exhalation takes place, the diaphragm rises and the rib cage contracts, decreasing the volume of the lungs and increasing pressure inside them. Now gases move out of the lungs until pressure is again equalized with the atmosphere.

Worked Example 8.5 Using Boyle's Law: Finding Volume at a Given Pressure

In a typical automobile engine, the fuel/air mixture in a cylinder is compressed from 1.0 atm to 9.5 atm. If the uncompressed volume of the cylinder is 750 mL, what is the volume when fully compressed?

ANALYSIS This is a Boyle's law problem because the volume and pressure in the cylinder change but the amount of gas and the temperature remain constant. According to Boyle's law, the pressure of the gas times its volume is constant:

$$P_1 V_1 = P_2 V_2$$

Knowing three of the four variables in this equation, we can solve for the unknown.

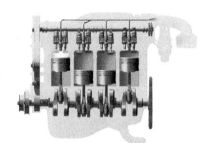

◀ A cut-away diagram of an internal combustion engine shows movement of pistons during expansion and compression cycles.

BALLPARK ESTIMATE Since the pressure *increases* approximately 10-fold (from 1.0 atm to 9.5 atm), the volume must *decrease* to approximately 1/10, from 750 mL to about 75 mL.

SOLUTION

STEP 1: **Identify known information.** Of the four variables in Boyle's law, we know P_1, V_1, and P_2.

STEP 2: **Identify answer and units.**

STEP 3: **Identify equation.** In this case, we simply substitute the known variables into Boyle's law and rearrange to isolate the unknown.

$P_1 = 1.0$ atm
$V_1 = 750$ mL
$P_2 = 9.5$ atm

$V_2 = ??$ mL

$$P_1 V_1 = P_2 V_2 \implies V_2 = \frac{P_1 V_1}{P_2}$$

STEP 4: **Solve.** Substitute the known information into the equation. Make sure units cancel so that the answer is given in the units of the unknown variable.

$$V_2 = \frac{P_1 V_1}{P_2} = \frac{(1.0 \text{ atm})(750 \text{ mL})}{(9.5 \text{ atm})} = 79 \text{ mL}$$

BALLPARK CHECK Our estimate was 75 mL.

PROBLEM 8.8
An oxygen cylinder used for breathing has a volume of 5.0 L at 90 atm pressure. What is the volume of the same amount of oxygen at the same temperature if the pressure is 1.0 atm? (Hint: Would you expect the volume of gas at this pressure to be greater than or less than the volume at 90 atm?)

PROBLEM 8.9
A sample of hydrogen gas at 273 K has a volume of 3.2 L at 4.0 atm pressure. What is the volume if the pressure is increased to 10.0 atm? If the pressure is decreased to 0.70 atm?

PROBLEM 8.10
A typical blood pressure measured using a sphygmomanometer is reported as 112/75 (see Chemistry in Action: Blood Pressure on p. 228). How would this pressure be recorded if the sphygmomanometer used units of psi instead of mmHg?

CHEMISTRY IN ACTION

Blood Pressure

Having your blood pressure measured is a quick and easy way to get an indication of the state of your circulatory system. Although blood pressure varies with age, a normal adult male has a reading near 120/80 mmHg, and a normal adult female has a reading near 110/70 mmHg. Abnormally high values signal an increased risk of heart attack and stroke.

Pressure varies greatly in different types of blood vessels. Usually, though, measurements are carried out on arteries in the upper arm as the heart goes through a full cardiac cycle. *Systolic pressure* is the maximum pressure developed in the artery just after contraction, as the heart forces the maximum amount of blood into the artery. *Diastolic pressure* is the minimum pressure that occurs at the end of the heart cycle.

Blood pressure is most often measured by a *sphygmomanometer*, a device consisting of a squeeze bulb, a flexible cuff, and a mercury manometer. (1) The cuff is placed around the upper arm over the brachial artery and inflated by the squeeze bulb to about 200 mmHg pressure, an amount great enough to squeeze the artery shut and prevent blood flow. Air is then slowly released from the cuff, and pressure drops (2). As cuff pressure reaches the systolic pressure, blood spurts through the artery, creating a turbulent tapping sound that can be heard through a stethoscope. The pressure registered on the manometer at the moment the first sounds are heard is the systolic blood pressure.

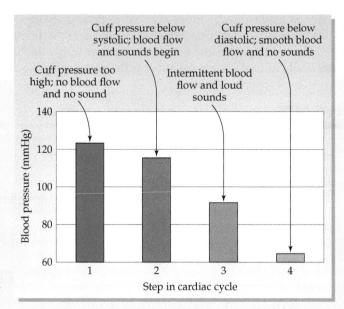

▲ The sequence of events during blood pressure measurement, including the sounds heard.

(3) Sounds continue until the pressure in the cuff becomes low enough to allow diastolic blood flow. (4) At this point, blood flow becomes smooth, no sounds are heard, and a diastolic blood pressure reading is recorded on the manometer. Readings are usually recorded as systolic/diastolic, for example, 120/80. The accompanying figure shows the sequence of events during measurement.

See Chemistry in Action Problems 8.102 and 103 at the end of the chapter.

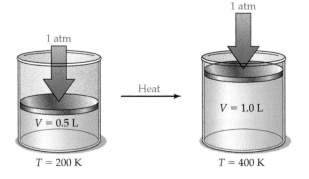

▲ The volume of the gas in the balloon increases as it is heated, causing a decrease in density and allowing the balloon to rise.

8.6 Charles's Law: The Relation between Volume and Temperature

Imagine that you again have a sample of gas inside a cylinder with a plunger at one end. What happens if you double the sample's kelvin temperature while letting the plunger move freely to keep the pressure constant? The gas particles move with twice as much energy and collide twice as forcefully with the walls. To maintain a constant pressure, the volume of the gas in the cylinder must double (Figure 8.14).

1 atm

$V = 0.5$ L

$T = 200$ K

Heat →

1 atm

$V = 1.0$ L

$T = 400$ K

▲ **Figure 8.14**
Charles's law.
The volume of a gas is directly proportional to its kelvin temperature at constant n and P. If the kelvin temperature of the gas is doubled, its volume doubles.

According to **Charles's law**, the volume of a fixed amount of gas at constant pressure is directly proportional to its kelvin temperature. Note the difference between *directly* proportional in Charles's law and *inversely* proportional in Boyle's law. Directly proportional quantities change in the same direction: as temperature goes up or down, volume also goes up or down (Figure 8.15).

Charles's law The volume of a gas is directly proportional to its kelvin temperature for a fixed amount of gas at a constant pressure. That is, V divided by T is constant when n and P are held constant.

$$V \propto T \quad \text{(In kelvins)}$$

$$\text{or } \frac{V}{T} = k \quad \text{(A constant value)}$$

$$\text{or } \frac{V_1}{T_1} = \frac{V_2}{T_2}$$

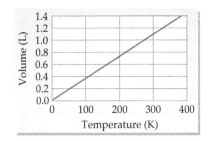

▲ **Figure 8.15**
Charles's law.
Volume is directly proportional to the kelvin temperature for a fixed amount of gas at a constant pressure. As the temperature goes up, the volume also goes up.

This observation is consistent with the kinetic–molecular theory. As temperature increases, the average kinetic energy of the gas molecules increases, as does the energy of molecular collisions with the interior surface of the container. The volume of the container must increase to maintain a constant pressure. As an example of Charles's law, think about what happens when a hot-air balloon is inflated. Heating causes the air inside to expand and fill the balloon. The air inside the balloon is less dense than the air outside the balloon, creating the buoyancy effect.

Worked Example 8.6 Using Charles's Law: Finding Volume at a Given Temperature

An average adult inhales a volume of 0.50 L of air with each breath. If the air is warmed from room temperature (20 °C = 293 K) to body temperature (37 °C = 310 K) while in the lungs, what is the volume of the air exhaled?

ANALYSIS This is a Charles's law problem because the volume and temperature of the air change while the amount and pressure remain constant. Knowing three of the four variables, we can rearrange Charles's law to solve for the unknown.

BALLPARK ESTIMATE Charles's law predicts an increase in volume directly proportional to the increase in temperature from 273 K to 310 K. The increase of less than 20 K represents a relatively small change compared to the initial temperature of 273 K. A 10% increase, for example, would be equal to a temperature change of 27 K; so a 20-K change would be less than 10%. We would therefore expect the volume to increase by less than 10%, from 0.50 L to a little less than 0.55 L.

SOLUTION

STEP 1: Identify known information. Of the four variables in Charles's law, we know T_1, V_1, and T_2.

$T_1 = 293 \text{ K}$
$V_1 = 0.50 \text{ L}$
$T_2 = 310 \text{ K}$

STEP 2: Identify answer and units.

$V_2 = \text{?? L}$

STEP 3: Identify equation. Substitute the known variables into Charles's law and rearrange to isolate the unknown.

$$\frac{V_1}{T_1} = \frac{V_2}{T_2} \quad \Rightarrow \quad V_2 = \frac{V_1 T_2}{T_1}$$

STEP 4: Solve. Substitute the known information into Charles's law; check to make sure units cancel.

$$V_2 = \frac{V_1 T_2}{T_1} = \frac{(0.50 \text{ L})(310 \text{ K})}{293 \text{ K}} = 0.53 \text{ L}$$

BALLPARK CHECK This is consistent with our estimate!

PROBLEM 8.11
A sample of chlorine gas has a volume of 0.30 L at 273 K and 1 atm pressure. What temperature (in °C) would be required to increase the volume to 1.0 L? To decrease the volume to 0.20 L?

8.7 Gay-Lussac's Law: The Relation between Pressure and Temperature

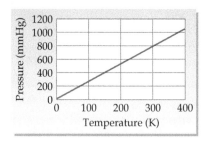

▲ **Figure 8.16**
Gay-Lussac's law.
Pressure is directly proportional to the temperature in kelvins for a fixed amount of gas at a constant volume. As the temperature goes up, the pressure also goes up.

Imagine next that you have a fixed amount of gas in a sealed container whose volume remains constant. What happens if you double the temperature (in kelvins)? The gas particles move with twice as much energy and collide with the walls of the container with twice as much force. Thus, the pressure in the container doubles. According to **Gay-Lussac's law**, the pressure of a fixed amount of gas at constant volume is directly proportional to its Kelvin temperature. As temperature goes up or down, pressure also goes up or down (Figure 8.16).

Gay-Lussac's law The pressure of a gas is directly proportional to its Kelvin temperature for a fixed amount of gas at a constant volume. That is, P divided by T is constant when n and V are held constant.

$$P \propto T \quad \text{(In kelvins)}$$

$$\text{or} \ \frac{P}{T} = k \quad \text{(A constant value)}$$

$$\text{or} \ \frac{P_1}{T_1} = \frac{P_2}{T_2}$$

According to the kinetic–molecular theory, the kinetic energy of molecules is directly proportional to absolute temperature. As the average kinetic energy of the molecules increases, the energy of collisions with the interior surface of the container increases, causing an increase in pressure. As an example of Gay-Lussac's law, think of what happens when an aerosol can is thrown into an incinerator. As the can gets hotter, pressure builds up inside and the can explodes (hence the warning statement on aerosol cans).

Worked Example 8.7 Using Gay-Lussac's Law: Finding Pressure at a Given Temperature

What does the inside pressure become if an aerosol can with an initial pressure of 4.5 atm is heated in a fire from room temperature (20 °C) to 600 °C?

ANALYSIS This is a Gay-Lussac's law problem because the pressure and temperature of the gas inside the can change while its amount and volume remain constant. We know three of the four variables in the equation for Gay-Lussac's law, and can find the unknown by substitution and rearrangement.

BALLPARK ESTIMATE Gay-Lussac's law states that pressure is directly proportional to temperature. Since the Kelvin temperature increases approximately threefold (from about 300 K to about 900 K), we expect the pressure to also increase by approximately threefold, from 4.5 atm to about 14 atm.

SOLUTION

STEP 1: **Identify known information.** Of the four variables in Gay-Lussac's law, we know P_1, T_1 and T_2. (Note that T must be in kelvins.)

$P_1 = 4.5 \text{ atm}$
$T_1 = 20\,°C = 293 \text{ K}$
$T_2 = 600\,°C = 873 \text{ K}$

STEP 2: **Identify answer and units.**

$P_2 = ?? \text{ atm}$

STEP 3: **Identify equation.** Substituting the known variables into Gay-Lussac's law, we rearrange to isolate the unknown.

$$\frac{P_1}{T_1} = \frac{P_2}{T_2} \quad \Rightarrow \quad P_2 = \frac{P_1 T_2}{T_1}$$

STEP 4: **Solve.** Substitute the known information into Gay-Lussac's law; check to make sure units cancel.

$$P_2 = \frac{P_1 T_2}{T_1} = \frac{(4.5 \text{ atm})(873 \text{ K})}{293 \text{ K}} = 13 \text{ atm}$$

BALLPARK CHECK Our estimate was 14 atm.

PROBLEM 8.12
Driving on a hot day causes tire temperature to rise. What is the pressure inside an automobile tire at 45 °C if the tire has a pressure of 30 psi at 15 °C? Assume that the volume and amount of air in the tire remain constant.

8.8 The Combined Gas Law

Since PV, V/T, and P/T all have constant values for a fixed amount of gas, these relationships can be merged into a **combined gas law**, which holds true whenever the amount of gas is fixed.

Combined gas law $\dfrac{PV}{T} = k$ (A constant value)

or $\dfrac{P_1 V_1}{T_1} = \dfrac{P_2 V_2}{T_2}$

If any five of the six quantities in this equation are known, the sixth quantity can be calculated. Furthermore, if any of the three variables T, P, or V is constant, that variable drops out of the equation, leaving behind Boyle's law, Charles's law, or Gay-Lussac's law. As a result, *the combined gas law is the only equation you need to remember for a fixed amount of gas.* Worked Example 8.8 gives a sample calculation.

Since $\dfrac{P_1 V_1}{T_1} = \dfrac{P_2 V_2}{T_2}$

At constant T: $\dfrac{P_1 V_1}{T} = \dfrac{P_2 V_2}{T}$ gives $P_1 V_1 = P_2 V_2$ (Boyle's law)

At constant P: $\dfrac{P V_1}{T_1} = \dfrac{P V_2}{T_2}$ gives $\dfrac{V_1}{T_1} = \dfrac{V_2}{T_2}$ (Charles's law)

At constant V: $\dfrac{P_1 V}{T_1} = \dfrac{P_2 V}{T_2}$ gives $\dfrac{P_1}{T_1} = \dfrac{P_2}{T_2}$ (Gay-Lussac's law)

Worked Example 8.8 Using the Combined Gas Law: Finding Temperature

A 6.3 L sample of helium gas stored at 25 °C and 1.0 atm pressure is transferred to a 2.0 L tank and maintained at a pressure of 2.8 atm. What temperature is needed to maintain this pressure?

ANALYSIS This is a combined gas law problem because pressure, volume, and temperature change while the amount of helium remains constant. Of the six variables in this equation, we know P_1, V_1, T_1, P_2, and V_2, and we need to find T_2.

BALLPARK ESTIMATE Since the volume goes down by a little more than a factor of about 3 (from 6.3 L to 2.0 L) and the pressure goes up by a little less than a factor of about 3 (from 1.0 atm to 2.8 atm), the two changes roughly offset each other, and so the temperature should not change much. Since the volume-decrease factor (3.2) is slightly greater than the pressure-increase factor (2.8), the temperature will drop slightly $(T \propto V)$.

SOLUTION

STEP 1: Identify known information. Of the six variables in combined gas law we know P_1, V_1, T_1, P_2, and V_2. (As always, T must be converted from Celsius degrees to kelvins.)

$P_1 = 1.0$ atm, $P_2 = 2.8$ atm
$V_1 = 6.3$ L, $V_2 = 2.0$ L
$T_1 = 25\,°C = 298$ K

STEP 2: Identify answer and units.

$T_2 = \text{?? kelvin}$

STEP 3: Identify the equation. Substitute the known variables into the equation for the combined gas law and rearrange to isolate the unknown.

$\dfrac{P_1 V_1}{T_1} = \dfrac{P_2 V_2}{T_2} \implies T_2 = \dfrac{P_2 V_2 T_1}{P_1 V_1}$

STEP 4: Solve. Solve the combined gas law equation for T_2; check to make sure units cancel.

$T_2 = \dfrac{P_2 V_2 T_1}{P_1 V_1} = \dfrac{(2.8 \text{ atm})(2.0 \text{ L})(298 \text{ K})}{(1.0 \text{ atm})(6.3 \text{ L})} = 260 \text{ K} (\Delta T = 2.38\,°C)$

BALLPARK CHECK The relatively small decrease in temperature (38 °C, or 13% compared to the original temperature) is consistent with our prediction.

PROBLEM 8.13

A weather balloon is filled with helium to a volume of 275 L at 22 °C and 752 mmHg. The balloon ascends to an altitude where the pressure is 480 mmHg, and the temperature is −32 °C. What is the volume of the balloon at this altitude?

🔑 **KEY CONCEPT PROBLEM 8.14**

A balloon is filled under the initial conditions indicated below. If the pressure is then increased to 2 atm while the temperature is increased to 50 °C, which balloon on the right, (a) or (b), represents the new volume of the balloon?

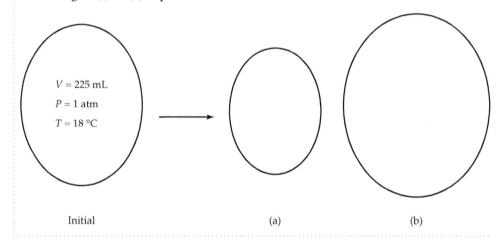

$V = 225$ mL

$P = 1$ atm

$T = 18$ °C

Initial   (a)   (b)

8.9 Avogadro's Law: The Relation between Volume and Molar Amount

Here we look at one final gas law, which takes changes in amount of gas into account. Imagine that you have two different volumes of a gas at the same temperature and pressure. How many moles does each sample contain? According to **Avogadro's law**, the volume of a gas is directly proportional to its molar amount at a constant pressure and temperature (Figure 8.17). A sample that contains twice the molar amount has twice the volume.

Avogadro's law The volume of a gas is directly proportional to its molar amount at a constant pressure and temperature. That is, V divided by n is constant when P and T are held constant.

Volume $(V) \propto$ Number of moles (n)

or $\dfrac{V}{n} = k$ (A constant value; the same for all gases)

or $\dfrac{V_1}{n_1} = \dfrac{V_2}{n_2}$

Because the particles in a gas are so tiny compared to the empty space surrounding them, there is no interaction among gas particles as proposed by the kinetic–molecular theory. As a result, the chemical identity of the particles does not matter and the value of the constant k in the equation $V/n = k$ is the same for all gases. It is therefore possible to compare the molar amounts of *any* two gases simply by comparing their volumes at the same temperature and pressure.

Notice that the *values* of temperature and pressure do not matter; it is only necessary that T and P be the same for both gases. To simplify comparisons of gas samples, however,

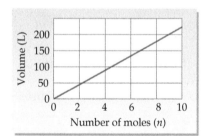

▲ **Figure 8.17**
Avogadro's law.
Volume is directly proportional to the molar amount, *n*, at a constant temperature and pressure. As the number of moles goes up, the volume also goes up.

it is convenient to define a set of conditions called **standard temperature and pressure (STP)**, which specifies a temperature of 0 °C (273 K) and a pressure of 1 atm (760 mmHg).

At standard temperature and pressure, 1 mol of any gas $(6.02 \times 10^{23}$ particles$)$ has a volume of 22.4 L, a quantity called the **standard molar volume** (Figure 8.18).

Standard temperature and pressure (STP) 0 °C (273.15 K); 1 atm (760 mmHg)

Standard molar volume of any ideal gas at STP 22.4 L/mol

◀ **Figure 8.18**
Avogadro's law.
Each of these 22.4 L bulbs contains 1.00 mol of gas at 0 °C and 1 atm pressure. Note that the volume occupied by 1 mol of gas is the same even though the mass (in grams) of 1 mol of each gas is different.

O₂
1.00 mol
32.0 g
22.4 L

He
1.00 mol
4.00 g
22.4 L

F₂
1.00 mol
38.0 g
22.4 L

Ar
1.00 mol
39.9 g
22.4 L

Worked Example 8.9 Using Avogadro's Law: Finding Moles in a Given Volume at STP

Use the standard molar volume of a gas at STP (22.4 L) to find how many moles of air at STP are in a room measuring 4.11 m wide by 5.36 m long by 2.58 m high.

ANALYSIS We first find the volume of the room and then use standard molar volume as a conversion factor to find the number of moles.

SOLUTION

STEP 1: **Identify known information.** We are given the room dimensions.

Length $= 5.36$ m
Width $= 4.11$ m
Height $= 2.58$ m

STEP 2: **Identify answer and units.**

Moles of air $= ??$ mol

STEP 3: **Identify the equation.** The volume of the room is the product of its three dimensions. Once we have the volume (in m³), we can convert to liters and use the molar volume at STP as a conversion factor to obtain moles of air.

$$\text{Volume} = (4.11 \text{ m})(5.36 \text{ m})(2.58 \text{ m}) = 56.8 \text{ m}^3$$
$$= 56.8 \text{ m}^3 \times \frac{1000 \text{ L}}{1 \text{ m}^3} = 5.68 \times 10^4 \text{ L}$$
$$1 \text{ mol} = 22.4 \text{ L} \rightarrow \frac{1 \text{ mol}}{22.4 \text{ L}}$$

STEP 4: **Solve.** Use the room volume and the molar volume at STP to set up an equation, making sure unwanted units cancel.

$$5.68 \times 10^4 \text{ L} \times \frac{1 \text{ mol}}{22.4 \text{ L}} = 2.54 \times 10^3 \text{ mol}$$

PROBLEM 8.15
How many moles of methane gas, CH_4, are in a 1.00×10^5 L storage tank at STP? How many grams of methane is this? How many grams of carbon dioxide gas could the same tank hold?

8.10 The Ideal Gas Law

The relationships among the four variables *P, V, T,* and *n* for gases can be combined into a single expression called the **ideal gas law**. If you know the values of any three of the four quantities, you can calculate the value of the fourth.

Ideal gas law $\dfrac{PV}{nT} = R$ (A constant value)

or $PV = nRT$

Gas constant (R) The constant R in the ideal gas law, $PV = nRT$.

The constant R in the ideal gas law (instead of the usual k) is called the **gas constant**. Its value depends on the units chosen for pressure, with the two most common values being

$$\text{For } P \text{ in atmospheres:} \quad R = 0.0821 \frac{L \cdot atm}{mol \cdot K}$$

$$\text{For } P \text{ in millimeters Hg:} \quad R = 62.4 \frac{L \cdot mmHg}{mol \cdot K}$$

In using the ideal gas law, it is important to choose the value of R having pressure units that are consistent with the problem and, if necessary, to convert volume into liters and temperature into kelvins.

Table 8.3 summarizes the various gas laws, and Worked Examples 8.10 and 8.11 show how to use the ideal gas law.

TABLE 8.3 A Summary of the Gas Laws

	Gas Law	Variables	Constant
Boyle's law	$P_1V_1 = P_2V_2$	P, V	n, T
Charles's law	$V_1/T_1 = V_2/T_2$	V, T	n, P
Gay-Lussac's law	$P_1/T_1 = P_2/T_2$	P, T	n, V
Combined gas law	$P_1V_1/T_1 = P_2V_2/T_2$	P, V, T	n
Avogadro's law	$V_1/n_1 = V_2/n_2$	V, n	P, T
Ideal gas law	$PV = nRT$	P, V, T, n	R

Worked Example 8.10 Using the Ideal Gas Law: Finding Moles

How many moles of air are in the lungs of an average person with a total lung capacity of 3.8 L? Assume that the person is at 1.0 atm pressure and has a normal body temperature of 37 °C.

ANALYSIS This is an ideal gas law problem because it asks for a value of n when P, V, and T are known: $n = PV/RT$. The volume is given in the correct unit of liters, but temperature must be converted to kelvins.

SOLUTION

STEP 1: **Identify known information.** We know three of the four variables in the ideal gas law.

$P = 1.0 \text{ atm}$
$V = 3.8 \text{ L}$
$T = 37\,°C = 310 \text{ K}$

STEP 2: **Identify answer and units.**

Moles of air, $n = \text{ ?? mol}$

STEP 3: **Identify the equation.** Knowing three of the four variables in the ideal gas law, we can rearrange and solve for the unknown variable, n. Note: because pressure is given in atm, we use the value of R that is expressed in atm:

$$R = 0.0821 \frac{L \cdot atm}{mol \cdot K}$$

$$PV = nRT \quad \Rightarrow \quad n = \frac{PV}{RT}$$

STEP 4: **Solve.** Substitute the known information and the appropriate value of R into the ideal gas law equation and solve for n.

$$n = \frac{PV}{RT} = \frac{(1.0 \text{ atm})(3.8 \text{ L})}{\left(0.0821 \dfrac{L \cdot atm}{mol \cdot K}\right)(310 \text{ K})} = 0.15 \text{ mol}$$

Worked Example 8.11 Using the Ideal Gas Law: Finding Pressure

Methane gas is sold in steel cylinders with a volume of 43.8 L containing 5.54 kg. What is the pressure in atmospheres inside the cylinder at a temperature of 20.0 °C (293.15 K)? The molar mass of methane (CH_4) is 16.0 g/mol.

ANALYSIS This is an ideal gas law problem because it asks for a value of P when V, T, and n are given. Although not provided directly, enough information is given so that we can calculate the value of n $(n = g/MW)$.

SOLUTION

STEP 1: **Identify known information.** We know two of the four variables in the ideal gas law; V, T, and can calculate the third, n, from the information provided.

$$V = 43.8\ L$$
$$T = 37\ °C = 310\ K$$

STEP 2: **Identify answer and units.**

Pressure, $P = ??\ atm$

STEP 3: **Identify equation.** First, calculate the number of moles, n, of methane in the cylinder by using molar mass (16.0 g/mol) as a conversion factor. Then use the ideal gas law to calculate the pressure.

$$n = (5.54\ \text{kg methane})\left(\frac{1000\ g}{1\ kg}\right)\left(\frac{1\ mol}{16.0\ g}\right) = 346\ \text{mol methane}$$

$$PV = nRT \quad \Rightarrow \quad P = \frac{nRT}{V}$$

STEP 4: **Solve.** Substitute the known information and the appropriate value of R into the ideal gas law equation and solve for P.

$$P = \frac{nRT}{V} = \frac{(346\ \text{mol})\left(0.0821\ \dfrac{L\cdot atm}{mol\cdot K}\right)(293\ K)}{43.8\ L} = 190\ atm$$

PROBLEM 8.16

An aerosol spray can of deodorant with a volume of 350 mL contains 3.2 g of propane gas (C_3H_8) as propellant. What is the pressure in the can at 20 °C?

PROBLEM 8.17

A helium gas cylinder of the sort used to fill balloons has a volume of 180 L and a pressure of 2200 psi (150 atm) at 25 °C. How many moles of helium are in the tank? How many grams?

🔑 **KEY CONCEPT PROBLEM 8.18**

Show the approximate level of the movable piston in drawings (a) and (b) after the indicated changes have been made to the initial gas sample (assume a constant pressure of 1 atm).

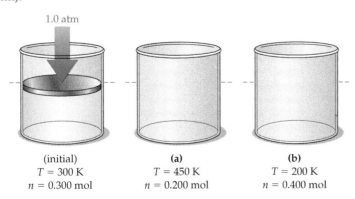

(initial)	(a)	(b)
$T = 300\ K$	$T = 450\ K$	$T = 200\ K$
$n = 0.300\ mol$	$n = 0.200\ mol$	$n = 0.400\ mol$

1.0 atm

8.11 Partial Pressure and Dalton's Law

According to the kinetic–molecular theory, each particle in a gas acts independently of all others because there are no attractive forces between them and they are so far apart. To any individual particle, the chemical identity of its neighbors is irrelevant. Thus, *mixtures* of gases behave the same as pure gases and obey the same laws.

Dry air, for example, is a mixture of about 21% oxygen, 78% nitrogen, and 1% argon by volume, which means that 21% of atmospheric air pressure is caused by O_2 molecules, 78% by N_2 molecules, and 1% by Ar atoms. The contribution of each gas in a mixture to the total pressure of the mixture is called the **partial pressure** of that gas. According to **Dalton's law**, the total pressure exerted by a gas mixture (P_{total}) is the sum of the partial pressures of the components in the mixture:

Partial pressure The contribution of a given gas in a mixture to the total pressure.

Dalton's law $P_{total} = P_{gas\ 1} + P_{gas\ 2} + g$

In dry air at a total air pressure of 760 mmHg, the partial pressure caused by the contribution of O_2 is 0.21×760 mmHg $= 160$ mmHg, the partial pressure of N_2 is 0.78×760 mmHg $= 593$ mmHg, and that of argon is 7 mmHg. *The partial pressure exerted by each gas in a mixture is the same pressure that the gas would exert if it were alone.* Put another way, the pressure exerted by each gas depends on the frequency of collisions of its molecules with the walls of the container. However, this frequency does not change when other gases are present, because the different molecules have no influence on one another.

To represent the partial pressure of a specific gas, we add the formula of the gas as a subscript to P, the symbol for pressure. You might see the partial pressure of oxygen represented as P_{O_2}, for instance. Moist air inside the lungs at 37 °C and atmospheric pressure has the following average composition at sea level. Note that P_{total} is equal to atmospheric pressure, 760 mmHg.

$$P_{total} = P_{N_2} + P_{O_2} + P_{CO_2} + P_{H_2O}$$
$$= 573\ mmHg + 100\ mmHg + 40\ mmHg + 47\ mmHg$$
$$= 760\ mmHg$$

The composition of air does not change appreciably with altitude, but the total pressure decreases rapidly. The partial pressure of oxygen in air therefore decreases with increasing altitude, and it is this change that leads to difficulty in breathing at high elevations.

Worked Example 8.12 Using Dalton's Law: Finding Partial Pressures

Humid air on a warm summer day is approximately 20% oxygen, 75% nitrogen, 4% water vapor, and 1% argon. What is the partial pressure of each component if the atmospheric pressure is 750 mmHg?

ANALYSIS According to Dalton's law, the partial pressure of any gas in a mixture is equal to the percent concentration of the gas times the total gas pressure (750 mmHg). In this case,

$$P_{total} = P_{O_2} + P_{N_2} + P_{H_2O} + P_{Ar}$$

SOLUTION

Oxygen partial pressure (P_{O_2}): $\quad 0.20 \times 750$ mmHg $= 150$ mmHg
Nitrogen partial pressure (P_{N_2}): $\quad 0.75 \times 750$ mmHg $= 560$ mmHg
Water vapor partial pressure (P_{H_2O}): $\quad 0.04 \times 750$ mmHg $= 30$ mmHg
Argon partial pressure (P_{Ar}): $\quad 0.01 \times 750$ mmHg $= 8$ mmHg

Total pressure $= 748$ mmHg $\rightarrow 750$ mmHg (rounding to 2 significant figures!)

Note that the sum of the partial pressures must equal the total pressure (within rounding error).

PROBLEM 8.19

Assuming a total pressure of 9.5 atm, what is the partial pressure of each component in the mixture of 98% helium and 2.0% oxygen breathed by deep-sea divers? How does the partial pressure of oxygen in diving gas compare with its partial pressure in normal air?

PROBLEM 8.20

Determine the percent composition of air in the lungs from the following composition in partial pressures: $P_{N_2} = 573$ mmHg, $P_{O_2} = 100$ mmHg, $P_{CO_2} = 40$ mmHg, $P_{H_2O} = 47$ mmHg; all at 37 °C and 1 atm pressure.

PROBLEM 8.21

The atmospheric pressure on the top of Mt. Everest, an altitude of 29,035 ft, is only 265 mmHg. What is the partial pressure of oxygen in the lungs at this altitude (assuming that the % O_2 is the same as in dry air)?

KEY CONCEPT PROBLEM 8.22

Assume that you have a mixture of He (MW = 4 amu) and Xe (MW = 131 amu) at 300 K. The total pressure of the mixture is 750 mmHg. What are the partial pressures of each of the gases? (blue = He; green = Xe)?

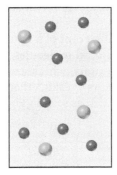

8.12 Liquids

Molecules are in constant motion in the liquid state, just as they are in gases. If a molecule happens to be near the surface of a liquid, and if it has enough energy, it can break free of the liquid and escape into the gas state, called **vapor**. In an open container, the now gaseous molecule will wander away from the liquid, and the process will continue until all the molecules escape from the container (Figure 8.19a). This, of course, is what happens during *evaporation*. We are all familiar with puddles of water evaporating after a rainstorm.

Vapor The gas molecules are in equilibrium with a liquid.

If the liquid is in a closed container, the situation is different because the gaseous molecules cannot escape. Thus, the random motion of the molecules occasionally brings them back into the liquid. After the concentration of molecules in the gas state has increased sufficiently, the number of molecules reentering the liquid becomes equal to the number escaping from the liquid (Figure 8.19b). At this point, a dynamic equilibrium exists, exactly as in a chemical reaction at equilibrium. Evaporation and condensation take place at the same rate, and the concentration of vapor in the container is constant as long as the temperature does not change.

Once molecules have escaped from the liquid into the gas state, they are subject to all the gas laws previously discussed. In a closed container at equilibrium, for example, the vapor molecules will make their own contribution to the total pressure of gases above the liquid according to Dalton's Law (Section 8.11). We call this contribution the **vapor pressure** of the liquid.

Vapor pressure The partial pressure of vapor molecules in equilibrium with a liquid.

The transfer of molecules between liquid and gas states.
(a) Molecules escape from an open container and drift away until the liquid has entirely evaporated.
(b) Molecules in a closed container cannot escape. Instead, they reach an equilibrium in which the rates of molecules leaving the liquid and returning to the liquid are equal, and the concentration of molecules in the gas state is constant.

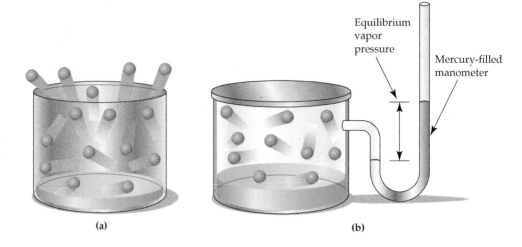

(a)   (b)

▲ **Because bromine is colored, it is possible to see its gaseous reddish vapor above the liquid.**

Normal boiling point The boiling point at a pressure of exactly 1 atmosphere.

Vapor pressure depends on both temperature and the chemical identity of a liquid. As the temperature rises, molecules become more energetic and more likely to escape into the gas state. Thus, vapor pressure rises with increasing temperature until ultimately it becomes equal to the pressure of the atmosphere. At this point, bubbles of vapor form under the surface and force their way to the top, giving rise to the violent action observed during a vigorous boil. At an atmospheric pressure of exactly 760 mmHg, boiling occurs at what is called the **normal boiling point**.

The vapor pressure and boiling point of a liquid will also depend on the intermolecular forces at work between liquid molecules. Ether molecules, for example, can engage in dipole–dipole interactions, which are weaker than the hydrogen bonds formed between water molecules. As a result, ether exhibits both lower vapor pressures and a lower boiling point than water, as seen in Figure 8.20.

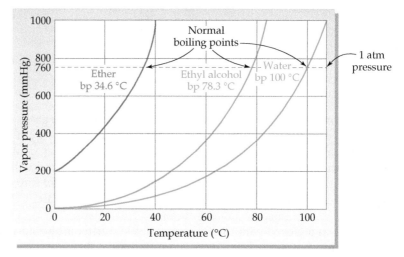

▲ **Figure 8.20**
A plot of the change of vapor pressure with temperature for ethyl ether, ethyl alcohol, and water. At a liquid's boiling point, its vapor pressure is equal to atmospheric pressure. Commonly reported boiling points are those at 760 mmHg.

If atmospheric pressure is higher or lower than normal, the boiling point of a liquid changes accordingly. At high altitudes, for example, atmospheric pressure is lower than at sea level, and boiling points are also lower. On top of Mt. Everest (29,035 ft; 8850 m), atmospheric pressure is about 245 mmHg and the boiling temperature of water is only 71 °C. If the atmospheric pressure is higher than normal, the boiling point is also higher. This principle is used in strong vessels known as *autoclaves*, in which water at high pressure is heated to the temperatures needed for sterilizing medical and dental instruments (170 °C).

Many familiar properties of liquids can be explained by the intermolecular forces just discussed. We all know, for instance, that some liquids, such as water or gasoline, flow easily when poured, whereas others, such as motor oil or maple syrup, flow sluggishly.

The measure of a liquid's resistance to flow is called its *viscosity*. Not surprisingly, viscosity is related to the ease with which individual molecules move around in the liquid and thus to the intermolecular forces present. Substances such as gasoline, which have small, nonpolar molecules, experience only weak intermolecular forces and have relatively low viscosities, whereas more polar substances such as glycerin $[C_3H_5(OH)_3]$ experience stronger intermolecular forces and so have higher viscosities.

Another familiar property of liquids is *surface tension*, the resistance of a liquid to spreading out and increasing its surface area. The beading-up of water on a newly waxed car and the ability of a water strider to walk on water are both due to surface tension.

Surface tension is caused by the difference between the intermolecular forces experienced by molecules at the surface of the liquid and those experienced by molecules in the interior. Molecules in the interior of a liquid are surrounded and experience maximum intermolecular forces, whereas molecules at the surface have fewer neighbors and feel weaker forces. Surface molecules are therefore less stable, and the liquid acts to minimize their number by minimizing the surface area (Figure 8.21).

▲ **Surface tension allows a water strider to walk on water without penetrating the surface.**

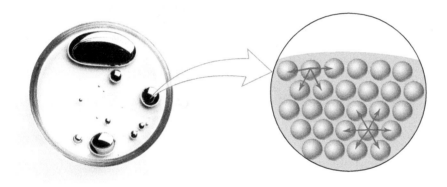

◀ **Figure 8.21**
Surface tension.
Surface tension is caused by the different forces experienced by molecules in the interior of a liquid and those on the surface. Molecules on the surface are less stable because they feel fewer attractive forces, so the liquid acts to minimize their number by minimizing surface area.

▶▶ Recall from Section 1.13 that specific heat is the amount of heat required to raise the temperature of 1g of a substance by 1 °C.

8.13 Water: A Unique Liquid

Ours is a world based on water. Water covers nearly 71% of the earth's surface, it accounts for 66% of the mass of an adult human body, and it is needed by all living things. The water in our blood forms the transport system that circulates substances throughout our body, and water is the medium in which all biochemical reactions are carried out. Largely because of its strong hydrogen bonding, water has many properties that are quite different from those of other compounds.

Water has the highest specific heat of any liquid, giving it the capacity to absorb a large quantity of heat while changing only slightly in temperature. As a result, large lakes and other bodies of water tend to moderate the air temperature and climate of surrounding areas. Another consequence of the high specific heat of water is that the human body is better able to maintain a steady internal temperature under changing outside conditions.

In addition to a high specific heat, water has an unusually high *heat of vaporization* (540 cal/g or 2.3 k J/g), meaning that it carries away a large amount of heat when it evaporates. You can feel the effect of water evaporation on your wet skin when the wind blows. Even when comfortable, your body is still relying for cooling on the heat carried away from the skin and lungs by evaporating water. The heat generated by the

▲ **The moderate year-round temperatures in San Francisco are due to the large heat capacity of the surrounding waters.**

chemical reactions of metabolism is carried by blood to the skin, where water moves through cell walls to the surface and evaporates. When metabolism, and therefore heat generation, speeds up, blood flow increases and capillaries dilate so that heat is brought to the surface faster.

Water is also unique in what happens as it changes from a liquid to a solid. Most substances are more dense as solids than as liquids because molecules are more closely packed in the solid than in the liquid. Water, however, is different. Liquid water has a maximum density of 1.000 g/mL at 3.98 °C but then becomes *less* dense as it cools. When it freezes, its density decreases still further to 0.917 g/mL.

As water freezes, each molecule is locked into position by hydrogen bonding to four other water molecules (Figure 8.22). The resulting structure has more open space than does liquid water, accounting for its lower density. As a result, ice floats on liquid water, and lakes and rivers freeze from the top down. If the reverse were true, fish would be killed in winter as they became trapped in ice at the bottom.

▶ **Figure 8.22**
Ice.
Ice consists of individual H_2O molecules held rigidly together in an ordered manner by hydrogen bonds. The open, cage-like crystal structure shows why ice is less dense than liquid water.

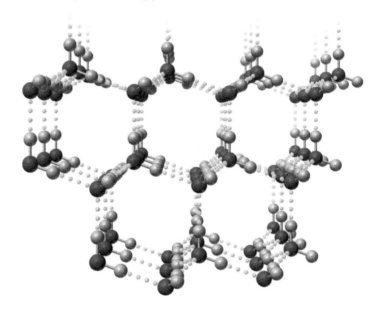

8.14 Solids

A brief look around us reveals that most substances are solids rather than liquids or gases. It is also obvious that there are many different kinds of solids. Some, such as iron and aluminum, are hard and metallic; others, such as sugar and table salt, are crystalline and easily broken; and still others, such as rubber and many plastics, are soft and amorphous.

▲ Crystalline solids, such as pyrite (left) and fluorite (right) have flat faces and distinct angles. The octahedral shape of pyrite and the cubic shape of fluorite reflect similarly ordered arrangements of particles at the atomic level.

The most fundamental distinction between solids is that some are crystalline and some are amorphous. A **crystalline solid** is one whose particles—whether atoms, ions, or molecules—have an ordered arrangement extending over a long range. This order on the atomic level is also seen on the visible level, because crystalline solids usually have flat faces and distinct angles.

Crystalline solids can be further categorized as ionic, molecular, covalent network, or metallic. *Ionic solids* are those like sodium chloride, whose constituent particles are ions. A crystal of sodium chloride is composed of alternating Na^+ and Cl^- ions ordered in a regular three-dimensional arrangement and held together by ionic bonds (see Figure 3.3). *Molecular solids* are those like sucrose or ice, whose constituent particles are molecules held together by the intermolecular forces discussed in Section 8.2. *Covalent network solids* are those like diamond (Figure 8.23) or quartz (SiO_2), whose atoms are linked together by covalent bonds into a giant three-dimensional array. In effect, a covalent network solid is one *very* large molecule.

Crystalline solid A solid whose atoms, molecules, or ions are rigidly held in an ordered arrangement.

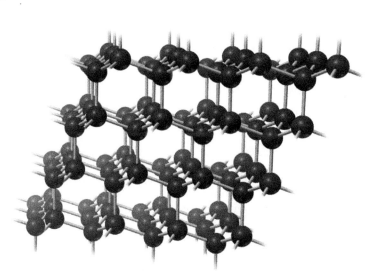

▲ **Figure 8.23**
Diamond. Diamond is a covalent network solid—one very large molecule of carbon atoms linked by covalent bonds.

Metallic solids, such as silver or iron, can be viewed as vast three-dimensional arrays of metal cations immersed in a sea of electrons that are free to move about. This continuous electron sea acts both as a glue to hold the cations together and as a mobile carrier of charge to conduct electricity. Furthermore, the fact that bonding attractions extend uniformly in all directions explains why metals are malleable rather than brittle. When a metal crystal receives a sharp blow, no spatially oriented bonds are broken; instead, the electron sea simply adjusts to the new distribution of cations.

An **amorphous solid**, by contrast with a crystalline solid, is one whose constituent particles are randomly arranged and have no ordered long-range structure. Amorphous solids often result when liquids cool before they can achieve internal order, or when their molecules are large and tangled together, as happens in many polymers. Glass is an amorphous solid, as are tar, the gemstone opal, and some hard candies. Amorphous solids differ from crystalline solids by softening over a wide temperature range rather than having sharp melting points and by shattering to give pieces with curved rather than planar faces.

Amorphous solid A solid whose particles do not have an orderly arrangement.

A summary of the different types of solids and their characteristics is given in Table 8.4.

TABLE 8.4 Types of Solids

Substance	Smallest Unit	Interparticle Forces	Properties	Examples
Ionic solid	Ions	Attraction between positive and negative ions	Brittle and hard; high mp; crystalline	NaCl, KI, $Ca_3(PO_4)_2$
Molecular solid	Molecules	Intermolecular forces	Soft; low to moderate mp; crystalline	Ice, wax, frozen CO_2, all solid organic compounds
Covalent network	Atoms	Covalent bonds	Very hard; very high mp; crystalline	Diamond, quartz (SiO_2), tungsten carbide (WC)
Metal or alloy	Metal atoms	Metallic bonding (attraction between metal ions and surrounding mobile electrons)	Lustrous; soft (Na) to hard (Ti); high melting; crystalline	Elements (Fe, Cu, Sn, . . .), bronze (CuSn alloy), amalgams (Hg+ other metals)
Amorphous solid	Atoms, ions, or molecules (including polymer molecules)	Any of the above	Noncrystalline; no sharp mp; able to flow (may be very slow); curved edges when shattered	Glasses, tar, some plastics

8.15 Changes of State

What happens when a solid is heated? As more and more energy is added, molecules begin to stretch, bend, and vibrate more vigorously, and atoms or ions wiggle about with more energy. Finally, if enough energy is added and the motions become vigorous enough, particles start to break free from one another and the substance starts to melt. Addition of more heat continues the melting process until all particles have broken free and are in the liquid phase. The quantity of heat required to completely melt a substance once it reaches its melting point is called its **heat of fusion**. After melting is complete, further addition of heat causes the temperature of the liquid to rise.

The change of a liquid into a vapor proceeds in the same way as the change of a solid into a liquid. When you first put a pan of water on the stove, all the added heat goes into raising the temperature of the water. Once the boiling point is reached, further absorbed heat goes into freeing molecules from their neighbors as they escape into the gas state. The quantity of heat needed to completely vaporize a liquid once it reaches its boiling point is called its **heat of vaporization**. A liquid with a low heat of vaporization, like rubbing alcohol (isopropyl alcohol), evaporates rapidly and is said to be *volatile*. If you spill a volatile liquid on your skin, you will feel a cooling effect as it evaporates because it is absorbing heat from your body.

It is important to know the difference between heat that is added or removed to change the *temperature* of a substance and heat that is added or removed to change the *phase* of a substance. Remember that temperature is a measure of the kinetic energy in a substance (see Section 7.1). When a substance is above or below its phase-change temperature (i.e., melting point or boiling point), adding or removing heat will simply change the kinetic energy and, hence, the temperature of the substance. The amount of heat needed to produce a given temperature change was presented previously (Section 1.13), but is worth presenting again here:

$$\text{Heat (cal or J)} = \text{Mass (g)} \times \text{Temperature change (°C)} \times \text{Specific heat} \left(\frac{\text{cal or J}}{\text{g} \times °C} \right)$$

In contrast, when a substance is at its phase-change temperature, heat that is added is being used to overcome the intermolecular forces holding particles in that phase. The temperature remains constant until *all* particles have been converted to the next phase. The energy needed to complete the phase change depends only on the amount

Heat of fusion The quantity of heat required to completely melt one gram of a substance once it has reached its melting point.

Heat of vaporization The quantity of heat needed to completely vaporize one gram of a liquid once it has reached its boiling point.

of the substance and the heat of fusion (for melting) or the heat of vaporization (for boiling).

$$\text{Heat (cal or J)} = \text{Mass (g)} \times \text{Heat of fusion}\left(\frac{\text{cal or J}}{g}\right)$$

$$\text{Heat (cal or J)} = \text{Mass (g)} \times \text{Heat of vaporization}\left(\frac{\text{cal or J}}{g}\right)$$

If the intermolecular forces are strong then large amounts of heat must be added to overcome these forces, and the heats of fusion and vaporization will be large. A list of heats of fusion and heats of vaporization for some common substances is given in Table 8.5. Butane, for example, has a small heat of vaporization since the predominant intermolecular forces in butane (dispersion) are relatively weak. Water, on the other hand, has a particularly high heat of vaporization because of its unusually strong hydrogen bonding interactions. Thus, water evaporates more slowly than many other liquids, takes a long time to boil away, and absorbs more heat in the process. A so-called *heating curve*, which indicates the temperature and state changes as heat is added, is shown in Figure 8.24.

TABLE 8.5 Melting Points, Boiling Points, Heats of Fusion, and Heats of Vaporization of Some Common Substances

Substance	Melting Point (°C)	Boiling Point (°C)	Heat of Fusion (cal/g; J/g)	Heat of Vaporization (cal/g; J/g)
Ammonia	−77.7	−33.4	84.0; 351	327; 1370
Butane	−138.4	−0.5	19.2; 80.3	92.5; 387
Ether	−116	34.6	23.5; 98.3	85.6; 358
Ethyl alcohol	−117.3	78.5	26.1; 109	200; 837
Isopropyl alcohol	−89.5	82.4	21.4; 89.5	159; 665
Sodium	97.8	883	14.3; 59.8	492; 2060
Water	0.0	100.0	79.7; 333	540; 2260

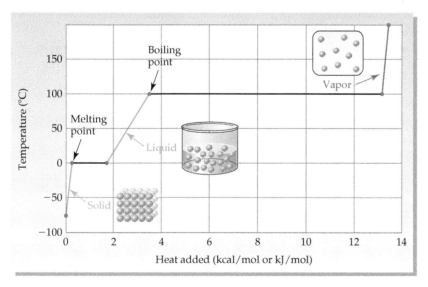

▲ **Figure 8.24**
A heating curve for water, showing the temperature and state changes that occur when heat is added.
The horizontal lines at 0 °C and 100 °C represent the heat of fusion and heat of vaporization, respectively.

Worked Example 8.13 Heat of Fusion: Calculating Total Heat of Melting

Naphthalene, an organic substance often used in mothballs, has a heat of fusion of 35.7 cal/g (149 J/g) and a molar mass of 128.0 g/mol. How much heat in kilocalories is required to melt 0.300 mol of naphthalene?

ANALYSIS The heat of fusion tells how much heat is required to melt 1 g. To find the amount of heat needed to melt 0.300 mol, we need a mole-to-mass conversion.

BALLPARK ESTIMATE Naphthalene has a molar mass of 128.0 g/mol, so 0.300 mol has a mass of about one-third this amount, or about 40 g. Approximately 35 cal or 150 J is required to melt 1 g, so we need about 40 times this amount of heat, or $(35 \times 40 = 1400 \text{ cal} = 1.4 \text{ kcal, or } 150 \times 40 = 6000 \text{ J} = 6.0 \text{ kJ})$.

SOLUTION

STEP 1: Identify known information. We know heat of fusion (cal/g), and the number of moles of naphthalene.

Heat of fusion = 35.7 cal/g, or 149 J/g

Moles of naphthalene = 0.300 mol

STEP 2: Identify answer and units.

Heat = ?? cal or J

STEP 3: Identify conversion factors. First convert moles of naphthalene to grams using the molar mass (128 g/mol) as a conversion factor. Then use the heat of fusion as a conversion factor to calculate the total heat necessary to melt the mass of naphthalene.

$(0.300 \text{ mol naphthalene})\left(\dfrac{128.0 \text{ g}}{1 \text{ mol}}\right) = 38.4 \text{ g napthalene}$

Heat of fusion = 35.7 cal/g or 149 J/g

STEP 4: Solve. Multiplying the mass of naphthalene by the heat of fusion then gives the answer.

$(38.4 \text{ g naphthalene})\left(\dfrac{35.7 \text{ cal}}{1 \text{ g naphthalene}}\right) = 1370 \text{ cal} = 1.37 \text{ kcal, or}$

$(38.4 \text{ g naphthalene})\left(\dfrac{149 \text{ J}}{1 \text{ g naphthalene}}\right) = 5720 \text{ J} = 5.72 \text{ kJ}$

BALLPARK CHECK The calculated result agrees with our estimate (1.4 kcal or 6.0 kJ)

PROBLEM 8.23

How much heat in kilocalories is required to melt and boil 1.50 mol of isopropyl alcohol (rubbing alcohol; molar mass = 60.0 g/mol)? The heat of fusion and heat of vaporization of isopropyl alcohol are given in Table 8.5.

PROBLEM 8.24

How much heat in kilojoules is released by the condensation of 2.5 mol of steam? The heat of vaporization is given in Table 8.5.

PROBLEM 8.25

The physical state of CO_2 depends on the temperature and pressure (see Chemistry in Action: CO_2 as an Environmentally Friendly Solvent on p. 245). In what state would you expect to find CO_2 at 50 atm and 25 °C?

CHEMISTRY IN ACTION

CO_2 as an Environmentally Friendly Solvent

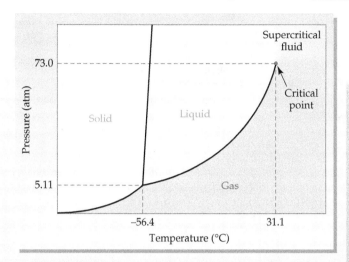

When you think of CO_2 you most likely think of the gas that is absorbed by plants for photosynthesis or exhaled by animals during respiration. You have also probably seen CO_2 in the form of dry ice, that very cold solid that sublimes to a gas. But how can CO_2 be a solvent? After all, carbon dioxide is a gas, not a liquid, at room temperature. Furthermore, CO_2 at atmospheric pressure does not become liquid even when cooled. When the temperature drops to $-78\,°C$ at 1 atm pressure, CO_2 goes directly from gas to solid (dry ice) without first becoming liquid. Only when the pressure is raised does liquid CO_2 exist. At a room temperature of 22.4 °C, a pressure of 60 atm is needed to force gaseous CO_2 molecules close enough together so they condense to a liquid. Even as a liquid, though, CO_2 is not a particularly good solvent. Only when it enters an unusual and rarely seen state of matter called the *supercritical state* does CO_2 become a remarkable solvent.

To understand the supercritical state of matter, consider the two factors that determine the physical state of a substance: temperature and pressure. In the solid state, molecules are packed closely together and do not have enough kinetic energy to overcome the intermolecular forces. If we increase the temperature, however, we can increase the kinetic energy so that the molecules can move apart and produce a phase change to either a liquid or a gas. In the gas state, molecules are too far apart to interact, but increasing the pressure will force molecules closer together, and, eventually, intermolecular attractions between molecules will cause them to condense into a liquid or solid state. This dependence of the physical state on temperature and pressure is represented by a *phase diagram*, such as the one shown here for CO_2.

The supercritical state represents a situation that is intermediate between liquid and gas. There is *some* space between molecules, but not much. The molecules are too far apart to be truly a liquid, yet they are too close together to be truly a gas. Supercritical CO_2 exists above the *critical point*, when the pressure is above 72.8 atm and the temperature is above 31.2 °C.

This pressure is high enough to force molecules close together and prevent them from expanding into the gas state. Above this temperature, however, the molecules have too much kinetic energy to condense into the liquid state.

Because open spaces already exist between CO_2 molecules, it is energetically easy for dissolved molecules to slip in, and supercritical CO_2 is therefore an extraordinarily good solvent. Among its many applications, supercritical CO_2 is used in the beverage and food-processing industries to decaffeinate coffee beans and to obtain spice extracts from vanilla, pepper, cloves, nutmeg, and other seeds. In the cosmetics and perfume industry, fragrant oils are extracted from flowers using supercritical CO_2. Perhaps the most important future application is the use of carbon dioxide for dry-cleaning clothes, thereby replacing environmentally harmful chlorinated solvents.

The use of supercritical CO_2 as a solvent has many benefits, including the fact that it is nontoxic and nonflammable. Most important, though, is that the technology is environmentally friendly. Industrial processes using CO_2 are designed as closed systems so that the CO_2 is recaptured after use and continually recycled. No organic solvent vapors are released into the atmosphere and no toxic liquids seep into groundwater supplies, as can occur with current procedures using chlorinated organic solvents. The future looks bright for this new technology.

See Chemistry in Action Problems 8.104 and 8.105 at the end of the chapter.

SUMMARY: REVISITING THE CHAPTER GOALS

1. What are the major intermolecular forces, and how do they affect the states of matter? There are three major types of *intermolecular forces*, which act to hold molecules near one another in solids and liquids. *Dipole–dipole forces* are the electrical attractions that occur between polar molecules. *London dispersion forces* occur between all molecules as a result of temporary molecular polarities due to unsymmetrical electron distribution. These forces increase in strength with molecular weight and with the surface area of molecules. *Hydrogen bonding*, the strongest of the three intermolecular forces, occurs between a hydrogen atom bonded to O, N, or F and a nearby O, N, or F atom (*see Problems 34–37, 116*).

2. How do scientists explain the behavior of gases? According to the *kinetic-molecular theory of gases*, the physical behavior of gases can be explained by assuming that they consist of particles moving rapidly at random, separated from other particles by great distances, and colliding without loss of energy. Gas pressure is the result of molecular collisions with a surface (*see Problems 29, 30, 40, 41, 53, 59, 68, 102, 103, 106*).

3. How do gases respond to changes in temperature, pressure, and volume? *Boyle's law* says that the volume of a fixed amount of gas at constant temperature is inversely proportional to its pressure ($P_1V_1 = P_2V_2$). *Charles's law* says that the volume of a fixed amount of gas at constant pressure is directly proportional to its Kelvin temperature ($V_1/T_1 = V_2/T_2$). *Gay-Lussac's law* says that the pressure of a fixed amount of gas at constant volume is directly proportional to its Kelvin temperature ($P_1/T_1 = P_2/T_2$). Boyle's law, Charles's law, and Gay-Lussac's law together give the *combined gas law* ($P_1V_1/T_1 = P_2V_2/T_2$), which applies to changing conditions for a fixed quantity of gas. *Avogadro's law* says that equal volumes of gases at the same temperature and pressure contain the same number of moles ($V_1/n_1 = V_2/n_2$) (*see Problems 26, 27, 32, 38–75, 107, 111, 112, 115*).

4. What is the ideal gas law? The four gas laws together give the *ideal gas law*, $PV = nRT$, which relates the effects of temperature, pressure, volume, and molar amount. At 0 °C and 1 atm pressure, called *standard temperature and pressure (STP)*, 1 mol of any gas (6.02×10^{23} molecules) occupies a volume of 22.4 L (*see Problems 76–85, 108–110, 113–115, 118, 119*).

5. What is partial pressure? The amount of pressure exerted by an individual gas in a mixture is called the *partial pressure* of the gas. According to *Dalton's law*, the total pressure exerted by the mixture is equal to the sum of the partial pressures of the individual gases (*see Problems 33, 86–89, 117*).

6. What are the various kinds of solids, and how do they differ? Solids are either crystalline or amorphous. *Crystalline solids* are those whose constituent particles have an ordered arrangement; *amorphous solids* lack internal order and do not have sharp melting points. There are several kinds of crystalline solids: *Ionic solids* are those such as sodium chloride, whose constituent particles are ions. *Molecular solids* are those such as ice, whose constituent particles are molecules held together by intermolecular forces. *Covalent network solids* are those such as diamond, whose atoms are linked together by covalent bonds into a giant three-dimensional array. *Metallic solids*, such as silver or iron, also consist of large arrays of atoms, but their crystals have metallic properties such as electrical conductivity (*see Problems 96–99*).

7. What factors affect a change of state? When a solid is heated, particles begin to move around freely at the *melting point*, and the substance becomes liquid. The amount of heat necessary to melt a given amount of solid at its melting point is its *heat of fusion*. As a liquid is heated, molecules escape from the surface of a liquid until an equilibrium is reached between liquid and gas, resulting in a *vapor pressure* of the liquid. At a liquid's *boiling point*, its vapor pressure equals atmospheric pressure, and the entire liquid is converted into gas. The amount of heat necessary to vaporize a given amount of liquid at its boiling point is called its *heat of vaporization* (*see Problems 27, 28, 31, 90–95, 98, 99, 104*).

KEY WORDS

Amorphous solid, *p. 241*

Avogadro's law, *p. 232*

Boiling point (bp), *p. 215*

Boyle's law, *p. 226*

Change of state, *p. 214*

Charles's law, *p. 229*

Combined gas law, *p. 231*

Crystalline solid, *p. 241*

Dalton's law, *p. 236*

Dipole–dipole force, *p. 216*

Gas constant (*R*), *p. 234*

Gas laws, *p. 225*

Gay-Lussac's law, *p. 230*

Heat of fusion, *p. 242*

Heat of vaporization, *p. 242*

Hydrogen bond, *p. 217*

Ideal gas, *p. 221*

Ideal gas law, *p. 233*

Intermolecular force, *p. 216*

Kinetic–molecular theory of gases, *p. 220*

London dispersion force, *p. 217*

Melting point (mp), *p. 215*

Normal boiling point, *p. 238*

Partial pressure, *p. 236*

Pressure (*P*), *p. 221*

Standard temperature and pressure (STP), *p. 233*

Standard molar volume, *p. 233*

Vapor, *p. 237*

Vapor pressure, *p. 237*

CONCEPT MAP: GASES, LIQUIDS, AND SOLIDS

Concept Map. The physical state of matter (solid, liquid, gas) depends on the strength of the intermolecular forces between molecules compared to the kinetic energy of the molecules. When the kinetic energy (i.e, temperature) is greater than the forces holding molecules in a given state, then a phase change occurs. Thus, the physical properties of matter (melting and boiling points, etc.) depend on the strength of the intermolecular forces between molecules, which depend on chemical structure and molecular shape. These relationships are reflected here in Figure 8.25.

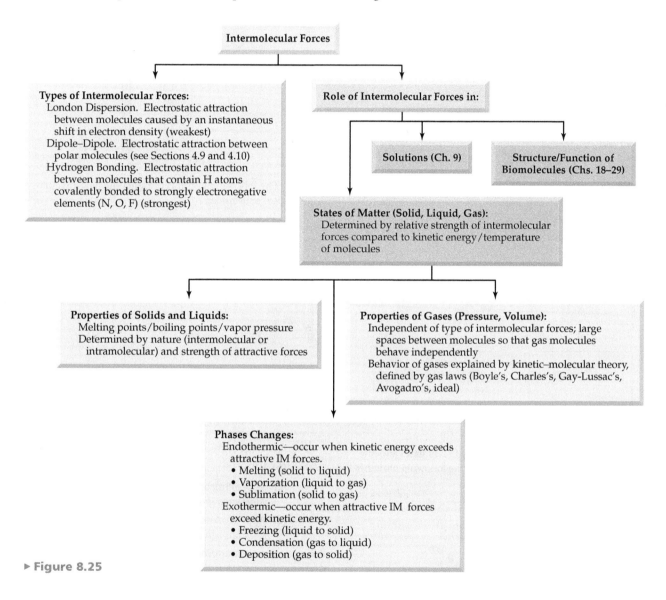

▶ **Figure 8.25**

UNDERSTANDING KEY CONCEPTS

8.26   Assume that you have a sample of gas in a cylinder with a movable piston, as shown in the following drawing:

Redraw the apparatus to show what the sample will look like after the following changes:

(a) The temperature is increased from 300 K to 450 K at constant pressure.

(b) The pressure is increased from 1 atm to 2 atm at constant temperature.

(c) The temperature is decreased from 300 K to 200 K and the pressure is decreased from 3 atm to 2 atm.

8.27   Assume that you have a sample of gas at 350 K in a sealed container, as represented in part (a). Which of the drawings (b)–(d) represents the gas after the temperature is lowered from 350 K to 150 K if the gas has a boiling point of 200 K? Which drawing represents the gas at 150 K if the gas has a boiling point of 100 K?

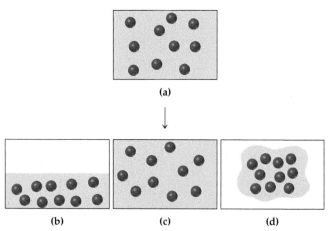

8.28   Assume that drawing (a) represents a sample of H_2O at 200 K. Which of the drawings (b)–(d) represents what the sample will look like when the temperature is raised to 300 K?

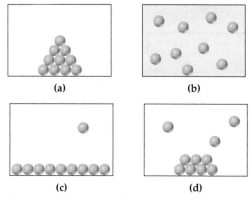

8.29   Three bulbs, two of which contain different gases and one of which is empty, are connected as shown in the following drawing:

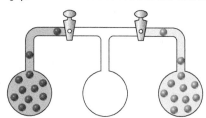

Redraw the apparatus to represent the gases after the stopcocks are opened and the system is allowed to come to equilibrium.

8.30   Redraw the following open-ended manometer to show what it would look like when stopcock A is opened.

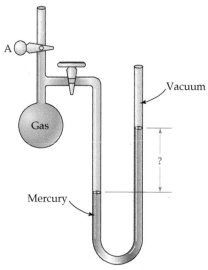

8.31   The following graph represents the heating curve of a hypothetical substance:

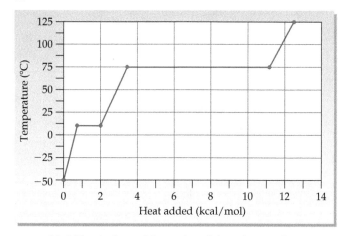

(a) What is the melting point of the substance?

(b) What is the boiling point of the substance?

(c) Approximately what is the heat of fusion for the substance in kcal/mol?

(d) Approximately what is the heat of vaporization for the substance in kcal/mol?

8.32   Show the approximate level of the movable piston in drawings (a)–(c) after the indicated changes have been made to the gas.

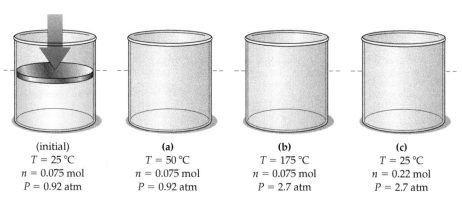

8.33   The partial pressure of the blue gas in the container represented in the picture is 240 mmHg. What are the partial pressures of the yellow and red gases? What is the total pressure inside the container?

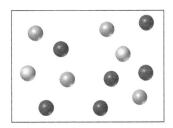

ADDITIONAL PROBLEMS

INTERMOLECULAR FORCES

8.34   What characteristic must a compound have to experience the following intermolecular forces?

    (a) London dispersion forces   **(b)** Dipole–dipole forces

    (c) Hydrogen bonding

8.35   Identify the predominant intermolecular force in each of the following substances.

    (a) N_2 **(b)** HCN   **(c)** CCl_4

    (d) NH_3 **(e)** CH_3Cl **(f)** CH_3COOH

8.36   Dimethyl ether (CH_3OCH_3) and ethanol (C_2H_5OH) have the same formula (C_2H_6O), but the boiling point of dimethyl ether is $-25\,°C$, while that of ethanol is $78\,°C$. Explain this difference in boiling points.

8.37   Iodine is a solid at room temperature $(mp = 113.5\,°C)$ while bromine is a liquid $(mp = -7\,°C)$. Explain this difference in terms of intermolecular forces.

GASES AND PRESSURE

8.38   How is 1 atm of pressure defined?

8.39   List four common units for measuring pressure.

8.40   What are the four assumptions of the kinetic–molecular theory of gases?

8.41   How does the kinetic–molecular theory of gases explain gas pressure?

8.42   Convert the following values into mmHg:

    (a) Standard pressure   **(b)** 25.3 psi   **(c)** 7.5 atm

    (d) 28.0 in. Hg   **(e)** 41.8 Pa

8.43   Atmospheric pressure at the top of Mt. Whitney in California is 440 mmHg.

    (a) How many atmospheres is this?

    (b) How many pascals is this?

8.44   What is the pressure (in mmHg) inside a container of gas connected to a mercury-filled, open-ended manometer of the sort shown in Figure 8.10 when the level in the arm connected to the container is 17.6 cm lower than the level in the arm open to the atmosphere and the atmospheric pressure reading outside the apparatus is 754.3 mmHg? What is the pressure inside the container in atm?

8.45   What is the pressure (in atmospheres) inside a container of gas connected to a mercury-filled, open-ended manometer of the sort shown in Figure 8.10 when the level in the arm connected to the container is 28.3 cm higher than the level in the arm open to the atmosphere, and the atmospheric pressure reading outside the apparatus is 1.021 atm? What is the pressure in mmHg?

BOYLE'S LAW

8.46   What is Boyle's law, and what variables must be kept constant for the law to hold?

8.47   Which assumption(s) of the kinetic–molecular theory explain the behavior of gases described by Boyle's Law? Explain your answer.

8.48   The pressure of gas in a 600.0 mL cylinder is 65.0 mmHg. What is the new volume when the pressure is increased to 385 mmHg?

8.49   The volume of a balloon is 2.85 L at 1.00 atm. What pressure is required to compress the balloon to a volume of 1.70 L?

8.50   The use of chlorofluorocarbons (CFCs) as refrigerants and propellants in aerosol cans has been discontinued as a result of concerns about the ozone layer. If an aerosol can contained 350 mL of CFC gas at a pressure of 5.0 atm, what volume would this gas occupy at 1.0 atm?

8.51   A balloon occupies a volume of 1.25 L at sea level where the ambient pressure is 1 atm. What volume would the balloon occupy at an altitude of 35,000 ft, where the air pressure is only 220 mmHg?

CHARLES'S LAW

8.52   What is Charles's law, and what variables must be kept constant for the law to hold?

8.53   Which assumption(s) of the kinetic–molecular theory explain the behavior of gases described by Charles's Law? Explain your answer.

8.54   A hot-air balloon has a volume of 960 L at 291 K. To what temperature (in °C) must it be heated to raise its volume to 1200 L, assuming the pressure remains constant?

8.55   A hot-air balloon has a volume of 875 L. What is the original temperature of the balloon if its volume changes to 955 L when heated to 56 °C?

8.56   A gas sample has a volume of 185 mL at 38 °C. What is its volume at 97 °C?

8.57   A balloon has a volume of 43.0 L at 25 °C. What is its volume at 2.8 °C?

GAY-LUSSAC'S LAW

8.58 What is Gay-Lussac's law, and what variables must be kept constant for the law to hold?

8.59 Which assumption(s) of the kinetic–molecular theory explain the behavior of gases described by Gay-Lussac's Law? Explain your answer.

8.60 A glass laboratory flask is filled with gas at 25 °C and 0.95 atm pressure, sealed, and then heated to 117 °C. What is the pressure inside the flask?

8.61 An aerosol can has an internal pressure of 3.85 atm at 25 °C. What temperature is required to raise the pressure to 18.0 atm?

COMBINED GAS LAW

8.62 A gas has a volume of 2.84 L at 1.00 atm and 0 °C. At what temperature does it have a volume of 7.50 L at 520 mmHg?

8.63 A compressed-air tank carried by scuba divers has a volume of 6.80 L and a pressure of 120 atm at 20 °C. What is the volume of air in the tank at 0 °C and 1.00 atm pressure (STP)?

8.64 When H_2 gas was released by the reaction of HCl with Zn, the volume of H_2 collected was 75.4 mL at 23 °C and 748 mmHg. What is the volume of the H_2 at 0 °C and 1.00 atm pressure (STP)?

8.65 What is the effect on the volume of a gas if you simultaneously:

(a) Halve its pressure and double its Kelvin temperature?

(b) Double its pressure and double its Kelvin temperature?

8.66 What is the effect on the pressure of a gas if you simultaneously:

(a) Halve its volume and double its Kelvin temperature?

(b) Double its volume and halve its Kelvin temperature?

8.67 A small cylinder of helium gas used for filling balloons has a volume of 2.30 L and a pressure of 1850 atm at 25 °C. How many balloons can you fill if each one has a volume of 1.5 L and a pressure of 1.25 atm at 25 °C?

AVOGADRO'S LAW AND STANDARD MOLAR VOLUME

8.68 Explain Avogadro's law using the kinetic–molecular theory of gases.

8.69 What conditions are defined as standard temperature and pressure (STP)?

8.70 How many molecules are in 1.0 L of O_2 at STP or 1.0 L? How may grams of O_2?

8.71 How many moles of gas are in a volume of 48.6 L at STP?

8.72 What is the mass of CH_4 in a sample that occupies a volume of 16.5 L at STP?

8.73 Assume that you have 1.75 g of the deadly gas hydrogen cyanide, HCN. What is the volume of the gas at STP?

8.74 A typical room is 4.0 m long, 5.0 m wide, and 2.5 m high. What is the total mass of the oxygen in the room assuming that the gas in the room is at STP and that air contains 21% oxygen and 79% nitrogen?

8.75 What is the total volume and number of moles of nitrogen in the room described in Problem 8.74?

IDEAL GAS LAW

8.76 What is the ideal gas law?

8.77 How does the ideal gas law differ from the combined gas law?

8.78 Which sample contains more molecules: 2.0 L of Cl_2 at STP, or 3.0 L of CH_4 at 300 K and 1150 mmHg? Which sample weighs more?

8.79 Which sample contains more molecules: 2.0 L of CO_2 at 300 K and 500 mmHg, or 1.5 L of N_2 at 57 °C and 760 mmHg? Which sample weighs more?

8.80 If 2.3 mol of He has a volume of 0.15 L at 294 K, what is the pressure in atm? In psi?

8.81 If 3.5 mol of O_2 has a volume of 27.0 L at a pressure of 1.6 atm, what is its temperature in °C?

8.82 If 15.0 g of CO_2 gas has a volume of 0.30 L at 310 K, what is its pressure in mmHg?

8.83 If 20.0 g of N_2 gas has a volume of 4.00 L and a pressure of 6.0 atm, what is its temperature in degrees celsius?

8.84 If 18.0 g of O_2 gas has a temperature of 350 K and a pressure of 550 mmHg, what is its volume?

8.85 How many moles of a gas will occupy a volume of 0.55 L at a temperature of 347 K and a pressure of 2.5 atm?

DALTON'S LAW AND PARTIAL PRESSURE

8.86 What is meant by *partial pressure*?

8.87 What is Dalton's law?

8.88 If the partial pressure of oxygen in air at 1.0 atm is 160 mmHg, what is its partial pressure on the summit of Mt. Whitney, where atmospheric pressure is 440 mmHg? Assume that the percent oxygen is the same.

8.89 Scuba divers who suffer from decompression sickness are treated in hyperbaric chambers using heliox (21% oxygen, 79% helium), at pressures up to 120 psi. Calculate the partial pressure of O_2 (in mmHg) in a hyperbaric chamber under these conditions.

LIQUIDS

8.90 What is the vapor pressure of a liquid?

8.91 What is a liquid's heat of vaporization?

8.92 What is the effect of pressure on a liquid's boiling point?

8.93 Which of the following substances would you expect to have the higher vapor pressure: CH_3OH or CH_3Cl? Explain

8.94 The heat of vaporization of water is 9.72 kcal/mol.

(a) How much heat (in kilocalories) is required to vaporize 3.00 mol of H_2O?

(b) How much heat (in kilocalories) is released when 320 g of steam condenses?

8.95 Patients with a high body temperature are often given "alcohol baths." The heat of vaporization of isopropyl alcohol (rubbing alcohol) is 159 cal/g. How much heat is removed from the skin by the evaporation of 190 g (about 1/2 a cup) of isopropyl alcohol?

SOLIDS

8.96 What is the difference between an amorphous and a crystalline solid?

8.97 List three kinds of crystalline solids, and give an example of each.

8.98 The heat of fusion of acetic acid, the principal organic component of vinegar, is 45.9 cal/g. How much heat (in kilocalories) is required to melt 1.75 mol of solid acetic acid?

8.99 The heat of fusion of sodium metal is 630 cal/mol. How much heat (in kilocalories) is required to melt 262 g of sodium?

CHEMISTRY IN ACTION

8.100 What evidence is there that global warming is occurring? [*Greenhouse Gases and Global Warming, p. 224*]

8.101 What are the three most important greenhouse gases? [*Greenhouse Gases and Global Warming, p. 224*]

8.102 What is the difference between a systolic and a diastolic pressure reading? Is a blood pressure of 180/110 within the normal range? [*Blood Pressure, p. 228*]

8.103 Convert the blood pressure reading in Problem 8.102 to atm. [*Blood Pressure, p. 228*]

8.104 What is a supercritical fluid? [CO_2 *as an Environmentally Friendly Solvent, p. 245*]

8.105 What are the environmental advantages of using supercritical CO_2 in place of chlorinated organic solvents? [CO_2 *as an Environmentally Friendly Solvent, p. 245*]

GENERAL QUESTIONS AND PROBLEMS

8.106 Use the kinetic–molecular theory to explain why gas pressure increases if the temperature is raised and the volume is kept constant.

8.107 Hydrogen and oxygen react according to the equation $2 H_2(g) + O_2(g) \longrightarrow 2 H_2O(g)$. According to Avogadro's law, how many liters of hydrogen are required to react with 2.5 L of oxygen at STP?

8.108 If 3.0 L of hydrogen and 1.5 L of oxygen at STP react to yield water, how many moles of water are formed? What gas volume does the water have at a temperature of 100 °C and 1 atm pressure?

8.109 Approximately 240 mL/min of CO_2 is exhaled by an average adult at rest. Assuming a temperature of 37 °C and 1 atm pressure, how many moles of CO_2 is this?

8.110 How many grams of CO_2 are exhaled by an average resting adult in 24 hours? (See Problem 8.109.)

8.111 Imagine that you have two identical containers, one containing hydrogen at STP and the other containing oxygen at STP. How can you tell which is which without opening them?

8.112 When fully inflated, a hot-air balloon has a volume of 1.6×10^5 L at an average temperature of 375 K and 0.975 atm. Assuming that air has an average molar mass of 29 g/mol, what is the density of the air in the hot-air balloon? How does this compare with the density of air at STP?

8.113 A 10.0 g sample of an unknown gas occupies 14.7 L at a temperature of 25 °C and a pressure of 745 mmHg. How many moles of gas are in the sample? What is the molar mass of the gas?

8.114 One mole of any gas has a volume of 22.4 L at STP. What are the molecular weights of the following gases, and what are their densities in grams per liter at STP?

    (a) CH_4 **(b)** CO_2 **(c)** O_2

8.115 Gas pressure outside the space shuttle is approximately 1×10^{-14} mm Hg at a temperature of approximately 1 K. If the gas is almost entirely hydrogen atoms (H, not H_2), what volume of space is occupied by 1 mol of atoms? What is the density of H gas in atoms per liter?

8.116 Ethylene glycol, $C_2H_6O_2$, has one OH bonded to each carbon.

    (a) Draw the Lewis dot structure of ethylene glycol.

    (b) Draw the Lewis dot structure of chloroethane, C_2H_5Cl.

    (c) Chloroethane has a slightly higher molar mass than ethylene glycol, but a much lower boiling point (3 °C versus 198 °C). Explain.

8.117 A rule of thumb for scuba diving is that the external pressure increases by 1 atm for every 10 m of depth. A diver using a compressed air tank is planning to descend to a depth of 25 m.

    (a) What is the external pressure at this depth? (Remember that the pressure at sea level is 1 atm.)

    (b) Assuming that the tank contains 20% oxygen and 80% nitrogen, what is the partial pressure of each gas in the diver's lungs at this depth?

8.118 The *Rankine* temperature scale used in engineering is to the Fahrenheit scale as the Kelvin scale is to the Celsius scale. That is, 1 Rankine degree is the same size as 1 Fahrenheit degree, and 0 °R = absolute zero.

    (a) What temperature corresponds to the freezing point of water on the Rankine scale?

    (b) What is the value of the gas constant R on the Rankine scale in $(L \cdot atm)/(°R \cdot mol)$?

8.119 Isooctane, C_8H_{18}, is the component of gasoline from which the term *octane rating* derives.

    (a) Write a balanced equation for the combustion of isooctane to yield CO_2 and H_2O.

    (b) Assuming that gasoline is 100% isooctane and that the density of isooctane is 0.792 g/mL, what mass of CO_2 (in kilograms) is produced each year by the annual U.S. gasoline consumption of 4.6×10^{10} L?

    (c) What is the volume (in liters) of this CO_2 at STP?

CHAPTER 9

Solutions

CONTENTS

◄ The giant sequoia relies on osmotic pressure—a colligative property of solutions—to transport water and nutrients from the roots to the treetops 300 ft up.

Up to this point, we have been concerned primarily with pure substances, both elements and compounds. In day-to-day life, however, most of the materials we come in contact with are mixtures. Air, for example, is a gaseous mixture of primarily oxygen and nitrogen; blood is a liquid mixture of many different components; and many rocks are solid mixtures of different minerals. In this chapter, we look closely at the characteristics and properties of mixtures, with particular attention to the uniform mixtures we call *solutions*.

9.1 Mixtures and Solutions

As we saw in Section 1.3, a *mixture* is an intimate combination of two or more substances, both of which retain their chemical identities. Mixtures can be classified as either *heterogeneous* or *homogeneous*, as indicated in Figure 9.1, depending on their appearance. **Heterogeneous mixtures** are those in which the mixing is not uniform and which therefore have regions of different composition. Rocky Road ice cream, for example, is a heterogeneous mixture, with something different in every spoonful. Granite and many other rocks are also heterogeneous, having a grainy character due to the heterogeneous mixing of different minerals. **Homogeneous mixtures** are those in which the mixing *is* uniform and that therefore have the same composition throughout. Seawater, a homogeneous mixture of soluble ionic compounds in water, is an example.

Homogeneous mixtures can be further classified as either *solutions* or *colloids*, according to the size of their particles. **Solutions**, the most important class of homogeneous mixtures, contain particles the size of a typical ion or small molecule—roughly 0.1–2 nm in diameter. **Colloids**, such as milk and fog, are also homogeneous in appearance but contain larger particles than solutions—in the range 2–500 nm diameter.

Liquid solutions, colloids, and heterogeneous mixtures can be distinguished in several ways. For example, liquid solutions are transparent (although they may be colored). Colloids may appear transparent if the particle size is small, but they have a murky or opaque appearance if the particle size is larger. Neither solutions nor small-particle colloids separate on standing, and the particles in both are too small to be removed by filtration. Heterogeneous mixtures and large-particle colloids, also known as "suspensions," are murky or opaque and their particles will slowly settle on prolonged standing. House paint is an example.

Heterogeneous mixture A nonuniform mixture that has regions of different composition.

Homogeneous mixture A uniform mixture that has the same composition throughout.

Solution A homogeneous mixture that contains particles the size of a typical ion or small molecule.

Colloid A homogeneous mixture that contains particles that range in diameter from 2 to 500 nm.

253

▶ **Figure 9.1**
Classification of mixtures.
The components in heterogeneous mixtures are not uniformly mixed, and the composition varies with location within the mixture. In homogeneous mixtures, the components are uniformly mixed at the molecular level.

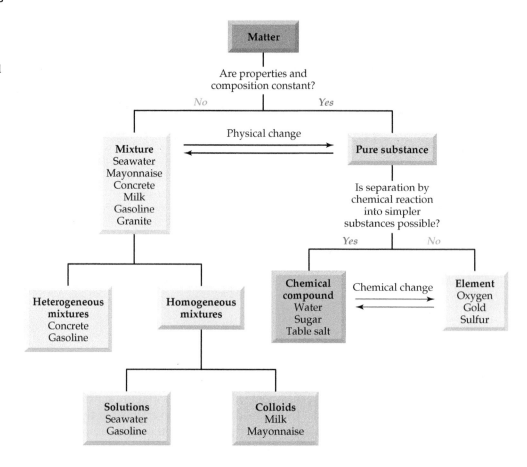

Table 9.1 gives some examples of solutions, colloids, and heterogeneous mixtures. It is interesting to note that blood has characteristics of all three. About 45% by volume of blood consists of suspended red and white cells, which settle slowly on standing; the remaining 55% is *plasma*, which contains ions in solution and colloidal protein molecules.

TABLE 9.1 **Some Characteristics of Solutions, Colloids, and Heterogeneous Mixtures**

Type of Mixture	Particle Size	Examples	Characteristics
Solution	<2.0 nm	Air, seawater, gasoline, wine	Transparent to light; does not separate on standing; nonfilterable
Colloid	2.0–500 nm	Butter, milk, fog, pearl	Often murky or opaque to light; does not separate on standing; nonfilterable
Heterogeneous	>500 nm	Blood, paint, aerosol sprays	Murky or opaque to light; separates on standing; filterable

Although we usually think of solids dissolved in liquids when we talk about solutions, solutions actually occur in all three phases of matter (Table 9.2). Metal alloys like 14-karat gold (58% gold with silver and copper) and brass (10–40% zinc with copper), for instance, are solutions of one solid with another. For solutions in which a gas or solid is dissolved in a liquid, the dissolved substance is called the **solute** and the liquid is called the **solvent**. In seawater, for example, the dissolved salts would be the solutes and water would be the solvent. When one liquid is dissolved in another, the minor component is usually considered the solute and the major component is the solvent.

Solute A substance that is dissolved in a solvent.

Solvent The substance in which another substance (the solute) is dissolved.

TABLE 9.2 Some Different Types of Solutions	
Type of Solution	**Example**
Gas in gas	Air (O_2, N_2, Ar, and other gases)
Gas in liquid	Seltzer water (CO_2 in water)
Gas in solid	H_2 in palladium metal
Liquid in liquid	Gasoline (mixture of hydrocarbons)
Liquid in solid	Dental amalgam (mercury in silver)
Solid in liquid	Seawater (NaCl and other salts in water)
Solid in solid	Metal alloys such as 14-karat gold (Au, Ag, and Cu)

PROBLEM 9.1

Classify the following liquid mixtures as heterogeneous or homogeneous. Further classify each homogeneous mixture as a solution or colloid.

(a) Orange juice   **(b)** Apple juice

(c) Hand lotion   **(d)** Tea

9.2 The Solution Process

What determines whether a substance is soluble in a given liquid? Solubility depends primarily on the strength of the attractions between solute and solvent particles relative to the strengths of the attractions within the pure substances. Ethyl alcohol is soluble in water, for example, because hydrogen bonding (Section 8.2) is nearly as strong between water and ethyl alcohol molecules as it is between water molecules alone or ethyl alcohol molecules alone.

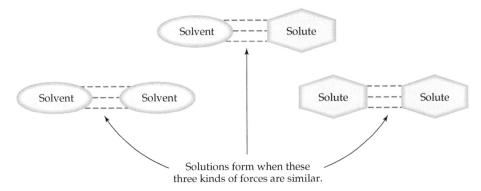

Solutions form when these three kinds of forces are similar.

A good rule of thumb for predicting solubility is that "like dissolves like," meaning that substances with similar intermolecular forces form solutions with one another, whereas substances with different intermolecular forces do not (Section 8.2).

Polar solvents dissolve polar and ionic solutes; nonpolar solvents dissolve nonpolar solutes. Thus, a polar, hydrogen-bonding compound like water dissolves ethyl alcohol and sodium chloride, whereas a nonpolar organic compound like hexane (C_6H_{14}) dissolves other nonpolar organic compounds like fats and oils. Water and oil, however, do not dissolve one another, as summed up by the old saying, "Oil and water don't mix." The intermolecular forces between water molecules are so strong that after an oil–water mixture is shaken, the water layer re-forms, squeezing out the oil molecules.

Water solubility is not limited to ionic compounds and ethyl alcohol. Many polar organic substances, such as sugars, amino acids, and even some proteins, dissolve in water. In addition, small, moderately polar organic molecules such as chloroform $(CHCl_3)$ are soluble in water to a limited extent. When mixed with water, a small amount of the organic compound dissolves, but the remainder forms a separate liquid layer. As the number of carbon atoms in organic molecules increases, though, water solubility decreases.

The process of dissolving an ionic solid in a polar liquid can be visualized as shown in Figure 9.2 for sodium chloride. When NaCl crystals are put in water, ions at the crystal surface come into contact with polar water molecules. Positively charged Na^+ ions are attracted to the negatively polarized oxygen of water, and negatively charged Cl^- ions are attracted to the positively polarized hydrogens. The combined forces of attraction between an ion and several water molecules pull the ion away from the crystal, exposing a fresh surface, until ultimately the crystal dissolves. Once in solution, Na^+ and Cl^- ions are completely surrounded by solvent molecules, a phenomenon called **solvation** (or, specifically for water, *hydration*). The water molecules form a loose shell around the ions, stabilizing them by electrical attraction.

Solvation The clustering of solvent molecules around a dissolved solute molecule or ion.

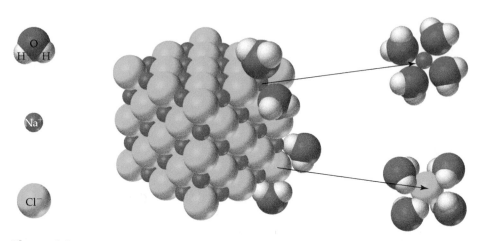

▲ **Figure 9.2**

Dissolution of an NaCl crystal in water.

Polar water molecules surround the individual Na^+ and Cl^- ions at an exposed edge or corner, pulling them from the crystal surface into solution and surrounding them. Note how the negatively polarized oxygens of water molecules cluster around Na^+ ions and the positively polarized hydrogens cluster around Cl^- ions.

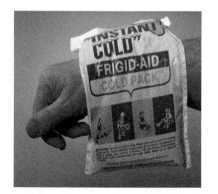

▲ Instant cold packs used to treat muscle strains and sprains often take advantage of the endothermic enthalpy of a solution of salts such as ammonium nitrate.

The dissolution of a solute in a solvent is a physical change, because the solution components retain their chemical identities. When sugar dissolves in water, for example, the individual sugar and water molecules still have the same chemical formulas as in the pure or undissolved state. Like all chemical and physical changes, the dissolution of a substance in a solvent has associated with it a heat change, or *enthalpy* change (Section 7.2). Some substances dissolve exothermically, releasing heat and warming the resultant solution, whereas other substances dissolve endothermically, absorbing heat and cooling the resultant solution. Calcium chloride, for example, *releases* 19.4 kcal/mol (81.2 kJ/mol) of heat energy when it dissolves in water, but ammonium nitrate (NH_4NO_3) *absorbs* 6.1 kcal/mol (25.5 kJ/mol) of heat energy. Athletes and others take advantage of both situations when they use instant hot packs or cold packs to treat injuries. Both hot and cold packs consist of a pouch of water and a dry chemical, such as $CaCl_2$ or $MgSO_4$ for hot packs, and NH_4NO_3 for cold packs. Squeezing the pack breaks the pouch and the solid dissolves, either raising or lowering the temperature.

Worked Example 9.1 Formation of Solutions

Which of the following pairs of substances would you expect to form solutions?

(a) Carbon tetrachloride (CCl_4) and hexane (C_6H_{14}).

(b) Octane (C_8H_{18}) and methyl alcohol (CH_3OH).

ANALYSIS Identify the kinds of intermolecular forces in each substance (Section 8.2). Substances with similar intermolecular forces tend to form solutions.

SOLUTION

(a) Hexane contains only C—H and C—C bonds, which are nonpolar. Carbon tetrachloride contains polar C—Cl bonds, but they are distributed symmetrically in the tetrahedral molecule so that it too is nonpolar. The major intermolecular force for both compounds is London dispersion forces, so they will form a solution.

(b) Octane contains only C—H and C—C bonds and so is nonpolar; the major intermolecular force is dispersion. Methyl alcohol contains polar C—O and O—H bonds; it is polar and forms hydrogen bonds. The intermolecular forces for the two substances are so dissimilar that they do not form a solution.

PROBLEM 9.2

Which of the following pairs of substances would you expect to form solutions?

(a) CCl_4 and water

(b) Benzene (C_6H_6) and $MgSO_4$

(c) Hexane (C_6H_{14}) and heptane (C_7H_{16})

(d) Ethyl alcohol (C_2H_5OH) and heptanol $(C_7H_{15}OH)$

9.3 Solid Hydrates

Some ionic compounds attract water strongly enough to hold on to water molecules even when crystalline, forming what are called *solid hydrates*. For example, the plaster of Paris used to make decorative objects and casts for broken limbs is calcium sulfate hemihydrate, $CaSO_4 \cdot \frac{1}{2}H_2O$. The dot between $CaSO_4$ and $\frac{1}{2}H_2O$ in the formula indicates that for every two $CaSO_4$ formula units in the crystal there is also one water molecule present.

$$CaSO_4 \cdot \tfrac{1}{2}H_2O \quad \text{A solid hydrate}$$

After being ground up and mixed with water to make plaster, $CaSO_4 \cdot \frac{1}{2}H_2O$ gradually changes into the crystalline dihydrate $CaSO_4 \cdot 2\,H_2O$, known as *gypsum*. During the change, the plaster hardens and expands in volume, causing it to fill a mold or shape itself closely around a broken limb. Table 9.3 lists some other ionic compounds that are handled primarily as hydrates.

TABLE 9.3 Some Common Solid Hydrates

Formula	Name	Uses
$AlCl_3 \cdot 6\,H_2O$	Aluminum chloride hexahydrate	Antiperspirant
$CaSO_4 \cdot 2\,H_2O$	Calcium sulfate dihydrate (gypsum)	Cements, wallboard molds
$CaSO_4 \cdot \frac{1}{2}H_2O$	Calcium sulfate hemihydrate (plaster of Paris)	Casts, molds
$CuSO_4 \cdot 5\,H_2O$	Copper(II) sulfate pentahydrate (blue vitriol)	Pesticide, germicide, topical fungicide
$MgSO_4 \cdot 7\,H_2O$	Magnesium sulfate heptahydrate (epsom salts)	Laxative, anticonvulsant
$Na_2B_4O_7 \cdot 10\,H_2O$	Sodium tetraborate decahydrate (borax)	Cleaning compounds, fireproofing agent
$Na_2S_2O_3 \cdot 5\,H_2O$	Sodium thiosulfate pentahydrate (hypo)	Photographic fixer

Hygroscopic Having the ability to pull water molecules from the surrounding atmosphere.

Still other ionic compounds attract water so strongly that they pull water vapor from humid air to become hydrated. Compounds that show this behavior, such as calcium chloride ($CaCl_2$), are called **hygroscopic** and are often used as drying agents. You might have noticed a small bag of a hygroscopic compound (probably silica gel, SiO_2) included in the packing material of a new MP3 player, camera, or other electronic device to keep humidity low during shipping.

PROBLEM 9.3

Write the formula of sodium sulfate decahydrate, known as Glauber's salt and used as a laxative.

PROBLEM 9.4

What mass of Glauber's salt must be used to provide 1.00 mol of sodium sulfate?

9.4 Solubility

We saw in Section 9.2 that ethyl alcohol is soluble in water because hydrogen bonding is nearly as strong between water and ethyl alcohol molecules as it is between water molecules alone or ethyl alcohol molecules alone. So similar are the forces in this particular case, in fact, that the two liquids are **miscible**, or mutually soluble in all proportions. Ethyl alcohol will continue to dissolve in water no matter how much is added.

Miscible Mutually soluble in all proportions.

Most substances, however, reach a solubility limit beyond which no more will dissolve in solution. Imagine, for instance that you are asked to prepare a saline solution (aqueous NaCl). You might measure out some water, add solid NaCl, and stir the mixture. Dissolution occurs rapidly at first but then slows down as more and more NaCl is added. Eventually the dissolution stops because an equilibrium is reached when the numbers of Na^+ and Cl^- ions leaving a crystal and going into solution are equal to the numbers of ions returning from solution to the crystal. At this point, the solution is said to be **saturated**. A maximum of 35.8 g of NaCl will dissolve in 100 mL of water at 20 °C. Any amount above this limit simply sinks to the bottom of the container and sits there.

Saturated solution A solution that contains the maximum amount of dissolved solute at equilibrium.

The equilibrium reached by a saturated solution is like the equilibrium reached by a reversible reaction (Section 7.7). Both are dynamic situations in which no *apparent* change occurs because the rates of forward and backward processes are equal. Solute particles leave the solid surface and reenter the solid from solution at the same rate.

$$\text{Solid solute} \underset{\text{Crystallize}}{\overset{\text{Dissolve}}{\rightleftharpoons}} \text{Solution}$$

Solubility The maximum amount of a substance that will dissolve in a given amount of solvent at a specified temperature.

The maximum amount of a substance that will dissolve in a given amount of a solvent at a given temperature, usually expressed in grams per 100 mL (g/100 mL), is called the substance's **solubility**. Solubility is a characteristic property of a specific solute–solvent combination, and different substances have greatly differing solubilities. Only 9.6 g of sodium hydrogen carbonate will dissolve in 100 mL of water at 20 °C, for instance, but 204 g of sucrose will dissolve under the same conditions.

9.5 The Effect of Temperature on Solubility

As anyone who has ever made tea or coffee knows, temperature often has a dramatic effect on solubility. The compounds in tea leaves or coffee beans, for instance, dissolve easily in hot water but not in cold water. The effect of temperature is different for every substance, however, and is usually unpredictable. As shown in Figure 9.3(a), the solubilities of most molecular and ionic solids increase with increasing temperature, but the solubilities of others (NaCl) are almost unchanged, and the solubilities of still others $[Ce_2(SO_4)_3]$ decrease with increasing temperature.

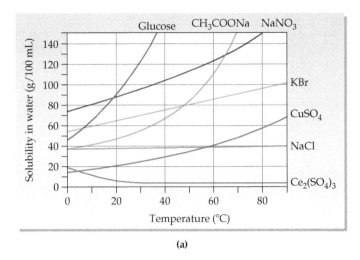

(a)

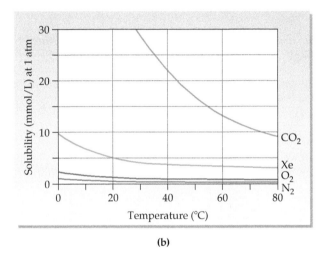

(b)

▲ **Figure 9.3**
Solubilities of some (a) solids and (b) gases, in water as a function of temperature.
Most solid substances become more soluble as temperature rises (although the exact relationship is usually complex), while the solubility of gases decreases.

Solids that are more soluble at high temperature than at low temperature can sometimes form what are called **supersaturated solutions**, which contain even more solute than a saturated solution. Suppose, for instance, that a large amount of a substance is dissolved at a high temperature. As the solution cools, the solubility decreases and the excess solute should precipitate to maintain equilibrium. But if the cooling is done very slowly, and if the container stands quietly, crystallization might not occur immediately and a supersaturated solution might result. Such a solution is unstable, however, and precipitation can occur dramatically when a tiny seed crystal is added or container disturbed to initiate crystallization (Figure 9.4).

Unlike solids, the influence of temperature on the solubility of gases *is* predictable: Addition of heat decreases the solubility of most gases, as seen in Figure 9.3(b) (helium is the only common exception). One result of this temperature-dependent decrease in gas solubility can sometimes be noted in a stream or lake near the outflow of warm water from an industrial operation. As water temperature increases, the concentration of dissolved oxygen in the water decreases, killing fish that cannot tolerate the lower oxygen levels.

Supersaturated solution A solution that contains more than the maximum amount of dissolved solute; a nonequilibrium situation.

▲ **Figure 9.4**
A supersaturated solution of sodium acetate in water.
When a tiny seed crystal is added, larger crystals rapidly grow and precipitate from the solution until equilibrium is reached.

Worked Example 9.2 Solubility of Gases: Effect of Temperature

From the following graph of solubility versus temperature for O_2, estimate the concentration of dissolved oxygen in water at 25 °C and at 35 °C. By what percentage does the concentration of O_2 change?

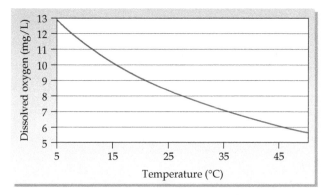

ANALYSIS The solubility of O_2 (on the y-axis) can be determined by finding the appropriate temperature (on the x-axis) and extrapolating. The percent change is calculated as

$$\frac{(\text{Solubility at } 25\,°C) - (\text{Solubility at } 35\,°C)}{(\text{Solubility at } 25\,°C)} \times 100$$

SOLUTION
From the graph we estimate that the solubility of O_2 at 25 °C is approximately 8.3 mg/L and at 35 °C is 7.0 mg/L. The percent change in solubility is

$$\frac{8.3 - 7.0}{8.3} \times 100 = 16\%$$

PROBLEM 9.5

A solution is prepared by dissolving 12.5 g of KBr in 20 mL of water at 60 °C (see Figure 9.3). Is this solution saturated, unsaturated, or supersaturated? What will happen if the solution is cooled to 10 °C?

9.6 The Effect of Pressure on Solubility: Henry's Law

Pressure has virtually no effect on the solubility of a solid or liquid, but it has a strong effect on the solubility of a gas. According to **Henry's law**, the solubility (or concentration) of a gas in a liquid is directly proportional to the partial pressure of the gas over the liquid. If the partial pressure of the gas doubles, solubility doubles; if the gas pressure is halved, solubility is halved (Figure 9.5).

▶▶▶ Recall from Section 8.11 that each gas in a mixture exerts a partial pressure independent of other gases present (Dalton's law of partial pressures).

▶ **Figure 9.5**
Henry's law.
The solubility of a gas is directly proportional to its partial pressure. An increase in pressure causes more gas molecules to enter solution until equilibrium is restored between the dissolved and undissolved gas.

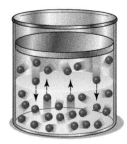

(a) Equilibrium   (b) Pressure increase   (c) Equilibrium restored

Henry's law   The solubility (or concentration) of a gas is directly proportional to the partial pressure of the gas if the temperature is constant. That is, concentration (C) divided by pressure (P) is constant when T is constant,

or $\dfrac{C}{P_{gas}} = k$ (At a constant temperature)

Henry's law can be explained using Le Châtelier's principle. In the case of a saturated solution of a gas in a liquid, an equilibrium exists whereby gas molecules enter and leave the solution at the same rate. When the system is stressed by increasing the pressure of the gas, more gas molecules go into solution to relieve that increase. Conversely, when the pressure of the gas is decreased, more gas molecules come out of solution to relieve the decrease.

▶▶ Le Châtelier's principle states that when a system at equilibrium is placed under stress, the equilibrium shifts to relieve that stress (Section 7.9).

$$[\text{Pressure increases} \longrightarrow]$$
$$\text{Gas} + \text{Solvent} \rightleftharpoons \text{Solution}$$

As an example of Henry's law in action, think about the fizzing that occurs when you open a bottle of soft drink or champagne. The bottle is sealed under greater than 1 atm of CO_2 pressure, causing some of the CO_2 to dissolve. When the bottle is opened, however, CO_2 pressure drops and gas comes fizzing out of solution.

Writing Henry's law in the form $P_{gas} = C/k$ shows that partial pressure can be used to express the concentration of a gas in a solution, a practice especially common in health-related sciences. Table 9.4 gives some typical values and illustrates the convenience of having the same unit for concentration of a gas in both air and blood. Compare the oxygen partial pressures in saturated alveolar air (air in the lungs) and in arterial blood, for instance. The values are almost the same because the gases dissolved in blood come to equilibrium with the same gases in the lungs.

TABLE 9.4   Partial Pressures and Normal Gas Concentrations in Body Fluids

Sample	Partial Pressure (mmHg)			
	P_{N_2}	P_{O_2}	P_{CO_2}	P_{H_2O}
Inspired air (dry)	597	159	0.3	3.7
Alveolar air (saturated)	573	100	40	47
Expired air (saturated)	569	116	28	47
Arterial blood	573	95	40	
Venous blood	573	40	45	
Peripheral tissues	573	40	45	

If the partial pressure of a gas over a solution changes while the temperature is constant, the new solubility of the gas can be found easily. Because C/P is a constant value at constant temperature, Henry's law can be restated to show how one variable changes if the other changes:

$$\frac{C_1}{P_1} = \frac{C_2}{P_2} = k \quad \text{(Where k is constant at a fixed temperature)}$$

Worked Example 9.3 gives an illustration of how to use this equation.

Worked Example **9.3** Solubility of Gases: Henry's Law

At a partial pressure of oxygen in the atmosphere of 159 mmHg, the solubility of oxygen in blood is 0.44 g/100 mL. What is the solubility of oxygen in blood at 11,000 ft, where the partial pressure of O_2 is 56 mmHg?

ANALYSIS According to Henry's law, the solubility of the gas divided by its pressure is constant:

$$\frac{C_1}{P_1} = \frac{C_2}{P_2}$$

Of the four variables in this equation, we know P_1, C_1, and P_2, and we need to find C_2.

BALLPARK ESTIMATE The pressure drops by a factor of about 3 (from 159 mmHg to 56 mmHg). Since the ratio of solubility to pressure is constant, the solubility must also drop by a factor of 3 (from 0.44 g/100 mL to about 0.15 g/100 mL).

SOLUTION

STEP 1: Identify known information. We have values for P_1, C_1, and P_2.

$P_1 = 159$ mmHg
$C_1 = 0.44$ g/100 mL
$P_2 = 56$ mmHg

STEP 2: Identify answer and units. We are looking for the solubility of O_2 (C_2) at a partial pressure P_2.

Solubility of O_2, $C_2 = $?? g/100 mL

STEP 3: Identify conversion factors or equations. In this case, we restate Henry's law to solve for C_2.

$$\frac{C_1}{P_1} = \frac{C_2}{P_2} \Rightarrow C_2 = \frac{C_1 P_2}{P_1}$$

STEP 4: Solve. Substitute the known values into the equation and calculate C_2.

$$C_2 = \frac{C_1 P_2}{P_1} = \frac{(0.44 \text{ g}/100 \text{ mL})(56 \text{ mmHg})}{159 \text{ mmHg}} = 0.15 \text{ g}/100 \text{ mL}$$

BALLPARK CHECK The calculated answer matches our estimate.

PROBLEM 9.6
At 20 °C and a partial pressure of 760 mmHg, the solubility of CO_2 in water is 0.169 g/100 mL at this temperature. What is the solubility of CO_2 at 2.5×10^4 mmHg?

PROBLEM 9.7
At a total atmospheric pressure of 1.00 atm, the partial pressure of CO_2 in air is approximately 4.0×10^{-4} atm. Using the data in Problem 9.6, what is the solubility of CO_2 in an open bottle of seltzer water at 20 °C?

PROBLEM 9.8
The atmospheric pressure at the top of Mt. Everest is only 265 mmHg. If the atmospheric composition is 21% oxygen, calculate the partial pressure of O_2 at this altitude and determine the percent saturation of hemoglobin under these conditions (see Chemistry in Action: Breathing and Oxygen Transport on p. 263).

9.7 Units of Concentration

Although we speak casually of a solution of, say, orange juice as either "dilute" or "concentrated," laboratory work usually requires an exact knowledge of a solution's concentration. As indicated in Table 9.5 on page 264, there are several common methods for expressing concentration. The units differ, but all the methods describe how much solute is present in a given quantity of solution.

CHEMISTRY IN ACTION

Breathing and Oxygen Transport

Like all other animals, humans need oxygen. When we breathe, the freshly inspired air travels through the bronchial passages and into the lungs. The oxygen then diffuses through the delicate walls of the approximately 150 million alveolar sacs of the lungs and into arterial blood, which transports it to all body tissues.

Only about 3% of the oxygen in blood is dissolved; the rest is chemically bound to *hemoglobin* molecules, large proteins with *heme* groups embedded in them. Each hemoglobin molecule contains four heme groups, and each heme group contains an iron atom that is able to bind 1 O_2 molecule. Thus, a single hemoglobin molecule can bind up to 4 molecules of oxygen. The entire system of oxygen transport and delivery in the body depends on the pickup and release of O_2 by hemoglobin (Hb) according to the following series of equilibria:

$$O_2(lungs) \rightleftharpoons O_2(blood) \quad (Henry's\ law)$$
$$Hb + 4\,O_2(blood) \rightleftharpoons Hb(O_2)_4$$
$$Hb(O_2)_4 \rightleftharpoons Hb + 4\,O_2\ (cell)$$

The delivery of oxygen depends on the concentration of O_2 in the various tissues, as measured by partial pressure (P_{O_2}, Table 9.4). The amount of oxygen carried by hemoglobin at any given value of P_{O_2} is usually expressed as a percent saturation and can be found from the curve shown in the accompanying figure. When $P_{O_2} = 100$ mmHg, the saturation in the lungs is 97.5%, meaning that each hemoglobin is carrying close to its maximum of 4 O_2 molecules. When $P_{O_2} = 26$ mmHg, however, the saturation drops to 50%.

So, how does the body ensure that enough oxygen is available to the various tissues? When large amounts of oxygen are needed—during a strenuous workout, for example—oxygen is released from hemoglobin to the hardworking, oxygen-starved muscle cells, where P_{O_2} is low. Increasing the supply of oxygen to the blood (by breathing harder and faster) shifts all the equilibria toward the right, according to Le Châtelier's principle (Section 7.9), to supply the additional O_2 needed by the muscles.

What about people living at high altitudes? In Leadville, CO, for example, where the altitude is 10,156 ft, the P_{O_2} in the lungs is only about 68 mmHg. Hemoglobin is only 90% saturated with O_2 at this pressure, meaning that less oxygen is available for delivery to the tissues. The body responds by producing erythropoietin (EPO), a hormone that stimulates the bone marrow to produce more red blood cells and hemoglobin molecules. The increase in Hb provides more capacity for O_2 transport and drives the Hb + O_2 equilibria to the right.

▲ **At high altitudes, the partial pressure of oxygen in the air is too low to saturate hemoglobin sufficiently. Additional oxygen is therefore needed.**

World-class athletes use the mechanisms of increased oxygen transport associated with higher levels of hemoglobin to enhance their performance. High-altitude training centers have sprung up, with living and training regimens designed to increase blood EPO levels. Unfortunately, some athletes have also tried to "cheat" by using injections of EPO and synthetic analogs, and "blood doping" to boost performance. This has led the governing bodies of many sports federations, including the Olympic Committee, to start testing for such abuse.

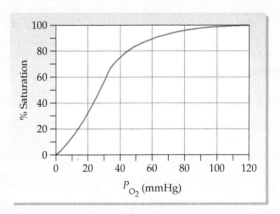

▲ **An oxygen-carrying curve for hemoglobin. The percent saturation of the oxygen binding sites on hemoglobin depends on the partial pressure of oxygen P_{O_2}.**

See Chemistry in Action Problem 9.90 at the end of the chapter.

TABLE **9.5** Some Units for Expressing Concentration		
Concentration Measure	**Solute Measure**	**Solution Measure**
Percent		
Mass/mass percent, (m/m)%	Mass (g)	Mass (g)
Volume/volume percent, (v/v)%	Volume*	Volume*
Mass/volume percent, (m/v)%	Mass (g)	Volume (mL)
Parts per million, ppm	Parts*	10^6 parts*
Parts per billion, ppb	Parts*	10^9 parts*
Molarity, M	Moles	Volume (L)

*Any units can be used as long as they are the same for both solute and solution.

Let us look at each of the concentration measures listed in Table 9.5 individually, beginning with *percent concentrations*.

Percent Concentrations

Percent concentrations express the amount of solute in one hundred units of solution. The amount of solute and the amount of solution can be represented in units of mass or volume. For solid solutions, such as a metal alloy, concentrations are typically expressed as **mass/mass percent concentration, (m/m)%**:

mass/mass percent concentration, (m/m)% Concentration expressed as the number of grams of solute per 100 grams of solution.

$$(m/m)\% \text{ concentration} = \frac{\text{Mass of solute (g)}}{\text{Mass of solution (g)}} \times 100\%$$

For example, the mass percent of copper in a red-gold ring that contains 19.20 g of gold and 4.80 g of copper would be calculated as:

$$(m/m)\% \text{ Cu} = \frac{\text{mass of Cu (g)}}{\text{mass of Cu (g)} + \text{mass of Au (g)}} \times 100\%$$

$$= \frac{4.80\,g}{4.80\,g + 19.20\,g} \times 100\% = 20.0\%$$

The concentration of a solution made by dissolving one liquid in another is often given by expressing the volume of solute as a percentage of the volume of final solution—the **volume/volume percent concentration, (v/v)%**.

volume/volume percent concentration, (v/v)% Concentration expressed as the number of milliliters of solute dissolved in 100 mL of solution.

$$(v/v)\% \text{ concentration} = \frac{\text{Volume of solute (mL)}}{\text{Volume of solution (mL)}} \times 100\%$$

For example, if 10.0 mL of ethyl alcohol is dissolved in enough water to give 100.0 mL of solution, the ethyl alcohol concentration is $(10.0\ mL/100.0\ mL) \times 100\% = 10.0\%\ (v/v)$.

A third common method for expressing percent concentration is to give the number of grams (mass) as a percentage of the number of milliliters (volume) of the final solution—called the **mass/volume percent concentration, (m/v)%**. Mathematically, (m/v)% concentration is found by taking the number of grams of solute per milliliter of solution and multiplying by 100%:

mass/volume percent concentration, (m/v)% Concentration expressed as the number of grams of solute per 100 mL of solution.

$$(m/v)\% \text{ concentration} = \frac{\text{Mass of solute (g)}}{\text{Volume of solution (mL)}} \times 100\%$$

For example, if 15 g of glucose is dissolved in enough water to give 100 mL of solution, the glucose concentration is 15 g/100 mL or 15% (m/v):

$$\frac{15\ g\ glucose}{100\ mL\ solution} \times 100\% = 15\%\ (m/v)$$

To prepare 100 mL of a specific mass/volume solution, the weighed solute is dissolved in just enough solvent to give a final volume of 100 mL, not in an initial volume of 100 mL solvent. (If the solute is dissolved in 100 mL of solvent, the final volume of the solution will likely be a bit larger than 100 mL, since the volume of the solute is included.) In practice, the appropriate amount of solute is weighed and placed in a *volumetric flask*, as shown in Figure 9.6. Enough solvent is then added to dissolve the solute, and further solvent is added until an accurately calibrated final volume is reached. The solution is then shaken until it is uniformly mixed. Worked Examples 9.4–9.7 illustrate how percent concentrations can be calculated for a solution, or how the percent concentration can be used as a conversion factor to determine the amount of solute in a given amount of solution.

(a)

(b)

(c)

◄**Figure 9.6**
Preparing a solution of known mass/volume percent concentration, (m/v)%.
(a) A measured number of grams of solute is placed in a volumetric flask.
(b) Enough solvent is added to dissolve the solute by swirling. (c) Further solvent is carefully added until the calibration mark on the neck of the flask is reached, and the solution is shaken until uniform.

Worked Example 9.4 Mass Percent as Conversion Factor: Mass of Solution to Mass of Solute

The percentage of gold in jewelry is typically reported in carats, with 24 carats representing 100% gold. A sample of 18-carat gold would contain 18 grams of gold in 24 grams of metal, which would equal a (m/m)% of 75%. Calculate the mass of gold in a 5.05 g ring that is 18-carat gold.

ANALYSIS We are given a concentration and the total mass of the sample solution (the gold alloy in the ring), and we need to find the mass of gold by rearranging the equation for (m/m)% concentration.

BALLPARK ESTIMATE A 75% (m/m) solution contains 75 g for every 100 g of solution, so 10 g contains 7.5 g. The mass of the ring is a little more than 5 g (or half of 10 g) so the amount of gold in the ring will be slightly more than half of 7.5 g, or ~3.8 g gold.

SOLUTION

$$(5.05 \text{ g})\left(\frac{75 \text{ g Au}}{100 \text{ g solution}}\right) = 3.79 \text{ g Au}$$

BALLPARK CHECK The calculated answer is consistent with our estimate of 3.8 g gold.

Worked Example 9.5 Volume Percent as Conversion Factor: Volume of Solution to Volume of Solute

How many milliliters of methyl alcohol are needed to prepare 75 mL of a 5.0% (v/v) solution?

ANALYSIS We are given a solution volume (75 mL) and a concentration [5.0% (v/v), meaning 5.0 mL solute/100 mL solution]. The concentration acts as a conversion factor for finding the amount of methyl alcohol needed.

BALLPARK ESTIMATE A 5% (v/v) solution contains 5 mL of solute in 100 mL of solution, so the amount of solute in 75 mL of solution must be about three-fourths of 5 mL, which means between 3 and 4 mL.

SOLUTION

$$(75 \text{ mL solution})\left(\frac{5.0 \text{ mL methyl alcohol}}{100 \text{ mL solution}}\right) = 3.8 \text{ mL methyl alcohol}$$

BALLPARK CHECK The calculated answer is consistent with our estimate of between 3 and 4 mL.

Worked Example 9.6 Solution Concentration: Mass/Volume Percent

A solution of heparin sodium, an anticoagulant for blood, contains 1.8 g of heparin sodium dissolved to make a final volume of 15 mL of solution. What is the mass/volume percent concentration of this solution?

ANALYSIS Mass/volume percent concentration is defined as the mass of the solute in grams divided by the volume of solution in milliliters and multiplied by 100%.

BALLPARK ESTIMATE The mass of solute (1.8 g) is smaller than the volume of solvent (15 mL) by a little less than a factor of 10. The weight/volume percent should thus be a little greater than 10%.

SOLUTION

$$(\text{m/v})\% \text{ concentration} = \frac{1.8 \text{ g heparin sodium}}{15 \text{ mL}} \times 100\% = 12\% \, (\text{m/v})$$

BALLPARK CHECK The calculated (m/v)% is reasonably close to our original estimate of 10%.

Worked Example 9.7 Mass/Volume Percent as Conversion Factor: Volume to Mass

How many grams of NaCl are needed to prepare 250 mL of a 1.5% (m/v) saline solution?

ANALYSIS We are given a concentration and a volume, and we need to find the mass of solute by rearranging the equation for (m/v)% concentration.

BALLPARK ESTIMATE The desired (m/v)% value, 1.5%, is between 1 and 2%. For a volume of 250 mL, we would need 2.5 g of solute for a 1% (m/v) solution and 5.0 g of solute for a 2% solution. Thus, for our 1.5% solution, we need a mass midway between 2.5 and 5.0 g, or about 3.8 g.

SOLUTION

$$\text{Since} \quad (\text{m/v})\% = \frac{\text{Mass of solute in g}}{\text{Volume of solution in mL}} \times 100\%$$

$$\text{then} \quad \text{Mass of solute in g} = \frac{(\text{Volume of solution in mL})\left[\,(\text{m/v})\,\right]\%}{100\%}$$

$$= \frac{(250)(1.5\%)}{100\%} = 3.75 \text{ g} = 3.8 \text{ g NaCl}$$

$$(2 \text{ significant figures})$$

BALLPARK CHECK The calculated answer matches our estimate.

PROBLEM 9.9

A metal alloy contains 15.8% nickel (m/m)%. What mass of the metal alloy would contain 36.5 g of nickel?

PROBLEM 9.10

How would you use a 500.0 mL volumetric flask to prepare a 7.5% (v/v) solution of acetic acid in water?

PROBLEM 9.11

In clinical lab reports, some concentrations are given in mg/dL. Convert a Ca^{2+} concentration of 8.6 mg/dL to mass/volume percent.

PROBLEM 9.12

What amounts of solute or solvent are needed to prepare the following solutions?

(a) Mass of glucose needed to prepare 125.0 mL of 16% (m/v) glucose $(C_6H_{12}O_6)$

(b) Volume of water needed to prepare a 2.0% (m/v) KCl solution using 1.20 g KCl

Parts per Million (ppm) or Parts per Billion (ppb)

The concentration units mass/mass percent (m/m)%, volume/volume percent (v/v)%, and mass/volume percent (w/v)% can also be defined as *parts per hundred* (pph) since 1% means one item per 100 items. When concentrations are very small, as often occurs in dealing with trace amounts of pollutants or contaminants, it is more convenient to use **parts per million (ppm)** or **parts per billion (ppb)**. The "parts" can be in any unit of either mass or volume as long as the units of both solute and solvent are the same:

Parts per million (ppm) Number of parts per one million (10^6) parts.

Parts per billion (ppb) Number of parts per one billion (10^9) parts.

$$ppm = \frac{\text{Mass of solute (g)}}{\text{Mass of solution (g)}} \times 10^6 \quad \text{or} \quad \frac{\text{Volume of solute (mL)}}{\text{Volume of solution (mL)}} \times 10^6$$

$$ppb = \frac{\text{Mass of solute (g)}}{\text{Mass of solution (g)}} \times 10^9 \quad \text{or} \quad \frac{\text{Volume of solute (mL)}}{\text{Volume of solution (mL)}} \times 10^9$$

To take an example, the maximum allowable concentration in air of the organic solvent benzene (C_6H_6) is currently set by government regulation at 1 ppm. A concentration of 1 ppm means that if you take a million "parts" of air in any unit—say, mL—then 1 of those parts is benzene vapor and the other 999,999 parts are other gases:

$$1 \text{ ppm} = \frac{1 \text{ mL}}{1,000,000 \text{ mL}} \times 10^6$$

Because the density of water is approximately 1.0 g/mL at room temperature, 1.0 L (or 1000 mL) of an aqueous solution weighs 1000 g. Therefore, when dealing with very dilute concentrations of solutes dissolved in water, ppm is equivalent to mg solute/L solution, and ppb is equivalent to μg solute/L solution. To demonstrate that these units are equivalent, the conversion from ppm to mg/L is as follows:

$$1 \text{ ppm} = \left(\frac{1 \text{ g solute}}{10^6 \text{ g solution}}\right)\left(\frac{1 \text{ mg solute}}{10^{-3} \text{ g solute}}\right)\left(\frac{10^3 \text{ g solution}}{1 \text{ L solution}}\right) = \frac{1 \text{ mg solute}}{1 \text{ L solution}}$$

Worked Example 9.8 ppm as Conversion Factor: Mass of Solution to Mass of Solute

The maximum allowable concentration of chloroform, $CHCl_3$, in drinking water is 100 ppb. What is the maximum amount (in grams) of chloroform allowed in a glass containing 400 g (400 mL) of water?

ANALYSIS We are given a solution amount (400 g) and a concentration (100 ppb). This concentration of 100 ppb means

$$100 \text{ ppb} = \frac{\text{Mass of solute (g)}}{\text{Mass of solution (g)}} \times 10^9$$

This equation can be rearranged to find the mass of solute.

SOLUTION

$$\text{Mass of solute (g)} = \frac{\text{Mass of solution (g)}}{10^9} \times 100 \text{ ppb}$$

$$= \frac{400 \text{ g}}{10^9} \times 100 \text{ ppb} = 4 \times 10^{-5} \text{ g (or 0.04 mg)}$$

BALLPARK CHECK The calculated answer matches our estimate.

PROBLEM 9.13

What is the concentration in ppm of sodium fluoride in tap water that has been fluoridated by the addition of 32 mg of NaF for every 20 kg of solution?

PROBLEM 9.14

The maximum amounts of lead and copper allowed in drinking water are 0.015 mg/kg for lead and 1.3 mg/kg for copper. Express these values in parts per million, and tell the maximum amount of each (in grams) allowed in 100 g of water.

Mole/Volume Concentration: Molarity

We saw in Chapter 6 that the various relationships between amounts of reactants and products in chemical reactions are calculated in *moles* (Sections 6.1–6.3). Thus, the most generally useful means of expressing concentration in the laboratory is **molarity (M)**, the number of moles of solute dissolved per liter of solution. For example, a solution made by dissolving 1.00 mol (58.5 g) of NaCl in enough water to give 1.00 L of solution has a concentration of 1.00 mol/L, or 1.00 M. The molarity of any solution is found by dividing the number of moles of solute by the number of liters of solution (solute + solvent):

$$\text{Molarity (M)} = \frac{\text{Moles of solute}}{\text{Liters of solution}}$$

Note that a solution of a given molarity is prepared by dissolving the solute in enough solvent to give a *final* solution volume of 1.00 L, not by dissolving it in an *initial* volume of 1.00 L. If an initial volume of 1.00 L was used, the final solution volume might be a bit larger than 1.00 L because of the additional volume of the solute. In practice, solutions are prepared using a volumetric flask, as shown previously in Figure 9.6.

Molarity can be used as a conversion factor to relate the volume of a solution to the number of moles of solute it contains. If we know the molarity and volume of a solution, we can calculate the number of moles of solute. If we know the number of moles of solute and the molarity of the solution, we can find the solution's volume.

$$\text{Molarity} = \frac{\text{Moles of solute}}{\text{Volume of solution (L)}}$$

$$\text{Moles of solute} = \text{Molarity} \times \text{Volume of solution}$$

$$\text{Volume of solution} = \frac{\text{Moles of solute}}{\text{Molarity}}$$

The flow diagram in Figure 9.7 shows how molarity is used in calculating the quantities of reactants or products in a chemical reaction, and Worked Examples 9.10 and 9.11 show how the calculations are done. Note that Problem 9.17 employs *millimolar* (mM) concentrations, which are useful in healthcare fields for expressing low concentrations such as are often found in body fluids (1 mM = 0.001 M).

Molarity (M) Concentration expressed as the number of moles of solute per liter of solution.

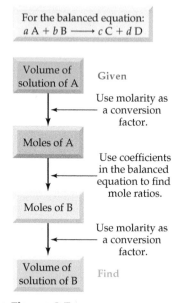

▲ **Figure 9.7**
Molarity and conversions.
A flow diagram summarizing the use of molarity for conversions between solution volume and moles to find quantities of reactants and products for chemical reactions in solution.

Worked Example 9.9 Solution Concentration: Molarity

What is the molarity of a solution made by dissolving 2.355 g of sulfuric acid (H_2SO_4) in water and diluting to a final volume of 50.0 mL? The molar mass of H_2SO_4 is 98.1 g/mol.

ANALYSIS Molarity is defined as moles of solute per liter of solution: $M = \text{mol/L}$. Thus, we must first find the number of moles of sulfuric acid by doing a mass to mole conversion, and then divide the number of moles by the volume of the solution.

BALLPARK ESTIMATE The molar mass of sulfuric acid is about 100 g/mol, so 2.355 g is roughly 0.025 mol. The volume of the solution is 50.0 mL, or 0.05 L, so we have about 0.025 mol of acid in 0.05 L of solution, which is a concentration of about 0.5 M.

SOLUTION

STEP 1: **Identify known information.** We know the mass of sulfuric acid and the final volume of solution.

Mass of $H_2SO_4 = 2.355$ g
Volume of solution $= 50.0$ mL

STEP 2: **Identify answer including units.** We need to find the molarity (M) in units of moles per liter.

$$\text{Molarity} = \frac{\text{Moles } H_2SO_4}{\text{Liters of solution}}$$

STEP 3: **Identify conversion factors and equations.** We know both the amount of solute and the volume of solution, but first we must make two conversions: convert mass of H_2SO_4 to moles of H_2SO_4, using molar mass as a conversion factor, and convert volume from milliliters to liters.

$$(2.355 \text{ g } H_2SO_4)\left(\frac{1 \text{ mol } H_2SO_4}{98.1 \text{ g } H_2SO_4}\right) = 0.0240 \text{ mol } H_2SO_4$$

$$(50.0 \text{ mL})\left(\frac{1 \text{ L}}{1000 \text{ mL}}\right) = 0.0500 \text{ L}$$

STEP 4: **Solve.** Substitute the moles of solute and volume of solution into the molarity expression.

$$\text{Molarity} = \frac{0.0240 \text{ mol } H_2SO_4}{0.0500 \text{ L}} = 0.480 \text{ M}$$

BALLPARK CHECK The calculated answer is close to our estimate, which was 0.5 M.

Worked Example 9.10 Molarity as Conversion Factor: Molarity to Mass

A blood concentration of 0.065 M ethyl alcohol (EtOH) is sufficient to induce a coma. At this concentration, what is the total mass of alcohol (in grams) in an adult male whose total blood volume is 5.6 L? The molar mass of ethyl alcohol is 46.0 g/mol. (Refer to the flow diagram in Figure 9.7 to identify which conversions are needed.)

ANALYSIS We are given a molarity (0.065 M) and a volume (5.6 L), which allows us to calculate the number of moles of alcohol in the blood. A mole to mass conversion then gives the mass of alcohol.

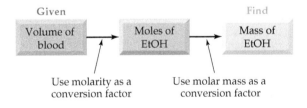

SOLUTION

$$(5.6 \text{ L blood})\left(\frac{0.065 \text{ mol EtOH}}{1 \text{ L blood}}\right) = 0.36 \text{ mol EtOH}$$

$$(0.36 \text{ mol EtOH})\left(\frac{46.0 \text{ g EtOH}}{1 \text{ mol EtOH}}\right) = 17 \text{ g EtOH}$$

Worked Example 9.11 Molarity as Conversion Factor: Molarity to Volume

In our stomachs, gastric juice that is about 0.1 M in HCl aids in digestion. How many milliliters of gastric juice will react completely with an antacid tablet that contains 500 mg of magnesium hydroxide? The molar mass of $Mg(OH)_2$ is 58.3 g/mol, and the balanced equation is

$$2\,HCl(aq) + Mg(OH)_2(aq) \longrightarrow MgCl_2(aq) + 2\,H_2O(l)$$

ANALYSIS We are given the molarity of HCl and need to find the volume. We first convert the mass of $Mg(OH)_2$ to moles and then use the coefficients in the balanced equation to find the moles of HCl that will react. Once we have the moles of HCl and the molarity in moles per liter, we can find the volume.

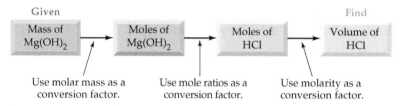

SOLUTION

$$\left[500\text{ mg } Mg(OH)_2\right]\left(\frac{1\text{ g}}{1000\text{ mg}}\right)\left[\frac{1\text{ mol } Mg(OH)_2}{58.3\text{ g } Mg(OH)_2}\right] = 0.008\ 58\text{ mol } Mg(OH)_2$$

$$\left[0.008\ 58\text{ mol } Mg(OH)_2\right]\left[\frac{2\text{ mol HCl}}{1\text{ mol } Mg(OH)_2}\right]\left(\frac{1\text{ L HCl}}{0.1\text{ mol HCl}}\right) = 0.2\text{ L }(200\text{ mL})$$

PROBLEM 9.15

What is the molarity of a solution that contains 50.0 g of vitamin B_1 hydrochloride (molar mass = 337 g/mol) in 160 mL of solution?

PROBLEM 9.16

How many moles of solute are present in the following solutions?
(a) 175 mL of 0.35 M $NaNO_3$
(b) 480 mL of 1.4 M HNO_3

PROBLEM 9.17

The concentration of cholesterol $(C_{27}H_{46}O)$ in blood is approximately 5.0 mM. How many grams of cholesterol are in 250 mL of blood?

PROBLEM 9.18

Calcium carbonate reacts with HCl according to the following equation:

$$2\,HCl(aq) + CaCO_3(aq) \longrightarrow CaCl_2(aq) + H_2O(l) + CO_2(g)$$

(a) How many moles of HCl are in 65 mL of 0.12 M HCl?
(b) What mass of calcium carbonate (in grams) is needed for complete reaction with the HCl in (a)?

9.8 Dilution

Many solutions, from orange juice to chemical reagents, are stored in high concentrations and then prepared for use by *dilution*—that is, by adding additional solvent to lower the concentration. For example, you might make up 1/2 gal of orange juice by adding water to a canned concentrate. In the same way, you might buy a medicine or chemical reagent as a concentrated solution and dilute it before use.

The key fact to remember about dilution is that the amount of *solute* remains constant; only the *volume* is changed by adding more solvent. If, for example, the initial and final concentrations are given in molarity, then we know that the number of moles of solute is the same both before and after dilution and can be determined by multiplying molarity times volume:

$$\text{Number of moles} = \text{Molarity (mol/L)} \times \text{Volume (L)}$$
$$M = \text{moles/volume}$$

Because the number of moles remains constant, we can set up the following equation, where M_c and V_c refer to the concentrated solution (before dilution), and M_d and V_d refer to the solution after dilution:

$$\text{Moles of solute} = M_c V_c = M_d V_d$$

This equation can be rewritten to solve for M_d, the concentration of the solution after dilution:

$$M_d = M_c \times \frac{V_c}{V_d} \quad \text{where} \quad \frac{V_c}{V_d} \quad \text{is a } dilution\ factor$$

The equation shows that the concentration after dilution (M_d) can be found by multiplying the initial concentration (M_c) by a **dilution factor**, which is simply the ratio of the initial and final solution volumes (V_c/V_d). If, for example, the solution volume *increases* by a factor of 5, from 10 mL to 50 mL, then the concentration must *decrease* to one-fifth of its initial value because the dilution factor is 10 mL/50 mL, or 1/5. Worked Example 9.12 shows how to use this relationship for calculating dilutions.

Dilution factor The ratio of the initial and final solution volumes (V_c/V_d).

The relationship between concentration and volume can also be used to find what volume of initial solution to start with to achieve a given dilution:

$$\text{Since} \quad M_c V_c = M_d V_d$$
$$\text{then} \quad V_c = V_d \times \frac{M_d}{M_c}$$

In this case, V_c is the initial volume that must be diluted to prepare a less concentrated solution with volume V_d. The initial volume is found by multiplying the final volume (V_d) by the ratio of the final and initial concentrations (M_d/M_c). For example, to decrease the concentration of a solution to 1/5 its initial value, the initial volume must be 1/5 the desired final volume. Worked Example 9.13 gives a sample calculation.

Although the preceding discussion, and the following Worked Examples, use concentration units of molarity, the dilution equation can be generalized to allow for the use of other concentration units. A more general equation would be $C_c V_c = C_d V_d$, where C refers to other concentration units, such as ppm, or m/v%.

Worked Example **9.12** Dilution of Solutions: Concentration

What is the final concentration if 75 mL of a 3.5 M glucose solution is diluted to a volume of 450 mL?

ANALYSIS The number of moles of solute is constant, so

$$M_c V_c = M_d V_d$$

Of the four variables in this equation, we know the initial concentration M_c (3.5 M), the initial volume V_c (75 mL), and the final volume V_d (450 mL), and we need to find the final concentration M_d.

BALLPARK ESTIMATE The volume increases by a factor of 6, from 75 mL to 450 mL, so the concentration must decrease by a factor of 6, from 3.5 M to about 0.6 M.

SOLUTION

Solving the above equation for M_d and substituting in the known values gives

$$M_d = \frac{M_c V_c}{V_d} = \frac{(3.5\ \text{M glucose})(75\ \text{mL})}{450\ \text{mL}} = 0.58\ \text{M glucose}$$

BALLPARK CHECK The calculated answer is close to our estimate of 0.6 M.

Worked Example 9.13 Dilution of Solutions: Volume

Aqueous NaOH can be purchased at a concentration of 1.0 M. How would you use this concentrated solution to prepare 750 mL of 0.32 M NaOH?

ANALYSIS The number of moles of solute is constant, so

$$M_c V_c = M_d V_d$$

Of the four variables in this equation, we know the initial concentration M_c (1.0 M), the final volume V_d (750 mL), and the final concentration M_d (0.32 M), and we need to find the initial volume V_c.

BALLPARK ESTIMATE We want the solution concentration to decrease by a factor of about 3, from 1.0 M to 0.32 M, which means we need to dilute the 1.0 M solution by a factor of 3. This means the final volume must be about three times greater than the initial volume. Because our final volume is to be 750 mL, we must start with an initial volume of about 250 mL.

SOLUTION

Solving the above equation for V_1 and substituting in the known values gives

$$V_c = \frac{V_d M_d}{M_c} = \frac{(750\ \text{mL})(0.32\ \text{M})}{1.0\ \text{M}} = 240\ \text{mL}$$

To prepare the desired solution, dilute 240 mL of 1.0 M NaOH with water to make a final volume of 750 mL.

BALLPARK CHECK The calculated answer (240 mL) is reasonably close to our estimate of 250 mL.

PROBLEM 9.19

Aqueous ammonia is commercially available at a concentration of 16.0 M. How much of the concentrated solution would you use to prepare 500.0 mL of a 1.25 M solution?

PROBLEM 9.20

The Environmental Protection Agency has set the limit for arsenic in drinking water at 0.010 ppm. To what volume would you need to dilute 1.5 L of water containing 5.0 ppm arsenic to reach the acceptable limit?

9.9 Ions in Solution: Electrolytes

▶▶▶ As we learned in Section 3.1, electricity can only flow through a medium containing charged particles that are free to move.

Look at Figure 9.8, which shows a light bulb connected to a power source through a circuit that is interrupted by two metal strips dipped into a beaker of liquid. When the strips are dipped into pure water, the bulb remains dark, but when they are dipped into an aqueous NaCl solution, the circuit is closed and the bulb lights. This simple demonstration shows that ionic compounds in aqueous solution can conduct electricity.

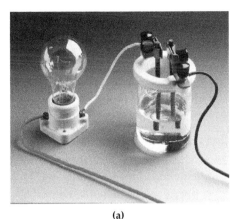

(a)   (b)

◄**Figure 9.8**
A simple demonstration shows that electricity can flow through a solution of ions.
(a) With pure water in the beaker, the circuit is incomplete, no electricity flows, and the bulb does not light. (b) With a concentrated NaCl solution in the beaker, the circuit is complete, electricity flows, and the light bulb glows.

Substances like NaCl that conduct an electric current when dissolved in water are called **electrolytes**. Conduction occurs because negatively charged Cl^- anions migrate through the solution toward the metal strip connected to the positive terminal of the power source, whereas positively charged Na^+ cations migrate toward the strip connected to the negative terminal. As you might expect, the ability of a solution to conduct electricity depends on the concentration of ions in solution. Distilled water contains virtually no ions and is nonconducting; ordinary tap water contains low concentrations of dissolved ions (mostly Na^+, K^+, Mg^{2+}, Ca^{2+}, and Cl^-) and is weakly conducting; and a concentrated solution of NaCl is strongly conducting.

Ionic substances like NaCl that ionize completely when dissolved in water are called **strong electrolytes**, and molecular substances like acetic acid (CH_3CO_2H) that are only partially ionized are **weak electrolytes**. Molecular substances like glucose that do not produce ions when dissolved in water are **nonelectrolytes**.

Electrolyte A substance that produces ions and therefore conducts electricity when dissolved in water.

Strong electrolyte A substance that ionizes completely when dissolved in water.

Weak electrolyte A substance that is only partly ionized in water.

Nonelectrolyte A substance that does not produce ions when dissolved in water.

Strong electrolyte; completely ionized

$$NaCl(s) \xrightarrow[\text{in water}]{\text{Dissolve}} Na^+(aq) + Cl^-(aq)$$

Weak electrolyte; partly ionized

$$CH_3CO_2H(l) \underset{\text{in water}}{\overset{\text{Dissolve}}{\rightleftharpoons}} CH_3CO_2^-(aq) + H^+(aq)$$

Nonelectrolyte; not ionized

$$Glucose(s) \underset{\text{in water}}{\overset{\text{Dissolve}}{\rightleftharpoons}} Glucose(aq)$$

9.10 Electrolytes in Body Fluids: Equivalents and Milliequivalents

What happens if NaCl and KBr are dissolved in the same solution? Because the cations $(K^+$ and $Na^+)$ and anions $(Cl^-$ and $Br^-)$ are all mixed together and no reactions occur between them, an identical solution could just as well be made from KCl and NaBr. Thus, we can no longer speak of having a NaCl + KBr solution; we can only speak of having a solution with four different ions in it.

A similar situation exists for blood and other body fluids, which contain many different anions and cations. Since they are all mixed together, it is difficult to "assign" specific cations to specific anions or to talk about specific ionic compounds. Instead, we are interested only in individual ions and in the total numbers of positive and negative charges. To discuss such mixtures, we use a new term—*equivalents* of ions.

For ions, one **equivalent (Eq)** is equal to the number of ions that carry 1 mol of charge. Of more practical use is the unit **gram-equivalent (g-Eq)**, which is the amount of ion (in grams) that contains one mole of charge. It can be calculated simply as the molar mass of the ion divided by the absolute value of its charge.

Equivalent For ions, the amount equal to 1 mol of charge.

Gram-equivalent For ions, the molar mass of the ion divided by the ionic charge.

$$\text{One gram-equivalent of ion} = \frac{\text{Molar mass of ion (g)}}{\text{Charge on ion}}$$

If the ion has a charge of +1 or −1, 1 gram-equivalent of the ion is simply the molar mass of the ion in grams. Thus, 1 gram-equivalent of Na^+ is 23 g, and 1 gram-equivalent of Cl^- is 35.5 g. If the ion has a charge of +2 or −2, however, 1 gram-equivalent is equal to the ion's formula weight in grams divided by 2. Thus, 1 gram-equivalent of Mg^{2+} is $(24.3\,g)/2 = 12.2\,g$, and 1 gram-equivalent of CO_3^{2-} is $[12.0\,g + (3 \times 16.0\,g)]/2 = 30.0\,g$. The gram-equivalent is a useful conversion factor when converting from volume of solution to mass of ions, as seen in Worked Example 9.14.

The number of equivalents of a given ion per liter of solution can be found by multiplying the molarity of the ion (moles per liter) by the charge on the ion. Because ion concentrations in body fluids are often low, clinical chemists find it more convenient to talk about *milliequivalents* of ions rather than equivalents. One milliequivalent (mEq) of an ion is 1/1000 of an equivalent. For example, the normal concentration of Na^+ in blood is 0.14 Eq/L, or 140 mEq/L.

$$1\ mEq = 0.001\ Eq \qquad 1\ Eq = 1000\ mEq$$

Note that the gram-equivalent for an ion can now be expressed as grams per equivalent or as mg per mEq.

Average concentrations of the major electrolytes in blood plasma are given in Table 9.6. As you might expect, the total milliequivalents of positively and negatively charged electrolytes must be equal to maintain electrical neutrality. Adding the milliequivalents of positive and negative ions in Table 9.6, however, shows a higher concentration of positive ions than negative ions. The difference, called the *anion gap*, is made up by the presence of negatively charged proteins and the anions of organic acids.

TABLE 9.6 Concentrations of Major Electrolytes in Blood Plasma	
Cation	**Concentration (mEq/L)**
Na^+	136–145
Ca^{2+}	4.5–6.0
K^+	3.6–5.0
Mg^{2+}	3
Anion	**Concentration (mEq/L)**
Cl^-	98–106
HCO_3^-	25–29
SO_4^{2-} and HPO_4^{2-}	2

Worked Example **9.14** Equivalents as Conversion Factors: Volume to Mass

The normal concentration of Ca^{2+} in blood is 5.0 mEq/L. How many milligrams of Ca^{2+} are in 1.00 L of blood?

ANALYSIS We are given a volume and a concentration in milliequivalents per liter, and we need to find an amount in milligrams. Thus, we need to calculate the gram-equivalent for Ca^{2+} and then use concentration as a conversion factor between volume and mass, as indicated in the following flow diagram:

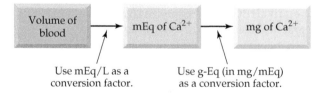

BALLPARK ESTIMATE The molar mass of calcium is 40.08 g/mol, and the calcium ion carries a charge of 2+. Thus, 1 g-Eq of Ca^{2+} equals about 20 g/Eq or 20 mg/mEq. This means that the 5.0 mEq of Ca^{2+} ions in 1.00 L of blood corresponds to a mass of 5.0 mEq Ca^{2+} × 20 mg/mEq = 100 mg Ca^{2+}.

SOLUTION

$$(1.00 \text{ L blood})\left(\frac{5.0 \text{ mEq Ca}^{2+}}{1.0 \text{ L blood}}\right)\left(\frac{20.04 \text{ mg Ca}^{2+}}{1 \text{ mEq Ca}^{2+}}\right) = 100 \text{ mg Ca}^{2+}$$

BALLPARK CHECK The calculated answer (100 mg of Ca^{2+} in 1.00 L of blood) matches our estimate.

PROBLEM 9.21

How many grams are in 1 Eq of the following ions? How many grams in 1 mEq?
(a) K^+ **(b)** Br^- **(c)** Mg^{2+} **(d)** SO_4^{2-} **(e)** Al^{3+} **(f)** PO_4^{3-}

PROBLEM 9.22

Look at the data in Table 9.6, and calculate how many milligrams of Mg^{2+} are in 250 mL of blood.

PROBLEM 9.23

A typical sports drink for electrolyte replacement contains 20 mEq/L of Na^+ and 10 mEq/L of K^+ ions (see Chemistry in Action: Electrolytes, Fluid Replacement, and Sports Drinks on p. 276). Convert these concentrations to m/v%.

9.11 Properties of Solutions

The properties of solutions are similar in many respects to those of pure solvents, but there are also some interesting and important differences. One such difference is that solutions have higher boiling points than the pure solvents; another is that solutions have lower freezing points. Pure water boils at 100.0 °C and freezes at 0.0 °C, for example, but a 1.0 M solution of NaCl in water boils at 101.0 °C and freezes at −3.7 °C.

The elevation of boiling point and the lowering of freezing point for a solution as compared with a pure solvent are examples of **colligative properties**—properties that depend on the *concentration* of a dissolved solute but not on its chemical identity. Other colligative properties are a lower vapor pressure for a solution compared with the pure solvent and *osmosis*, the migration of solvent molecules through a semipermeable membrane.

Colligative property A property of a solution that depends only on the number of dissolved particles, not on their chemical identity.

Colligative Properties

- Vapor pressure is lower for a solution than for a pure solvent.
- Boiling point is higher for a solution than for a pure solvent.
- Freezing point is lower for a solution than for a pure solvent.
- Osmosis occurs when a solution is separated from a pure solvent by a semipermeable membrane.

Vapor-Pressure Lowering in Solutions

We said in Section 8.13 that the vapor pressure of a liquid depends on the equilibrium between molecules entering and leaving the liquid surface. Only those molecules at the surface of the liquid that are sufficiently energetic will evaporate. If, however, some of the liquid (solvent) molecules at the surface are replaced by other (solute) particles that do not evaporate, then the rate of evaporation of solvent molecules decreases and the

CHEMISTRY IN ACTION

Electrolytes, Fluid Replacement, and Sports Drinks

Electrolytes are essential in many physiological processes, and significant changes in electrolyte levels can be potentially life-threatening if not addressed quickly. Heavy and continuous diarrhea from conditions such as cholera can result in dehydration and very low sodium levels in the body (hyponatremia). Restoration of electrolytes can be accomplished by oral rehydration therapy (ORT). The introduction of ORT in developing countries decreased infant mortality from diarrhea, which had previously been the leading cause of death in children under 5 years of age. A typical ORT solution contains sodium (75 mEq/L), potassium (75b mEq/L), chloride (65 mEq/L), citrate (10 mEq/L), and glucose (75 mmol/L). Heavy sweating during strenuous exercise can also lead to dehydration and loss of electrolytes.

The composition of sweat is highly variable, but the typical concentration for the Na^+ ion is about 30–40 mEq/L, and that of K^+ ion is about 5–10 mEq/L. In addition, there are small amounts of other metal ions, such as Mg^{2+}, and there are sufficient Cl^- ions (35–50 mEq/L) to balance the positive charge of all these cations. If water and electrolytes are not replaced, dehydration, hyperthermia and heat stroke, dizziness, nausea, muscle cramps, impaired kidney function, and other difficulties ensue. As a rule of thumb, a sweat loss equal to 5% of body weight—about 3.5 L for a 150 lb person—is the maximum amount that can be safely allowed for a well-conditioned athlete.

Plain water works perfectly well to replace sweat lost during short bouts of activity up to a few hours in length, but a carbohydrate–electrolyte beverage, or "sports drink," is much superior for rehydrating during and after longer activity in which substantial amounts of electrolytes have been lost. Some of the better known sports drinks are little more than overpriced sugar–water solutions, but others are carefully formulated and highly effective for fluid replacement. Nutritional research has shown that a serious sports drink should meet the following criteria. There are several dry-powder mixes on the market to choose from.

- The drink should contain 6–8% of soluble complex carbohydrates (about 15 g per 8 oz serving) and only a small amount of simple sugar for taste. The complex carbohydrates, which usually go by the name "maltodextrin," provide a slow release of glucose into the bloodstream. Not only does the glucose provide a steady source of energy, it also enhances the absorption of water from the stomach.

▲ **Drinking water to replace fluids is adequate for short periods of activity, but extended exercise requires replacement of fluid and electrolytes, such as those found in sports drinks.**

- The drink should contain electrolytes to replenish those lost in sweat. Concentrations of approximately 20 mEq/L for Na^+ ions, 10 mEq/L for K^+ ion, and 4 mEq/L for Mg^{2+} ions are recommended. These amounts correspond to about 100 mg sodium, 100 mg potassium, and 25 mg magnesium per 8 oz serving.

- The drink should be noncarbonated because carbonation can cause gastrointestinal upset during exercise, and it should not contain caffeine, which acts as a diuretic.

- The drink should taste good so the athlete will want to drink it. Thirst is a poor indicator of fluid requirements, and most people will drink less than needed unless a beverage is flavored.

In addition to complex carbohydrates, electrolytes, and flavorings, some sports drinks also contain vitamin A (as beta-carotene), vitamin C (ascorbic acid), and selenium, which act as antioxidants to protect cells from damage. Some drinks also contain the amino acid glutamine, which appears to lessen lactic acid buildup in muscles and thus helps muscles bounce back more quickly after an intense workout.

See Chemistry in Actions Problems 9.91 and 9.92 at the end of the chapter.

vapor pressure of a solution is lower than that of the pure solvent (Figure 9.9). Note that the *identity* of the solute particles is irrelevant; only their concentration matters.

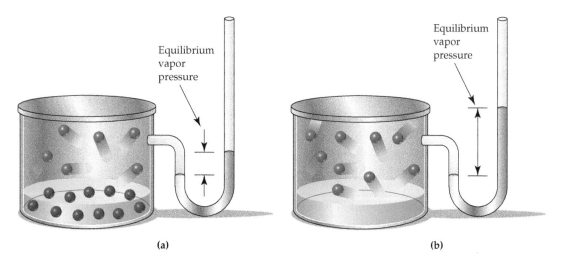

▲ **Figure 9.9**
Vapor-pressure lowering of solution.
(a) The vapor pressure of a solution is lower than (b) the vapor pressure of the pure solvent because fewer solvent molecules are able to escape from the surface of the solution.

Boiling Point Elevation of Solutions

One consequence of the vapor-pressure–lowering for a solution is that the boiling point of the solution is higher than that of the pure solvent. Recall from Section 8.13 that boiling occurs when the vapor pressure of a liquid reaches atmospheric pressure. But because the vapor pressure of a solution is lower than that of the pure solvent at a given temperature, the solution must be heated to a higher temperature for its vapor pressure to reach atmospheric pressure. Figure 9.10 shows a close-up plot of vapor pressure versus temperature for pure water and for a 1.0 M NaCl solution. The vapor pressure of pure water reaches atmospheric pressure (760 mmHg) at 100.0 °C, but the vapor pressure of the NaCl solution does not reach the same point until 101.0 °C.

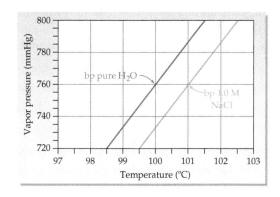

◄ **Figure 9.10**
Vapor pressure and temperature.
A close-up plot of vapor pressure versus temperature for pure water (red curve) and for a 1.0 M NaCl solution (blue curve). Pure water boils at 100.0 °C, but the solution does not boil until 101.0 °C.

For each mole of solute particles added, regardless of chemical identity, the boiling point of 1 kg of water is raised by 0.51 °C, or

$$\Delta T_{\text{boiling}} = \left(0.51\,°C\frac{\text{kg water}}{\text{mol particles}}\right)\left(\frac{\text{mol particles}}{\text{kg water}}\right)$$

The addition of 1 mol of a molecular substance like glucose to 1 kg of water therefore raises the boiling point from 100.0 °C to 100.51 °C. The addition of 1 mol of NaCl per kilogram of water, however, raises the boiling point by 2 × 0.51 °C = 1.02 °C because the solution contains 2 mol of solute particles—Na$^+$ and Cl$^-$ ions.

Worked Example **9.15** Properties of Solutions: Boiling Point Elevation

What is the boiling point of a solution of 0.75 mol of KBr in 1.0 kg of water?

ANALYSIS The boiling point increases 0.51 °C for each mole of solute per kilogram of water. Since KBr is a strong electrolyte, there are 2 moles of ions (K^+ and Br^-) for every 1 mole of KBr that dissolves.

BALLPARK ESTIMATE The boiling point will increase about 0.5 °C for every 1 mol of ions in 1 kg of water. Since 0.75 mol of KBr produce 1.5 mol of ions, the boiling point should increase by (1.5 mol ions) × (0.5 °C/mol ions) = 0.75 °C.

SOLUTION

$$\Delta T_{\text{boiling}} = \left(0.51 \,°C\frac{\text{kg water}}{\text{mol ions}}\right)\left(\frac{2 \text{ mol ions}}{1 \text{ mol KBr}}\right)\left(\frac{0.75 \text{ mol KBr}}{1.0 \text{ kg water}}\right) = 0.77 \,°C$$

The normal boiling point of pure water is 100 °C, so the boiling point of the solution increases to 100.77 °C.

BALLPARK CHECK The 0.77 °C increase is consistent with our estimate of 0.75 °C.

PROBLEM 9.24

A solution is prepared by dissolving 0.67 mol of $MgCl_2$ in 0.50 kg of water.

(a) How many moles of ions are present in solution?

(b) What is the change in the boiling point of the aqueous solution?

PROBLEM 9.25

When 1.0 mol of HF is dissolved in 1.0 kg of water, the boiling point of the resulting solution is 100.5 °C. Is HF a strong or weak electrolyte? Explain.

KEY CONCEPT PROBLEM 9.26

The following diagram shows plots of vapor pressure versus temperature for a solvent and a solution.

(a) Which curve represents the pure solvent and which the solution?

(b) What is the approximate boiling point elevation for the solution?

(c) What is the approximate concentration of the solution in mol/kg, if 1 mol of solute particles raises the boiling point of 1 kg of solvent by 3.63 °C?

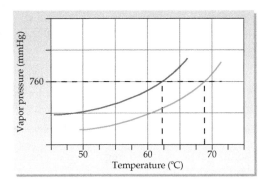

Freezing Point Depression of Solutions

Just as solutions have lower vapor pressure and consequently higher boiling points than pure solvents, they also have lower freezing points. Motorists in cold climates take advantage of this effect when they add "antifreeze" to the water in automobile cooling systems. Antifreeze is a nonvolatile solute, usually ethylene glycol ($HOCH_2CH_2OH$), that is added in sufficient concentration to lower the freezing point below the lowest expected outdoor temperature. In the same way, salt sprinkled on icy roads lowers the freezing point of ice below the road temperature and thus causes ice to melt.

Freezing point depression has much the same cause as vapor pressure lowering and boiling point elevation. Solute molecules are dispersed between solvent molecules throughout the solution, thereby making it more difficult for solvent molecules to come together and organize into ordered crystals.

For each mole of nonvolatile solute particles, the freezing point of 1 kg of water is lowered by 1.86 °C, or

$$\Delta T_{\text{freezing}} = \left(-1.86\,°C\,\frac{\text{kg water}}{\text{mol particles}}\right)\left(\frac{\text{mol particles}}{\text{kg water}}\right)$$

Thus, addition of 1 mol of antifreeze to 1 kg of water lowers the freezing point from 0.00 °C to −1.86 °C, and addition of 1 mol of NaCl (2 mol of particles) to 1 kg of water lowers the freezing point from 0.00 °C to −3.72 °C.

Worked Example 9.16 Properties of Solutions: Freezing Point Depression

The cells of a tomato contain mostly an aqueous solution of sugar and other substances. If a typical tomato freezes at −2.5 °C, what is the concentration of dissolved particles in the tomato cells (in moles of particles per kg of water)?

ANALYSIS The freezing point decreases by 1.86 °C for each mole of solute dissolved in 1 kg of water. We can use the decrease in freezing point (2.5 °C) to find the amount of solute per kg of water.

BALLPARK ESTIMATE The freezing point will decrease by about 1.9 °C for every 1 mol of solute particles in 1 kg of water. To lower the freezing point by 2.5 °C (about 30% more) will require about 30% more solute, or 1.3 mol.

SOLUTION

$$\Delta T_{\text{freezing}} = -2.5\,°C$$

$$= \left(-1.86\,°C\,\frac{\text{kg water}}{\text{mol solute particles}}\right)\left(\frac{??\ \text{mol solute particles}}{1.0\ \text{kg water}}\right)$$

We can rearrange this expression to

$$(-2.5\,°C)\left(\frac{1}{-1.86\,°C}\,\frac{\text{mol solute particles}}{\text{kg water}}\right) = 1.3\,\frac{\text{mol solute particles}}{\text{kg water}}$$

BALLPARK CHECK The calculated answer agrees with our estimate of 1.3 mol/kg.

PROBLEM 9.27
What is the freezing point of a solution of 1.0 mol of glucose in 1.0 kg of water?

PROBLEM 9.28
When 0.5 mol of a certain ionic substance is dissolved in 1.0 kg of water, the freezing point of the resulting solution is −2.8 °C. How many ions does the substance give when it dissolves?

9.12 Osmosis and Osmotic Pressure

Certain materials, including those that make up the membranes around living cells, are *semipermeable*. They allow water and other small molecules to pass through, but they block the passage of large solute molecules or ions. When a solution and a pure solvent, or two solutions of different concentration, are separated

Osmosis The passage of solvent through a semipermeable membrane separating two solutions of different concentration.

by a semipermeable membrane, solvent molecules pass through the membrane in a process called **osmosis**. Although the passage of solvent through the membrane takes place in both directions, passage from the pure solvent side to the solution side is favored and occurs more often. As a result, the amount of liquid on the pure solvent side decreases, the amount of liquid on the solution side increases, and the concentration of the solution decreases.

For the simplest explanation of osmosis, let us look at what happens on the molecular level. As shown in Figure 9.11, a solution inside a bulb is separated by a semipermeable membrane from pure solvent in the outer container. Solvent molecules in the outer container, because of their somewhat higher concentration, approach the membrane more frequently than do molecules in the bulb, thereby passing through more often and causing the liquid level in the attached tube to rise.

▶ **Figure 9.11**

The phenomenon of osmosis.
A solution inside the bulb is separated from pure solvent in the outer container by a semipermeable membrane. Solvent molecules in the outer container have a higher concentration than molecules in the bulb and therefore pass through the membrane more frequently. The liquid in the tube therefore rises until an equilibrium is reached. At equilibrium, the osmotic pressure exerted by the column of liquid in the tube is sufficient to prevent further net passage of solvent.

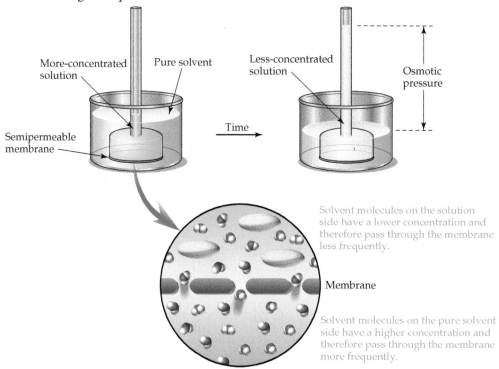

As the liquid in the tube rises, its increased weight creates an increased pressure that pushes solvent back through the membrane until the rates of forward and reverse passage become equal and the liquid level stops rising. The amount of pressure necessary to achieve this equilibrium is called the **osmotic pressure** (π) of the solution and can be determined from the expression

Osmotic pressure The amount of external pressure that must be applied to a solution to prevent the net movement of solvent molecules across a semipermeable membrane.

$$\pi = \left(\frac{n}{V}\right)RT$$

where n is the number of moles of particles in the solution, V is the solution volume, R is the gas constant (Section 8.10), and T is the absolute temperature of the solution. Note the similarity between this equation for the osmotic pressure of a solution and the equation for the pressure of an ideal gas, $P = (n/V)RT$. In both cases, the pressure has units of atmospheres.

Osmotic pressures can be extremely high, even for relatively dilute solutions. The osmotic pressure of a 0.15 M NaCl solution at 25 °C, for example, is 7.3 atm, a value that supports a difference in water level of approximately 250 ft!

As with other colligative properties, the amount of osmotic pressure depends only on the concentration of solute particles, not on their identity. Thus, it is convenient to use a new unit, *osmolarity* (osmol), to describe the concentration of particles in solution. The **osmolarity** of a solution is equal to the number of moles of dissolved particles (ions or molecules) per liter of solution. A 0.2 M glucose solution, for instance, has

Osmolarity (osmol) The sum of the molarities of all dissolved particles in a solution.

an osmolarity of 0.2 osmol, but a 0.2 M solution of NaCl has an osmolarity of 0.4 osmol because it contains 0.2 mol of Na^+ ions and 0.2 mol of Cl^- ions.

Osmosis is particularly important in living organisms because the membranes around cells are semipermeable. The fluids both inside and outside cells must therefore have the same osmolarity to prevent buildup of osmotic pressure and consequent rupture of the cell membrane.

In blood, the plasma surrounding red blood cells has an osmolarity of approximately 0.30 osmol and is said to be **isotonic** with (that is, has the same osmolarity as) the cell contents. If the cells are removed from plasma and placed in 0.15 M NaCl (called *physiological saline solution*), they are unharmed because the osmolarity of the saline solution (0.30 osmol) is the same as that of plasma. If, however, red blood cells are placed in pure water or in any solution with an osmolarity much lower than 0.30 osmol (a **hypotonic** solution), water passes through the membrane into the cell, causing the cell to swell up and burst, a process called *hemolysis*.

Finally, if red blood cells are placed in a solution having an osmolarity greater than the cell contents (a **hypertonic** solution), water passes out of the cells into the surrounding solution, causing the cells to shrivel, a process called *crenation*. Figure 9.12 shows red blood cells under all three conditions: isotonic, hypotonic, and hypertonic. Therefore, it is critical that any solution used intravenously be isotonic to prevent red blood cells from being destroyed.

Isotonic Having the same osmolarity.

Hypotonic Having an osmolarity *less than* the surrounding blood plasma or cells.

Hypertonic Having an osmolarity *greater than* the surrounding blood plasma or cells.

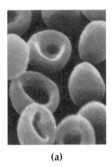
(a)

(b)

(c)

◀**Figure 9.12**
Red blood cells.
In an isotonic solution the blood cells are normal in appearance (a), but the cells in a hypotonic solution (b) are swollen because of water gain, and those in a hypertonic solution (c) are shriveled because of water loss.

Worked Example 9.17 Properties of Solutions: Osmolarity

The solution of glucose commonly used intravenously has a concentration of 5.0% (m/v) glucose. What is the osmolarity of this solution? The molar mass of glucose is 180 g/mol.

ANALYSIS Since glucose is a molecular substance that does not give ions in solution, the osmolarity of the solution is the same as the molarity. Recall from Section 9.7 that a solution of 5.0% (m/v) glucose has a concentration of 5.0 g glucose per 100 mL of solution, which is equivalent to 50 g per liter of solution. Thus, finding the molar concentration of glucose requires a mass to mole conversion.

BALLPARK ESTIMATE One liter of solution contains 50 g of glucose ($MW = 180\,g/mol$). Thus, 50 g of glucose is equal to a little more than 0.25 mol, so a solution concentration of 50 g/L is equal to about 0.25 osmol, or 0.25 M.

SOLUTION

STEP 1: **Identify known information.** We know the (m/v)% concentration of the glucose solution.

STEP 2: **Identify answer and units.** We are looking for osmolarity, which in this case is equal to the molarity of the solution because glucose is a molecular substance and does not dissociate into ions.

$$5.0\%\,(m/v) = \frac{5.0\,g\,glucose}{100\,mL\,solution} \times 100\%$$

$$Osmolarity = Molarity = ??\,mol/liter$$

STEP 3: **Identify conversion factors.** The (m/v)% concentration is defined as grams of solute per 100 mL of solution, and molarity is defined as moles of solute per liter of solution. We will need to convert from milliliters to liters and then use molar mass to convert grams of glucose to moles of glucose.

$$\frac{\text{g glucose}}{100 \text{ mL}} \times \frac{1000 \text{ mL}}{\text{L}} \longrightarrow \frac{\text{g glucose}}{\text{L}}$$

$$\frac{\text{g glucose}}{\text{L}} \times \frac{1 \text{ mol glucose}}{180 \text{ g glucose}} \longrightarrow \frac{\text{moles glucose}}{\text{L}}$$

STEP 4: **Solve.** Starting with the (m/v)% glucose concentration, we first find the number of grams of glucose in 1 L of solution and then convert to moles of glucose per liter.

$$\left(\frac{5.0 \text{ g glucose}}{100 \text{ mL solution}}\right)\left(\frac{1000 \text{ mL}}{1 \text{ L}}\right) = \frac{50 \text{ g glucose}}{\text{L solution}}$$

$$\left(\frac{50 \text{ g glucose}}{1 \text{ L}}\right)\left(\frac{1 \text{ mol}}{180 \text{ g}}\right) = 0.28 \text{ M glucose} = 0.28 \text{ osmol}$$

BALLPARK CHECK The calculated osmolarity is reasonably close to our estimate of 0.25 osmol.

Worked Example 9.18 Properties of Solutions: Osmolarity

What mass of NaCl is needed to make 1.50 L of a 0.300 osmol solution? The molar mass of NaCl is 58.44 g/mol.

ANALYSIS Since NaCl is an ionic substance that produces 2 mol of ions (Na^+, Cl^-) when it dissociates, the osmolarity of the solution is twice the molarity. From the volume and the osmolarity we can determine the moles of NaCl needed and then perform a mole to mass conversion.

SOLUTION

STEP 1: **Identify known information.** We know the volume and the osmolarity of the final NaCl solution.

$V = 1.50$ L

$$0.300 \text{ osmol} = \left(\frac{0.300 \text{ mol ions}}{\text{L}}\right)$$

STEP 2: **Identify answer and units.** We are looking for the mass of NaCl.

Mass of NaCl = ?? g

STEP 3: **Identify conversion factors.** Starting with osmolarity in the form (moles NaCl/L), we can use volume to determine the number of moles of solute. We can then use molar mass for the mole to mass conversion.

$$\left(\frac{\text{moles NaCl}}{\text{L}}\right) \times (\text{L}) = \text{moles NaCl}$$

$$(\text{moles NaCl}) \times \left(\frac{\text{g NaCl}}{\text{mole NaCl}}\right) = \text{g NaCl}$$

STEP 4: **Solve.** Use the appropriate conversions, remembering that NaCl produces two ions per formula unit, to find the mass of NaCl.

$$\left(\frac{0.300 \text{ mol ions}}{\text{L}}\right)\left(\frac{1 \text{ mol NaCl}}{2 \text{ mol ions}}\right)(1.50 \text{ L}) = 0.225 \text{ mol NaCl}$$

$$(0.225 \text{ mol NaCl})\left(\frac{58.44 \text{ g NaCl}}{\text{mol NaCl}}\right) = 13.1 \text{ g NaCl}$$

PROBLEM 9.29

What is the osmolarity of the following solutions?

(a) 0.35 M KBr

(b) 0.15 M glucose + 0.05 M K_2SO_4

PROBLEM 9.30

A typical oral rehydration solution (ORS) for infants contains 90 mEq/L Na^+, 20 mEq/L K^+, 110 mEq/L Cl^-, and 2.0% (m/v) glucose (MW = 180 g/mol).

(a) Calculate the concentration of each ORS component in units of molarity.

(b) What is the osmolarity of the solution, and how does it compare with the osmolarity of blood plasma?

9.13 Dialysis

Dialysis is similar to osmosis, except that the pores in a dialysis membrane are larger than those in an osmotic membrane so that both solvent molecules and small solute particles can pass through, but large colloidal particles such as proteins cannot pass. (The exact dividing line between a "small" molecule and a "large" one is imprecise, and dialysis membranes with a variety of pore sizes are available.) Dialysis membranes include animal bladders, parchment, and cellophane.

Perhaps the most important medical use of dialysis is in artificial kidney machines, where *hemodialysis* is used to cleanse the blood of patients whose kidneys malfunction (Figure 9.13). Blood is diverted from the body and pumped through a long cellophane dialysis tube suspended in an isotonic solution formulated to contain many of the same components as blood plasma. These substances—glucose, NaCl, NaHCO₃, and KCl— have the same concentrations in the dialysis solution as they do in blood so that they have no net passage through the membrane.

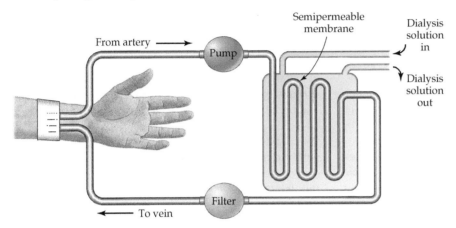

◄ **Figure 9.13**

Operation of a hemodialysis unit used for purifying blood.
Blood is pumped from an artery through a coiled semipermeable membrane of cellophane. Small waste products pass through the membrane and are washed away by an isotonic dialysis solution.

Small waste materials such as urea pass through the dialysis membrane from the blood to the solution side where they are washed away, but cells, proteins, and other important blood components are prevented from passing through the membrane because of their larger size. In addition, the dialysis fluid concentration can be controlled so that imbalances in electrolytes are corrected. The wash solution is changed every 2 h, and a typical hemodialysis procedure lasts for 4–7 h.

As noted above, colloidal particles are too large to pass through a semipermeable membreane. Protein molecules, in particular, do not cross semipermeable membranes and thus play an essential role in determining the osmolarity of body fluids. The distribution of water and solutes across the capillary walls that separate blood plasma from the fluid

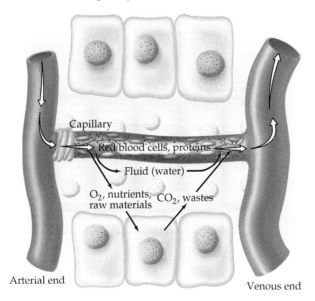

◄ **The delivery of oxygen and nutrients to the cells and the removal of waste products are regulated by osmosis.**

surrounding cells is controlled by the balance between blood pressure and osmotic pressure. The pressure of blood inside the capillary tends to push water out of the plasma (filtration), but the osmotic pressure of colloidal protein molecules tends to draw water into the plasma (reabsorption). The balance between the two processes varies with location in the body. At the arterial end of a capillary, where blood pumped from the heart has a higher pressure, filtration is favored, At the venous end, where blood pressure is lower, reabsorption is favored, causing waste products from metabolism to enter the bloodstream, to be removed by the kidneys.

CHEMISTRY IN ACTION

Timed-Release Medications

There is much more in most medications than medicine. Even something as simple as a generic aspirin tablet contains a binder to keep it from crumbling, a filler to bring it to the right size and help it disintegrate in the stomach, and a lubricant to keep it from sticking to the manufacturing equipment. Timed-release medications are more complex still.

The widespread use of timed-release medication dates from the introduction of Contac decongestant in 1961. The original idea was simple: tiny beads of medicine were encapsulated by coating them with varying thicknesses of a slow-dissolving polymer. Those beads with a thinner coat dissolve and release their medicine more rapidly; those with a thicker coat dissolve more slowly. Combining the right number of beads with the right thicknesses into a single capsule makes possible the gradual release of medication over a predictable time.

The technology of timed-release medications has become much more sophisticated in recent years, and the kinds of medications that can be delivered have become more numerous. Some medicines, for instance, either damage the stomach lining or are destroyed by the highly acidic environment in the stomach but can be delivered safely if given an *enteric coating*. The enteric coating is a polymeric material formulated so that it is stable in acid but reacts and is destroyed when it passes into the more basic environment of the intestines.

More recently, dermal patches have been developed to deliver drugs directly by diffusion through the skin. Patches are available to treat conditions from angina to motion sickness, as well as nicotine patches to help reduce cigarette cravings. One clever new device for timed release of medication through the skin uses the osmotic effect to force a drug from its reservoir. Useful only for drugs that do not dissolve in water, the device is divided into two compartments, one containing medication covered by a perforated membrane and the other containing a hygroscopic material (Section 9.3) covered by a semipermeable membrane. As moisture from the air diffuses through the membrane into the compartment with the hygroscopic material, the buildup of osmotic pressure squeezes the medication out of the other compartment through tiny holes.

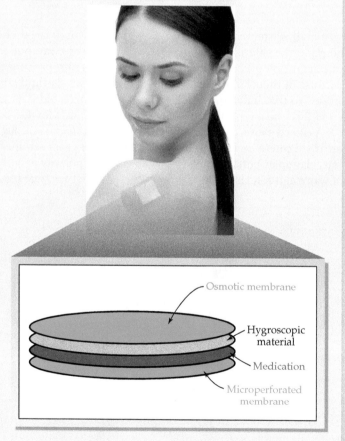

▲ The small beads of medicine are coated with different thicknesses of a slow-dissolving polymer so that they dissolve and release medicine at different times.

See Chemistry in Action Problem 9.93 at the end of the chapter.

SUMMARY: REVISITING THE CHAPTER GOALS

1. What are solutions, and what factors affect solubility? Mixtures are classified as either *heterogeneous*, if the mixing is nonuniform, or *homogeneous*, if the mixing is uniform. *Solutions* are homogeneous mixtures that contain particles the size of ions and molecules (<2.0 nm diameter), whereas larger particles (2.0–500 nm diameter) are present in *colloids*.

The maximum amount of one substance (the *solute*) that can be dissolved in another (the *solvent*) is called the substance's *solubility*. Substances tend to be mutually soluble when their intermolecular forces are similar. The solubility in water of a solid often increases with temperature, but the solubility of a gas always decreases with temperature. Pressure significantly affects gas solubilities, which are directly proportional to their partial pressure over the solution (*Henry's law*) (*see Problems 36–43, 94, 105*).

2. How is the concentration of a solution expressed? The concentration of a solution can be expressed in several ways, including molarity, weight/weight percent composition, weight/volume percent composition, and parts per million (or billion). Osmolarity is used to express the total concentration of dissolved particles (ions and molecules). Molarity, which expresses concentration as the number of moles of solute per liter of solution, is the most useful method when calculating quantities of reactants or products for reactions in aqueous solution (*see Problems 44–65, 86, 88, 89, 91, 94–105, 107, 108*).

3. How are dilutions carried out? A dilution is carried out by adding more solvent to an existing solution. Only the amount of solvent changes; the amount of solute remains the same. Thus, the molarity times the volume of the dilute solution is equal to the molarity times the volume of the concentrated solution: $M_c V_c = M_d V_d$ (*see Problems 35, 66–71, 98*).

4. What is an electrolyte? Substances that form ions when dissolved in water and whose water solutions therefore conduct an electric current are called *electrolytes*. Substances that ionize completely in water are *strong electrolytes*, those that ionize partially are *weak electrolytes*, and those that do not ionize are *nonelectrolytes*. Body fluids contain small amounts of many different electrolytes, whose concentrations are expressed as moles of ionic charge, or equivalents, per liter (*see Problems 32,33, 72–79, 97, 108*).

5. How do solutions differ from pure solvents in their behavior? In comparing a solution to a pure solvent, the solution has a lower vapor pressure at a given temperature, a higher boiling point, and a lower melting point. Called *colligative properties*, these effects depend only on the number of dissolved particles, not on their chemical identity (*see Problems 32, 33, 43, 80–83, 108*).

6. What is osmosis? *Osmosis* occurs when solutions of different concentration are separated by a semipermeable membrane that allows solvent molecules to pass but blocks the passage of solute ions and molecules. Solvent flows from the more dilute side to the more concentrated side until sufficient *osmotic pressure* builds up and stops the flow. An effect similar to osmosis occurs when membranes of larger pore size are used. In *dialysis*, the membrane allows the passage of solvent and small dissolved molecules but prevents passage of proteins and larger particles (*see Problems 31, 84, 85, 87*).

KEY WORDS

Colligative property, *p. 275*

Colloid, *p. 253*

Dilution factor, *p. 271*

Electrolyte, *p. 273*

Equivalent (Eq), *p. 273*

Gram-equivalent (g-Eq), *p. 273*

Henry's law, *p. 261*

Heterogeneous mixture, *p. 253*

Homogeneous mixture, *p. 253*

Hygroscopic, *p. 258*

Hypertonic, *p. 281*

Hypotonic, *p. 281*

Isotonic, *p. 281*

Mass/mass percent concentration, (m/m)%, *p. 264*

mass/volume percent concentration, (m/v)%, *p. 264*

Miscible, *p. 258*

Molarity (M), *p. 268*

Nonelectrolyte, *p. 273*

Osmolarity (osmol), *p. 280*

Osmosis, *p. 280*

Osmotic pressure, *p. 280*

Parts per billion (ppb), *p. 267*

Parts per million (ppm), *p. 267*

Saturated solution, *p. 258*

Solubility, *p. 258*

Solute, *p. 254*

Solution, *p. 253*

Solvation, *p. 256*

Solvent, *p. 254*

Strong electrolyte, *p. 273*

Supersaturated solution, *p. 259*

Volume/volume percent concentration, (v/v)%, *p. 264*

Weak electrolyte, *p. 273*

CONCEPT MAP: SOLUTIONS

Formation of a solution depends on many factors, including the attractive forces between solute and solvent particles, temperature, and pressure (gases). The extent to which a solute dissolves in solution can be expressed either qualitatively or using quantitative concentration units. The most common concentration unit in chemical applications is molarity (moles of solute/L solution), which is also useful in quantitative relationships involving reactions that take place in solution. Colligative properties of solution, including boiling and freezing points, will vary with the amount of solute dissolved in solution. These relationships are illustrated in the concept map in Figure 9.14.

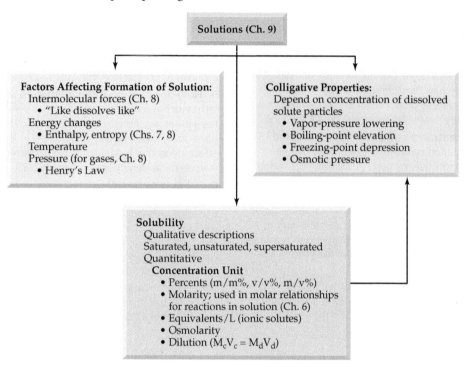

▲ **Figure 9.14**

UNDERSTANDING KEY CONCEPTS

9.31 Assume that two liquids are separated by a semipermeable membrane, with pure solvent on the right side, and a solution of a solute on the left side. Make a drawing that shows the situation after equilibrium is reached.

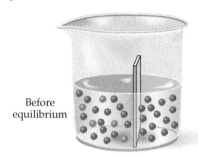

Before equilibrium

9.32 When 1 mol of HCl is added to 1 kg of water, the boiling point increases by 1.0 °C, but when 1 mol of acetic acid, CH_3CO_2H, is added to 1 kg of water, the boiling point increases by only 0.5 °C. Explain.

9.33 HF is a weak electrolyte and HBr is a strong electrolyte. Which of the curves in the figure represents the change in the boiling point of an aqueous solution when 1 mole of HF is added to 1 kg of water, and which represents the change when 1 mol of HBr is added?

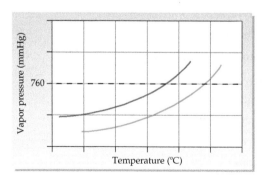

9.34 Assume that you have two full beakers, one containing pure water (blue) and the other containing an equal volume of a 10% (w/v) solution of glucose (green). Which of the drawings (a)–(c) best represents the two beakers after they have stood uncovered for several days and partial evaporation has occurred? Explain.

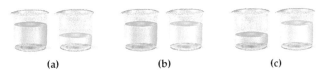

(a) (b) (c)

9.35 A beaker containing 150.0 mL of 0.1 M glucose is represented by (a). Which of the drawings (b)–(d) represents the

solution that results when 50.0 mL is withdrawn from (a) and then diluted by a factor of 4?

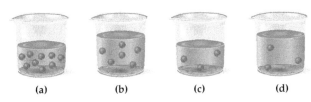

(a) (b) (c) (d)

ADDITIONAL PROBLEMS

SOLUTIONS AND SOLUBILITY

9.36 What is the difference between a homogeneous mixture and a heterogeneous one?

9.37 How can you tell a solution from a colloid?

9.38 What characteristic of water allows it to dissolve ionic solids?

9.39 Why does water not dissolve motor oil?

9.40 Which of the following are solutions?

    (a) Italian salad dressing   **(b)** Rubbing alcohol

    (c) Algae in pond water   **(d)** Black coffee

9.41 Based on the predominant intermolecular forces, which of the following pairs of liquids are likely to be miscible?

    (a) H_2SO_4 and H_2O **(b)** C_8H_{18} and C_6H_6

    (c) CH_2Cl_2, and H_2O **(d)** CS_2 and CCl_4

9.42 The solubility of NH_3 gas in water at an NH_3 pressure of 760.0 mmHg is 51.8 g/100 mL. What is the solubility of NH_3 if its partial pressure is reduced to 225.0 mmHg?

9.43 The solubility of CO_2 gas in water is 0.15 g/100 mL at a CO_2 pressure of 760 mmHg. What is the solubility of CO_2 in a soft drink (which is mainly water) that was bottled under a CO_2 pressure of 4.5 atm?

CONCENTRATION AND DILUTION OF SOLUTIONS

9.44 Is a solution highly concentrated if it is saturated? Is a solution saturated if it is highly concentrated?

9.45 How is mass/volume percent concentration defined and for what types of solutions is it typically used?

9.46 How is molarity defined?

9.47 How is volume/volume percent concentration defined and for what types of solutions is it typically used?

9.48 How would you prepare 750.0 mL of a 6.0% (v/v) ethyl alcohol solution?

9.49 A dilute aqueous solution of boric acid, H_3BO_3 is often used as an eyewash. How would you prepare 500.0 mL of a 0.50% (m/v) boric acid solution?

9.50 Describe how you would prepare 250 mL of a 0.10 M NaCl solution.

9.51 Describe how you would prepare 1.50 L of a 7.50% (m/v) $Mg(NO_3)_2$ solution.

9.52 What is the mass/volume percent concentration of the following solutions?

    (a) 0.078 mol KCl in 75 mL of solution

    (b) 0.044 mol sucrose $(C_{12}H_{22}O_{11})$ in 380 mL of solution

9.53 The concentration of glucose in blood is approximately 90 mg/100 mL. What is the mass/volume percent concentration of glucose? What is the molarity of glucose?

9.54 How many moles of each substance are needed to prepare the following solutions?

    (a) 50.0 mL of 8.0% (m/v) KCl (MW $=$ 74.55 g/mol)

    (b) 200.0 mL of 7.5% (m/v) acetic acid (MW $=$ 60.05 g/mol)

9.55 Which of the following solutions is more concentrated?

    (a) 0.50 M KCl or 5.0% (m/v) KCl

    (b) 2.5% (m/v) $NaHSO_4$ or 0.025 M $NaHSO_4$

9.56 If you had only 23 g of KOH remaining in a bottle, how many milliliters of 10.0% (m/v) solution could you prepare? How many milliliters of 0.25 M solution?

9.57 Over-the-counter hydrogen peroxide (H_2O_2) solutions are 3% (m/v). What is this concentration in moles per liter?

9.58 The lethal dosage of potassium cyanide (KCN) in rats is 10 mg KCN per kilogram of body weight. What is this concentration in parts per million?

9.59 The maximum concentration set by the U.S. Environmental Protection Agency for lead in drinking water is 15 ppb. (*Hint*: 1 ppb $=$ 1 $\mu g/L$)

    (a) What is this concentration in milligrams per liter?

    (b) How many liters of water contaminated at this maximum level must you drink to consume 1.0 μg of lead?

9.60 What is the molarity of the following solutions?

    (a) 12.5 g $NaHCO_3$ in 350.0 mL solution

    (b) 45.0 g H_2SO_4 in 300.0 mL solution

    (c) 30.0 g NaCl dissolved to make 500.0 mL solution

9.61 How many grams of solute are in the following solutions?

    (a) 200 mL of 0.30 M acetic acid, CH_3CO_2H

    (b) 1.50 L of 0.25 M NaOH

    (c) 750 mL of 2.5 M nitric acid, HNO_3

9.62 How many milliliters of a 0.75 M HCl solution do you need to obtain 0.0040 mol of HCl?

9.63 Nalorphine, a relative of morphine, is used to combat withdrawal symptoms in heroin users. How many milliliters of a 0.40% (m/v) solution of nalorphine must be injected to obtain a dose of 1.5 mg?

9.64 A flask containing 450 mL of 0.50 M H_2SO_4 was accidentally knocked to the floor. How many grams of $NaHCO_3$ do you need to put on the spill to neutralize the acid according to the following equation?

$$H_2SO_4(aq) + 2\,NaHCO_3(aq) \longrightarrow$$
$$Na_2SO_4(aq) + 2\,H_2O(l) + 2\,CO_2(g)$$

9.65 Sodium thiosulfate $(Na_2S_2O_3)$, the major component in photographic fixer solution, reacts with silver bromide to dissolve it according to the following reaction:

$$AgBr(s) + 2\,Na_2S_2O_3(aq) \longrightarrow$$
$$Na_3Ag(S_2O_3)_2(aq) + NaBr(aq)$$

(a) How many moles of $Na_2S_2O_3$ would be required to react completely with 0.450 g of AgBr?

(b) How many mL of 0.02 M $Na_2S_2O_3$ contain this number of moles?

9.66 What is the final volume of an orange juice prepared from 100.0 mL of orange juice concentrate if the final juice is to be 20.0% of the strength of the original?

9.67 What is the final volume of NaOH solution prepared from 100.0 mL of 0.500 M NaOH if you wanted the final concentration to be 0.150 M?

9.68 An aqueous solution that contains 285 ppm of potassium nitrate (KNO_3) is being used to feed plants in a garden. What volume of this solution is needed to prepare 2.0 L of a solution that is 75 ppm in KNO_3?

9.69 What is the concentration of a NaCl solution, in (m/v)%, prepared by diluting 65 mL of a saturated solution, which has a concentration of 37 (m/v)%, to 480 mL?

9.70 Concentrated (12.0 M) hydrochloric acid is sold for household and industrial purposes under the name "muriatic acid." How many milliliters of 0.500 M HCl solution can be made from 25.0 mL of 12.0 M HCl solution?

9.71 Dilute solutions of $NaHCO_3$ are sometimes used in treating acid burns. How many milliliters of 0.100 M $NaHCO_3$ solution are needed to prepare 750.0 mL of 0.0500 M $NaHCO_3$ solution?

ELECTROLYTES

9.72 What is an electrolyte?

9.73 Give an example of a strong electrolyte and a nonelectrolyte.

9.74 What does it mean when we say that the concentration of Ca^{2+} in blood is 3.0 mEq/L?

9.75 What is the total anion concentration (in mEq/L) of a solution that contains 5.0 mEq/L Na^+, 12.0 mEq/L Ca^{2+}, and 2.0 mEq/L Li^+?

9.76 Kaochlor, a 10% (m/v) KCl solution, is an oral electrolyte supplement administered for potassium deficiency. How many milliequivalents of K^+ are in a 30 mL dose?

9.77 Calculate the gram-equivalent for each of the following ions:

(a) Ca^{2+} (b) K^+

(c) SO_4^{2-} (d) PO_4^{3-}

9.78 Look up the concentration of Cl^- ion in blood in Table 9.6. How many milliliters of blood would be needed to obtain 1.0 g of Cl^- ions?

9.79 Normal blood contains 3 mEq/L of Mg^{2+}. How many milligrams of Mg^{2+} are present in 150.0 mL of blood?

PROPERTIES OF SOLUTIONS

9.80 Which lowers the freezing point of 2.0 kg of water more, 0.20 mol NaOH or 0.20 mol $Ba(OH)_2$? Both compounds are strong electrolytes. Explain.

9.81 Which solution has the higher boiling point, 0.500 M glucose or 0.300 M KCl? Explain.

9.82 Methanol, CH_3OH, is sometimes used as an antifreeze for the water in automobile windshield washer fluids. How many moles of methanol must be added to 5.00 kg of water to lower its freezing point to $-10.0\,°C$? (For each mole of solute, the freezing point of 1 kg of water is lowered $1.86\,°C$.)

9.83 Hard candy is prepared by dissolving pure sugar and flavoring in water and heating the solution to boiling. What is the boiling point of a solution produced by adding 650 g of cane sugar (molar mass 342.3 g/mol) to 1.5 kg of water? (For each mole of nonvolatile solute, the boiling point of 1 kg of water is raised $0.51\,°C$.)

OSMOSIS

9.84 Why do red blood cells swell up and burst when placed in pure water?

9.85 What does it mean when we say that a 0.15 M NaCl solution is isotonic with blood, whereas distilled water is hypotonic?

9.86 Which of the following solutions has the higher osmolarity?

(a) 0.25 M KBr or 0.20 M Na_2SO_4

(b) 0.30 M NaOH or 3.0% (m/v) NaOH

9.87 Which of the following solutions will give rise to a greater osmotic pressure at equilibrium: 5.00 g of NaCl in 350.0 mL water or 35.0 g of glucose in 400.0 mL water? For NaCl, MW = 58.5 amu; for glucose, MW = 180 amu.

9.88 A pickling solution for preserving food is prepared by dissolving 270 g of NaCl in 3.8 L of water. Calculate the osmolarity of the solution.

9.89 An isotonic solution must be approximately 0.30 osmol. How much KCl is needed to prepare 175 mL of an isotonic solution?

CHEMISTRY IN ACTION

9.90 How does the body increase oxygen availability at high altitude? [*Breathing and Oxygen Transport, p. 263*]

9.91 What are the major electrolytes in sweat, and what are their approximate concentrations in mEq/L? [*Electrolytes, Fluid Replacement, and Sports Drinks, p. 276*]

9.92 Why is a sports drink more effective than plain water for rehydration after extended exercise? [*Electrolytes, Fluid Replacement, and Sports Drinks, p. 276*]

9.93 How does an enteric coating on a medication work? [*Timed-Release Medications, p. 284*]

GENERAL QUESTIONS AND PROBLEMS

9.94 Hyperbaric chambers, which provide high pressures (up to 6 atm) of either air or pure oxygen, are used to treat a variety of conditions, ranging from decompression sickness in deep-sea divers to carbon monoxide poisoning.

(a) What is the partial pressure of O_2 (in millimeters of Hg) in a hyperbaric chamber pressurized to 5 atm with air that is 18% in O_2?

(b) What is the solubility of O_2 (in grams per 100 mL) in the blood at this partial pressure? The solubility of O_2 is 2.1 g/100 mL for $P_{O_2} = 1$ atm.

9.95 Express the solubility of O_2 in Problem 9.94(b) in units of molarity.

9.96 Uric acid, the principal constituent of some kidney stones, has the formula $C_5H_4N_4O_3$. In aqueous solution, the solubility of uric acid is only 0.067 g/L. Express this concentration in (m/v)%, in parts per million, and in molarity.

9.97 Emergency treatment of cardiac arrest victims sometimes involves injection of a calcium chloride solution directly into the heart muscle. How many grams of $CaCl_2$ are administered in an injection of 5.0 mL of a 5.0% (m/v) solution? How many milliequivalents of Ca^{2+}?

9.98 Nitric acid, HNO_3, is available commercially at a concentration of 16 M.

(a) What volume would you need to obtain 0.150 mol HNO_3?

(b) To what volume must you dilute this volume of HNO_3 from part (a) to prepare a 0.20 M solution?

9.99 One test for vitamin C (ascorbic acid, $C_6H_8O_6$) is based on the reaction of the vitamin with iodine:

$$C_6H_8O_6(aq) + I_2(aq) \longrightarrow C_6H_6O_6(aq) + 2\,HI(aq)$$

(a) A 25.0 mL sample of a fruit juice requires 13.0 mL of 0.0100 M I_2 solution for reaction. How many moles of ascorbic acid are in the sample?

(b) What is the molarity of ascorbic acid in the fruit juice?

(c) The Food and Drug Administration recommends that 60 mg of ascorbic acid be consumed per day. How many milliliters of the fruit juice in part (a) must a person drink to obtain the recommended dosage?

9.100 *Ringer's solution*, used in the treatment of burns and wounds, is prepared by dissolving 8.6 g of NaCl, 0.30 g of KCl, and 0.33 g of $CaCl_2$ in water and diluting to a volume of 1.00 L. What is the molarity of each component?

9.101 What is the osmolarity of Ringer's solution (see Problem 9.100)? Is it hypotonic, isotonic, or hypertonic with blood plasma (0.30 osmol)?

9.102 The typical dosage of statin drugs for the treatment of high cholesterol is 10 mg. Assuming a total blood volume of 5.0 L, calculate the (m/v)% concentration of drug in the blood in units of g/100 mL.

9.103 Assuming the density of blood in healthy individuals is approximately 1.05 g/mL, report the concentration of drug in Problem 9.102 in units of ppm.

9.104 In all 50 states, a person with a blood alcohol concentration of 0.080% (v/v) is considered legally drunk. What volume of total alcohol does this concentration represent, assuming a blood volume of 5.0 L?

9.105 Ammonia, NH_3, is very soluble in water (51.8 g/L at 20 °C and 760 mmHg).

(a) Show how NH_3 can hydrogen bond to water.

(b) What is the solubility of ammonia in water in moles per liter?

9.106 Cobalt(II) chloride, a blue solid, can absorb water from the air to form cobalt(II) chloride hexahydrate, a pink solid. The equilibrium is so sensitive to moisture in the air that $CoCl_2$ is used as a humidity indicator.

(a) Write a balanced equation for the equilibrium. Be sure to include water as a reactant to produce the hexahydrate.

(b) How many grams of water are released by the decomposition of 2.50 g of cobalt(II) chloride hexahydrate?

9.107 How many milliliters of 0.150 M $BaCl_2$ are needed to react completely with 35.0 mL of 0.200 M Na_2SO_4? How many grams of $BaSO_4$ will be formed?

9.108 Many compounds are only partially dissociated into ions in aqueous solution. Trichloroacetic acid (CCl_3CO_2H), for instance, is partially dissociated in water according to the equation

$$CCl_3CO_2H(aq) \rightleftharpoons H^+(aq) + CCl_3CO_2^-(aq)$$

For a solution prepared by dissolving 1.00 mol of trichloroacetic acid in 1.00 kg of water, 36.0% of the trichloroacetic acid dissociates to form H^+ and $CCl_3CO_2^-$ ions.

(a) What is the total concentration of dissolved ions and molecules in 1 kg of water?

(b) What is the freezing point of this solution? (The freezing point of 1 kg of water is lowered 1.86 °C for each mole of solute particles.)

Acids and Bases

CONTENTS

◄ Acids are found in many of the foods we eat, including tomatoes, peppers, and these citrus fruits.

A cids! The word evokes images of dangerous, corrosive liquids that eat away everything they touch. Although a few well-known substances such as sulfuric acid (H_2SO_4) do indeed fit this description, most acids are relatively harmless. In fact, many acids, such as ascorbic acid (vitamin C), are necessary for life. We have already touched on the subject of acids and bases on several occasions, but the time has come for a more detailed study.

10.1 Acids and Bases in Aqueous Solution

Let us take a moment to review what we said about acids and bases in Sections 3.11 and 5.10 before going on to a more systematic study:

- An acid is a substance that produces hydrogen ions, H^+, when dissolved in water.
- A base is a substance that produces hydroxide ions, OH^-, when dissolved in water.
- The neutralization reaction of an acid with a base yields water plus a *salt*, an ionic compound composed of the cation from the base and the anion from the acid.

The above definitions of acids and bases were proposed in 1887 by the Swedish chemist Svante Arrhenius and are useful for many purposes. The definitions are limited, however, because they refer only to reactions that take place in aqueous solutions. (We will see shortly how the definitions can be broadened.) Another issue is that the H^+ ion is so reactive it does not exist in water. Instead, H^+ reacts with H_2O to give the **hydronium ion**, H_3O^+, as mentioned in Section 3.11. When gaseous HCl dissolves in water, for instance, H_3O^+ and Cl^- are formed. As described in Section 4.9, electrostatic potential maps show that the hydrogen of HCl is positively polarized and electron-poor (blue), whereas the oxygen of water is negatively polarized and electron-rich (red):

Hydronium ion The H_3O^+ ion, formed when an acid reacts with water.

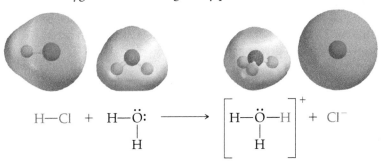

Thus, the Arrhenius definition is updated to acknowledge that an acid yields H_3O^+ in water rather than H^+. In practice, however, the notations H_3O^+ and $H^+(aq)$ are often used interchangeably.

The Arrhenius definition of a base is correct as far as it goes, but it is important to realize that the OH^- ions "produced" by the base can come from either of two sources. Metal hydroxides, such as $NaOH$, KOH, and $Ba(OH)_2$, are ionic compounds that already contain OH^- ions and merely release those ions when they dissolve in water. Some molecular compounds such as ammonia, however, are not ionic and contain no OH^- ions in their structure. Nonetheless, they can act as bases to produce OH^- ions in reactions with water, as will be seen in Section 10.3.

10.2 Some Common Acids and Bases

Acids and bases are present in a variety of foods and consumer products. Acids generally have a sour taste, and nearly every sour food contains an acid: Lemons, oranges, and grapefruit contain citric acid, for instance, and sour milk contains lactic acid. Bases are not so obvious in foods, but most of us have them stored under the kitchen or bathroom sink. Bases are present in many household cleaning agents, from perfumed bar soap, to ammonia-based window cleaners, to the substance you put down the drain to dissolve hair, grease, and other materials that clog it.

Some of the most common acids and bases are listed below. It is a good idea at this point to learn their names and formulas, because we will refer to them often.

- **Sulfuric acid, H_2SO_4,** is probably the most important raw material in the chemical and pharmaceutical industries, and it is manufactured in greater quantity worldwide than any other industrial chemical. Over 45 million tons are prepared in the United States annually for use in many hundreds of industrial processes, including the preparation of phosphate fertilizers. Its most common consumer use is as the acid found in automobile batteries. As anyone who has splashed battery acid on his or her skin or clothing knows, sulfuric acid is highly corrosive and can cause painful burns.

- **Hydrochloric acid, HCl,** or *muriatic acid*, as it was historically known, has many industrial applications, including its use in metal cleaning and in the manufacture of high-fructose corn syrup. Aqueous HCl is also present as "stomach acid" in the digestive systems of most mammals.

- **Phosphoric acid, H_3PO_4,** is used in vast quantities in the manufacture of phosphate fertilizers. In addition, it is also used as an additive in foods and toothpastes. The tart taste of many soft drinks is due to the presence of phosphoric acid.

- **Nitric acid, HNO_3,** is a strong oxidizing agent that is used for many purposes, including the manufacture of ammonium nitrate fertilizer and military explosives. When spilled on the skin, it leaves a characteristic yellow coloration because of its reaction with skin proteins.

- **Acetic acid, CH_3CO_2H,** is the primary organic constituent of vinegar. It also occurs in all living cells and is used in many industrial processes such as the preparation of solvents, lacquers, and coatings.

- **Sodium hydroxide, $NaOH$,** also called *caustic soda* or *lye*, is the most commonly used of all bases. Industrially, it is used in the production of aluminum from its ore, in the production of glass, and in the manufacture of soap from animal fat. Concentrated solutions of $NaOH$ can cause severe burns if allowed to sit on the skin for long. Drain cleaners often contain $NaOH$ because it reacts with the fats and proteins found in grease and hair.

- **Calcium hydroxide, $Ca(OH)_2$,** or *slaked lime*, is made industrially by treating lime (CaO) with water. It has many applications, including its use in mortars and cements. An aqueous solution of $Ca(OH)_2$ is often called *limewater*.

- **Magnesium hydroxide, $Mg(OH)_2$,** or *milk of magnesia*, is an additive in foods, toothpaste, and many over-the-counter medications. Antacids such as Rolaids™, Mylanta™, and Maalox™, for instance, all contain magnesium hydroxide.

▲ Common household cleaners typically contain bases ($NaOH$, NH_3). Soap is manufactured by the reaction of vegetable oils and animal fats with the bases $NaOH$ and KOH.

- **Ammonia, NH$_3$,** is used primarily as a fertilizer, but it also has many other industrial applications, including the manufacture of pharmaceuticals and explosives. A dilute solution of ammonia is frequently used around the house as a glass cleaner.

10.3 The Brønsted–Lowry Definition of Acids and Bases

The Arrhenius definition of acids and bases discussed in Section 10.1 applies only to processes that take place in an aqueous solution. A far more general definition was proposed in 1923 by the Danish chemist Johannes Brønsted and the English chemist Thomas Lowry. A **Brønsted–Lowry acid** is any substance that is able to give a hydrogen ion, H$^+$, to another molecule or ion. A hydrogen *atom* consists of a proton and an electron, so a hydrogen *ion*, H$^+$, is simply a proton. Thus, we often refer to acids as *proton donors*. The reaction need not occur in water, and a Brønsted–Lowry acid need not give appreciable concentrations of H$_3$O$^+$ ions in water.

Different acids can supply different numbers of H$^+$ ions, as we saw in Section 3.11. Acids with one proton to donate, such as HCl or HNO$_3$, are called *monoprotic acids*; H$_2$SO$_4$ is a *diprotic acid* because it has two protons to donate, and H$_3$PO$_4$ is a *triprotic acid* because it has three protons to donate. Notice that the acidic H atoms (that is, the H atoms that are donated as protons) are bonded to electronegative atoms, such as chlorine or oxygen.

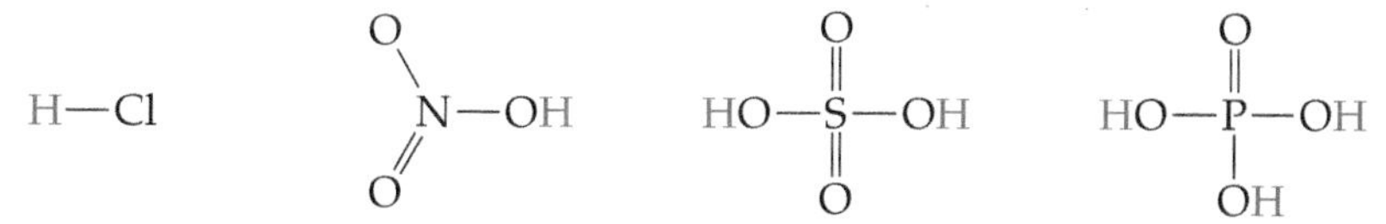

Brønsted–Lowry acid A substance that can donate a hydrogen ion, H$^+$, to another molecule or ion.

| Hydrochloric acid (monoprotic) | Nitric acid (monoprotic) | Sulfuric acid (diprotic) | Phosphoric acid (triprotic) |

Acetic acid (CH$_3$CO$_2$H), an example of an organic acid, actually has a total of 4 hydrogens, but only the one bonded to the electronegative oxygen is positively polarized and therefore acidic. The 3 hydrogens bonded to carbon are not acidic. Most organic acids are similar in that they contain many hydrogen atoms, but only the one in the —CO$_2$H group (blue in the electrostatic potential map) is acidic:

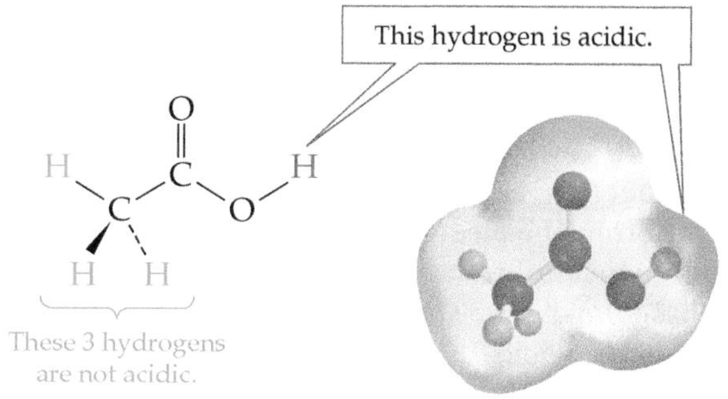

Acetic acid will react with water to produce H$_3$O$^+$ ions (Arrhenius acid definition) by donating a proton (Brønsted–Lowry acid definition) to water, as shown:

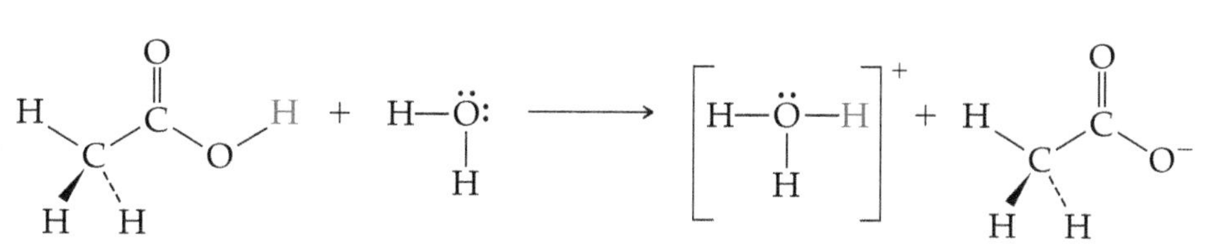

Whereas a Brønsted–Lowry acid is a substance that *donates* H$^+$ ions, a **Brønsted–Lowry base** is a substance that *accepts* H$^+$ ions from an acid. Ammonia will react

Brønsted–Lowry base A substance that can accept H$^+$ ions from an acid.

with water to produce OH^- ions (Arrhenius base definition) by accepting a proton (Brønsted–Lowry base definition), as shown:

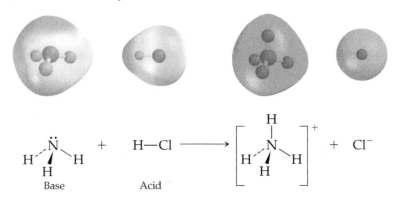

This OH^- ion comes from H_2O.

$$H-\overset{\overset{\textstyle H}{|}}{\underset{\underset{\textstyle H}{|}}{\ddot{N}}}-H(g) + H_2O(l) \rightleftharpoons H-\overset{\overset{\textstyle H}{|}}{\underset{\underset{\textstyle H}{|}}{\overset{+}{N}}}-H(aq) + OH^-(aq)$$

As with the acids, reactions involving Brønsted–Lowry bases need not occur in water, and the Brønsted–Lowry base need not give appreciable concentrations of OH^- ions in water. Gaseous NH_3, for example, acts as a base to accept H^+ from gaseous HCl and yield the ionic solid $NH_4^+ Cl^-$:

$$\underset{\text{Base}}{H-\overset{\ddot{N}}{\underset{H}{\diagup \diagdown}}-H} + \underset{\text{Acid}}{H-Cl} \longrightarrow \left[H-\overset{\overset{\textstyle H}{|}}{\underset{H}{\diagup \diagdown}}-H \right]^+ + Cl^-$$

Putting the acid and base definitions together, *an acid–base reaction is one in which a proton is transferred.* The general reaction between proton-donor acids and proton-acceptor bases can be represented as

Electrons on base form bond with H^+ from acid.

$$B: + H-A \rightleftharpoons B\overset{+}{-}H + A^-$$

$$B:^- + H-A \rightleftharpoons B-H + A^-$$

where the abbreviation HA represents a Brønsted–Lowry acid and B: or B:$^-$ represents a Brønsted–Lowry base. Notice in these acid–base reactions that both electrons in the product B—H bond come from the base, as indicated by the curved arrow flowing from the electron pair of the base to the hydrogen atom of the acid. Thus, the B—H bond that forms is a coordinate covalent bond. In fact, a Brønsted–Lowry base *must* have such a lone pair of electrons; without them, it could not accept H^+ from an acid.

▶▶▶ Recall from Section 4.4 that a coordinate covalent bond is one where both electrons are donated by the same atom.

A base can either be neutral (B:) or negatively charged (B:$^-$). If the base is neutral, then the product has a positive charge (BH^+) after H^+ has been added. Ammonia is an example:

Adding an H^+ creates positive charge.

$$\underset{\substack{\text{Ammonia} \\ \text{(a neutral base, B:)}}}{H-\overset{\overset{\textstyle H}{|}}{\underset{\underset{\textstyle H}{|}}{N}}:} + H-A \rightleftharpoons \underset{\text{Ammonium ion}}{H-\overset{\overset{\textstyle H}{|}}{\underset{\underset{\textstyle H}{|}}{\overset{+}{N}}}-H} + :A^-$$

If the base is negatively charged, then the product is neutral (BH). Hydroxide ion is an example:

$$H—\overset{..}{\underset{..}{O}}{:}^{-} \quad + \quad H—A \rightleftharpoons H—\overset{..}{\underset{..}{O}}—H \;+\; :A^{-}$$

Hydroxide ion
(a negatively charged
base, B:⁻)

Water

An important consequence of the Brønsted–Lowry definitions is that the *products* of an acid–base reaction can also behave as acids and bases. Many acid–base reactions are reversible, although in some cases the equilibrium constant for the reaction is quite large. For example, suppose we have as a forward reaction an acid HA donating a proton to a base B to produce A⁻. This product A⁻ is a base because it can act as a proton acceptor in the reverse reaction. At the same time, the product BH⁺ acts as an acid because it may donate a proton in the reverse reaction:

▶▶ When the equilibrium constant for a reaction is greater than 1, the forward reaction is favored. When the equilibrium constant is less than 1, the reverse reaction is favored (Section 7.8).

Double arrow indicates reversible reaction.

$$B: \;+\; H—A \rightleftharpoons :A^{-} \;+\; B—\overset{+}{H}$$

Base   Acid   Base   Acid

Conjugate acid–base pair

Pairs of chemical species such as B, BH⁺ and HA, A⁻ are called **conjugate acid–base pairs**. They are species that are found on opposite sides of a chemical reaction whose formulas differ by only one H⁺. Thus, the product anion A⁻ is the **conjugate base** of the reactant acid HA, and HA is the **conjugate acid** of the base A⁻. Similarly, the reactant B is the conjugate base of the product acid BH⁺, and BH⁺ is the conjugate acid of the base B. The number of protons in a conjugate acid–base pair is always one greater than the number of protons in the base of the pair. To give some examples, acetic acid and acetate ion, the hydronium ion and water, and the ammonium ion and ammonia all make conjugate acid–base pairs:

Conjugate acid–base pair Two substances whose formulas differ by only a hydrogen ion, H⁺.

Conjugate base The substance formed by loss of H⁺ from an acid.

Conjugate acid The substance formed by addition of H⁺ to a base.

Conjugate acids $\left\{\begin{array}{l} CH_3\overset{O}{\overset{\|}{C}}OH \rightleftharpoons H^+ + CH_3\overset{O}{\overset{\|}{C}}O^- \\ H_3O^+ \rightleftharpoons H^+ + H_2O \\ NH_4^+ \rightleftharpoons H^+ + NH_3 \end{array}\right.$ Conjugate bases

Worked Example 10.1 Acids and Bases: Identifying Brønsted–Lowry Acids and Bases

Identify each of the following as a Brønsted–Lowry acid or base:

(a) PO_4^{3-} **(b)** $HClO_4$ **(c)** CN^-

ANALYSIS A Brønsted–Lowry acid must have a hydrogen that it can donate as H⁺, and a Brønsted–Lowry base must have an atom with a lone pair of electrons that can bond to H⁺. Typically, a Brønsted–Lowry base is an anion derived by loss of H⁺ from an acid.

SOLUTION

(a) The phosphate anion (PO_4^{3-}) has no proton to donate, so it must be a Brønsted–Lowry base. It is derived by loss of 3 H⁺ ions from phosphoric acid, H_3PO_4.

(b) Perchloric acid $(HClO_4)$ is a Brønsted–Lowry acid because it can donate an H⁺ ion.

(c) The cyanide ion (CN^-) has no proton to donate, so it must be a Brønsted-Lowry base. It is derived by loss removal of an H⁺ ion from hydrogen cyanide, HCN.

Worked Example 10.2 Acids and Bases: Identifying Conjugate Acid–Base Pairs

Write formulas for

(a) The conjugate acid of the cyanide ion, CN^-

(b) The conjugate base of perchloric acid, $HClO_4$

ANALYSIS A conjugate acid is formed by adding H^+ to a base; a conjugate base is formed by removing H^+ from an acid.

SOLUTION

(a) HCN is the conjugate acid of CN^-

(b) ClO_4^- is the conjugate base of $HClO_4$.

PROBLEM 10.1

Which of the following would you expect to be Brønsted–Lowry acids?

(a) HCO_2H (b) H_2S (c) $SnCl_2$

PROBLEM 10.2

Which of the following would you expect to be Brønsted–Lowry bases?

(a) SO_3^{2-} (b) Ag^+ (c) F^-

PROBLEM 10.3

Write formulas for:

(a) The conjugate acid of HS^- (b) The conjugate acid of PO_4^{3-}

(c) The conjugate base of H_2CO_3 (d) The conjugate base of NH_4^+

🔑 KEY CONCEPT PROBLEM 10.4

For the reaction shown here, identify the Brønsted–Lowry acids, bases, and conjugate acid–base pairs.

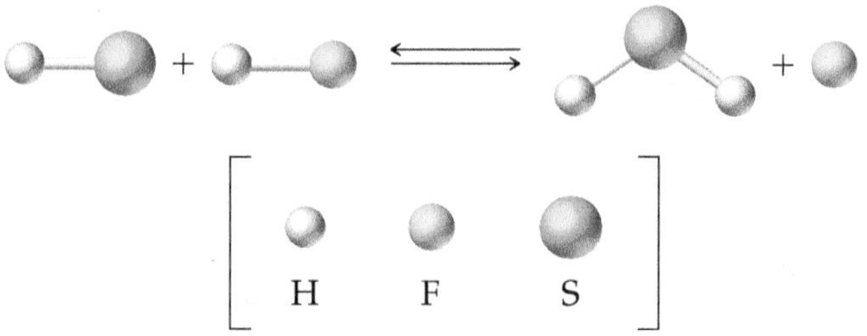

10.4 Acid and Base Strength

Some acids and bases, such as sulfuric acid (H_2SO_4), hydrochloric acid (HCl), or sodium hydroxide (NaOH), are highly corrosive. They react readily and, in contact with skin, can cause serious burns. Other acids and bases are not nearly as reactive. Acetic acid $(CH_3COOH$, the major component in vinegar) and phosphoric acid (H_3PO_4) are found in many food products. Why are some acids and bases relatively "safe," while others must be handled with extreme caution? The answer lies in how easily they produce the active ions for an acid (H^+) or a base (OH^-).

As indicated in Table 10.1, acids differ in their ability to give up a proton. The six acids at the top of the table are **strong acids**, meaning that they give up a proton easily and are essentially 100% **dissociated**, or split apart into ions, in water. Those remaining are **weak acids**, meaning that they give up a proton with difficulty and are substantially less than 100% dissociated in water. In a similar way, the conjugate bases at the

Strong acid An acid that gives up H^+ easily and is essentially 100% dissociated in water.

Dissociation The splitting apart of an acid in water to give H^+ and an anion.

Weak acid An acid that gives up H^+ with difficulty and is less than 100% dissociated in water.

TABLE 10.1 Relative Strengths of Acids and Conjugate Bases

		ACID		CONJUGATE BASE			
Increasing acid strength ↑	Strong acids: 100% dissociated	Perchloric acid	$HClO_4$	ClO_4^-	Perchlorate ion	Little or no reaction as bases	**Increasing base strength**
		Sulfuric acid	H_2SO_4	HSO_4^-	Hydrogen sulfate ion		
		Hydriodic acid	HI	I^-	Iodide ion		
		Hydrobromic acid	HBr	Br^-	Bromide ion		
		Hydrochloric acid	HCl	Cl^-	Chloride ion		
		Nitric acid	HNO_3	NO_3^-	Nitrate ion		
		Hydronium ion	H_3O^+	H_2O	**Water**		
	Weak acids	Hydrogen sulfate ion	HSO_4^-	SO_4^{2-}	Sulfate ion	Very weak bases	
		Phosphoric acid	H_3PO_4	$H_2PO_4^-$	Dihydrogen phosphate ion		
		Nitrous acid	HNO_2	NO_2^-	Nitrite ion		
		Hydrofluoric acid	HF	F^-	Fluoride ion		
		Acetic acid	CH_3COOH	CH_3COO^-	Acetate ion		
	Very weak acids	Carbonic acid	H_2CO_3	HCO_3^-	Bicarbonate ion	Weak bases	
		Dihydrogen phosphate ion	$H_2PO_4^-$	HPO_4^{2-}	Hydrogen phosphate ion		
		Ammonium ion	NH_4^+	NH_3	Ammonia		
		Hydrocyanic acid	HCN	CN^-	Cyanide ion		
		Bicarbonate ion	HCO_3^-	CO_3^{2-}	Carbonate ion		
		Hydrogen phosphate ion	HPO_4^{2-}	PO_4^{3-}	Phosphate ion		
		Water	H_2O	OH^-	**Hydroxide ion**	Strong base	↓

top of the table are **weak bases** because they have little affinity for a proton, and the conjugate bases at the bottom of the table are **strong bases** because they grab and hold a proton tightly.

Note that diprotic acids, such as sulfuric acid H_2SO_4, undergo two stepwise dissociations in water. The first dissociation yields HSO_4^- and occurs to the extent of nearly 100%, so H_2SO_4 is a strong acid. The second dissociation yields SO_4^{2-} and takes place to a much lesser extent because separation of a positively charged H^+ from the negatively charged HSO_4^- anion is difficult. Thus, HSO_4^- is a weak acid:

$$H_2SO_4(l) + H_2O(l) \longrightarrow H_3O^+(aq) + HSO_4^-(aq)$$
$$HSO_4^-(aq) + H_2O(l) \rightleftharpoons H_3O^+(aq) + SO_4^{2-}(aq)$$

Perhaps the most striking feature of Table 10.1 is the inverse relationship between acid strength and base strength. **The stronger the acid, the weaker its conjugate base; the weaker the acid, the stronger its conjugate base.** HCl, for example, is a strong acid, so Cl^- is a very weak base. H_2O, however, is a very weak acid, so OH^- is a strong base.

Why is there an inverse relationship between acid strength and base strength? To answer this question, think about what it means for an acid or base to be strong or weak. A strong acid H—A is one that readily gives up a proton, meaning that its conjugate base A^- has little affinity for the proton. But this is exactly the definition of a weak base—a substance that has little affinity for a proton. As a result, the reverse

Weak base A base that has only a slight affinity for H^+ and holds it weakly.

Strong base A base that has a high affinity for H^+ and holds it tightly.

reaction occurs to a lesser extent, as indicated by the size of the forward and reverse arrows in the reaction:

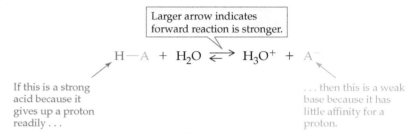

Larger arrow indicates forward reaction is stronger.

$$H{-}A + H_2O \rightleftarrows H_3O^+ + A^-$$

If this is a strong acid because it gives up a proton readily . . .

. . . then this is a weak base because it has little affinity for a proton.

In the same way, a weak acid is one that gives up a proton with difficulty, meaning that its conjugate base has a high affinity for the proton. But this is just the definition of a strong base—a substance that has a high affinity for the proton. The reverse reaction now occurs more readily.

$$H{-}A + H_2O \rightleftarrows H_3O^+ + A^-$$

If this is a weak acid because it gives up a proton with difficulty . . .

Larger arrow indicates reverse reaction is stronger.

. . . then this is a strong base because it has a high affinity for a proton.

Knowing the relative strengths of different acids as shown in Table 10.1 makes it possible to predict the direction of proton-transfer reactions. *An acid–base proton-transfer equilibrium always favors reaction of the stronger acid with the stronger base and formation of the weaker acid and base.* That is, the proton always leaves the stronger acid (whose weaker conjugate base cannot hold the proton) and always ends up in the weaker acid (whose stronger conjugate base holds the proton tightly). Put another way, in a contest for the proton, the stronger base always wins.

Stronger acid + Stronger base $\rightleftarrows$ Weaker base + Weaker acid

To try out this rule, compare the reactions of acetic acid with water and with hydroxide ion. The idea is to write the equation, identify the acid on each side of the arrow, and then decide which acid is stronger and which is weaker. For example, the reaction of acetic acid with water to give acetate ion and hydronium ion is favored in the reverse direction, because acetic acid is a weaker acid than H_3O^+:

$$\overset{O}{\overset{\|}{CH_3C}OH} + H_2O \rightleftarrows \overset{O}{\overset{\|}{CH_3C}O^-} + H_3O^+$$

Weaker acid   Stronger acid   Reverse reaction is favored.

This base holds the proton less tightly . . .   . . . than this base does.

On the other hand, the reaction of acetic acid with hydroxide ion to give acetate ion and water is favored in the forward direction, because acetic acid is a stronger acid than H_2O :

$$\overset{O}{\overset{\|}{CH_3C}OH} + OH^- \rightleftarrows \overset{O}{\overset{\|}{CH_3C}O^-} + H_2O$$

Stronger acid   Weaker acid   Forward reaction is favored.

This base holds the proton more tightly . . .   . . . than this base does.

CHEMISTRY IN ACTION

GERD—Too Much Acid or Not Enough?

Strong acids are very caustic substances that can dissolve even metals, and no one would think of ingesting them. However, the major component of the gastric juices secreted in the stomach is hydrochloric acid—a strong acid—and the acidic environment in the stomach is vital to good health and nutrition.

Stomach acid is essential for the digestion of proteins and for the absorption of certain micronutrients, such as calcium, magnesium, iron, and vitamin B_{12}. It also creates a sterile environment in the gut by killing yeast and bacteria that may be ingested. If these gastric juices leak up into the esophagus, the tube through which food and drink enter the stomach, they can cause the burning sensation in the chest or throat known as either heartburn or acid indigestion. Persistent irritation of the esophagus is known as gastro-esophageal reflux disease (GERD) and, if untreated, can lead to more serious health problems.

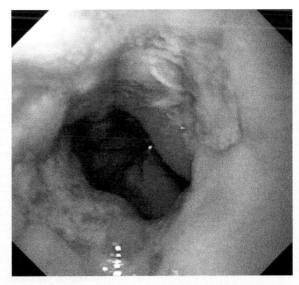

▲ **If not treated, GERD can cause ulcers and scarring of esophageal tissue.**

Hydrogen ions and chloride ions are secreted separately from the cytoplasm of parietal cells lining the stomach and then combine to form HCl that is usually close to 0.10 M. The HCl is then released into the stomach cavity, where the concentration is diluted to about 0.01–0.001 M. Unlike the esophagus, the stomach is coated by a thick mucus layer that protects the stomach wall from damage by this caustic solution.

Those who suffer from acid indigestion can obtain relief by using over-the-counter antacids, such as TUMS™ or Rolaids™ (see Section 10.12, p. 316). Chronic conditions such as GERD, however, are often treated with prescription medications. GERD can be treated by two classes of drugs. Proton-pump inhibitors (PPI), such as Prevacid™ and Prilosec™, prevent the production of the H^+ ions in the parietal cells, while H_2-receptor blockers (Tagamet™, Zantac™, and Pepcid™) prevent the release of stomach acid into the lumen. Both drugs effectively decrease the production of stomach acid to ease the symptoms of GERD.

Ironically, GERD can also be caused by not having enough stomach acid—a condition known as *hypochlorhydria*. The valve that controls the release of stomach contents to the small intestine is triggered by acidity. If this valve fails to open because the stomach is not acidic enough, the contents of the stomach can be churned back up into the esophagus.

See Chemistry in Action Problems 10.94 and 10.95 at the end of the chapter.

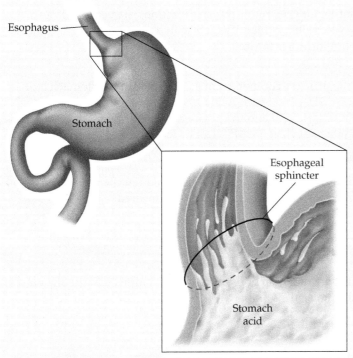

▲ **The burning sensation and other symptoms associated with GERD are caused by the reflux of the acidic contents of the stomach into the esophagus.**

Worked Example 10.3 Acid/Base Strength: Predicting Direction of H-transfer Reactions

Write a balanced equation for the proton-transfer reaction between phosphate ion (PO_4^{3-}) and water, and determine in which direction the equilibrium is favored.

ANALYSIS Look in Table 10.1 to see the relative acid and base strengths of the species involved in the reaction. The acid–base proton-transfer equilibrium will favor reaction of the stronger acid and formation of the weaker acid.

SOLUTION
Phosphate ion is the conjugate base of a weak acid (HPO_4^{2-}) and is therefore a relatively strong base. Table 10.1 shows that HPO_4^{2-} is a stronger acid than H_2O, and OH^- is a stronger base than PO_4^{3-}, so the reaction is favored in the reverse direction:

$$PO_4^{3-}(aq) \; + \; H_2O(l) \; \rightleftharpoons \; HPO_4^{3-}(aq) \; + \; OH^-(aq)$$

Weaker base   Weaker acid   Stronger acid   Stronger base

PROBLEM 10.5
Use Table 10.1 to identify the stronger acid in the following pairs:
(a) H_2O or NH_4^+ (b) H_2SO_4 or CH_3CO_2H (c) HCN or H_2CO_3

PROBLEM 10.6
Use Table 10.1 to identify the stronger base in the following pairs:
(a) F^- or Br^- (b) OH^- or HCO_3^-

PROBLEM 10.7
Write a balanced equation for the proton-transfer reaction between a hydrogen phosphate ion and a hydroxide ion. Identify each acid–base pair, and determine in which direction the equilibrium is favored.

PROBLEM 10.8
Hydrochloric acid is the primary component of gastric juice in the stomach (see Chemistry in Action: GERD—Too Much Acid or Not Enough? on p. 299). The reaction between hydrochloric acid and the carbonate ion, the primary active ingredient in antacid tablets such as TUMS®, can be written as

$$HCl(aq) + CO_3^{2-}(aq) \rightleftharpoons HCO_3^-(aq) + Cl^-(aq)$$

Identify the conjugate acid–base pairs in the reaction, and rewrite the arrows in the reaction to indicate if the forward or reverse reaction is favored.

🔑 KEY CONCEPT PROBLEM 10.9

From this electrostatic potential map of the amino acid alanine, identify the most acidic hydrogens in the molecule:

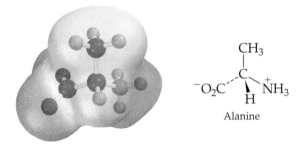

Alanine

10.5 Acid Dissociation Constants

The reaction of a weak acid with water, like any chemical equilibrium, can be described by an equilibrium equation (Section 7.8), where square brackets indicate the concentrations of the enclosed species in molarity (moles per liter).

For the reaction $HA(aq) + H_2O(l) \rightleftharpoons H_3O^+(aq) + A^-(aq)$

We have $K = \dfrac{[H_3O^+][A^-]}{[HA][H_2O]}$

Because water is a solvent as well as a participant for the reaction, its concentration is essentially constant and has no effect on the equilibrium. Therefore, we usually put the equilibrium constant K and the water concentration $[H_2O]$ together to make a new constant called the **acid dissociation constant, (K_a)**. The acid dissociation constant is simply the hydronium ion concentration $[H_3O^+]$ times the conjugate base concentration $[A^-]$ divided by the undissociated acid concentration $[HA]$:

$$\text{Acid dissociation constant}   K_a = K[H_2O] = \frac{[H_3O^+][A^-]}{[HA]}$$

Acid dissociation constant, (K_a)
The equilibrium constant for the dissociation of an acid (HA), equal to $[H^+][A^-]/[HA]$.

For a strong acid, the H_3O^+ and A^- concentrations are much larger than the HA concentration, so K_a is very large. In fact, the K_a values for strong acids such as HCl are so large that it is difficult and not very useful to measure them. For a weak acid, however, the H_3O^+ and A^- concentrations are smaller than the HA concentration, so K_a is small. Table 10.2 gives K_a values for some common acids and illustrates several important points:

- Strong acids have K_a values much greater than 1 because dissociation is favored.
- Weak acids have K_a values much less than 1 because dissociation is not favored.
- Donation of each successive H^+ from a polyprotic acid is more difficult than the one before it, so K_a values become successively lower.
- Most organic acids, which contain the $-CO_2H$ group, have K_a values near 10^{-5}.

TABLE 10.2 Some Acid Dissociation Constants, K_a, at 25 °C

Acid	K_a	Acid	K_a
Hydrofluoric acid (HF)	3.5×10^{-4}	*Polyprotic acids*	
Hydrocyanic acid (HCN)	4.9×10^{-10}	Sulfuric acid	
Ammonium ion (NH_4^+)	5.6×10^{-10}	H_2SO_4	Large
		HSO_4^-	1.2×10^{-2}
Organic acids		Phosphoric acid	
Formic acid (HCOOH)	1.8×10^{-4}	H_3PO_4	7.5×10^{-3}
Acetic acid (CH_3COOH)	1.8×10^{-5}	$H_2PO_4^-$	6.2×10^{-8}
Propanoic acid (CH_3CH_2COOH)	1.3×10^{-5}	HPO_4^{2-}	2.2×10^{-13}
		Carbonic acid	
Ascorbic acid (vitamin C)	7.9×10^{-5}	H_2CO_3	4.3×10^{-7}
		HCO_3^-	5.6×10^{-11}

PROBLEM 10.10

Benzoic acid $(C_7H_5CO_2H)$ has $K_a = 6.5 \times 10^{-5}$ and citric acid $(C_6H_8O_7)$ has $K_a = 7.2 \times 10^{-4}$. Which is the stronger conjugate base, benzoate $(C_7H_5CO_2^-)$ or citrate $(C_6H_7O_7^-)$?

10.6 Water as Both an Acid and a Base

Water is neither an acid nor a base in the Arrhenius sense because it does not contain appreciable concentrations of either H_3O^+ or OH^-. In the Brønsted–Lowry sense, however, water can act as *both* an acid and a base. When in contact with a base, water reacts as a Brønsted–Lowry acid and *donates* a proton to the base. In its reaction with ammonia, for example, water donates H^+ to ammonia to form the ammonium ion:

$$NH_3 \; + \; H_2O \; \longrightarrow \; NH_4^+ \; + \; OH^-$$

| Ammonia | Water | Ammonium ion | Hydroxide ion |
| (base) | (acid) | (acid) | (base) |

When in contact with an acid, water reacts as a Brønsted–Lowry base and *accepts* H^+ from the acid. This, of course, is exactly what happens when an acid such as HCl dissolves in water, as discussed in Section 10.1.

Water uses two electrons to form a bond to H^+.

$$H-\overset{..}{\underset{|}{\overset{}{O}}}: \; + \; H-Cl \; \longrightarrow \; H-\overset{..}{\underset{|}{\overset{+}{O}}}-H \; + \; Cl^-$$

Water (An acid) Hydronium ion
(A base)

Substances like water, which can react as either an acid or a base depending on the circumstances, are said to be **amphoteric** (am-pho-**tare**-ic). When water acts as an acid, it donates H^+ and becomes OH^-; when it acts as a base, it accepts H^+ and becomes H_3O^+. (*Note:* HCO^{3-}, H_2PO^{4-} and HPO_4^{2-} are also amphoteric.)

Amphoteric A substance that can react as either an acid or a base.

Dissociation of Water

We have seen how water can act as an acid when a base is present and as a base when an acid is present. But what about when no other acids or bases are present? In this case, one water molecule acts as an acid while another water molecule acts as a base, reacting to form the hydronium and hydroxide ions:

$$H_2O(l) \; + \; H_2O(l) \; \rightleftharpoons \; H_3O^+(aq) \; + \; OH^-(aq)$$

Because each dissociation reaction yields 1 H_3O^+ ion and 1 OH^- ion, the concentrations of the 2 ions are identical. Also, the equilibrium arrows indicate that this reaction favors reactants, so that not many H_3O^+ and OH^- ions are present at equilibrium. At 25 °C, the concentration of each is 1.00×10^{-7} M. We can write the equilibrium constant expression for the dissociation of water as

$$K = \frac{[H_3O^+][OH^-]}{[H_2O][H_2O]}$$

where $[H_3O^+] = [OH^-] = 1.00 \times 10^{-7}$ M (at 25 °C)

▶▶▶ Refer to discussion of equilibria involving pure liquids and solids in Section 7.8.

Ion-product constant for water (K_w) The product of the H_3O^+ and OH^- molar concentrations in water or any aqueous solution ($K_w = [H_3O^+][OH^-] = 1.00 \times 10^{-14}$).

As a pure substance the concentration of water is essentially constant. We can therefore put the water concentrations $[H_2O]$ together to make a new constant called the **ion-product constant for water** (K_w), which is simply the H_3O^+ concentration times the OH^- concentration. At 25 °C, $K_w = 1.00 \times 10^{-14}$.

Ion-product constant for water $K_w = K[H_2O][H_2O]$
$$= [H_3O^+][OH^-]$$
$$= 1.0 \times 10^{-14} \quad (\text{at } 25 \text{ °C})$$

The importance of the equation $K_w = [H_3O^+][OH^-]$ is that it applies to all aqueous solutions, not just to pure water. Since the product of $[H_3O^+]$ times $[OH^-]$ is always constant for any solution, we can determine the concentration of one species if we know the concentration of the other. If an acid is present in solution, for instance, so that $[H_3O^+]$ is large, then $[OH^-]$ must be small. If a base is present in solution so that $[OH^-]$ is large, then $[H_3O^+]$ must be small. For example, for a 0.10 M HCl solution, we know that $[H_3O^+] = 0.10$ M because HCl is 100% dissociated. Thus, we can calculate that $[OH^-] = 1.0 \times 10^{-13}$ M:

$$\text{Since }\; K_w \times [H_3O^+][OH^-] = 1.00 \times 10^{-14}$$

$$\text{we have }\; [OH^-] = \frac{K_w}{[H_3O^+]} = \frac{1.00 \times 10^{-14}}{0.10} = 1.0 \times 10^{-13}\text{ M}$$

Similarly, for a 0.10 M NaOH solution, we know that $[OH^-] = 0.10$ M, so $[H_3O^+] = 1.0 \times 10^{-13}$ M:

$$[H_3O^+] = \frac{K_w}{[OH^-]} = \frac{1.00 \times 10^{-14}}{0.10} = 1.0 \times 10^{-13}\text{ M}$$

Solutions are identified as acidic, neutral, or basic (*alkaline*) according to the value of their H_3O^+ and OH^- concentrations:

Acidic solution: $[H_3O^+] > 10^{-7}$ M   and $[OH^-] < 10^{-7}$ M
Neutral solution: $[H_3O^+] = 10^{-7}$ M   and $[OH^-] = 10^{-7}$ M
Basic solution: $[H_3O^+] < 10^{-7}$ M   and $[OH^-] > 10^{-7}$ M

Worked Example **10.4** Water Dissociation Constant: Using K_w to Calculate $[OH^-]$

Milk has an H_3O^+ concentration of 4.5×10^{-7} M. What is the value of $[OH^-]$? Is milk acidic, neutral, or basic?

ANALYSIS The OH^- concentration can be found by dividing K_w by $[H_3O^+]$. An acidic solution has $[H_3O^+] > 10^{-7}$ M, a neutral solution has $[H_3O^+] = 10^{-7}$ M, and a basic solution has $[H_3O^+] < 10^{-7}$ M.

BALLPARK ESTIMATE Since the H_3O^+ concentration is slightly *greater* than 10^{-7} M, the OH^- concentration must be slightly *less* than 10^{-7} M, on the order of 10^{-8}.

SOLUTION

$$[OH^-] = \frac{K_w}{[H_3O^+]} = \frac{1.00 \times 10^{-14}}{4.5 \times 10^{-7}} = 2.2 \times 10^{-8}\text{ M}$$

Milk is slightly acidic because its H_3O^+ concentration is slightly larger than 1×10^{-7} M.

BALLPARK CHECK The OH^- concentration is of the same order of magnitude as our estimate.

PROBLEM 10.11
Identify the following solutions as either acidic or basic. What is the value of $[OH^-]$ in each?
(a) Household ammonia, $[H_3O^+] = 3.1 \times 10^{-12}$ M
(b) Vinegar, $[H_3O^+] = 4.0 \times 10^{-3}$ M

10.7 Measuring Acidity in Aqueous Solution: pH

In many fields, from medicine to chemistry to winemaking, it is necessary to know the exact concentration of H_3O^+ or OH^- in a solution. If, for example, the H_3O^+ concentration in blood varies only slightly from a value of 4.0×10^{-8} M, death can result.

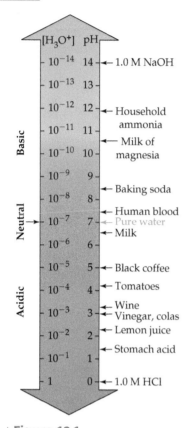

▲ Figure 10.1

The pH scale and the pH values of some common substances.

A low pH corresponds to a strongly acidic solution, a high pH corresponds to a strongly basic solution, and a pH of 7 corresponds to a neutral solution.

p function The negative common logarithm of some variable, $pX = -\log(X)$.

pH A measure of the acid strength of a solution; the negative common logarithm of the H_3O^+ concentration.

Although correct, it is nevertheless awkward or, in some instances inconvenient, to refer to low concentrations of H_3O^+ using molarity. Fortunately, there is an easier way to express and compare H_3O^+ concentrations—the *pH scale.*

The pH of an aqueous solution is a number, usually between 0 and 14, that indicates the H_3O^+ concentration of the solution. A pH smaller than 7 corresponds to an acidic solution, a pH larger than 7 corresponds to a basic solution, and a pH of exactly 7 corresponds to a neutral solution. The pH scale and pH values of some common substances are shown in Figure 10.1.

Mathematically, a **p function** is defined as the negative common logarithm of some variable. The **pH** of a solution, therefore, is the negative common logarithm of the H_3O^+ concentration:

$$\mathbf{pH} = -\log[H^+] \ (\text{or}[H_3O^+])$$

If you have studied logarithms, you may remember that the common logarithm of a number is the power to which 10 must be raised to equal the number. The pH definition can therefore be restated as

$$[H_3O^+] = 10^{-pH}$$

For example, in neutral water at 25 °C, where $[H_3O^+] = 1 \times 10^{-7}$ M, the pH is 7; in a strong acid solution where $[H_3O^+] = 1 \times 10^{-1}$ M, the pH is 1; and in a strong base solution where $[H_3O^+] = 1 \times 10^{-14}$ M, the pH is 14:

Acidic solution: pH < 7, $[H_3O^+] > 1 \times 10^{-7}$ M
Neutral solution: pH = 7, $[H_3O^+] = 1 \times 10^{-7}$ M
Basic solution: pH > 7, $[H_3O^+] < 1 \times 10^{-7}$ M

Keep in mind that the pH scale covers an enormous range of acidities because it is a *logarithmic* scale, which involves powers of 10 (Figure 10.2). A change of only 1 pH unit means a 10-fold change in $[H_3O^+]$, a change of 2 pH units means a 100-fold change in $[H_3O^+]$, and a change of 12 pH units means a change of 10^{12} (a trillion) in $[H_3O^+]$.

To get a feel for the size of the quantities involved, think of a typical backyard swimming pool, which contains about 100,000 L of water. You would have to add only 0.10 mol of HCl (3.7 g) to lower the pH of the pool from 7.0 (neutral) to 6.0, but you would have to add 10,000 mol of HCl (370 kg!) to lower the pH of the pool from 7.0 to 1.0.

The logarithmic pH scale is a convenient way of reporting the relative acidity of solutions, but using logarithms can also be useful when calculating H_3O^+ and OH^- concentrations. Remember that the equilibrium between H_3O^+ and OH^- in aqueous solutions is expressed by K_w, where

$$K_w = [H_3O^+][OH^-] = 1 \times 10^{-14} \quad (\text{at } 25 \,°C)$$

If we convert this equation to its negative logarithmic form, we obtain

$$-\log(K_w) = -\log[H_3O^+] - \log[OH^-]$$
$$-\log(1 \times 10^{-14}) = -\log[H_3O^+] - \log[OH^-]$$
$$or \quad 14.00 = pH + pOH$$

The logarithmic form of the K_w equation can simplify the calculation of solution pH from OH^- concentration, as demonstrated in Worked Example 10.7.

Worked Example 10.5 Measuring Acidity: Calculating pH from $[H_3O^+]$

The H_3O^+ concentration in coffee is about 1×10^{-5} M. What pH is this?

ANALYSIS The pH is the negative common logarithm of the H_3O^+ concentration: $pH = -\log[H_3O^+]$.

SOLUTION

Since the common logarithm of 1×10^{-5} M is -5.0, the pH is 5.0.

Worked Example 10.6 Measuring Acidity: Calculating $[H_3O^+]$ from pH

Lemon juice has a pH of about 2. What $[H_3O^+]$ is this?

ANALYSIS In this case, we are looking for the $[H_3O^+]$, where $[H_3O^+] = 10^{-pH}$.

SOLUTION
Since pH = 2.0, $[H_3O^+] = 10^{-2} = 1 \times 10^{-2}$ M.

Worked Example 10.7 Measuring Acidity: Using K_w to Calculate $[H_3O^+]$ and pH

A cleaning solution is found to have $[OH^-] = 1 \times 10^{-3}$ M. What is the pH?

ANALYSIS To find pH, we must first find the value of $[H_3O^+]$ by using the equation $[H_3O^+] = K_w/[OH^-]$. Alternatively, we can calculate the pOH of the solution and then use the logarithmic form of the K_w equation: pH = 14.00 − pOH.

SOLUTION
Rearranging the K_w equation, we have

$$[H_3O^+] = \frac{K_w}{[OH^-]} = \frac{1.00 \times 10^{-14}}{1 \times 10^{-3}} = 1 \times 10^{-11} \text{ M}$$
$$pH = -\log(1 \times 10^{-11}) = 11.0$$

Using the logarithmic form of the K_w equation, we have

$$pH = 14.0 - pOH = 14.0 - (-\log[OH^-])$$
$$pH = 14.0 - (-\log(1 \times 10^{-3}))$$
$$pH = 14.0 - 3.0 = 11.0$$

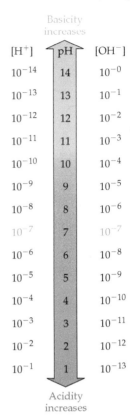

▲ **Figure 10.2**
The relationship of the pH scale to H^+ and OH^- concentrations.

Worked Example 10.8 Measuring Acidity: Calculating pH of Strong Acid Solutions

What is the pH of a 0.01 M solution of HCl?

ANALYSIS To find pH, we must first find the value of $[H_3O^+]$.

SOLUTION
Since HCl is a strong acid (Table 10.1), it is 100% dissociated, and the H_3O^+ concentration is the same as the HCl concentration: $[H_3O^+] = 0.01$ M, or 1×10^{-2} M, and pH = 2.0.

PROBLEM 10.12
Calculate the pH of the solutions in Problem 10.11.

PROBLEM 10.13
Give the hydronium ion and hydroxide ion concentrations of solutions with the following values of pH. Which of the solutions is most acidic? Which is most basic?
(a) pH 13.0   (b) pH 3.0   (c) pH 8.0

PROBLEM 10.14
Which solution would have the higher pH: 0.010 M HNO_2 or 0.010 M HNO_3? Explain.

10.8 Working with pH

Converting between pH and H_3O^+ concentration is easy when the pH is a whole number, but how do you find the H_3O^+ concentration of blood, which has a pH of 7.4, or the pH of a solution with $[H_3O^+] = 4.6 \times 10^{-3}$ M? Sometimes it is sufficient to make an estimate. The pH of blood (7.4) is between 7 and 8, so the H_3O^+ concentration of blood must be between 1×10^{-7} and 1×10^{-8} M. To be exact about finding pH values, though, requires a calculator.

Converting from pH to $[H_3O^+]$ requires finding the *antilogarithm* of the negative pH, which is done on many calculators with an "INV" key and a "log" key. Converting from $[H_3O^+]$ to pH requires finding the logarithm, which is commonly done with a "log" key and an "expo" or "EE" key for entering exponents of 10. Consult your calculator instructions if you are not sure how to use these keys. Remember that the sign of the number given by the calculator must be changed from minus to plus to get the pH.

The H_3O^+ concentration in blood with pH $= 7.4$ is

$$[H_3O^+] = \text{antilog}(-7.4) = 4 \times 10^{-8} \text{ M}$$

The pH of a solution with $[H_3O^+] = 4.6 \times 10^{-3}$ M is

$$pH = -\log(4.6 \times 10^{-3}) = -(-2.34) = 2.34$$

A note about significant figures: an antilogarithm contains the same number of significant figures as the original number has to the right of the decimal point. A logarithm contains the same number of digits to the right of the decimal point as the number of significant figures in the original number.

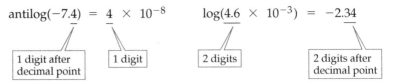

Worked Example 10.9 Working with pH: Converting a pH to $[H_3O^+]$

Soft drinks usually have a pH of approximately 3.1. What is the $[H_3O^+]$ concentration in a soft drink?

ANALYSIS To convert from a pH value to an $[H_3O^+]$ concentration requires using the equation $[H_3O^+] = 10^{-pH}$, which requires finding an antilogarithm on a calculator.

BALLPARK ESTIMATE Because the pH is between 3.0 and 4.0, the $[H_3O^+]$ must be between 1×10^{-3} and 1×10^{-4}. A pH of 3.1 is very close to 3.0, so the $[H_3O^+]$ must be just slightly below 1×10^{-3} M.

SOLUTION
Entering the negative pH on a calculator (-3.1) and pressing the "INV" and "log" keys gives the answer 7.943×10^{-4}, which must be rounded off to 8×10^{-4} because the pH has only one digit to the right of the decimal point.

BALLPARK CHECK The calculated $[H_3O^+]$ of 8×10^{-4} M is between 1×10^{-3} M and 1×10^{-4} M and, as we estimated, just slightly below 1×10^{-3} M. (Remember, 8×10^{-4} is 0.8×10^{-3}.)

Worked Example 10.10 Working with pH: Calculating pH for Strong Acid Solutions

What is the pH of a 0.0045 M solution of $HClO_4$?

ANALYSIS Finding pH requires first finding $[H_3O^+]$ and then using the equation $pH = -\log[H_3O^+]$. Since $HClO_4$ is a strong acid (see Table 10.1), it is 100% dissociated, and so the H_3O^+ concentration is the same as the $HClO_4$ concentration.

BALLPARK ESTIMATE Because $[H_3O^+] = 4.5 \times 10^{-3}$ M is close to midway between 1×10^{-2} M and 1×10^{-3} M, the pH must be close to the midway point between 2.0 and 3.0. (Unfortunately, because the logarithm scale is not linear, trying to estimate the midway point is not a simple process.)

SOLUTION
$[H_3O^+] = 0.0045$ M $= 4.5 \times 10^{-3}$ M. Taking the negative logarithm gives pH $= 2.35$.

BALLPARK CHECK The calculated pH is consistent with our estimate.

Worked Example 10.11 Working with pH: Calculating pH for Strong Base Solutions

What is the pH of a 0.0032 M solution of NaOH?

ANALYSIS Since NaOH is a strong base, the OH^- concentration is the same as the NaOH concentration. Starting with the OH^- concentration, finding pH requires either using the K_w equation to find $[H_3O^+]$ or calculating pOH and then using the logarithmic form of the K_w equation.

BALLPARK ESTIMATE Because $[OH^-] = 3.2 \times 10^{-3}$ M is close to midway between 1×10^{-2} M and 1×10^{-3} M, the pOH must be close to the midway point between 2.0 and 3.0. Subtracting the pOH from 14 would therefore yield a pH between 11 and 12.

SOLUTION
$$[OH^-] = 0.0032 \text{ M} = 3.2 \times 10^{-3} \text{ M}$$
$$[H_3O^+] = \frac{K_w}{(3.2 \times 10^{-3})} = 3.1 \times 10^{-12} \text{ M}$$

Taking the negative logarithm gives pH $= -\log(3.1 \times 10^{-12}) = 11.51$. Alternatively, we can calculate pOH and subtract from 14.00 using the logarithmic form of the K_w equation. For $[OH^-] = 0.0032$ M,
$$pOH = -\log(3.2 \times 10^{-3}) = 2.49$$
$$pH = 14.00 - 2.49 = 11.51$$

Since the given OH^- concentration included two significant figures, the final pH includes two significant figures beyond the decimal point.

BALLPARK CHECK The calculated pH is consistent with our estimate.

PROBLEM 10.15
Identify the following solutions as acidic or basic, estimate $[H_3O^+]$ and $[OH^-]$ values for each, and rank them in order of increasing acidity:
(a) Saliva, pH $= 6.5$
(b) Pancreatic juice, pH $= 7.9$
(c) Orange juice, pH $= 3.7$
(d) Wine, pH $= 3.5$

PROBLEM 10.16
Calculate the pH of the following solutions and report it to the correct number of significant figures:
(a) Seawater with $[H_3O^+] = 5.3 \times 10^{-9}$ M
(b) A urine sample with $[H_3O^+] = 8.9 \times 10^{-6}$ M

PROBLEM 10.17
What is the pH of a 0.0025 M solution of HCl?

10.9 Laboratory Determination of Acidity

Acid–base indicator A dye that changes color depending on the pH of a solution.

The pH of water is an important indicator of water quality in applications ranging from swimming pool and spa maintenance to municipal water treatment. There are several ways to measure the pH of a solution. The simplest but least accurate method is to use an **acid–base indicator**, a dye that changes color depending on the pH of the solution. For example, the well-known dye *litmus* is red below pH 4.8 but blue above pH 7.8 and the indicator *phenolphthalein* (fee-nol-**thay**-lean) is colorless below pH 8.2 but red above pH 10. To make pH determination particularly easy, test kits are available that contain a mixture of indicators known as *universal indicator* to give approximate pH measurements in the range 2–10 (Figure 10.3a). Also available are rolls of "pH paper," which make it possible to determine pH simply by putting a drop of solution on the paper and comparing the color that appears to the color on a calibration chart (Figure 10.3b).

▶ **Figure 10.3**
Finding pH.
(a) The color of universal indicator in solutions of known pH from 1 to 12. (b) Testing pH with a paper strip. Comparing the color of the strip with the code on the package gives the approximate pH.

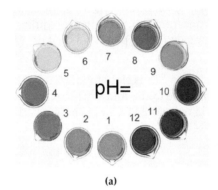

(a)

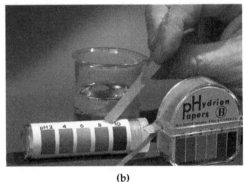

(b)

A much more accurate way to determine pH uses an electronic pH meter like the one shown in Figure 10.4. Electrodes are dipped into the solution, and the pH is read from the meter.

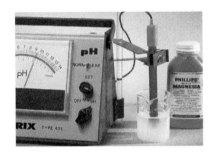

▲ **Figure 10.4**
Using a pH meter to obtain an accurate reading of pH.
Is milk of magnesia acidic or basic?

Buffer A combination of substances that act together to prevent a drastic change in pH; usually a weak acid and its conjugate base.

10.10 Buffer Solutions

Much of the body's chemistry depends on maintaining the pH of blood and other fluids within narrow limits. This is accomplished through the use of **buffers**—combinations of substances that act together to prevent a drastic change in pH.

Most buffers are mixtures of a weak acid and a roughly equal concentration of its conjugate base—for example, a solution that contains 0.10 M acetic acid and 0.10 M acetate ion. If a small amount of OH^- is added to a buffer solution, the pH increases, but not by much because the acid component of the buffer neutralizes the added OH^-. If a small amount of H_3O^+ is added to a buffer solution, the pH decreases, but again not by much because the base component of the buffer neutralizes the added H_3O^+.

To see why buffer solutions work, look at the equation for the acid dissociation constant of an acid HA.

For the reaction: $HA(aq) + H_2O(l) \rightleftharpoons A^-(aq) + H_3O^+(aq)$

we have $$K_a = \frac{[H_3O^+][A^-]}{[HA]}$$

Rearranging this equation shows that the value of $[H_3O^+]$, and thus the pH, depends on the ratio of the undissociated acid concentration to the conjugate base concentration, $[HA]/[A^-]$:

$$[H_3O^+] = K_a \frac{[HA]}{[A^-]}$$

In the case of the acetic acid–acetate ion buffer, for instance, we have

$$CH_3CO_2H(aq) + H_2O(l) \rightleftharpoons H_3O^+(aq) + CH_3CO_2^-(aq)$$
$$(0.10 \text{ M}) \qquad\qquad\qquad (0.10 \text{ M})$$

and $\quad [H_3O^+] = K_a \dfrac{[CH_3CO_2H]}{[CH_3CO_2^-]}$

Initially, the pH of the 0.10 M acetic acid–0.10 M acetate ion buffer solution is 4.74. When acid is added, most will be removed by reaction with $CH_3CO_2^-$. The equilibrium reaction shifts to the left, and as a result the concentration of CH_3CO_2H increases and the concentration of $CH_3CO_2^-$ decreases. As long as the changes in $[CH_3CO_2H]$ and $[CH_3CO_2^-]$ are relatively small, however, the ratio of $[CH_3CO_2H]$ to $[CH_3CO_2^-]$ changes only slightly, and there is little change in the pH.

When base is added to the buffer, most will be removed by reaction with CH_3CO_2H. The equilibrium shifts to the right, and so the concentration of CH_3CO_2H decreases and the concentration of $CH_3CO_2^-$ increases. Here too, though, as long as the concentration changes are relatively small, there is little change in the pH.

The ability of a buffer solution to resist changes in pH when acid or base is added is illustrated in Figure 10.5. Addition of 0.010 mol of H_3O^+ to 1.0 L of pure water changes the pH from 7 to 2, and addition of 0.010 mol of OH^- changes the pH from 7 to 12. A similar addition of acid to 1.0 L of a 0.10 M acetic acid–0.10 M acetate ion buffer, however, changes the pH from only 4.74 to 4.68, and addition of base changes the pH from only 4.74 to 4.85.

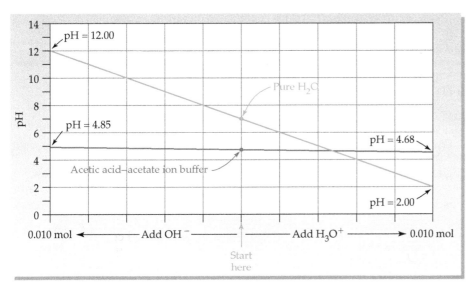

▲ **Figure 10.5**
A comparison of the change in pH.
When 0.010 mol of acid or 0.010 mol of base are added to 1.0 L of pure water and to 1.0 L of a 0.10 M acetic acid–0.10 M acetate ion buffer, the pH of the water varies between 12 and 2, while the pH of the buffer varies only between 4.85 and 4.68.

As we did with K_w, we can convert the rearranged K_a equation to its logarithmic form to obtain

$$pH = pK_a - \log\left(\frac{[HA]}{[A^-]}\right)$$

$$\text{or}\quad pH = pK_a + \log\left(\frac{[A^-]}{[HA]}\right)$$

This expression is known as the **Henderson–Hasselbalch equation** and is very useful in buffer applications, particularly in biology and biochemistry. Examination of the Henderson–Hasselbalch equation provides useful insights into how to prepare a buffer and into the factors that affect the pH of a buffer solution.

Henderson–Hasselbalch equation
The logarithmic form of the K_a equation for a weak acid, used in applications involving buffer solutions.

The effective pH range of a buffer will depend on the pK_a of the acid HA and on the relative concentrations of HA and conjugate base A^-. In general, the most effective buffers meet the following conditions:

- The pK_a for the weak acid should be close to the desired pH of the buffer solution.
- The ratio of $[HA]$ to $[A^-]$ should be close to 1, so that neither additional acid nor additional base changes the pH of the solution dramatically.
- The molar amounts of HA and A^- in the buffer should be approximately 10 times greater than the molar amounts of either acid or base you expect to add so that the ratio $[A^-]/[HA]$ does not undergo a large change.

The pH of body fluids is maintained by three major buffer systems. Two of these buffers, the carbonic acid–bicarbonate ($H_2CO_3 - HCO_3^-$) system and the dihydrogen phosphate–hydrogen phosphate ($H_2PO_4 - HPO_4^{2-}$) system, depend on weak acid–conjugate base interactions exactly like those of the acetate buffer system described previously:

$$H_2CO_3(aq) + H_2O(l) \rightleftharpoons HCO_3^-(aq) + H_3O^+(aq) \qquad pK_a = 6.37$$
$$H_2PO_4^-(aq) + H_2O(l) \rightleftharpoons HPO_4^{2-}(aq) + H_3O^+(aq) \qquad pK_a = 7.21$$

The third buffer system depends on the ability of proteins to act as either proton acceptors or proton donors at different pH values.

LOOKING AHEAD ▶▶▶ In Chapter 29, we will see how the regulation of blood pH by the bicarbonate buffer system is particularly important in preventing *acidosis* and *alkalosis*.

Worked Example 10.12 Buffers: Selecting a Weak Acid for a Buffer Solution

Which of the organic acids in Table 10.2 would be the most appropriate for preparing a pH 4.15 buffer solution?

ANALYSIS The pH of the buffer solution depends on the pK_a of the weak acid. Remember that $pK_a = -\log(K_a)$.

SOLUTION
The K_a and pK_a values for the four organic acids in Table 10.2 are tabulated below. The ascorbic acid ($pK_a = 4.10$) will produce a buffer solution closest to the desired pH of 4.15.

Organic Acid	K_a	pK_a
Formic acid (HCOOH)	1.8×10^{-4}	3.74
Acetic acid (CH_3COOH)	1.8×10^{-5}	4.74
Propanoic acid (CH_3CH_2COOH)	1.3×10^{-5}	4.89
Ascorbic acid (vitamin C)	7.9×10^{-5}	4.10

Worked Example 10.13 Buffers: Calculating the pH of a Buffer Solution

What is the pH of a buffer solution that contains 0.100 M HF and 0.120 M NaF? The K_a of HF is 3.5×10^{-4}, and so $pK_a = 3.46$.

ANALYSIS The Henderson–Hasselbalch equation can be used to calculate the pH of a buffer solution: $pH = pK_a + \log\left(\dfrac{[F^-]}{[HF]}\right)$.

BALLPARK ESTIMATE If the concentrations of F^- and HF were equal, the log term in our equation would be zero, and the pH of the solution would be equal to the pK_a for HF, which means pH = 3.46. However, since the concentration of the conjugate base ($[F^-] = 0.120$ M) is slightly higher than the concentration of the conjugate acid ($[HF] = 0.100$ M), then the pH of the buffer solution will be slightly higher (more basic) than the pK_a.

SOLUTION

$$pH = pK_a + \log\left(\frac{[F^-]}{[HF]}\right)$$

$$pH = 3.46 + \log\left(\frac{0.120}{0.100}\right) = 3.46 + 0.08 = 3.54$$

BALLPARK CHECK   The calculated pH of 3.54 is consistent with the prediction that the final pH will be slightly higher than the pK_a of 3.46.

Worked Example 10.14 Buffers: Measuring the Effect of Added Base on pH

What is the pH of 1.00 L of the 0.100 M hydrofluoric acid–0.120 M fluoride ion buffer system described in Worked Example 10.13 after 0.020 mol of NaOH is added?

ANALYSIS   Initially, the 0.100 M HF–0.120 M NaF buffer has pH $= 3.54$, as calculated in Worked Example 10.13. The added base will react with the acid as indicated in the neutralization reaction,

$$HF(aq) + OH^-(aq) \longrightarrow H_2O(l) + F^-(aq)$$

which means $[HF]$ decreases and $[F^-]$ increases. With the pK_a and the concentrations of HF and F^- known, pH can be calculated using the Henderson–Hasselbalch equation.

BALLPARK ESTIMATE   After the neutralization reaction, there is more conjugate base (F^-) and less conjugate acid (HF), and so we expect the pH to increase slightly from the initial value of 3.54.

SOLUTION
When 0.020 mol of NaOH is added to 1.00 L of the buffer, the HF concentration *decreases* from 0.100 M to 0.080 M as a result of an acid–base reaction. At the same time, the F^- concentration *increases* from 0.120 M to 0.140 M because additional F^- is produced by the neutralization. Using these new values gives

$$pH = 3.46 + \log\left(\frac{0.140}{0.080}\right) = 3.46 + 0.24 = 3.70$$

The addition of 0.020 mol of base causes the pH of the buffer to rise only from 3.54 to 3.70.

BALLPARK CHECK   The final pH, 3.70, is slightly more basic than the initial pH of 3.54, consistent with our prediction.

PROBLEM 10.18
What is the pH of 1.00 L of the 0.100 M hydrofluoric acid–0.120 M fluoride ion buffer system described in Worked Example 10.13 after 0.020 mol of HNO_3 is added?

PROBLEM 10.19
The ammonia/ammonium buffer system is sometimes used to optimize polymerase chain reactions (PCR) used in DNA studies. The equilibrium for this buffer can be written as

$$NH_4^+(aq) + H_2O(l) \rightleftharpoons H_3O^+(aq) + NH_3(aq)$$

Calculate the pH of a buffer that contains 0.050 M ammonium chloride and 0.080 M ammonia. The K_a of ammonium is 5.6×10^{-10}.

PROBLEM 10.20
What is the ratio of bicarbonate ion to carbonic acid $([HCO_3^-]/[H_2CO_3])$ in blood serum that has a pH of 7.40? (see Chemistry in Action: Buffers in the Body: Acidosis and Alkalosis on p. 312).

CHEMISTRY IN ACTION

Buffers in the Body: Acidosis and Alkalosis

A group of teenagers at a rock concert experience a collective fainting spell. A person taking high doses of aspirin for chronic pain appears disoriented and is having trouble breathing. A person with type 1 diabetes complains of tiredness and stomach pains. An athlete who recently completed a highly strenuous workout suffers from muscle cramps and nausea. A patient on an HIV drug regimen experiences increasing weakness and numbness in the hands and feet. What do all these individuals have in common? They are all suffering from abnormal fluctuations in blood pH, resulting in conditions known as *acidosis* (pH < 7.35) or *alkalosis* (pH > 7.45).

Each of the fluids in our bodies has a pH range suited to its function, as shown in the accompanying table. The stability of cell membranes, the shapes of huge protein molecules that must be folded in certain ways to function, and the activities of enzymes are all dependent on appropriate H_3O^+ concentrations. Blood plasma and the interstitial fluid surrounding cells, which together compose one-third of body fluids, have a slightly basic pH with a normal range of 7.35–7.45. The highly complex series of reactions and equilibria that take place throughout the body are very sensitive to pH—variations of even a few tenths of a pH unit can produce severe physiological symptoms.

pH of Body Fluids

Fluid	pH
Blood plasma	7.4
Interstitial fluid	7.4
Cytosol	7.0
Saliva	5.8–7.1
Gastric juice	1.6–1.8
Pancreatic juice	7.5–8.8
Intestinal juice	6.3–8.0
Urine	4.6–8.0
Sweat	4.0–6.8

Maintaining the pH of blood serum in its optimal range is accomplished by the carbonic acid–bicarbonate buffer system (Section 10.10), which depends on the relative amounts of CO_2 and bicarbonate dissolved in the blood. Because carbonic acid is unstable and therefore in equilibrium with CO_2 and water, there is an extra step in the bicarbonate buffer mechanism:

$$CO_2(aq) + H_2O(l) \rightleftharpoons$$
$$H_2CO_3(aq) \rightleftharpoons HCO_3^-(aq) + H_3O^+(aq)$$

As a result, the bicarbonate buffer system is intimately related to the elimination of CO_2, which is continuously produced in cells and transported to the lungs to be exhaled. Anything that significantly shifts the balance between dissolved CO_2 and HCO_3^- can upset these equilibria and raise or lower the pH. How does this happen, and how does the body compensate?

▲ **Hyperventilation, the rapid breathing due to excitement or stress, removes CO_2 and increases blood pH resulting in respiratory alkalosis.**

The relationships between the bicarbonate buffer system, the lungs, and the kidneys are shown in the figure on the next page. Under normal circumstances, the reactions shown in the figure are in equilibrium. Addition of excess acid (red arrows) causes formation of H_2CO_3 and results in lowering of H_3O^+ concentration. Removal of acid (blue arrows) causes formation of more H_3O^+ by dissociation of H_2CO_3. The maintenance of pH by this mechanism is supported by a reserve of bicarbonate ions in body fluids. Such a buffer can accommodate large additions of H_3O^+ before there is a significant change in the pH.

Additional backup to the bicarbonate buffer system is provided by the kidneys. Each day a quantity of acid equal to that produced in the body is excreted in the urine. In the process, the kidney returns HCO_3^- to the extracellular fluids, where it becomes part of the bicarbonate reserve.

Respiratory acidosis can be caused by a decrease in respiration, which leads to a buildup of excess CO_2 in the blood and a corresponding decrease in pH. This could be caused by a blocked air passage due to inhaled food—removal of the blockage restores normal breathing and a return to the optimal pH. *Metabolic acidosis* results from an excess of other acids in the blood that reduce the bicarbonate concentration. High doses of aspirin (acetylsalicylic acid, Section 17.5), for example, increase the hydronium ion concentration and decrease the pH. Strenuous exercise generates excess lactate in the muscles, which is released into the bloodstream (Section 23.11). The liver converts lactate into glucose, which is the body's major source of energy; this process consumes bicarbonate ions, which decreases the pH. Some HIV drug therapies can damage cellular mitochondria (Section 21.3), resulting in a buildup of lactic acid in the cells and bloodstream. In the case of a person with diabetes, lack of insulin causes the body to start burning fat, which generates ketones and keto acids (Chapter 16), organic compounds that lower the blood pH.

The body attempts to correct acidosis by increasing the rate and depth of respiration—breathing faster "blows off" CO_2, shifting the CO_2–bicarbonate equilibrium to the left and raising the pH. The net effect is rapid reversal of the acidosis.

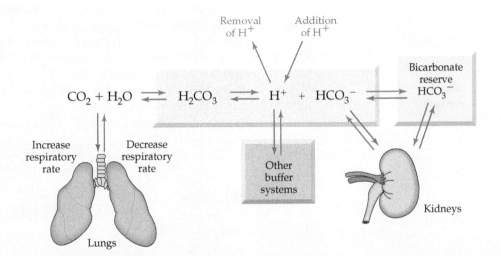

Although this may be sufficient for cases of respiratory acidosis, it provides only temporary relief for metabolic acidosis. A long-term solution depends on removal of excess acid by the kidneys, which can take several hours.

What about our teenage fans? In their excitement they have hyperventilated—their increased breathing rate has removed too much CO_2 from their blood and they are suffer-

ing from *respiratory alkalosis*. The body responds by "fainting" to decrease respiration and restore the CO_2 levels in the blood. When they regain consciousness, they will be ready to rock once again.

See Chemistry in Action Problems 10.96 and 10.97 at the end of the chapter.

🔑 KEY CONCEPT PROBLEM 10.21

A buffer solution is prepared using CN^- (from NaCN salt) and HCN in the amounts indicated. The K_a for HCN is 4.9×10^{-10}. Calculate the pH of the buffer solution.

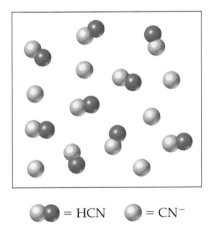

10.11 Acid and Base Equivalents

We said in Section 9.10 that it is sometimes useful to think in terms of ion *equivalents* (Eq) and *gram-equivalents* (g-Eq) when we are primarily interested in an ion itself rather than the compound that produced the ion. For similar reasons, it can also be useful to consider acid or base equivalents and gram-equivalents.

Equivalent of acid Amount of an acid that contains 1 mole of H^+ ions.

Equivalent of base Amount of base that contains 1 mole of OH^- ions.

When dealing with ions, the property of interest was the charge on the ion. Therefore, 1 Eq of an ion was defined as the number of ions that carry 1 mol of charge, and 1 g-Eq of any ion was defined as the molar mass of the ion divided by the ionic charge. For acids and bases, the property of interest is the number of H^+ ions (for an acid) or the number of OH^- ions (for a base) per formula unit. Thus, 1 **equivalent of acid** contains 1 mol of H^+ ions, and 1 g-Eq of an acid is the mass in grams that contains 1 mol of H^+ ions. Similarly, 1 **equivalent of base** contains 1 mol of OH^- ions, and 1 g-Eq of a base is the mass in grams that contains 1 mol of OH^- ions:

$$\text{One gram-equivalent of acid} = \frac{\text{Molar mass of acid (g)}}{\text{Number of } H^+ \text{ ions per formula unit}}$$

$$\text{One gram-equivalent of base} = \frac{\text{Molar mass of base (g)}}{\text{Number of } OH^- \text{ ions per formula unit}}$$

Thus 1 g-Eq of the monoprotic acid HCl is

$$1 \text{ g-Eq HCl} = \frac{36.5 \text{ g}}{1 \text{ } H^+ \text{ per HCl}} = 36.5 \text{ g}$$

which is equal to molar mass of the acid, but one gram-equivalent of the diprotic acid H_2SO_4 is

$$1 \text{ g-Eq } H_2SO_4 = \frac{98.0 \text{ g}}{2 \text{ } H^+ \text{ per } H_2SO_4} = 49.0 \text{ g}$$

which is the molar mass divided by 2, because 1 mol of H_2SO_4 contains 2 mol of H^+.

$$\text{One equivalent of } H_2SO_4 = \frac{\text{Molar mass of } H_2SO_4}{2} = \frac{98.0 \text{ g}}{2} = 49.0 \text{ g}$$

Divide by 2 because H_2SO_4 is diprotic.

Using acid–base equivalents has two practical advantages: First, they are convenient when only the acidity or basicity of a solution is of interest rather than the identity of the acid or base. Second, they show quantities that are chemically equivalent in their properties; 36.5 g of HCl and 49.0 g of H_2SO_4 are chemically equivalent quantities because each reacts with 1 Eq of base. *One equivalent of any acid neutralizes one equivalent of any base.*

Because acid–base equivalents are so useful, clinical chemists sometimes express acid and base concentrations in *normality* rather than molarity. The **normality (N)** of an acid or base solution is defined as the number of equivalents (or milliequivalents) of acid or base per liter of solution. For example, a solution made by dissolving 1.0 g-Eq (49.0 g) of H_2SO_4 in water to give 1.0 L of solution has a concentration of 1.0 Eq/L, which is 1.0 N. Similarly, a solution that contains 0.010 Eq/L of acid is 0.010 N and has an acid concentration of 10 mEq/L:

Normality (N) A measure of acid (or base) concentration expressed as the number of acid (or base) equivalents per liter of solution.

$$\text{Normality (N)} = \frac{\text{Equivalents of acid or base}}{\text{Liters of solution}}$$

The values of molarity (M) and normality (N) are the same for monoprotic acids, such as HCl, but are not the same for diprotic or triprotic acids. A solution made by diluting 1.0 g-Eq (49.0 g = 0.50 mol) of the diprotic acid H_2SO_4 to a volume of 1.0 L has a *normality* of 1.0 N but a *molarity* of 0.50 M. For any acid or base, normality is always equal to molarity times the number of H^+ or OH^- ions produced per formula unit:

Normality of acid = (Molarity of acid) × (Number of H^+ ions produced per formula unit)
Normality of base = (Molarity of base) × (Number of OH^- ions produced per formula unit)

Worked Example 10.15 Equivalents: Mass to Equivalent Conversion for Diprotic Acid

How many equivalents are in 3.1 g of the diprotic acid H_2S? The molar mass of H_2S is 34.0 g.

ANALYSIS The number of acid or base equivalents is calculated by doing a gram to mole conversion using molar mass as the conversion factor and then multiplying by the number of H^+ ions produced.

BALLPARK ESTIMATE The 3.1 g is a little less than 0.10 mol of H_2S. Since it is a diprotic acid, (two H^+ per mole), this represents a little less than 0.2 Eq of H_2S.

SOLUTION

$$(3.1 \text{ g } H_2S)\left(\frac{1 \text{ mol } H_2S}{34.0 \text{ g } H_2S}\right)\left(\frac{2 \text{ Eq } H_2S}{1 \text{ mol } H_2S}\right) = 0.18 \text{ Eq } H_2S$$

BALLPARK CHECK The calculated value of 0.18 is consistent with our prediction of a little less than 0.2 Eq of H_2S.

Worked Example 10.16 Equivalents: Calculating Equivalent Concentrations

What is the normality of a solution made by diluting 6.5 g of H_2SO_4 to a volume of 200 mL? What is the concentration of this solution in milliequivalents per liter? The molar mass of H_2SO_4 is 98.0 g.

ANALYSIS Calculate how many equivalents of H_2SO_4 are in 6.5 g by using the molar mass of the acid as a conversion factor and then determine the normality of the acid.

SOLUTION

STEP 1: **Identify known information.** We know the molar mass of H_2SO_4, the mass of H_2SO_4 to be dissolved, and the final volume of solution.

MW of H_2SO_4 = 98.0 g/mol
Mass of H_2SO_4 = 6.5 g
Volume of solution = 200 mL

STEP 2: **Identify answer including units.** We need to calculate the normality of the final solution.

Normality = ?? (equiv./L)

STEP 3: **Identify conversion factors.** We will need to convert the mass of H_2SO_4 to moles, and then to equivalents of H_2SO_4. We will then need to convert volume from mL to L.

$$(6.5 \text{ g } H_2SO_4)\left(\frac{1 \text{ mol } H_2SO_4}{98.0 \text{ g } H_2SO_4}\right)\left(\frac{2 \text{ Eq } H_2SO_4}{1 \text{ mol } H_2SO_4}\right)$$
$$= 0.132 \text{ Eq } H_2SO_4 \text{ (don't round yet!)}$$
$$(200 \text{ mL})\left(\frac{1 \text{ L}}{1000 \text{ mL}}\right) = 0.200 \text{ L}$$

STEP 4: **Solve.** Dividing the number of equivalents by the volume yields the Normality.

$$\frac{0.132 \text{ Eq } H_2SO_4}{0.200 \text{ L}} = 0.66 \text{ N}$$

The concentration of the sulfuric acid solution is 0.66 N, or 660 mEq/L.

PROBLEM 10.22
How many equivalents are in the following?
(a) 5.0 g HNO_3
(b) 12.5 g $Ca(OH)_2$
(c) 4.5 g H_3PO_4

PROBLEM 10.23
What are the normalities of the solutions if each sample in Problem 10.22 is dissolved in water and diluted to a volume of 300.0 mL?

10.12 Some Common Acid–Base Reactions

Among the most common of the many kinds of Brønsted–Lowry acid–base reactions are those of an acid with hydroxide ion, an acid with bicarbonate or carbonate ion, and an acid with ammonia or a related nitrogen-containing compound. Let us look briefly at each of the three types.

Reaction of Acids with Hydroxide Ion

One equivalent of an acid reacts with 1 Eq of a metal hydroxide to yield water and a salt in a neutralization reaction:

$$\underset{\text{(An acid)}}{HCl(aq)} + \underset{\text{(A base)}}{KOH(aq)} \longrightarrow \underset{\text{(Water)}}{H_2O(l)} + \underset{\text{(A salt)}}{KCl(aq)}$$

Such reactions are usually written with a single arrow because their equilibria lie far to the right and they have very large equilibrium constants ($K = 5 \times 10^{15}$; Section 7.8). The net ionic equation (Section 5.8) for all such reactions makes clear why acid–base equivalents are useful and why the properties of the acid and base disappear in neutralization reactions: The equivalent ions for the acid (H^+) and the base (OH^-) are used up in the formation of water.

$$H^+(aq) + OH^-(aq) \longrightarrow H_2O(l)$$

PROBLEM 10.24

Maalox, an over-the-counter antacid, contains aluminum hydroxide, $Al(OH)_3$, and magnesium hydroxide, $Mg(OH)_2$. Write balanced equations for the reaction of both with stomach acid (HCl).

Reaction of Acids with Bicarbonate and Carbonate Ion

Bicarbonate ion reacts with acid by accepting H^+ to yield carbonic acid, H_2CO_3. Similarly, carbonate ion accepts 2 protons in its reaction with acid. Carbonic acid is unstable, however, rapidly decomposing to carbon dioxide gas and water:

$$H^+(aq) + HCO_3^-(aq) \longrightarrow [H_2CO_3(aq)] \longrightarrow H_2O(l) + CO_2(g)$$
$$2\,H^+(aq) + CO_3^{2-}(aq) \longrightarrow [H_2CO_3(aq)] \longrightarrow H_2O(l) + CO_2(g)$$

Most metal carbonates are insoluble in water—marble, for example, is almost pure calcium carbonate, $CaCO_3$—but they nevertheless react easily with aqueous acid. In fact, geologists often test for carbonate-bearing rocks by putting a few drops of aqueous HCl on the rock and watching to see if bubbles of CO_2 form (Figure 10.6). This reaction is also responsible for the damage to marble and limestone artwork caused by acid rain (See Chemistry in Action: Acid Rain on p. 320). The most common application involving carbonates and acid, however, is the use of antacids that contain carbonates, such as TUMS™ or Rolaids™, to neutralize excess stomach acid.

▲ **Figure 10.6**
Marble.
Marble, which is primarily $CaCO_3$, releases bubbles of CO_2 when treated with hydrochloric acid.

PROBLEM 10.25

Write a balanced equation for each of the following reactions:
(a) $HCO_3^-(aq) + H_2SO_4(aq) \longrightarrow$?
(b) $CO_3^{2-}(aq) + HNO_3(aq) \longrightarrow$?

Reaction of Acids with Ammonia

Acids react with ammonia to yield ammonium salts, such as ammonium chloride, NH_4Cl, most of which are water-soluble:

$$NH_3(aq) + HCl(aq) \rightarrow NH_4Cl(aq)$$

Living organisms contain a group of compounds called *amines*, which contain nitrogen atoms bonded to carbon. Amines react with acids just as ammonia does, yielding water-soluble salts. Methylamine, for example, an organic compound found in rotting fish, reacts with HCl:

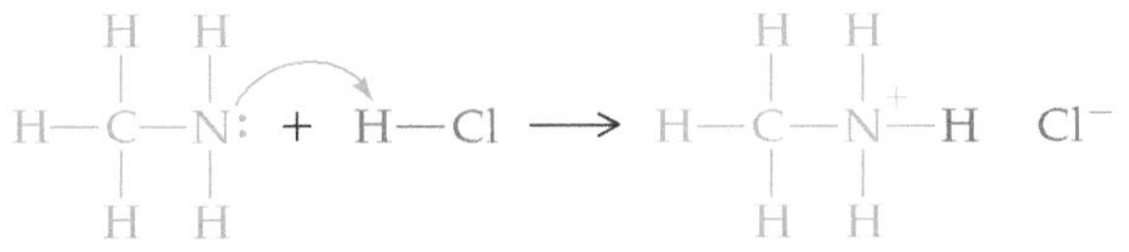

Methylamine   Methylammonium chloride

LOOKING AHEAD ▶▶▶ In Chapter 15, we will see that amines occur in all living organisms, both plant and animal, as well as in many pharmaceutical agents. Amines called amino acids form the building blocks from which proteins are made, as we will see in Chapter 18.

PROBLEM 10.26

What products would you expect from the reaction of ammonia and sulfuric acid in aqueous solution?

$$2 NH_3(aq) + H_2SO_4(aq) \longrightarrow ?$$

PROBLEM 10.27

Show how ethylamine $(C_2H_5NH_2)$ reacts with hydrochloric acid to form an ethylammonium salt.

10.13 Titration

Determining the pH of a solution gives the solution's H_3O^+ concentration but not necessarily its total acid concentration. That is because the two are not the same thing. The H_3O^+ concentration gives only the amount of acid that has dissociated into ions, whereas total acid concentration gives the sum of dissociated plus undissociated acid. In a 0.10 M solution of acetic acid, for instance, the total acid concentration is 0.10 M, yet the H_3O^+ concentration is only 0.0013 M $(pH = 2.89)$ because acetic acid is a weak acid that is only about 1% dissociated.

The total acid or base concentration of a solution can be found by carrying out a **titration** procedure, as shown in Figure 10.7. Let us assume, for instance, that we want to find the acid concentration of an HCl solution. (Likewise, we might need to find the base concentration of an NaOH solution.) We begin by measuring out a known volume of the HCl solution and adding an acid–base indicator. Next, we fill a calibrated glass tube called a *buret* with an NaOH solution of known concentration, and we slowly add the NaOH to the HCl until neutralization is complete (the *end point*), identified by a color change in the indicator.

Reading from the buret gives the volume of the NaOH solution that has reacted with the known volume of HCl. Knowing both the concentration and volume of the NaOH solution then allows us to calculate the molar amount of NaOH, and the coefficients in the balanced equation allow us to find the molar amount of HCl that has been neutralized. Dividing the molar amount of HCl by the volume of the HCl solution

Titration A procedure for determining the total acid or base concentration of a solution.

▶ **Figure 10.7**

Titration of an acid solution of unknown concentration with a base solution of known concentration.
(a) A measured volume of the acid solution is placed in the flask along with an indicator. (b) The base of known concentration is then added from a buret until the color change of the indicator shows that neutralization is complete (the *end point*).

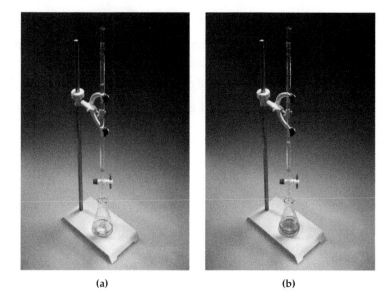

(a)   (b)

gives the concentration. The calculation thus involves mole–volume conversions just like those done in Section 9.7. Figure 10.8 shows a flow diagram of the strategy, and Worked Example 10.17 shows how to calculate total acid concentration.

When the titration involves a neutralization reaction in which one mole of acid reacts with one mole of base, such as that shown in Figure 10.8, then the moles of acid and base needed for complete reaction can be represented as

$$M_{acid} \times V_{acid} = M_{base} \times V_{base}$$

When the coefficients for the acid and base in the balanced neutralization reaction are not the same, such as in the reaction of a diprotic acid (H_2SO_4) with a monoprotic base (NaOH), then we can use equivalents of acid and base instead of moles, and Normality instead of Molarity:

$$(Eq)_{acid} = (Eq)_{base}$$
$$N_{acid} \times V_{acid} = N_{base} \times V_{base.}$$

We can convert between Normality and Molarity as described in Section 10.11.

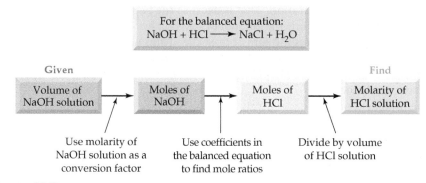

For the balanced equation:
$$NaOH + HCl \longrightarrow NaCl + H_2O$$

Given   Find

| Volume of NaOH solution | Moles of NaOH | Moles of HCl | Molarity of HCl solution |

Use molarity of NaOH solution as a conversion factor

Use coefficients in the balanced equation to find mole ratios

Divide by volume of HCl solution

▲ **Figure 10.8**

A flow diagram for an acid–base titration.
This diagram summarizes the calculations needed to determine the concentration of an HCl solution by titration with an NaOH solution of known concentration. The steps are similar to those shown in Figure 9.7.

Worked Example 10.17 Titrations: Calculating Total Acid Concentration

When a 5.00 mL sample of household vinegar (dilute aqueous acetic acid) is titrated, 44.5 mL of 0.100 M NaOH solution is required to reach the end point. What is the acid concentration of the vinegar in moles per liter, equivalents per liter, and milliequivalents per liter? The neutralization reaction is

$$CH_3CO_2H(aq) + NaOH(aq) \longrightarrow CH_3CO_2^-Na^+(aq) + H_2O(l)$$

ANALYSIS To find the molarity of the vinegar, we need to know the number of moles of acetic acid dissolved in the 5.00 mL sample. Following a flow diagram similar to Figure 10.8, we use the volume and molarity of NaOH to find the number of moles. From the chemical equation, we use the mole ratio to find the number of moles of acid, and then divide by the volume of the acid solution. Because acetic acid is a monoprotic acid, the normality of the solution is numerically the same as its molarity.

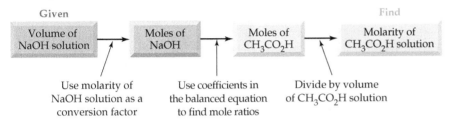

BALLPARK ESTIMATE The 5.00 mL of vinegar required nearly nine times as much NaOH solution (44.5 mL) for complete reaction. Since the neutralization stoichiometry is 1:1, the molarity of the acetic acid in the vinegar must be nine times greater than the molarity of NaOH, or approximately 0.90 M.

SOLUTION
Substitute the known information and appropriate conversion factors into the flow diagram, and solve for the molarity of the acetic acid:

$$(44.5 \text{ mL NaOH})\left(\frac{0.100 \text{ mol NaOH}}{1000 \text{ mL}}\right)\left(\frac{1 \text{ mol CH}_3CO_2H}{1 \text{ mol NaOH}}\right)$$

$$\times \left(\frac{1}{0.005\ 00 \text{ L}}\right) = 0.890 \text{ M CH}_3CO_2H$$

$$= 0.890 \text{ N CH}_3CO_2H$$

Expressed in milliequivalents, this concentration is

$$\frac{0.890 \text{ Eq}}{L} \times \frac{1000 \text{ mEq}}{1 \text{ Eq}} = 890 \text{ mEq/L}$$

BALLPARK CHECK The calculated result (0.890 M) is very close to our estimate of 0.90 M.

PROBLEM 10.28
A titration is carried out to determine the concentration of the acid in an old bottle of aqueous HCl whose label has become unreadable. What is the HCl concentration if 58.4 mL of 0.250 M NaOH is required to titrate a 20.0 mL sample of the acid?

CHEMISTRY IN ACTION

Acid Rain

As the water that evaporates from oceans and lakes condenses into raindrops, it dissolves small quantities of gases from the atmosphere. Under normal conditions, rain is slightly acidic, with a pH close to 5.6, because of atmospheric CO_2 that dissolves to form carbonic acid:

$$CO_2(aq) + H_2O(l) \rightleftharpoons$$
$$H_2CO_3(aq) \rightleftharpoons HCO_3^-(aq) + H_3O^+(aq)$$

In recent decades, however, the acidity of rainwater in many industrialized areas of the world has increased by a factor of over 100, to a pH between 3 and 3.5.

The primary cause of this so-called *acid rain* is industrial and automotive pollution. Each year, large power plants and smelters pour millions of tons of sulfur dioxide (SO_2) gas into the atmosphere, where some is oxidized by air to produce sulfur trioxide (SO_3). Sulfur oxides then dissolve in rain to form dilute sulfurous acid (H_2SO_3) and sulfuric acid (H_2SO_4):

$$SO_2(g) + H_2O(l) \longrightarrow H_2SO_3(aq)$$
$$SO_3(g) + H_2O(l) \longrightarrow H_2SO_4(aq)$$

Nitrogen oxides produced by the high-temperature reaction of N_2 with O_2 in coal-burning plants and in automobile engines further contribute to the problem. Nitrogen dioxide (NO_2) dissolves in water to form dilute nitric acid (HNO_3) and nitric oxide (NO):

$$3\,NO_2(g) + H_2O(l) \longrightarrow 2\,HNO_3(aq) + NO(g)$$

Oxides of both sulfur and nitrogen have always been present in the atmosphere, produced by such natural sources as volcanoes and lightning bolts, but their amounts have increased dramatically over the last century because of industrialization. The result is a notable decrease in the pH of rainwater in more densely populated regions, including Europe and the eastern United States.

Many processes in nature require such a fine pH balance that they are dramatically upset by the shift that has occurred in the pH of rain. Some watersheds contain soils that have high "buffering capacity" and so are able to neutralize acidic compounds in acid rain. Other areas, such as the northeastern United States and eastern Canada, where soil-buffering capacity is poor, have experienced negative ecological effects. Acid rain releases aluminum salts from soil, and the ions then wash into streams. The low pH and increased aluminum levels are so toxic to fish and other organisms that many lakes and streams in these areas are devoid of aquatic life. Massive tree die-offs have occurred throughout central and eastern Europe as acid rain has lowered the pH of the soil and has leached nutrients from leaves.

Fortunately, acidic emissions in the United States have been greatly reduced in recent years as a result of the Clean Air Act

▲ This limestone statue adorning the Rheims Cathedral in France has been severely eroded by acid rain.

Hydrogen ion concentration as pH from measurements made at the Central Analytical Laboratory, 1996

National Atmospheric Deposition Program/National Trends Network
http://nadp.sws.uiuc.edu

Hydrogen ion concentration as pH from measurements made at the Central Analytical Laboratory, 2009

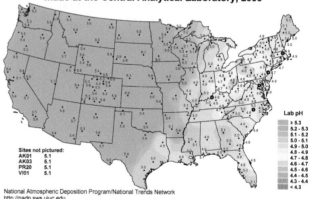

National Atmospheric Deposition Program/National Trends Network
http://nadp.sws.uiuc.edu

▲ These maps compare the average pH of precipitation in the United States in 1996 and in 2009. During this period, total acid deposition in much of the eastern United States decreased substantially.

Amendments of 1990. Industrial emissions of SO_2 and nitrogen oxides decreased by over 40% from 1990 to 2007, resulting in a decrease in acid rain depositions, particularly in the eastern United States and Canada (see accompanying figure). While significant reductions have been realized, most environmental scientists agree that additional reductions in these pollutant

emissions are necessary to ensure the recovery of affected lakes and streams.

See Chemistry in Action Problems 10.98 and 10.99 at the end of the chapter.

PROBLEM 10.29

How many milliliters of 0.150 M NaOH are required to neutralize 50.0 mL of 0.200 M H_2SO_4? The balanced neutralization reaction is:

$$H_2SO_4(aq) + 2\,NaOH(aq) \longrightarrow Na_2SO_4(aq) + 2\,H_2O(l).$$

PROBLEM 10.30

A 21.5 mL sample of a KOH solution of unknown concentration requires 16.1 mL of 0.150 M H_2SO_4 solution to reach the end point in a titration.

(a) How many moles of H_2SO_4 were necessary to reach the end point? How many equivalents?

(b) What is the molarity of the KOH solution?

PROBLEM 10.31

Titration of a 50.00 ml sample of acid rain required 9.30 mL of 0.0012 M NaOH to reach the end point. What was the total $[H_3O^+]$ in the rain sample? What was the pH? (see Chemistry in Action: Acid Rain on p. 320).

10.14 Acidity and Basicity of Salt Solutions

It is tempting to think of all salt solutions as neutral; after all, they come from the neutralization reaction between an acid and a base. In fact, salt solutions can be neutral, acidic, or basic, depending on the ions present, because some ions react with water to produce H_3O^+ and some ions react with water to produce OH^-. To predict the acidity of a salt solution, it is convenient to classify salts according to the acid and base from which they are formed in a neutralization reaction. The classification and some examples are given in Table 10.3.

TABLE 10.3 Acidity and Basicity of Salt Solutions

Anion Derived from Acid That Is:	Cation Derived from Base That Is:	Solution	Example
Strong	Weak	Acidic	NH_4Cl, NH_4NO_3
Weak	Strong	Basic	$NaHCO_3$, KCH_3CO_2
Strong	Strong	Neutral	$NaCl$, KBr, $Ca(NO_3)_2$
Weak	Weak	More information needed	

The general rule for predicting the acidity or basicity of a salt solution is that the stronger partner from which the salt is formed dominates. That is, a salt formed from a strong acid and a weak base yields an acidic solution because the strong acid dominates; a salt formed from a weak acid and a strong base yields a basic solution because the base dominates; and a salt formed from a strong acid and a strong base yields a neutral solution because neither acid nor base dominates. Here are some examples.

Salt of Strong Acid + Weak Base ⟶ Acidic Solution

A salt such as NH_4Cl, which can be formed by reaction of a strong acid (HCl) with a weak base (NH_3), yields an acidic solution. The Cl^- ion does not react with water, but the NH_4^+ ion is a weak acid that gives H_3O^+ ions:

$$NH_4^+(aq) + H_2O(l) \rightleftharpoons NH_3(aq) + H_3O^+(aq)$$

Salt of Weak Acid + Strong Base ⟶ Basic Solution

A salt such as sodium bicarbonate, which can be formed by reaction of a weak acid (H_2CO_3) with a strong base (NaOH), yields a basic solution. The Na^+ ion does not react with water, but the HCO_3^- ion is a weak base that gives OH^- ions:

$$HCO_3^-(aq) + H_2O(l) \rightleftharpoons H_2CO_3(aq) + OH^-(aq)$$

Salt of Strong Acid + Strong Base ⟶ Neutral Solution

A salt such as NaCl, which can be formed by reaction of a strong acid (HCl) with a strong base (NaOH), yields a neutral solution. Neither the Cl^- ion nor the Na^+ ion reacts with water.

Salt of Weak Acid + Weak Base

Both cation and anion in this type of salt react with water, so we cannot predict whether the resulting solution will be acidic or basic without quantitative information. The ion that reacts to the greater extent with water will govern the pH—it may be either the cation or the anion.

Worked Example 10.18 Acidity and Basicity of Salt Solutions

Predict whether the following salts produce an acidic, basic, or neutral solution:

(a) $BaCl_2$ (b) NaCN   (c) NH_4NO_3

ANALYSIS Look in Table 10.1 to see the classification of acids and bases as strong or weak.

SOLUTION

(a) $BaCl_2$ gives a neutral solution because it is formed from a strong acid (HCl) and a strong base $[Ba(OH)_2]$.

(b) NaCN gives a basic solution because it is formed from a weak acid (HCN) and a strong base (NaOH).

(c) NH_4NO_3 gives an acidic solution because it is formed from a strong acid (HNO_3) and a weak base (NH_3).

PROBLEM 10.32

Predict whether the following salts produce an acidic, basic, or neutral solution:

(a) K_2SO_4 (b) Na_2HPO_4 (c) MgF_2 (d) NH_4Br

SUMMARY: REVISITING THE CHAPTER GOALS

1. What are acids and bases? According to the *Brønsted–Lowry definition*, an acid is a substance that donates a hydrogen ion (a proton, H^+) and a base is a substance that accepts a hydrogen ion. Thus, the generalized reaction of an acid with a base involves the reversible transfer of a proton:

$$B: + H{-}A \rightleftharpoons A:^- + H{-}B^+$$

In aqueous solution, water acts as a base and accepts a proton from an acid to yield a *hydronium ion*, H_3O^+. Reaction of an acid with a metal hydroxide, such as KOH, yields water and a salt; reaction with bicarbonate ion (HCO_3^-) or carbonate ion (CO_3^{2-}) yields water, a salt, and CO_2 gas; and reaction with ammonia yields an ammonium salt (*see Problems 33, 37, 38, 42, 43, 60, 94, 100, 102*).

2. What effect does the strength of acids and bases have on their reactions? Different acids and bases differ in their ability to give up or accept a proton. A *strong acid* gives up a proton easily and is 100% *dissociated* in aqueous solution; a *weak acid* gives up a proton with difficulty, is only slightly dissociated in water, and establishes an equilibrium between dissociated and undissociated forms. Similarly, a *strong base* accepts and holds a proton readily, whereas a *weak base* has a low affinity for a proton and establishes an equilibrium in aqueous solution. The two substances that are related by the gain or loss of a proton are called a *conjugate acid–base pair*. The exact strength of an acid is defined by an *acid dissociation constant*, K_a:

For the reaction $HA + H_2O \rightleftharpoons H_3O^+ + A^-$

we have $K_a = \dfrac{[H_3O^+][A^-]}{[HA]}$

A proton-transfer reaction always takes place in the direction that favors formation of the weaker acid (*see Problems 34–36, 38–41, 44–55, 58–65, 99, 104, 108*).

3. What is the ion-product constant for water? Water is *amphoteric*; that is, it can act as either an acid or a base. Water also dissociates slightly into H_3O^+ ions and OH^- ions; the product of whose concentrations in any aqueous solution is the *ion-product constant for water*, $K_w = [H_3O^+][OH^-] = 1.00 \times 10^{-14}$ at 25 °C (*see Problems 56, 69–71, 101*).

4. What is the pH scale for measuring acidity? The acidity or basicity of an aqueous solution is given by its *pH*, defined as the negative logarithm of the hydronium ion concentration, $[H_3O^+]$. A pH below 7 means an acidic solution; a pH equal to 7 means a neutral solution; and a pH above 7 means a basic solution (*see Problems 57, 61–71, 76, 78, 94, 96–101, 104, 110*).

5. What is a buffer? The pH of a solution can be controlled through the use of a *buffer* that acts to remove either added H_3O^+ ions or added OH^- ions. Most buffer solutions consist of roughly equal amounts of a weak acid and its conjugate base. The bicarbonate buffer present in blood and the hydrogen phosphate buffer present in cells are particularly important examples (*see Problems 72–79, 105, 107*).

6. How is the acid or base concentration of a solution determined? Acid (or base) concentrations are determined in the laboratory by *titration* of a solution of unknown concentration with a base (or acid) solution of known strength until an indicator signals that neutralization is complete (*see Problems 80–93, 103, 106, 109, 110*).

CONCEPT MAP: ACIDS AND BASES

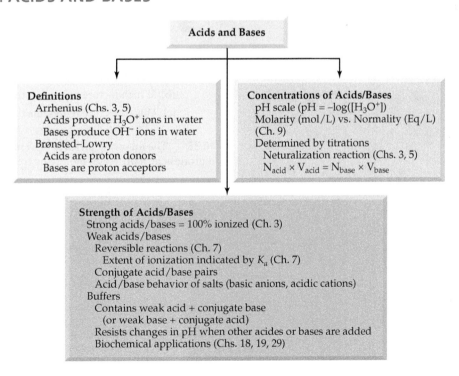

▲ **Figure 10.9**

Acids and bases play important roles in many chemical and biochemical processes, and many common substances are classified as acids or bases. Acid and base behavior is related to the ability to exchange protons, or to form H_3O^+ or OH^- ions, respectively, in water. Strong acids and bases ionize completely in aqueous solution, while weak acids/bases ionize only partially and establish an equilibrium with their conjugates. The relationship between these concepts and some of their practical and/or quantitative applications are illustrated in Figure 10.9.

KEY WORDS

Acid dissociation constant (K_a), *p. 301*

Acid–base indicator, *p. 308*

Amphoteric, *p. 302*

Brønsted–Lowry acid, *p. 293*

Brønsted–Lowry base, *p. 293*

Buffer, *p. 308*

Conjugate acid, *p. 295*

Conjugate acid–base pair, *p. 295*

Conjugate base, *p. 295*

Dissociation, *p. 296*

Equivalent of acid, *p. 314*

Equivalent of base, *p. 314*

Gram-equivalent of acid, *p. 314*

Gram-equivalent of base, *p. 314*

Henderson–Hasselbalch equation, *p. 309*

Hydronium ion, *p. 291*

Ion-product constant for water (K_w), *p. 302*

Normality (N), *p. 314*

p function, *p. 304*

pH, *p. 304*

Strong acid, *p. 296*

Strong base, *p. 297*

Titration, *p. 317*

Weak acid, *p. 296*

Weak base, *p. 297*

UNDERSTANDING KEY CONCEPTS

10.33 An aqueous solution of OH^-, represented as a blue sphere, is allowed to mix with a solution of an acid H_nA, represented as a red sphere. Three possible outcomes are depicted by boxes (1)–(3), where the green spheres represent A^{n-}, the anion of the acid:

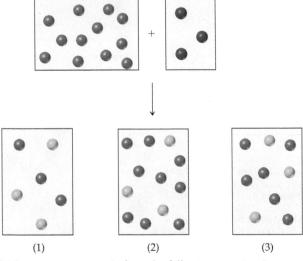

Which outcome corresponds to the following reactions?

(a) $HF + OH^- \longrightarrow H_2O + F^-$

(b) $H_2SO_3 + 2\,OH^- \longrightarrow 2\,H_2O + SO_3^{2-}$

(c) $H_3PO_4 + 3\,OH^- \longrightarrow 3\,H_2O + PO_4^{3-}$

10.34 Electrostatic potential maps of acetic acid (CH_3CO_2H) and ethyl alcohol (CH_3CH_2OH) are shown. Identify the most acidic hydrogen in each, and tell which of the two is likely to be the stronger acid.

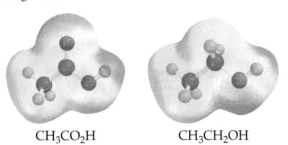

$$CH_3CO_2H \qquad CH_3CH_2OH$$

10.35 The following pictures represent aqueous acid solutions. Water molecules are not shown.

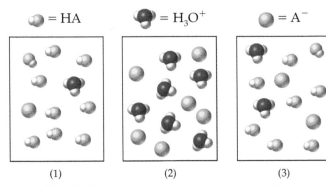

(a) Which picture represents the weakest acid?

(b) Which picture represents the strongest acid?

(c) Which picture represents the acid with the smallest value of K_a?

10.36 The following pictures represent aqueous solutions of a diprotic acid H_2A. Water molecules are not shown.

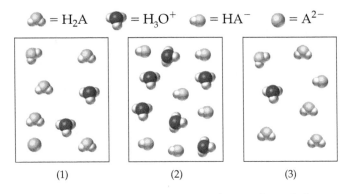

(a) Which picture represents a solution of a weak diprotic acid?

(b) Which picture represents an impossible situation?

10.37 Assume that the red spheres in the buret represent H_3O^+ ions, the blue spheres in the flask represent OH^- ions, and you are carrying out a titration of the base with the acid. If the volumes in the buret and the flask are identical and the concentration of the acid in the buret is 1.00 M, what is the concentration of the base in the flask?

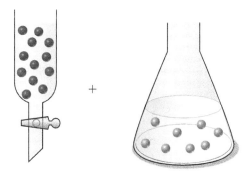

ADDITIONAL PROBLEMS

ACIDS AND BASES

10.38 What happens when a strong acid such as HBr is dissolved in water?

10.39 What happens when a weak acid such as CH_3CO_2H is dissolved in water?

10.40 What happens when a strong base such as KOH is dissolved in water?

10.41 What happens when a weak base such as NH_3 is dissolved in water?

10.42 What is the difference between a monoprotic acid and a diprotic acid? Give an example of each.

10.43 What is the difference between H^+ and H_3O^+?

10.44 Which of the following are strong acids? Look at Table 10.1 if necessary.

(a) $HClO_4$ (b) H_2CO_3 (c) H_3PO_4
(d) NH_4^+ (e) HI (f) $H_2PO_4^-$

10.45 Which of the following are weak bases? Look at Table 10.1 if necessary.

(a) NH_3 (b) $Ca(OH)_2$ (c) HPO_4^{2-}
(d) LiOH (e) CN^- (f) NH_2^-

BRØNSTED–LOWRY ACIDS AND BASES

10.46 Identify the following substances as a Brønsted–Lowry base, a Brønsted–Lowry acid, or neither:

(a) HCN (b) $CH_3CO_2^-$ (c) $AlCl_3$
(d) H_2CO_3 (e) Mg^{2+} (f) $CH_3NH_3^+$

10.47 Label the Brønsted–Lowry acids and bases in the following equations, and tell which substances are conjugate acid–base pairs.

(a) $CO_3^{2-}(aq) + HCl(aq) \longrightarrow$
$HCO_3^-(aq) + Cl^-(aq)$

(b) $H_3PO_4(aq) + NH_3(aq) \longrightarrow$
$H_2PO_4^-(aq) + NH_4^+(aq)$

(c) $NH_4^+(aq) + CN^-(aq) \rightleftharpoons NH_3(aq) + HCN(aq)$

(d) $HBr(aq) + OH^-(aq) \longrightarrow H_2O(l) + Br^-(aq)$

(e) $H_2PO_4^-(aq) + N_2H_4(aq) \rightleftharpoons$
$HPO_4^{2-}(aq) + N_2H_5^+(aq)$

10.48 Write the formulas of the conjugate acids of the following Brønsted–Lowry bases:

(a) $ClCH_2CO_2^-$ (b) C_5H_5N
(c) SeO_4^{2-} (d) $(CH_3)_3N$

10.49 Write the formulas of the conjugate bases of the following Brønsted–Lowry acids:

(a) HCN (b) $(CH_3)_2NH_2^+$
(c) H_3PO_4 (d) $HSeO_3^-$

10.50 The hydrogen-containing anions of many polyprotic acids are amphoteric. Write equations for HCO_3^- and $H_2PO_4^-$ acting as bases with the strong acid HCl and as acids with the strong base NaOH.

10.51 Write balanced equations for proton-transfer reactions between the listed pairs. Indicate the conjugate pairs, and determine the favored direction for each equilibrium.

(a) HCl and PO_4^{3-} (b) HCN and SO_4^{2-}
(c) $HClO_4$ and NO_2^- (d) CH_3O^- and HF

10.52 Sodium bicarbonate ($NaHCO_3$), also known as baking soda, is a common home remedy for acid indigestion and is also used to neutralize acid spills in the laboratory. Write a balanced chemical equation for the reaction of sodium bicarbonate with

(a) Gastric juice (HCl) (b) Sulfuric acid (H_2SO_4)

10.53 Refer to Section 10.12 to write balanced equations for the following acid–base reactions:

(a) $LiOH + HNO_3 \longrightarrow$ (b) $BaCO_3 + HI \longrightarrow$
(c) $H_3PO_4 + KOH \longrightarrow$ (d) $Ca(HCO_3)_2 + HCl \longrightarrow$
(e) $Ba(OH)_2 + H_2SO_4 \longrightarrow$

ACID AND BASE STRENGTH: K_a AND pH

10.54 How is K_a defined? Write the equation for K_a for the generalized acid HA.

10.55 Rearrange the equation you wrote in Problem 10.54 to solve for $[H_3O^+]$ in terms of K_a.

10.56 How is K_w defined, and what is its numerical value at 25 °C?

10.57 How is pH defined?

10.58 A solution of 0.10 M HCl has a pH = 1.00, whereas a solution of 0.10 M CH_3COOH has a pH = 2.88. Explain.

10.59 Calculate $[H_3O^+]$ for the 0.10 M CH_3COOH solution in Problem 10.58. What percent of the weak acid is dissociated?

10.60 Write the expressions for the acid dissociation constants for the three successive dissociations of phosphoric acid, H_3PO_4, in water.

10.61 Based on the K_a values in Table 10.1, rank the following solutions in order of increasing pH: 0.10 M HCOOH, 0.10 M HF, 0.10 M H_2CO_3, 0.10 M HSO_4^-, 0.10 M NH_4^+.

10.62 The electrode of a pH meter is placed in a sample of urine, and a reading of 7.9 is obtained. Is the sample acidic, basic, or neutral? What is the concentration of H_3O^+ in the urine sample?

10.63 A 0.10 M solution of the deadly poison hydrogen cyanide, HCN, has a pH of 5.2. Calculate the $[H_3O^+]$ of the solution. Is HCN a strong or a weak acid?

10.64 Human sweat can have a pH ranging from 4.0–6.8. Calculate the range of $[H_3O^+]$ in normal human sweat. How many orders of magnitude does this range represent?

10.65 Saliva has a pH range of 5.8–7.1. Approximately what is the H_3O^+ concentration range of saliva?

10.66 What is the approximate pH of a 0.02 M solution of a strong monoprotic acid? Of a 0.02 M solution of a strong base, such as KOH?

10.67 Calculate the pOH of each solution in Problems 10.62–10.65.

10.68 Without using a calculator, match the H_3O^+ concentrations of the following solutions, (a)–(d), to the corresponding pH, i–iv:

(a) Fresh egg white: $[H_3O^+] = 2.5 \times 10^{-8}$ M
(b) Apple cider: $[H_3O^+] = 5.0 \times 10^{-4}$ M
(c) Household ammonia: $[H_3O^+] = 2.3 \times 10^{-12}$ M
(d) Vinegar (acetic acid): $[H_3O^+] = 4.0 \times 10^{-3}$ M

i. pH = 3.30   ii. pH = 2.40   iii. pH = 11.64   iv. pH = 7.60

10.69 What are the OH^- concentration and pOH for each solution in Problem 10.68? Rank the solutions according to increasing acidity.

10.70 What are the H_3O^+ and OH^- concentrations of solutions that have the following pH values?

(a) pH 4   (b) pH 11   (c) pH 0
(d) pH 1.38   (e) pH 7.96

10.71 About 12% of the acid in a 0.10 M solution of a weak acid dissociates to form ions. What are the H_3O^+ and OH^- concentrations? What is the pH of the solution?

BUFFERS

10.72 What are the two components of a buffer system? How does a buffer work to hold pH nearly constant?

10.73 Which system would you expect to be a better buffer: $HNO_3 + Na^+NO_3^-$, or $CH_3CO_2H + CH_3CO_2^-Na^+$? Explain.

10.74 The pH of a buffer solution containing 0.10 M acetic acid and 0.10 M sodium acetate is 4.74.

(a) Write the Henderson–Hasselbalch equation for this buffer.
(b) Write the equations for reaction of this buffer with a small amount of HNO_3 and with a small amount of NaOH.

10.75 Which of the following buffer systems would you use if you wanted to prepare a solution having a pH of approximately 9.5?

(a) 0.08 M $H_2PO_4^-$ / 0.12 M HPO_4^{2-}
(b) 0.08 M NH_4^+ / 0.12 M NH_3

10.76 What is the pH of a buffer system that contains 0.200 M hydrocyanic acid (HCN) and 0.150 M sodium cyanide (NaCN)? The pK_a of hydrocyanic acid is 9.31.

10.77 Consider 1.00 L of the buffer system described in Problem 10.76.

(a) What are the $[HCN]$ and $[CN^-]$ after 0.020 mol of HCl is added? What is the pH?
(b) What are the $[HCN]$ and $[CN^-]$ after 0.020 mol of NaOH is added? What is the pH?

10.78 What is the pH of a buffer system that contains 0.15 M NH_4^+ and 0.10 M NH_3? The pK_a of NH_4^+ is 9.25.

10.79 How many moles of NaOH must be added to 1.00 L of the solution described in Problem 10.78 to increase the pH to 9.25? (Hint: What is the $[NH_3]/[NH_4^+]$ when the pH = pK_a?)

CONCENTRATIONS OF ACID AND BASE SOLUTIONS

10.80 What does it mean when we talk about acid *equivalents* and base *equivalents*?

10.81 How does normality compare to molarity for monoprotic and polyprotic acids??

10.82 Calculate the gram-equivalent for each of the following acids and bases.

(a) HNO_3 (b) H_3PO_4 (c) KOH   (d) $Mg(OH)_2$

10.83 What mass of each of the acids and bases in Problem 10.82 is needed to prepare 500 mL of 0.15 N solution?

10.84 How many milliliters of 0.0050 N KOH are required to neutralize 25 mL of 0.0050 N H_2SO_4? To neutralize 25 mL of 0.0050 M H_2SO_4?

10.85 How many equivalents are in 75.0 mL of 0.12 M H_2SO_4 solution? In 75.0 mL of a 0.12 M H_3PO_4 solution?

10.86 How many equivalents of an acid or base are in the following?

(a) 0.25 mol $Mg(OH)_2$
(b) 2.5 g $Mg(OH)_2$
(c) 15 g CH_3CO_2H

10.87 What mass of citric acid (triprotic, $C_6H_5O_7H_3$) contains 152 mEq of citric acid?

10.88 What are the molarity and the normality of a solution made by dissolving 5.0 g of $Ca(OH)_2$ in enough water to make 500.0 mL of solution?

10.89 What are the molarity and the normality of a solution made by dissolving 25 g of citric acid (triprotic, $C_6H_5O_7H_3$) in enough water to make 800 mL of solution?

10.90 Titration of a 12.0 mL solution of HCl requires 22.4 mL of 0.12 M NaOH. What is the molarity of the HCl solution?

10.91 How many equivalents are in 15.0 mL of 0.12 M $Ba(OH)_2$ solution? What volume of 0.085 M HNO_3 is required to reach the end point when titrating 15.0 mL of this solution?

10.92 Titration of a 10.0 mL solution of KOH requires 15.0 mL of 0.0250 M H_2SO_4 solution. What is the molarity of the KOH solution?

10.93 If 35.0 mL of a 0.100 N acid solution is needed to reach the end point in titration of 21.5 mL of a base solution, what is the normality of the base solution?

CHEMISTRY IN ACTION

10.94 The concentration of HCl when released to the stomach cavity is diluted to between 0.01 and 0.001 M [*GERD—Too Much Acid or Not Enough? p. 299*]

(a) What is the pH range in the stomach cavity?

(b) Write a balanced equation for the neutralization of stomach acid by $NaHCO_3$.

(c) How many grams of $NaHCO_3$ are required to neutralize 15.0 mL of a solution having a pH of 1.8?

10.95 What are the functions of the acidic gastric juices in the stomach? [*GERD—Too Much Acid or Not Enough? p. 299*]

10.96 Metabolic acidosis is often treated by administering bicarbonate intravenously. Explain how this treatment can increase blood serum pH. [*Buffers in the Body: Acidosis and Alkalosis, p. 312*]

10.97 Which body fluid is most acidic? Which is most basic? [*Buffers in the Body: Acidosis and Alkalosis, p. 312*]

10.98 Rain typically has a pH of about 5.6. What is the H_3O^+ concentration in rain? [*Acid Rain, p. 320*]

10.99 Acid rain with a pH as low as 1.5 has been recorded in West Virginia. [*Acid Rain, p. 320*]

(a) What is the H_3O^+ concentration in this acid rain?

(b) How many grams of HNO_3 must be dissolved to make 25 L of solution that has a pH of 1.5?

GENERAL QUESTIONS AND PROBLEMS

10.100 A solution is prepared by bubbling 15.0 L of HCl(*g*) at 25 °C and 1 atm into 250.0 mL of water.

(a) Assuming all the HCl dissolves in the water, how many moles of HCl are in solution?

(b) What is the pH of the solution?

10.101 The dissociation of water into H_3O^+ and OH^- ions depends on temperature. At 0 °C the $[H_3O^+] = 3.38 \times 10^{-8}$ M, at 25 °C the $[H_3O^+] = 1.00 \times 10^{-7}$ M, and at 50 °C the $[H_3O^+] = 2.34 \times 10^{-7}$ M.

(a) Calculate the pH of water at 0 °C and 50 °C.

(b) What is the value of K_w at 0 °C and 50 °C?

(c) Is the dissociation of water endothermic or exothermic?

10.102 Alka-Seltzer™, a drugstore antacid, contains a mixture of $NaHCO_3$, aspirin, and citric acid, $C_6H_5O_7H_3$. Why does Alka-Seltzer™ foam and bubble when dissolved in water? Which ingredient is the antacid?

10.103 How many milliliters of 0.50 M NaOH solution are required to titrate 40.0 mL of a 0.10 M H_2SO_4 solution to an end point?

10.104 Which solution contains more acid, 50 mL of a 0.20 N HCl solution or 50 mL of a 0.20 N acetic acid solution? Which has a higher hydronium ion concentration? Which has a lower pH?

10.105 One of the buffer systems used to control the pH of blood involves the equilibrium between $H_2PO_4^-$ and HPO_4^{2-}. The pK_a for $H_2PO_4^-$ is 7.21.

(a) Write the Henderson–Hasselbalch equation for this buffer system.

(b) What HPO_4^{2-} to $H_2PO_4^-$ ratio is needed to maintain the optimum blood pH of 7.40?

10.106 A 0.15 N solution of HCl is used to titrate 30.0 mL of a $Ca(OH)_2$ solution of unknown concentration. If 140.0 mL of HCl is required, what is the normality of the $Ca(OH)_2$ solution? What is the molarity?

10.107 Which of the following combinations produces an effective buffer solution? Assuming equal concentrations of each acid and its conjugate base, calculate the pH of each buffer solution.

(a) NaF and HF

(b) $HClO_4$ and $NaClO_4$

(c) NH_4Cl and NH_3

(d) KBr and HBr

10.108 One method of analyzing ammonium salts is to treat them with NaOH and then heat the solution to remove the NH_3 gas formed.

$$NH_4^+(aq) + OH^-(aq) \longrightarrow NH_3(g) + H_2O(l)$$

(a) Label the Brønsted–Lowry acid–base pairs.

(b) If 2.86 L of NH_3 at 60 °C and 755 mmHg is produced by the reaction of NH_4Cl, how many grams of NH_4Cl were in the original sample?

10.109 One method of reducing acid rain is "scrubbing" the combustion products before they are emitted from power plant smoke stacks. The process involves addition of an aqueous suspension of lime (CaO) to the combustion chamber and stack, where the lime reacts with SO_2 to give calcium sulfite ($CaSO_3$):

$$CaO(aq) + SO_2(g) \longrightarrow CaSO_3(aq)$$

(a) How much lime (in g) is needed to remove 1 mol of SO_2?

(b) How much lime (in kg) is needed to remove 1 kg of SO_2?

10.110 Sodium oxide, Na_2O, reacts with water to give NaOH.

(a) Write a balanced equation for the reaction.

(b) What is the pH of the solution prepared by allowing 1.55 g of Na_2O to react with 500.0 mL of water? Assume that there is no volume change.

(c) How many milliliters of 0.0100 M HCl are needed to neutralize the NaOH solution prepared in (b)?

Nuclear Chemistry

CONTENTS

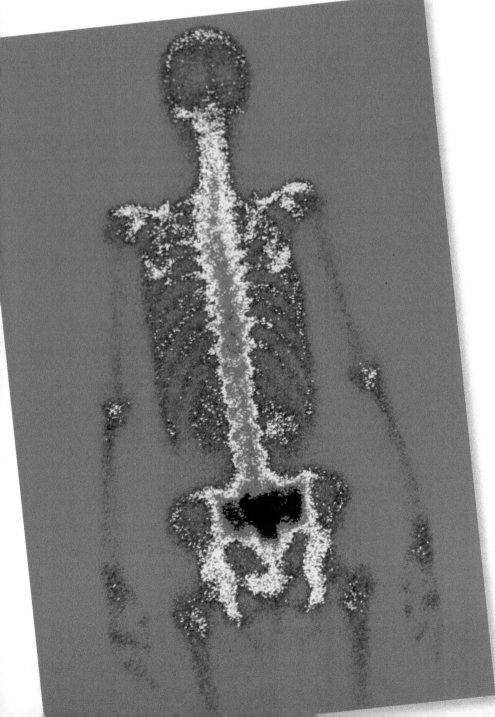

◄ Many medical diagnostic techniques, including this total body bone scan, take advantage of the properties of radioactive isotopes.

CHAPTER GOALS

1. **What is a nuclear reaction, and how are equations for nuclear reactions balanced?**
   THE GOAL: Be able to write and balance equations for nuclear reactions. (◄◄◄ A, B, C.)

2. **What are the different kinds of radioactivity?**
   THE GOAL: Be able to list the characteristics of three common kinds of radiation—$\alpha, \beta,$ and γ (alpha, beta, and gamma).

3. **How are the rates of nuclear reactions expressed?**
   THE GOAL: Be able to explain half-life and calculate the quantity of a radioisotope remaining after a given number of half-lives.

4. **What is ionizing radiation?**
   THE GOAL: Be able to describe the properties of the different types of ionizing radiation and their potential for harm to living tissue.

5. **How is radioactivity measured?**
   THE GOAL: Be able to describe the common units for measuring radiation.

6. **What is transmutation?**
   THE GOAL: Be able to explain nuclear bombardment and balance equations for nuclear bombardment reactions. (◄◄◄ A, B, and C.)

7. **What are nuclear fission and nuclear fusion?**
   THE GOAL: Be able to explain nuclear fission and nuclear fusion.

In all of the reactions we have discussed thus far, only the *bonds* between atoms have changed; the chemical identities of atoms themselves have remained unchanged. Anyone who reads the paper or watches television knows, however, that atoms *can* change, often resulting in the conversion of one element into another. Atomic weapons, nuclear energy, and radioactive radon gas in our homes are all topics of societal importance, and all involve *nuclear chemistry*—the study of the properties and reactions of atomic nuclei.

11.1 Nuclear Reactions

Recall from Section 2.2 that an atom is characterized by its *atomic number, Z,* and its *mass number, A*. The atomic number, written below and to the left of the element symbol, gives the number of protons in the nucleus and identifies the element. The mass number, written above and to the left of the element symbol, gives the total number of **nucleons**, a general term for both protons (p) and neutrons (n). The most common isotope of carbon, for example, has 12 nucleons: 6 protons and 6 neutrons: $^{12}_{6}C$.

Nucleon A general term for both protons and neutrons.

Mass number $\longrightarrow$ $^{12}_{6}C$ $\longleftarrow$ 6 protons

Atomic number $\longrightarrow$ Carbon-12 6 neutrons / 12 nucleons

Atoms with identical atomic numbers but different mass numbers are called *isotopes*, and the nucleus of a specific isotope is called a **nuclide**. Thirteen isotopes of carbon are known—two occur commonly (^{12}C and ^{13}C) and one (^{14}C) is produced in small amounts in the upper atmosphere by the action of neutrons from cosmic rays on ^{14}N. The remaining 10 carbon isotopes have been produced artificially. Only the two commonly occurring isotopes are stable indefinitely; the others undergo spontaneous **nuclear reactions**, which change their nuclei. Carbon-14, for example, is an unstable isotope that slowly decomposes and is converted to nitrogen-14 plus an electron, a process we can write as

$$^{14}_{6}C \longrightarrow {}^{14}_{7}N + {}^{0}_{-1}e$$

The electron is often written as $^{0}_{-1}e$, where the superscript 0 indicates that the mass of an electron is essentially zero when compared with that of a proton or neutron, and the subscript -1 indicates that the charge is -1. (The subscript in this instance is not

▶▶ The different isotopes of an atom each have the same number of protons and only differ in their number of neutrons (Section 2.3).

Nuclide The nucleus of a specific isotope of an element.

Nuclear reaction A reaction that changes an atomic nucleus, usually causing the change of one element into another.

329

a true atomic number; in Section 11.4 the purpose of representing the electron this way will become clear.)

Nuclear reactions, such as the spontaneous decay of ^{14}C, are distinguished from chemical reactions in several ways:

- A *nuclear* reaction involves a change in an atom's nucleus, usually producing a different element. A *chemical* reaction, by contrast, involves only a change in distribution of the outer-shell electrons around the atom and never changes the nucleus itself or produces a different element.
- Different isotopes of an element have essentially the same behavior in chemical reactions but often have completely different behavior in nuclear reactions.
- The rate of a nuclear reaction is unaffected by a change in temperature or pressure or by the addition of a catalyst.
- The nuclear reaction of an atom is essentially the same whether it is in a chemical compound or in an uncombined, elemental form.
- The energy change accompanying a nuclear reaction can be up to several million times greater than that accompanying a chemical reaction. The nuclear transformation of 1.0 g of uranium-235 releases 3.4×10^8 kcal (1.4×10^9 kJ), for example, whereas the chemical combustion of 1.0 g of methane releases only 12 kcal (50 kJ).

11.2 The Discovery and Nature of Radioactivity

The discovery of *radioactivity* dates to the year 1896 when the French physicist Henri Becquerel made a remarkable observation. While investigating the nature of phosphorescence—the luminous glow of some minerals and other substances that remains when the light is suddenly turned off—Becquerel happened to place a sample of a uranium-containing mineral on top of a photographic plate that had been wrapped in black paper and put in a drawer to protect it from sunlight. On developing the plate, Becquerel was surprised to find a silhouette of the mineral. He concluded that the mineral was producing some kind of unknown radiation, which passed through the paper and exposed the photographic plate.

Radioactivity The spontaneous emission of radiation from a nucleus.

Marie Sklodowska Curie and her husband, Pierre, took up the challenge and began a series of investigations into this new phenomenon, which they termed **radioactivity**. They found that the source of the radioactivity was the element uranium (U) and that two previously unknown elements, which they named polonium (Po) and radium (Ra), were also radioactive. For these achievements, Becquerel and the Curies shared the 1903 Nobel Prize in physics.

Further work on radioactivity by the English scientist Ernest Rutherford established that there were at least two types of radiation, which he named *alpha* (α) and *beta* (β) after the first two letters of the Greek alphabet. Shortly thereafter, a third type of radiation was found and named for the third Greek letter, *gamma* (γ).

Subsequent studies showed that when the three kinds of radiation are passed between two plates with opposite electrical charges, each is affected differently. Alpha radiation bends toward the negative plate and must therefore have a positive charge. Beta radiation, by contrast, bends toward the positive plate and must have a negative charge, whereas gamma radiation does not bend toward either plate and has no charge (Figure 11.1).

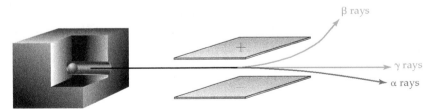

▲ **Figure 11.1**
The effect of an electric field on α, β, and γ, radiation.
The radioactive source in the shielded box emits radiation, which passes between the two electrically charged plates. Alpha radiation is deflected toward the negative plate, β radiation is deflected toward the positive plate, and γ radiation is not deflected.

Another difference among the three kinds of radiation soon became apparent when it was discovered that alpha and beta radiations are composed of small particles with a measurable mass, whereas **gamma (γ) radiation** consists of high-energy electromagnetic waves and has no mass. Rutherford was able to show that a **beta (β) particle** is an electron (e^-) and that an **alpha (α) particle** is actually a helium nucleus, He^{2+}. (Recall that a helium *atom* consists of two protons, two neutrons, and two electrons. When the two electrons are removed, the remaining helium nucleus, or α particle, has only the two protons and two neutrons.)

Yet a third difference among the three kinds of radiation is their penetrating power. Because of their relatively large mass, α particles move slowly (up to about $1/10$ the speed of light) and can be stopped by a few sheets of paper or by the top layer of skin. Beta particles, because they are much lighter, move at up to $9/10$ the speed of light and have about 100 times the penetrating power of α particles. A block of wood or heavy protective clothing is necessary to stop β radiation, which can otherwise penetrate the skin and cause burns and other damage. Gamma rays move at the speed of light $(3.00 \times 10^8 \, m/s)$ and have about 1000 times the penetrating power of α particles. A lead block several inches thick is needed to stop γ radiation, which can otherwise penetrate and damage the body's internal organs.

The characteristics of the three kinds of radiation are summarized in Table 11.1. Note that an α particle, even though it is an ion with a $+2$ charge, is usually written using the symbol ^4_2He without the charge. A β particle is usually written $^0_{-1}e$, as noted previously.

Gamma (γ) radiation Radioactivity consisting of high-energy light waves.

▶ ▶ See Chemistry in Action: Atoms and Light on p. 66 in Chapter 2 for a discussion of gamma rays and the rest of the electromagnetic spectrum.

Beta (β) particle An electron (e^-), emitted as radiation.

Alpha (α) particle A helium nucleus (He^{2+}), emitted as α radiation.

TABLE 11.1 Characteristics of α, β, and γ Radiation

Type of Radiation	Symbol	Charge	Composition	Mass (AMU)	Velocity	Relative Penetrating Power
Alpha	α, ^4_2He	+2	Helium nucleus	4	Up to 10% speed of light	Low (1)
Beta	β, $^0_{-1}e$	−1	Electron	1/1823	Up to 90% speed of light	Medium (100)
Gamma	γ, $^0_0\gamma$	0	High-energy radiation	0	Speed of light $(3.00 \times 10^8 \, m/s)$	High (1000)

11.3 Stable and Unstable Isotopes

Every element in the periodic table has at least one radioactive isotope, or **radioisotope**, and more than 3300 radioisotopes are known. Their radioactivity is the result of having unstable nuclei, although the exact causes of this instability are not fully understood. Radiation is emitted when an unstable radioactive nucleus, or **radionuclide**, spontaneously changes into a more stable one.

For elements in the first few rows of the periodic table, stability is associated with a roughly equal number of neutrons and protons (Figure 11.2). Hydrogen, for example, has stable ^1_1H (protium) and ^2_1H (deuterium) isotopes, but its ^3_1H isotope (tritium) is radioactive. As elements get heavier, the number of neutrons relative to protons in stable nuclei increases. Lead-208 $\left(^{208}_{82}Pb\right)$, for example, the most abundant stable isotope of lead, has 126 neutrons and 82 protons in its nuclei. Nevertheless, of the 35 known isotopes of lead, only 3 are stable whereas 32 are radioactive. In fact, there are only 264 stable isotopes among all the elements. All isotopes of elements with atomic numbers higher than that of bismuth (83) are radioactive.

Most of the more than 3300 known radioisotopes have been made in high-energy particle accelerators by reactions that will be described in Section 11.10. Such isotopes are called *artificial radioisotopes* because they are not found in nature. All isotopes of the transuranium elements (those heavier than uranium) are artificial. The much smaller number of radioactive isotopes found in Earth's crust, such as $^{238}_{92}U$, are called *natural radioisotopes*.

Radioisotope A radioactive isotope.

Radionuclide The nucleus of a radioactive isotope.

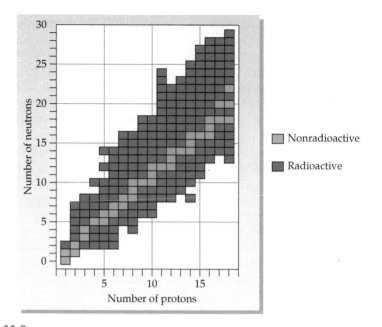

▲ **Figure 11.2**

A plot of the numbers of neutrons and protons for known isotopes of the first 18 elements. Stable (nonradioactive) isotopes of these elements have equal or nearly equal numbers of neutrons and protons.

Aside from their radioactivity, different radioisotopes of the same element have the same chemical properties as stable isotopes, which accounts for their great usefulness as *tracers*. A chemical compound tagged with a radioactive atom undergoes exactly the same reactions as its nonradioactive counterpart. The difference is that the tagged compound can be located with a radiation detector and its location determined, as discussed in Chemistry in Action: Body Imaging on page 348.

11.4 Nuclear Decay

Think for a minute about the consequences of α and β radiation. If radioactivity involves the spontaneous emission of a small particle from an unstable atomic nucleus, then the nucleus itself must undergo a change. With that understanding of radioactivity came the startling discovery that atoms of one element can change into atoms of another element, something that had previously been thought impossible. The spontaneous emission of a particle from an unstable nucleus is called **nuclear decay**, or *radioactive decay*, and the resulting change of one element into another is called **transmutation**.

Nuclear decay The spontaneous emission of a particle from an unstable nucleus.

Transmutation The change of one element into another.

> **Nuclear decay:** Radioactive element $\longrightarrow$ New element + Emitted particle

We now look at what happens to a nucleus when nuclear decay occurs.

Alpha Emission

When an atom of uranium-238 ($^{238}_{92}U$) emits an α particle, the nucleus loses 2 protons and 2 neutrons. Because the number of protons in the nucleus has now changed from 92 to 90, the *identity* of the atom has changed from uranium to thorium. Furthermore, since the total number of nucleons has decreased by 4, uranium-238 has become thorium-234 ($^{234}_{90}Th$) (Figure 11.3).

Note that the equation for a nuclear reaction is not balanced in the usual chemical sense because the kinds of atoms are not the same on both sides of the arrow. Instead, we say that a nuclear equation is balanced when the number of nucleons on both sides of the equation is the same and when the sums of the charges on the nuclei plus any ejected subatomic particles (protons or electrons) are the same on both sides of the

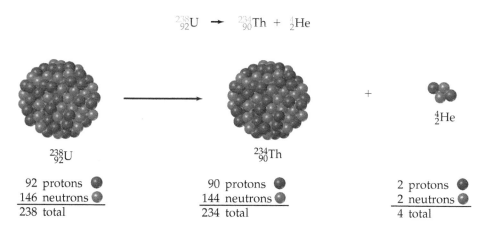

$$^{238}_{92}\text{U} \longrightarrow {}^{234}_{90}\text{Th} + {}^4_2\text{He}$$

$^{238}_{92}\text{U}$

92 protons	90 protons	2 protons
146 neutrons	144 neutrons	2 neutrons
238 total	234 total	4 total

$^{234}_{90}\text{Th}$

^4_2He

equation. In the decay of $^{238}_{92}\text{U}$ to give ^4_2He and $^{234}_{90}\text{Th}$, for example, there are 238 nucleons and 92 nuclear charges on both sides of the nuclear equation.

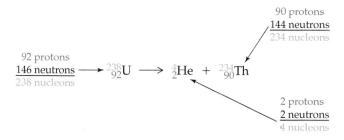

Worked Example 11.1 Balancing Nuclear Reactions: Alpha Emission

Polonium-208 is one of the α emitters studied by Marie Curie. Write the equation for the α decay of polonium-208, and identify the element formed.

ANALYSIS Look up the atomic number of polonium (84) in the periodic table, and write the known part of the nuclear equation, using the standard symbol for polonium-208:

$$^{208}_{84}\text{Po} \longrightarrow {}^4_2\text{He} + ?$$

Then, calculate the mass number and atomic number of the product element, and write the final equation.

SOLUTION
The mass number of the product is $208 - 4 = 204$, and the atomic number is $84 - 2 = 82$. A look at the periodic table identifies the element with atomic number 82 as lead (Pb).

$$^{208}_{84}\text{Po} \longrightarrow {}^4_2\text{He} + {}^{204}_{82}\text{Pb}$$

Check your answer by making sure that the mass numbers and atomic numbers on the two sides of the equation are balanced:

Mass numbers: $208 = 4 + 204$ Atomic numbers: $84 = 2 + 82$

PROBLEM 11.1
High levels of radioactive radon-222 ($^{222}_{86}\text{Rn}$) have been found in many homes built on radium-containing rock, leading to the possibility of health hazards. What product results from α emission by radon-222?

PROBLEM 11.2
What isotope of radium (Ra) is converted into radon-222 by α emission?

Beta Emission

Whereas α emission leads to the loss of two protons and two neutrons from the nucleus, β emission involves the *decomposition* of a neutron to yield an electron and a proton. This process can be represented as

$$^1_0n \longrightarrow {}^1_1p + {}^{\;0}_{-1}e$$

where the electron $\left({}^{\;0}_{-1}e\right)$ is ejected as a β particle, and the proton is retained by the nucleus. Note that the electrons emitted during β radiation come from the *nucleus* and not from the occupied orbitals surrounding the nucleus. The decomposition of carbon-14 to form nitrogen-14 in Section 11.1 is an example of beta decay.

The net result of β emission is that the atomic number of the atom *increases* by 1 because there is a new proton. The mass number of the atom remains the same, however, because a neutron has changed into a proton, leaving the total number of nucleons unchanged. For example, iodine-131 $\left({}^{131}_{53}I\right)$, a radioisotope used in detecting thyroid problems, undergoes nuclear decay by β emission to yield xenon-131 $\left({}^{131}_{54}Xe\right)$:

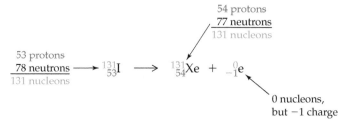

Note that the superscripts (mass numbers) are balanced in this equation because a β particle has a mass near zero, and the subscripts are balanced because a β particle has a charge of -1.

Worked Example 11.2 Balancing Nuclear Reactions: Beta Emission

Write a balanced nuclear equation for the β decay of chromium-55.

ANALYSIS Write the known part of the nuclear equation:

$$^{55}_{24}Cr \longrightarrow {}^{\;0}_{-1}e + ?$$

Then calculate the mass number and atomic number of the product element, and write the final equation.

SOLUTION
The mass number of the product stays at 55, and the atomic number increases by 1, $24 + 1 = 25$, so the product is manganese-55.

$$^{55}_{24}Cr \longrightarrow {}^{\;0}_{-1}e + {}^{55}_{25}Mn$$

Check your answer by making sure that the mass numbers and atomic numbers on the two sides of the equation are balanced:

Mass numbers: $55 = 0 + 55$ Atomic numbers: $24 = -1 + 25$

PROBLEM 11.3
Strontium-89 is a short-lived β emitter often used in the treatment of bone tumors. Write a nuclear equation for the decay of strontium-89.

PROBLEM 11.4
Write nuclear equations for the formation of each of the following nuclides by β emission.
(a) ^3_2He (b) $^{210}_{83}Bi$ (c) $^{20}_{10}Ne$

Gamma Emission

Emission of γ rays, unlike the emission of α and β particles, causes no change in mass or atomic number because γ rays are simply high-energy electromagnetic waves. Although γ emission can occur alone, it usually accompanies α or β emission as a mechanism for the new nucleus that results from a transmutation to release some extra energy.

Since γ emission affects neither mass number nor atomic number, it is often omitted from nuclear equations. Nevertheless, γ rays are of great importance. Their penetrating power makes them by far the most dangerous kind of external radiation for humans and also makes them useful in numerous medical applications. Cobalt-60, for example, is used in cancer therapy as a source of penetrating γ rays that kill cancerous tissue.

$$^{60}_{27}\text{Co} \longrightarrow {}^{60}_{28}\text{Ni} + {}^{0}_{-1}\text{e} + {}^{0}_{0}\gamma$$

Positron Emission

In addition to α, β, and γ radiation, there is another common type of radioactive decay process called *positron emission*, which involves the conversion of a proton in the nucleus into a neutron plus an ejected **positron**, ${}^{0}_{1}\text{e}$ or β^{+}. A positron, which can be thought of as a "positive electron," has the same mass as an electron but a positive charge. This process can be represented as

$$^{1}_{1}\text{p} \longrightarrow {}^{1}_{0}\text{n} + {}^{0}_{1}\text{e}$$

The result of positron emission is a decrease in the atomic number of the product nucleus because a proton has changed into a neutron, but no change in the mass number. Potassium-40, for example, undergoes positron emission to yield argon-40, a nuclear reaction important in geology for dating rocks. Note once again that the sum of the two subscripts on the right of the nuclear equation $(18 + 1 = 19)$ is equal to the subscript in the $^{40}_{19}\text{K}$ nucleus on the left.

Positron A "positive electron," which has the same mass as an electron but a positive charge.

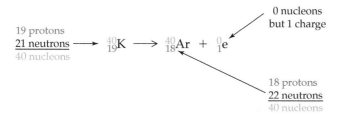

Electron Capture

Electron capture, symbolized E.C., is a process in which the nucleus captures an inner-shell electron from the surrounding electron cloud, thereby converting a proton into a neutron, and energy is released in the form of gamma rays. The mass number of the product nucleus is unchanged, but the atomic number decreases by 1, just as in positron emission. The conversion of mercury-197 into gold-197 is an example:

Electron capture (E.C.) A process in which the nucleus captures an inner-shell electron from the surrounding electron cloud, thereby converting a proton into a neutron.

80 protons
117 neutrons
197 nucleons

Inner-shell electron

79 protons
118 neutrons
197 nucleons

$$^{197}_{80}\text{Hg} + {}^{0}_{-1}\text{e} \longrightarrow {}^{197}_{79}\text{Au}$$

Do not plan on using this reaction to get rich, however. Mercury-197 is not one of the naturally occurring isotopes of Hg and is typically produced by transmutation reactions as discussed in Section 11.10.

In Figure 11.2 we see that most of the stable isotopes of the lighter elements have nearly the same number of neutrons and protons. With this fact in mind, we can often predict the most likely decay mode: unstable isotopes that have more protons than neutrons are more likely to undergo β decay to convert a proton to a neutron, while unstable isotopes having more neutrons than protons are more likely to undergo either positron emission or electron capture to convert a neutron to a proton. Also, the very heavy isotopes ($Z > 83$) will most likely undergo α-decay to lose both neutrons and protons to decrease the atomic number. Characteristics of the five kinds of radioactive decay processes are summarized in Table 11.2.

TABLE 11.2 A Summary of Radioactive Decay Processes

Process	Symbol	Change in Atomic Number	Change in Mass Number	Change in Number of Neutrons
α emission	$^4_2$He or α	−2	−4	−2
β emission	$^0_{-1}$e or β^-*	+1	0	−1
γ emission	$^0_0\gamma$ or γ	0	0	0
Positron emission	$^0_1$e or β^+*	−1	0	+1
Electron capture	E.C.	−1	0	+1

*Superscripts are used to indicate the charge associated with the two forms of beta decay; β^-, or a beta particle, carries a −1 charge, while β^+, or a positron, carries a +1 charge.

Worked Example 11.3 Balancing Nuclear Reactions: Electron Capture, Positron Emission

Write balanced nuclear equations for the following processes:

(a) Electron capture by polonium-204: $^{204}_{84}$Po $+ ^0_{-1}$e $\longrightarrow$?

(b) Positron emission from xenon-118: $^{118}_{54}$Xe $\longrightarrow ^0_1$e $+$?

ANALYSIS The key to writing nuclear equations is to make sure that the number of nucleons is the same on both sides of the equation and that the number of charges is the same.

SOLUTION

(a) In electron capture, the mass number is unchanged and the atomic number decreases by 1, giving bismuth-204: $^{204}_{84}$Po $+ ^0_{-1}$e $\longrightarrow ^{204}_{83}$Bi.

Check your answer by making sure that the number of nucleons and the number of charges are the same on both sides of the equation:

Mass number: $204 + 0 = 204$ Atomic number: $84 + (-1) = 83$

(b) In positron emission, the mass number is unchanged and the atomic number decreases by 1, giving iodine-118: $^{118}_{54}$Xe $\longrightarrow ^0_1$e $+ ^{118}_{53}$I.

CHECK! Mass number: $118 = 0 + 118$ Atomic number: $54 = 1 + 53$

PROBLEM 11.5

Write nuclear equations for positron emission from the following radioisotopes:

(a) $^{38}_{20}$Ca   **(b)** $^{118}_{54}$Xe   **(c)** $^{79}_{37}$Rb

PROBLEM 11.6

Write nuclear equations for the formation of the following radioisotopes by electron capture:

(a) $^{62}_{29}$Cu   **(b)** $^{110}_{49}$In   **(c)** $^{81}_{35}$Br

The red arrow in this graph indicates the changes that occur in the nucleus of an atom during a nuclear reaction. Identify the isotopes involved as product and reactant, and name the type of decay process.

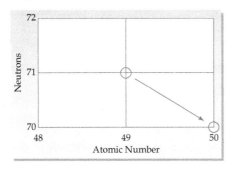

11.5 Radioactive Half-Life

The rate of radioactive decay varies greatly from one radioisotope to another. Some radioisotopes, such as uranium-238, decay at a barely perceptible rate over billions of years, but others, such as carbon-17, decay within thousandths of a second.

Rates of nuclear decay are measured in units of **half-life ($t_{1/2}$)**, defined as the amount of time required for one-half of a radioactive sample to decay. For example, the half-life of iodine-131 is 8.021 days. If today you have 1.000 g of $^{131}_{53}I$, then 8.021 days from now you will have only 50% of that amount (0.500 g) because one-half of the sample will have decayed into $^{131}_{54}Xe$. After 8.021 more days (16.063 days total), you will have only 25% (0.250 g) of your original $^{131}_{53}I$ sample; after another 8.021 days (24.084 days total), you will have only 12.5% (0.125 g); and so on. Each passage of a half-life causes the decay of one-half of whatever sample remains. The half-life of any particular isotope is the same no matter what the size of the sample, the temperature, or any other external conditions. There is no known way to slow down, speed up, or otherwise change the characteristics of radioactive decay.

Half-life ($t_{1/2}$) The amount of time required for one-half of a radioactive sample to decay.

$$1.000 \text{ g } ^{131}_{53}I \xrightarrow[\text{days}]{8} 0.500 \text{ g } ^{131}_{53}I \xrightarrow[\text{days}]{8} 0.250 \text{ g } ^{131}_{53}I \xrightarrow[\text{days}]{8} 0.125 \text{ g } ^{131}_{53}I \longrightarrow$$

| | One half-life | Two half-lives (16 days total) | Three half-lives (24 days total) |

100%   50% remaining   25% remaining   12.5% remaining

The fraction of radioisotope remaining after the passage of each half-life is represented by the curve in Figure 11.4 and can be calculated as

$$\text{fraction remaining} = (0.5)^n$$

where n is the number of half-lives that have elapsed.

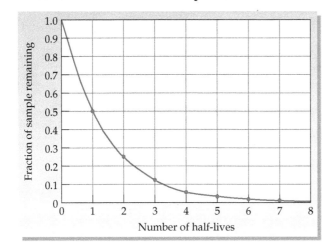

◀ **Figure 11.4**

The decay of a radioactive nucleus over time.

All nuclear decays follow this curve, whether the half-lives are measured in years, days, minutes, or seconds. That is, the fraction of sample remaining after one half-life is 0.50, the fraction remaining after two half-lives is 0.25, the fraction remaining after three half-lives is 0.125, and so on.

CHEMISTRY IN ACTION

Medical Uses of Radioactivity

The origins of nuclear medicine date from 1901, when the French physician Henri Danlos first used radium in the treatment of a tubercular skin lesion. Since that time, the use of radioactivity has become a crucial part of modern medical care, both diagnostic and therapeutic. Current nuclear techniques can be grouped into three classes: (1) *in vivo* procedures, (2) radiation therapy, and (3) imaging procedures. The first two are described here, and the third one is described on page 348 in the Chemistry in Action: Body Imaging.

In Vivo Procedures

In vivo studies—those that take place inside the body—are carried out to assess the functioning of a particular organ or body system. A *radiopharmaceutical* agent is administered, and its path in the body—whether absorbed, excreted, diluted, or concentrated—is determined by analysis of blood or urine samples.

Among the many *in vivo* procedures utilizing radioactive agents is a simple method for the determination of whole-blood volume, a common indicator used in the diagnosis of congestive heart failure, hypertension, and renal failure. A known quantity of red blood cells labeled with radioactive chromium-51 is injected into the patient and allowed to circulate to be distributed evenly throughout the body. After a suitable interval, a blood sample is taken and blood volume is calculated by comparing the concentration of labeled cells in the blood with the quantity of labeled cells injected. This and similar procedures are known as *isotope dilution* and are described by

$$R_{sample} = R_{tracer}\left(\frac{W_{sample}}{W_{system} + W_{tracer}}\right)$$

where R_{sample} is the counting rate (a measure of radioactivity) of the analyzed sample, R_{tracer} is the counting rate of the tracer added to the system, and W refers to either the mass or volume of the analyzed sample, added tracer, or total system as indicated.

Therapeutic Procedures

Therapeutic procedures—those in which radiation is purposely used as a weapon to kill diseased tissue—involve either external or internal sources of radiation. External radiation therapy for the treatment of cancer is often carried out with γ rays emanating from a cobalt-60 source. The highly radioactive source is shielded by a thick lead container and has a small opening directed toward the site of the tumor. By focusing the radiation beam on the tumor, the tumor receives the full exposure while exposure of surrounding parts of the body is minimized. Nevertheless, enough healthy tissue is affected so that most patients treated in this manner suffer the effects of radiation sickness.

Internal radiation therapy is a much more selective technique than external therapy. In the treatment of thyroid disease, for

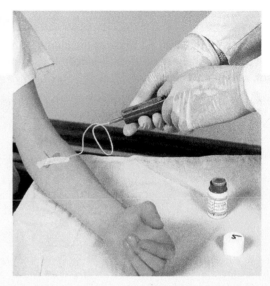

▲ **A person's blood volume can be found by injecting a small amount of radioactive chromium-51 and measuring the dilution factor.**

example, a radioactive substance such as iodine-131 is administered. This powerful β emitter is incorporated into the iodine-containing hormone thyroxine, which concentrates in the thyroid gland. Because β particles penetrate no farther than several millimeters, the localized ^{131}I produces a high radiation dose that destroys only the surrounding diseased tissue. To treat some tumors, such as those in the female reproductive system, a radioactive source is placed physically close to the tumor for a specific amount of time.

Boron neutron-capture therapy (BNCT) is a relatively new technique in which boron-containing drugs are administered to a patient and concentrate in the tumor site. The tumor is then irradiated with a neutron beam from a nuclear reactor. The boron absorbs a neutron and undergoes transmutation to produce an alpha particle and a lithium nucleus. These highly energetic particles have very low penetrating power and can kill nearby tumor tissue while sparing the healthy surrounding tissue. Because one disadvantage of BNCT is the need for access to a nuclear reactor, this treatment is available only in limited locations.

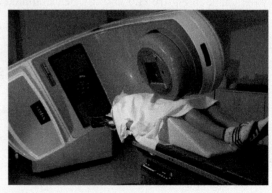

▲ **A cancer patient receiving radiotherapy treatments, a therapeutic application of radioactive isotopes.**

See Chemistry in Action Problems 11.70 and 11.71 at the end of the chapter.

One of the better known half-life applications is radiocarbon dating to determine the age of archaeological artifacts. The method is based on the slow and constant production of radioactive carbon-14 atoms in the upper atmosphere by bombardment of nitrogen atoms with neutrons from cosmic rays. Carbon-14 atoms combine with oxygen to yield $^{14}CO_2$, which slowly mixes with ordinary $^{12}CO_2$ and is then taken up by plants during photosynthesis. When these plants are eaten by animals, carbon-14 enters the food chain and is distributed evenly throughout all living organisms.

As long as a plant or animal is living, a dynamic equilibrium is established in which the organism excretes or exhales the same amount of ^{14}C that it takes in. As a result, the ratio of ^{14}C to ^{12}C in the living organism is the same as that in the atmosphere—about 1 part in 10^{12}. When the plant or animal dies, however, it no longer takes in more ^{14}C. Thus, the $^{14}C/^{12}C$ ratio in the organism slowly decreases as ^{14}C undergoes radioactive decay. At 5730 years (one ^{14}C half-life) after the death of the organism, the $^{14}C/^{12}C$ ratio has decreased by a factor of 2; at 11,460 years after death, the $^{14}C/^{12}C$ ratio has decreased by a factor of 4; and so on. By measuring the amount of ^{14}C remaining in the traces of any once-living organism, archaeologists can determine how long ago the organism died. The accuracy of the technique lessens as a sample gets older, but artifacts with an age of 1000–20,000 years can be dated with reasonable accuracy.

The half-lives of some useful radioisotopes are given in Table 11.3. As you might expect, radioisotopes that are used internally for medical applications have fairly short half-lives so that they decay rapidly and do not remain in the body for prolonged periods.

TABLE 11.3 Half-Lives of Some Useful Radioisotopes

Radioisotope	Symbol	Radiation	Half-Life	Use
Tritium	^3_1H	β	12.33 years	Biochemical tracer
Carbon-14	$^{14}_6C$	β	5730 years	Archaeological dating
Sodium-24	$^{24}_{11}Na$	β	14.959 hours	Examining circulation
Phosphorus-32	$^{32}_{15}P$	β	14.262 days	Leukemia therapy
Potassium-40	$^{40}_{19}K$	β, β^+	1.277×10^9 years	Geological dating
Cobalt-60	$^{60}_{27}Co$	β, γ	5.271 years	Cancer therapy
Arsenic-74	$^{74}_{33}As$	β^+	17.77 days	Locating brain tumors
Technetium-99m*	$^{99m}_{43}Tc$	γ	6.01 hours	Brain scans
Iodine-131	$^{131}_{53}I$	β	8.021 days	Thyroid therapy
Uranium-235	$^{235}_{92}U$	α, γ	7.038×10^8 years	Nuclear reactors

*The m in technetium-99m stands for *metastable*, meaning that the nucleus undergoes γ emission but does not change its mass number or atomic number.

Worked Example 11.4 Nuclear Reactions: Half-Life

Phosphorus-32, a radioisotope used in leukemia therapy, has a half-life of about 14 days. Approximately what percentage of a sample remains after 8 weeks?

ANALYSIS Determine how many half-lives have elapsed. For an integral number of half-lives, we can multiply the starting amount (100%) by $1/2$ for each half-life that has elapsed.

SOLUTION
Since one half-life of $^{32}_{15}P$ is 14 days (2 weeks), 8 weeks represents four half-lives. The fraction that remains after 8 weeks is thus

Four half-lives

$$\text{Final Percentage} = 100\% \times (0.5)^4 = 100\% \times \left(\tfrac{1}{2} \times \tfrac{1}{2} \times \tfrac{1}{2} \times \tfrac{1}{2}\right)$$
$$= 100\% \times \tfrac{1}{16} = 6.25\%$$

Worked Example 11.5 Nuclear Reactions: Half-Life

As noted in Table 11.3, iodine-131 has a half-life of about 8 days. Approximately what fraction of a sample remains after 20 days?

ANALYSIS Determine how many half-lives have elapsed. For a non-integral number (i.e., fraction) of half-lives, use the equation below to determine the fraction of radioisotope remaining.

$$\text{fraction remaining} = (0.5)^n$$

BALLPARK ESTIMATE Since the half-life of iodine-131 is 8 days, an elapsed time of 20 days is 2.5 half-lives. The fraction remaining should be between 0.25 (fraction remaining after two half-lives) and 0.125 (fraction remaining after three half-lives). Since the relationship between the number of half-lives and fraction remaining is not linear (see Figure 11.4), the fraction remaining will not be exactly halfway between these values but instead will be slightly closer to the lower fraction, say 0.17.

SOLUTION

$$\text{fraction remaining} = (0.5)^n = (0.5)^{2.5} = 0.177$$

BALLPARK CHECK The fraction remaining is close to our estimate of 0.17.

PROBLEM 11.8

The half-life of carbon-14, an isotope used in archaeological dating, is 5730 years. What percentage of $^{14}_{6}C$ remains in a sample estimated to be 17,000 years old?

PROBLEM 11.9

A 1.00 mL sample of red blood cells containing chromium-51 as a tracer was injected into a patient. After several hours a 5.00 mL sample of blood was drawn and its activity compared to the activity of the injected tracer sample. If the collected sample activity was 0.10% of the original tracer, calculate the total blood volume of the patient (see Chemistry in Action: Medical Uses of Radioactivity, p. 338).

⊶ **KEY CONCEPT PROBLEM 11.10**

What is the half-life of the radionuclide that shows the following decay curve?

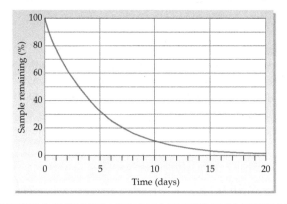

11.6 Radioactive Decay Series

When a radioactive isotope decays, nuclear change occurs and a different element is formed. Often, this newly formed nucleus is stable, but sometimes the product nucleus is itself radioactive and undergoes further decay. In fact, some radioactive nuclei undergo an extended **decay series** of nuclear disintegrations before they ultimately reach a nonradioactive product. This is particularly true for the isotopes of heavier elements. Uranium-238, for example, undergoes a series of 14 sequential nuclear reactions, ultimately stopping at lead-206 (Figure 11.5).

Decay series A sequential series of nuclear disintegrations leading from a heavy radioisotope to a nonradioactive product.

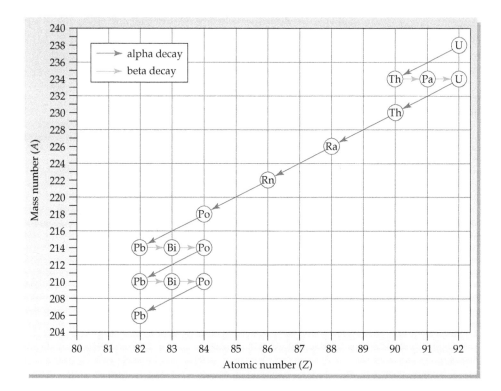

◄ **Figure 11.5**
The decay series from $^{238}_{92}U$ to $^{206}_{82}Pb$. Each isotope except for the last is radioactive and undergoes nuclear decay. The long slanted arrows represent α emissions, and the short horizontal arrows represent β emissions.

One of the intermediate radionuclides in the uranium-238 decay series is radium-226. Radium-226 has a half-life of 1600 years and undergoes α decay to produce radon-222, a gas. Rocks, soil, and building materials that contain radium are sources of radon-222, which can seep through cracks in basements and get into the air inside homes and other buildings. Radon itself is a gas that passes in and out of the lungs without being incorporated into body tissue. If, however, a radon-222 atom should happen to undergo alpha decay while in the lungs, the result is the solid decay product polonium-218. Further decay of the ^{218}Po emits α particles, which can damage lung tissue.

11.7 Ionizing Radiation

High-energy radiation of all kinds is often grouped together under the name **ionizing radiation**. This includes not only α particles, β particles, and γ rays but also *X rays* and *cosmic rays*. **X rays** are like γ rays; they have no mass and consist of high-energy electromagnetic radiation. The only difference between them is that the energy of X rays is somewhat less than that of γ rays (see Chemistry in Action: Atoms and Light in Chapter 2). **Cosmic rays** are not rays at all but are a mixture of high-energy particles that shower Earth from outer space. They consist primarily of protons, along with some α and β particles.

The interaction of any kind of ionizing radiation with a molecule knocks out an orbital electron, converting the atom or molecule into an extremely reactive ion:

$$\text{Molecule} \xrightarrow[\text{radiation}]{\text{ionizing}} \text{Ion} + e^-$$

This reactive ion can react with other molecules nearby, creating still other fragments that can in turn cause further reactions. In this manner, a large dose of ionizing radiation can destroy the delicate balance of chemical reactions in living cells, ultimately causing the death of an organism.

Ionizing radiation A general name for high-energy radiation of all kinds.

X rays Electromagnetic radiation with an energy somewhat less than that of γ rays.

Cosmic rays A mixture of high-energy particles—primarily of protons and various atomic nuclei—that shower Earth from outer space.

A small dose of ionizing radiation may not cause visible symptoms but can nevertheless be dangerous if it strikes a cell nucleus and damages the genetic machinery inside. The resultant changes might lead to a genetic mutation, to cancer, or to cell death. The nuclei of rapidly dividing cells, such as those in bone marrow, the lymph system, the lining of the intestinal tract, or an embryo, are the most readily damaged. Because cancer cells are also rapidly dividing they are highly susceptible to the effects of ionizing radiation, which is why radiation therapy is an effective treatment for many types of cancer (see Chemistry in Action: Medical Uses of Radioactivity on p. 338). Some properties of ionizing radiation are summarized in Table 11.4.

TABLE 11.4 Some Properties of Ionizing Radiation

Type of Radiation	Energy Range*	Penetrating Distance in Water**
α	3–9 MeV	0.02–0.04 mm
β	0–3 MeV	0–4 mm
X	100 eV–10 keV	0.01–1 cm
γ	10 keV–10 MeV	1–20 cm

* The energies of subatomic particles are often measured in electron volts (eV): 1 eV = 6.703×10^{-19} cal, or 2.805×10^{-18} J.
** Distance at which one-half of the radiation is stopped.

The effects of ionizing radiation on the human body vary with the energy of the radiation, its distance from the body, the length of exposure, and the location of the source outside or inside the body. When coming from outside the body, γ rays and X rays are potentially more harmful than α and β particles because they pass through clothing and skin and into the body's cells. Alpha particles are stopped by clothing and skin, and β particles are stopped by wood or several layers of clothing. These types of radiation are much more dangerous when emitted within the body, however, because all their radiation energy is given up to the immediately surrounding tissue. Alpha emitters are especially hazardous internally and are almost never used in medical applications.

Health professionals who work with X rays or other kinds of ionizing radiation protect themselves by surrounding the source with a thick layer of lead or other dense material. Protection from radiation is also afforded by controlling the distance between the worker and the radiation source because radiation intensity (I) decreases with the square of the distance from the source. The intensities of radiation at two different distances, 1 and 2, are given by the equation

$$\frac{I_1}{I_2} = \frac{d_2{}^2}{d_1{}^2}$$

For example, suppose a source delivers 16 units of radiation at a distance of 1.0 m. Doubling the distance to 2.0 m decreases the radiation intensity to one-fourth:

$$\frac{16 \text{ units}}{I_2} = \frac{(2 \text{ m})^2}{(1 \text{ m})^2}$$

$$I_2 = 16 \text{ units} \times \frac{1 \text{ m}^2}{4 \text{ m}^2} = 4 \text{ units}$$

Worked Example 11.6 Ionizing Radiation: Intensity versus Distance from the Source

If a radiation source gives 75 units of radiation at a distance of 2.4 m, at what distance does the source give 25 units of radiation?

ANALYSIS Radiation intensity (I) decreases with the square of the distance (d) from the source according to the equation

$$\frac{I_1}{I_2} = \frac{d_2{}^2}{d_1{}^2}$$

We know three of the four variables in this equation (I_1, I_2, and d_1), and we need to find d_2.

BALLPARK ESTIMATE In order to decrease the radiation intensity from 75 units to 25 units (a factor of 3), the distance must *increase* by a factor of $\sqrt{3} = 1.7$. Thus, the distance should increase from 2.4 m to about 4 m.

SOLUTION

STEP 1: **Identify known information.** We know three of the four variables.

STEP 2: **Identify answer and units.**

STEP 3: **Identify equation.** Rearrange the equation relating intensity and distance to solve for d_2.

STEP 4: **Solve.** Substitute in known values so that unwanted units cancel.

$I_1 = 75$ units
$I_2 = 25$ units
$d_1 = 2.4$ m

$d_2 = ???$ m

$$\frac{I_1}{I_2} = \frac{d_2^{\,2}}{d_1^{\,2}}$$

$$d_2^{\,2} = \frac{I_1 d_1^{\,2}}{I_2} \quad\Rightarrow\quad d_2 = \sqrt{\frac{I_1 d_1^{\,2}}{I_2}}$$

$$d_2 = \sqrt{\frac{(75 \text{ units})(2.4 \text{ m})^2}{(25 \text{ units})}} = 4.2 \text{ m}$$

BALLPARK CHECK The calculated result is consistent with our estimate of about 4 m.

PROBLEM 11.11

A β-emitting radiation source gives 250 units of radiation at a distance of 4.0 m. At what distance does the radiation drop to one-tenth its original value?

11.8 Detecting Radiation

Small amounts of naturally occurring radiation have always been present, but people have been aware of it only within the past 100 years. The problem is that radiation is invisible. We cannot see, hear, smell, touch, or taste radiation, no matter how high the dose. We can, however, detect radiation by taking advantage of its ionizing properties.

The simplest device for detecting exposure to radiation is the photographic film badge worn by people who routinely work with radioactive materials. The film is protected from exposure to light, but any other radiation striking the badge causes the film to fog (remember Becquerel's discovery). At regular intervals, the film is developed and compared with a standard to indicate the radiation exposure.

The most versatile method for measuring radiation in the laboratory is the *scintillation counter*, a device in which a substance called a *phosphor* emits a flash of light when struck by radiation. The number of flashes are counted electronically and converted into an electrical signal.

Perhaps the best-known method for detecting and measuring radiation is the *Geiger counter*, an argon-filled tube containing two electrodes (Figure 11.6). The inner walls of the tube are coated with an electrically conducting material and given a negative charge, and a wire in the center of the tube is given a positive charge. As radiation enters the tube through a thin window, it strikes and ionizes argon atoms, which briefly conduct a tiny electric current between the walls and the center electrode. The passage of the current is detected, amplified, and used to produce a clicking sound or to register on a meter. The more radiation that enters the tube, the more frequent the clicks. Geiger counters are useful for seeking out a radiation source in a large area and for gauging the intensity of emitted radiation.

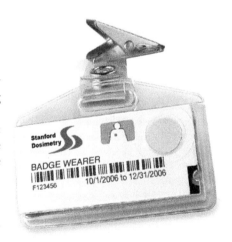

▲ This photographic film badge is a common device for monitoring radiation exposure.

▶ **Figure 11.6**
A Geiger counter for measuring radiation.
As radiation enters the tube through a thin window, it ionizes argon atoms and produces electrons that conduct a tiny electric current between the walls and the center electrode. The current flow then registers on the meter.

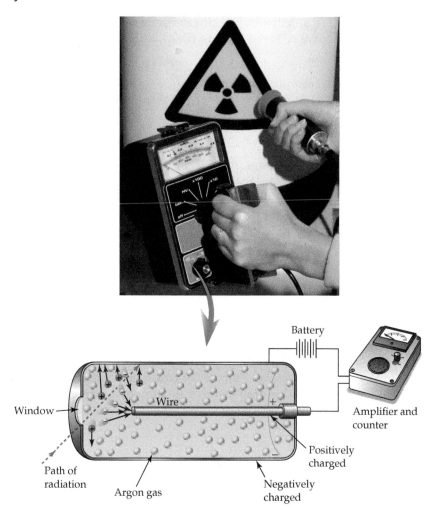

11.9 Measuring Radiation

Radiation intensity is expressed in different ways, depending on what characteristic of the radiation is measured (Table 11.5). Some units measure the number of nuclear decay events, while others measure exposure to radiation or the biological consequences of radiation.

TABLE 11.5 Common Units for Measuring Radiation

Unit	Quantity Measured	Description
Curie (Ci)	Decay events	Amount of radiation equal to 3.7×10^{10} disintegrations per second
Roentgen (R)	Ionizing intensity	Amount of radiation producing 2.1×10^{9} charges per cubic centimeter of dry air
Rad	Energy absorbed per gram of tissue	1 rad = 1 R
Rem	Tissue damage	Amount of radiation producing the same damage as 1 R of X rays
Sievert (Sv)	Tissue damage	1 Sv = 100 rem

CHEMISTRY IN ACTION

Irradiated Food

The idea of irradiating food to kill harmful bacteria is not new; it goes back almost as far as the earliest studies on radiation. Not until the 1940s did serious work get under way, however, when U.S. Army scientists found that irradiation increased the shelf-life of ground beef. Nevertheless, widespread civilian use of the technique has been a long time in coming, spurred on in recent years by outbreaks of food poisoning that resulted in several deaths.

The principle of food irradiation is simple: exposure of contaminated food to ionizing radiation—usually γ rays produced by cobalt-60 or cesium-137—destroys the genetic material of any bacteria or other organisms present, thereby killing them. Irradiation will not, however, kill viruses or prions (see Chemistry in Action: Prions: Proteins That Cause Disease in Chapter 18), the cause of "mad-cow" disease. The amount of radiation depends on the desired effect. For example, to delay ripening of fruit may require a dose of 0.25 – 0.75 kGy, while sterilization of packaged meat requires a much higher dose of 25 – 70 kGy. The food itself undergoes little if any change when irradiated and does not itself become radioactive. The only real argument against food irradiation, in fact, is that it is *too* effective. Knowing that irradiation will kill nearly all harmful organisms, a food processor might be tempted to cut back on normal sanitary practices!

Food irradiation has been implemented to a much greater extent in Europe than in the United States. The largest marketers of irradiated food are Belgium, France, and the Netherlands, which irradiate between 10,000 and 20,000 tons of food per year. Currently, over 40 countries permit food irradiation and over 500,000 metric tons of food are treated annually worldwide.

▲ **Irradiating food kills bacteria and extends shelf life. Most irradiated food products are labeled with the Radura symbol (in green) to inform the public that the food product was exposed to radiation.**

One of the major concerns in the United States is the possible generation of *radiolytic products*, compounds formed in food by exposure to ionizing radiation. The U.S. Food and Drug Administration, after studying the matter extensively, has declared that food irradiation is safe and that it does not appreciably alter the vitamin or other nutritional content of food. Spices, fruits, pork, and vegetables were approved for irradiation in 1986, followed by poultry in 1990 and red meat, particularly ground beef, in 1997. In 2000, approval was extended to whole eggs and sprouting seeds. Should the food industry adopt irradiation of meat as its standard practice, occurrences of *E. coli* and *salmonella* contaminations, resulting in either massive product recalls or serious health concerns for consumers will become a thing of the past.

See Chemistry in Action Problems 11.72 and 11.73 at the end of the chapter.

- **Curie** The *curie* (Ci), the *millicurie* (mCi), and the *microcurie* (μCi) measure the number of radioactive disintegrations occurring each second in a sample. One curie is the decay rate of 1 g of radium, equal to 3.7×10^{10} disintegrations per second; 1 mCi = 0.001 Ci = 3.7×10^7 disintegrations per second; and 1 μCi = 0.000 001 Ci = 3.7×10^4 disintegrations per second.

  The dosage of a radioactive substance administered orally or intravenously is usually given in millicuries. To calculate the size of a dose, it is necessary to determine the decay rate of the isotope solution per milliliter. Because the emitter concentration is constantly decreasing as it decays, the activity must be measured immediately before administration. Suppose, for example, that a solution containing iodine-131 for a thyroid-function study is found to have a decay rate of 0.020 mCi/mL and the dose administered is to be 0.050 mCi. The amount of the solution administered must be

$$\frac{0.05 \text{ mCi}}{\text{Dose}} \times \frac{1 \text{ mL } ^{131}\text{I solution}}{0.020 \text{ mCi}} = 2.5 \text{ mL } ^{131}\text{I solution/dose}$$

- **Roentgen** The *roentgen* (R) is a unit for measuring the ionizing intensity of γ or X radiation. In other words, the roentgen measures the capacity of the radiation for affecting matter. One roentgen is the amount of radiation that produces 2.1×10^9 units of charge in 1 cm^3 of dry air at atmospheric pressure. Each collision of ionizing radiation with an atom produces one ion, or one unit of charge.

- **Rad** The *rad* (radiation absorbed dose) is a unit for measuring the energy absorbed per gram of material exposed to a radiation source and is defined as the absorption of 1×10^{-5} J of energy per gram. The energy absorbed varies with the type of material irradiated and the type of radiation. For most purposes, though, the roentgen and the rad are so close that they can be considered identical when used for X rays and γ rays: 1 R = 1 rad.
- **Rem** The *rem* (roentgen equivalent for man) measures the amount of tissue damage caused by radiation. One rem is the amount of radiation that produces the same effect as 1 R of X rays. Rems are the preferred units for medical purposes because they measure equivalent doses of different kinds of radiation. The rem is calculated as

$$\text{Rems} = \text{rads} \times \text{RBE}$$

where RBE is a *relative biological effectiveness* factor, which takes into account the differences in energy and of the different types of radiation. Although the actual biological effects of radiation depend greatly on both the source and the energy of the radiation, the RBE of X rays, γ rays, and β particles are essentially equivalent (RBE = 1), while the accepted RBE for α particles is 20. For example, 1 rad of α radiation causes 20 times more tissue damage than 1 rad of γ rays, but 1 rem of α radiation and 1 rem of γ rays cause the same amount of damage. Thus, the rem takes both ionizing intensity and biological effect into account, whereas the rad deals only with intensity.

- **SI Units** In the SI system, the *becquerel* (Bq) is defined as one disintegration per second. The SI unit for energy absorbed is the *gray* (Gy; 1 Gy = 100 rad). For radiation dose, the SI unit is the *sievert* (Sv), which is equal to 100 rem.

The biological consequences of different radiation doses are given in Table 11.6. Although the effects seem frightening, the average radiation dose received annually by most people is only about 0.27 rem. About 80% of this *background radiation* comes from natural sources (rocks and cosmic rays); the remaining 20% comes from consumer products and from medical procedures such as X rays. The amount due to emissions from nuclear power plants and to fallout from testing of nuclear weapons in the 1950s is barely detectable.

TABLE 11.6 Biological Effects of Short-Term Radiation on Humans

Dose (rem)	Biological Effects
0–25	No detectable effects
25–100	Temporary decrease in white blood cell count
100–200	Nausea, vomiting, longer-term decrease in white blood cells
200–300	Vomiting, diarrhea, loss of appetite, listlessness
300–600	Vomiting, diarrhea, hemorrhaging, eventual death in some cases
Above 600	Eventual death in nearly all cases

PROBLEM 11.12

Radiation released during the 1986 Chernobyl nuclear power plant disaster is expected to increase the background radiation level worldwide by about 5 mrem. By how much will this increase the annual dose of the average person? Express your answer as a percentage.

PROBLEM 11.13

A solution of selenium-75, a radioisotope used in the diagnosis of pancreatic disease, is found just prior to administration to have an activity of 44 μCi/mL. If 3.98 mL were delivered intravenously to the patient, what dose of Se-75 (in μCi) did the patient receive?

PROBLEM 11.14

A typical food irradiation application for the inhibition of sprout formation in potatoes applies a dose of 0.20 kGy. What is this dose in units of rad if the radiation is predominantly γ rays? If it is predominantly α particles? (See Chemistry in Action: Irradiated Food on p. 345.)

11.10 Artificial Transmutation

Very few of the approximately 3300 known radioisotopes occur naturally. Most are made from stable isotopes by **artificial transmutation**, the change of one atom into another brought about by nuclear bombardment reactions.

When an atom is bombarded with a high-energy particle, such as a proton, a neutron, an α particle, or even the nucleus of another element, an unstable nucleus is created in the collision. A nuclear change then occurs, and a different element is produced. For example, transmutation of ^{14}N to ^{14}C occurs in the upper atmosphere when neutrons produced by cosmic rays collide with atmospheric nitrogen. In the collision, a neutron dislodges a proton (^{1}H) from the nitrogen nucleus as the neutron and nucleus fuse together:

$$^{14}_{7}N + {}^{1}_{0}n \longrightarrow {}^{14}_{6}C + {}^{1}_{1}H$$

Artificial transmutation can lead to the synthesis of entirely new elements never before seen on Earth. In fact, all the *transuranium elements*—those elements with atomic numbers greater than 92—have been produced by bombardment reactions. For example, plutonium-241 (^{241}Pu) can be made by bombardment of uranium-238 with α particles:

$$^{238}_{92}U + {}^{4}_{2}He \longrightarrow {}^{241}_{94}Pu + {}^{1}_{0}n$$

Plutonium-241 is itself radioactive, with a half-life of 14.35 years, decaying by β emission to yield americium-241, which in turn decays by α emission with a half-life of 432.2 years. (If the name *americium* sounds vaguely familiar, it is because this radioisotope is used in smoke detectors.)

$$^{241}_{94}Pu \longrightarrow {}^{241}_{95}Am + {}^{0}_{-1}e$$

Note that all the equations just given for artificial transmutations are balanced. The sum of the mass numbers and the sum of the charges are the same on both sides of each equation.

Artificial transmutation The change of one atom into another brought about by a nuclear bombardment reaction.

▲ Smoke detectors contain a small amount of americium-241. The α particles emitted by this radioisotope ionize the air within the detector, causing it to conduct a tiny electric current. When smoke enters the chamber, conductivity drops and an alarm is triggered.

Worked Example **11.7** Balancing Nuclear Reactions: Transmutation

Californium-246 is formed by bombardment of uranium-238 atoms. If 4 neutrons are also formed, what particle is used for the bombardment?

ANALYSIS First write an incomplete nuclear equation incorporating the known information:

$$^{238}_{92}U + ? \longrightarrow {}^{246}_{98}Cf + 4{}^{1}_{0}n$$

Then find the numbers of nucleons and charges necessary to balance the equation. In this instance, there are 238 nucleons on the left and $246 + 4 = 250$ nucleons on the right, so the bombarding particle must have $250 - 238 = 12$ nucleons. Furthermore, there are 92 nuclear charges on the left and 98 on the right, so the bombarding particle must have $98 - 92 = 6$ protons.

SOLUTION
The missing particle is $^{12}_{6}C$.

$$^{238}_{92}U + {}^{12}_{6}C \longrightarrow {}^{246}_{98}Cf + 4{}^{1}_{0}n$$

CHEMISTRY IN ACTION

Body Imaging

We are all familiar with the appearance of a standard X-ray image, produced when X rays pass through the body and the intensity of the radiation that exits is recorded on film. X-ray imaging is, however, only one of a host of noninvasive imaging techniques that are now in common use.

Among the most widely used imaging techniques are those that give diagnostic information about the health of various parts of the body by analyzing the distribution pattern of a radioactively tagged substance in the body. A radiopharmaceutical agent that is known to concentrate in a specific organ or other body part is injected into the body, and its distribution pattern is monitored by an external radiation detector such as a γ ray camera. Depending on the medical condition, a diseased part might concentrate more of the radiopharmaceutical than normal and thus show up on the film as a radioactive hot spot against a cold background. Alternatively, the diseased part might concentrate less of the radiopharmaceutical than normal and thus show up as a cold spot on a hot background.

Among the radioisotopes most widely used for diagnostic imaging is technetium-99m, whose short half-life of only 6 hours minimizes the patient's exposure to radioactivity. Enhanced body images, such as the brain scan shown in the accompanying photograph, are an important tool in the diagnosis of cancer and many other medical conditions.

Several other techniques now used in medical diagnosis are made possible by *tomography*, a technique in which computer processing allows production of images through "slices" of the body. In X-ray tomography, commonly known as *CAT* or *CT* scanning (computerized tomography), the X-ray source and an array of detectors move rapidly in a circle around a patient's body, collecting up to 90,000 readings. CT scans can detect structural abnormalities such as tumors without the use of radioactive materials.

Combining tomography with radioisotope imaging gives cross-sectional views of regions that concentrate a radioactive substance.

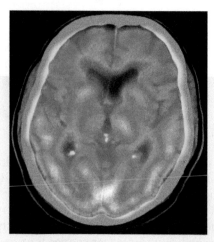

▲ **This enhanced image of the brain of a 72-year old male was obtained using PET following injection of 20 mCi of Tc-99m. The results can be used to distinguish between dementia and depression.**

One such technique, *positron emission tomography* (PET), utilizes radioisotopes that emit positrons and ultimately yield γ rays. Oxygen-15, nitrogen-13, carbon-11, and fluorine-18 are commonly used for PET because they can be readily incorporated into many physiologically active compounds. An ^{18}F-labeled glucose derivative, for instance, is useful for imaging brain regions that respond to various stimuli. The disadvantage of PET scans is that the necessary radioisotopes are so short-lived that they must be produced on-site immediately before use. The cost of PET is therefore high, because a hospital must install and maintain the necessary nuclear facility.

Magnetic resonance imaging (MRI) is a medical imaging technique that uses powerful magnetic and radio-frequency fields to interact with specific nuclei in the body (usually the nuclei of hydrogen atoms) to generate images in which the contrast between soft tissues is much better than that seen with CT. The original name for this technique was *nuclear* magnetic resonance imaging, but the *nuclear* was eliminated because in the public mind this word conjured up negative images of ionizing radiation. Ironically, MRI does not involve any nuclear radiation at all.

See Chemistry in Action Problems 11.74 and 11.75 at the end of the chapter.

PROBLEM 11.15

What isotope results from α decay of the americium-241 in smoke detectors?

PROBLEM 11.16

The element berkelium, first prepared at the University of California at Berkeley in 1949, is made by α bombardment of $^{241}_{95}$Am. Two neutrons are also produced during the reaction. What isotope of berkelium results from this transmutation? Write a balanced nuclear equation.

PROBLEM 11.17

Write a balanced nuclear equation for the reaction of argon-40 with a proton:

$$^{40}_{18}\text{Ar} + {}^{1}_{1}\text{H} \longrightarrow ? + {}^{1}_{0}\text{n}$$

PROBLEM 11.18
Technetium-99*m* (Tc-99*m*) is used extensively in diagnostic applications, including positron emission tomography (PET) scans (see Chemistry in Action: Body Imaging on p. 348). The half-life of Tc-99*m* is 6 hours. How long will it take for the Tc-99*m* activity to decrease to 0.1% of its original activity?

11.11 Nuclear Fission and Nuclear Fusion

In the preceding section, we saw that particle bombardment of various elements causes artificial transmutation and results in the formation of new, usually heavier elements. Under very special conditions with a very few isotopes, however, different kinds of nuclear events occur. Certain very heavy nuclei can split apart, and certain very light nuclei can fuse together. The two resultant processes—**nuclear fission** for the fragmenting of heavy nuclei and **nuclear fusion** for the joining together of light nuclei—have changed the world since their discovery in the late 1930s and early 1940s.

The huge amounts of energy that accompany these nuclear processes are the result of mass-to-energy conversions and are predicted by Einstein's equation

$$E = mc^2$$

where E = energy, m = mass change associated with the nuclear reaction, and c = the speed of light (3.0×10^8 m/s). Based on this relationship, a mass change as small as 1 µg results in a release of 2.15×10^4 kcal (9.00×104 kJ) of energy!

Nuclear fission The fragmenting of heavy nuclei.

Nuclear fusion The joining together of light nuclei.

Nuclear Fission

Uranium-235 is the only naturally occurring isotope that undergoes nuclear fission. When this isotope is bombarded by a stream of relatively slow-moving neutrons, its nucleus splits to give isotopes of other elements. The split can take place in more than 400 ways, and more than 800 different fission products have been identified. One of the more frequently occurring pathways generates barium-142 and krypton-91, along with 2 additional neutrons plus the 1 neutron that initiated the fission:

$$^{1}_{0}n + {}^{235}_{92}U \longrightarrow {}^{142}_{56}Ba + {}^{91}_{36}Kr + 3\,{}^{1}_{0}n$$

As indicated by the balanced nuclear equation above, *one* neutron is used to initiate fission of a ^{235}U nucleus, but *three* neutrons are released. Thus, a nuclear **chain reaction** can be started: 1 neutron initiates one fission that releases 3 neutrons. Those 3 neutrons initiate three new fissions that release 9 neutrons. The 9 neutrons initiate nine fissions that release 27 neutrons, and so on at an ever-faster pace (Figure 11.7). It is worth noting that the neutrons produced by fission reactions are highly energetic. They possess penetrating power greater than α and β particles, but less than γ rays. In a nuclear fission reactor, the neutrons must first be slowed down to allow them to react. If the sample size is small, many of the neutrons escape before initiating additional fission events, and the chain reaction stops. If a sufficient amount of ^{235}U is present, however—an amount called the **critical mass**—then the chain reaction becomes self-sustaining. Under high-pressure conditions that confine the ^{235}U to a small volume, the chain reaction occurs so rapidly that a nuclear explosion results. For ^{235}U, the critical mass is about 56 kg, although the amount can be reduced to approximately 15 kg by placing a coating of ^{238}U around the ^{235}U to reflect back some of the escaping neutrons.

Chain reaction A reaction that, once started, is self-sustaining.

Critical mass The minimum amount of radioactive material needed to sustain a nuclear chain reaction.

An enormous quantity of heat is released during nuclear fission—the fission of just 1.0 g of uranium-235 produces 3.4×10^8 kcal (1.4×109 kJ) for instance. This heat can be used to convert water to steam, which can be harnessed to turn huge generators and produce electric power. Although the United States, France, and Japan are responsible for nearly 50% of all nuclear power generated worldwide, only about 19% of the

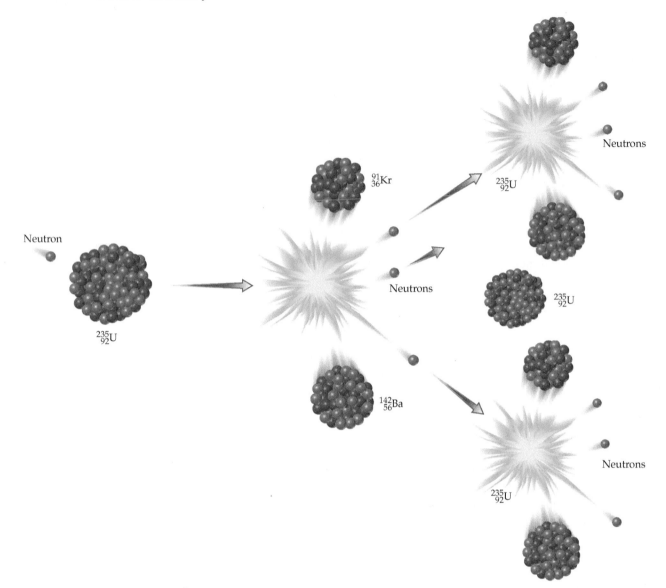

▲ **Figure 11.7**
A chain reaction.
Each fission event produces additional neutrons that induce more fissions. The rate of the process increases at each stage. Such chain reactions usually lead to the formation of many different fission products in addition to the two indicated.

electricity consumed in the United States is nuclear-generated. In France, nearly 80% of electricity is generated by nuclear power plants.

Two major objections that have caused much public debate about nuclear power plants are safety and waste disposal. Although a nuclear explosion is not possible under the conditions that typically exist in a power plant, there is a serious potential radiation hazard should an accident rupture the containment vessel holding the nuclear fuel and release radioactive substances to the environment. There have been several such instances in the last 35 years, most notably Three Mile Island in Pennsylvania (1979), Chernobyl in the Ukraine (1986), and the more recent Fukushima reactor damaged by the tsunami in Japan (2011). Perhaps even more important is the problem posed by disposal of radioactive wastes from nuclear plants. Many of these wastes have such long half-lives that hundreds or even thousands of years must elapse before they will be safe for humans to approach. How to dispose of such hazardous materials safely is an unsolved problem.

PROBLEM 11.19

What other isotope besides tellurium-137 is produced by nuclear fission of uranium-235?

$$^{235}_{92}\text{U} + ^{1}_{0}\text{n} \longrightarrow ^{137}_{52}\text{Te} + 2\,^{1}_{0}\text{n} + ?$$

Nuclear Fusion

Just as heavy nuclei such as ^{235}U release energy when they undergo *fission*, very light nuclei such as the isotopes of hydrogen release enormous amounts of energy when they undergo *fusion*. In fact, it is just such a fusion reaction of hydrogen nuclei to produce helium that powers our sun and other stars. Among the processes thought to occur in the sun are those in the following sequence leading to helium-4:

$$^{1}_{1}\text{H} + ^{2}_{1}\text{H} \longrightarrow ^{3}_{2}\text{He}$$

$$^{3}_{2}\text{He} + ^{3}_{2}\text{He} \longrightarrow ^{4}_{2}\text{He} + 2\,^{1}_{1}\text{H}$$

$$^{3}_{2}\text{He} + ^{1}_{1}\text{H} \longrightarrow ^{4}_{2}\text{He} + ^{0}_{1}\text{e}$$

Under the conditions found in stars, where the temperature is on the order of 2×10^7 K and pressures approach 10^5 atmospheres, nuclei are stripped of all their electrons and have enough kinetic energy that nuclear fusion readily occurs. The energy of our sun, and all the stars, comes from thermonuclear fusion reactions in their core that fuse hydrogen and other light elements, transmuting them into heavier elements. On Earth, however, the necessary conditions for nuclear fusion are not easily created. For more than 50 years scientists have been trying to create the necessary conditions for fusion in laboratory reactors, including the Tokamak Fusion Test Reactor (TFTR) at Princeton, New Jersey, and the Joint European Torus (JET) at Culham, England. Recent advances in reactor design have raised hopes that a commercial fusion reactor will be realized within the next 20 years.

If the dream becomes reality, controlled nuclear fusion can provide the ultimate cheap, clean power source. The fuel is deuterium (^2H), available in the oceans in limitless amounts, and there are few radioactive by-products.

PROBLEM 11.20

One of the possible reactions for nuclear fusion involves the collision of 2 deuterium nuclei. Complete the reaction by identifying the missing particle:

$$^{2}_{1}\text{H} + ^{2}_{1}\text{H} \longrightarrow ^{1}_{0}n + ?$$

SUMMARY: REVISITING THE CHAPTER GOALS

1. What is a nuclear reaction, and how are equations for nuclear reactions balanced? A *nuclear reaction* is one that changes an atomic nucleus, causing the change of one element into another. Loss of an α particle leads to a new atom whose atomic number is 2 less than that of the starting atom. Loss of a β particle leads to an atom whose atomic number is 1 greater than that of the starting atom:

$$\alpha \text{ emission: } ^{238}_{92}\text{U} \longrightarrow ^{234}_{90}\text{Th} + ^{4}_{2}\text{He}$$

$$\beta \text{ emission: } ^{131}_{53}\text{I} \longrightarrow ^{131}_{54}\text{Xe} + ^{0}_{-1}\text{e}$$

A nuclear reaction is balanced when the sum of the *nucleons* (protons and neutrons) is the same on both sides of the reaction arrow and when the sum of the charges on the nuclei plus any ejected subatomic particles is the same (see *Problems 22, 24, 26, 38, 40, 41, 44–53, 81, 82, 84, 85, 90–95*).

2. What are the different kinds of radioactivity? *Radioactivity* is the spontaneous emission of radiation from the nucleus of an unstable atom. The three major kinds of radiation are called *alpha* (α), *beta* (β), and *gamma* (γ). Alpha radiation consists of helium nuclei, small particles containing 2 protons and

2 neutrons ($^4_2$He); β radiation consists of electrons ($^0_{-1}$e); and γ radiation consists of high-energy light waves. Every element in the periodic table has at least one radioactive isotope, or *radioisotope* (*see Problems 22, 25, 27, 29, 30–32, 40, 41, 44–47, 49, 81, 82, 93*).

3. How are the rates of nuclear reactions expressed? The rate of a nuclear reaction is expressed in units of *half-life* ($t_{1/2}$), where one half-life is the amount of time necessary for one half of the radioactive sample to decay (*see Problems 21, 23, 28, 29, 54–59, 77, 83, 85*).

4. What is ionizing radiation? High-energy radiation of all types—α particles, β particles, γ rays, and X rays—is called *ionizing radiation*. When any of these kinds of radiation strikes an atom, it dislodges an orbital electron and gives a reactive ion that can be lethal to living cells. Gamma rays and X rays are the most penetrating and most harmful types of external radiation; α and β particles are the most dangerous types of internal radiation because of their high energy and the resulting damage to surrounding tissue (*see Problems 33–37, 63, 65, 72, 76, 84, 86, 87*).

5. How is radioactivity measured? Radiation intensity is expressed in different ways according to the property being measured. The *curie* (*Ci*) measures the number of radioactive disintegrations per second in a sample; the *roentgen* (*R*) measures the ionizing ability of radiation. The *rad* measures the amount of radiation energy absorbed per gram of tissue; and the *rem* measures the amount of tissue damage caused by radiation. Radiation effects become noticeable with a human exposure of 25 rem and become lethal at an exposure above 600 rem (*see Problems 60–69, 79, 80*).

6. What is transmutation? *Transmutation* is the change of one element into another brought about by a nuclear reaction. Most known radioisotopes do not occur naturally but are made by bombardment of an atom with a high-energy particle. In the ensuing collision between particle and atom, a nuclear change occurs and a new element is produced by *artificial transmutation* (*see Problems 38, 39, 48, 50, 51, 53, 90, 94, 95*).

7. What are nuclear fission and nuclear fusion? With a very few isotopes, including $^{235}_{92}$U, the nucleus is split apart by neutron bombardment to give smaller fragments. A large amount of energy is released during this *nuclear fission*, leading to use of the reaction for generating electric power. *Nuclear fusion* results when small nuclei such as those of tritium ($^3_1$H) and deuterium ($^2_1$H) combine to give a heavier nucleus (*see Problems 42, 43, 48, 88, 91, 92*).

KEY WORDS

Alpha (α) particle, *p. 331*

Artificial transmutation, *p. 347*

Beta (β) particle, *p. 331*

Chain reaction, *p. 349*

Cosmic rays, *p. 341*

Critical mass, *p. 349*

Decay series, *p. 341*

Electron capture (E.C.), *p. 335*

Gamma (γ) radiation, *p. 331*

Half-life ($t_{1/2}$) *p. 337*

Ionizing radiation, *p. 341*

Nuclear decay, *p. 332*

Nuclear fission, *p. 349*

Nuclear fusion, *p. 349*

Nuclear reaction, *p. 329*

Nucleon, *p. 329*

Nuclide, *p. 329*

Positron, *p. 335*

Radioactivity, *p. 330*

Radioisotope, *p. 331*

Radionuclide, *p. 331*

Transmutation, *p. 332*

X rays, *p. 341*

UNDERSTANDING KEY CONCEPTS

11.21 Magnesium-28 decays by β emission to give aluminum-28. If yellow spheres represent $^{28}_{12}$Mg atoms and blue spheres represent $^{28}_{13}$Al atoms, how many half-lives have passed in the following sample?

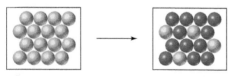

11.22 Write a balanced nuclear equation to represent the decay reaction described in Problem 11.21.

11.23 Refer to Figure 11.4 and then make a drawing similar to those in Problem 11.21 representing the decay of a sample of $^{28}_{12}$Mg after approximately four half-lives have passed.

11.24 Write the symbol of the isotope represented by the following drawing. Blue spheres represent neutrons and red spheres represent protons.

11.25 Shown in the following graph is a portion of the decay series for plutonium-241 ($^{241}_{94}$Pu). The series has two kinds of arrows: shorter arrows pointing right and longer arrows pointing left. Which arrow corresponds to an α emission, and which to a β emission? Explain.

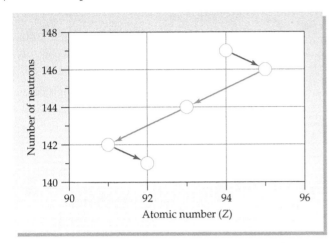

11.26   Identify and write the symbol for each of the five nuclides in the decay series shown in Problem 11.25.

11.27   Identify the isotopes involved, and tell the type of decay process occurring in the following nuclear reaction:

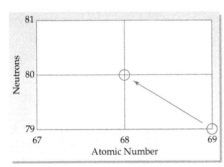

11.28   What is the half-life of the radionuclide that shows the following decay curve?

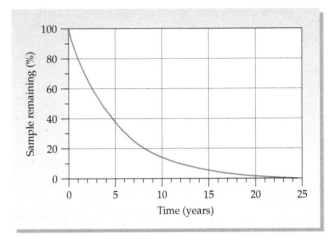

11.29   What is wrong with the following decay curve? Explain.

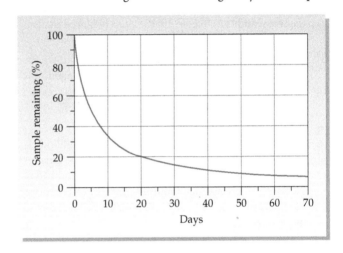

ADDITIONAL PROBLEMS

RADIOACTIVITY

11.30   What does it mean to say that a substance is radioactive?

11.31   Describe how α radiation, β radiation, γ radiation, positron emission, and electron capture differ.

11.32   List three of the five ways in which a nuclear reaction differs from a chemical reaction.

11.33   What happens when ionizing radiation strikes an atom in a chemical compound?

11.34   How does ionizing radiation lead to cell damage?

11.35   What are the main sources of background radiation?

11.36   How can a nucleus emit an electron during β decay when there are no electrons present in the nucleus to begin with?

11.37   What is the difference between an α particle and a helium atom?

NUCLEAR DECAY AND TRANSMUTATION

11.38   What does it mean to say that a nuclear equation is balanced?

11.39   What are transuranium elements, and how are they made?

11.40   What happens to the mass number and atomic number of an atom that emits an α particle? A β particle?

11.41   What happens to the mass number and atomic number of an atom that emits a γ ray? A positron?

11.42   How does nuclear fission differ from normal radioactive decay?

11.43   What characteristic of uranium-235 fission causes a chain reaction?

11.44   What products result from radioactive decay of the following β emitters?

(a) $^{35}_{16}S$ (b) $^{24}_{10}Ne$ (c) $^{90}_{38}Sr$

11.45   What radioactive nuclides will produce the following products following α decay?

(a) $^{186}_{76}Os$ (b) $^{204}_{85}At$ (c) $^{241}_{94}Pu$

11.46   Identify the starting radioisotopes needed to balance each of these nuclear reactions:

(a) $? + {}^{4}_{2}He \longrightarrow {}^{113}_{49}In$ (b) $? + {}^{4}_{2}He \longrightarrow {}^{13}_{7}N + {}^{1}_{0}n$

11.47 Identify the radioisotope product needed to balance each of these nuclear reactions:

(a) $^{26}_{11}Na \longrightarrow ? + ^{0}_{-1}e$ (b) $^{212}_{83}Bi \longrightarrow ? + ^{4}_{2}He$

11.48 Balance the following equations for the nuclear fission of $^{235}_{92}U$:

(a) $^{235}_{92}U + ^{1}_{0}n \longrightarrow ^{160}_{62}Sm + ^{72}_{30}Zn + ? \, ^{1}_{0}n$

(b) $^{235}_{92}U + ^{1}_{0}n \longrightarrow ^{87}_{35}Br + ? + 3 \, ^{1}_{0}n$

11.49 Complete the following nuclear equations and identify each as α decay, β decay, positron emission, or electron capture:

(a) $^{126}_{50}Sn \longrightarrow ? + ^{126}_{51}Sb$

(b) $^{210}_{88}Ra \longrightarrow ? + ^{206}_{86}Rn$

(c) $^{76}_{36}Kr + ? \longrightarrow ^{76}_{35}Br$

11.50 For centuries, alchemists dreamed of turning base metals into gold. The dream finally became reality when it was shown that mercury-198 can be converted into gold-198 when bombarded by neutrons. What small particle is produced in addition to gold-198? Write a balanced nuclear equation for the reaction.

11.51 Cobalt-60 (half-life = 5.3 years) is used to irradiate food, to treat cancer, and to disinfect surgical equipment. It is produced by irradiation of cobalt-59 in a nuclear reactor. It decays to nickel-60. Write nuclear equations for the formation and decay reactions of cobalt-60.

11.52 Bismuth-212 attaches readily to monoclonal antibodies and is used in the treatment of various cancers. This bismiuth-212 is formed after the parent isotope undergoes a decay series consisting of four α decays and one β decay. (the decays could be in any order). What is the parent isotope for this decay series?

11.53 Meitnerium-266 ($^{266}_{109}Mt$) was prepared in 1982 by bombardment of bismuth-209 atoms with iron-58. What other product must also have been formed? Write a balanced nuclear equation for the transformation.

HALF-LIFE

11.54 What does it mean when we say that strontium-90, a waste product of nuclear power plants, has a half-life of 28.8 years?

11.55 How many half lives must pass for the mass of a radioactive sample to decrease to 35% of the original mass? To 10%?

11.56 Selenium-75, a β emitter with a half-life of 120 days, is used medically for pancreas scans.

(a) Approximately how long would it take for a 0.050 g sample of selenium-75 to decrease to 0.010 g?

(b) Approximately how much selenium-75 would remain from a 0.050 g sample that has been stored for one year? (*Hint:* How many half-lives are in one year?)

11.57 Approximately how long would it take a sample of selenium-75 to lose 75% of its radioactivity? To lose 99%? (See Problem 11.56.)

11.58 The half-life of mercury-197 is 64.1 hours. If a patient undergoing a kidney scan is given 5.0 ng of mercury-197, how much will remain after 7 days? After 30 days?

11.59 Gold-198, a β emitter used to treat leukemia, has a half-life of 2.695 days. The standard dosage is about 1.0 mCi/kg body weight.

(a) What is the product of the β emission of gold-198?

(b) How long does it take a 30.0 mCi sample of gold-198 to decay so that only 3.75 mCi remains?

(c) How many millicuries are required in a single dosage administered to a 70.0 kg adult?

MEASURING RADIOACTIVITY

11.60 Describe how a Geiger counter works.

11.61 Describe how a film badge works.

11.62 Describe how a scintillation counter works.

11.63 Why are rems the preferred units for measuring the health effects of radiation?

11.64 Approximately what amount (in rems) of short-term exposure to radiation produces noticeable effects in humans?

11.65 Match each unit in the left column with the property being measured in the right column:

1. curie   (a) Ionizing intensity of radiation

2. rem   (b) Amount of tissue damage

3. rad   (c) Number of disintegrations per second

4. roentgen (d) Amount of radiation per gram of tissue

11.66 Technetium-99*m* is used for radioisotope-guided surgical biopsies of certain bone cancers. A patient must receive an injection of 28 mCi of technetium-99*m* 6–12 hours before surgery. If the activity of the solution is 15 mCi, what volume should be injected?

11.67 Sodium-24 is used to study the circulatory system and to treat chronic leukemia. It is administered in the form of saline (NaCl) solution, with a therapeutic dosage of 180 μCi/kg body weight.

(a) What dosage (in mCi) would be administered to a 68 kg adult patient?

(b) How many milliliters of a 6.5 mCi/mL solution are needed to treat a 68 kg adult?

11.68 A selenium-75 source is producing 300 rem at a distance of 2.0 m?

(a) What is its intensity at 16 m?

(b) What is its intensity at 25 m?

11.69 If a radiation source has an intensity of 650 rem at 1.0 m, what distance is needed to decrease the intensity of exposure to below 25 rem, the level at which no effects are detectable?

CHEMISTRY IN ACTION

11.70 What are the three main classes of techniques used in nuclear medicine? Give an example of each. [*Medical Uses of Radioactivity*, p. 338]

11.71 A 2 mL solution containing 1.25 μCi/mL is injected into the bloodstream of a patient. After dilution, a 1.00 mL sample is withdrawn and found to have an activity of

2.6 × 10^{-4} μCi. Calculate total blood volume. [*Medical Uses of Radioactivity, p. 338*]

11.72 What is the purpose of food irradiation, and how does it work? [*Irradiated Food, p. 345*]

11.73 What kind of radiation is used to treat food? [*Irradiated Food, p. 345*]

11.74 What are the advantages of CT and PET relative to conventional X rays? [*Body Imaging, p. 348*]

11.75 What advantages does MRI have over CT and PET imaging? [*Body Imaging, p. 348*]

GENERAL QUESTIONS AND PROBLEMS

11.76 Film badge dosimeters typically include filters to target specific types of radiation. A film badge is constructed that includes a region containing a tin foil filter, a region containing a plastic film filter, and a region with no filter. Which region monitors exposure to α-radiation? Which monitors exposure to β-radiation? Which monitors γ-radiation? Explain.

11.77 Some dried beans with a $^{14}C/^{12}C$ ratio one-eighth of the current value are found in an old cave. How old are the beans?

11.78 Harmful chemical spills can often be cleaned up by treatment with another chemical. For example, a spill of H_2SO_4 might be neutralized by addition of $NaHCO_3$. Why is it that the harmful radioactive wastes from nuclear power plants cannot be cleaned up as easily?

11.79 Why is a scintillation counter or Geiger counter more useful for determining the existence and source of a new radiation leak than a film badge?

11.80 A Geiger counter records an activity of 28 counts per minute (cpm) when located at a distance of 10 m. What will be the activity (in cpm) at a distance of 5 m?

11.81 Most of the stable isotopes for elements lighter than Ca-40 have equal numbers of protons and neutrons in the nucleus. What would be the most probable decay mode for an isotope that had more protons than neutrons? More neutrons than protons?

11.82 Technetium-99*m*, used for brain scans and to monitor heart function, is formed by decay of molybdenum-99.

(a) By what type of decay does ^{99}Mo produce ^{99m}Tc?

(b) Molybdenum-99 is formed by neutron bombardment of a natural isotope. If one neutron is absorbed and there are no other by-products of this process, from what isotope is ^{99}Mo formed?

11.83 The half-life of technetium-99*m* (Problem 11.82) is 6.01 hours. If a sample with an initial activity of 15 μCi is injected into a patient, what is the activity in 24 hours, assuming that none of the sample is excreted?

11.84 Plutonium-238 is an α emitter used to power batteries for heart pacemakers.

(a) Write the balanced nuclear equation for this emission.

(b) Why is a pacemaker battery enclosed in a metal case before being inserted into the chest cavity?

11.85 Sodium-24, a beta-emitter used in diagnosing circulation problems, has a half-life of 15 hours.

(a) Write the balanced nuclear equation for this emission.

(b) What fraction of sodium-24 remains after 50 hours?

11.86 High levels of radioactive fallout after the 1986 accident at the Chernobyl nuclear power plant in what is now Ukraine resulted in numerous miscarriages in humans and many instances of farm animals born with severe defects. Why are embryos and fetuses particularly susceptible to the effects of radiation?

11.87 One way to demonstrate the dose factor of ionizing radiation (penetrating distance × ionizing energy) is to think of radiation as cookies. Imagine that you have four cookies—an α cookie, a β cookie, a γ cookie, and a neutron cookie. Which one would you eat, which would you hold in your hand, which would you put in your pocket, and which would you throw away?

11.88 What are the main advantages of nuclear fission relative to nuclear fusion as an energy source? What are the drawbacks?

11.89 Although turning lead into gold in a nuclear reactor is technologically feasible (Problem 11.50), it is not economical. It is far easier to convert gold into lead. The process involves a series of neutron bombardments, and can be summarized as

$$^{197}_{79}\text{Au} + ?\,^{1}_{0}n \longrightarrow \,^{204}_{82}\text{Pb} + ?\,^{0}_{-1}e$$

How many neutrons and β particles are involved?

11.90 Balance the following transmutation reactions:

(a) $^{253}_{99}\text{Es} + ? \longrightarrow \,^{256}_{101}\text{Md} + \,^{1}_{0}n$

(b) $^{250}_{98}\text{Cf} + \,^{11}_{5}\text{B} \longrightarrow ? + 4\,^{1}_{0}n$

11.91 The most abundant isotope of uranium, ^{238}U, does not undergo fission. In a *breeder reactor*, however, a ^{238}U atom captures a neutron and emits 2 beta particles to make a fissionable isotope of plutonium, which can then be used as fuel in a nuclear reactor. Write the balanced nuclear equation.

11.92 Boron is used in *control rods* for nuclear reactors because it can absorb neutrons to keep a chain reaction from becoming supercritical, and decays by emitting alpha particles. Balance the equation:

$$^{10}_{5}\text{B} + \,^{1}_{0}n \longrightarrow ? + \,^{4}_{2}\text{He}$$

11.93 Thorium-232 decays by a 10-step series, ultimately yielding lead-208. How many α particles and how many β particles are emitted?

11.94 Californium-246 is formed by bombardment of uranium-238 atoms. If four neutrons are formed as by-products, what particle is used for the bombardment?

11.95 The most recently discovered element 117 (Ununseptium, Uus) was synthesized by nuclear transmutation reactions in which berkelium-249 was bombarded with calcium-48. Two isotopes of Uus were identified:

$$^{48}_{20}\text{Ca} + \,^{249}_{97}\text{Bk} \longrightarrow \,^{294}_{117}\text{Uus} + ?\,^{1}_{0}n$$

$$^{48}_{20}\text{Ca} + \,^{249}_{97}\text{Bk} \longrightarrow \,^{293}_{117}\text{Uus} + ?\,^{1}_{0}n$$

How many neutrons are produced in each reaction?

CHAPTER 12

Introduction to Organic Chemistry: Alkanes

CONTENTS

◄ The gasoline, kerosene, and other products of this petroleum refinery are primarily mixtures of simple organic compounds called alkanes.

The study of chemistry progressed in the 1700s as scientists isolated substances from the world around them and examined their properties. Researchers began to notice differences between the properties of compounds obtained from living sources and those obtained from minerals. As a result, the term *organic chemistry* was introduced to describe the study of compounds derived from living organisms, while *inorganic chemistry* was used to refer to the study of compounds from minerals.

It was long believed that organic compounds could only be obtained from a living source; this concept, known as *vitalism*, hindered the study of these types of molecules because vitalist chemists believed that organic materials could not be synthesized from inorganic components. It wasn't until 1828 that Friedrich Wöhler first prepared an organic compound, urea, from an inorganic salt, ammonium cyanate, disproving the theory of vitalism and truly pioneering the field of organic chemistry.

Today, we know that there are no fundamental differences between organic and inorganic compounds: The same scientific principles are applicable to both. The only common characteristic of compounds from living sources is that they contain the element carbon as their primary component. Thus, organic chemistry is now defined as the study of carbon-based compounds.

Why is carbon special? The answer derives from its position in the periodic table. As a group 4A nonmetal, carbon atoms have the unique ability to form four strong covalent bonds. Also, unlike atoms of other elements, carbon atoms can readily form strong bonds with other carbon atoms to produce long chains and rings. As a result, only carbon is able to form such a diverse and immense array of compounds, from methane with 1 carbon atom to DNA with billions of carbons.

12.1 The Nature of Organic Molecules

Let us begin a study of **organic chemistry**—the chemistry of carbon compounds—by reviewing what we have seen in earlier chapters about the structures of organic molecules:

Organic chemistry The study of carbon compounds.

- **Carbon is tetravalent; it always forms four bonds** (Section 4.2). In methane, for example, carbon is connected to 4 hydrogen atoms:

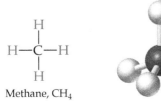

Methane, CH_4

- **Organic molecules have covalent bonds** (Section 4.2). In ethane, for example, the bonds result from the sharing of 2 electrons, either between 2 C atoms or a C and an H atom:

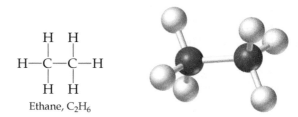

Ethane, C_2H_6

- **When carbon bonds to a more electronegative element, polar covalent bonds result** (Section 4.9). In chloromethane, for example, the electronegative chlorine atom attracts electrons more strongly than carbon, resulting in polarization of the C—Cl bond so that carbon and hydrogens have a partial positive charge, $\delta+$, and chlorine has a partial negative charge, $\delta-$. It is useful to think of polar covalent bonds in this manner, as it will later help to explain their reactivity. In electrostatic potential maps (Section 4.9), the chlorine atom is therefore in the red region of the map and the carbon atom in the blue region:

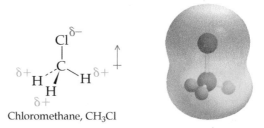

Chloromethane, CH_3Cl

- **Carbon forms multiple covalent bonds by sharing more than 2 electrons with a neighboring atom** (Section 4.3). In ethylene, for example, the 2 carbon atoms share 4 electrons in a double bond; in acetylene (also called ethyne), the 2 carbons share 6 electrons in a triple bond:

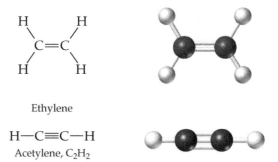

Ethylene

H—C≡C—H

Acetylene, C_2H_2

- **Organic molecules have specific three-dimensional shapes** (Section 4.8). When carbon is bonded to 4 atoms, as in methane, CH_4, the bonds are oriented toward the four corners of a regular tetrahedron with carbon in the center. Such three-dimensionality is commonly shown using normal lines for bonds in the plane of the page, dashed lines for bonds receding behind the page, and wedged lines for bonds coming out of the page:

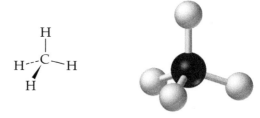

- **Organic molecules often contain nitrogen and oxygen in addition to carbon and hydrogen** (Section 4.7). Nitrogen can form single, double, and triple bonds to carbon, while oxygen can form single and double bonds. Hydrogen can only form single bonds to carbon:

$$C-N \quad C-O \quad C-H$$
$$C=N \quad C=O$$
$$C\equiv N$$

Covalent bonding makes organic compounds quite different from the inorganic compounds we have been concentrating on up to this point. For example, inorganic compounds such as NaCl have high melting points and high boiling points because they consist of large numbers of oppositely charged ions held together by strong electrical attractions. By contrast, organic compounds consist of atoms joined by covalent bonds, forming individual molecules. Because the organic molecules are attracted to one another only by weak non-ionic intermolecular forces, organic compounds generally have lower melting and boiling points than inorganic salts. As a result, many simple organic compounds are liquids or low melting solids at room temperature, and a few are gases.

Other important differences between organic and inorganic compounds include solubility and electrical conductivity. Whereas many inorganic compounds dissolve in water to yield solutions of ions that conduct electricity, most organic compounds are insoluble in water, and almost all of those that are soluble do not conduct electricity. Only small polar organic molecules, such as glucose and ethyl alcohol, or large molecules with many polar groups, such as some proteins, interact with water molecules through both dipole–dipole interactions and/or hydrogen bonding and thus dissolve in water. This lack of water solubility for organic compounds has important practical consequences, varying from the difficulty in removing greasy dirt and cleaning up environmental oil spills to drug delivery.

▶ ▶ Other unique properties of ionic compounds are discussed in Section 3.4.

▶ ▶ Recall from Section 8.11 the various intermolecular forces: dipole–dipole forces, London dispersion forces, and hydrogen bonds.

▶ ▶ Section 9.9 explores how anions and cations in solution conduct electric current.

▶ ▶ Recall from Section 9.2 that a compound is only soluble when the intermolecular forces between solvent and solute are comparable in strength to the intermolecular forces of the pure solvent or solute.

◄ **Oil spills can be a serious environmental problem because oil is insoluble in water.**

LOOKING AHEAD ▶ ▶ The interior of a living cell is largely a water solution that contains many hundreds of different compounds. In later chapters, we will see how cells use membranes composed of water-insoluble organic molecules to enclose their watery interiors and to regulate the flow of substances across the cell boundary.

12.2 Families of Organic Molecules: Functional Groups

More than 18 *million* organic compounds are described in the scientific literature. Each of these 18 million compounds has unique chemical and physical properties, and many of them also have unique biological properties (both desired and undesired). How can we ever understand them all?

Chemists have learned through experience that organic compounds can be classified into families according to their structural features, and that the chemical behavior of family members is often predictable based on their specific grouping of atoms. Instead of 18 million compounds with seemingly random chemical reactivity, there are just a few general families of organic compounds whose chemistry falls into simple patterns.

Functional group An atom or group of atoms within a molecule that has a characteristic physical and chemical behavior.

The structural features that allow us to classify organic compounds into distinct chemical families are called **functional groups**. A functional group is an atom or group of atoms that has a characteristic physical and chemical behavior. Each functional group is always part of a larger molecule, and a molecule may have more than one class of functional group present, as we shall soon see. An important property of functional groups is that a given functional group *tends to undergo the same reactions in every molecule that contains it*. For example, the carbon–carbon double bond is a common functional group. Ethylene (C_2H_4), the simplest compound with a double bond, undergoes many chemical reactions similar to those of oleic acid ($C_{18}H_{34}O_2$), a much larger and more complex compound that also contains a double bond. Both, for example, react with hydrogen gas in the same manner, as shown in Figure 12.1. These identical reactions with hydrogen are typical: *The chemistry of an organic molecule is primarily determined by the functional groups it contains, not by its size or complexity.*

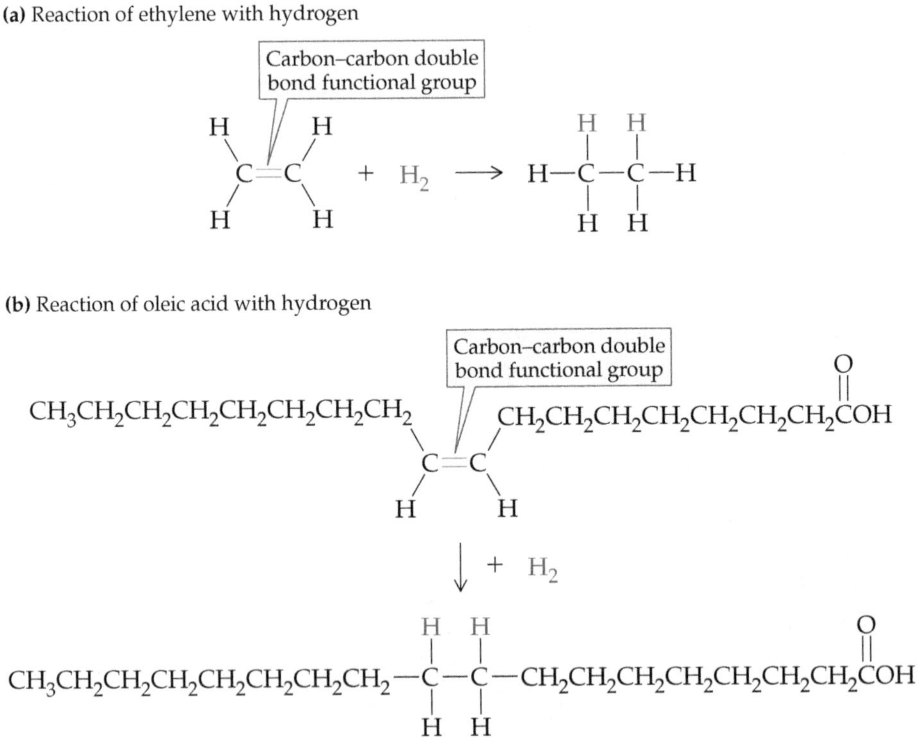

▶ **Figure 12.1**
The reactions of (a) ethylene and (b) oleic acid with hydrogen.
The carbon–carbon double-bond functional group adds 2 hydrogen atoms in both cases, regardless of the complexity of the rest of the molecule.

(a) Reaction of ethylene with hydrogen

(b) Reaction of oleic acid with hydrogen

Table 12.1 lists some of the most important families of organic molecules and their distinctive functional groups. Compounds that contain a C═C double bond, for instance, are in the *alkene* family; compounds that have an —OH group bound to a tetravalent carbon are in the *alcohol* family; and so on. To aid in identifying the organic functional groups you will encounter, we have included an Organic Functional Group Flow Scheme (Figure 12.5) at the end of the chapter; it should be used in conjunction with Table 12.1. You will find it helpful as you proceed through the remainder of this text.

Much of the chemistry discussed in this and the next five chapters is the chemistry of the families listed in Table 12.1, so it is best to learn the names and become familiar with their structures now. Note that they fall into four groups:

Hydrocarbon An organic compound that contains only carbon and hydrogen.

- The first four families in Table 12.1 are **hydrocarbons**, organic compounds that contain only carbon and hydrogen. *Alkanes* have only single bonds and contain

TABLE 12.1 Some Important Families of Organic Molecules

FAMILY NAME	FUNCTIONAL GROUP STRUCTURE*	SIMPLE EXAMPLE	LINE STRUCTURE	NAME ENDING
Alkane	Contains only C—H and C—C single bonds	$CH_3CH_2CH_3$ Propane		*-ane*
Alkene	$\overset{\backslash}{\underset{/}{C}}=\overset{/}{\underset{\backslash}{C}}$	$H_2C{=}CH_2$ Ethylene		*-ene*
Alkyne	$-C{\equiv}C-$	$H-C{\equiv}C-H$ Acetylene (Ethyne)	$H{=\!\!=\!\!=}H$	*-yne*
Aromatic		Benzene		None
Alkyl halide	$-\overset{\mid}{\underset{\mid}{C}}-X$ (X=F, Cl, Br, I)	CH_3CH_2Cl Ethyl chloride		None
Alcohol	$-\overset{\mid}{\underset{\mid}{C}}-O-H$	CH_3CH_2OH Ethyl alcohol (Ethanol)		*-ol*
Ether	$-\overset{\mid}{\underset{\mid}{C}}-O-\overset{\mid}{\underset{\mid}{C}}-$	$CH_3CH_2-O-CH_2CH_3$ Diethyl ether		None
Amine	$-\overset{\mid}{\underset{\mid}{C}}-N\overset{/}{\backslash}$	$CH_3CH_2NH_2$ Ethylamine		*-amine*
Aldehyde	$-\overset{\mid}{\underset{\mid}{C}}-\overset{O}{\overset{\|}{C}}-H$	$CH_3-\overset{O}{\overset{\|}{C}}-H$ Acetaldehyde (Ethanal)		*-al*
Ketone	$-\overset{\mid}{\underset{\mid}{C}}-\overset{O}{\overset{\|}{C}}-\overset{\mid}{\underset{\mid}{C}}-$	$CH_3-\overset{O}{\overset{\|}{C}}-CH_3$ Acetone		*-one*
Carboxylic acid	$-\overset{\mid}{\underset{\mid}{C}}-\overset{O}{\overset{\|}{C}}-OH$	$CH_3-\overset{O}{\overset{\|}{C}}-OH$ Acetic acid		*-ic acid*
Anhydride	$-\overset{\mid}{\underset{\mid}{C}}-\overset{O}{\overset{\|}{C}}-O-\overset{O}{\overset{\|}{C}}-\overset{\mid}{\underset{\mid}{C}}-$	$CH_3-\overset{O}{\overset{\|}{C}}-O-\overset{O}{\overset{\|}{C}}-CH_3$ Acetic anhydride		None
Ester	$-\overset{\mid}{\underset{\mid}{C}}-\overset{O}{\overset{\|}{C}}-O-\overset{\mid}{\underset{\mid}{C}}-$	$CH_3-\overset{O}{\overset{\|}{C}}-O-CH_3$ Methyl acetate		*-ate*
Amide	$-\overset{\mid}{\underset{\mid}{C}}-\overset{O}{\overset{\|}{C}}-NH_2, -\overset{\mid}{\underset{\mid}{C}}-\overset{O}{\overset{\|}{C}}-N-H,$ $-\overset{\mid}{\underset{\mid}{C}}-\overset{O}{\overset{\|}{C}}-\overset{\mid}{N}-$	$CH_3-\overset{O}{\overset{\|}{C}}-NH_2$ Acetamide		*-amide*
Thiol	$-\overset{\mid}{\underset{\mid}{C}}-SH$	CH_3CH_2SH Ethyl thiol		None
Disulfide	$C-S-S-C$	CH_3SSCH_3 Dimethyl disulfide		None
Sulfide	$C-S-C$	$CH_3CH_2SCH_3$ Ethyl methyl sulfide		None

*The bonds whose connections are not specified are assumed to be attached to carbon or hydrogen atoms in the rest of the molecule.

no functional groups. As we will see, the absence of functional groups makes alkanes relatively unreactive. *Alkenes* contain a carbon–carbon double-bond functional group; *alkynes* contain a carbon–carbon triple-bond functional group; and *aromatic* compounds contain a six-membered ring of carbon atoms with three alternating double bonds.

- The next four families in Table 12.1 have functional groups that contain only single bonds and have a carbon atom bonded to an electronegative atom. *Alkyl halides* have a carbon–halogen bond; *alcohols* have a carbon–oxygen bond; *ethers* have two carbons bonded to the same oxygen; and *amines* have a carbon–nitrogen bond.
- The next six families in Table 12.1 have functional groups that contain a carbon–oxygen double bond: *aldehydes, ketones, carboxylic acids, anhydrides, esters*, and *amides*.
- The remaining three families in Table 12.1 have functional groups that contain sulfur: *thioalcohols* (known simply as *thiols*), *sulfides*, and *disulfides*. These three families play an important role in protein function (Chapter 18).

Worked Example 12.1 Molecular Structures: Identifying Functional Groups

To which family of organic compounds do the following compounds belong? Explain.

(a)
(b)
(c)
(d)
(e)
(f)

ANALYSIS Use the Organic Functional Group Flow Scheme (Figure 12.5, see end of chapter) and Table 12.1 to identify each functional group, and name the corresponding family to which the compound belongs. Begin by determining what elements are present and whether multiple bonds are present.

SOLUTION

(a) This compound contains only carbon and hydrogen atoms, so it is a *hydrocarbon*. There is only one carbon–carbon double bond, so it is an *alkene*.

(b) This compound contains an oxygen and has only single bonds. The presence of the O—H group bonded to tetravalent carbon identifies this compound as an *alcohol*.

(c) This compound also contains only carbon and hydrogen atoms, which identifies it as a *hydrocarbon*. It has three double bonds in a ring. The six-membered carbon ring with alternating double bonds also identifies this compound as an *aromatic* hydrocarbon compound.

(d) This molecule contains an oxygen that is double bonded to a carbon (a *carbonyl group*, discussed in Chapter 16), and there is no singly bound oxygen or nitrogen also connected to the carbon. The carbon–oxygen double bond is connected to two other carbons (as opposed to a hydrogen); that identifies this compound as a *ketone*.

(e) Many of the organic molecules we will come across have more than one functional group present in the same molecule; in these cases we will classify the molecule as belonging to multiple functional group families. This molecule contains oxygen and nitrogen in addition to carbon and hydrogen, so it is not a hydrocarbon. The presence of the carbonyl group further classifies this molecule, but here we run into a problem: one —NH$_2$ is attached to the carbonyl but the other —NH_2 is not. This leads us to conclude that there are two functional groups present: an *amide* and an *amine*:

amine
NH_2
amide
$CH_3—CH—C—NH_2$
$\overset{\|}{O}$

(f) This molecule also contains two functional groups: a ring containing alternating carbon–carbon single and double bonds as well as an S—S group. From our flow scheme, we trace the double bond to indicate we have an aromatic hydrocarbon, while the sulfurs indicate the presence of a disulfide:

$—CH_2—CH—CH_3$
$\overset{|}{S—S—CH_3}$

aromatic

disulfide

Worked Example 12.2 Molecular Structures: Drawing Functional Groups

Given the family of organic compounds to which the compound belongs, propose structures for compounds having the following chemical formulas.

(a) An amine having the formula C_2H_7N
(b) An alkyne having the formula C_3H_4
(c) An ether having the formula $C_4H_{10}O$

ANALYSIS Identify the functional group for each compound from Table 12.1. Once the atoms in this functional group are eliminated from the chemical formula, the remaining structure can be determined. (Remember that each carbon atom forms four bonds, nitrogen forms three bonds, oxygen forms two bonds, and hydrogen forms only one bond.)

SOLUTION

(a) Amines have a C—NH_2 group. Eliminating these atoms from the formula leaves 1 C atom and 5 H atoms. Since only the carbons are capable of forming more than one bond, the 2 C atoms must be bonded together. The remaining H atoms are then bonded to the carbons until each C has 4 bonds.

$$H—\overset{\overset{\displaystyle H}{|}}{\underset{\underset{\displaystyle H}{|}}{C}}—\overset{\overset{\displaystyle H}{|}}{\underset{\underset{\displaystyle H}{|}}{C}}—N\overset{\nearrow H}{\searrow_H}$$

(b) The alkynes contain a C≡C bond. This leaves 1 C atom and 4 H atoms. Attach this C to one of the carbons in the triple bond, and then distribute the H atoms until each carbon has a full complement of four bonds.

$$H—\overset{\overset{\displaystyle H}{|}}{\underset{\underset{\displaystyle H}{|}}{C}}—C≡C—H$$

(c) The ethers contain a C—O—C group. Eliminating these atoms leaves 2 C atoms and 10 H atoms. The C atoms can be distributed on either end of the ether group, and the H atoms are then distributed until each carbon atom has a full complement of four bonds.

$$H—\overset{\overset{\displaystyle H}{|}}{\underset{\underset{\displaystyle H}{|}}{C}}—\overset{\overset{\displaystyle H}{|}}{\underset{\underset{\displaystyle H}{|}}{C}}—O—\overset{\overset{\displaystyle H}{|}}{\underset{\underset{\displaystyle H}{|}}{C}}—\overset{\overset{\displaystyle H}{|}}{\underset{\underset{\displaystyle H}{|}}{C}}—H \quad \text{or} \quad H—\overset{\overset{\displaystyle H}{|}}{\underset{\underset{\displaystyle H}{|}}{C}}—\overset{\overset{\displaystyle H}{|}}{\underset{\underset{\displaystyle H}{|}}{C}}—\overset{\overset{\displaystyle H}{|}}{\underset{\underset{\displaystyle H}{|}}{C}}—O—\overset{\overset{\displaystyle H}{|}}{\underset{\underset{\displaystyle H}{|}}{C}}—H$$

PROBLEM 12.1

Many organic compounds contain more than one functional group. Locate and identify the functional groups in **(a)** lactic acid, from sour milk; **(b)** methyl methacrylate, used in making Lucite and Plexiglas; and **(c)** phenylalanine, an amino acid found in proteins.

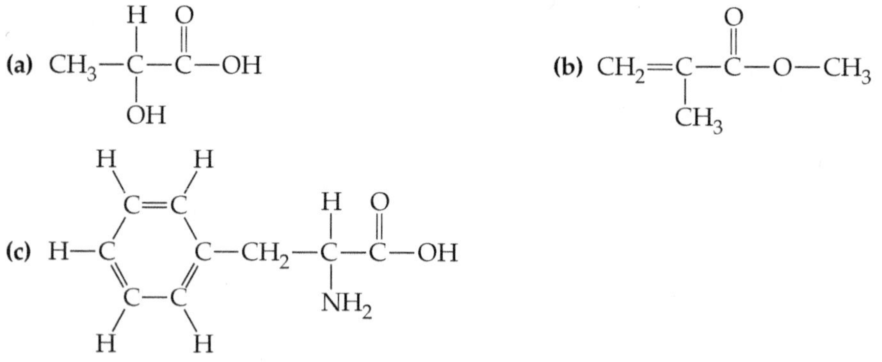

(a) $CH_3-\overset{\displaystyle H}{\underset{\displaystyle OH}{C}}-\overset{\displaystyle O}{C}-OH$

(b) $CH_2{=}\overset{}{\underset{\displaystyle CH_3}{C}}-\overset{\displaystyle O}{C}-O-CH_3$

(c) $H-C\overset{\displaystyle H \quad H}{\underset{}{}}$ ... $C-CH_2-\overset{\displaystyle H}{\underset{\displaystyle NH_2}{C}}-\overset{\displaystyle O}{C}-OH$

PROBLEM 12.2

Propose structures for molecules that fit the following descriptions:

(a) C_3H_6O containing an aldehyde functional group
(b) C_3H_6O containing a ketone functional group
(c) $C_3H_6O_2$ containing a carboxylic acid functional group

12.3 The Structure of Organic Molecules: Alkanes and Their Isomers

Alkane A hydrocarbon that has only single bonds.

Hydrocarbons that contain only single bonds belong to the family of organic molecules called **alkanes**. Imagine how 1 carbon and 4 hydrogens can combine, and you will realize there is only one possibility: methane, CH_4. Now, imagine how 2 carbons and 6 hydrogens can combine—only ethane, CH_3CH_3, is possible. Likewise, with the combination of 3 carbons with 8 hydrogens—only propane, $CH_3CH_2CH_3$, is possible. The general rule for *all* hydrocarbons except methane is that each carbon *must* be bonded to at least one other carbon. The carbon atoms bond together to form the "backbone" of the compound, with the hydrogens on the periphery. The general formula for alkanes is C_nH_{2n+2}, where n is the number of carbons in the compound.

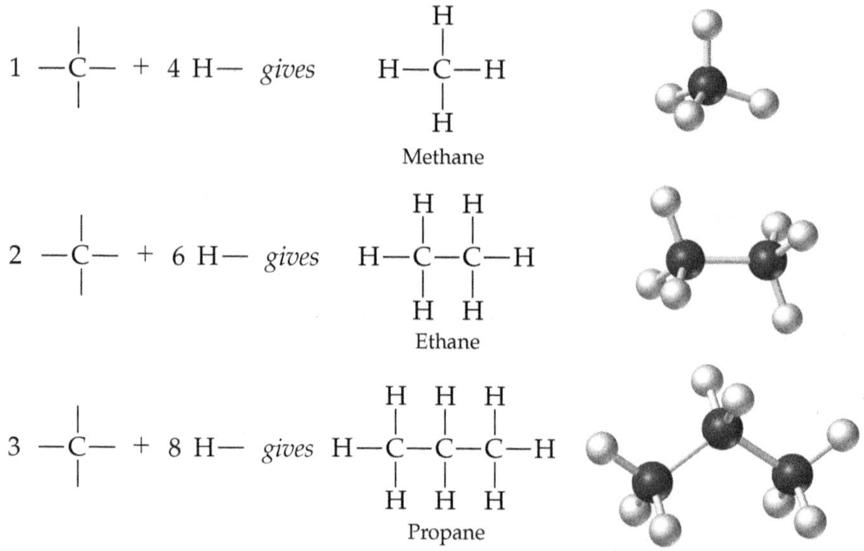

$$1 \; -\overset{|}{\underset{|}{C}}- \; + \; 4\,H- \quad gives \quad H-\overset{\displaystyle H}{\underset{\displaystyle H}{C}}-H$$

Methane

$$2 \; -\overset{|}{\underset{|}{C}}- \; + \; 6\,H- \quad gives \quad H-\overset{\displaystyle H}{\underset{\displaystyle H}{C}}-\overset{\displaystyle H}{\underset{\displaystyle H}{C}}-H$$

Ethane

$$3 \; -\overset{|}{\underset{|}{C}}- \; + \; 8\,H- \quad gives \quad H-\overset{\displaystyle H}{\underset{\displaystyle H}{C}}-\overset{\displaystyle H}{\underset{\displaystyle H}{C}}-\overset{\displaystyle H}{\underset{\displaystyle H}{C}}-H$$

Propane

As larger numbers of carbons and hydrogens combine, the ability to form *isomers* arises. Compounds that have the same molecular formula but different structural formulas are called **isomers** of one another. For example, there are two ways in which molecules that have the formula C_4H_{10} can be formed. The 4 carbons can either be joined in a contiguous row or have a branched arrangement:

Isomers Compounds with the same molecular formula but different structures.

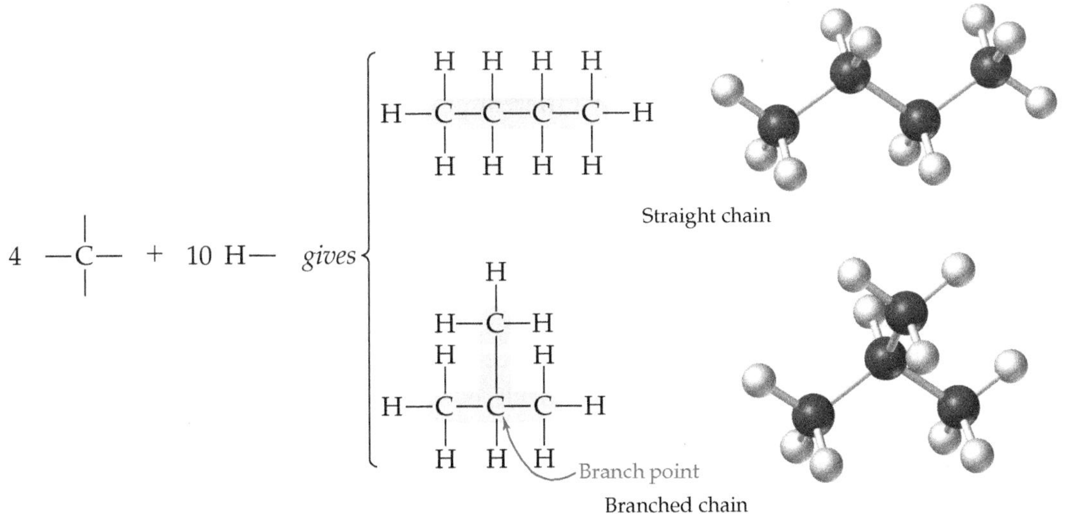

Straight chain

$$4 \quad -\overset{|}{\underset{|}{C}}- \quad + \quad 10 \text{ H}- \quad gives$$

Branch point

Branched chain

The same is seen with the molecules that have the formula C_5H_{12}, for which three isomers are possible:

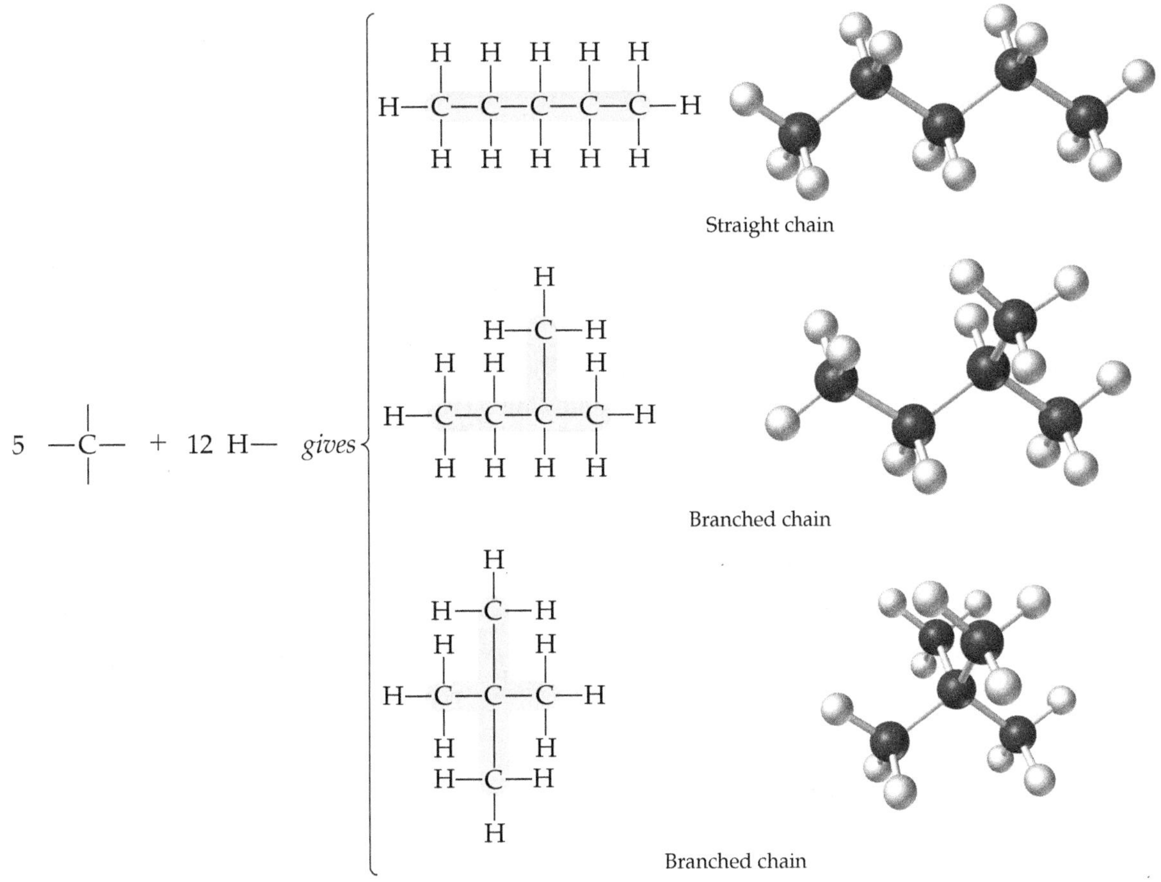

Straight chain

$$5 \quad -\overset{|}{\underset{|}{C}}- \quad + \quad 12 \text{ H}- \quad gives$$

Branched chain

Branched chain

Compounds with all their carbons connected in a continuous chain are called **straight-chain alkanes**; those with a branching connection of carbons are called **branched-chain alkanes**. Note that in a straight-chain alkane, you can draw a line through all the carbon atoms without lifting your pencil from the paper. In a branched-chain alkane, however, you must either lift your pencil from the paper or retrace your steps to draw a line through all the carbons.

Straight-chain alkane An alkane that has all its carbons connected in a row.

Branched-chain alkane An alkane that has a branching connection of carbons.

Constitutional isomers Compounds with the same molecular formula but different connections among their atoms.

The two isomers of C_4H_{10} and the three isomers of C_5H_{12} shown above are **constitutional isomers**—compounds with the same molecular formula but with different connections among their constituent atoms. Needless to say, the number of possible alkane isomers grows rapidly as the number of carbon atoms increases.

Constitutional isomers of a given molecular formula are chemically distinct from one another. They have different structures, physical properties (such as melting and boiling points), and potentially different physiological properties. When the molecular formula contains atoms other than carbon and hydrogen, the constitutional isomers obtained can also be **functional group isomers**: isomers that differ in both molecular connection and family classification. In these cases the differences between isomers can be dramatic. For example, ethyl alcohol and dimethyl ether both have the formula C_2H_6O, but ethyl alcohol is a liquid with a boiling point of 78.5 °C and dimethyl ether is a gas with a boiling point of +23 °C. While ethyl alcohol is a depressant of the central nervous system, dimethyl ether is a nontoxic compound with anesthetic properties at high concentrations. Clearly, molecular formulas by themselves are not very useful in organic chemistry; a knowledge of structure is also necessary.

Functional group isomer Isomers having the same chemical formula but belonging to different chemical families due to differences in bonding; ethyl alcohol and dimethyl ether are examples of functional group isomers.

Ethyl alcohol
C_2H_6O

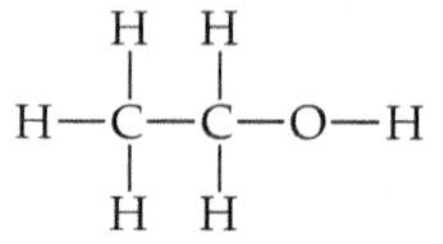

Dimethyl ether
C_2H_6O

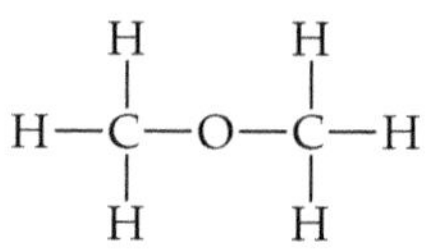

Worked Example 12.3 Molecular Structures: Drawing Isomers

Draw all isomers that have the formula C_6H_{14}.

ANALYSIS Knowing that all the carbons must be bonded together to form the molecule, find all possible arrangements of the 6 carbon atoms. Begin with the isomer that has all 6 carbons in a straight chain, then draw the isomer that has 5 carbons in a straight chain, using the remaining carbon to form a branch, then repeat for the isomer having 4 carbons in a straight chain and 2 carbons in branches. Once each carbon backbone is drawn, arrange the hydrogens around the carbons to complete the structure. (Remember that each carbon can only have *four* bonds total.)

SOLUTION

The straight-chain isomer contains all 6 carbons bonded to form a chain with no branches. The branched isomers are drawn by starting with either a 5-carbon chain or a 4-carbon chain, and adding the extra carbons as branches in the middle of the chain. Hydrogens are added until each carbon has a full complement of four bonds.

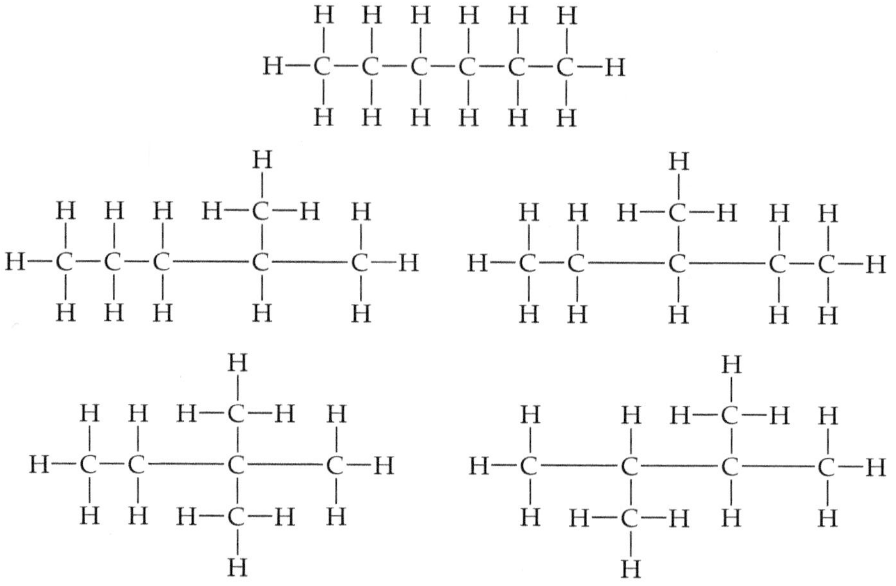

PROBLEM 12.3
Draw the straight-chain isomer with the formula (**a**) C_7H_{16}; (**b**) C_9H_{20}.

PROBLEM 12.4
Draw the two branched-chain isomers with the formula C_7H_{16}, where the longest chain in the molecule is 6 carbons long.

12.4 Drawing Organic Structures

Drawing structural formulas that show every atom and every bond in a molecule is both time-consuming and awkward, even for relatively small molecules. Much easier is the use of **condensed structures**, which are simpler but still show the essential information about which functional groups are present and how atoms are connected. In condensed structures, C—C and C—H single bonds are not necessarily shown; rather, they are "understood." If a carbon atom has 3 hydrogens bonded to it, we write CH_3; if the carbon has 2 hydrogens bonded to it, we write CH_2; and so on. For example, the 4-carbon, straight-chain alkane called butane and its branched-chain isomer (2-methylpropane) can be written as the following condensed structures:

Condensed structure A shorthand way of drawing structures in which C—C and C—H bonds are understood rather than shown.

▸▸▸ Condensed structures were explored in Section 4.7.

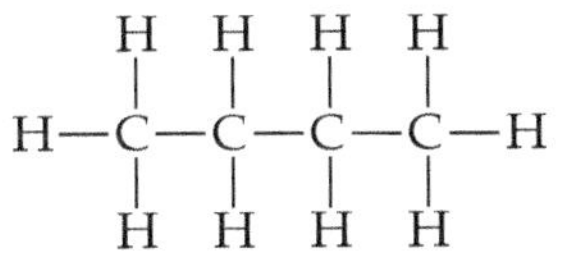

H H H H
| | | |
H—C—C—C—C—H = $CH_3CH_2CH_2CH_3$
| | | |
H H H H

Butane

Structural formula   Condensed formula

              H
              |
          H—C—H
          H | H
          | | |
H—C—C—C—H = CH_3CHCH_3 CH_3
  | | |
  H H H

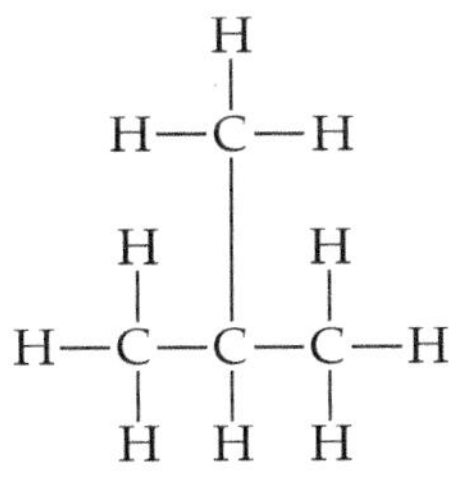

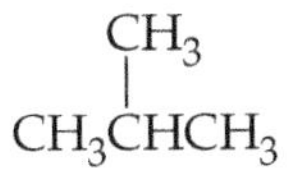

2-Methylpropane

Structural formula   Condensed formula

Note in these condensed structures for butane and 2-methylpropane that the horizontal bonds between carbons are not usually shown—the CH_3 and CH_2 units are simply placed next to one another—but that the vertical bond in 2-methylpropane *is* shown for clarity.

Occasionally, as a further simplification, not all the CH_2 groups (called **methylenes**) are shown. Instead, CH_2 is shown once in parentheses, with a subscript indicating the number of methylene units strung together. For example, the 6-carbon straight-chain alkane (hexane) can be written as

Methylene Another name for a CH_2 unit.

$$CH_3CH_2CH_2CH_2CH_2CH_3 = CH_3(CH_2)_4CH_3$$

Worked Example 12.4 Molecular Structures: Writing Condensed Structures

Write condensed structures for the isomers from Worked Example 12.3.

ANALYSIS Eliminate all horizontal bonds, substituting reduced formula components (CH_3, CH_2, and so on) for each carbon in the compound. Show vertical bonds to branching carbons for clarity.

SOLUTION

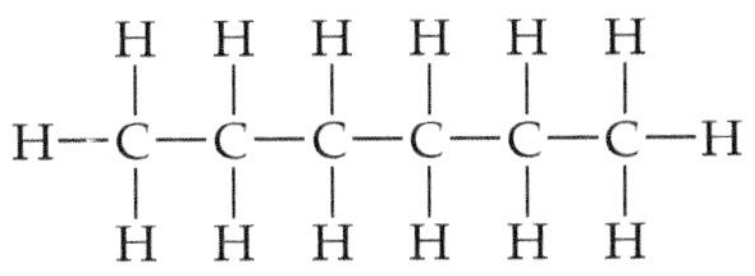

H H H H H H
| | | | | |
H--C—C—C—C—C—C—H ⟶ $CH_3CH_2CH_2CH_2CH_2CH_3$ or
| | | | | | $CH_3(CH_2)_4CH_3$
H H H H H H

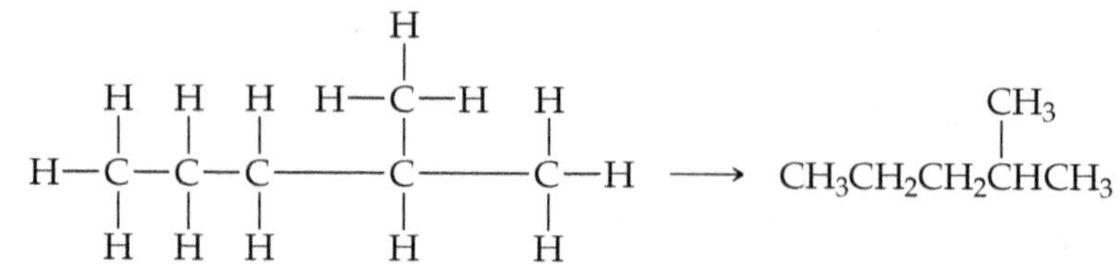

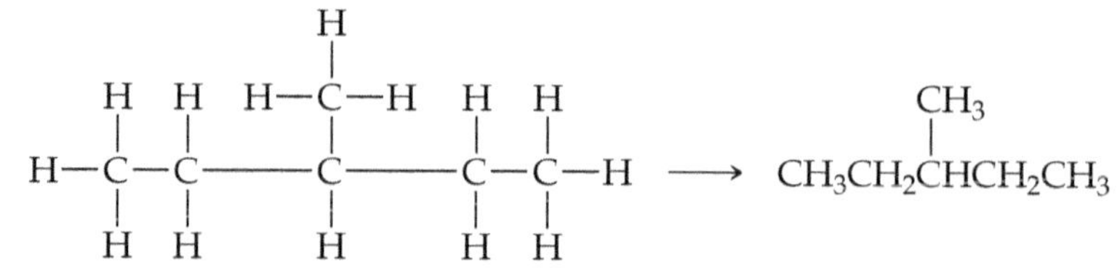

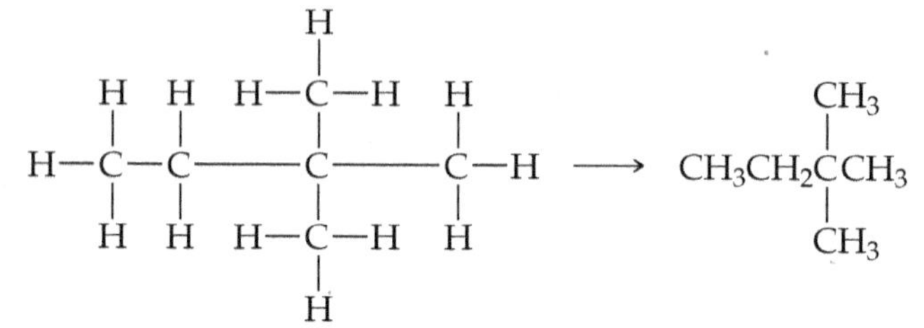

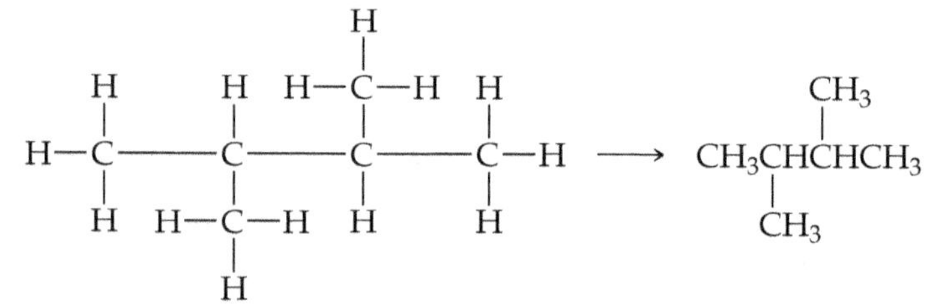

$$\text{H—C—C—C} \overline{\quad\quad} \text{C} \overline{\quad\quad} \text{C—H} \longrightarrow CH_3CH_2CH_2CHCH_3$$

with pendant CH3 group; product: CH₃CH₂CH₂CHCH₃ with CH3 above

$$\longrightarrow CH_3CH_2CHCH_2CH_3$$

with CH3 above second carbon

$$\longrightarrow CH_3CH_2CCH_3$$

with CH3 above and CH3 below the C

$$\longrightarrow CH_3CHCHCH_3$$

with CH3 above and CH3 below

PROBLEM 12.5

Draw the following three isomers of C_5H_{12} as condensed structures:

(a) 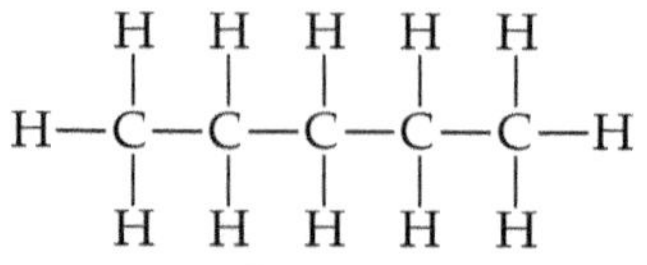
$$H-\underset{\underset{H}{|}}{\overset{\overset{H}{|}}{C}}-\underset{\underset{H}{|}}{\overset{\overset{H}{|}}{C}}-\underset{\underset{H}{|}}{\overset{\overset{H}{|}}{C}}-\underset{\underset{H}{|}}{\overset{\overset{H}{|}}{C}}-\underset{\underset{H}{|}}{\overset{\overset{H}{|}}{C}}-H$$
Pentane

(b) 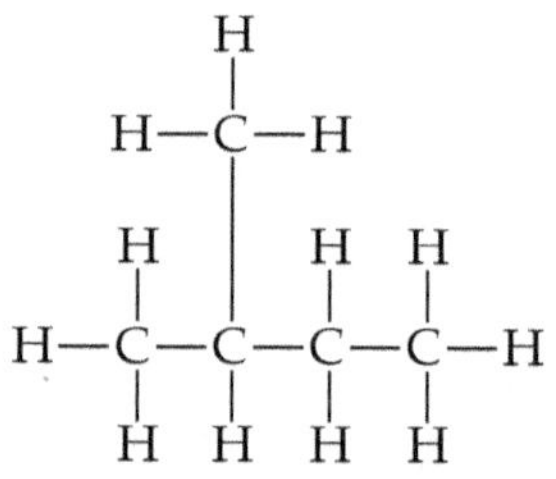
$$H-\underset{\underset{H}{|}}{\overset{\overset{H}{|}}{C}}-\underset{\underset{H}{|}}{\overset{\overset{H-C-H}{|}}{C}}-\underset{\underset{H}{|}}{\overset{\overset{H}{|}}{C}}-\underset{\underset{H}{|}}{\overset{\overset{H}{|}}{C}}-H$$
2-Methylbutane

(c) 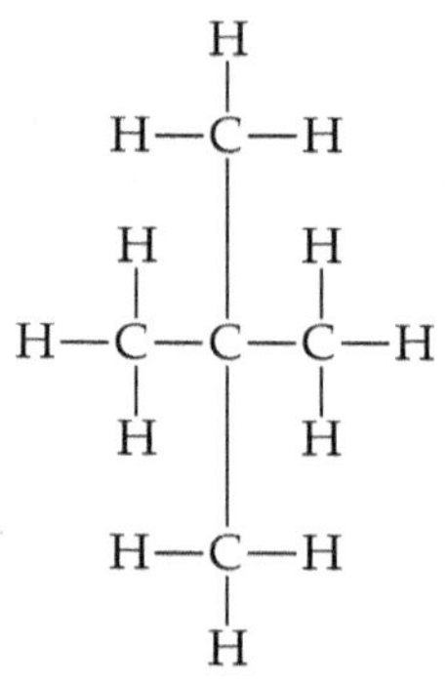
$$H-\underset{\underset{H}{|}}{\overset{\overset{H}{|}}{C}}-\underset{\underset{H-C-H}{|}}{\overset{\overset{H-C-H}{|}}{C}}-\underset{\underset{H}{|}}{\overset{\overset{H}{|}}{C}}-H$$
2,2-Dimethylpropane

Another way of representing organic molecules is to use **line (or line-angle)**
structures, which are structures in which the symbols C and H do not appear. Instead,
a chain of carbon atoms and their associated hydrogens are represented by a zigzag
arrangement of short lines, with any branches off the main chain represented by
additional lines. The line structure for 2-methylbutane, for instance, is

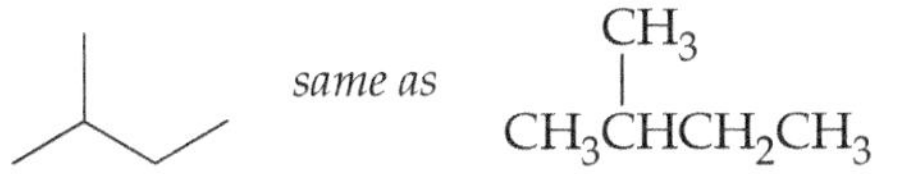

$$\textit{same as} \quad \begin{array}{c} CH_3 \\ | \\ CH_3CHCH_2CH_3 \end{array}$$

Line structure Also known as line-
angle structure; a shorthand way of
drawing structures in which carbon
and hydrogen atoms are not explicitly
shown. Instead, a carbon atom is understood to be wherever a line begins
or ends and at every intersection of
two lines, and hydrogens are understood to be wherever they are needed
to have each carbon form four bonds.

Line structures are a simple and quick way to represent organic molecules without
the clutter arising from showing all carbons and hydrogens present. Chemists, biolo-
gists, pharmacists, doctors, and nurses all use line structures to conveniently convey to
one another very complex organic structures. Another advantage is that a line structure gives a more realistic depiction of the angles seen in a carbon chain.

Drawing a molecule in this way is simple, provided one follows these guidelines:

1. Each carbon–carbon bond is represented by a line.
2. Anywhere a line ends or begins, as well as any vertex where two lines meet,
    represents a carbon atom.
3. Any atom other than another carbon or a hydrogen attached to a carbon must
    be shown.
4. Since a neutral carbon atom forms four bonds, all bonds not shown for any
    carbon are understood to be the number of carbon–hydrogen bonds needed to
    have the carbon form four bonds.

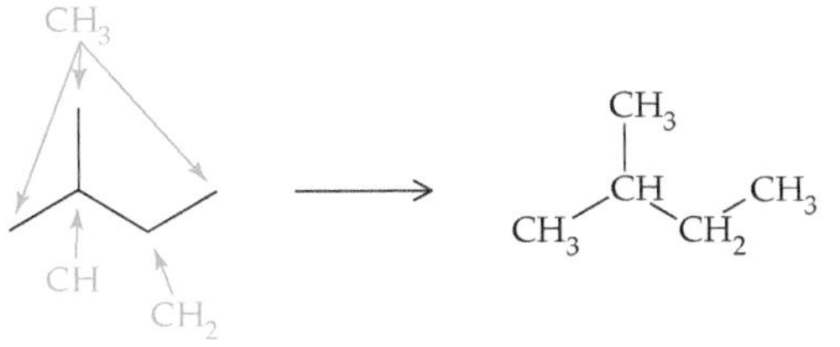

Converting line structures to structural formulas or to condensed structures is
simply a matter of correctly interpreting each line ending and each intersection in a
line structure. For example, the common pain reliever ibuprofen has the condensed
and line structures

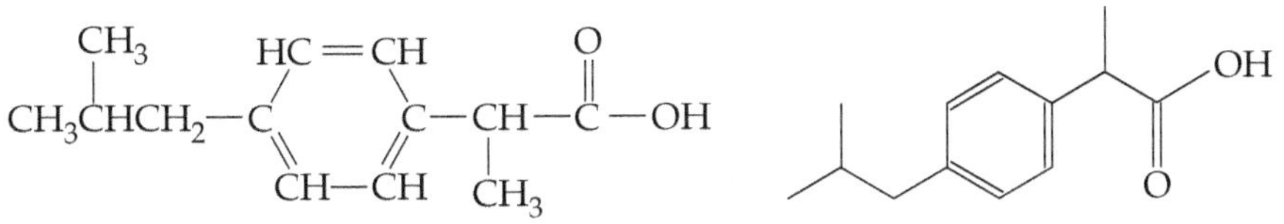

Finally, it is important to note that chemists and biochemists often use a mixture
of structural formulas, condensed structures, and line structures to represent the molecules they study. As you progress through this textbook, you will see many complicated molecules represented in this way, so it is a good idea to get used to thinking
interchangeably in all three formats.

Worked Example 12.5 Molecular Structures: Converting Condensed Structures
to Line Structures

Convert the following condensed structures to line structures:

(a) $$\begin{array}{c} CH_3 \\ | \\ CH_3CH_2CHCHCH_2CH_3 \\ | \\ CH_3 \end{array}$$

(b) $$\begin{array}{c} OH \quad\ Cl \\ |\qquad | \\ CH_3CHCH—C\ CH_2CH_3 \\ \quad\ |\quad\ | \\ \quad\ CH_3\ CH_3 \end{array}$$

ANALYSIS Find the longest continuous chain of carbon atoms in the condensed structure. Begin the line structure by drawing a zigzag line in which the number of vertices plus line ends equals the number of carbon atoms in the chain. Show branches coming off the main chain by drawing vertical lines at the vertices as needed. Show all atoms that are not carbons or are not hydrogens attached to carbons.

SOLUTION

(a) Begin by drawing a zigzag line in which the total number of ends + vertices equals the number of carbons in the longest chain (here 6, with the carbons numbered for clarity):

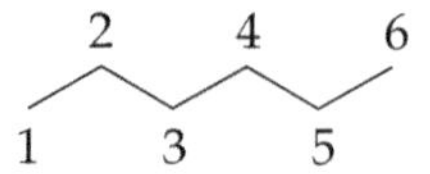

Looking at the condensed structure, you see CH_3 groups on carbons 3 and 4; these two methyl groups are represented by lines coming off those carbons in the line structure:

This is the complete line structure. Notice that the hydrogens are not shown, but understood. For example, carbon 4 has three bonds shown: one to carbon 3, one to carbon 5, and one to the branch methyl group; the fourth bond this carbon must have is understood to be to a hydrogen.

(b) Proceed as in (a), drawing a zigzag line for the longest chain of carbon atoms, which again contains 6 carbons. Next draw a line coming off each carbon bonded to a CH_3 group (carbons 3 and 4). Both the OH and the Cl groups must be shown to give the final structure:

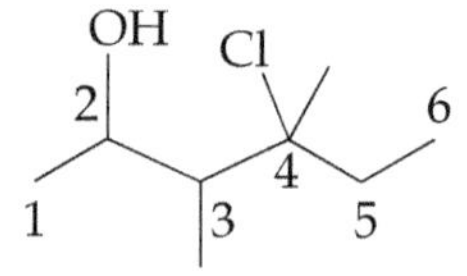

Note from this line structure that it does not matter in such a two-dimensional drawing what direction you show for a group that branches off the main chain, as long as it is attached to the correct carbon. This is true for condensed structures as well. Quite often, the direction that a group is shown coming off a main chain of carbon atoms is chosen simply for aesthetic reasons.

Worked Example 12.6 Molecular Structures: Converting Line Structures to Condensed Structures

Convert the following line structures to condensed structures:

(a)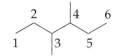

(b)

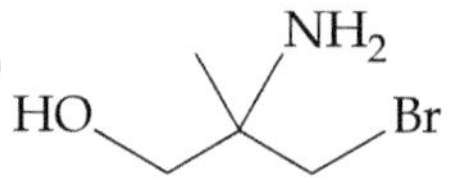

ANALYSIS Convert all vertices and line ends to carbons. Write in any noncarbon atoms and any hydrogens bonded to a noncarbon atom. Add hydrogens as needed so that each carbon has four groups attached. Remove lines connecting carbons except for branches.

SOLUTION

(a) Anywhere a line ends and anywhere two lines meet, write a C:

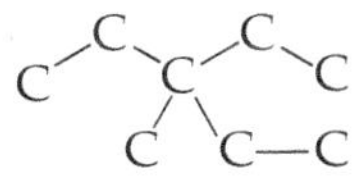

Because there are no atoms other than carbons and hydrogens in this molecule, the next step is to add hydrogens as needed to have four bonds for each carbon:

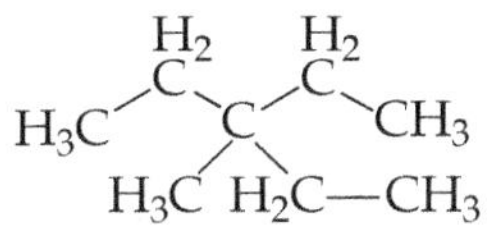

Finally, eliminate all lines except for branches to get the condensed structure:

$$CH_3CH_2 \overset{\overset{\displaystyle CH_3}{\displaystyle |}}{\underset{\underset{\displaystyle CH_2CH_3}{\displaystyle |}}{C}} CH_2CH_3$$

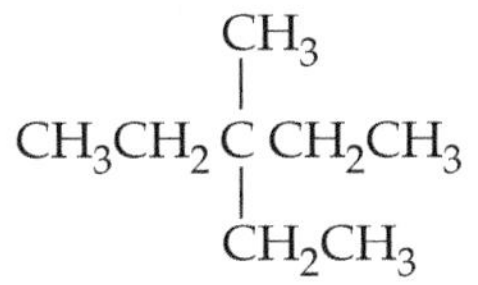

(b) Begin the condensed structure with a drawing showing a carbon at each line end and at each intersection of two lines:

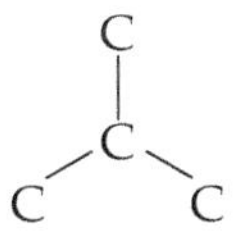

Next, write in all the noncarbon atoms and the hydrogen bonded to the oxygen. Then, add hydrogens so that each carbon forms four bonds:

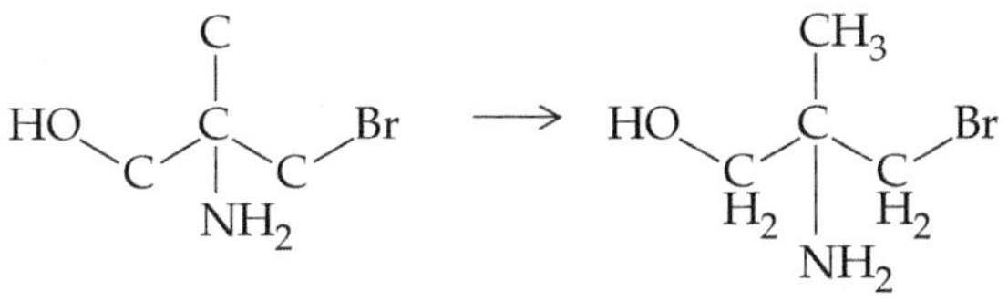

Eliminate all lines except for branches for the completed condensed structure:

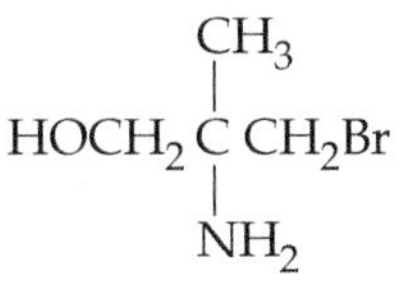

$$HOCH_2 \overset{\overset{\displaystyle CH_3}{\displaystyle |}}{\underset{\underset{\displaystyle NH_2}{\displaystyle |}}{C}} CH_2Br$$

PROBLEM 12.6

Convert the following condensed structures to line structures:

(a)
$$CH_3CH_2 \overset{\overset{\displaystyle CH_2CH_3}{\displaystyle |}}{\underset{\underset{\displaystyle CH_2OH}{\displaystyle |}}{C}} {-}CH_2CH_2CH_3$$

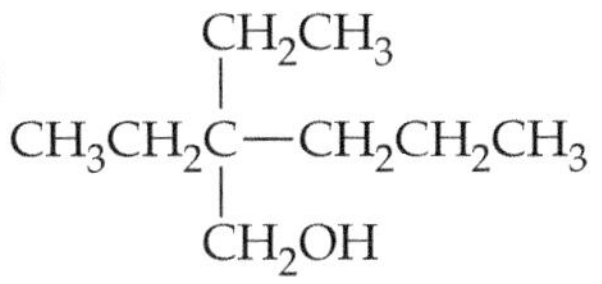

(b)
$$CH_3CH \overset{\overset{\displaystyle CH_2CH_3}{\displaystyle |}}{\underset{\underset{\displaystyle CH_3CHCH_2CH_3}{\displaystyle |}}{C}} H \, CH_2 \overset{\overset{\displaystyle CH_3}{\displaystyle |}}{C} HCH_3$$

(c)
$$CH_3 \overset{\overset{\displaystyle Br}{\displaystyle |}}{\underset{\underset{\displaystyle CH_3}{\displaystyle |}}{C}} {-}CH CH_2CH_2 \overset{\overset{\displaystyle Cl}{\displaystyle |}}{\underset{\underset{\displaystyle CHCH_2CH_3}{\displaystyle |}}{C}} HCH_2CH_3$$

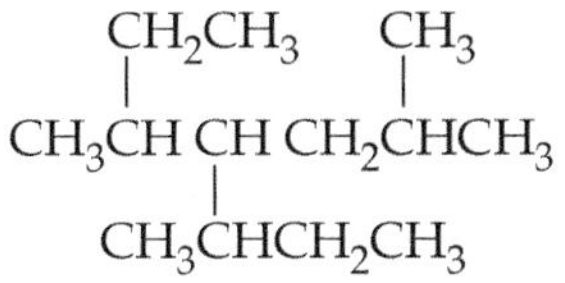

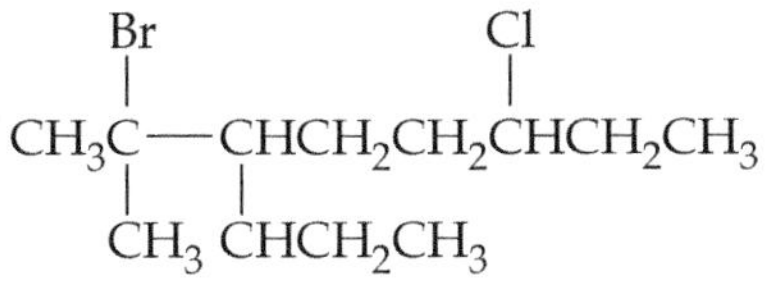

PROBLEM 12.7
Convert the following line structures to condensed structures:

(a)

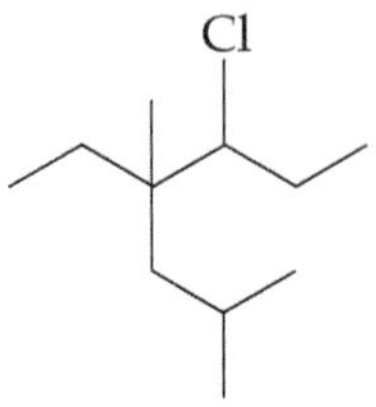

(b)

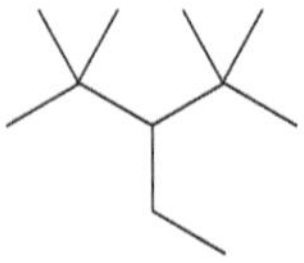

PROBLEM 12.8
Draw both condensed and line structures for the chemicals listed in Problem 12.2.

12.5 The Shapes of Organic Molecules

Every carbon atom in an alkane has its four bonds pointing toward the four corners of a tetrahedron, but chemists do not usually worry about three-dimensional shapes when writing condensed structures. Condensed structures do not imply any particular three-dimensional shape; they only indicate the connections between atoms without specifying geometry. Line structures do try to give some limited feeling for the shape of a molecule, but even here, the ability to show three-dimensional shape is limited unless dashed and wedged lines are used for the bonds (Section 4.8).

Butane, for example, has no one single shape because *rotation* takes place around carbon–carbon single bonds. The two parts of a molecule joined by a carbon–carbon single bond in a noncyclic structure are free to spin around the bond, giving rise to an infinite number of possible three-dimensional geometries, or **conformations**. The various conformations of a molecule such as butane are called **conformers** of one another. Conformers differ from one another as a result of rotation around carbon–carbon single bonds. Although the conformers of a given molecule have different three-dimensional shapes and different energies, the conformers cannot be separated from one another. A given butane molecule might be in its fully extended conformation at one instant but in a twisted conformation an instant later (Figure 12.2). An actual sample of butane contains a great many molecules that are constantly changing conformation. At any given instant, however, most of the molecules have the least crowded, lowest-energy extended conformation shown in Figure 12.2a. The same is true for all other alkanes: At any given instant, most molecules are in the least crowded conformation.

Conformation The specific three-dimensional arrangement of atoms in a molecule achieved specifically through rotations around carbon–carbon single bonds.

Conformer Molecular structures having identical connections between atoms and directly interconvertible through C—C bond rotations; that is, they represent identical compounds.

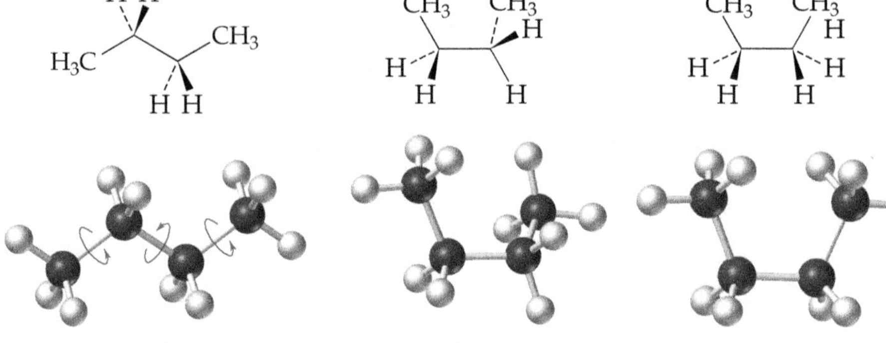

▶ **Figure 12.2**
Some conformations of butane (there are many others as well). The least crowded, extended conformation in (a) is the lowest-energy one, while the eclipsed conformation shown in (c) is the highest-energy one.

(a)   (b)   (c)

As long as any two structures have identical connections between atoms, and are interconvertible either by "flipping" the molecule or through C—C bond rotations, they are conformers of each other and represent the same compound, no matter how the structures are drawn. It is important to remember that no bonds are broken and reformed when interconverting conformers. Sometimes, you have to mentally rotate structures to see whether they are conformers or actually different molecules. To see that the following two structures represent conformers of the same compound rather than two isomers, picture one of them flipped right to left so that the red CH_3 groups are on the same side:

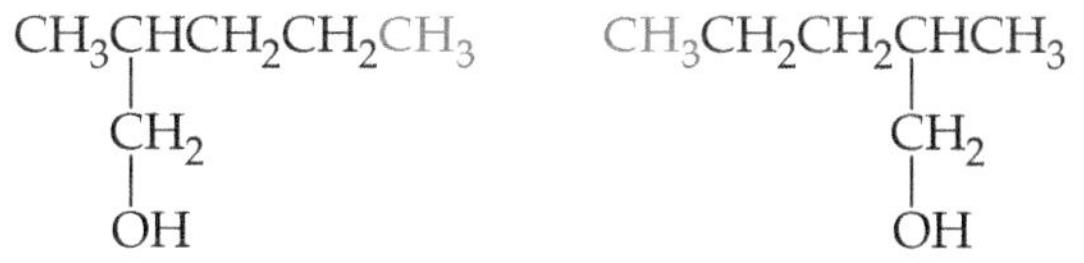

$$CH_3CHCH_2CH_2CH_3 \qquad CH_3CH_2CH_2CHCH_3$$
$$| \qquad\qquad\qquad\qquad |$$
$$CH_2 \qquad\qquad\qquad\qquad CH_2$$
$$| \qquad\qquad\qquad\qquad |$$
$$OH \qquad\qquad\qquad\qquad OH$$

Another way to determine whether two structures are conformers is to name each one using the IUPAC nomenclature rules (Section 12.6). If two structures have the same name, they are conformers of the same compound.

Worked Example 12.7 Molecular Structures: Identifying Conformers

The following structures all have the formula C_7H_{16}. Which of them represent the same molecule?

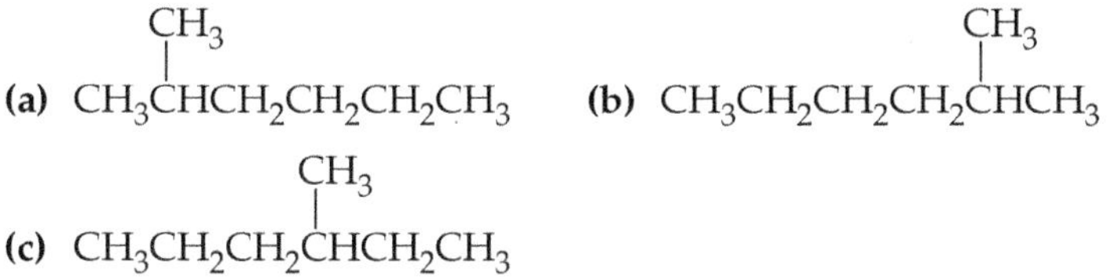

$$\qquad CH_3 \qquad\qquad\qquad\qquad\qquad CH_3$$
$$\qquad | \qquad\qquad\qquad\qquad\qquad\qquad |$$
(a) $CH_3CHCH_2CH_2CH_2CH_3$ (b) $CH_3CH_2CH_2CH_2CHCH_3$

$$\qquad\qquad\qquad CH_3$$
$$\qquad\qquad\qquad |$$
(c) $CH_3CH_2CH_2CHCH_2CH_3$

ANALYSIS Pay attention to the *connections* between atoms. Do not get confused by the apparent differences caused by writing a structure right to left versus left to right. Begin by identifying the longest chain of carbon atoms in the molecule.

SOLUTION
Molecule (a) has a straight chain of 6 carbons with a $—CH_3$ branch on the second carbon from the end. Molecule (b) also has a straight chain of 6 carbons with a $—CH_3$ branch on the second carbon from the end and is therefore identical to (a). That is, (a) and (b) are conformers of the same molecule. The only difference between (a) and (b) is that one is written "forward" and one is written "backward." Molecule (c), by contrast, has a straight chain of 6 carbons with a $—CH_3$ branch on the *third* carbon from the end and is therefore an isomer of (a) and (b).

Worked Example 12.8 Molecular Structures: Identifying Conformers and Isomers

Are the following pairs of compounds the same (conformers), isomers, or unrelated?

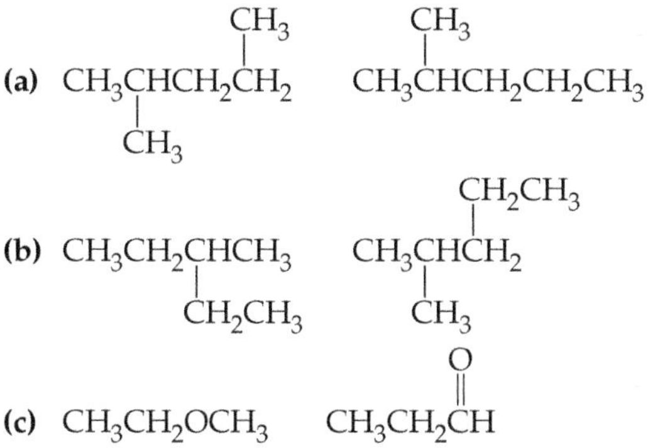

$$\qquad CH_3 \qquad\qquad CH_3$$
$$\qquad | \qquad\qquad\qquad |$$
(a) $CH_3CHCH_2CH_2 \qquad CH_3CHCH_2CH_2CH_3$
$$\qquad |$$
$$\qquad CH_3$$

$$\qquad\qquad\qquad\qquad\qquad\qquad CH_2CH_3$$
$$\qquad\qquad\qquad\qquad\qquad\qquad |$$
(b) $CH_3CH_2CHCH_3 \qquad CH_3CHCH_2$
$$\qquad\qquad |\qquad\qquad\qquad\qquad\qquad |$$
$$\qquad\qquad CH_2CH_3 \qquad\qquad CH_3$$

$$\qquad\qquad\qquad\qquad\qquad\qquad O$$
$$\qquad\qquad\qquad\qquad\qquad\qquad \|$$
(c) $CH_3CH_2OCH_3 \qquad CH_3CH_2CH$

ANALYSIS First compare molecular formulas to see if the compounds are related, and then look at the structures to see if they are the same compound or isomers. Find the longest continuous carbon chain in each, and then compare the locations of the substituents connected to the longest chain.

SOLUTION

(a) Both compounds have the same molecular formula (C_6H_{14}), so they are related. Since the —CH_3 group is on the second carbon from the end of a 5-carbon chain in both cases, these structures represent the same compound and are conformers of each other.

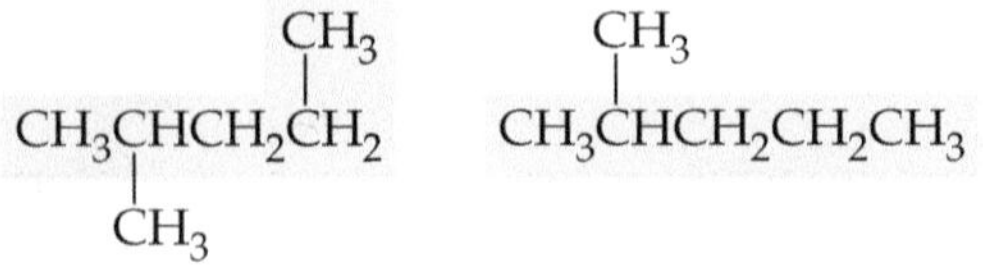

$$CH_3CHCH_2CH_2 \quad CH_3CHCH_2CH_2CH_3$$

with CH_3 substituents as shown:

$$\underset{\underset{CH_3}{|}}{\overset{\overset{CH_3}{|}}{CH_3CHCH_2CH_2}} \qquad \overset{\overset{CH_3}{|}}{CH_3CHCH_2CH_2CH_3}$$

(b) Both compounds have the same molecular formula (C_6H_{14}), and the longest chain in each is 5 carbon atoms. A comparison shows, however, that the —CH_3 group is on the middle carbon atom in one structure and on the second carbon atom in the other. These compounds are isomers of each other.

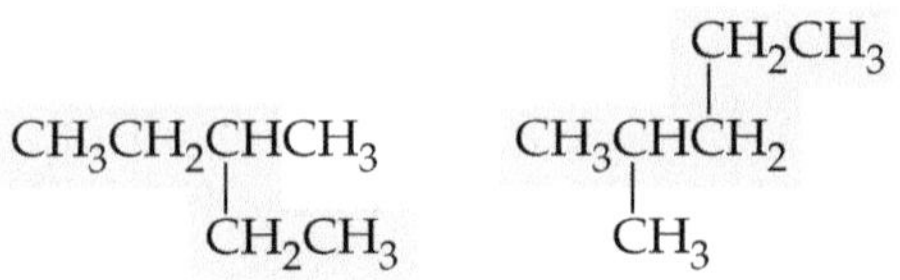

$$\underset{\underset{CH_2CH_3}{|}}{CH_3CH_2CHCH_3} \qquad \overset{\overset{CH_2CH_3}{|}}{\underset{\underset{CH_3}{|}}{CH_3CHCH_2}}$$

(c) These compounds have different formulas (C_3H_8O and C_3H_6O), so they are unrelated; they are neither conformers nor isomers of each other.

PROBLEM 12.9

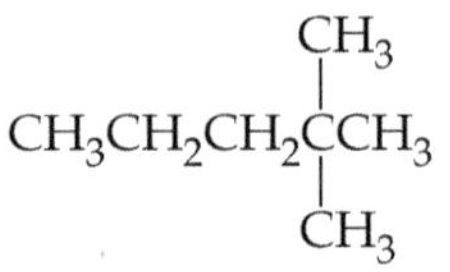

Which of the following structures are conformers?

$$\textbf{(a)} \quad \overset{\overset{CH_3}{|}}{CH_2CH_2} \overset{\overset{CH_3}{|}}{CHCH_2CH_3}$$

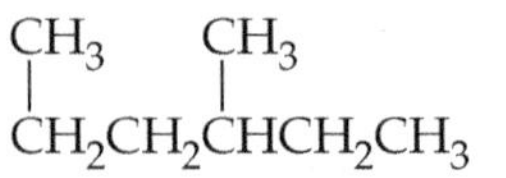

$$\textbf{(b)} \quad \overset{\overset{CH_3}{|}}{CH_3CH_2CH_2} \underset{\underset{CH_3}{|}}{CCH_3}$$

$$\textbf{(c)} \quad \overset{\overset{CH_3}{|}}{CH_3CH_2CHCH_2CH_2CH_3}$$

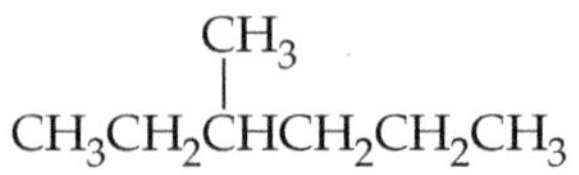

PROBLEM 12.10

In total, there are 18 isomers with the formula C_8H_{18}. Draw condensed structures for as many as you can that have only one or two —CH_3 groups as branch points (there are 9 isomers that fit these conditions). Convert the condensed structures you drew to line structures.

12.6 Naming Alkanes

When relatively few pure organic chemicals were known, new compounds were named at the whim of their discoverer. Thus, urea is a crystalline substance first isolated from urine, and the barbiturates were named by their discoverer in honor of his friend Barbara. As more and more compounds became known, however, the need for a systematic method of naming compounds became apparent.

The system of naming (*nomenclature*) now used is one devised by the International Union of Pure and Applied Chemistry, IUPAC (pronounced **eye**-you-pack). In the IUPAC system for organic compounds, a chemical name has three parts: *prefix*, *parent*, and *suffix*. The prefix specifies the location of functional groups and other **substituents** in the molecule; the parent tells how many carbon atoms are present

Substituent An atom or group of atoms attached to a parent compound.

in the longest continuous chain; and the suffix identifies what family the molecule belongs to:

Straight-chain alkanes are named by counting the number of carbon atoms and adding the family suffix -*ane*. With the exception of the first four compounds—*meth*ane, *eth*ane, *prop*ane, and *but*ane—whose parent names have historical origins, the alkanes are named from Greek numbers according to the number of carbons present (Table 12.2). Thus, *pent*ane is the 5-carbon alkane, *hex*ane is the 6-carbon alkane, and so on. Straight-chain alkanes have no substituents, so prefixes are not needed. The first ten alkane names are so common that they should be memorized.

TABLE 12.2 Names of Straight-Chain Alkanes

Number of Carbons	Structure	Name
1	CH_4	*Methane*
2	CH_3CH_3	*Ethane*
3	$CH_3CH_2CH_3$	*Propane*
4	$CH_3CH_2CH_2CH_3$	*Butane*
5	$CH_3CH_2CH_2CH_2CH_3$	*Pentane*
6	$CH_3CH_2CH_2CH_2CH_2CH_3$	*Hexane*
7	$CH_3CH_2CH_2CH_2CH_2CH_2CH_3$	*Heptane*
8	$CH_3CH_2CH_2CH_2CH_2CH_2CH_2CH_3$	*Octane*
9	$CH_3CH_2CH_2CH_2CH_2CH_2CH_2CH_2CH_3$	*Nonane*
10	$CH_3CH_2CH_2CH_2CH_2CH_2CH_2CH_2CH_2CH_3$	*Decane*

Substituents, such as $-CH_3$ and $-CH_2CH_3$, that branch off the main chain are called **alkyl groups**. An alkyl group can be thought of as the part of an alkane that remains when 1 hydrogen atom is removed to create an available bonding site. For example, removal of a hydrogen from methane gives the **methyl group,** $-CH_3$, and removal of a hydrogen from ethane gives the **ethyl group,** $-CH_2CH_3$. Notice that these alkyl groups are named simply by replacing the -*ane* ending of the parent alkane with an -*yl* ending:

Alkyl group The part of an alkane that remains when a hydrogen atom is removed.

Methyl group The $-CH_3$ alkyl group.

Ethyl group The $-CH_2CH_3$ alkyl group.

Alkyl groups are derived from a parent alkane.

$$\underset{\text{Methane}}{H-\overset{\displaystyle H}{\underset{\displaystyle H}{C}}-H} \xrightarrow{\text{Remove one H}} -\overset{\displaystyle H}{\underset{\displaystyle H}{C}}-H = -CH_3 \text{ Methyl group}$$

$$\underset{\text{Ethane}}{H-\overset{\displaystyle H}{\underset{\displaystyle H}{C}}-\overset{\displaystyle H}{\underset{\displaystyle H}{C}}-H} \xrightarrow{\text{Remove one H}} -\overset{\displaystyle H}{\underset{\displaystyle H}{C}}-\overset{\displaystyle H}{\underset{\displaystyle H}{C}}-H = -CH_2CH_3 \text{ Ethyl group}$$

Both methane and ethane have only one "kind" of hydrogen. It does not matter which of the 4 methane hydrogens is removed, so there is only one possible methyl group. Similarly, it does not matter which of the 6 equivalent ethane hydrogens is removed, so only one ethyl group is possible.

The situation is more complex for larger alkanes, which contain more than one kind of hydrogen. Propane, for example, has two different kinds of hydrogens. Removal of any one of the 6 hydrogens attached to an end carbon yields a straight-chain alkyl group called **propyl**, whereas removal of either one of the 2 hydrogens attached to the central carbon yields a branched-chain alkyl group called **isopropyl**:

Propyl group The straight-chain alkyl group $-CH_2CH_2CH_3$.

Isopropyl group The branched-chain alkyl group $-CH(CH_3)_2$.

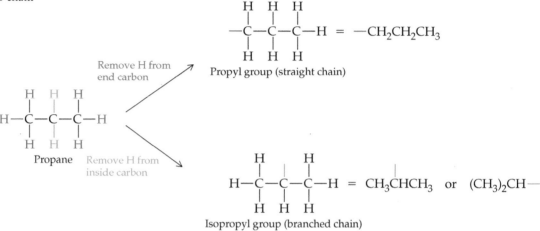

It is important to realize that alkyl groups are not compounds but rather are simply partial structures that help us name compounds. The names of some common alkyl groups are listed in Figure 12.3; you will want to commit them to memory.

▶ **Figure 12.3**
The most common alkyl groups found in organic molecules are shown here; the red bond shows the attachment the group has to the rest of the molecule.*

Some Common Alkyl Groups*

CH_3-
Methyl

CH_3CH_2-
Ethyl

$CH_3CH_2CH_2-$
n-Propyl

$CH_3\overset{\displaystyle CH_3}{\underset{|}{CH}}-$
Isopropyl

$CH_3CH_2CH_2CH_2-$
n-Butyl

$CH_3\overset{|}{\underset{|}{CH}}CH_2CH_3$
sec-Butyl

$CH_3\overset{\displaystyle CH_3}{\underset{|}{CH}}CH_2-$
Isobutyl

$CH_3\overset{\displaystyle CH_3}{\underset{\displaystyle CH_3}{\underset{|}{\overset{|}{C}}}}CH_3$
tert-Butyl

The red bond shows the connection to the rest of the molecule.

Notice that four butyl (4-carbon) groups are listed in Figure 12.3: butyl, *sec*-butyl, isobutyl, and *tert*-butyl. The prefix *sec*- stands for *secondary*, and the prefix *tert*- stands for *tertiary*, referring to the number of other carbon atoms attached to the branch point. There are four possible substitution patterns for carbons attached to four atoms and these are designated *primary, secondary, tertiary,* and *quaternary. It is important to note that these designations strictly apply to carbons having only single bonds.* A **primary (1°) carbon atom** has 1 other carbon attached to it (typically indicated as an —R group in the molecular structure), a **secondary (2°) carbon atom** has 2 other carbons attached, a **tertiary (3°) carbon atom** has 3 other carbons attached, and a **quaternary (4°) carbon atom** has 4 other carbons attached:

Primary (1°) carbon atom A carbon atom with 1 other carbon attached to it.

Secondary (2°) carbon atom A carbon atom with 2 other carbons attached to it.

Tertiary (3°) carbon atom A carbon atom with 3 other carbons attached to it.

Quaternary (4°) carbon atom A carbon atom with 4 other carbons attached to it.

$R-\overset{\displaystyle H}{\underset{\displaystyle H}{\underset{|}{\overset{|}{C}}}}-H$

Primary carbon (1°) has one other carbon attached.

$R-\overset{\displaystyle R}{\underset{\displaystyle H}{\underset{|}{\overset{|}{C}}}}-H$

Secondary carbon (2°) has two other carbons attached.

$R-\overset{\displaystyle R}{\underset{\displaystyle R}{\underset{|}{\overset{|}{C}}}}-H$

Tertiary carbon (3°) has three other carbons attached.

$R-\overset{\displaystyle R}{\underset{\displaystyle R}{\underset{|}{\overset{|}{C}}}}-R$

Quaternary carbon (4°) has four other carbons attached.

*The symbol **R** is used here and in later chapters as a general abbreviation for any organic substituent.* You should think of it as representing the **R**est of the molecule, which we are not bothering to specify. The R is used to allow you to focus on a particular structural feature of a molecule without the "clutter" of the other atoms in the molecule detracting from it. The R might represent a methyl, ethyl, or propyl group, or any of a vast number of other possibilities. For example, the generalized formula $R-OH$ for an alcohol might refer to an alcohol as simple as CH_3OH or CH_3CH_2OH or one as complicated as cholesterol, shown here:

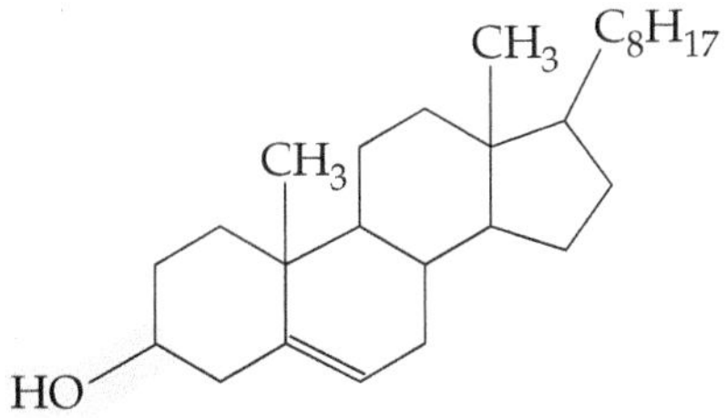

Branched-chain alkanes can be named by following four steps:

STEP 1: **Name the main chain.** Find the longest continuous chain of carbons, and name the chain according to the number of carbon atoms it contains. The longest chain may not be immediately obvious because it is not always written on one line; you may have to "turn corners" to find it.

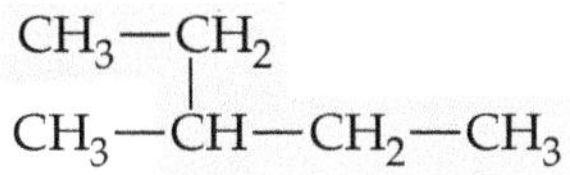

$$CH_3-CH_2$$
$$CH_3-CH-CH_2-CH_3$$

Name as a substituted pentane, not as a substituted butane, because the *longest* chain has five carbons.

STEP 2: **Number the carbon atoms in the main chain,** beginning at the end nearer the first branch point:

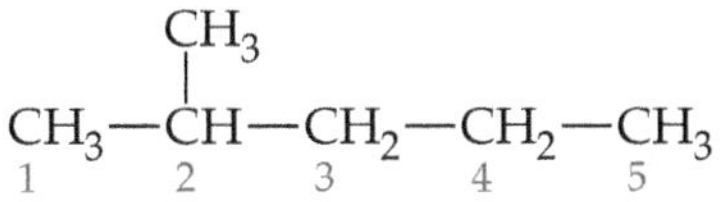

$$CH_3$$
$$\underset{1}{CH_3}-\underset{2}{CH}-\underset{3}{CH_2}-\underset{4}{CH_2}-\underset{5}{CH_3}$$

The first (and only) branch occurs at C2 if we start numbering from the left, but would occur at C4 if we started from the right by mistake.

STEP 3: **Identify the branching substituents, and number each** according to its point of attachment to the main chain:

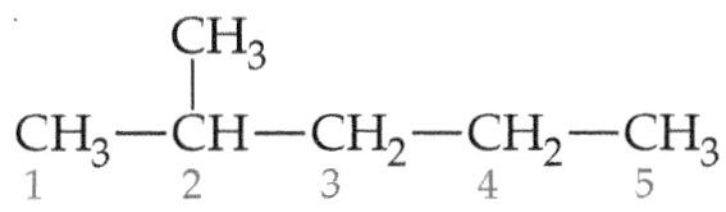

$$CH_3$$
$$\underset{1}{CH_3}-\underset{2}{CH}-\underset{3}{CH_2}-\underset{4}{CH_2}-\underset{5}{CH_3}$$

The main chain is a pentane. There is one $-CH_3$ substituent group connected to C2 of the chain.

If there are two substituents on the same carbon, assign the same number to both. There must always be as many numbers in the name as there are substituents.

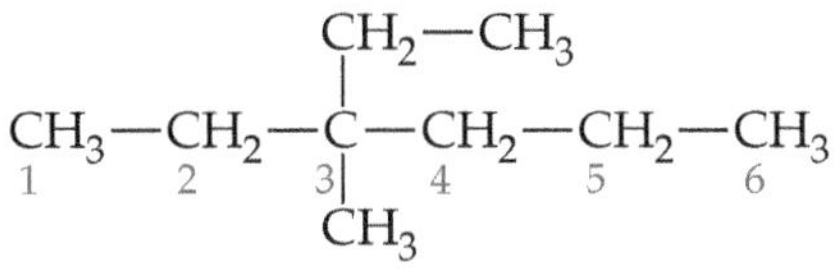

$$CH_2-CH_3$$
$$\underset{1}{CH_3}-\underset{2}{CH_2}-\underset{3}{C}-\underset{4}{CH_2}-\underset{5}{CH_2}-\underset{6}{CH_3}$$
$$CH_3$$

The main chain is a hexane. There are two substituents, a $-CH_3$ and a $-CH_2CH_3$, both connected to C3 of the chain.

STEP 4: **Write the name as a single word,** using hyphens to separate the numbers from the different prefixes and commas to separate numbers, if necessary. If two or more different substituent groups are present, cite them in alphabetical order. If two or more identical substituents are present, use one of the prefixes *di-*, *tri-*, *tetra-*, and so forth, but do not use these prefixes for alphabetizing purposes.

$$CH_3$$
$$|$$
$$\underset{1}{CH_3}-\underset{2}{CH}-\underset{3}{CH_2}-\underset{4}{CH_2}-\underset{5}{CH_3}$$

2-Methylpentane (a 5-carbon main chain with a 2-methyl substituent)

$$CH_2-CH_3$$
$$|$$
$$\underset{1}{CH_3}-\underset{2}{CH_2}-\underset{3}{C}-\underset{4}{CH_2}-\underset{5}{CH_2}-\underset{6}{CH_3}$$
$$|$$
$$CH_3$$

3-Ethyl-3-methylhexane (a 6-carbon main chain with 3-ethyl and 3-methyl substituents cited alphabetically)

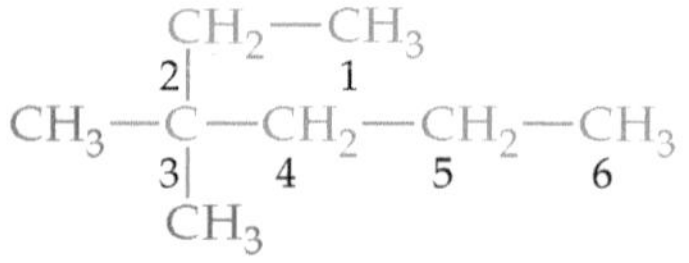

$$\overset{2}{CH_2}-\overset{1}{CH_3}$$
$$|$$
$$\underset{}{CH_3}-\underset{3}{C}-\underset{4}{CH_2}-\underset{5}{CH_2}-\underset{6}{CH_3}$$
$$|$$
$$CH_3$$

3,3-Dimethylhexane (a 6-carbon main chain with two 3-methyl substitutents)

Worked Example 12.9 Naming Organic Compounds: Alkanes

What is the IUPAC name of the following alkanes?

$$\overset{CH_3}{\overset{|}{}} \qquad \overset{CH_3}{\overset{|}{}}$$

(a) 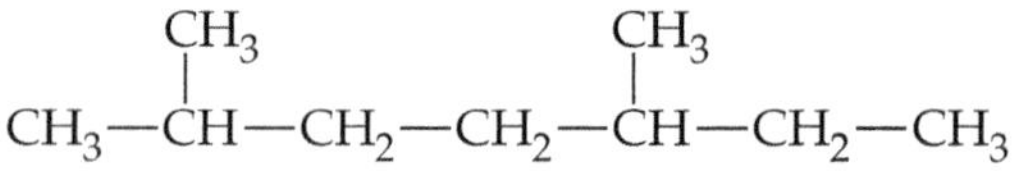 $CH_3-CH-CH_2-CH_2-CH-CH_2-CH_3$

(b)

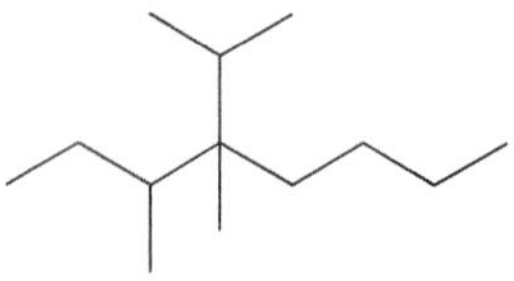

ANALYSIS Follow the four steps outlined in the text.

SOLUTION

(a) STEP 1: The longest continuous chain of carbon atoms is seven, so the main chain is a *hept*ane.

STEP 2: Number the main chain beginning at the end nearer the first branch:

$$\overset{CH_3}{\overset{|}{}} \qquad \overset{CH_3}{\overset{|}{}}$$
$$\underset{1}{CH_3}-\underset{2}{CH}-\underset{3}{CH_2}-\underset{4}{CH_2}-\underset{5}{CH}-\underset{6}{CH_2}-\underset{7}{CH_3}$$

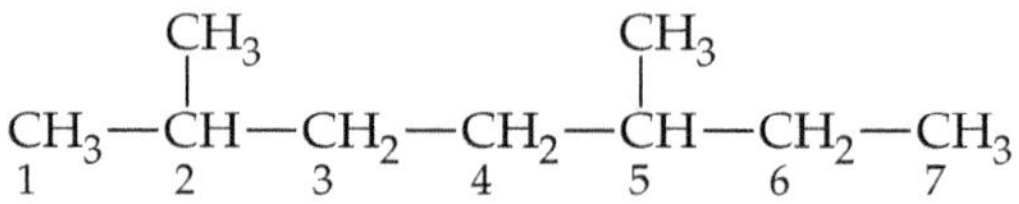

STEP 3: Identify and number the substituents (a 2-methyl and a 5-methyl in this case):

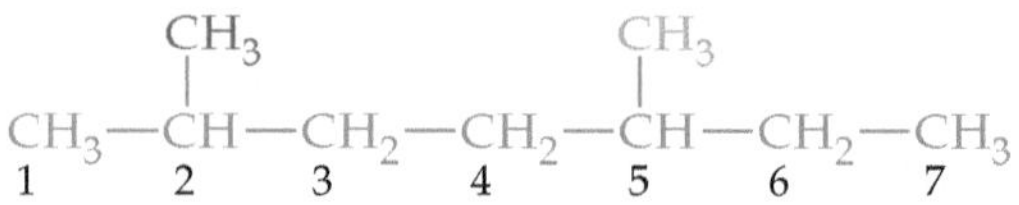

$$\overset{CH_3}{\overset{|}{}} \qquad \overset{CH_3}{\overset{|}{}}$$
$$\underset{1}{CH_3}-\underset{2}{CH}-\underset{3}{CH_2}-\underset{4}{CH_2}-\underset{5}{CH}-\underset{6}{CH_2}-\underset{7}{CH_3}$$

Substituents: 2-methyl and 5-methyl

STEP 4: Write the name as one word, using the prefix *di*- because there are two methyl groups. Separate the two numbers by a comma, and use a hyphen between the numbers and the word.

Name: 2, 5-Dimethylheptane

(b) STEP 1: The longest continuous chain of carbon atoms is eight, so the main chain is an *oct*ane.

STEP 2: Number the main chain beginning at the end nearer the first branch:

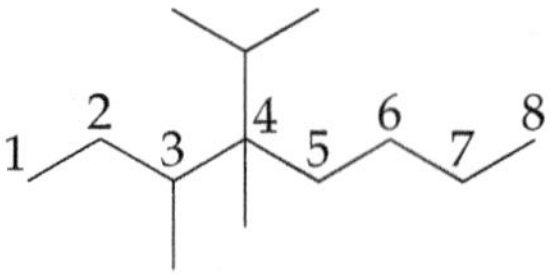

STEP 3: Identify and number the substituents:

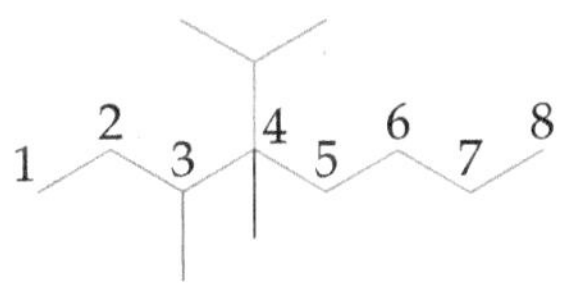

3-methyl, 4-methyl, 4-isopropyl

STEP 4: Write the name as one word, again using the prefix *di-* because there are two methyl groups.

Name: 3, 4-Dimethyl-4-isopropyloctane

Worked Example 12.10 Molecular Structure: Identifying 1°, 2°, 3°, and 4° Carbons

Identify each carbon atom in the following molecule as primary, secondary, tertiary, or quaternary.

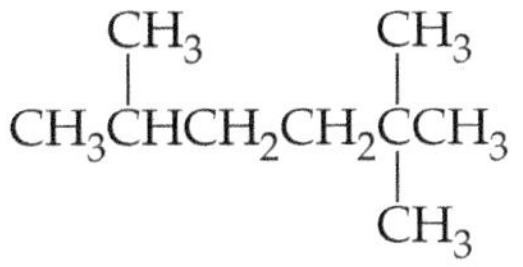

ANALYSIS Look at each carbon atom in the molecule, count the number of other carbon atoms attached, and make the assignment accordingly: primary (1 carbon attached); secondary (2 carbons attached); tertiary (3 carbons attached); quaternary (4 carbons attached).

SOLUTION

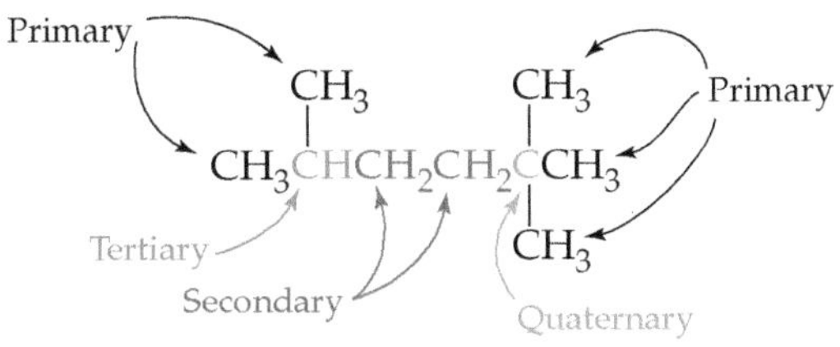

Worked Example 12.11 Molecular Structures: Drawing Condensed Structures from Names

Draw condensed and line structures corresponding to the following IUPAC names:

(a) 2,3-Dimethylpentane

(b) 3-Ethylheptane

ANALYSIS Starting with the parent chain, add the named alkyl substituent groups to the appropriately numbered carbon atom(s).

SOLUTION

(a) The parent chain has 5 carbons (*pent*ane), with two methyl groups ($-CH_3$) attached to the second and third carbon in the chain:

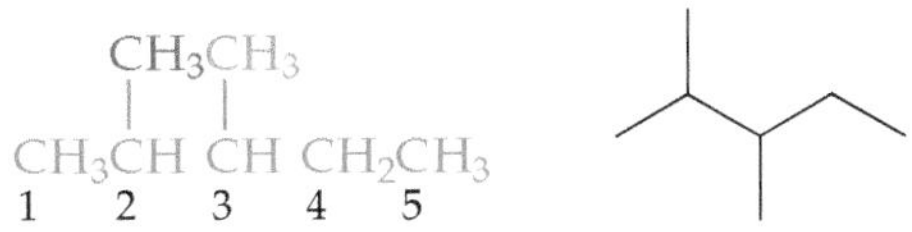

(b) The parent chain has 7 carbons (*hept*ane), with one ethyl group ($-CH_2CH_3$) attached to the third carbon in the chain:

$$CH_2CH_3$$
$$|$$
$$\underset{1 \quad 2 \quad 3 \quad 4 \quad 5 \quad 6 \quad 7}{CH_3CH_2CHCH_2CH_2CH_2CH_3}$$

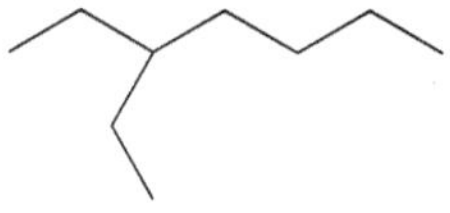

PROBLEM 12.11

Identify each carbon in the molecule shown in Worked Example 12.9b as primary, secondary, tertiary, or quaternary.

PROBLEM 12.12

What are the IUPAC names of the following alkanes?

(a)
$$CH_2-CH_3 \qquad\qquad CH_3$$
$$| \qquad\qquad\qquad\qquad |$$
$$CH_3-CH-CH_2-CH_2-CH_2-CH-CH_3$$

(b)
$$CH_2-CH_3$$
$$|$$
$$CH_3-CH_2-CH_2-CH_2-C-CH_2-CH_3$$
$$|$$
$$CH_2-CH_3$$

PROBLEM 12.13

Draw both condensed and line structures corresponding to the following IUPAC names and label each carbon as primary, secondary, tertiary, or quaternary:

(a) 3-Methylhexane   **(b)** 3,4-Dimethyloctane   **(c)** 2,2,4-Trimethylpentane

PROBLEM 12.14

Draw and name alkanes that meet the following descriptions:

(a) A 5-carbon alkane with a tertiary carbon atom

(b) A 7-carbon alkane that has both a tertiary and a quaternary carbon atom

---

KEY CONCEPT PROBLEM 12.15

What are the IUPAC names of the following alkanes?

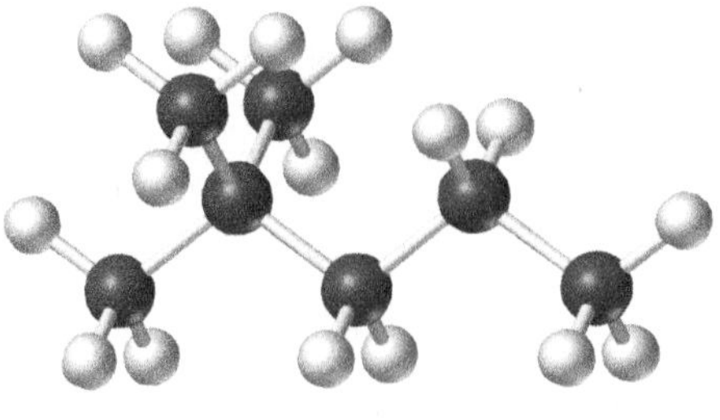

(a) 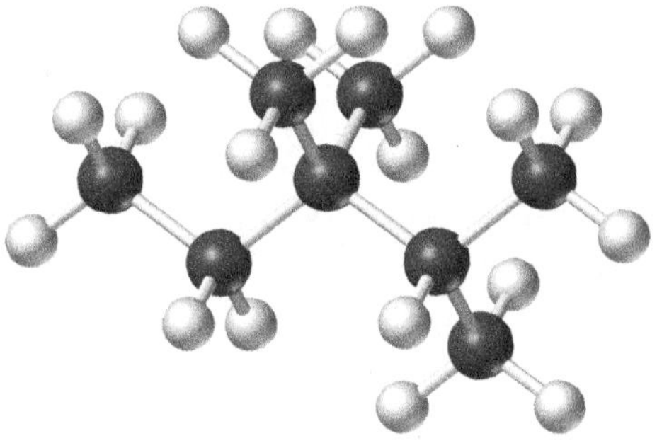   (b)

12.7 Properties of Alkanes

▶▶▶ Review the effects of London dispersion forces on molecules in Section 8.11.

Alkanes contain only nonpolar C—C and C—H bonds, so the only intermolecular forces influencing them are weak London dispersion forces. The effect of these forces is shown in the regularity with which the melting and boiling points of straight-chain alkanes increase with molecular size (Figure 12.4). The first four alkanes—methane, ethane, propane, and butane—are gases at room temperature and pressure. Alkanes

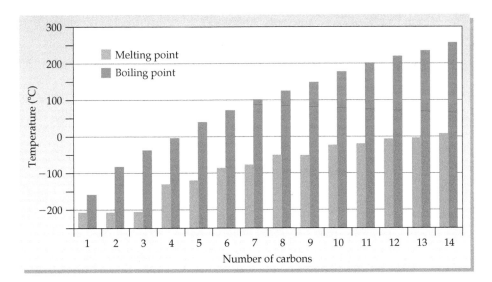

◀ **Figure 12.4**
The boiling and melting points for the C_1—C_{14} straight-chain alkanes increase with molecular size.

with 5–15 carbon atoms are liquids; those with 16 or more carbon atoms are generally low-melting, waxy solids.

In keeping with their low polarity, alkanes are insoluble in water but soluble in nonpolar organic solvents, including other alkanes. Because alkanes are generally less dense than water, they float on its surface. Low-molecular-weight alkanes are volatile and must be handled with care because their vapors are flammable. Mixtures of alkane vapors and air can explode when ignited by a single spark.

The physiological effects of alkanes are limited. Methane, ethane, and propane gases are nontoxic, but the danger of inhaling them lies in potential suffocation due to lack of oxygen. Breathing the vapor of larger alkanes in large concentrations can induce loss of consciousness. There is also a danger in breathing droplets of liquid alkanes because they dissolve nonpolar substances in lung tissue and cause pneumonia-like symptoms.

Mineral oil, petroleum jelly, and paraffin wax are mixtures of higher alkanes. All are harmless to body tissue and are used in numerous food and medical applications. Mineral oil passes through the body unchanged and is sometimes used as a laxative. Petroleum jelly (sold as Vaseline) softens, lubricates, and protects the skin. Paraffin wax is used in candle making, on surfboards, and in home canning. See Chemistry in Action box on page 385 for more surprising uses of alkanes.

▶▶ Recall from Section 9.2 the rule of thumb when predicting solubility: "like dissolves like."

Properties of Alkanes:

- Odorless or mild odor; colorless; tasteless; nontoxic
- Nonpolar; insoluble in water but soluble in nonpolar organic solvents; less dense than water
- Flammable; otherwise not very reactive

12.8 Reactions of Alkanes

Alkanes do not react with acids, bases, or most other common laboratory *reagents* (a substance that causes a reaction to occur). Their only major reactions are with oxygen (combustion) and with halogens (halogenation). Both of these reaction types have complicated mechanisms and occur through the intermediacy of free radicals (Section 13.8).

Combustion

Most of you probably get to school everyday using some sort of transportation that uses gasoline, which is a mixture of alkanes. To power a vehicle, that mixture of alkanes must be converted into energy. The reaction of an alkane with oxygen is called **combustion**, an oxidation reaction that commonly takes place in a controlled manner

Combustion A chemical reaction that produces a flame, usually because of burning with oxygen.

MASTERING REACTIONS

Organic Chemistry and the Curved Arrow Formalism

Starting with this chapter and continuing on through the remainder of this text, you will be exploring the world of organic chemistry and its close relative, biochemistry. Both of these areas of chemistry are much more "visual" than those you have been studying; organic chemists, for example, look at how and why reactions occur by examining the flow of electrons. For example, consider the following reaction of 2-iodopropane with sodium cyanide:

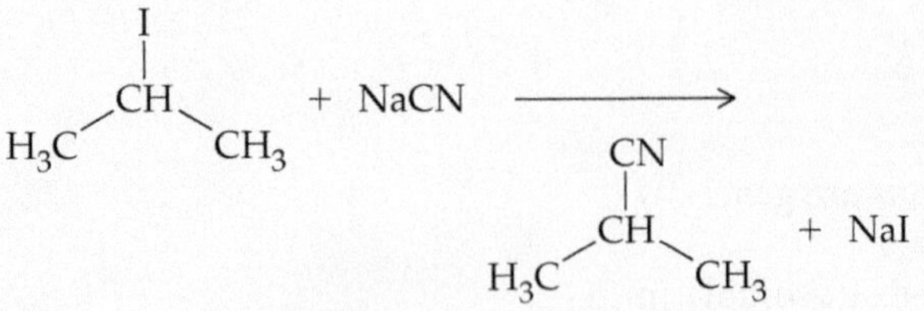

This seemingly simple process (known as a *substitution reaction*, discussed in Chapter 13) is not adequately described by the equation. To help to understand what may really be going on, organic chemists use what is loosely described as "electron pushing" and have adopted what is known as *curved arrow formalism* to represent it. The movement of electrons is depicted using curved arrows, where the number of electrons corresponds to the head of the arrow. Single-headed arrows represent movement of one electron, while a double-headed arrow indicates the movement of two:

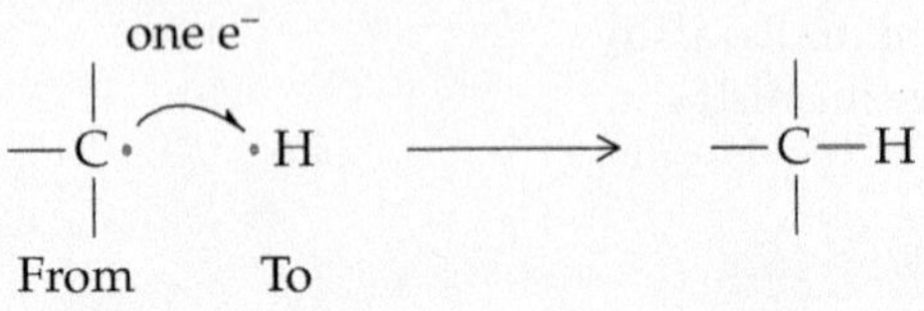

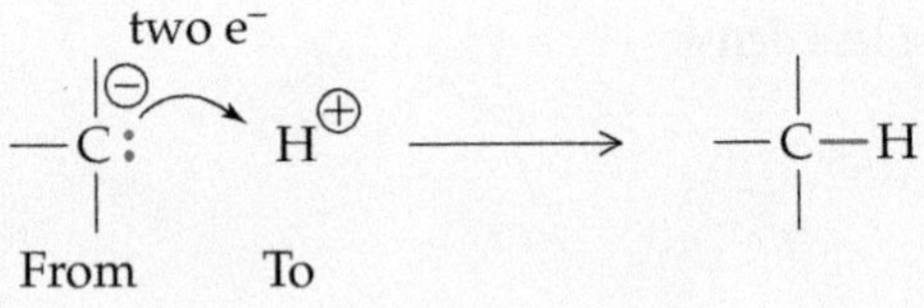

The convention is to show the movement *from* an area of high electron density (the start of the arrow) *to* one of lower electron density (the head of the arrow). Using curved arrow formalism, we can examine the reaction of 2-iodopropane with sodium cyanide in more detail. There are two distinct paths by which this reaction can occur:

Path 1

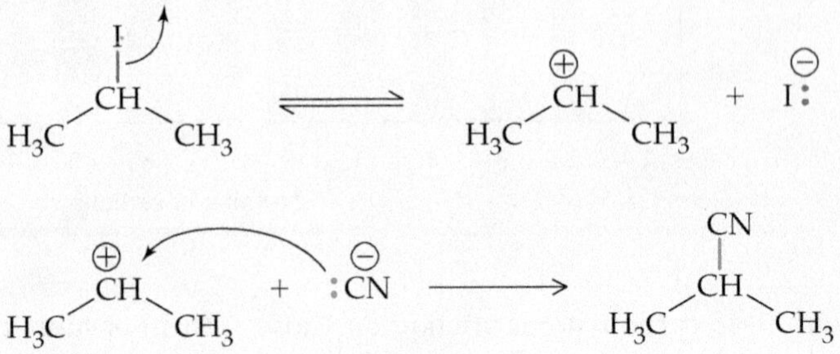

Path 2

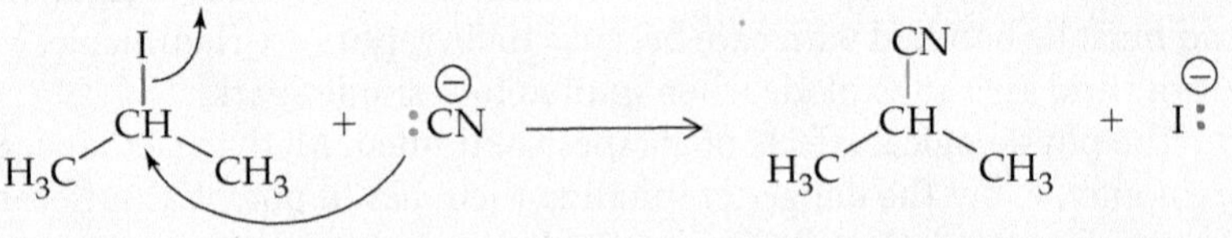

Notice that while both pathways lead ultimately to the same product, the curved arrow formalism shows us that they have significantly different ways of occurring. Although it is not important right now to understand which of the two paths is actually operative (it turns out to be a function of solvent), concentrations, catalysts, temperature, and other conditions) it is important that you get used to thinking of reactions as an "electron flow" of sorts. Throughout the next six chapters, you will see more of these "Mastering Reactions" boxes; they are intended to give you a little more insight into the otherwise seemingly random reactions that organic molecules undergo.

See Mastering Reactions Problems 12.76 and 12.77 at the end of the chapter.

▶▶▶ Combustion reactions are exothermic, as we learned in Section 7.3.

in an engine or furnace. Carbon dioxide and water are the products of complete combustion of any hydrocarbon, and a large amount of heat is released (ΔH is a negative number.) Some examples were given in Table 7.1.

$$CH_4(g) + 2\,O_2(g) \longrightarrow CO_2(g) + 2\,H_2O(g) \quad \Delta H = -213\ \text{kcal/mol}\ (-891\ \text{kJ/mol})$$

When hydrocarbon combustion is incomplete because of faulty engine or furnace performance, carbon monoxide and carbon-containing soot are among the products. Carbon monoxide is a highly toxic and dangerous substance, especially so because it has no odor and can easily go undetected (See the Chemistry in Action feature "CO and NO: Pollutants or Miracle Molecules?" in Chapter 4). Breathing air that contains as little as 2% CO for only one hour can cause respiratory and nervous system damage or death. The supply of oxygen to the brain is cut off by carbon monoxide because it binds strongly to blood hemoglobin at the site where oxygen is normally bound. By contrast with CO, CO_2 is nontoxic and causes no harm, except by suffocation when present in high concentration.

PROBLEM 12.16
Write a balanced equation for the complete combustion of ethane with oxygen.

The second notable reaction of alkanes is *halogenation*, the replacement of an alkane hydrogen by a chlorine or bromine in a process initiated by heat or light. Halogenation is important because it is used to prepare both a number of molecules that are key industrial solvents (such as dichloromethane, chloroform, and carbon tetrachloride) as well as others (such as bromoethane) that are used for the preparation of other larger organic molecules. In a halogenation reaction, only one H at a time is replaced; however, if allowed to react for a long enough time, all H's will be replaced with halogens. Complete chlorination of methane, for example, yields carbon tetrachloride:

$$CH_4 \ + \ 4\,Cl_2 \ \xrightarrow{\text{Heat or light}} \ CCl_4 \ + \ 4\,HCl$$

Although the above equation for the reaction of methane with chlorine is balanced, it does not fully represent what actually happens. In fact, this reaction, like many organic reactions, yields a mixture of products:

$CH_4 \ + \ Cl_2 \ \longrightarrow \ CH_3Cl \ + \ HCl$

$\quad\quad\quad\quad\quad \xrightarrow{Cl_2} \ CH_2Cl_2 \ + \ HCl$

$\quad\quad\quad\quad\quad\quad\quad\quad \xrightarrow{Cl_2} \ CHCl_3 \ + \ HCl$

$\quad\quad\quad\quad\quad\quad\quad\quad\quad\quad\quad \xrightarrow{Cl_2} \ CCl_4 \ + \ HCl$

CH_3Cl, chloromethane
CH_2Cl_2, dichloromethane
$CHCl_3$, chloroform
CCl_4, carbon tetrachloride

When we write the equation for an organic reaction, our attention is usually focused on converting a particular reactant into a desired product; any minor by-products and inorganic compounds (such as the HCl formed in the chlorination of methane) are often of little interest and are ignored. Thus, it is not always necessary to balance the equation for an organic reaction as long as the reactant, the major product, and any necessary reagents and conditions are shown. A chemist who plans to convert methane into bromomethane might therefore, write the equation as

$$CH_4 \ \xrightarrow[\text{Light, heat}]{Br_2} \ CH_3Br$$ Like many equations for organic reactions, this equation is not balanced.

In using this convention, it is customary to put reactants and reagents above the arrow and conditions, solvents, and catalysts below the arrow.

PROBLEM 12.17
Write the structures of all six possible products with either 1 or 2 chlorine atoms that form in the reaction of propane with Cl_2.

12.9 Cycloalkanes

The organic compounds described thus far have all been open-chain, or *acyclic*, alkanes. **Cycloalkanes**, which contain rings of carbon atoms, are also well known and are widespread throughout nature. To form a closed ring requires an additional

Cycloalkane An alkane that contains a ring of carbon atoms.

C—C bond and the loss of 2 H atoms; the general formula for cycloalkanes, therefore, is C_nH_{2n}, which, as we will find in the next chapter, is the same as that for alkenes. Compounds of all ring sizes from 3 through 30 and beyond have been prepared in the laboratory. The two simplest cycloalkanes—cyclopropane and cyclobutane—contain 3 and 4 carbon atoms, respectively:

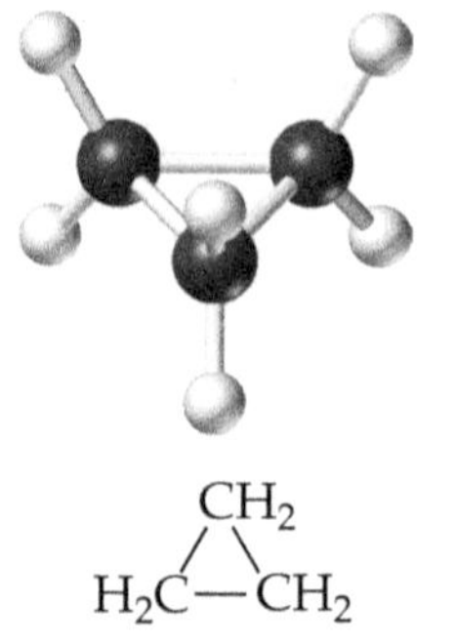

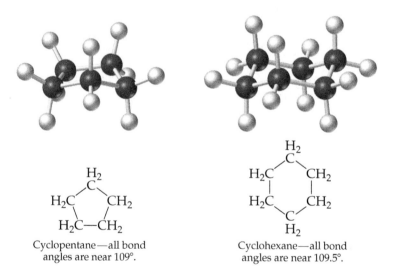

$$CH_2$$
$$H_2C—CH_2$$
Cyclopropane
(mp −128 °C, bp −33 °C)

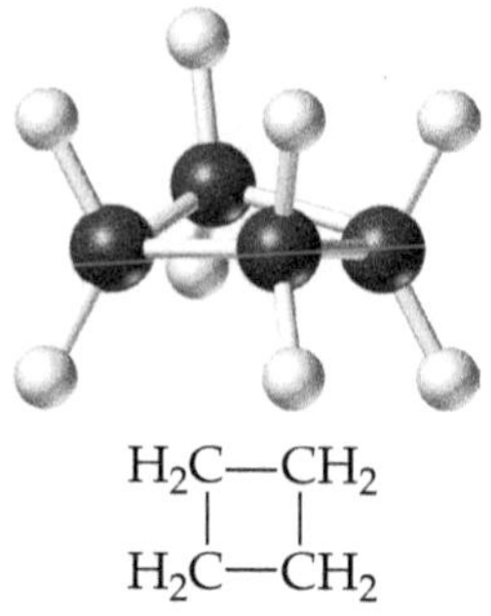

$$H_2C—CH_2$$
$$H_2C—CH_2$$
Cyclobutane
(mp −50 °C, bp −12 °C)

Note that if we flatten the rings in cyclopropane and cyclobutane, the C—C—C bond angles are 60° and 90°, respectively—values that are considerably compressed from the normal tetrahedral value of 109.5°. As a result, these compounds are less stable and more reactive than other cycloalkanes. The five-membered (cyclopentane) ring has nearly ideal bond angles, and so does the six-membered (cyclohexane) ring. Both cyclopentane and cyclohexane accomplish this nearly ideal state by adopting a puckered, nonplanar shape called a *chair conformation*, further discussion of which, while important, is beyond the scope of this textbook. Both cyclopentane and cyclohexane rings are therefore stable, and many naturally occurring and biochemically active molecules, such as the steroids (Chapter 28), contain such rings.

Cyclic and acyclic alkanes are similar in many of their properties. Cyclopropane and cyclobutane are gases at room temperature, whereas larger cycloalkanes are liquids or solids. Like alkanes, cycloalkanes are nonpolar, insoluble in water, and flammable. Because of their cyclic structures, however, cycloalkane molecules are more rigid and less flexible than their open-chain counterparts. Rotation is not possible around the carbon–carbon bonds in cycloalkanes without breaking open the ring.

$$H_2$$
$$C$$
$$H_2C \qquad CH_2$$
$$H_2C—CH_2$$
Cyclopentane—all bond
angles are near 109°.

$$H_2$$
$$C$$
$$H_2C \qquad CH_2$$
$$H_2C \qquad CH_2$$
$$C$$
$$H_2$$
Cyclohexane—all bond
angles are near 109.5°.

CHEMISTRY IN ACTION

Surprising Uses of Petroleum

Whenever the word "petroleum" is mentioned, the first thing that comes to most people's mind is gasoline and oil. Petroleum, arising from the decay of ancient plants and animals, is found deep below the earth's crust; it is, simply put, a mixture of hydrocarbons of varying sizes. Petroleum's worth as both a portable, energy-dense fuel and as the starting point of many industrial chemicals makes it one of the world's most important commodities. Current estimates put 90% of vehicular fuel needs worldwide as being met by oil. In addition, 40% of total energy consumption in the United States is petroleum-based, but petroleum is responsible for only 2% of electricity generation. In an effort to create a "greener" environment and more sustainable energy, a great fervor has developed to find alternative energy sources. Wind, solar, biodiesel, and geothermal are but a few of the emerging technologies that have been pushed into the forefront; but a question arises: Can we completely eliminate the need for petroleum from our lives, even if we could find an alternative energy for transportation purposes?

Petrochemicals are chemical products derived specifically from petroleum and generally refer to those products that are not used for fuels. When crude oil is refined and cracked (the process during which complex organic molecules found in oil are converted into simpler molecules by the breaking of carbon–carbon bonds), a number of fractions having different boiling ranges are obtained. The lower boiling fractions contain the simplest alkanes and alkenes, many of which are important chemical feedstocks. A feedstock is a material that is used as the starting point for the preparation of more complex ones. The primary petrochemicals obtained can be broken down into three categories:

1. Alkenes (or olefins; Chapter 13): primarily ethylene, propylene, and butadiene. Ethylene and propylene are important sources of industrial chemicals and plastics products.
2. Aromatics (Chapter 13): most important among these are benzene, toluene, and the xylenes. These raw materials are used for making a variety of compounds, from dyes and synthetic detergents, to plastics and synthetic fibers, to pharmaceutical starting materials.
3. Synthesis gas: a mixture of carbon monoxide and hydrogen used to make methanol (which is used as both a solvent and feedstock for other products).

What specific types of products are made from these petrochemicals? Let's look at a few:

Lubricants such as light machine oils, motor oils, and greases are products used to keep almost all mechanical devices running smoothly and to prevent them from seizing up

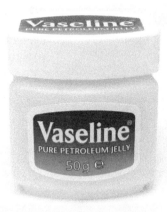

▲ **Petroleum jelly, originally an unwanted by-product of drilling, has found many uses in today's average household.**

under high-use conditions. Look at the mixer or the blender in your kitchen: Lubricants are responsible for keeping it running efficiently and quietly. Wax is another raw petroleum product. These paraffin waxes are used to make candles and polishes as well as food packaging such as milk cartons. The shine you see on the fruit in your local supermarket is also a result of the use of wax.

Most of the rubber soles found on today's shoes are derived from butadiene. Natural rubber becomes sticky when hot and stiff when cold, but man-made rubber stays much more flexible. Car tires are also made from synthetic rubber, which makes them much safer to drive on. Today, the demand for synthetic rubber is four-times greater than for natural rubber.

Other alkenes obtained from the refining of petroleum, such as ethylene and propylene, are used to make plastics that are used in turn to make the clothes you wear, the carpet you walk on, the CDs and DVDs that entertain you, and hundreds of other products we take for granted.

One very interesting petroleum-derived material was once considered a nuisance by-product of oil drilling. "Black rod wax" is a paraffin-like substance that forms on oil-drilling rigs, causing the drills to malfunction. Workers had to scrape the thick, viscous material off to keep the drills running. However, they found that when applied to cuts and burns it would cause these injuries to heal faster. A young chemist named Robert Chesebrough obtained some of this material to see if it had commercial potential. After purification he obtained a light-colored gel that he named vaseline, or petroleum jelly. Chesebrough demonstrated the product by burning his skin with acid or an open flame, then spreading the ointment on his injuries and showing how his past injuries had healed by his miracle product.

As you can see, petroleum has many uses that are key in our everyday lives. Although lessening its use as a fuel for transportation can help to conserve what reserves we have, its complete elimination from our lives is, at this point in time, nearly impossible.

See Chemistry in Action Problems 12.74 and 12.75 at the end of the chapter.

12.10 Drawing and Naming Cycloalkanes

Even condensed structures become awkward when we work with large molecules that contain rings. Thus, line structures are used almost exclusively in drawing cycloalkanes, with *polygons* used for the cyclic parts of the molecules. A triangle represents cyclopropane, a square represents cyclobutane, a pentagon represents cyclopentane, and so on.

Cyclopropane   Cyclobutane   Cyclopentane   Cyclohexane   Cycloheptane

Methylcyclohexane, for example, looks like this in a line structure:

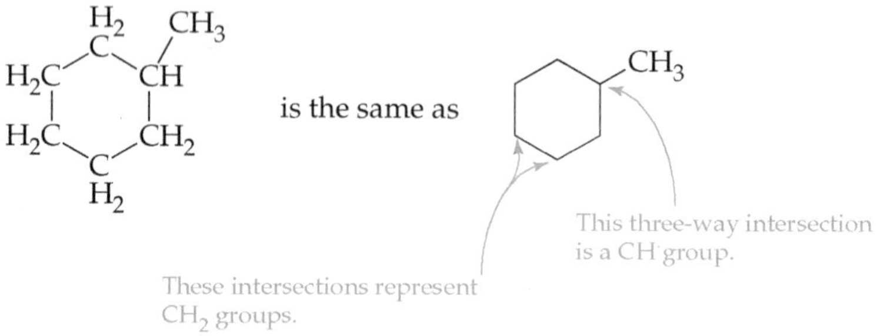

is the same as

This three-way intersection is a CH group.

These intersections represent CH$_2$ groups.

Cycloalkanes are named by a straightforward extension of the rules for naming open-chain alkanes. In most cases, only two steps are needed:

STEP 1: **Use the cycloalkane name as the parent.** That is, compounds are named as alkyl-substituted cycloalkanes rather than as cycloalkyl-substituted alkanes. If there is only one substituent on the ring, it is not even necessary to assign a number because all ring positions are identical.

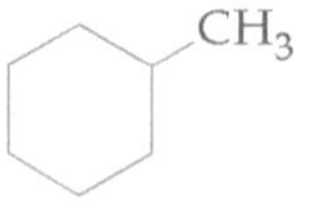

Parent compound: Cyclohexane
Name: Methylcyclohexane
(not cyclohexylmethane)

STEP 2: **Identify and number the substituents.** Start numbering at the group that has alphabetical priority, and proceed around the ring in the direction that gives the second substituent the lower possible number.

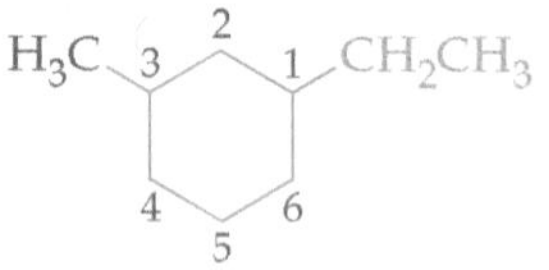

1-ethyl-3-methylcyclohexane
(not 1-ethyl-5-methylcyclohexane or
1-methyl-3-ethylcyclohexane or
1-methyl-5-ethylcyclohexane)

Worked Example 12.12 Naming Organic Compounds: Cycloalkanes

What is the IUPAC name of the following cycloalkane?

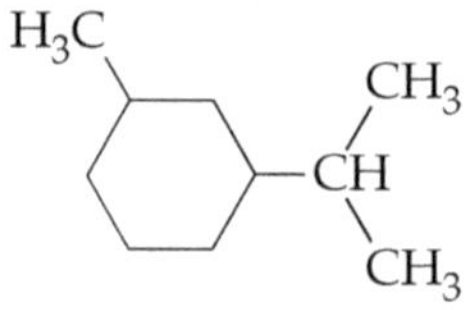

ANALYSIS First identify the parent cycloalkane, then add the positions and identity of any substituents.

SOLUTION

STEP 1: The parent cycloalkane contains 6 carbons (*hexane*); hence, *cyclohexane*.

STEP 2: There are two substituents; a *methyl* ($-CH_3$) and an *isopropyl* (CH_3CHCH_3). Alphabetically, the isopropyl group is given priority (number 1); the methyl group is then found on the third carbon in the ring.

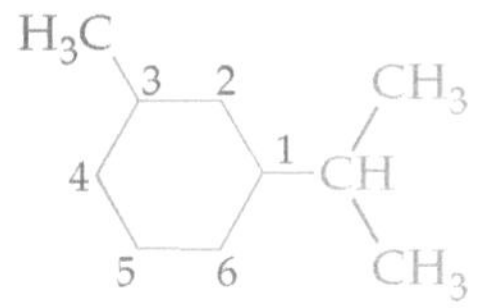

1-isopropyl-3-methylcyclohexane

Worked Example **12.13** Molecular Structures: Drawing Line Structures for Cycloalkanes

Draw a line structure for 1,4-dimethylcyclohexane.

ANALYSIS This structure consists of a 6-carbon ring with two methyl groups attached at positions 1 and 4. Draw a hexagon to represent a cyclohexane ring, and attach a $-CH_3$ group at an arbitrary position that becomes the first carbon in the chain, designated as C1. Then count around the ring to the fourth carbon (C4), and attach another $-CH_3$ group.

SOLUTION

Note that the second methyl group is written here as H_3C- because it is attached on the left side of the ring.

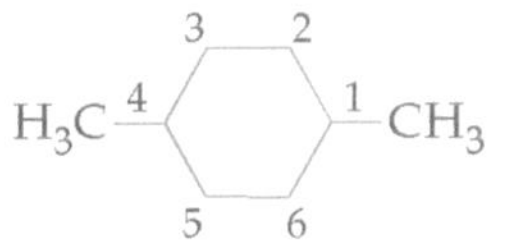

1,4-dimethylcyclohexane

PROBLEM 12.18
What are the IUPAC names of the following cycloalkanes?

(a)

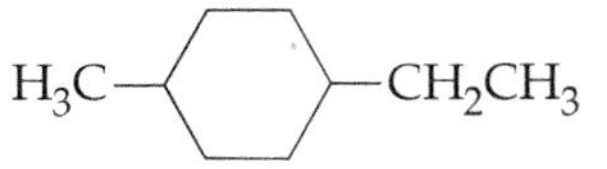

(b)

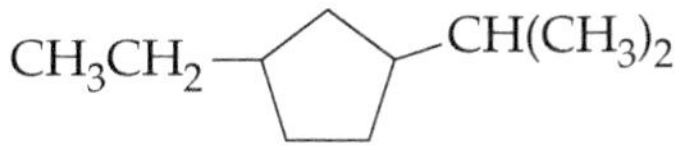

PROBLEM 12.19
Draw line structures that represent the following IUPAC names:
(a) 1,1-Diethylcyclohexane
(b) 1,3,5-Trimethylcycloheptane

PROBLEM 12.20
In the box Chemistry in Action: Surprising Uses of Petroleum, three alkenes were mentioned as being important materials obtained from the refining of petroleum: ethylene, propylene, and butadiene.
(a) What consumer products are manufactured with ethylene and propylene?
(b) Butadiene is used in the manufacture of synthetic rubber. Why is this more desired than natural rubber?

KEY CONCEPT PROBLEM 12.21

What is the IUPAC name of the following cycloalkane?

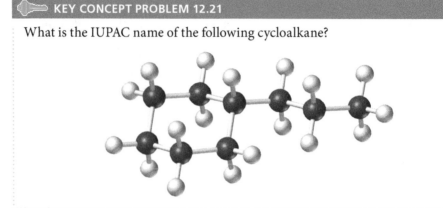

SUMMARY: REVISITING THE CHAPTER GOALS

1. What are the basic properties of organic compounds? Compounds made up primarily of carbon atoms are classified as organic. Many organic compounds contain carbon atoms that are joined in long chains by a combination of single (C—C), double (C=C), or triple (C≡C) bonds. In this chapter, we focused primarily on *alkanes*, hydrocarbon compounds that contain only single bonds between all C atoms (*see Problems 29, 31, 32*).

2. What are functional groups, and how are they used to classify organic molecules? Organic compounds can be classified into various families according to the functional groups they contain. A *functional group* is a part of a larger molecule and is composed of a group of atoms that has characteristic structure and chemical reactivity. A given functional group undergoes nearly the same chemical reactions in every molecule where it occurs (*see Problems 25, 34–37, 66, 73*).

3. What are isomers? *Isomers* are compounds that have the same formula but different structures. Isomers that differ in their connections among atoms are called *constitutional isomers*. When atoms other than carbon and hydrogen are present, the ability to have *functional group isomers* arises; these are molecules that, due to the differences in their connections, have not only different structures but also belong to different families of organic molecules (*see Problems 28, 38–51*).

4. How are organic molecules drawn? Organic compounds can be represented by *structural formulas* in which all atoms and bonds are shown, by *condensed structures* in which not all bonds are drawn, or by *line structures* in which the carbon skeleton

is represented by lines and the locations of C and H atoms are understood (*see Problems 22–24, 44, 45, 48, 49–51*).

5. What are alkanes and cycloalkanes, and how are they named? Compounds that contain only carbon and hydrogen are called *hydrocarbons*, and hydrocarbons that have only single bonds are called *alkanes*. A *straight-chain alkane* has all its carbons connected in a row, a *branched-chain alkane* has a branching connection of atoms somewhere along its chain, and a *cycloalkane* has a ring of carbon atoms. Alkanes have the general formula C_nH_{2n+2}, whereas cycloalkanes have the formula C_nH_{2n}. Straight-chain alkanes are named by adding the family ending *-ane* to a parent; this tells how many carbon atoms are present. Branched-chain alkanes are named by using the longest continuous chain of carbon atoms for the parent and then identifying the *alkyl groups* present as branches off the main chain. The positions of the substituent groups on the main chain are identified by numbering the carbons in the chain so that the substituents have the lowest number. Cycloalkanes are named by adding *cyclo-* as a prefix to the name of the alkane (*see Problems 25, 27, 52, 61, 67*).

6. What are the general properties and chemical reactions of alkanes? Alkanes are generally soluble only in nonpolar organic solvents, have weak intermolecular forces, and are nontoxic. Their principal chemical reactions are *combustion*, a reaction with oxygen that gives carbon dioxide and water, and *halogenation*, a reaction in which hydrogen atoms are replaced by chlorine or bromine (*see Problems 62–65, 70, 76, 77*).

CONCEPT MAP: INTRODUCTION TO ORGANIC CHEMISTRY FAMILIES

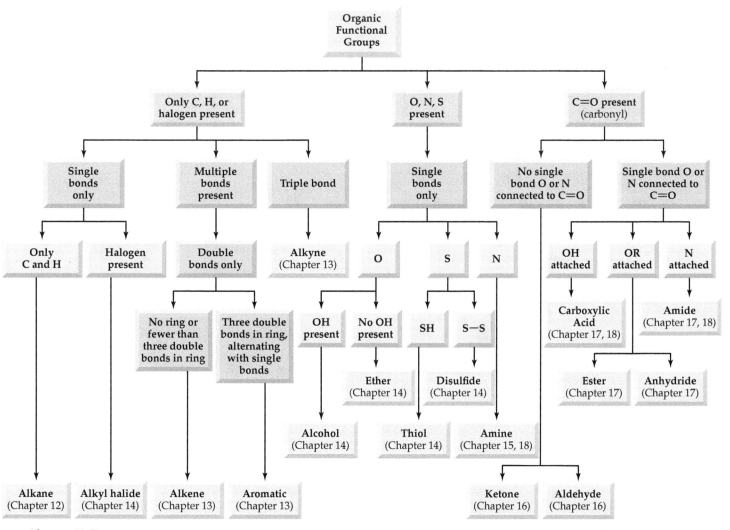

▲ **Figure 12.5**

Functional Group Flow Scheme. Learning to classify organic molecules by the families to which they belong is a crucial skill you need to develop, since the chemistry that both organic and biological molecules undergo is directly related to their functional groups. The flow scheme in Figure 12.5 will aid you in this classification. First introduced in Section 12.2, it will be a key reference as you proceed through the rest of the chapters in this book. As we discuss each family in later chapters, sections of it will be reproduced and expanded to help also tie in the chemistry that those functional groups undergo.

KEY WORDS

Alkane, *p. 364*

Alkyl group, *p. 375*

Branched-chain alkane, *p. 365*

Combustion, *p.381*

Condensed structure, *p. 367*

Conformation, *p. 372*

Conformer, *p. 372*

Constitutional isomers, *p. 366*

Cycloalkane, *p. 383*

Ethyl group, *p. 375*

Functional group, *p. 360*

Functional group isomer, *p. 366*

Hydrocarbon, *p. 360*

Isomers, *p. 365*

Isopropyl group, *p. 376*

Line structure, *p. 369*

Methyl group, *p. 375*

Methylene group, *p. 367*

Organic chemistry, *p. 357*

Primary (1°) carbon atom, *p. 376*

Propyl group, *p. 376*

Quaternary (4°) carbon atom, *p. 376*

Secondary (2°) carbon atom, *p. 376*

Straight-chain alkane, *p. 365*

Substituent, *p. 374*

Tertiary (3°) carbon atom, *p. 376*

SUMMARY OF REACTIONS

1. **Combustion of an alkane with oxygen (Section 12.8):**

$$CH_4 + 2\,O_2 \longrightarrow CO_2 + 2\,H_2O$$

2. **Halogenation of an alkane to yield an alkyl halide (Section 12.8):**

$$CH_4 + Cl_2 \longrightarrow CH_3Cl + HCl$$

UNDERSTANDING KEY CONCEPTS

12.22 How many hydrogen atoms are needed to complete the hydrocarbon formulas for the following carbon backbones?

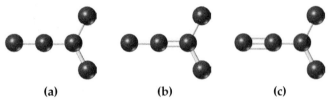

     (a)   (b)   (c)

12.23 Convert the following models into condensed structures (black = C; white = H; red = O):

    (a)   (b)

12.24 Convert the following models into line drawings (black = C; white = H; red = O; blue = N):

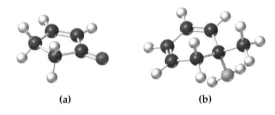

    (a)   (b)

12.25 Convert the following models into line drawings and identify the functional groups in each:

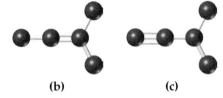

    (a)   (b)

12.26 Give systematic names for the following alkanes:

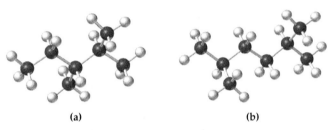

    (a)   (b)

12.27 Give systematic names for the following cycloalkanes:

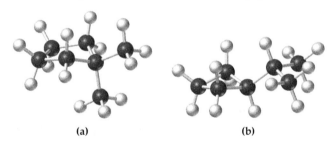

    (a)   (b)

12.28 The following two compounds are isomers, even though both can be named 1,3-dimethylcyclopentane. What is the difference between them?

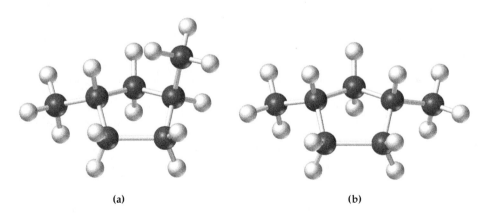

       (a)   (b)

ADDITIONAL PROBLEMS

ORGANIC MOLECULES AND FUNCTIONAL GROUPS

12.29 What characteristics of carbon make possible the existence of so many different organic compounds?

12.30 What are functional groups, and why are they important?

12.31 Why are most organic compounds nonconducting and insoluble in water?

12.32 What is meant by the term *polar covalent bond*? Give an example of such a bond.

12.33 For each of the following, give an example of a member compound containing 5 carbons total:

(a) Alcohol (b) Amide (c) Carboxylic acid (d) Ester

12.34 Identify the circled functional groups in the following molecules:

(a)

(b)

12.35 Identify the functional groups in the following molecules:

(a)

Vitamin A

(b)

Ramipril
(a new generation antihypertensive)

12.36 Propose structures for molecules that fit the following descriptions:

(a) An aldehyde with the formula $C_5H_{10}O$

(b) An ester with the formula $C_6H_{12}O_2$

(c) A compound with the formula C_3H_7NOS that is both an amide and a thiol

12.37 Propose structures for molecules that fit the following descriptions:

(a) An amide with the formula C_4H_9NO

(b) An aldehyde that has a ring of carbons, $C_6H_{10}O$

(c) An aromatic compound that is also an ether, $C_8H_{10}O$

ALKANES AND ISOMERS

12.38 What requirement must be met for two compounds to be isomers?

12.39 If one compound has the formula C_5H_{10} and another has the formula C_4H_{10}, are the two compounds isomers? Explain.

12.40 What is the difference between a secondary carbon and a tertiary carbon? What about the difference between a primary carbon and a quaternary carbon?

12.41 Why is it not possible for a compound to have a *quintary* carbon (five R groups attached to C)?

12.42 Give examples of compounds that meet the following descriptions:

(a) An alkane with 2 tertiary carbons

(b) A cycloalkane with only secondary carbons

12.43 Give examples of compounds that meet the following descriptions:

(a) A branched-chain alkane with only primary and quaternary carbons

(b) A cycloalkane with three substituents

12.44 (a) There are two isomers with the formula C_4H_{10}. Draw both the condensed and line structure for each isomer.

(b) Using the structures you drew in (a) as a starting point, draw both the condensed and line structures for the four isomeric alcohols having the chemical formula $C_4H_{10}O$.

(c) Using the structures you drew in (a) as a starting point, draw both the condensed and line structures for the three isomeric ethers having the chemical formula $C_4H_{10}O$.

12.45 Write condensed structures for the following molecular formulas. (You may have to use rings and/or multiple bonds in some instances.)

(a) C_2H_7N (b) C_4H_8 (Write the line structure as well.)

(c) C_2H_4O (d) CH_2O_2 (Write the line structure as well.)

12.46 How many isomers can you write that fit the following descriptions?

(a) Alcohols with formula $C_5H_{12}O$

(b) Amines with formula C_3H_9N

(c) Ketones with formula $C_5H_{10}O$

12.47 How many isomers can you write that fit the following descriptions?

(a) Aldehydes with formula $C_5H_{10}O$

(b) Esters with formula $C_4H_8O_2$

(c) Carboxylic acids with formula $C_4H_8O_2$

12.48 Which of the following pairs of structures are identical, which are isomers, and which are unrelated?

(a) 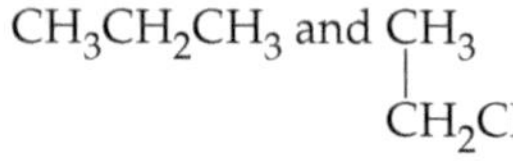 $CH_3CH_2CH_3$ and $\underset{\underset{CH_2CH_3}{|}}{CH_3}$

(b) 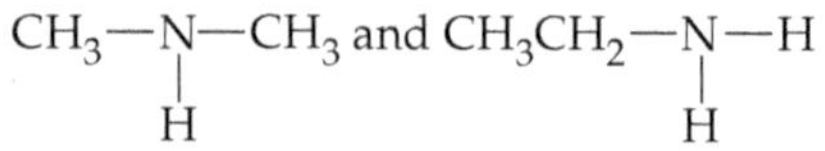 $CH_3-\underset{\underset{H}{|}}{N}-CH_3$ and $CH_3CH_2-\underset{\underset{H}{|}}{N}-H$

(c) 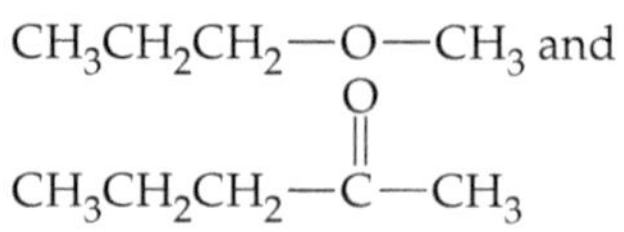 $CH_3CH_2CH_2-O-CH_3$ and

$CH_3CH_2CH_2-\overset{\overset{O}{\|}}{C}-CH_3$

(d) 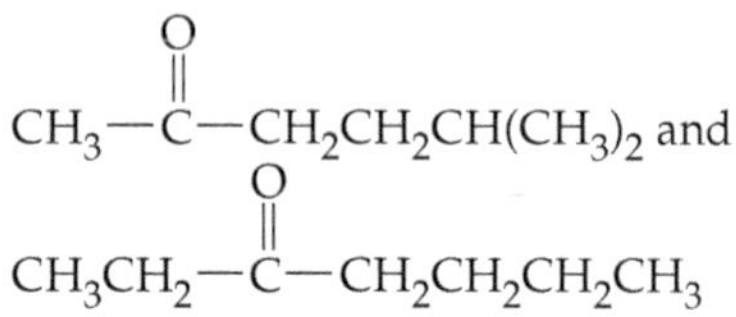 $CH_3-\overset{\overset{O}{\|}}{C}-CH_2CH_2CH(CH_3)_2$ and

$CH_3CH_2-\overset{\overset{O}{\|}}{C}-CH_2CH_2CH_2CH_3$

(e) 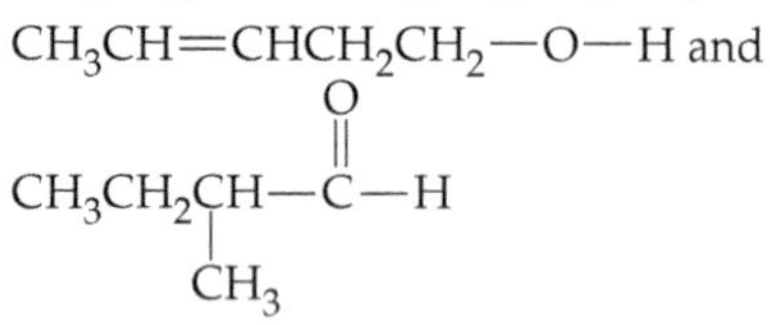 $CH_3CH=CHCH_2CH_2-O-H$ and

$CH_3CH_2\underset{\underset{CH_3}{|}}{CH}-\overset{\overset{O}{\|}}{C}-H$

12.49 Which structure(s) in each group represent the same compound, and which represent isomers?

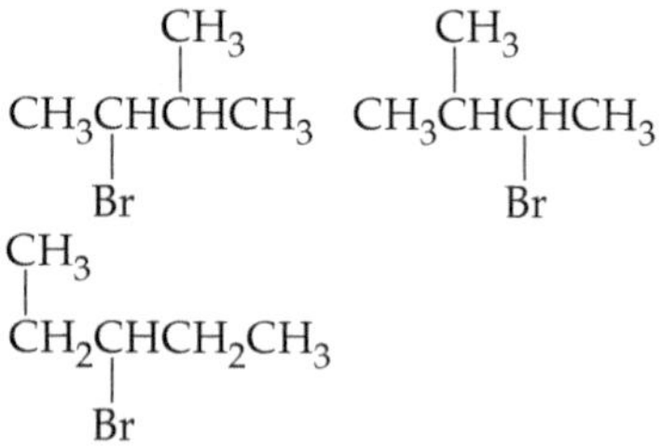

(a) 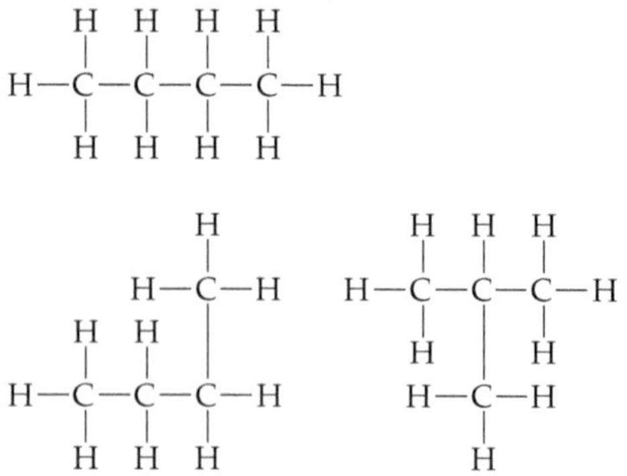 $H-\overset{\overset{H}{|}}{\underset{\underset{H}{|}}{C}}-\overset{\overset{H}{|}}{\underset{\underset{H}{|}}{C}}-\overset{\overset{H}{|}}{\underset{\underset{H}{|}}{C}}-\overset{\overset{H}{|}}{\underset{\underset{H}{|}}{C}}-H$

(b)

$H-\overset{\overset{H}{|}}{\underset{\underset{H}{|}}{C}}-H$

$H-\overset{\overset{H}{|}}{\underset{\underset{H}{|}}{C}}-\overset{\overset{H}{|}}{\underset{\underset{H}{|}}{C}}-\overset{\overset{H}{|}}{\underset{\underset{H}{|}}{C}}-H$

(c)

$H-\overset{\overset{H}{|}}{\underset{\underset{H}{|}}{C}}-\overset{\overset{H}{|}}{\underset{\underset{H}{|}}{C}}-\overset{\overset{H}{|}}{\underset{\underset{H}{|}}{C}}-H$

$H-\overset{\overset{H}{|}}{\underset{\underset{H}{|}}{C}}-H$

$\underset{\underset{Br}{|}}{CH_3\overset{\overset{CH_3}{|}}{CH}CHCH_3}$ $\underset{\underset{Br}{|}}{CH_3\overset{\overset{CH_3}{|}}{CH}CHCH_3}$

$\underset{\underset{Br}{|}}{\overset{\overset{CH_3}{|}}{CH_2}CHCH_2CH_3}$

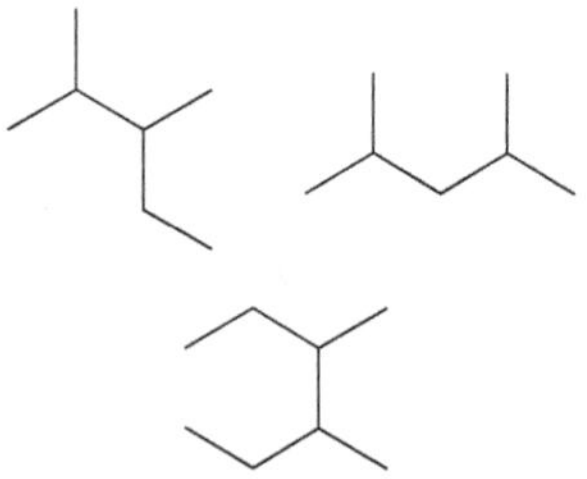

12.50 What is wrong with the following structures?

(a) $CH_3=CHCH_2CH_2OH$

(b) 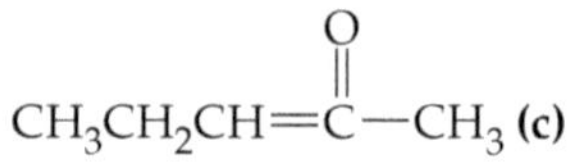 $CH_3CH_2CH=\overset{\overset{O}{\|}}{C}-CH_3$ (c) $CH_2CH_2CH_2C\equiv\overset{\overset{CH_3}{|}}{C}CH_3$

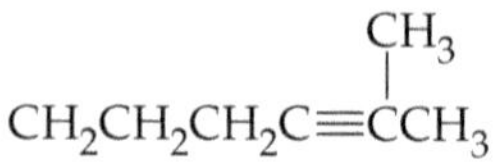

12.51 There are two things wrong with the following structure. What are they?

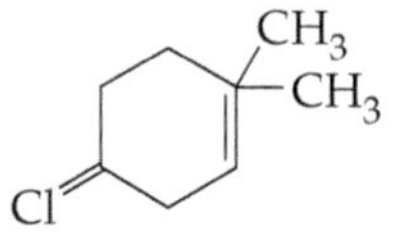

ALKANE NOMENCLATURE

12.52 What are the IUPAC names of the following alkanes?

(a) 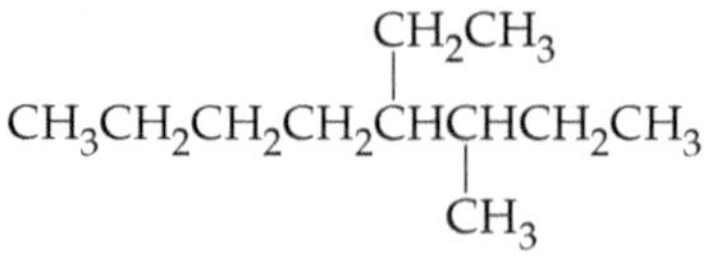 $CH_3CH_2CH_2CH_2\underset{\underset{CH_3}{|}}{\overset{\overset{CH_2CH_3}{|}}{CH}}CHCH_2CH_3$

(b) 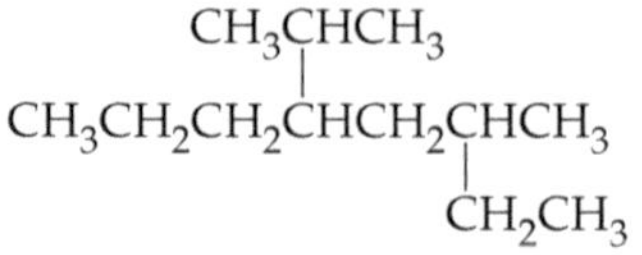 $CH_3CH_2CH_2\underset{\underset{CH_2CH_3}{|}}{\overset{\overset{CH_3CHCH_3}{|}}{CH}}CH_2CHCH_3$

(c) 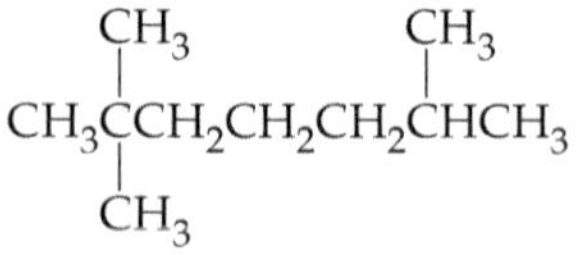 $CH_3\underset{\underset{CH_3}{|}}{\overset{\overset{CH_3}{|}}{C}}CH_2CH_2CH_2\overset{\overset{CH_3}{|}}{CH}CH_3$

(d) 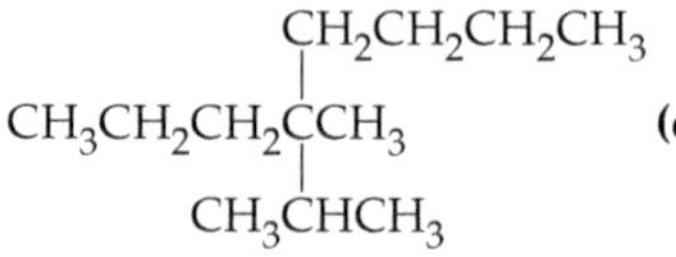 $CH_3CH_2CH_2\underset{\underset{CH_3CHCH_3}{|}}{\overset{\overset{CH_2CH_2CH_2CH_3}{|}}{C}}CH_3$

(e) 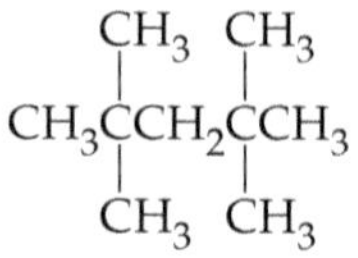 $CH_3\underset{\underset{CH_3}{|} \underset{\underset{CH_3}{}}{}}{\overset{\overset{CH_3}{|}}{C}}CH_2\underset{\underset{CH_3}{|}}{\overset{\overset{CH_3}{|}}{C}}CH_3$

(f) 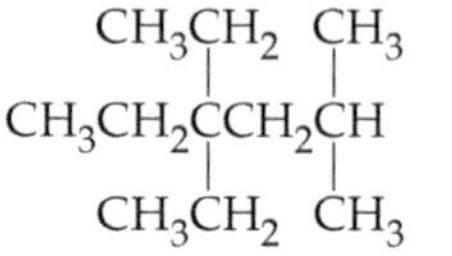 $CH_3CH_2\underset{\underset{CH_3CH_2}{} \underset{\underset{CH_3}{}}{}}{\overset{\overset{CH_3CH_2}{} \overset{\overset{CH_3}{}}{}}{C}}CH_2CH$

(g) 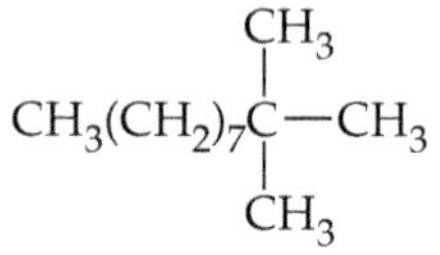 $CH_3(CH_2)_7\underset{\underset{CH_3}{|}}{\overset{\overset{CH_3}{|}}{C}}-CH_3$

12.53 Give IUPAC names for the five isomers with the formula C_6H_{14}.

12.54 Write condensed structures for the following compounds:

(a) 4-*tert*-Butyl-3,3,5-trimethylheptane

(b) 2,4-Dimethylpentane

(c) 4,4-Diethyl-3-methyloctane

(d) 3-Isopropyl-2,3,6,7-tetramethylnonane

(e) 3-Isobutyl-1-isopropyl-5-methylcycloheptane

(f) 1,1,3-Trimethylcyclopentane

12.55 Draw line structures for the following cycloalkanes:

(a) 1,1-Dimethylcyclopropane

(b) 1,2,3,4-Tetramethylcyclopentane

(c) Ethylhexane   (d) Cycloheptane

(e) 1-Methyl-3-propylcyclohexane

(f) 1-*sec*-Butyl-4-isopropylcyclooctane

12.56 Name the following cycloalkanes:

(a)

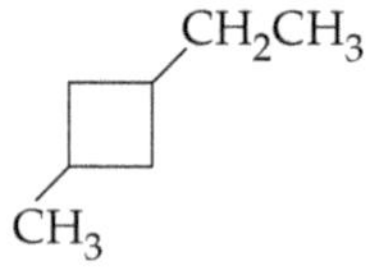

(b)

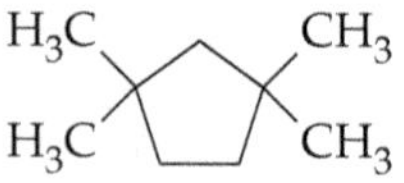

(c)

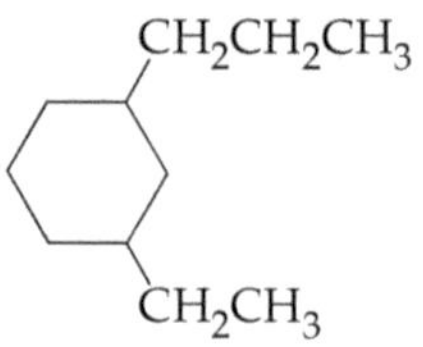

(d)

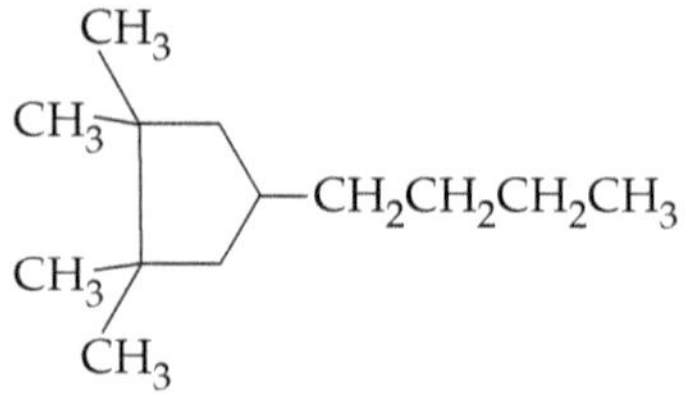

12.57 Name the following cycloalkanes:

(a)

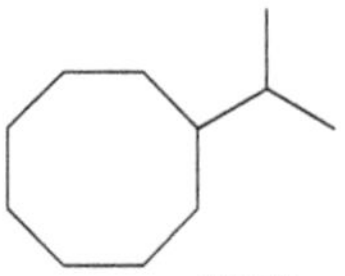

(b)

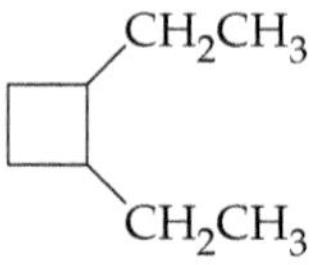

(c)  H_2C——CH_3

12.58 The following names are incorrect. Tell what is wrong with each, and provide the correct names.

(a)
$$CH_3$$
$$CH_3CCH_2CH_2CH_3$$
$$CH_3$$
2,2-Methylpentane

(b)
$$CH_3 \quad CH_3$$
$$CH{-}CH_2{-}CH$$
$$CH_3 \quad CH_3$$
1,1-Diisopropylmethane

(c)
$$CH_3$$
$$CH_3CHCH_2{-}\square$$
1-Cyclobutyl-2-methylpropane

12.59 The following names are incorrect. Write the structural formula that agrees with the apparent name, and then write the correct name of the compound.

(a) 2-Ethylbutane
(b) 2-Isopropyl-2-methylpentane
(c) 5-Ethyl-1,1-methylcyclopentane
(d) 3-Ethyl-3,5,5-trimethylhexane
(e) 1,2-Dimethyl-4-ethylcyclohexane
(f) 2,4-Diethylpentane
(g) 5,5,6,6-Methyl-7,7-ethyldecane

12.60 Draw structures and give IUPAC names for the nine isomers of C_7H_{16}.

12.61 Draw the structural formulas and name all cyclic isomers with the formula C_5H_{10}.

REACTIONS OF ALKANES

12.62 Propane, commonly known as LP gas, burns in air to yield CO_2 and H_2O. Write a balanced equation for the reaction.

12.63 Write a balanced equation for the combustion of isooctane, C_8H_{16}, a component of gasoline.

12.64 Write the formulas of the three singly chlorinated isomers formed when 2,2-dimethylbutane reacts with Cl_2 in the presence of light.

12.65 Write the formulas of the seven doubly brominated isomers formed when 2,2-dimethylbutane reacts with Br_2 in the presence of light.

GENERAL QUESTIONS AND PROBLEMS

12.66 Identify the indicated functional groups in the following molecules:

(a) Testosterone, a male sex hormone

(b) Thienamycin, an antibiotic

12.67 The line structure for aspartame is shown below:

Identify carbons a–d as primary, secondary, tertiary, or quaternary.

12.68 Consider the compound shown in Problem 12.66a; how many tertiary carbons does it have?

12.69 If someone reported the preparation of a compound with the formula C_3H_9 most chemists would be skeptical. Why?

12.70 Most lipsticks are about 70% castor oil and wax. Why is lipstick more easily removed with petroleum jelly than with water?

12.71 When pentane is exposed to Br_2 in the presence of light, a halogenation reaction occurs. Write the formulas of:

(a) All possible products containing only one bromine.
(b) All possible products containing two bromines that are *not* on the same carbon.

12.72 Which do you think has a higher boiling point, pentane or neopentane (2,2-dimethylpropane)? Why?

12.73 Propose structures for the following:

(a) An aldehyde, C_4H_8O
(b) An iodo-substituted alkene, C_5H_9I
(c) A cycloalkane, C_7H_{14}
(d) A diene (dialkene), C_5H_8

CHEMISTRY IN ACTION

12.74 What is a chemical feedstock? [*Surprising Uses of Petroleum, p. 385*]

12.75 Why is the demand for synthetic rubber greater than that of natural rubber? [*Surprising Uses of Petroleum, p. 385*]

MASTERING REACTIONS

12.76 When ethyl alcohol is treated with acid, the initially formed intermediate is known as an oxonium ion:

$$CH_3{-}CH_2{-}\overset{..}{\underset{..}{O}}H \;+\; H^+ \;\rightleftharpoons\; CH_3{-}CH_2{-}\overset{H}{\underset{+}{\underset{|}{O}H}}$$

Using the curved arrow formalism, show how this process most likely occurs.

12.77 Consider the following two-step process:

$$CH_3{-}\overset{..}{\underset{..}{S}}H \;+\; {}^-{:}\overset{..}{O}H \;\rightleftharpoons\; CH_3{-}\overset{..}{\underset{..}{S}}{:}^- \;+\; H\overset{..}{O}H$$

$$CH_3{-}\overset{..}{\underset{..}{S}}{:}^- \;+\; CH_3{-}\overset{..}{\underset{..}{I}}{:} \;\longrightarrow\; CH_3{-}\overset{..}{\underset{..}{S}}{-}CH_3 \;+\; {}^-{:}\overset{..}{\underset{..}{I}}{:}$$

Using the curved arrow formalism, show how each step of this process is most likely to occur.

Scientific Notation

What Is Scientific Notation?

The numbers that you encounter in chemistry are often either very large or very small. For example, there are about 33,000,000,000,000,000,000,000 H_2O molecules in 1.0 mL of water, and the distance between the H and O atoms in an H_2O molecule is 0.000 000 000 095 7 m. These quantities are more conveniently written in *scientific notation* as 3.3×10^{22} molecules and 9.57×10^{-11} m, respectively. In scientific notation (also known as *exponential notation*), a quantity is represented as a number between 1 and 10 multiplied by a power of 10. In this kind of expression, the small raised number to the right of the 10 is the exponent.

Number	Exponential Form	Exponent
1,000,000	1×10^6	6
100,000	1×10^5	5
10,000	1×10^4	4
1,000	1×10^3	3
100	1×10^2	2
10	1×10^1	1
1		
0.1	1×10^{-1}	-1
0.01	1×10^{-2}	-2
0.001	1×10^{-3}	-3
0.000 1	1×10^{-4}	-4
0.000 01	1×10^{-5}	-5
0.000 001	1×10^{-6}	-6
0.000 000 1	1×10^{-7}	-7

Numbers greater than 1 have *positive* exponents, which tell how many times a number must be *multiplied* by 10 to obtain the correct value. For example, the expression 5.2×10^3 means that 5.2 must be multiplied by 10 three times:

$$5.2 \times 10^3 = 5.2 \times 10 \times 10 \times 10 = 5.2 \times 1000 = 5200$$

Note that doing this means moving the decimal point three places to the right:

$$5200.$$
$$123$$

The value of a positive exponent indicates *how many places to the right the decimal point must be moved* to give the correct number in ordinary decimal notation.

Numbers less than 1 have *negative exponents,* which tell how many times a number must be *divided* by 10 (or multiplied by one-tenth) to obtain the correct value. Thus, the expression 3.7×10^{-2} means that 3.7 must be divided by 10 two times:

$$3.7 \times 10^{-2} = \frac{3.7}{10 \times 10} = \frac{3.7}{100} = 0.037$$

Note that doing this means moving the decimal point two places to the left:

$$0.037$$
$$21$$

The value of a negative exponent indicates *how may places to the left the decimal point must be moved* to give the correct number in ordinary decimal notation.

Representing Numbers in Scientific Notation

How do you convert a number from ordinary notation to scientific notation? If the number is greater than or equal to 10, shift the decimal point to the *left* by n places until you obtain a number between 1 and 10. Then, multiply the result by 10^n. For example, the number 8137.6 is written in scientific notation as 8.1376×10^3:

Number of places decimal
point was shifted to the left

$$8137.6 = 8.1376 \times 10^3$$

Shift decimal point to the left
by 3 places to get a number
between 1 and 10

When you shift the decimal point to the left by three places, you are in effect dividing the number by $10 \times 10 \times 10 = 1000 = 10^3$. Therefore, you must multiply the result by 10^3 so that the value of the number is unchanged.

To convert a number less than 1 to scientific notation, shift the decimal point to the *right* by n places until you obtain a number between 1 and 10. Then, multiply the result by 10^{-n}. For example, the number 0.012 is written in scientific notation as 1.2×10^{-2}:

Number of places decimal
point was shifted to the right

$$0.012 = 1.2 \times 10^{-2}$$

Shift decimal point to the right
by 2 places to get a number
between 1 and 10

When you shift the decimal point to the right by two places, you are in effect multiplying the number by $10 \times 10 = 100 = 10^2$. Therefore, you must multiply the result by 10^{-2} so that the value of the number is unchanged. ($10^2 \times 10^{-2} = 10^0 = 1$.)

The following table gives some additional examples. To convert from scientific notation to ordinary notation, simply reverse the preceding process. Thus, to write the number 5.84×10^4 in ordinary notation, drop the factor of 10^4 and move the decimal point 4 places to the *right* ($5.84 \times 10^4 = 58{,}400$). To write the number 3.5×10^{-1} in ordinary notation, drop the factor of 10^{-1} and move the decimal point 1 place to the *left* ($3.5 \times 10^{-1} = 0.35$). Note that you don't need scientific notation for numbers between 1 and 10 because $10^0 = 1$.

Number	Scientific Notation
58,400	5.84×10^4
0.35	3.5×10^{-1}
7.296	$7.296 \times 10^0 = 7.296 \times 1$

Mathematical Operations with Scientific Notation

Addition and Subtraction in Scientific Notation

To add or subtract two numbers expressed in scientific notation, both numbers must have the same exponent. Thus, to add 7.16×10^3 and 1.32×10^2, first write the latter number as 0.132×10^3 and then add:

$$
\begin{array}{r}
7.16\ \times 10^3 \\
+0.132 \times 10^3 \\
\hline
7.29\ \times 10^3
\end{array}
$$

The answer has three significant figures. (Significant figures are discussed in Section 2.4.) Alternatively, you can write the first number as 71.6×10^2 and then add:

$$
\begin{array}{r}
7.16 \times 10^2 \\
+\ 1.32 \times 10^2 \\
\hline
72.9\ \ \times 10^2 = 7.29 \times 10^3
\end{array}
$$

Subtraction of these two numbers is carried out in the same manner.

$$
\begin{array}{r}
7.16\ \ \times 10^3 \\
-0.132 \times 10^3 \\
\hline
7.03\ \ \times 10^3
\end{array}
\quad \text{or} \quad
\begin{array}{r}
7.16 \times 10^2 \\
-1.32 \times 10^2 \\
\hline
70.3 \times 10^2 = 7.03 \times 10^3
\end{array}
$$

Multiplication in Scientific Notation

To multiply two numbers expressed in scientific notation, multiply the factors in front of the powers of 10 and then add the exponents. For example,

$$
(2.5 \times 10^4)(4.7 \times 10^7) = (2.5)(4.7) \times 10^{4+7} = 10 \times 10^{11} = 1.2 \times 10^{12}
$$
$$
(3.46 \times 10^5)(2.2 \times 10^{-2}) = (3.46)(2.2) \times 10^{5+(-2)} = 7.6 \times 10^3
$$

Both answers have two significant figures.

Division in Scientific Notation

To divide two numbers expressed in scientific notation, divide the factors in front of the powers of 10 and then subtract the exponent in the denominator from the exponent in the numerator. For example,

$$
\frac{3 \times 10^6}{7.2 \times 10^2} = \frac{3}{7.2} \times 10^{6-2} = 0.4 \times 10^4 = 4 \times 10^3 \ (\text{1 significant figure})
$$

$$
\frac{7.50 \times 10^{-5}}{2.5 \times 10^{-7}} = \frac{7.50}{2.5} \times 10^{-5-(-7)} = 3.0 \times 10^2 \ (\text{2 significant figures})
$$

Scientific Notation and Electronic Calculators

With a scientific calculator you can carry out calculations in scientific notation. You should consult the instruction manual for your particular calculator to learn how to enter and manipulate numbers expressed in an exponential format. On most calculators, you enter the number $A \times 10^n$ by (i) entering the number A, (ii) pressing a key labeled EXP or EE, and (iii) entering the exponent n. If the exponent is negative, you press a key labeled $+/-$ before entering the value of n. (Note that you do not enter the number 10.) The calculator displays the number $A \times 10^n$ with the number A on the left followed by some space and then the exponent n. For example,

$$
4.625 \times 10^2 \quad \text{is displayed as} \quad 4.625\ 02
$$

To add, subtract, multiply, or divide exponential numbers, use the same sequence of keystrokes as you would in working with ordinary numbers. When you add or subtract on a calculator, the numbers need not have the same exponent; the calculator automatically takes account of the different exponents. Remember, though, that the calculator often gives more digits in the answer than the allowed number of significant figures. It's sometimes helpful to outline the calculation on paper, as in the preceding examples, to keep track of the number of significant figures.

PROBLEM A.1

Perform the following calculations, expressing the results in scientific notation with the correct number of significant figures. (You don't need a calculator for these.)

(a) $(1.50 \times 10^4) + (5.04 \times 10^3)$

(b) $(2.5 \times 10^{-2}) - (5.0 \times 10^{-3})$

(c) $(6.3 \times 10^{15}) \times (10.1 \times 10^3)$

(d) $(2.5 \times 10^{-3}) \times (3.2 \times 10^{-4})$

(e) $(8.4 \times 10^4) \div (3.0 \times 10^6)$

(f) $(5.530 \times 10^{-2}) \div (2.5 \times 10^{-5})$

ANSWERS

(a) 2.00×10^4 (b) 2.0×10^{-2} (c) 6.4×10^{19}

(d) 8.0×10^{-7} (e) 2.8×10^{-2} (f) 2.2×10^3

PROBLEM A.2

Perform the following calculations, expressing the results in scientific notation with the correct number of significant figures. (Use a calculator for these.)

(a) $(9.72 \times 10^{-1}) + (3.4823 \times 10^2)$

(b) $(3.772 \times 10^3) - (2.891 \times 10^4)$

(c) $(1.956 \times 10^3) \div (6.02 \times 10^{23})$

(d) $3.2811 \times (9.45 \times 10^{21})$

(e) $(1.0015 \times 10^3) \div (5.202 \times 10^{-9})$

(f) $(6.56 \times 10^{-6}) \times (9.238 \times 10^{-4})$

ANSWERS

(a) 3.4920×10^2 (b) -2.514×10^4 (c) 3.25×10^{-21}

(d) 3.10×10^{22} (e) 1.925×10^{11} (f) 6.06×10^{-9}

Conversion Factors

Length SI Unit: Meter (m)

1 meter = 0.001 kilometer (km)

= 100 centimeters (cm)

= 1.0936 yards (yd)

1 centimeter = 10 millimeters (mm)

= 0.3937 inch (in.)

1 nanometer = 1×10^{-9} meter

1 Angstrom (Å) = 1×10^{-10} meter

1 inch = 2.54 centimeters

1 mile = 1.6094 kilometers

Volume SI Unit: Cubic meter (m^3)

1 cubic meter = 1000 liters (L)

1 liter = 1000 cubic centimeters (cm^3)

= 1000 milliliters (mL)

= 1.056710 quarts (qt)

1 cubic inch = 16.4 cubic centimeters

Temperature SI Unit: Kelvin (K)

0 K = $-273.15\,°C$

= $-459.67\,°F$

$°F = (9/5)°C + 32°; °F = (1.8 \times °C) + 32°$

$°C = (5/9)(°F - 32°); °C = \dfrac{(°F - 32°)}{1.8}$

$K = °C + 273.15°$

Mass SI Unit: Kilogram (kg)

1 kilogram = 1000 grams (g)

= 2.205 pounds (lb)

1 gram = 1000 milligrams (mg)

= 0.03527 ounce (oz)

1 pound = 453.6 grams

1 atomic mass unit = 1.66054×10^{-24} gram

Pressure SI Unit: Pascal (Pa)

1 pascal = 9.869×10^{-6} atmosphere

1 atmosphere = 101,325 pascals

= 760 mmHg (Torr)

= 14.70 lb/in^2

Energy SI Unit: Joule (J)

1 joule = 0.23901 calorie (cal)

1 calorie = 4.184 joules

1 Calorie (nutritional unit) = 1000 calories

= 1 kcal

Glossary

1,4 Link A glycosidic link between the hemiacetal hydroxyl group at C1 of one sugar and the hydroxyl group at C4 of another sugar.

Acetal A compound that has two ether-like —OR groups bonded to the same carbon atom.

Acetyl coenzyme A (acetyl-CoA) Acetyl-substituted coenzyme A—the common intermediate that carries acetyl groups into the citric acid cycle.

Acetyl group A $CH_3C{=}O$ group.

Achiral The opposite of chiral; having no right- or left-handedness and no nonsuper-imposable mirror images.

Acid A substance that provides H^+ ions in water.

Acid dissociation constant (K_a) The equilibrium constant for the dissociation of an acid (HA), equal to $[H^+][A^-]/[HA]$

Acidosis The abnormal condition associated with a blood plasma pH below 7.35; may be respiratory or metabolic.

Acid-base indicator A dye that changes color depending on the pH of a solution.

Activation (of an enzyme) Any process that initiates or increases the action of an enzyme.

Activation energy (E_{act}) The amount of energy necessary for reactants to surmount the energy barrier to reaction; affects reaction rate.

Active site A pocket in an enzyme with the specific shape and chemical makeup necessary to bind a substrate.

Active transport Movement of substances across a cell membrane with the assistance of energy (for example, from ATP).

Actual Yield The amount of product actually formed in a reaction.

Acyl group An $RC{=}O$ group.

Addition reaction A general reaction type in which a substance X—Y adds to the multiple bond of an unsaturated reactant to yield a saturated product that has only single bonds.

Addition reaction, aldehydes and ketones Addition of an alcohol or other compound to the carbon-oxygen double bond to give a carbon-oxygen single bond.

Adenosine triphosphate (ATP) The principal energy-carrying molecule; removal of a phosphoryl group to give ADP releases free energy.

Aerobic In the presence of oxygen.

Agonist A substance that interacts with a receptor to cause or prolong the receptor's normal biochemical response.

Alcohol A compound that has an —OH group bonded to a saturated, alkane-like carbon atom, R—OH.

Alcoholic fermentation The anaerobic breakdown of glucose to ethanol plus carbon dioxide by the action of yeast enzymes.

Aldehyde A compound that has a carbonyl group bonded to one carbon and one hydrogen, RCHO.

Aldose A monosaccharide that contains an aldehyde carbonyl group.

Alkali metal An element in group 1A of the periodic table.

Alkaline earth metal An element in group 2A of the periodic table.

Alkaloid A naturally occurring nitrogen-containing compound isolated from a plant; usually basic, bitter, and poisonous.

Alkalosis The abnormal condition associated with a blood plasma pH above 7.45; may be respiratory or metabolic.

Alkane A hydrocarbon that has only single bonds.

Alkene A hydrocarbon that contains a carbon-carbon double bond.

Alkoxide ion The anion resulting from deprotonation of an alcohol, RO^-.

Alkoxy group An —OR group.

Alkyl group The part of an alkane that remains when a hydrogen atom is removed.

Alkyl halide A compound that has an alkyl group bonded to a halogen atom, R—X.

Alkyne A hydrocarbon that contains a carbon-carbon triple bond.

Allosteric control An interaction in which the binding of a regulator at one site on a protein affects the protein's ability to bind another molecule at a different site.

Allosteric enzyme An enzyme whose activity is controlled by the binding of an activator or inhibitor at a location other than the active site.

Alpha (α) particle A helium nucleus (He^{2+}), emitted as α-radiation.

Alpha- (α-) amino acid An amino acid in which the amino group is bonded to the carbon atom next to the —COOH group.

Alpha- (α-) helix Secondary protein structure in which a protein chain forms a right-handed coil stabilized by hydrogen bonds between peptide groups along its backbone.

Amide A compound that has a carbonyl group bonded to a carbon atom and a nitrogen atom group, $RCONR_2'$, where the R′ groups may be alkyl groups or hydrogen atoms.

Amine A compound that has one or more organic groups bonded to nitrogen; primary, RNH_2; secondary, R_2NH; or tertiary, R_3N.

Amino acid A molecule that contains both an amino group and a carboxylic acid functional group.

Amino acid pool The entire collection of free amino acids in the body.

Amino group The —NH_2 functional group.

Amino-terminal (N-terminal) amino acid The amino acid with the free —NH^{3+} group at the end of a protein.

Ammonium ion A positive ion formed by addition of hydrogen to ammonia or an amine (may be primary, secondary, or tertiary).

Ammonium salt An ionic compound composed of an ammonium cation and an anion; an amine salt.

Amorphous solid A solid whose particles do not have an orderly arrangement.

Amphoteric Describing a substance that can react as either an acid or a base.

Anabolism Metabolic reactions that build larger biological molecules from smaller pieces.

Anaerobic In the absence of oxygen.

Anion A negatively charged ion.

Anomeric carbon atom The hemiacetal C atom in a cyclic sugar; the C atom bonded to an —OH group and an O in the ring.

Anomers Cyclic sugars that differ only in positions of substituents at the hemiacetal carbon (the anomeric carbon); the α form has the —OH on the opposite side from the —CH_2OH; the β form has the —OH on the same side as the —CH_2OH.

Antagonist A substance that blocks or inhibits the normal biochemical response of a receptor.

Antibody (immunoglobulin) Glycoprotein molecule that identifies antigens.

Anticodon A sequence of three ribonucleotides on tRNA that recognizes the complementary sequence (the codon) on mRNA.

Antigen A substance foreign to the body that triggers the immune response.

Antioxidant A substance that prevents oxidation by reacting with an oxidizing agent.

Aromatic The class of compounds containing benzene-like rings.

Artificial transmutation The change of one atom into another brought about by a nuclear bombardment reaction.

Atom The smallest and simplest particle of an element.

Atomic mass unit (amu) A convenient unit for describing the mass of an atom; 1 amu = 1/12 the mass of a carbon-12 atom.

Atomic number (Z) The number of protons in an atom.

Atomic theory A set of assumptions proposed by English scientist John Dalton to explain the chemical behavior of matter.

Atomic weight The weighted average mass of an element's atoms.

ATP synthase The enzyme complex in the inner mitochondrial membrane at which hydrogen ions cross the membrane and ATP is synthesized from ADP.

Autoimmune disease Disorder in which the immune system identifies normal body components as antigens and produces antibodies to them.

Avogadro's law Equal volumes of gases at the same temperature and pressure contain equal numbers of molecules (V/n = constant, or $V_1/n_1 = V_2/n_2$).

Avogadro's number (N_A) The number of units in 1 mole of anything; 6.02×10^{23}.

Balanced equation Describing a chemical equation in which the numbers and kinds of atoms are the same on both sides of the reaction arrow.

Base A substance that provides OH^- ions in water.

Base pairing The pairing of bases connected by hydrogen bonding (G-C and A-T), as in the DNA double helix.

Beta- (β-) Oxidation pathway A repetitive series of biochemical reactions that degrades fatty acids to acetyl-SCoA by removing carbon atoms two at a time.

Beta (β) particle An electron (e⁻), emitted as β radiation.

Beta- (β-) Sheet Secondary protein structure in which adjacent protein chains either in the same molecule or in different molecules are held in place by hydrogen bonds along the backbones.

Bile Fluid secreted by the liver and released into the small intestine from the gallbladder during digestion; contains bile acids, bicarbonate ion, and other electrolytes.

Bile acids Steroid acids derived from cholesterol that are secreted in bile.

Binary compound A compound formed by combination of two different elements.

Blood clot A network of fibrin fibers and trapped blood cells that forms at the site of blood loss.

Blood plasma Liquid portion of the blood; an extracellular fluid.

Blood serum Fluid portion of blood remaining after clotting has occurred.

Boiling point (bp) The temperature at which liquid and gas are in equilibrium.

Bond angle The angle formed by three adjacent atoms in a molecule.

Bond dissociation energy The amount of energy that must be supplied to break a bond and separate the atoms in an isolated gaseous molecule.

Bond length The optimum distance between nuclei in a covalent bond.

Boyle's law The pressure of a gas at constant temperature is inversely proportional to its volume ($PV = $ constant, or $P_1V_1 = P_2V_2$).

Branched-chain alkane An alkane that has a branching connection of carbons.

Brønsted-Lowry acid A substance that can donate a hydrogen ion, H⁺, to another molecule or ion.

Brønsted-Lowry base A substance that can accept H⁺ from an acid.

Buffer A combination of substances that act together to prevent a drastic change in pH; usually a weak acid and its conjugate base.

Carbohydrate A member of a large class of naturally occurring polyhydroxy ketones and aldehydes.

Carbonyl compound Any compound that contains a carbonyl group $C=O$.

Carbonyl group A functional group that has a carbon atom joined to an oxygen atom by a double bond, $C=O$.

Carbonyl-group substitution reaction A reaction in which a new group replaces (substitutes for) a group attached to a carbonyl-group carbon in an acyl group.

Carboxyl group The —COOH functional group.

Carboxyl-terminal (C-terminal) amino acid The amino acid with the free —COO⁻ group at the end of a protein.

Carboxylate anion The anion that results from ionization of a carboxylic acid, RCOO⁻.

Carboxylic acid A compound that has a carbonyl group bonded to a carbon atom and an —OH group, RCOOH.

Carboxylic acid salt An ionic compound containing a carboxylate anion and a cation.

Catabolism Metabolic reaction pathways that break down food molecules and release biochemical energy.

Catalyst A substance that speeds up the rate of a chemical reaction but is itself unchanged.

Cation A positively charged ion.

Centromeres The central regions of chromosomes.

Chain reaction A reaction that, once started, is self-sustaining.

Change of state The conversion of a substance from one state to another—for example, from a liquid to a gas.

Charles's law The volume of a gas at constant pressure is directly proportional to its Kelvin temperature ($V/T = $ constant, or $V_1/T_1 = V_2/T_2$).

Chemical change A change in the chemical makeup of a substance.

Chemical compound A pure substance that can be broken down into simpler substances by chemical reactions.

Chemical equation An expression in which symbols and formulas are used to represent a chemical reaction.

Chemical equilibrium A state in which the rates of forward and reverse reactions are the same.

Chemical formula A notation for a chemical compound using element symbols and subscripts to show how many atoms of each element are present.

Chemical reaction A process in which the identity and composition of one or more substances are changed.

Chemistry The study of the nature, properties, and transformations of matter.

Chiral carbon atom (chirality center) A carbon atom bonded to four different groups.

Chiral Having right- or left-handedness; able to have two different mirror-image forms.

Chromosome A complex of proteins and DNA; visible during cell division.

Cis-trans isomers Alkenes that have the same connections between atoms but differ in their three-dimensional structures because of the way that groups are attached to different sides of the double bond. The cis isomer has hydrogen atoms on the same side of the double bond; the trans isomer has them on opposite sides.

Citric acid cycle The series of biochemical reactions that breaks down acetyl groups to produce energy carried by reduced coenzymes and carbon dioxide.

Clones Identical copies of organisms, cells, or DNA segments from a single ancestor.

Codon A sequence of three ribonucleotides in the messenger RNA chain that codes for a specific amino acid; also the three nucleotide sequence (a stop codon) that stops translation.

Coefficient A number placed in front of a formula to balance a chemical equation.

Coenzyme An organic molecule that acts as an enzyme cofactor.

Cofactor A nonprotein part of an enzyme that is essential to the enzyme's catalytic activity; a metal ion or a coenzyme.

Colligative property A property of a solution that depends only on the number of dissolved particles, not on their chemical identity.

Colloid A homogeneous mixture that contains particles that range in diameter from 2 to 500 nm.

Combined gas law The product of the pressure and volume of a gas is proportional to its temperature ($PV/T = $ constant, or $P_1V_1/T_1 = P_2V_2/T_2$).

Combustion A chemical reaction that produces a flame, usually because of burning with oxygen.

Competititve (enzyme) inhibition Enzyme regulation in which an inhibitor competes with a substrate for binding to the enzyme active site.

Concentration A measure of the amount of a given substance in a mixture.

Concentration gradient A difference in concentration within the same system.

Condensed structure A shorthand way of drawing structures in which $C-C$ and $C-H$ bonds are understood rather than shown.

Conformation The specific three-dimensional arrangement of atoms in a molecule at a given instant.

Conformers Molecular structures having identical connections between atoms.

Conjugate acid The substance formed by addition of H⁺ to a base.

Conjugate acid-base pair Two substances whose formulas differ by only a hydrogen ion, H⁺.

Conjugate base The substance formed by loss of H⁺ from an acid.

Conjugated protein A protein that incorporates one or more non-amino acid units in its structure.

Constitutional isomers Compounds with the same molecular formula but different connections among their atoms.

Conversion factor An expression of the relationship between two units.

Coordinate covalent bond The covalent bond that forms when both electrons are donated by the same atom.

Cosmic rays A mixture of high-energy particles—primarily of protons and various atomic nuclei—that shower the earth from outer space.

Covalent bond A bond formed by sharing electrons between atoms.

Critical mass The minimum amount of radioactive material needed to sustain a nuclear chain reaction.

Crystalline solid A solid whose atoms, molecules, or ions are rigidly held in an ordered arrangement.

Cycloalkane An alkane that contains a ring of carbon atoms.

Cycloalkene A cyclic hydrocarbon that contains a double bond.

Cytoplasm The region between the cell membrane and the nuclear membrane in a eukaryotic cell.

Cytosol The fluid part of the cytoplasm surrounding the organelles within a cell.

***d*-Block element** A transition metal element that results from the filling of d orbitals.

D-Sugar Monosaccharide with the —OH group on the chiral carbon atom farthest from the carbonyl group pointing to the right in a Fischer projection.

Dalton's law The total pressure exerted by a mixture of gases is equal to the sum of the partial pressures exerted by each individual gas.

Decay series A sequential series of nuclear disintegrations leading from a heavy radioisotope to a nonradioactive product.

Degree of unsaturation The number of carbon-carbon double bonds in a molecule.

Dehydration The loss of water from an alcohol to yield an alkene.

Denaturation The loss of secondary, tertiary or quaternary protein structure due to disruption of noncovalent interactions and/or disulfide bonds that leaves peptide bond and primary structure intact.

Density The physical property that relates the mass of an object to its volume; mass per unit volume.

Deoxyribonucleotide A nucleotide containing 2-deoxy-D-ribose.

Diabetes mellitus A chronic condition due to either insufficient insulin or failure of insulin to activate crossing of cell membranes by glucose.

Diastereomers Stereoisomers that are not mirror images of each other.

Digestion A general term for the breakdown of food into small molecules.

Dilution factor The ratio of the initial and final solution volumes (V_1/V_2).

Dipole-dipole force The attractive force between positive and negative ends of polar molecules.

Disaccharide A carbohydrate composed of two monosaccharides.

Dissociation The splitting apart of an acid in water to give H^+ and an anion.

Disulfide A compound that contains a sulfur-sulfur bond, RS-SR.

Disulfide bond (in protein) An S-S bond formed between two cysteine side chains; can join two peptide chains together or cause a loop in a peptide chain.

DNA (deoxyribonucleic acid) The nucleic acid that stores genetic information; a polymer of deoxyribonucleotides.

Double bond A covalent bond formed by sharing two electron pairs.

Double helix Two strands coiled around each other in a screwlike fashion; in most organisms the two polynucleotides of DNA form a double helix.

Drug Any substance that alters body function when it is introduced from an external source.

Eicosanoid A lipid derived from a 20-carbon unsaturated carboxylic acid.

Electrolyte A substance that produces ions and therefore conducts electricity when dissolved in water.

Electron A negatively charged subatomic particle.

Electron affinity The energy released on adding an electron to a single atom in the gaseous state.

Electron capture A process in which the nucleus captures an inner-shell electron from the surrounding electron cloud, thereby converting a proton into a neutron.

Electron configuration The specific arrangement of electrons in an atom's shells and subshells.

Electron shell A grouping of electrons in an atom according to energy.

Electron subshell A grouping of electrons in a shell according to the shape of the region of space they occupy.

Electron-dot symbol An atomic symbol with dots placed around it to indicate the number of valence electrons.

Electron-transport chain The series of biochemical reactions that passes electrons from reduced coenzymes to oxygen and is coupled to ATP formation.

Electronegativity The ability of an atom to attract electrons in a covalent bond.

Element A fundamental substance that can't be broken down chemically into any simpler substance.

Elimination reaction A general reaction type in which a saturated reactant yields an unsaturated product by losing groups from two adjacent carbon atoms.

Enantiomers, optical isomers The two mirror-image forms of a chiral molecule.

Endergonic A nonspontaneous reaction or process that absorbs free energy and has a positive ΔG.

Endocrine system A system of specialized cells, tissues, and ductless glands that excretes hormones and shares with the nervous system the responsibility for maintaining constant internal body conditions and responding to changes in the environment.

Endothermic A process or reaction that absorbs heat and has a positive ΔH.

Energy The capacity to do work or supply heat.

Enthalpy A measure of the amount of energy associated with substances involved in a reaction.

Enthalpy change (ΔH) An alternative name for heat of reaction.

Entropy (S) The amount of disorder in a system.

Entropy change (ΔS) A measure of the increase in disorder ($\Delta S = +$) or decrease in disorder ($\Delta S = -$) as a chemical reaction or physical change occurs.

Enzyme A protein or other molecule that acts as a catalyst for a biological reaction.

Equilibrium constant (K) Value of the equilibrium constant expression for a given reaction.

Equivalent For ions, the amount equal to 1 mol of charge.

Equivalent of acid Amount of an acid that contains 1 mole of H^+ ions.

Equivalent of base Amount of base that contains 1 mole of OH^- ions.

Erythrocytes Red blood cells; transporters of blood gases.

Essential amino acid An amino acid that cannot be synthesized by the body and thus must be obtained in the diet.

Ester A compound that has a carbonyl group bonded to a carbon atom and an $-OR'$ group, RCOOR'.

Esterification The reaction between an alcohol and a carboxylic acid to yield an ester plus water.

Ether A compound that has an oxygen atom bonded to two organic groups, R$-$O$-$R.

Ethyl group The $-CH_2CH_3$ alkyl group.

Exergonic A spontaneous reaction or process that releases free energy and has a negative ΔG.

Exon A nucleotide sequence in DNA that is part of a gene and codes for part of a protein.

Exothermic A process or reaction that releases heat and has a negative ΔH.

Extracellular fluid Fluid outside cells.

f-Block element An inner transition metal element that results from the filling of f orbitals.

Facilitated diffusion Passive transport across a cell membrane with the assistance of a protein that changes shape.

Factor-label method A problem-solving procedure in which equations are set up so that unwanted units cancel and only the desired units remain.

Fat A mixture of triacylglycerols that is solid because it contains a high proportion of saturated fatty acids.

Fatty acid A long-chain carboxylic acid; those in animal fats and vegetable oils often have 12–22 carbon atoms.

Feedback control Regulation of an enzyme's activity by the product of a reaction later in a pathway.

Fermentation The production of energy under anaerobic conditions.

Fibrin Insoluble protein that forms the fiber framework of a blood clot.

Fibrous protein A tough, insoluble protein whose protein chains form fibers or sheets.

Filtration (kidney) Filtration of blood plasma through a glomerulus and into a kidney nephron.

Fischer projection Structure that represents chiral carbon atoms as the intersections of two lines, with the horizontal lines representing bonds pointing out of the page and the vertical lines representing bonds pointing behind the page. For sugars, the aldehyde or ketone is at the top.

Formula unit The formula that identifies the smallest neutral unit of a compound.

Formula weight The sum of the atomic weights of the atoms in one formula unit of any compound.

Free radical An atom or molecule with an unpaired electron.

Free-energy change (ΔG) The criterion for spontaneous change (negative ΔG; $\Delta G = \Delta H - T\Delta S$).

Functional group An atom or group of atoms within a molecule that has a characteristic structure and chemical behavior.

Functional group isomer Isomers having the same chemical formula but belonging to different chemical families due to differences in bonding; ethyl alcohol and dimethyl ether are examples of functional group isomers.

Gamma (γ) radiation Radioactivity consisting of high-energy light waves.

Gas A substance that has neither a definite volume nor a definite shape.

Gas constant (R) The constant R in the ideal gas law, $PV = nRT$.

Gas laws A series of laws that predict the influence of pressure (P), volume (V), and temperature (T) on any gas or mixture of gases.

Gay-Lussac's law For a fixed amount of gas at a constant voume, pressure is directly proportional to the Kelvin temperature ($P/T = $ constant, or $P_1/T_1 = P_2/T_2$).

Gene Segment of DNA that directs the synthesis of a single polypeptide.

Genetic (enzyme) control Regulation of enzyme activity by control of the synthesis of enzymes.

Genetic code The sequence of nucleotides, coded in triplets (codons) in mRNA, that determines the sequence of amino acids in protein synthesis.

Genome All of the genetic material in the chromosomes of an organism; its size is given as the number of base pairs.

Genomics The study of whole sets of genes and their functions.

Globular protein A water-soluble protein whose chain is folded in a compact shape with hydrophilic groups on the outside.

Glomerular filtrate Fluid that enters the nephron from the glomerulus; filtered blood plasma.

Gluconeogenesis The biochemical pathway for the synthesis of glucose from non-carbohydrates, such as lactate, amino acids, or glycerol.

Glycerophospholipid (phosphoglyceride) A lipid in which glycerol is linked by ester bonds to two fatty acids and one phosphate, which is in turn linked by another ester bond to an amino alcohol (or other alcohol).

Glycogenesis The biochemical pathway for synthesis of glycogen.

Glycogenolysis The biochemical pathway for breakdown of glycogen to free glucose.

Glycol A dialcohol, or diol having the two —OH groups on adjacent carbons.

Glycolipid A lipid with a fatty acid bonded to the $C2—NH_2$ and a sugar bonded to the $C1—OH$ group of sphingosine.

Glycolysis The biochemical pathway that breaks down a molecule of glucose into two molecules of pyruvate plus energy.

Glycoprotein A protein that contains a short carbohydrate chain.

Glycoside A cyclic acetal formed by reaction of a monosaccharide with an alcohol, accompanied by loss of H_2O.

Glycosidic bond Bond between the anomeric carbon atom of a monosaccharide and an —OR group.

Gram-equivalent For ions, the molar mass of the ion divided by the ionic charge.

Group One of the 18 vertical columns of elements in the periodic table.

Guanosine diphosphate (GDP) An energy-carrying molecule that can gain or lose a phosphoryl group to transfer energy.

Guanosine triphosphate (GTP) An energy-carrying molecule similar to ATP; removal of a phosphoryl group to give GDP releases free energy.

Half-life ($t_{1/2}$) The amount of time required for one-half of a radioactive sample to decay.

Halogen An element in group 7A of the periodic table.

Halogenation (alkene) The addition of Cl_2 or Br_2 to a multiple bond to give a 1,2-dihalide product.

Halogenation (aromatic) The substitution of a halogen group (—X) for a hydrogen on an aromatic ring.

Heat The kinetic energy transferred from a hotter object to a colder object when the two are in contact.

Heat of fusion The quantity of heat required to completely melt a substance once it has reached its melting point.

Heat of reaction (ΔH) The amount of heat absorbed or released in a reaction.

Heat of vaporization The quantity of heat needed to completely vaporize a liquid once it has reached its boiling point.

Hemiacetal A compound with both an alcohol-like —OH group and an ether-like —OR group bonded to the same carbon atom.

Hemostasis The stopping of bleeding.

Henderson-Hasselbalch equation The logarithmic form of the K_a equation for a weak acid, used in applications involving buffer solutions.

Henry's law The solubility of a gas in a liquid is directly proportional to its partial pressure over the liquid at constant temperature.

Heterocycle A ring that contains nitrogen or some other atom in addition to carbon.

Heterogeneous mixture A nonuniform mixture that has regions of different composition.

Heterogeneous nuclear RNA The initially synthesized mRNA strand containing both introns and exons.

Homogeneous mixture A uniform mixture that has the same composition throughout.

Hormone A chemical messenger secreted by cells of the endocrine system and transported through the bloodstream to target cells with appropriate receptors where it elicits a response.

Hydration The addition of water to a multiple bond to give an alcohol product.

Hydrocarbon An organic compound that contains only carbon and hydrogen.

Hydrogen bond The attraction between a hydrogen atom bonded to an electronegative O, N, or F atom and another nearby electronegative O, N, or F atom.

Hydrogenation The addition of H_2 to a multiple bond to give a saturated product.

Hydrohalogenation The addition of HCl or HBr to a multiple bond to give an alkyl halide product.

Hydrolysis A reaction in which a bond or bonds are broken and the H— and —OH of water add to the atoms of the broken bond or bonds.

Hydronium ion The H_3O^+ ion, formed when an acid reacts with water.

Hydrophilic Water-loving; a hydrophilic substance dissolves in water.

Hydrophobic Water-fearing; a hydrophobic substance does not dissolve in water.

Hygroscopic Having the ability to pull water molecules from the surrounding atmosphere.

Hyperglycemia Higher-than-normal blood glucose concentration.

Hypertonic Having an osmolarity greater than the surrounding blood plasma or cells.

Hypoglycemia Lower-than-normal blood glucose concentration.

Hypotonic Having an osmolarity less than the surrounding blood plasma or cells.

Ideal gas A gas that obeys all the assumptions of the kinetic-molecular theory.

Ideal gas law A general expression relating pressure, volume, temperature, and amount for an ideal gas: $PV = nRT$.

Immune response Defense mechanism of the immune system dependent on the recognition of specific antigens, including viruses, bacteria, toxic substances, and infected cells; either cell-mediated or antibody-mediated.

Induced-fit model A model of enzyme action in which the enzyme has a flexible active site that changes shape to best fit the substrate and catalyze the reaction.

Inflammation Result of the inflammatory response: includes swelling, redness, warmth, and pain.

Inflammatory response A nonspecific defense mechanism triggered by antigens or tissue damage.

Inhibition (of an enzyme) Any process that slows or stops the action of an enzyme.

Inner transition metal element An element in one of the 14 groups shown separately at the bottom of the periodic table.

Intermolecular force A force that acts between molecules and holds molecules close to one another in liquids and solids.

Interstitial fluid Fluid surrounding cells: an extracellular fluid.

Intracellular fluid Fluid inside cells.

Intron A portion of DNA between coding regions of a gene (exons); is transcribed and then removed from final messenger RNA.

Ion An electrically charged atom or group of atoms.

Ion-product constant for water (K_w) The product of the H_3O^+ and OH^- molar concentrations in water or any aqueous solution ($K_w = [H_3O^+][OH^-] = 1.00 \times 10^{-14}$).

Ionic bond The electrical attractions between ions of opposite charge in a crystal.

Ionic compound A compound that contains ionic bonds.

Ionic equation An equation in which ions are explicitly shown.

Ionic solid A crystalline solid held together by ionic bonds.

Ionization energy The energy required to remove one electron from a single atom in the gaseous state.

Ionizing radiation A general name for high-energy radiation of all kinds.

Irreversible (enzyme) inhibition Enzyme deactivation in which an inhibitor forms covalent bonds to the active site, permanently blocking it.

Isoelectric point (pI) The pH at which a sample of an amino acid has equal number of + and − charges.

Isomers Compounds with the same molecular formula but different structures.

Isopropyl group The branched-chain alkyl group —$CH(CH_3)_2$.

Isotonic Having the same osmolarity.

Isotopes Atoms with identical atomic numbers but different mass numbers.

Ketoacidosis Lowered blood pH due to accumulation of ketone bodies.

Ketogenesis The synthesis of ketone bodies from acetyl-SCoA.

Ketone A compound that has a carbonyl group bonded to two carbons in organic groups that can be the same or different, $R_2C=O$, RCOR′.

Ketone bodies Compounds produced in the liver that can be used as fuel by muscle and brain tissue; 3-hydroxybutyrate, ace-toacetate, and acetone.

Ketose A monosaccharide that contains a ketone carbonyl group.

Kinetic energy The energy of an object in motion.

Kinetic-molecular theory (KMT) of gases A group of assumptions that explain the behavior of gases.

L-Sugar Monosaccharide with the —OH group on the chiral carbon atom farthest from the carbonyl group pointing to the left in a Fischer projection.

Law of conservation of energy Energy can be neither created nor destroyed in any physical or chemical change.

Law of conservation of mass Matter can be neither created nor destroyed in any physical or chemical change.

Le Châtelier's principle When a stress is applied to a system in equilibrium, the equilibrium shifts to relieve the stress.

Lewis base A compound containing an unshared pair of electrons.

Lewis structure A molecular representation that shows both the connections among atoms and the locations of lone-pair valence electrons.

Limiting reagent The reactant that runs out first in a chemical reaction.

Line structure A shorthand way of drawing structures in which atoms aren't shown; instead, a carbon atom is understood to be at every intersection of lines, and hydrogens are filled in mentally.

Lipid A naturally occurring molecule from a plant or animal that is soluble in nonpolar organic solvents.

Lipid bilayer The basic structural unit of cell membranes; composed of two parallel sheets of membrane lipid molecules arranged tail to tail.

Lipogenesis The biochemical pathway for synthesis of fatty acids from acetyl-CoA.

Lipoprotein A lipid-protein complex that transports lipids.

Liposome A spherical structure in which a lipid bilayer surrounds a water droplet.

Liquid A substance that has a definite volume but that changes shape to fit its container.

London dispersion force The short-lived attractive force due to the constant motion of electrons within molecules.

Lone pair A pair of electrons that is not used for bonding.

Main group element An element in one of the two groups on the left or the six groups on the right of the periodic table.

Markovnikov's rule In the addition of HX to an alkene, the H becomes attached to the carbon that already has the most H's, and the X becomes attached to the carbon that has fewer H's.

Mass A measure of the amount of matter in an object.

Mass/mass percent concentration [(m/m)%] Concentration expressed as the number of grams of solute per 100 grams of solution.

Mass number (A) The total number of protons and neutrons in an atom.

Mass/volume percent concentration [(m/v)%] Concentration expressed as the number of grams of solute per 100 mL of solution.

Matter The physical material that makes up the universe; anything that has mass and occupies space.

Melting point (mp) The temperature at which solid and liquid are in equilibrium.

Messenger RNA (mRNA) The RNA that carries the code transcribed from DNA and directs protein synthesis.

Metal A malleable element with a lustrous appearance that is a good conductor of heat and electricity.

Metalloid An element whose properties are intermediate between those of a metal and a nonmetal.

Methyl group The $-CH_3$ alkyl group.

Methylene Another name for a $-CH_2$ unit.

Micelle A spherical cluster formed by the aggregation of soap or detergent molecules so that their hydrophobic ends are in the center and their hydrophilic ends are on the surface.

Miscible Mutually soluble in all proportions.

Mitochondrial matrix The space surrounded by the inner membrane of a mitochondrion.

Mitochondrion (plural, mitochondria) An egg-shaped organelle where small molecules

are broken down to provide the energy for an organism.

Mixture A blend of two or more substances, each of which retains its chemical identity.

Mobilization (of triacylglycerols) Hydrolysis of triacylglycerols in adipose tissue and release of fatty acids into the bloodstream.

Molar mass The mass in grams of one mole of a substance, numerically equal to the molecular weight.

Molarity (M) Concentration expressed as the number of moles of solute per liter of solution.

Mole The amount of a substance corresponding to 6.02×10^{23} units.

Molecular compound A compound that consists of molecules rather than ions.

Molecular formula A formula that shows the numbers and kinds of atoms in one molecule of a compound.

Molecular weight The sum of the atomic weights of the atoms in a molecule.

Molecule A group of atoms held together by covalent bonds.

Monomer A small molecule that is used to prepare a polymer.

Monosaccharide (simple sugar) A carbohydrate with 3–7 carbon atoms.

Mutagen A substance that causes mutations.

Mutarotation Change in rotation of plane-polarized light resulting from the equilibrium between cyclic anomers and the open-chain form of a sugar.

Mutation An error in base sequence that is carried along in DNA replication.

Native protein A protein with the shape (secondary, tertiary, and quaternary structure) in which it exists naturally in living organisms.

Net ionic equation An equation that does not include spectator ions.

Neurotransmitter A chemical messenger that travels between a neuron and a neighboring neuron or other target cell to transmit a nerve impulse.

Neutralization reaction The reaction of an acid with a base.

Neutron An electrically neutral subatomic particle.

Nitration The substitution of a nitro group $(-NO_2)$ for a hydrogen on an aromatic ring.

Noble gas An element in group 8A of the periodic table.

Noncovalent forces Forces of attraction other than covalent bonds that can act between molecules or within molecules.

Nonelectrolyte A substance that does not produce ions when dissolved in water.

Nonessential amino acid One of 11 amino acids that are synthesized in the body and are therefore not necessary in the diet.

Nonmetal An element that is a poor conductor of heat and electricity.

Normal boiling point The boiling point at a pressure of exactly 1 atmosphere.

Normality (N) A measure of acid (or base) concentration expressed as the number of acid (or base) equivalents per liter of solution.

Nuclear decay The spontaneous emission of a particle from an unstable nucleus.

Nuclear fission The fragmenting of heavy nuclei.

Nuclear fusion The joining together of light nuclei.

Nuclear reaction A reaction that changes an atomic nucleus, usually causing the change of one element into another.

Nucleic acid A polymer of nucleotides.

Nucleon A general term for both protons and neutrons.

Nucleoside A 5-carbon sugar bonded to a cyclic amine base; like a nucleotide but missing the phosphate group.

Nucleotide A 5-carbon sugar bonded to a cyclic amine base and one phosphate group (a nucleoside monophosphate); monomer for nucleic acids.

Nucleus The dense, central core of an atom that contains protons and neutrons.

Nuclide The nucleus of a specific isotope of an element.

Octet rule Main-group elements tend to undergo reactions that leave them with 8 valence electrons.

Oil A mixture of triacylglycerols that is liquid because it contains a high proportion of unsaturated fatty acids.

Orbital A region of space within an atom where an electron in a given subshell can be found.

Organic chemistry The study of carbon compounds.

Osmolarity (osmol) The sum of the molarities of all dissolved particles in a solution.

Osmosis The passage of solvent through a semipermeable membrane separating two solutions of different concentration.

Osmotic pressure The amount of external pressure applied to the more concentrated solution to halt the passage of solvent molecules across a semipermeable membrane.

Oxidation The loss of one or more electrons by an atom.

Oxidation number A number that indicates whether an atom is neutral, electron-rich, or electron-poor.

Oxidation-Reduction, or Redox, reaction A reaction in which electrons are transferred from one atom to another.

Oxidative deamination Conversion of an amino acid $-NH_2$ group to an α-keto group, with removal of NH_4^+.

Oxidative phosphorylation The synthesis of ATP from ADP using energy released in the electron-transport chain.

Oxidizing agent A reactant that causes an oxidation by taking electrons from or increasing the oxidation number of another reactant.

p-Block element A main group element that results from the filling of p orbitals.

p function The negative common logarithm of some variable, $pX = -(\log X)$.

Partial pressure The pressure exerted by a gas in a mixture.

Parts per billion (ppb) Number of parts of solute (in mass or volume) per one billion parts of solution.

Parts per million (ppm) Number of parts of solute (in mass or volume) per one million parts of solution.

Passive transport Movement of a substance across a cell membrane without the use of energy, from a region of higher concentration to a region of lower concentration.

Pentose phosphate pathway The biochemical pathway that produces ribose (a pentose), NADPH, and other sugar phosphates from glucose; an alternative to glycolysis.

Peptide bond An amide bond that links two amino acids together.

Percent yield The percent of the theoretical yield actually obtained from a chemical reaction.

Period One of the seven horizontal rows of elements in the periodic table.

Periodic table A table of the elements in order of increasing atomic number and grouped according to their chemical similarities.

pH A measure of the acid strength of a solution; the negative common logarithm of the H_3O^+ concentration.

Phenol A compound that has an —OH group bonded directly to an aromatic, benzene-like ring, Ar—OH.

Phenyl The C_6H_5— group.

Phosphate ester A compound formed by reaction of an alcohol with phosphoric acid; may be a monoester, $ROPO_3H_2$; a diester, $(RO)_2PO_3H$; or a triester, $(RO)_3PO$; also may be a di- or triphosphate.

Phospholipid A lipid that has an ester link between phosphoric acid and an alcohol (glycerol or sphingosine).

Phosphoryl group The —$PO_3{}^{2-}$ group in organic phosphates.

Phosphorylation Transfer of a phosphoryl group, —$PO_3{}^{2-}$, between organic molecules.

Physical change A change that does not affect the chemical makeup of a substance or object.

Physical quantity A physical property that can be measured.

Polar covalent bond A bond in which the electrons are attracted more strongly by one atom than by the other.

Polyatomic ion An ion that is composed of more than one atom.

Polymer A large molecule formed by the repetitive bonding together of many smaller molecules.

Polymorphism A variation in DNA sequence within a population.

Polysaccharide (complex carbohydrate) A carbohydrate that is a polymer of monosaccharides.

Polyunsaturated fatty acid A long-chain fatty acid that has two or more carbon-carbon double bonds.

Positron A "positive electron," which has the same mass as an electron but a positive charge.

Potential energy Energy that is stored because of position, composition, or shape.

Precipitate An insoluble solid that forms in solution during a chemical reaction.

Pressure The force per unit area pushing against a surface.

Primary carbon atom A carbon atom with one other carbon attached to it.

Primary protein structure The sequence in which amino acids are linked by peptide bonds in a protein.

Product A substance that is formed in a chemical reaction and is written on the right side of the reaction arrow in a chemical equation.

Property A characteristic useful for identifying a substance or object.

propyl group The straight-chain alkyl group —$CH_2CH_2CH_3$.

Protein A large biological molecule made of many amino acids linked together through amide (peptide) bonds.

Proton A positively charged subatomic particle.

Pure substance A substance that has uniform chemical composition throughout.

Quaternary ammonium ion A positive ion with four organic groups bonded to the nitrogen atom.

Quaternary ammonium salt An ionic compound composed of a quaternary ammonium ion and an anion.

Quaternary carbon atom A carbon atom with four other carbons attached to it.

Quaternary protein structure The way in which two or more protein chains aggregate to form large, ordered structures.

Radioactivity The spontaneous emission of radiation from a nucleus.

Radioisotope A radioactive isotope.

Radionuclide The nucleus of a radioactive isotope.

Reabsorption (kidney) Movement of solutes out of filtrate in a kidney tubule.

Reactant A substance that undergoes change in a chemical reaction and is written on the left side of the reaction arrow in a chemical equation.

Reaction mechanism A description of the individual steps by which old bonds are broken and new bonds are formed in a reaction.

Reaction rate A measure of how rapidly a reaction occurs.

Rearrangement reaction A general reaction type in which a molecule undergoes bond reorganization to yield an isomer.

Receptor A molecule or portion of a molecule with which a hormone, neurotransmitter, or other biochemically active molecule interacts to initiate a response in a target cell.

Recombinant DNA DNA that contains segments from two different species.

Reducing agent A reactant that causes a reduction by giving up electrons or increasing the oxidation number of another reactant.

Reducing sugar A carbohydrate that reacts in basic solution with a mild oxidizing agent.

Reduction The gain of one or more electrons by an atom.

Reductive deamination Conversion of an α-keto acid to an amino acid by reaction with $NH_4{}^+$.

Regular tetrahedron A geometric figure with four identical triangular faces.

Replication The process by which copies of DNA are made when a cell divides.

Residue (amino acid) An amino acid unit in a polypeptide.

Resonance The phenomenon where the true structure of a molecule is an average among two or more conventional structures.

Reversible reaction A reaction that can go in either the forward direction or the reverse direction, from products to reactants or reactants to products.

Ribonucleotide A nucleotide containing D-ribose.

Ribosomal RNA (rRNA) The RNA that is complexed with proteins in ribosomes.

Ribosome The structure in the cell where protein synthesis occurs; composed of protein and rRNA.

Ribozyme RNA that acts as an enzyme.

RNA (ribonucleic acids) The nucleic acids (messenger, transfer, and ribosomal) responsible for putting the genetic information to use in protein synthesis; polymers of ribonucleotides.

Rounding off A procedure used for deleting nonsignificant figures.

s-Block element A main group element that results from the filling of an s orbital.

Salt An ionic compound formed from reaction of an acid with a base.

Saponification The reaction of an ester with aqueous hydroxide ion to yield an alcohol and the metal salt of a carboxylic acid.

Saturated A molecule whose carbon atoms bond to the maximum number of hydrogen atoms.

Saturated fatty acid A long-chain carboxylic acid containing only carbon-carbon single bonds.

Saturated solution A solution that contains the maximum amount of dissolved solute at equilibrium.

Scientific Method Systematic process of observation, hypothesis, and experimentation to expand and refine a body of knowledge.

Scientific notation A number expressed as the product of a number between 1 and 10, times the number 10 raised to a power.

Second messenger Chemical messenger released inside a cell when a hydrophilic hormone or neurotransmitter interacts with a receptor on the cell surface.

Secondary carbon atom A carbon atom with two other carbons attached to it.

Secondary protein structure Regular and repeating structural patterns (for example, α-helix, β-sheet) created by hydrogen bonding between backbone atoms in neighboring segments of protein chains.

Secretion (kidney) Movement of solutes into filtrate in a kidney tubule.

SI units Units of measurement defined by the International System of Units.

Side chain (amino acid) The group bonded to the carbon next to the carboxyl group in an amino acid; different in different amino acids.

Significant figures The number of meaningful digits used to express a value.

Simple diffusion Passive transport by the random motion of diffusion through the cell membrane.

Simple protein A protein composed of only amino acid residues.

Single bond A covalent bond formed by sharing one electron pair.

Single-nucleotide polymorphism Common single-base-pair variation in DNA.

Soap The mixture of salts of fatty acids formed on saponification of animal fat.

Solid A substance that has a definite shape and volume.

Solubility The maximum amount of a substance that will dissolve in a given amount of solvent at a specified temperature.

Solute A substance dissolved in a liquid.

Solution A homogeneous mixture that contains particles the size of a typical ion or small molecule.

Solvation The clustering of solvent molecules around a dissolved solute molecule or ion.

Solvent The liquid in which another substance is dissolved.

Specific gravity The density of a substance divided by the density of water at the same temperature.

Specific heat The amount of heat that will raise the temperature of 1 g of a substance by 1 °C.

Specificity (enzyme) The limitation of the activity of an enzyme to a specific substrate, specific reaction, or specific type of reaction.

Spectator ion An ion that appears unchanged on both sides of a reaction arrow.

Sphingolipid A lipid derived from the amino alcohol sphingosine.

Spontaneous process A process or reaction that, once started, proceeds on its own without any external influence.

Standard molar volume The volume of one mole of a gas at standard temperature and pressure (22.4 L).

Standard temperature and pressure (STP) Standard conditions for a gas, defined as 0 °C (273 K) and 1 atm (760 mmHg) pressure.

State of matter The physical state of a substance as a solid, a liquid, or a gas.

Stereoisomers Isomers that have the same molecular and structural formulas, but different spatial arrangements of their atoms.

Sterol A lipid whose structure is based on the following tetracyclic (four-ring) carbon skeleton.

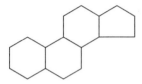

Straight-chain alkane An alkane that has all its carbons connected in a row.

Strong acid An acid that gives up H^+ easily and is essentially 100% dissociated in water.

Strong base A base that has a high affinity for H^+ and holds it tightly.

Strong electrolyte A substance that ionizes completely when dissolved in water.

Structural formula A molecular representation that shows the connections among atoms by using lines to represent covalent bonds.

Subatomic particles Three kinds of fundamental particles from which atoms are made: protons, neutrons, and electrons.

Substituent An atom or group of atoms attached to a parent compound.

Substitution reaction A general reaction type in which an atom or group of atoms in a molecule is replaced by another atom or group of atoms.

Substrate A reactant in an enzyme catalyzed reaction.

Sulfonation The substitution of a sulfonic acid group ($—SO_3H$) for a hydrogen on an aromatic ring.

Supersaturated solution A solution that contains more than the maximum amount of dissolved solute; a nonequilibrium situation.

Synapse The place where the tip of a neuron and its target cell lie adjacent to each other.

Telomeres The ends of chromosomes; in humans, contain long series of repeating groups of nucleotides.

Temperature The measure of how hot or cold an object is.

Tertiary carbon atom A carbon atom with three other carbons attached to it.

Tertiary protein structure The way in which an entire protein chain is coiled and folded into its specific three-dimensional shape.

Theoretical yield The amount of product formed assuming complete reaction of the limiting reagent.

Thiol A compound that contains an $—SH$ group, $R—SH$.

Titration A procedure for determining the total acid or base concentration of a solution.

Transamination The interchange of the amino group of an amino acid and the keto group of an α-keto acid.

Transcription The process by which the information in DNA is read and used to synthesize RNA.

Transfer RNA (tRNA) The RNA that transports amino acids into position for protein synthesis.

Transition metal element An element in one of the 10 smaller groups near the middle of the periodic table.

Translation The process by which RNA directs protein synthesis.

Transmutation The change of one element into another.

Triacylglycerol (triglyceride) A triester of glycerol with three fatty acids.

Triple bond A covalent bond formed by sharing three electron pairs.

Turnover number The maximum number of substrate molecules acted upon by one molecule of enzyme per unit time.

Uncompetitive (enzyme) inhibition Enzyme regulation in which an inhibitor binds to an enzyme elsewhere than at the active site, thereby changing the shape of the enzyme's active site and reducing its efficiency.

Unit A defined quantity used as a standard of measurement.

Unsaturated A molecule that contains a carbon–carbon multiple bond, to which more hydrogen atoms can be added.

Unsaturated fatty acid A long-chain carboxylic acid containing one or more carbon-carbon double bonds.

Urea cycle The cyclic biochemical pathway that produces urea for excretion.

Valence electron An electron in the outermost, or valence, shell of an atom.

Valence shell The outermost electron shell of an atom.

Valence-shell electron-pair repulsion (VSEPR) model A method for predicting molecular shape by noting how many electron charge clouds surround atoms and assuming that the clouds orient as far away from one another as possible.

Vapor The gas molecules in equilibrium with a liquid.

Vapor pressure The partial pressure of gas molecules in equilibrium with a liquid.

Vitamin An organic molecule, essential in trace amounts that must be obtained in the diet because it is not synthesized in the body.

Volume/volume percent concentration [(v/v)%] Concentration expressed as the number of milliliters of solute dissolved in 100 mL of solution.

Wax A mixture of esters of long-chain carboxylic acids with long-chain alcohols.

Weak acid An acid that gives up H^+ with difficulty and is less than 100% dissociated in water.

Weak base A base that has only a slight affinity for H^+ and holds it weakly.

Weak electrolyte A substance that is only partly ionized in water.

Weight A measure of the gravitational force that the earth or other large body exerts on an object.

Whole blood Blood plasma plus blood cells.

X rays Electromagnetic radiation with an energy somewhat less than that of γ rays.

Zwitterion A neutral dipolar ion that has one + charge and one − charge.

Zymogen A compound that becomes an active enzyme after undergoing a chemical change.

Index

Chapter Outline

I. Matter and its properties (Sections 1.1–1.2).
  A. Matter is anything that is physically real (Section 1.1).
  B. Properties are the characteristics of matter.
    1. Physical properties are those properties that can be measured without altering the identity of a substance. Examples include mass, melting point, boiling point, and color.
    2. Chemical properties must be determined by changing the identity of the substance. Examples include rusting, combustion, and chemical reactivity.
    3. A physical change does not alter the identity of a substance.
    4. A chemical change is a process in which one or more substances undergoes a change in identity.
  C. States of matter (Section 1.2).
    1. The states of matter are solid, liquid, and gas.
      a. Solids have definite volume and definite shape.
      b. Liquids have definite volume and indefinite shape.
      c. Gases have indefinite volume and indefinite shape.
    2. Changes of state are melting, boiling, condensing, and freezing.
II. Classification of matter (Sections 1.3–1.6).
  A. Mixtures (Section 1.3).
    1. Mixtures vary in composition and properties.
    2. Mixtures can be separated by physical methods.
  B. Pure substances.
    1. Pure substances include chemical compounds and chemical elements.
    2. Pure substances don't vary in composition and properties.
    3. Chemical compounds can be broken down to elements by chemical change.
    4. Chemical elements can't be broken down.
  C. Chemical elements (Sections 1.4–1.5).
    1. There are 118 elements; 91 of them occur naturally (Section 1.4).
    2. Elements are represented by one- or two-letter symbols.
    3. The symbols for elements can be combined to produce chemical formulas.
    4. Elements are presented in a table—the periodic table (Section 1.5).
    5. Elements can be classified as metals, nonmetals, or metalloids.
      a. Metals are solids that are lustrous, brittle, malleable, and good conductors of heat and electricity.
      b. Nonmetals may be solid, liquid, or gas and are poor conductors.
      c. Metalloids have characteristics intermediate between metals and nonmetals.
  D. Chemical reactions (Section 1.6).
      a. A chemical reaction represents a chemical change between pure substances.
      b. In a chemical reaction, the reactants are written on the left, the products are written on the right, and an arrow connects them.
III. Measurements (Sections 1.7–1.8).
  A. Physical quantities (Section 1.7).
    1. All physical quantities consist of a number plus a unit.
      a. SI units, the standard units for scientists, are the kilogram, the meter, and the kelvin.
      b. Metric units are the gram, the meter, the liter, and the degree Celsius.

      c. Other units, such as those for speed and concentration, can be derived from SI and metric units.

   2. Prefixes are used with units to indicate multiples of 10.

  B. Measuring mass, length, and volume (Section 1.8).

    1. Measuring mass.

      a. Mass is the amount of matter in a substance.

      b. Mass differs from weight (a measure of the gravitational pull exerted on an object).

      c. The SI unit of mass is the kilogram, but in chemistry the gram and milligram are more often used.

    2. Measuring length.

      a. The meter is the standard unit for length.

    3. Measuring volume.

      a. Volume is the amount of space that a substance occupies.

      b. Units for volume are the liter (L) and the cubic meter (m^3)—the SI unit.

IV. Numbers in measurement (Sections 1.9–1.11).

  A. Significant figures (Section 1.9).

    1. All measurements have a degree of uncertainty.

    2. For any measurement, the number of digits known with certainty, plus one digit considered uncertain, is known as the number of significant figures.

    3. Rules for significant figures:

      a. Zeroes in the middle of a number are always significant.

      b. Zeroes at the beginning of a number are never significant.

      c. Zeroes at the end of a number but after a decimal point are significant.

      d. Zeroes at the end of a number but before an implied decimal point may or may not be significant.

    4. Some numbers are exact and have an unlimited number of significant figures.

  B. Scientific notation (Section 1.10).

    1. In scientific notation, a number is written as the product of a number between 1 and 10 times 10 raised to a power.

      a. For numbers greater than 10, the power of 10 is positive.

      b. For numbers less than 1, the power of 10 is negative.

    2. Scientific notation is helpful in indicating the number of significant figures in a number.

  C. Rounding off numbers (Section 1.11).

    1. Numbers must be rounded off if they contain more digits than are significant.

    2. Rounding in calculations.

      a. In multiplication or division, the result can't have more significant figures than any of the original numbers.

      b. In addition or subtraction, the result can't have more digits to the right of the decimal point than any of the original numbers.

    3. Rules of rounding:

      a. If the digit to be removed is 4 or less, drop it and remove all following digits.

      b. If the digit to be removed is 5 or greater, add 1 to the digit to the left of the digit you drop.

      c. Round off after all steps in a calculation have been carried out.

  D. Problem solving (Section 1.12).

    1. Converting a quantity from one unit to another.

      a. In the *factor-label* method:

    (quantity in old units) x (conversion factor) = (quantity in new units).

        i. The conversion factor is a fraction that converts one unit to another.

        ii. All conversion factors are equal to 1.

      b. In the factor-label method, units are treated as numbers.

      c. In the factor-label method, all unwanted units cancel.

    2. Problem solving techniques.
        a. Identify the information known.
        b. Identify the information needed in the answer.
        c. Use conversion factors to convert the given information to the answer.
        d. Make a "ballpark" estimate of the answer and compare it to the calculated answer.
V. Temperature, heat, and energy (Section 1.13).
    A. Measuring temperature.
        1. Units of temperature are the degree Fahrenheit, the degree Celsius, and the kelvin.
        2. Temperature in °C = Temperature in K – 273.15°.
        3. $°F = \left(\dfrac{9\,°F}{5\,°C} \times °C\right) + 32\,°F.$
        4. $°C = \dfrac{5\,°C}{9\,°F} \times (°F - 32\,°F).$
    B. Energy and heat.
        1. All chemical reactions are accompanied by a change in energy.
            a. Potential energy is stored energy.
            b. Kinetic energy is the energy of motion.
        2. Heat is the energy transferred from a hotter object to a cooler object when the two are in contact.
        3. Units of energy are the joule (SI) and the calorie.
        4. $\text{Specific heat} = \dfrac{\text{calories}}{\text{grams} \times °C}$
VI. Density and specific gravity (Section 1.14).
    A. Density.
        1. Density = Mass (g) / Volume (mL or cm^3).
        2. Density is temperature dependent.
    B. Specific gravity.
        1. $\text{Specific gravity} = \dfrac{\text{density of substance (g/mL)}}{\text{density of water (1 g/mL)}}.$
        2. Specific gravity has no units.

Solutions to Chapter 1 Problems

1.1   *Change in physical properties*:   (a) grinding of a metal   (d) a puddle evaporating
Change in chemical properties: (b) fruit ripening   (c) wood burning

1.2   At 10°C, acetic acid is a solid.

1.3   *Mixtures*: (a) concrete (heterogeneous);   (d) wood (heterogeneous)
Pure substances: (b) helium (element);   (c) a lead weight (element)

1.4   *Physical changes*: (a) dissolving sugar in water
Chemical change: (b) production of carbon dioxide by heating limestone; (c) frying an
egg; (d) conversion of salicylic acid to acetylsalicylic acid

1.5   The process is a chemical change because the product is different in composition from the
reactant.

1.6   (a) 2 (Na); (b) 1 (W); (c) 6 (Sr); (d) 5 (Ti); (e) 4 (F);   (f) 3 (Sn).

1.7   (a) Ammonia (NH_3) contains one nitrogen atom and three hydrogen atoms.
(b) Sodium bicarbonate ($NaHCO_3$) contains one sodium atom, one hydrogen atom, one
   carbon atom, and three oxygen atoms.
(c) Octane (C_8H_{18}) contains eight carbon atoms and eighteen hydrogen atoms.
(d) Vitamin C ($C_6H_8O_6$) contains six carbon atoms, eight hydrogen atoms, and six oxygen
   atoms.

1.8

Element	Name	Number in Periodic Table
(a) B	boron	5
(b) Si	silicon	14
(c) Ge	germanium	32
(d) As	arsenic	33
(e) Sb	antimony	51
(f) Te	tellurium	52

The metalloids appear on a diagonal boundary between metals and nonmetals.

1.9   Mercury is a metal. Physical properties that lead to its toxicity include the solubility of
mercury-containing compounds and the persistence of mercury vapor. Chemical properties
include the tendency of mercury and mercury vapor to form soluble toxic compounds.

1.10 (a) 1 cm = 1 centimeter = 0.01 m   (b) 1 dg = 1 decigram = 0.1 g
(c) 1 km = 1 kilometer = 1000 m   (d) 1 μs = microsecond = 0.000 001 s
(e) 1 ng = 1 nanogram = 0.000 000 001 g

1.11

Number	Significant Figures	Reason
(a) 3.45 m	3	
(b) 0.1400 kg	4	Rule 3
(c) 10.003 L	5	Rule 1
(d) 35 cents	Exact	

1.12 32.3 °C. The answer has three significant figures.

1.13 In scientific notation, a number is written as the product of a number between 1 and 10 times 10 raised to a power. In (a), 58 g = 5.8 x 10^1 g.

Value	Scientific Notation
(a) 0.058 g	5.8 x 10^{-2} g
(b) 46,792 m	4.6792 x 10^4 m
(c) 0.006 072 cm	6.072 x 10^{-3} cm
(d) 345.3 kg	3.453 x 10^2 kg

1.14

Value in Scientific Notation	Value in Standard Notation
(a) 4.885 x 10^4 mg	48,850 mg
(b) 8.3 x 10^{-6} m	0.000 0083 m
(c) 4.00 x 10^{-2} m	0.0400 m

1.15 (a) 6.3000 x 10^5 (b) 1.30 x 10^3 (c) 7.942 x 10^{11}

1.16 (a) 2.30 g   (b) 188.38 mL   (c) 0.009 L   (d) 1.000 kg

1.17 Remember:
(1) The sum or difference of two numbers can't have more digits to the right of the decimal point than either of the two numbers.
(2) The product or quotient of two numbers can't have more significant figures than either of the two numbers.

Calculation	Rounded to:
(a) 4.87 mL + 46.0 mL = 50.87 mL	50.9 mL
(b) 3.4 x 0.023 g = 0.0782 g	0.078 g
(c) 19.333 m − 7.4 m = 11.933 m	11.9 m
(d) 55 mg − 4.671 mg + 0.894 mg = 51.223 mg	51 mg
(e) 62,911 ÷ 611 = 102.96399	103

1.18

(a) $16.0 \text{ oz} \times \dfrac{28.35 \text{ g}}{1 \text{ oz}} = 454 \text{ g}$ (b) $2500 \text{ mL} \times \dfrac{1 \text{ L}}{1000 \text{ mL}} = 2.5 \text{ L}$

(c) $99.0 \text{ L} \times \dfrac{1 \text{ qt}}{0.9464 \text{ L}} = 105 \text{ qt}$

1.19

$0.840 \text{ quart} \times \dfrac{1 \text{ L}}{1.057 \text{ quart}} \times \dfrac{1000 \text{ mL}}{1 \text{ L}} = 795 \text{ mL}$

1.20 This is a *long* unit conversion! Remember that all units must cancel at the end, except for the units needed in the final answer (meters and seconds). Nautical miles must be converted to meters, and hours must be converted to seconds. Also remember the definition of a knot—1 nautical mile per hour.

$\dfrac{14.3 \text{ naut. mi}}{1 \text{ hr}} \times \dfrac{6076.1155 \text{ ft}}{1 \text{ naut. mi}} \times \dfrac{0.3048 \text{ m}}{1 \text{ ft}} \times \dfrac{1 \text{ hr}}{60 \text{ min}} \times \dfrac{1 \text{ min}}{60 \text{ s}} = 7.36 \text{ m/s}$

1.21

$$2 \times 0.324 \text{ g} \times \frac{1000 \text{ mg}}{1 \text{ g}} \times \frac{1}{135 \text{ lb}} \times \frac{2.205 \text{ lb}}{1 \text{ kg}} = 10.6 \frac{\text{mg}}{\text{kg}}$$

$$2 \times 0.324 \text{ g} \times \frac{1000 \text{ mg}}{1 \text{ g}} \times \frac{1}{40 \text{ lb}} \times \frac{2.205 \text{ lb}}{1 \text{ kg}} = 36 \frac{\text{mg}}{\text{kg}}$$

1.22 From Section 1.13, we find the formula:

$$(°F - 32 \text{ °F}) \times \frac{5 \text{ °C}}{9 \text{ °F}} = °C$$

Substituting 136°F into the preceding formula:

$$(136 \text{ °F} - 32 \text{ °F}) \times \frac{5 \text{ °C}}{9 \text{ °F}} = 57.8 \text{ °C}$$

To find the temperature in kelvins, add the temperature in degrees Celsius to 273.15 since the size of a degree is the same in both kelvins and degrees Celsius.

$$(273.15 + 57.8) \text{ K} = 331.0 \text{ K}$$

1.23 39 °C = 102 °F

1.24

$$\text{Heat (cal)} = \text{mass (g)} \times \text{temperature change (°C)} \times \text{specific heat} \left(\frac{\text{cal}}{\text{g} \cdot \text{°C}} \right)$$

$$= 350 \text{ g} \times (25 \text{ °C} - 3 \text{ °C}) \times \frac{1.0 \text{ cal}}{\text{g} \cdot \text{°C}}$$

$$= 7700 \text{ cal} = 7.7 \times 10^3 \text{ cal}$$

Ballpark check: The temperature change is approximately 20 °C. The mass of Coca-Cola times the temperature change equals 7000, a number close to the exact solution.

1.25

$$\text{Specific heat} = \frac{\text{calories}}{\text{grams} \times \text{°C}}$$

$$\text{Specific heat} = \frac{161 \text{ cal}}{75 \text{ g} \times 10.0 \text{ °C}} = \frac{0.21 \text{ cal}}{\text{g} \cdot \text{°C}}, \quad \frac{674 \text{ J}}{75 \text{ g} \times 10.0 \text{ °C}} = \frac{0.90 \text{ J}}{\text{g} \cdot \text{°C}}$$

1.26

$$\text{Density} = \frac{\text{Mass}}{\text{Volume}} = \frac{17.4 \text{ g}}{27.3 \text{ cm}^3} = \frac{0.637 \text{ g}}{\text{cm}^3}$$

The sample will float since it is less dense than water.

1.27

$$12.37 \text{ g} \times \frac{1 \text{ mL}}{1.474 \text{ g}} = 8.392 \text{ mL}$$

Ballpark check: Since the density of chloroform is approximately 1.5, the volume needed is about two-thirds of the mass needed.

1.28 Battery acid is more dense than water.

Understanding Key Concepts

1.29 Blue (from top to bottom): helium (He), neon (Ne), argon (Ar), krypton (Kr), xenon (Xe), radon (Rn).
Red (from top to bottom): copper (Cu), silver (Ag), gold (Au).

1.30 Green: boron (B) – metalloid
Blue: bromine (Br) – nonmetal
Red: vanadium (V) – metal

1.31 The element, americium (Am), is a metal.

1.32 The specific gravity is found by reading the liquid level on the scale of the hydrometer.
(a) The specific gravity of this solution is 0.978.
(b) The answer has three significant figures.
(c) The solution is less dense than water.

1.33

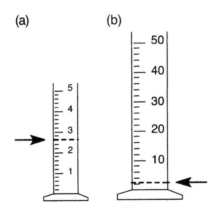

The smaller graduated cylinder is more precise for two reasons. (1) The distance between two gradations represents a smaller volume, making it easier to measure volumes more accurately. (2) The percent error is greater when a small volume is measured in a large graduated cylinder.

1.34 The length of the pencil is either 8.0 cm or 3 1/8 in.

1.35 The liquid level is 0.11 mL before dispensing the sample and 0.25 mL after dispensing, indicating a sample size of 0.14 mL.

1.36 If two identical hydrometers are placed in ethanol and in chloroform, the hydrometer in chloroform will float higher. Since a hydrometer bulb sinks until it displaces a volume of liquid equal to its mass, it displaces a smaller volume of chloroform, the denser liquid, and the bulb floats higher.

Chemistry and the Properties of Matter

1.37 A physical change doesn't alter the identity of a substance; it alters only its physical state. A chemical change results in a change in chemical identity of a substance.

1.38 *Physical changes:* (a) boiling water; (d) breaking of glass
Chemical changes: (b) decomposing water by passing a current through it; (c) exploding of potassium when placed in water

1.39 *Physical changes:* (a) making lemonade; (d) whipping cream
Chemical changes: (b) frying eggs; (c) burning a candle; (e) leaves changing color

States and Classification of Matter

1.40 A *gas* is a substance that has no definite shape or volume.
A *liquid* has no definite shape but has a definite volume.
A *solid* has a definite volume and a definite shape.

1.41 Melting, boiling, condensation, and freezing are all changes of state. *Melting* occurs when a solid is heated and becomes a liquid. *Boiling* occurs when a liquid is heated and becomes a gas. *Condensation* occurs when a gas is cooled and becomes a liquid. *Freezing* occurs when a liquid is cooled and becomes a solid. All changes of state are physical changes.

1.42 Sulfur dioxide is a gas at 298 K (25 °C).

1.43 No. At 25 °F (–4 °C), butane is a liquid.

1.44 *Mixtures:* (a) pea soup; (b) seawater; (d) urine; (f) multivitamin tablet
Pure substances: (c) propane (C_3H_8); (e) lead

1.45 (a) gasoline—(i) mixture; (iii) liquid
(b) iodine—(ii) solid; (v) chemical element
(c) water—(iii) liquid; (vi) chemical compound
(d) air—(i) mixture; (iv) gas
(e) blood—(i) mixture; (iii) liquid
(f) sodium bicarbonate—(ii) solid; (vi) chemical compound
(g) gaseous ammonia—(iv) gas; (vi) chemical compound
(h) silicon—(ii) solid); (v) chemical element

1.46   *Reactant*   *Products*

Hydrogen peroxide ⟶ Water + Oxygen
chemical compound   *chemical compound   element*

1.47   *Reactants*   *Products*

Sodium + Water ⟶ Hydrogen + Sodium hydroxide
element chemical compound   element   chemical compound

Elements and Their Symbols

1.48 *Metals* are elements that are solids at room temperature (except for Hg), are lustrous and malleable, and are good conductors of heat and electricity.

Nonmetals are elements that are gases or brittle solids (except for Br) and are poor conductors.

Metalloids are elements that have properties intermediate between those of metals and nonmetals.

1.49 Oxygen (O) is the most abundant element in both the Earth's crust and in the human body.

1.50 (a) Gadolinium (Gd); (b) Germanium (Ge); (c) Technetium (Tc); (d) Arsenic (As); (e) Cadmium (Cd)

1.51 (a) Nitrogen (b) Potassium (c) Chlorine (d) Ca (e) P (f) Mn

1.52 (a) The symbol for bromine is Br (the second letter in a symbol is never capitalized).
(b) The symbol for manganese is Mn (Mg is the symbol for magnesium).
(c) The symbol for carbon is C (Ca is the symbol for calcium).
(d) The symbol for potassium is K; (Po is the symbol for polonium).

1.53 (a) Carbon dioxide has the formula CO_2 (the number 2 is a subscript).
(b) The O in carbon dioxide must be capitalized to show that it is composed of carbon and oxygen.
(c) Table salt is composed of sodium (Na) and chlorine (Cl).

1.54 Carbon, hydrogen, nitrogen, and oxygen are present in glycine. The formula $C_2H_5NO_2$ represents 10 atoms.

1.55 Carbon (6 atoms), hydrogen (12 atoms), and oxygen (6 atoms) are present in glucose.

1.56 Ibuprofen: $C_{13}H_{18}O_2$

1.57 (a) metal   (b) metalloid   (c) nonmetal   (d) nonmetal

Physical Quantities: Definitions and Units

1.58 A *physical quantity* is a physical property that can be measured; it consists of a number plus a unit.

1.59

Quantity	SI Unit	Metric Unit
Mass	kilogram (kg)	gram (g)
Volume	cubic meter (m^3)	liter (L)
Length	meter (m)	meter (m)
Temperature	kelvin (K)	degree celsius (°C)

1.60 (a) cubic centimeter   (b) decimeter   (c) millimeter   (d) nanoliter
(e) milligram   (f) cubic meter

1.61 (a) ng   (b) cm   (c) μL   (d) μm   (e) mg

1.62

$$1 \text{ mg} \times \frac{10^{-3} \text{ g}}{1 \text{ mg}} \times \frac{10^{12} \text{ pg}}{1 \text{ g}} = 10^9 \text{ pg}$$

$$35 \text{ ng} \times \frac{10^{-9} \text{ g}}{1 \text{ ng}} \times \frac{10^{12} \text{ pg}}{1 \text{ g}} = 3.5 \times 10^4 \text{ pg}$$

1.63

$$1 \text{ L} \times \frac{10^6 \text{ } \mu\text{L}}{1 \text{ L}} = 10^6 \text{ } \mu\text{L} \text{ ; } \quad 20 \text{ mL} \times \frac{10^3 \text{ } \mu\text{L}}{1 \text{ mL}} = 2 \times 10^4 \text{ } \mu\text{L}$$

Scientific Notation and Significant Figures

1.64 (a) 9.457×10^3 (b) 7×10^{-5} (c) 2.000×10^{10}
(d) 1.2345×10^{-2} (e) 6.5238×10^2

1.65 (a) 5280   (b) 0.082 05
(c) 0.000 018 4   (d) 63,700

1.66 (a) six   (b) three   (c) three   (d) four
(e) 1–5   (f) 2–3

1.67 (a) five   (b) three   (c) four   (d) one   (e) three

1.68 (a) 7926 mi; 7900 mi; 7926.38 mi   (b) $7.926\,381 \times 10^3$ mi

1.69 (a) 1.4×10^4 km   (b) 2.6×10^1 °C   (c) 1.1×10^3 °C
(d) 1×10^{-5} mm   (e) 1.1×10^{-1} nm

1.70 (a) 12.1 g   (b) 96.19 cm   (c) 263 mL   (d) 20.9 mg

1.71 (a) 3.3×10^4 ft   (b) 15 m^2 (c) 0.30 cm^3 (d) 81 cm^3

Unit Conversions and Problem Solving

1.72 (a) 0.3614 cg   (b) 0.0120 ML   (c) 0.0144 mm   (d) 60.3 ng   (e) 1.745 dL
(f) 1.5×10^5 cm

1.73

(a) $56.4 \text{ mi} \times \frac{1.609 \text{ km}}{1 \text{ mi}} = 90.7 \text{ km}$

$56.4 \text{ mi} \times \frac{1.609 \text{ km}}{1 \text{ mi}} \times \frac{1 \text{ Mm}}{10^3 \text{ km}} = 9.07 \times 10^{-2} \text{ Mm}$

(b) $2.0 \text{ L} \times \frac{1.057 \text{ qt}}{1 \text{ L}} = 2.1 \text{ qt}$

$2.0 \text{ L} \times \frac{10^3 \text{ mL}}{1 \text{ L}} \times \frac{1 \text{ fl oz}}{29.57 \text{ mL}} = 68 \text{ fl oz}$

(c) $7.0 \text{ ft} \times \dfrac{12 \text{ in.}}{1 \text{ ft}} = 84.0 \text{ in.}; \ 84.0 \text{ in.} + 2.0 \text{ in} = 86.0 \text{ in.}$

$86.0 \text{ in.} \times \dfrac{1 \text{ cm}}{0.3937 \text{ in.}} = 218 \text{ cm}; \quad 218 \text{ cm} \times \dfrac{1 \text{ m}}{100 \text{ cm}} = 2.18 \text{ m}$

(d) $1.35 \text{ lb} \times \dfrac{1 \text{ kg}}{2.205 \text{ lb}} = 0.612 \text{ kg}; \quad 0.612 \text{ kg} \times \dfrac{10^4 \text{ dg}}{1 \text{ kg}} = 6.12 \times 10^3 \text{ dg}$

1.74 (a) 97.8 kg   (b) 0.133 mL   (c) 0.46 ng   (d) 2.99 Mm

1.75 (a) 1.25×10^5 m   (b) 6.285×10^{-3} kg   (c) 4.735×10^2 mL   (d) 6.74×10^{-4} km

1.76

(a) $\dfrac{100 \text{ km}}{1 \text{ hr}} \times \dfrac{0.6214 \text{ mi}}{1 \text{ km}} = \dfrac{62.1 \text{ mi}}{1 \text{ hr}}$

(b) $\dfrac{62.1 \text{ mi}}{1 \text{ hr}} \times \dfrac{5280 \text{ ft}}{1 \text{ mi}} \times \dfrac{1 \text{ hr}}{60 \text{ min}} \times \dfrac{1 \text{ min}}{60 \text{ s}} = \dfrac{91.1 \text{ ft}}{1 \text{ s}}$

1.77

(a) $\dfrac{1200 \text{ ft}}{1 \text{ s}} \times \dfrac{1 \text{ mi}}{5280 \text{ ft}} \times \dfrac{60 \text{ s}}{1 \text{ min}} \times \dfrac{60 \text{ min}}{1 \text{ hr}} = \dfrac{820 \text{ mi}}{1 \text{ hr}}$

(b) $\dfrac{1200 \text{ ft}}{1 \text{ s}} \times \dfrac{0.3048 \text{ m}}{1 \text{ ft}} = \dfrac{370 \text{ m}}{1 \text{ s}}$

1.78

(a) $6 \times 10^{-6} \text{ m} \times \dfrac{10^2 \text{ cm}}{1 \text{ m}} = 6 \times 10^{-4} \text{ cm}$

(b) $1 \text{ cm} \times \dfrac{1 \text{ cell}}{6 \times 10^{-4} \text{ cm}} = 2 \times 10^3 \text{ cells}$

$1 \text{ in.} \times \dfrac{1 \text{ cell}}{6 \times 10^{-6} \text{ m}} \times \dfrac{1 \text{ m}}{39.37 \text{ in}} = 4 \times 10^3 \text{ cells}$

1.79 $1 \text{ ft}^2 = (0.3048 \text{ m})^2 = 0.09290 \text{ m}^2$

$418{,}000 \text{ m}^2 \times \dfrac{1 \text{ ft}^2}{0.0929 \text{ m}^2} = 4.50 \times 10^6 \text{ ft}^2$

1.80

$\dfrac{200 \text{ mg}}{1 \text{ dL}} \times \dfrac{10 \text{ dL}}{1 \text{ L}} \times 5 \text{ L} = 10^4 \text{ mg}; \ 10^4 \text{ mg} \times \dfrac{1 \text{ g}}{10^3 \text{ mg}} = 10 \text{ g cholesterol}$

1.81

$1200 \text{ mg} \times \dfrac{1.0 \text{ cup}}{290 \text{ mg}} = 4.1 \text{ cups}$

1.82

$\dfrac{1.2 \times 10^4 \text{ cells}}{1 \text{ mm}^3} \times \dfrac{10^6 \text{ mm}^3}{1 \text{ L}} \times 5 \text{ L} = 6 \times 10^{10} \text{ cells}$

Energy, Heat, and Temperature

1.83 273.15 K – 195.8 = 77.4 K

$$°F = \left(\frac{9°F}{5°C} \times °C\right) + 32°F = \left(\frac{9°F}{5°C} \times (-195.8°C)\right) + 32°F = -352.4°F + 32°F = -320.4 °F$$

1.84

Heat (cal) = mass (g) x temperature change (°C) x specific heat $\left(\frac{cal}{g \cdot °C}\right)$

$\qquad$ = 30.0 g x (30.0 °C – 10.0 °C) x $\frac{0.895\ cal}{g \cdot °C}$ = 537 cal = 0.537 kcal

537 cal x $\frac{4.18\ J}{1\ cal}$ = 2240 J = 2.24 kJ

1.85

Temperature change (°C) = $\dfrac{\text{heat (cal)}}{\text{mass (g) x specific heat} \left(\frac{cal}{g \cdot °C}\right)}$

Temperature change (°C) = $\dfrac{25.7\ cal}{18.4\ g\ \times\ 0.215 \left(\frac{cal}{g \cdot °C}\right)}$ = 6.50 °C

Final temperature = 20.0 °C + 6.5 °C = 26.5 °C

1.86

Specific heat = $\dfrac{cal}{g \cdot °C}$ = $\dfrac{23\ cal}{5.0\ g\ \times\ 50\ °C}$ = 0.092 $\dfrac{cal}{g \cdot °C}$ = 0.38 $\dfrac{J}{g \cdot °C}$

1.87

Heat (cal) = mass (g) x temperature change (°C) x specific heat $\left(\frac{cal}{g \cdot °C}\right)$

Mass of fat = $\dfrac{0.94\ g}{1\ cm^3}$ x 10 cm³ = 9.4 g

Heat (cal) = 9.4 g x 10 °C x 0.45 $\left(\dfrac{cal}{g \cdot °C}\right)$ = 42 cal (180 J)

1.88

For mercury: Temperature change (°C) = $\dfrac{250\ cal}{150\ g\ \times\ 0.033\ \frac{cal}{g \cdot °C}}$ = 51 °C

$\qquad$ Final temp = 25 °C + 51 °C = 76 °C

For iron: Temperature change (°C) = $\dfrac{250\ cal}{150\ g\ \times\ 0.106\ \frac{cal}{g \cdot °C}}$ = 15.7 °C

$\qquad$ · Final temp = 25.0 °C + 15.7 °C = 40.7 °C

1.89

$$\text{Specific heat} = \frac{\text{cal}}{\text{g} \cdot °\text{C}} = \frac{100 \text{ cal}}{125 \text{ g} \times 28 °\text{C}} = 0.029 \frac{\text{cal}}{\text{g} \cdot °\text{C}} \ (0.12 \frac{\text{J}}{\text{g} \cdot °\text{C}})$$

The calculated value for specific heat, 0.029 cal/g ·°C, is closest in value to the specific heat of gold, 0.031 cal/g ·°C.

Density and Specific Gravity

1.90

$$250 \text{ mg} \times \frac{1 \text{ g}}{10^3 \text{ mg}} \times \frac{1 \text{ cm}^3}{1.40 \text{ g}} = 0.179 \text{ cm}^3$$

1.91 From the expression for density, we know that 1 L of hydrogen has a mass of 0.0899 g. We need to find the number of liters that have a mass of 1.0078 g.

$$1.0078 \text{ g} \times \frac{1 \text{ L}}{0.0899 \text{ g}} = 11.2 \text{ L}$$

1.92 To find the density of lead, divide the mass of lead by the volume of the bar in cm^3. 0.500 cm × 1.55 cm × 25.00 cm = 19.38 cm^3.

$$\frac{220.9 \text{ g}}{19.38 \text{ cm}^3} = 11.4 \frac{\text{g}}{\text{cm}^3}$$

1.93 The volume of lithium is 0.82 cm × 1.45 cm × 1.25 cm = 1.5 cm^3.

$$\frac{0.794 \text{ g}}{1.5 \text{ cm}^3} = 0.53 \frac{\text{g}}{\text{cm}^3}$$

1.94 The density of ethanol at 25 °C is equal to its specific gravity at 25 °C times the density of water at 25 °C.

$$0.787 \times \frac{0.997 \text{ g}}{1 \text{ mL}} = 0.785 \frac{\text{g}}{\text{mL}}; \ 125 \text{ g} \times \frac{1 \text{ mL}}{0.785 \text{ g}} = 159 \text{ mL}$$

1.95 Use the same reasoning shown in the previous problem.

$$\text{density} = 1.1088 \times \frac{0.997 \text{ g}}{1 \text{ mL}} = \frac{1.112 \text{ g}}{1 \text{ mL}}$$

$$1.00 \text{ L} \times \frac{1000 \text{ mL}}{1 \text{ L}} \times \frac{1.112 \text{ g}}{1 \text{ mL}} = 1.111 \times 10^3 \text{ g} = 1.11 \text{ kg}$$

Chemistry in Action

1.96 ASA contains nine carbons, eight hydrogens, and four oxygens, totaling 21 atoms. It is a solid at room temperature.

1.97 Only soluble forms of mercury are toxic. Hg_2Cl_2 passes through the body before it can be chemically converted to a soluble form, but methyl mercury chloride is soluble.

1.98

$$(28\,°F - 32\,°F)\ \text{x}\ \frac{5\,°C}{9\,°F}\ =\ -2.2\,°C\ =\ 271\ K$$

1.99

$$°F = \left(\frac{9\,°F}{5\,°C}\ \text{x}\ °C\right) + 32\,°F$$

For °C = 37 °C, °F = 99 °F.   For °C = 47 °C, °F = 117 °F

1.100 (a) BMI = 29   (b) BMI = 23.7   (c) BMI = 24.4

Individual (a), with a body mass index that borders on obese, is most likely to have increased health risks.

1.101

$$5.0\ \text{lb}\ \text{x}\ \frac{454\ g}{1\ \text{lb}}\ \text{x}\ \frac{1\ mL}{0.94\ g}\ \text{x}\ \frac{1\ L}{10^3\ mL}\ =\ 2.4\ L$$

General Questions and Problems

1.102 Element 117 lies beneath astatine in the periodic table. It is expected to be a nonmetallic, nonconducting solid and to have chemical behavior similar to the elements above it.

1.103 The white solid is a chemical compound, and the brown gas and molten metal are elements.

1.104

$$3.125\ \text{in.}\ \text{x}\ \frac{2.54\ cm}{1\ \text{in.}}\ =\ 7.94\ cm$$

The difference in the calculated length (7.94 cm) and the measured length (8.0 cm) is due to the lack of precision of the ruler and to rounding.

1.105 One carat = 200 mg = 0.200 g

$$\frac{0.200\ g}{1\ \text{carat}}\ \text{x}\ 44.4\ \text{carat}\ =\ 8.88\ g$$

1.106

(a) $350\ \text{kcal}\ \text{x}\ \dfrac{1\ \text{x}\ 10^3\ \text{cal}}{1\ \text{kcal}}\ =\ 3.50\ \text{x}\ 10^5\ \text{cal};\ 3.50\ \text{x}\ 10^5\ \text{cal}\ \text{x}\ \dfrac{4.18\ J}{\text{cal}}\ =\ 1.46\ \text{x}\ 10^6\ J$

(b) Temperature change (°C) $= \dfrac{\text{heat (cal)}}{\text{mass (g)}\ \text{x}\ \text{specific heat}\left(\frac{\text{cal}}{\text{g}\cdot°C}\right)}$

mass = 35.5 kg = $3.55\ \text{x}\ 10^4$ g; heat = $3.50\ \text{x}\ 10^5$ cal

Temperature change (°C) $= \dfrac{3.50\ \text{x}\ 10^5\ \text{cal}}{3.55\ \text{x}\ 10^4\ \text{g}\ \text{x}\ 1.00\left(\frac{\text{cal}}{\text{g}\cdot°C}\right)}\ =\ 9.86\ °C$

1.107

(a) $\dfrac{9.0 \text{ mg}}{1 \text{ kg}}$ x 130 lb x $\dfrac{1 \text{ kg}}{2.21 \text{ lb}}$ = 530 mg

(b) $\dfrac{9.0 \text{ mg}}{1 \text{ kg}}$ x 40 lb x $\dfrac{1 \text{ kg}}{2.21 \text{ lb}}$ = 163 mg

To receive the recommended dose, the child would thus need about 1.3 of the 125 mg tablets.

1.108 3.9×10^{-2} g/dL iron, 8.3×10^{-3} g/dL calcium, 2.24×10^{-1} g/dL cholesterol

1.109

(a) $2.027 \times 10^5 \text{ ft}^3$ x $\dfrac{0.0283 \text{ m}^3}{\text{ft}^3}$ x $\dfrac{1 \times 10^3 \text{ L}}{\text{m}^3}$ = $5.74 \times 10^6 \text{ L}$

(b) $5.74 \times 10^6 \text{ L}$ x $\dfrac{0.174 \text{ g}}{1 \text{ L}}$ x $\dfrac{1 \text{ kg}}{1 \times 10^3 \text{ g}}$ = $9.99 \times 10^2 \text{ kg}$

(c) $5.74 \times 10^6 \text{ L}$ x $\dfrac{1.20 \text{ g}}{1 \text{ L}}$ x $\dfrac{1 \text{ kg}}{1 \times 10^3 \text{ g}}$ = $6.89 \times 10^3 \text{ kg}$

1.110

$75 \dfrac{\text{mL}}{\text{beat}}$ x $72 \dfrac{\text{beats}}{\text{min}}$ x $60 \dfrac{\text{min}}{\text{hr}}$ x $24 \dfrac{\text{hr}}{\text{day}}$ = $7.8 \times 10^6 \dfrac{\text{mL}}{\text{day}}$

1.111

15 g x $\dfrac{1000.0 \text{ mL}}{50.00 \text{ g}}$ = 300 mL

1.112

0.14 mL x $\dfrac{0.963 \text{ g}}{1 \text{ mL}}$ = 0.13 g

1.113 (a) The effective range of an alcohol thermometer in °C is 115 °C + 78.5 °C = 193.5 °C. Since a Fahrenheit degree is 9/5 of a Celsius degree, the range in °F is 9/5 x 193.5 = 348°F

(b) The thermometer can contain either 0.79 g alcohol or 13.6 g mercury.

1.114

$\dfrac{85 \text{ mg}}{100 \text{ mL}}$ x $\dfrac{1 \text{ g}}{10^3 \text{mg}}$ x $\dfrac{10^3 \text{ mL}}{1 \text{ L}}$ x $\dfrac{0.9464 \text{ L}}{1 \text{ qt}}$ x $\dfrac{1 \text{ qt}}{2 \text{ pt}}$ x 11 pt = 4.4 g

4.4 g x $\dfrac{1 \text{ lb}}{454 \text{ g}}$ = 0.0097 lb

1.115

$\dfrac{3000 \text{ mL}}{1 \text{ day}}$ x $\dfrac{5 \text{ g}}{100 \text{ mL}}$ x $\dfrac{4 \text{ kcal}}{1 \text{ g}}$ = 600 kcal/day

1.116

$\left(\dfrac{100 \text{ mL}}{1 \text{ kg}} \times 10 \text{ kg}\right)$ + $\left(\dfrac{50 \text{ mL}}{1 \text{ kg}} \times 10 \text{ kg}\right)$ + $\left(\dfrac{20 \text{ mL}}{1 \text{ kg}} \times 35 \text{ kg}\right)$ = 2200 mL

1.117

$$7.5 \text{ grains} \times \frac{1 \text{ fluidram}}{10 \text{ grains}} \times \frac{3.72 \text{ mL}}{1 \text{ fluidram}} = 2.8 \text{ mL}$$

1.118

Heat (cal) = mass (g) × temperature change (°C) × specific heat $\left(\dfrac{\text{cal}}{\text{g} \cdot \text{°C}}\right)$

For water: specific heat = 1.00 cal /(g·°C);

$$\text{mass} = 3.00 \text{ L} \times \frac{10^3 \text{ mL}}{1 \text{ L}} \times \frac{1.00 \text{ g}}{1 \text{ mL}} = 3.00 \times 10^3 \text{ g};$$
$$\text{temperature change} = 90.0 \text{ °C} - 18.0 \text{ °C} = 72.0 \text{ °C}$$

$$\text{Calories needed} = 3.00 \times 10^3 \text{ g} \times 72.0\text{°C} \times \frac{1.00 \text{ cal}}{\text{g} \cdot \text{°C}} = 2.16 \times 10^5 \text{ cal} = 216 \text{ kcal}$$

$$216 \text{ kcal} \times \frac{1.0 \text{ tbsp}}{100 \text{ kcal}} = 2.2 \text{ tbsp butter}$$

1.119

$$\text{Specific heat} = \frac{\text{cal}}{\text{g} \cdot \text{°C}} = \frac{1350 \text{ cal}}{1620 \text{ g} \times 7.8 \text{ °C}} = 0.107 \frac{\text{cal}}{\text{g} \cdot \text{°C}} = 0.448 \frac{\text{J}}{\text{g} \cdot \text{°C}}$$

The calculated specific heat, 0.107 cal/g · °C, is closer to the value for iron than for gold.

1.120

$$\frac{1620 \text{ g}}{205 \text{ mL}} = 7.90 \frac{\text{g}}{\text{mL}}$$

The value calculated for density very nearly agrees with the density of iron (7.86 g/mL).

1.121

$$2.01 \times 10^{11} \text{ lb} \times \frac{454 \text{ g}}{1 \text{ lb}} \times \frac{1 \text{ mL}}{1.83 \text{ g}} \times \frac{1 \text{ L}}{1000 \text{ mL}} = 4.99 \times 10^{10} \text{ L}$$

1.122 Use the dimensions of the cork and of the lead to find their respective volumes. Multiply the volume of each substance by its density to arrive at the mass of each.
Volume of cork: 1.30 cm x 5.50 cm x 3.00 cm = 21.5 cm³
Volume of lead: (1.15 cm)³ = 1.52 cm³

Mass of cork: Mass of lead:

$$21.5 \text{ cm}^3 \times \frac{0.235 \text{ g}}{1 \text{ cm}^3} = 5.05 \text{ g cork} \qquad 1.52 \text{ cm}^3 \times \frac{11.35 \text{ g}}{1 \text{ cm}^3} = 17.3 \text{ g lead}$$

Add the two masses, and divide by the sum of the two volumes to find the density of the combination.

$$\text{Density} = \frac{5.05 \text{ g} + 17.3 \text{ g}}{21.5 \text{ cm}^3 + 1.52 \text{ cm}^3} = \frac{22.40 \text{ g}}{23.0 \text{ cm}^3} = 0.974 \text{ g/cm}^3$$

The combination will float because its density is less than the density of water.

1.123 At the crossover point, °F = °C.

$$\text{°F} = \left(\frac{9 \text{ °F}}{5 \text{ °C}} \times \text{°C}\right) + 32 \text{ °F} \qquad \text{If °C = °F, °F} = \frac{9}{5} \text{°F} + 32°; \ 5 \text{ °F} = 9 \text{ °F} + 160°$$

The crossover temperature is °F = °C = −40°.

Self-Test for Chapter 1

1. Write the full name of these units:
    (a) μm (b) dL (c) Mg (d) L (e) ng

2. Write the abbreviation for each of the following units:
    (a) kiloliter (b) picogram (c) centimeter (d) hectoliter

3. | *Quantity* | *Significant Figures?* |

    (a) 1.0037 g
    (b) 0.0080 L
    (c) 0.008 L
    (d) 2 aspirin
    (e) 273,000 mi

4. Express the following in scientific notation:
    (a) 0.000 070 3 g   (b) 137,100 m   (c) 0.011 L   (d) 18,371,008 mm
    How many significant figures do each of these quantities have?

5. Round the following to three significant figures:
    (a) 807.3 L   (b) 4,773,112 people   (c) 0.00127 g   (d) 10370 μm
    Express each of these quantities in scientific notation.

6. Convert the following quantities:
    (a) 256 g = _____ lb   (b) 417 mm = _____ m
    (c) 2.0 gallons = _____ L   (d) 2.17 m = _____ inches
    (e) 35 °C = _____ °F   (f) 298 K = _____ °C
    (g) 175 mL = _____ fl oz   (h) 175 mg = _____ oz

7. If the specific heat of gold is 0.031 cal/g °C, how many calories does it take to heat 10 g of gold from 0 °C to 100 °C?

8. If the density of ethanol is 0.7893 g/mL, how many grams does 275 mL of ethanol weigh?

Multiple Choice

1. Which of the following is not an SI unit?
    (a) kg (b) L (c) m (d) K

2. How many significant figures does the number 4500 have?
    (a) 2 (b) 3 (c) 4 (d) any of the above

3. Which of the following quantities is larger than a gram?
    (a) 1 nanogram (b) 1 dekagram (c) 1 centigram (d) 1 microgram

4. Which of the following conversion factors do you need for converting 3.2 lb/qt to kg/L?
    (a) $\dfrac{1 \text{ kg}}{2.2 \text{ lb}}$ x $\dfrac{1 \text{ qt}}{0.95 \text{ L}}$ (b) $\dfrac{2.2 \text{ lb}}{1 \text{ kg}}$ x $\dfrac{1 \text{ qt}}{0.95 \text{ L}}$ (c) $\dfrac{2.2 \text{ lb}}{1 \text{ kg}}$ x $\dfrac{0.95 \text{ L}}{1 \text{ qt}}$ (d) $\dfrac{1 \text{ kg}}{2.2 \text{ lb}}$ x $\dfrac{0.95 \text{ L}}{1 \text{ qt}}$

5. When written in scientific notation, the exponent in the number 0.000 007 316 is:
    (a) 10^{-6} (b) 6 (c) -6 (d) 10^6

6.   The change of state that occurs when a gas is cooled to a liquid is called:
     (a) boiling   (b) melting   (c) evaporation   (d) condensation

7.   How many zeros are significant in the number 0.007 006?
     (a) 1   (b) 2   (c) 3   (d) 4

8.   All of the following have uniform composition except: (a) element   (b) solution   (c) pure substance   (d) chemical compound

9.   To measure the amount of heat needed to raise the temperature of a given substance, you need to know all of the following except:
     (a) the mass of the substance   (b) the specific heat of the substance   (c) the density of the substance   (d) the initial and final temperature

10. For which of the following is specific gravity a useful measure?
     (a) to describe the amount of solids in urine   (b) to indicate the amount of heat necessary to raise the temperature of one gram of a substance by 1°C   (c) to determine if an object will float on water

Sentence Completion

1.   The fundamental SI units are _____, _____, _____, and _____.

2.   Physical quantities are described by a _____ and a _____.

3.   The amount of heat necessary to raise the temperature of one gram of a substance by one degree is the substance's _____ _____.

4.   _____ is the symbol for the element bismuth.

5.   The number 0.003 06 has _____ significant figures.

6.   To convert from grams to pounds, use the conversion factor _____.

7.   A _____ substance can be beaten or rolled into different shapes.

8.   The method used for converting units is called the _____ _____ method.

9.   _____ _____ is the density of a substance divided by the density of water at the same temperature.

10. The size of a degree is the same in both _____ and _____ units.

Chapter 1

True or False

1. The units of specific gravity are g/mL.

2. The number 0.07350 has four significant figures.

3. The sum of 57.35 and 1.3 has four significant figures.

4. The conversion factor 1.057 quarts/liter is used to convert quarts into liters.

5. Rust formation is a chemical change.

6. The temperature in °C is always a larger number than the temperature in K.

7. Raising the temperature of 10 g of water by 10 °C takes less heat than raising the temperature of 10 g of gold by 10 °C.

8. Mass measures the amount of matter in an object.

9. Ice is more dense than water.

10. A nanogram is larger than a picogram.

Match each entry on the left with its partner on the right.

1. 50037   (a) Converts pounds to kilograms

2. 1 centimeter   (b) 0.1 grams

3. $\dfrac{2.205 \text{ lb}}{1 \text{ kg}}$ (c) Larger than one inch

4. 263 K   (d) −17.8 °C

5. 1 dekagram   (e) Five significant figures

6. 0.048   (f) SI unit of volume measure

7. 1 m^3 (g) Converts kilograms to pounds

8. 1 liter   (h) 10 grams

9. 1 decimeter   (i) −10 °C

10. $\dfrac{1 \text{ kg}}{2.205 \text{ lb}}$ (j) Smaller than one inch

11. 0°F   (k) Metric unit of volume measure

12. 1 decigram   (l) Two significant figures

Chapter Outline

I.   Atomic Theory (Sections 2.1–2.3).
   A. Fundamental assumptions about atoms (Section 2.1).
      1. All matter is composed of atoms.
      2. The atoms of each element are different from the atoms of all other elements.
      3. Chemical compounds consist of elements combined in definite proportions.
      4. Chemical reactions only change the way that atoms are combined in compounds; the atoms themselves are unchanged.
   B. Nature of the atom (Sections 2.1).
      1. Atoms are very small (~10^{-11} m in diameter).
      2. Atoms consist of subatomic particles.
         a. A proton is positively charged and has a mass of 1.6726×10^{-24} g.
         b. A neutron has no charge and has a mass of 1.6749×10^{-24} g.
         c. An electron is negatively charged and has a mass of 9.1093×10^{-28} g.
      3. The masses of atoms are expressed in relative terms.
         a. Under this system, a carbon atom with six protons and six neutrons is given a mass of exactly 12 atomic mass units (amu).
         b. Consequently, a proton and a neutron each have a mass of approximately 1 amu.
      4. Atoms are held together by the interplay of attractive and repulsive forces of positively charged protons and negatively charged electrons.
      5. Protons and neutrons are located in the nucleus of an atom, and electrons move about the nucleus.
      6. The size of the nucleus is small compared to the size of the atom.
   C. Composition of atoms (Section 2.2).
      1. Atoms of different elements differ from each other according to how many protons they contain.
      2. Z stands for the number of protons an atom has and is known as the atomic number.
      3. The number of electrons in an atom is the same as the number of protons.
      4. The mass number A stands for the number of protons plus the number of neutrons.
   D. Isotopes and atomic weight (Section 2.3).
      1. Isotopes are atoms of the same element that differ only in the number of neutrons.
      2. Isotopes are represented by showing the mass number as a superscript on the left side of the symbol for the chemical element; the atomic number is shown as a subscript on the left side.
      3. Most elements occur in nature as a mixture of isotopes.
      4. The atomic weight of an element can be calculated if the percent of contributing isotopes is known.
II. The Periodic Table (Sections 2.4–2.5).
   A. The periodic table is a classification of elements according to their properties (Section 2.4).
      1. Elements are arranged by increasing atomic number in seven rows called periods.
      2. Elements are also arranged in 18 vertical columns called groups.
         a. Main group elements occur on the left and right of the periodic table.
         b. Transition metal groups occur in the middle of the periodic table.
         c. Inner transition metal groups are shown separately at the bottom.
      3. The elements in each group have similar chemical properties.

B. Chemical characteristics of groups of elements (Section 2.5).
   1. Group 1A—Alkali metals (Li, Na, K, Rb, Cs, Fr).
      a. Shiny, soft, low-melting.
      b. React violently with water.
   2. Group 2A—Alkaline earth metals (Be, Mg, Ca, Sr, Ba, Ra).
      a. Lustrous, shiny metals.
      b. Less reactive than metals in group 1A.
   3. Group 7A—Halogens (F, Cl, Br, I, At).
      a. Corrosive, nonmetals (except At).
      b. Found in nature only in combination with other elements.
   4. Group 8A—Noble gases (He, Ne, Ar, Kr, Xe, Rn). Extremely unreactive.
C. Neighboring groups have similar behaviors.
   1. Metals.
      a. Found on the left side of the periodic table.
      b. Silvery, ductile, good conductors.
   2. Nonmetals.
      a. Found on the right side of the periodic table.
      b. Eleven of the 17 nonmetals are gases.
      c. Solid nonmetals are brittle and are poor conductors of electricity.
   3. Metalloids.
      a. Occur on the boundary between metals and nonmetals.
      b. Have intermediate chemical behavior.
III. Electrons (Sections 2.6–2.9).
  A. The properties of the elements are due to the distribution of electrons in their atoms (Section 2.6).
  B. Location of electrons.
   1. Electrons are located in specific regions about the nucleus.
   2. The energies of electrons are quantized.
   3. The locations of electrons are described by shells, subshells and orbitals.
      a. Shells.
         i. Shells describe the energy level of an electron.
         ii. Shells are related to an electron's distance from the nucleus.
      b. Subshells.
         i. Subshells describe the energy levels of electrons within each shell.
         ii. The four types of subshell are *s, p, d,* and *f.*
      c. Orbitals.
         i. Orbitals are the regions of subshells in which electrons of a specific energy can be found.
         ii. An *s* subshell contains one orbital, a *p* subshell contains three orbitals, a *d* subshell contains five orbitals, and an *f* subshell contains seven orbitals.
         iii. Each orbital can hold two electrons, and they must be of opposite spin.
         iv. An *s* orbital is spherical, and a *p* orbital is dumbbell-shaped.
   4. Since the exact position of electrons can't be specified, orbitals are often referred to as electron clouds.
  C. Electron configurations (Section 2.7).
   1. The specific arrangement of electrons in an atom's shells and subshells is known as its electron configuration.
   2. This arrangement can be predicted by using three rules.
      a. Electrons occupy the lowest orbitals available within each subshell.
         i. Within each shell, the subshell energy levels increase in the order *s, p, d, f.*
      b. Each orbital can hold only two electrons, and they must be of opposite spin.
      c. If two or more orbitals have the same energy, each orbital is half filled before any orbital is completely filled.

3. The number of electrons in each subshell is given by a superscript.

D. Electron configuration and the periodic table (Sections 2.8–2.9).

1. Properties of elements are determined by their location in the periodic table (Section 2.8).

2. The periodic table is divided into four regions.

a. Elements in groups 1A and 2A are *s*-block elements because they result from filling *s* orbitals.

b. Groups 3A–8A are *p*-block elements.

c. Transition metals are *d*-block elements.

d. Inner transition metals are *f*-block elements.

3. The periodic table can be used as a reminder of the order of orbital filling.

4. Elements within a group of the periodic table have similar electronic configurations of their valence electronic shells and thus similar chemical behavior.

5. The valence electrons in a compound can be represented by electron dots (Section 2.9).

Solutions to Chapter 2 Problems

2.1

$$150 \times 10^{12} \text{ atoms} \times \frac{56 \text{ amu}}{1 \text{ atom}} \times \frac{1.660\ 539 \times 10^{-24} \text{ g}}{1 \text{ amu}} = 1.39 \times 10^{-8} \text{ g}$$

2.2

(a) $1.0 \text{ g} \times \dfrac{1 \text{ amu}}{1.660\ 539 \times 10^{-24} \text{ g}} \times \dfrac{1 \text{ atom}}{1.0 \text{ amu}} = 6.0 \times 10^{23} \text{ atoms}$

(b) $12.0 \text{ g} \times \dfrac{1 \text{ amu}}{1.660\ 539 \times 10^{-24} \text{ g}} \times \dfrac{1 \text{ atom}}{12.0 \text{ amu}} = 6.02 \times 10^{23} \text{ atoms}$

(c) $23.0 \text{ g} \times \dfrac{1 \text{ amu}}{1.660\ 539 \times 10^{-24} \text{ g}} \times \dfrac{1 \text{ atom}}{23.0 \text{ amu}} = 6.02 \times 10^{23} \text{ atoms}$

2.3   In each of the preceding examples, the mass in grams equals the mass in amu, and the number of atoms in all three samples is identical.

2.4   In comparing the volume of the nucleus to the volume of the atom, the terms $4/3\ \pi$ cancel.

$$(\text{radius}_{\text{nucleus}})^3 \div (\text{radius}_{\text{atom}})^3 = (1.5 \times 10^{-15} \text{ m}^3)^3 \div (1.44 \times 10^{-10})^3 \times 100\%$$

$$= (3.375 \times 10^{-45} \text{ m}^3) \div (2.986 \times 10^{-30}) \times 100\%$$

$$= 1.1 \times 10^{-13}\%$$

Thus, $1.1 \times 10^{-13}\%$ of the volume of a gold atom is occupied by the nucleus.

2.5   (a) Re   (b) Sr   (c) Te

2.6   Recall that the *atomic number* (*Z*) shows how many protons an atom contains. Cobalt, with an atomic number of 27, thus contains 27 protons.
Cobalt also contains 27 electrons, since the number of protons equals the number of electrons.
The *mass number* (*A*) shows the number of protons plus the number of neutrons. To find the number of neutrons in an atom, subtract the atomic number from the mass number.
For cobalt: Mass number – atomic number = 60 – 27 = 33.
The cobalt atom has 33 neutrons.

2.7   Contribution from ^{39}K: 93.12% of 38.96 amu = 36.28 amu
Contribution from ^{41}K: 6.88% of 40.96 amu =   2.82 amu
_ _
Atomic weight = 39.10 amu

The calculated value agrees exactly with the reported value.

2.8   Both bromine isotopes have 35 protons. The isotope with mass number 79 has 44 neutrons, and the isotope with mass number 81 has 46 neutrons.
The atomic number is written at the lower left of the element symbol, and the mass number is written at the upper left.

$^{79}_{35}$Br   and $^{81}_{35}$Br

2.9

$^{35}_{17}$Cl $^{37}_{17}$Cl

2.10   Aluminum is in group 3A (or 13) and period 3.

2.11   The group 1B element in period 5 is silver (Ag).
The group 2A element in period 4 is calcium (Ca).

2.12   *Group 5A Element*   *Period*
_ _ _ _ _ _ _ _ _ _ _ _ _
Nitrogen (N)   2
Phosphorus (P)   3
Arsenic (As)   4
Antimony (Sb)   5
Bismuth (Bi)   6

2.13   Metals: titanium (Ti), scandium (Sc)
Nonmetals: selenium (Se), argon (Ar), astatine (At)
Metalloids: tellurium (Te)

2.14   (a) Krypton: (ii) nonmetal; (iv) main group element; (v) noble gas
(b) Strontium: (i) metal; (iv) main group element
(c) Nitrogen: (ii) nonmetal; (iv) main group element
(d) Cobalt: (i) metal; (iii) transition element

2.15   Thirteen He-4 nuclei, plus four neutrons, would be needed.

2.16   (a) Sodium; Group 1A; Period 3; metal   (b) Oxygen; Group 6A; Period 2; nonmetal

2.17   Twelve electrons are present in this atom, which is magnesium.

2.18   Sulfur is a main-group element (Group 6A) that is a nonmetal. The last electron is found in a 3*p* orbital.

2.19 To find the electron configuration of an atom, first find its atomic number. For C (carbon), the atomic number is 6; thus, carbon has 6 protons and 6 electrons. Then assign electrons to the proper orbitals. For carbon, the electron configuration is $1s^2\, 2s^2\, 2p^2$.

Element	Atomic Number	Electron Configuration
(a) C (carbon)	6	$1s^2\, 2s^2\, 2p^2$
(b) P (phosphorus)	15	$1s^2\, 2s^2\, 2p^6\, 3s^2\, 3p^3$
(c) Cl (chlorine)	17	$1s^2\, 2s^2\, 2p^6\, 3s^2\, 3p^5$
(d) K (potassium)	19	$1s^2\, 2s^2\, 2p^6\, 3s^2\, 3p^6\, 4s^1$

2.20 Element 33 (As): $1s^2\, 2s^2\, 2p^6\, 3s^2\, 3p^6\, 4s^2\, 3d^{10}\, 4p^3$. The $4p$ subshell is incompletely filled. Notice that only one electron occupies each orbital of the $4p$ subshell.

$\uparrow\ \uparrow\ \uparrow\quad 4p^3$

2.21 The atom has 31 electrons (and 31 protons) and can be identified as gallium.

2.22 (a) F: $1s^2\, 2s^2\, 2p^5$; [He] $\mathbf{2s^2\ 2p^5}$ (b) Al: $1s^2\, 2s^2\, 2p^6\, 3s^2\, 3p^1$; [Ne] $\mathbf{3s^2\ 3p^1}$

(c) As: $1s^2\, 2s^2\, 2p^6\, 3s^2\, 3p^6\, 4s^2\, 3d^{10}\, 4p^3$; [Ar] $\mathbf{4s^2}\, 3d^{10}\, \mathbf{4p^3}$
(Valence electrons are bold.)

2.23 In group 2A, all elements have the outer-shell configuration ns^2.

2.24 Chlorine, in group 7A (17), has seventeen electrons. Its electron configuration is $1s^2\, 2s^2$ $2p^6\, 3s^2\, 3p^5$. Two electrons are in shell 1, eight electrons are in shell 2, and seven electrons are in shell 3. The outer shell configuration is $3s^2\, 3p^5$.

2.25 The elements form group 6A (16) and have the general valence-shell configuration $ns^2 np^4$.

2.26

·Ẋ·

2.27

:Ṙṅ: ·Ṗb·   :Ẋė: ·Ra·

2.28 The wavelength of red light lies between 700–780 nm, and the wavelength of blue light lies between 400–480 nm. Blue light is associated with higher energy.

Understanding Key Concepts

2.29

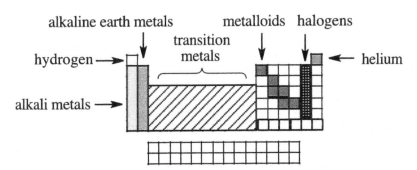

2.30 The element marked in red is a gas (fluorine—group 7A).
The element marked in blue has atomic number 79 (gold).
All elements in group 2A have chemical behavior similar to the element marked in green
(calcium). These include beryllium, magnesium, strontium, barium, and radium.

2.31

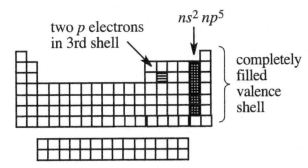

2.32 Selenium (Z = 34) is the element whose orbital-filling diagram is shown. Notice that it is
possible to identify the element by counting its electrons, which equal the number of
protons and give the value of Z.

2.33 As: $1s^2\,2s^2\,2p^6\,3s^2\,3p^6$ ⇅   ⇅ ⇅ ⇅ ⇅ ⇅   ↑ ↑ ↑
                                                4s   3d   4p

Atomic Theory and the Composition of Atoms

2.34 (1) All matter is composed of atoms.
(2) The atoms of a given element differ from the atoms of all other elements.
(3) Chemical compounds consist of atoms combined in specific proportions.
(4) Chemical reactions change only the way that atoms are combined in compounds; the
atoms themselves are unchanged.

2.35 Atoms of different elements differ in the number of protons and electrons they have.

2.36

(a) Bi: $208.9804 \text{ amu} \times \dfrac{1.660\ 539 \times 10^{-24} \text{ g}}{1 \text{ amu}} = 3.470201 \times 10^{-22} \text{ g}$

(b) Xe: $131.29 \text{ amu} \times \dfrac{1.660\ 539 \times 10^{-24} \text{ g}}{1 \text{ amu}} = 2.1801 \times 10^{-22} \text{ g}$

(c) He: $4.0026 \text{ amu} \times \dfrac{1.660\ 539 \times 10^{-24} \text{ g}}{1 \text{ amu}} = 6.6465 \times 10^{-24} \text{ g}$

2.37

(a) $\dfrac{2.66 \times 10^{-23} \text{ g}}{1 \text{ atom O}} \times \dfrac{1 \text{ amu}}{1.660\ 539 \times 10^{-24} \text{ g}} = 16.0 \text{ amu}$

(b) $\dfrac{1.31 \times 10^{-22} \text{ g}}{1 \text{ atom Br}} \times \dfrac{1 \text{ amu}}{1.660\ 539 \times 10^{-24} \text{ g}} = 78.9 \text{ amu}$

2.38

$6.022 \times 10^{23} \text{ atoms} \times \dfrac{1.660\ 539 \times 10^{-24} \text{ g}}{1 \text{ amu}} \times \dfrac{14.01 \text{ amu}}{1 \text{ atom}} = 14.01 \text{ g}$

2.39

$6.022 \times 10^{23} \text{ atoms} \times \dfrac{1.660\ 539 \times 10^{-24} \text{ g}}{1 \text{ amu}} \times \dfrac{16.00 \text{ amu}}{1 \text{ atom}} = 16.00 \text{ g}$

2.40

$15.99 \text{ g} \times \dfrac{1 \text{ amu}}{1.660\ 539 \times 10^{-24} \text{ g}} \times \dfrac{1 \text{ atom}}{15.99 \text{ amu}} = 6.022 \times 10^{23} \text{ atoms}$

2.41

$12.00 \text{ g} \times \dfrac{1 \text{ amu}}{1.660\ 539 \times 10^{-24} \text{ g}} \times \dfrac{1 \text{ atom}}{12.00 \text{ amu}} = 6.022 \times 10^{23} \text{ atoms}$

2.42

Particle	Mass in amu	Charge
Proton	1.007 276	+1
Neutron	1.008 665	0
Electron	$5.485\ 799 \times 10^{-4}$	−1

2.43 Protons and neutrons are found in a dense central region called the nucleus. Electrons move about the nucleus in large, specifically defined regions called orbitals.

2.44

Isotope	Argon-36	Argon-38	Argon-40
Number of neutrons	18	20	22

2.45

Isotope	(a) $^{27}_{13}\text{Al}$	(b) $^{28}_{14}\text{Si}$	(c) $^{11}_{5}\text{B}$	(d) $^{115}_{47}\text{Ag}$
Number of protons	13	14	5	47
Number of neutrons	14	14	6	68
Number of electrons	13	14	5	47

2.46 Symbols (a) and (c) represent isotopes because they have the same atomic number but different mass numbers.

2.47 (a) fluorine-19 (b) neon-19 (c) fluorine-21 (d) magnesium-21

2.48

(a) $^{14}_{6}C$ (b) $^{39}_{19}K$ (c) $^{20}_{10}Ne$

2.49

(a) $^{120}_{50}Sn$ (b) $^{56}_{26}Fe$ (c) $^{226}_{88}Ra$

2.50

$^{12}_{6}C$ – six neutrons $^{13}_{6}C$ – seven neutrons $^{14}_{6}C$ – eight neutrons

2.51

$^{99}_{43}Tc$

2.52 Contribution from ^{63}Cu: 69.17% of 62.93 amu = 43.53 amu
Contribution from ^{65}Cu: 30.83% of 64.93 amu = 20.02 amu
– –
Average atomic weight = 63.55 amu

2.53 Contribution from ^{7}Li: 92.58% of 7.016 amu = 6.495 amu
Contribution from ^{6}Li: 7.42% of 6.015 amu = 0.446 amu
– –
Average atomic weight = 6.941 amu

The Periodic Table

2.54 The third period in the periodic table contains 8 elements because 8 electrons are needed to fill the *s* subshell (2 electrons) and *p* subshell (6 electrons) of the third shell.

2.55 The fourth period contains 18 elements because 18 electrons are needed to fill the *s* subshell (2 electrons) and *p* subshell (6 electrons) of the fourth shell, plus the *d* subshell (10 electrons) of the third shell.

2.56 Americium (Am; atomic number 95) is a metal.

2.57 The *p* subshell is being filled for the metalloid elements.

2.58 (a) They are metals.
(b) They are transition metals.
(c) The 3*d* subshell is being filled.

2.59 (a) They are metals.
(b) They are lanthanides, which are a subgroup of the inner transition elements.
(c) The 4*f* subshell is being filled.

2.60 (a) Rubidium: (i) metal; (v) main group element; (vii) alkali metal
(b) Tungsten: (i) metal; (iv) transition element
(c) Germanium: (iii) metalloid; (v) main group element
(d) Krypton: (ii) nonmetal; (v) main group element; (vi) noble gas

2.61 (a) Calcium: (i) metal; (v) main group element; (viii) alkaline earth metal
(b) Palladium: (i) metal; (iv) transition element
(c) Carbon: (ii) nonmetal; (v) main group element
(d) Radon: (ii) nonmetal; (v) main group element; (vi) noble gas

2.62 Selenium is chemically similar to sulfur.

2.63 Any element in Group 1A other than hydrogen is chemically similar to potassium.

2.64 The alkali metal family is composed of lithium, sodium, potassium, rubidium, cesium, and francium.

2.65 Fluorine, chlorine, bromine, iodine, and astatine make up the halogen family.

Electron Configuration

2.66 A maximum of two electrons can go into an orbital.

2.67 An *s* orbital is spherical and centered on the nucleus. A *p* orbital is dumbbell-shaped, and the three *p* orbitals extend out from the nucleus at 90° angles to each other.

2.68 First shell—2 electrons
Second shell—8 electrons
Third shell—18 electrons

2.69 The third shell contains nine orbitals: one *s* orbital, three *p* orbitals, and five *d* orbitals. The fourth shell contains sixteen orbitals: one *s* orbital, three *p* orbitals, five *d* orbitals, and seven *f* orbitals.

2.70 The third shell contains three subshells: 3*s*, 3*p*, 3*d*. The fourth shell contains four subshells: 4*s*, 4*p*, 4*d*, 4*f*. The fifth shell contains five subshells: 5*s*, 5*p*, 5*d*, 5*f*, and an additional subshell.

2.71 It would contain nine orbitals and would be filled by 18 electrons.

2.72 Ten electrons are present; the element is neon.

2.73 22 electrons are present; the element is titanium.

2.74   (a) Sulfur   (b) Bromine   (c) Silicon

$\uparrow\downarrow \;\; \uparrow \;\; \uparrow$ $\uparrow\downarrow \;\; \uparrow\downarrow \;\; \uparrow$ $\uparrow \;\; \uparrow \;\; -$

$3p^4$ $4p^5$ $3p^2$

2.75   (a) Rubidium   (b) Niobium   (c) Rhodium

$\uparrow$ $\uparrow\downarrow \;\; \uparrow \;\; \uparrow \;\; \uparrow \;\; - \; -$ $\uparrow\downarrow \;\; \uparrow\downarrow \;\; \uparrow\downarrow \;\; \uparrow \;\; \uparrow \;\; \uparrow$

$5s$ $5s$ $4d$ $5s$ $4d$

2.76

Element	Sulfur	Bromine	Silicon	Rubidium	Niobium	Rhodium
Number of unpaired electrons	2	1	2	1	3	3

2.77

Element	*Electron configuration*
(a) Ti	$1s^2 \, 2s^2 \, 2p^6 \, 3s^2 \, 3p^6 \, 4s^2 \, 3d^2$
(b) P	$1s^2 \, 2s^2 \, 2p^6 \, 3s^2 \, 3p^3$
(c) Ar	$1s^2 \, 2s^2 \, 2p^5 \, 3s^2 \, 3p^6$
(d) La	$1s^2 \, 2s^2 \, 2p^6 \, 3s^2 \, 3p^6 \, 4s^2 \, 3d^{10} \, 4p^6 \, 5s^2 \, 4d^{10} \, 5p^6 \, 6s^2 \, 5d^1$

2.78   The element with atomic number 12 (Mg) has two electrons in its valence shell.

$\cdot \text{Mg} \cdot$

2.79   The number of valence electrons for elements in a main group is the same as the group number. Thus, group 4A elements have four valence electrons.

2.80   Beryllium: $2s$ Arsenic: $4p$

2.81   Group 5A(15) has the configuration $ns^2 \, np^3$.

2.82

Element:	(a) Kr	(b) C	(c) Ca	(d) K	(e) B	(f) Cl
Number of valence-shell electrons:	8	4	2	1	3	7

$:\!\overset{\displaystyle\cdot\cdot}{\underset{\displaystyle\cdot\cdot}{\text{Kr}}}\!:$ $\cdot \overset{\displaystyle\cdot}{\text{C}} \cdot$ $\cdot \text{Ca} \cdot$ $\cdot \text{K}$ $\cdot \overset{\displaystyle\cdot}{\text{B}} \cdot$ $:\!\overset{\displaystyle\cdot\cdot}{\underset{\displaystyle\cdot\cdot}{\text{Cl}}}\!\cdot$

2.83   Group 6A: $ns^2 \, np^4$;   Group 2A: ns^2

Chemistry in Action

2.84   A normal light microscope can't reach the degree of precision of a scanning tunneling microscope.

2.85   (a) The character is 12 iron atoms wide.

(b) $12 \text{ atoms} \times \dfrac{126 \text{ pm}}{1 \text{ atom}} \times \dfrac{1 \text{ cm}}{1 \times 10^{10} \text{ pm}} = 1.51 \times 10^{-7} \text{ cm}$

2.86 Hydrogen and helium are the first two elements made in stars.

2.87 A gravitational collapse of stars results in the synthesis of elements heavier than iron and produces an explosion known as a supernova.

2.88

	Higher Energy	*Lower Energy*
(a)	ultraviolet	infrared
(b)	gamma waves	microwaves
(c)	X rays	visible light

2.89 Ultraviolet rays are more damaging to the skin because they are of higher energy than visible light.

General Questions and Problems

2.90 Helium, neon, argon, krypton, xenon, and radon make up the noble gas family.

2.91 Hydrogen can be placed in group 1A because it has one electron in its outermost (only) electron shell. Hydrogen can be placed in group 7A because only one electron is needed to fill its outermost (only) electron shell.

2.92 Tellurium has a greater atomic weight because its nuclei contain, on the average, more neutrons than an iodine nucleus.

2.93 The undiscovered element beneath francium has the atomic number 119.

2.94 Pb: $1s^2\, 2s^2\, 2p^6\, 3s^2\, 3p^6\, 4s^2\, 3d^{10}\, 4p^6\, 5s^2\, 4d^{10}\, 5p^6\, 6s^2\, 4f^{14}\, 5d^{10}\, 6p^2$
Shell 1: 2 electrons   Shell 2: 8 electrons   Shell 3: 18 electrons
Shell 4: 32 electrons   Shell 5: 18 electrons   Shell 6: 4 electrons

2.95 Highest-energy occupied subshell: (a) $I - 5p$; (b) $Sc - 3d$; (c) $As - 4p$; (d) $Al - 3p$

2.96 Contribution from ^{79}Br: 50.69% of 78.92 amu = 40.00 amu
Contribution from ^{81}Br: 49.31% of 80.91 amu = 39.90 amu

$$\text{Average atomic weight} = 79.90 \text{ amu}$$

2.97 (a) One atom of carbon has a mass of 12 amu. In grams:

$$12 \text{ amu} \times \frac{1.660\ 539 \times 10^{-24} \text{ g}}{1 \text{ amu}} = 1.99 \times 10^{-23} \text{ g}$$

(b) $\dfrac{12 \text{ amu}}{1 \text{ atom}} \times \dfrac{1.660\ 539 \times 10^{-24} \text{ g}}{1 \text{ amu}} \times 6.02 \times 10^{23} \text{ atoms} = 12 \text{ g}$

(c) Based on the answer to part (b), we predict that 6.02×10^{23} sodium atoms will weigh about 23 grams.

2.98   The unidentified element is strontium, which occurs directly below calcium in group 2A and thus has similar chemical behavior. Strontium is a metal, has 38 protons, and is in the fifth period.

$$\cdot \text{Sr} \cdot$$

2.99   (a) Ge: $1s^2 \, 2s^2 \, 2p^6 \, 3s^2 \, 3p^6 \, 4s^2 \, 3d^{10} \, 4p^2$; [Ar] $4s^2 \, 3d^{10} \, 4p^2$

(b) The outer-shell electrons of germanium are in the $4s$ and $4p$ orbitals.

2.100 Tin, a metal, has an electron configuration by shell of 2 8 18 18 4.

2.101

$$8.6 \text{ mg} \; \times \; \frac{1 \text{ g}}{10^3 \text{ mg}} \; \times \; \frac{1 \text{ amu}}{1.660\,539 \times 10^{-24} \text{ g}} \; \times \; \frac{1 \text{ atom}}{40.08 \text{ amu}} = 1.3 \times 10^{20} \text{ atoms}$$

2.102 (a) Electrons must fill the $4s$ subshell before entering the $3d$ subshell. The correct configuration:

$$1s^2 \, 2s^2 \, 2p^6 \, 3s^2 \, 3p^6 \, 4s^2 \, 3d^8$$

(b) Electrons must fill the $2s$ subshell before entering the $2p$ subshell. The correct configuration:

$$1s^2 \, 2s^2 \, 2p^3$$

(c) Silicon has 14 electrons. The p orbitals must be half-filled before any one orbital is completely filled. The correct configuration:

$$1s^2 \, 2s^2 \, 2p^6 \, 3s^2 \; \underset{3p}{\uparrow \; \uparrow} \; \_\_$$

(d) The $3s$ electrons must have opposite spins. The correct configuration:

$$1s^2 \, 2s^2 \, 2p^6 \; \underset{3s}{\uparrow\downarrow}$$

2.103 Count the electrons in each example to arrive at the atomic number. Then look up the answer in the periodic table.
(a) Cr   (b) Cu   (c) Mo   (d) Ag

2.104 An electron will fill or half-fill a d subshell instead of filling an s subshell of a higher shell.

2.105 Au: $1s^2 \, 2s^2 \, 2p^6 \, 3s^2 \, 3p^6 \, 4s^2 \, 3d^{10} \, 4p^6 \, 5s^2 \, 4d^{10} \, 5p^6 \, 6s^1 \, 4f^{14} \, 5d^{10}$

2.106 The last orbital filled in element 117 is $7p$.

Self-Test for Chapter 2

Multiple Choice

1. Which of the following is a metalloid?
   (a) carbon (b) aluminum (c) silicon (d) phosphorus

2. Which of the following has a partially filled *d* subshell?
   (a) calcium (b) vanadium (c) zinc (d) arsenic

3. Which of the following is not a part of atomic theory?
   (a) All metal is composed of atoms. (b) The atoms of each element are different from the atoms of other elements. (c) In chemical compounds, atoms are combined in specific proportions. (d) Chemical reactions only change the way that atoms are combined.

4. How many isotopes of hydrogen are there?
   (a) one (b) two (c) three (d) can't be determined

5. What holds protons and neutrons together in the nucleus?
   (a) attraction (b) repulsion (c) electrons (d) internuclear forces

6. Which of the following has a mass number of 33?
   (a) $^{74}_{33}$As (b) $^{35}_{17}$Cl (c) $^{32}_{16}$S (d) $^{33}_{16}$S

7. In which order are subshells usually filled?
   (a) *s, p, d, f*   (b) *d, f, p, s*   (c) *s, p, f, d*   (d) *s, d, p, f*

8. The element with atomic number 38 is:
   (a) an alkali metal (b) an alkaline earth metal (c) a transition metal (d) a metalloid

9. The element that has atomic weight = 91 and has 40 electrons is:
   (a) protactinium (b) niobium (c) antimony (d) zirconium

10. The element that has electron configuration $1s^2\ 2s^2\ 2p^6\ 3s^2\ 3p^6\ 4s^2\ 3d^7$ is:
    (a) copper (b) rhodium (c) arsenic (d) cobalt

11. An element that has electrons in its *f* subshell is:
    (a) europium (b) technetium (c) antimony (d) xenon

12. $^{195}_{78}$X is the symbol for:
    (a) gold (b) platinum (c) iridium (d) iron

Sentence Completion

1.   A _____ orbital is dumbbell-shaped.

2.   An atomic mass unit is also known as a _____.

3.   The nucleus of an atom is made up of _____ and _____.

4. The _____ _____ indicates the number of protons in an atom.

5. The electrons in an atom are grouped by energy into _____.

6. Elements belonging to the same _____ have similar chemical properties.

7. The atomic number of aluminum is _____.

8. Protons, neutrons, and electrons are known as _____ _____.

9. Atoms having the same number of protons but different numbers of neutrons are called _____.

10. The third shell contains _____ electrons.

11. The word _____ means that electrons can have certain energy values and no others.

True or False

1. Bismuth is a metal.

2. The mass of an electron is approximately 1 amu.

3. A 4s electron is higher in energy than a 3d electron.

4. Isotopes have the same number of protons but different numbers of neutrons.

5. An atom's atomic number indicates the number of protons and neutrons the atom has.

6. Elements in group 2A are more reactive than elements in group 1A.

7. Elements in the same period have similar chemical properties.

8. More elements are metals than are nonmetals.

9. All compounds consist of atoms combined in specific proportions.

10. A subshell contains only two electrons.

11. An element can have the same number of protons, neutrons, and electrons.

12. Atomic weight always increases with atomic number.

Match each entry on the left with its partner on the right.

1. $1s^2\,2s^2$

(a) Mendeleev

2. Group

(b) Number of protons in an element

3. Atomic mass unit

(c) Reactive metals

4. Formulated the periodic table

(d) Average mass of a large number of an element's atoms

5. Neutron

(e) Column in the periodic table

6. $^{28}_{14}\text{Si}$

(f) Row in the periodic table

7. Group 1A

(g) Element with atomic mass of 14 amu

8. Atomic number

(h) Electron configuration of beryllium

9. $^{29}_{14}\text{Si}$

(i) Element having 15 neutrons

10. Atomic weight

(j) Subatomic particle with zero charge

11. $^{14}_{7}\text{N}$

(k) Dalton

12. Period

(l) Element with atomic number 14

Chapter Outline

I. Ions (Sections 3.1–3.2).
  A. Ions are formed when a neutral atom either gains an electron (to form an anion) or loses an electron (to form a cation).
    1. Ionization energy measures the ease with which an atom gives up an electron.
      a. Energy must be supplied in order to remove an electron.
      b. Elements on the far left of the periodic table have smaller ionization energies and lose electrons more easily.
      c. Elements on the far right of the periodic table have larger ionization energies and lose electrons with difficulty.
    2. Electron affinity measures the ease with which an atom gains an electron.
      a. Energy is released when an atom gains an electron.
      b. Elements on the far right of the periodic table have larger electron affinities and gain electrons easily.
      c. Elements on the far left of the periodic table have smaller electron affinities and gain electrons less easily.
  B. Main group elements in the middle of the periodic table neither lose or gain electrons easily.
II. Formation of ionic compounds (Sections 3.3–3.5).
  A. Compounds formed between an element on the far left side of the periodic table and an element on the far right of the periodic table are electronically neutral (Section 3.3).
    1. These compounds consist of a large number of cations and anions packed together in a regular arrangement in a crystal.
    2. The bonds between ions in the crystal are known as ionic bonds.
    3. The crystal is known as an ionic solid.
  B. Properties of ionic compounds (Section 3.4).
    1. Ionic compounds are crystalline.
    2. Solutions of ionic compounds conduct electricity.
    3. Ionic compounds are high-melting.
    4. Many, but not all, ionic compounds are water-soluble.
  C. The octet rule (Section 3.5).
    1. Main group elements undergo reactions that leave them with eight valence electrons – an octet.
III. Ions of some common elements (Sections 3.6–3.8).
  A. Cations (Section 3.6).

    1. Group 1A $M\cdot \longrightarrow M^+ + e^-$

    2. Group 2A $\cdot M \cdot \longrightarrow M^{2+} + 2e^-$

    3. Group 3A Al^{3+} is the only common cation.
    4. Transition metals form cations, but the charge on these cations is not as predictable as it is for main group elements.

B. Anions.

1. Group 6A $:\ddot{X}: + \ 2e^- \longrightarrow \ :\ddot{\underset{..}{X}}:^{2-}$

2. Group 7A $:\ddot{X}: + \ e^- \longrightarrow \ :\ddot{\underset{..}{X}}:^{-}$

C. Group 4A, group 5A, and group 8A elements don't usually form cations or anions.
D. Naming ions (Section 3.7).
   1. Main group cations are named by identifying the metal and then adding the word "ion."
   2. Transition metal cations are named by identifying the metal, specifying the charge, and adding the word "ion."
   3. Anions are named by replacing the end of the name of the element with -*ide* and adding the word "ion."
   4. Polyatomic ions (Section 3.8).
      a. Polyatomic ions are composed of more than one atom.
      b. Subscripts in polyatomic ions indicate how many of each ion are present in the formula unit (no subscripts are necessary if only one ion is present).
      c. The names of polyatomic ions should be memorized.
IV. Ionic compounds (Sections 3.9–3.11).
  A. Formulas of ionic compounds (Section 3.9).
   1. Formulas are written so that the number of positive charges equals the number of negative charges.
      a. Cations are listed first, anions second.
      b. It is not necessary to write the charges of the ions.
      c. Use parentheses around a polyatomic ion if it has a subscript.
   2. A formula unit shows the simplest neutral unit of an ionic compound.
  B. Naming ionic compounds (Section 3.10).
   1. Ionic compounds are named by citing the cation and then the anion, with a space between the two words.
   2. If the cation can exhibit more than one charge, the charge must be specified.
  C. Acids and bases (Section 3.11).
   1. Acids are compounds that provide H^+ ions in solution.
   2. Bases are compounds that provide OH^- ions in solution.
   3. Some acids and bases can each provide more than one H^+ or OH^- ion in solution.

Solutions to Chapter 3 Problems

3.1   The Mg^{2+} ion is a cation.

3.2   The S^{2-} ion is an anion.

3.3   The ion shown, O^{-2}, is an anion because it has two more negative charges than positive charges.

3.4   Figure 3.1 shows approximate ionization energies for helium, neon, argon and krypton. In line with this trend, it is predicted that the ionization energy of xenon should be somewhat less than that of krypton but greater than the ionization energy of most other elements.

3.5   (a) According to Figure 3.1, B ($Z = 5$) loses an electron more easily than Be ($Z = 4$).
(b) Ca ($Z = 20$) loses an electron more easily than Co ($Z = 27$).
(c) Sc ($Z = 21$) loses an electron more easily than Se($Z = 34$).

3.6   (a) According to Figure 3.1, H gains an electron more easily than He. Because the electron affinity for He is zero, it does not accept an electron.
(b) S gains an electron more easily than Si.
(c) Cr gains an electron more easily than Mn.

3.7   *Ionic liquids:*   *Other ionic substances:*
Liquid or low-melting at room temperature   High-melting solids
High viscosity   Low viscosity
Low to moderate electrical conductivity   Highly conducting if molten or in solution

3.8   Potassium (atomic number 19): $1s^2\,2s^2\,2p^6\,3s^2\,3p^6\,4s^1$
Argon (atomic number 18): $1s^2\,2s^2\,2p^6\,3s^2\,3p^6$
Potassium can attain the noble-gas configuration of argon by losing an electron from its $4s$ subshell, forming the K^+ cation.

3.9   Aluminum (atomic number 13): $1s^2\,2s^2\,2p^6\,3s^2\,3p^1$
Neon (atomic number 10): $1s^2\,2s^2\,2p^6$
Aluminum can attain the noble-gas configuration of neon by losing three electrons, two from its $3s$ subshell and one from its $3p$ subshell, resulting in the formation of the Al^{3+} ion.

3.10

$$X{:} \;+\; {:}\ddot{Y}{:} \;\longrightarrow\; X^{2+} \;+\; {:}\ddot{\underset{..}{Y}}{:}^{\,2-}$$

Y gains electrons, and X loses electrons.

3.11   Molybdenum, a transition metal, is more likely to form a cation than an anion.

3.12

(a) $:\!\dot{\ddot{Se}}\!\cdot \;+\; 2\,e^- \;\longrightarrow\; :\!\ddot{\underset{..}{Se}}\!:^{\,2-}$; $Se \;+\; 2\,e^- \;\longrightarrow\; Se^{2-}$

(b) $\cdot Ba \cdot \;\longrightarrow\; Ba^{2+} \;+\; 2\,e^-$; $Ba \;\longrightarrow\; Ba^{2+} \;+\; 2\,e^-$

(c) $:\!\ddot{Br}\!\cdot \;+\; e^- \;\longrightarrow\; :\!\ddot{\underset{..}{Br}}\!:^{-}$; $Br \;+\; e^- \;\longrightarrow\; Br^-$

3.13
$$\frac{1\ L}{35\ g} \;\times\; \frac{454\ g}{1\ lb} \;\times\; \frac{1\ gal}{3.79\ L} \;=\; \frac{3.4\ gal}{1\ lb}$$

3.14   (a) Cu^{2+} copper(II) ion (cupric ion)   (b) F^- fluoride ion
(c) Mg^{2+} magnesium ion   (d) S^{2-} sulfide ion

3.15   (a) Ag^+ (b) Fe^{2+} (c) Cu^+ (d) Te^{2-}

3.16 Na^+ sodium ion; K^+ potassium ion;
Ca^{2+} calcium ion; Cl^- chloride ion

3.17 (a) NO_3^- nitrate ion   (b) CN^- cyanide ion
(c) OH^- hydroxide ion   (d) HPO_4^{2-} hydrogen phosphate ion

3.18 *Group 1A*: Na^+, K^+ *Group 2A*: Mg^{2+}, Ca^{2+}
Transition metal: Fe^{2+} *Halogen*: Cl^-

3.19 (a) The two ions are Ag^+ and I^-. Since they have the same charge, only one of each ion is needed. The formula is AgI.
(b) Ions: Ag^+, O^{2-}. Two Ag^+ ions will balance the O^{2-} ion. The formula is Ag_2O.
(c) The ions are Ag^+ and PO_4^{3-}. Three Ag^+ ions are needed to balance the charge of the PO_4^{3-} anion. The formula is Ag_3PO_4.

3.20 (a) Na_2SO_4 (b) $FeSO_4$ (c) $Cr_2(SO_4)_3$

3.21 $(NH_4)_2CO_3$

3.22 $Al_2(SO_4)_3$ $Al(CH_3CO_2)_3$

3.23 Use the periodic table to identify the elements present and use the rules described in Section 3.10 to write the formulas. The formulas are K_2S (blue), $BaBr_2$ (red), and Al_2O_3 (green).

3.24 Since there are three calcium ions for every two nitride ions, the formula is Ca_3N_2. Calcium ion has a +2 charge, and nitride ion has a –3 charge.

3.25 Ag_2S—silver(I) sulfide. The charge on silver is +1.

3.26 (a) SnO_2 tin(IV) oxide   (b) $Ca(CN)_2$ calcium cyanide
(c) Na_2CO_3 sodium carbonate   (d) Cu_2SO_4 copper(I) sulfate
(e) $Ba(OH)_2$ barium hydroxide   (f) $Fe(NO_3)_2$ iron(II) nitrate

3.27 (a) Li_3PO_4 (b) $CuCO_3$ (c) $Al_2(SO_3)_3$ (d) CuF (e) $Fe_2(SO_4)_3$ (f) NH_4Cl

3.28 Cr_2O_3 chromium(III) oxide

3.29 Acids provide H^+ ions when dissolved in water.
Bases provide OH^- ions when dissolved in water.

Acids: HF $\xrightarrow{\text{dissolve in water}}$ H^+ + F^-

           HCN $\xrightarrow{\text{dissolve in water}}$ H^+ + CN^-

Bases: $Ca(OH)_2$ $\xrightarrow{\text{dissolve in water}}$ Ca^{2+} + $2\ OH^-$

           $LiOH$ $\xrightarrow{\text{dissolve in water}}$ Li^+ + OH^-

3.30 Solution (a) represents HCl; the drawing shows that there are equal numbers of cations and anions in solution. Solution (b) represents H_2SO_4; two cations are present for each anion.

Understanding Key Concepts

3.31

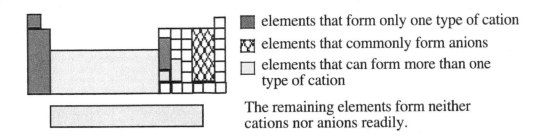

■ elements that form only one type of cation

▨ elements that commonly form anions

□ elements that can form more than one type of cation

The remaining elements form neither cations nor anions readily.

3.32

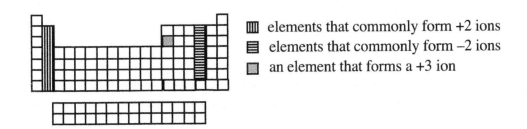

▥ elements that commonly form +2 ions

▤ elements that commonly form –2 ions

▨ an element that forms a +3 ion

3.33   Drawing (a) shows an ion that has two more electrons than protons and thus represents an O^{2-} ion.
Drawing (b) represents Na^+, an ion with one more proton than electron.
(c) Ca^{2+} (d) Fe^{2+}

3.34   Drawing (a) represents a sodium atom, and drawing (b) represents an Na^+ ion. The Na atom is larger because its $3s$ electron lies in an orbital that is farther from the nucleus.

3.35   Drawing (a) represents a chlorine atom, and drawing (b) represents a Cl^- anion. The anion is larger because its extra electron is not as tightly held by the positively charged nucleus as are the electrons of the atom.

3.36 $FeCl_2$: iron (II) chloride or ferrous chloride $FeCl_3$: iron (III) chloride or ferric chloride
FeO: iron (II) oxide or ferrous oxide Fe_2O_3: iron (III) oxide or ferric oxide
$PbCl_2$: lead (II) chloride $PbCl_4$: lead (IV) chloride
PbO: lead (II) oxide PbO_2: lead (IV) oxide

3.37   Use the ratios of atoms to assign answers. Picture (a) represents ZnS, because one cation is present for each anion. Picture (b) represents $PbBr_2$, (c) represents CrF_3, and (d) represents Al_2O_3.

Ions and Ionic Bonding

3.38   (a) $Ca \rightarrow Ca^{2+} + 2\,e^-$ (b) $Au \rightarrow Au^+ + e^-$
       (c) $F + e^- \rightarrow F^-$ (d) $Cr \rightarrow Cr^{3+} + 3\,e^-$

3.39   (a) P^{3-} $1s^2\,2s^2\,2p^6\,3s^2\,3p^6$ (b) Li^+ $1s^2$
       (c) Co^{2+} $1s^2\,2s^2\,2p^6\,3s^2\,3p^6\,4s^2\,3d^5$
       (d) Tl^{3+} $1s^2\,2s^2\,2p^6\,3s^2\,3p^6\,4s^2\,3d^{10}\,4p^6\,5s^2\,4d^{10}\,5p^6\,4f^{14}\,5d^{10}$

3.40   (a) False. A cation is formed by *loss* of one or more electrons from an atom. (b), (c) False. Group 4A elements rarely form ions. (d) True.

3.41   (a) False. Ions have a regular arrangement in ionic solids.   (b) False. Ions vary in size.
       (c) True.   (d) False. Ionic solids have high melting points and boiling points.

Ions and the Octet Rule

3.42   The *octet rule* states that main group atoms undergo reactions in order to achieve a noble gas electron configuration with eight outer-shell electrons.

3.43   Electrons belonging to hydrogen and helium occupy the first shell, which can hold only two electrons. Thus, even though H^- has the configuration of a noble gas (He), it can't have an electron octet.

3.44 Se^{2-} An ion with 34 protons and 36 electrons has a –2 charge.

3.45 Sc^{2+} An ion with 21 protons and 19 electrons has a +2 charge.

3.46   (a) $X^{2+} = Sr^{2+}$; $X = Sr$ The strontium ion has the same electron configuration as the noble gas krypton.
       (b) $X^- = Br^-$; $X = Br$ The bromide ion also has the same electron configuration as the noble gas krypton.

3.47 $Z^{3+} = Ga^{3+}$; $Z = Ga$. The Z^{3+} cation has 31 protons and 28 electrons.

3.48   (a) Rb^+ $1s^2\,2s^2\,2p^6\,3s^2\,3p^6\,4s^2\,3d^{10}\,4p^6$
       (b) Br^- $1s^2\,2s^2\,2p^6\,3s^2\,3p^6\,4s^2\,3d^{10}\,4p^6$
       (c) S^{2-} $1s^2\,2s^2\,2p^6\,3s^2\,3p^6$
       (d) Ba^{2+} $1s^2\,2s^2\,2p^6\,3s^2\,3p^6\,4s^2\,3d^{10}\,4p^6\,5s^2\,4d^{10}\,5p^6$
       (e) Al^{3+} $1s^2\,2s^2\,2p^6$

3.49   (a) Ca^{2+} (b) O^{2-} (c) Ti^{2+} (d) K^+ (e) Al^{3+}

Periodic Properties and Ion Formation

3.50   (a) O   (b) Li   (c) Zn   (d) N

3.51   (a) S   (b) I   (c) Br

3.52 None of the ions are stable because all lack eight outer-shell electrons.

3.53 (a) Magnesium forms only the Mg^{2+} cation.
(b) Tin forms both the Sn^{2+} and Sn^{4+} cations.
(c) Mercury forms Hg_2^{2+} and Hg^{2+} cations.
(d) Al forms the Al^{3+} cation.

3.54 Cr^{2+}: $1s^2\,2s^2\,2p^6\,3s^2\,3p^6\,3d^4$
Cr^{3+}: $1s^2\,2s^2\,2p^6\,3s^2\,3p^6\,3d^3$

3.55 Co : $1s^2\,2s^2\,2p^6\,3s^2\,3p^6\,3d^7\,4s^2$
Co^{2+}: $1s^2\,2s^2\,2p^6\,3s^2\,3p^6\,3d^7$
Co^{3+}: $1s^2\,2s^2\,2p^6\,3s^2\,3p^6\,3d^6$

3.56 The ionization energy of Li^+ is much greater than that of Li. Li readily loses an electron to form an ion with eight outer-shell electrons, but Li^+ would need to lose one electron from a stable octet in order to form the Li^{2+} cation.

3.57 (a) $K \rightarrow K^+ + e^-$ loss of an electron by K
$K^+ + e^- \rightarrow K$ gain of an electron by K^+
(b) The second equation is the reverse of the first equation.
(c) Ionization energy of $K = -$ (electron affinity of K^+)

Symbols, Formulas, and Names for Ions

3.58 (a) S^{2-} sulfide ion (b) Sn^{2+} tin(II) ion (c) Sr^{2+} strontium ion
(d) Mg^{2+} magnesium ion (e) Au^+ gold(I) ion

3.59 (a) Cr^{2+} chromous ion chromium(II) ion
(b) Fe^{3+} ferric ion iron(III) ion
(c) Hg^{2+} mercuric ion mercury(II) ion

3.60 (a) Se^{2-} (b) O^{2-} (c) Ag^+

3.61 (a) Fe^{2+} (b) Sn^{4+} (c) Pb^{2+} (d) Cr^{3+}

3.62 (a) OH^- (b) HSO_4^- (c) $CH_3CO_2^-$ (d) MnO_4^- (e) OCl^- (f) NO_3^-
(g) CO_3^{2-} (h) $Cr_2O_7^{2-}$

3.63 (a) NO_2^- nitrite ion (b) CrO_4^{2-} chromate ion
(c) NH_4^+ ammonium ion (d) HPO_4^{2-} hydrogen phosphate ion

Names and Formulas for Ionic Compounds

3.64 (a) $Al_2(SO_4)_3$ (b) Ag_2SO_4 (c) $ZnSO_4$ (d) $BaSO_4$

3.65 (a) $SrCO_3$ (b) $Fe_2(CO_3)_3$ (c) $(NH_4)_2CO_3$ (d) $Sn(CO_3)_2$

3.66 (a) NaF (b) KNO_3 (c) $CaCO_3$ (d) NH_4NO_3

3.67 (a) C (b) $CuSO_4$ (c) Na_3PO_4

3.68

	S^{2-}	Cl^-	PO_4^{3-}	CO_3^{2-}
Copper(II)	CuS	$CuCl_2$	$Cu_3(PO_4)_2$	$CuCO_3$
Ca^{2+}	CaS	$CaCl_2$	$Ca_3(PO_4)_2$	$CaCO_3$
NH_4^+	$(NH_4)_2S$	NH_4Cl	$(NH_4)_3PO_4$	$(NH_4)_2CO_3$
Ferric ion	Fe_2S_3	$FeCl_3$	$FePO_4$	$Fe_2(CO_3)_3$

3.69

	O^{2-}	HSO_4^-	HPO_4^{2-}	$C_2O_4^{2-}$
K^+	K_2O	$KHSO_4$	K_2HPO_4	$K_2C_2O_4$
Ni^{2+}	NiO	$Ni(HSO_4)_2$	$NiHPO_4$	NiC_2O_4
NH_4^+	$(NH_4)_2O$	NH_4HSO_4	$(NH_4)_2HPO_4$	$(NH_4)_2C_2O_4$
Chromous	CrO	$Cr(HSO_4)_2$	$CrHPO_4$	CrC_2O_4

3.70

copper(II) sulfide	copper(II) chloride	copper(II) phosphate	copper(II) carbonate
calcium sulfide	calcium chloride	calcium phosphate	calcium carbonate
ammonium sulfide	ammonium chloride	ammonium phosphate	ammonium carbonate
ferric sulfide	ferric chloride	ferric phosphate	ferric carbonate

3.71

potassium oxide	potassium bisulfate	potassium hydrogen phosphate	potassium oxalate
nickel(II) oxide	nickel(II) bisulfate	nickel(II) hydrogen phosphate	nickel(II) oxalate
ammonium oxide	ammonium bisulfate	ammonium hydrogen phosphate	ammonium oxalate
chromous oxide	chromous bisulfate	chromous hydrogen phosphate	chromous oxalate

3.72   (a) $MgCO_3$ magnesium carbonate   (b) $Ca(CH_3CO_2)_2$ calcium acetate
(c) $AgCN$ silver(I) cyanide   (d) $Na_2Cr_2O_7$ sodium dichromate

3.73   (a) $Fe(OH)_2$ iron(II) hydroxide   (b) $KMnO_4$ potassium permanganate
(c) Na_2CrO_4 sodium chromate   (d) $Ba_3(PO_4)_2$ barium phosphate

3.74 $Ca_3(PO_4)_2$ (d) is the correct formula because the six positive charges from the three Ca^{2+} ions are balanced by the six negative charges of the two PO_4^{3-} ions.

3.75   (a) $Al_2(SO_4)_3$ (b) $(NH_4)_3PO_4$ (c) Rb_2SO_4

Acids and Bases

3.76   An acid provides H^+ ions when dissolved in water. A base provides OH^- ions when dissolved in water.

3.77   Acids: H_2CO_3, HCN
Bases: $Mg(OH)_2$, KOH

3.78

(a) $H_2CO_3 \xrightarrow{\text{dissolve in water}} 2\,H^+ + CO_3^{2-}$

(b) $HCN \xrightarrow{\text{dissolve in water}} H^+ + CN^-$

(c) $Mg(OH)_2$ $\xrightarrow{\text{dissolve in water}}$ Mg^{2+} +   2 OH^-

(d)   KOH $\xrightarrow{\text{dissolve in water}}$ K^+ + OH^-

3.79 (a) carbonate anion   (b) cyanide anion

Chemistry in Action

3.80 The bulky cations can't pack in an orderly way and thus don't crystallize at room temperature.

3.81 They are nonvolatile (important in a very low-pressure environment), viscous (allowing them to be coated with a thin metallic film to form a parabolic reflective surface), and inexpensive (relative to the cost of a conventional lens).

3.82 The RDI for sodium is 2300 mg, which is equivalent to 4 g of table salt.

3.83 Most of the calcium present in the body is found in bones and teeth.

3.84 Sodium protects against fluid loss and is necessary for muscle contraction and transmission of nerve impulses.

3.85 Fe^{2+} is a component of hemoglobin, which is responsible for transport of oxygen in the blood.

3.86

Ion	Name	Charge	Total Charge
Ca^{2+}	calcium ion	2+	10 x (2+) = 20+
PO_4^{3-}	phosphate ion	3–	6 x (3–) = 18–
OH^-	hydroxide ion	1–	2 x (1–) = 2–

The formula correctly represents a neutral compound because the number of positive charges equals the number of negative charges.

3.87 $Ca_{10}(PO_4)_6(OH)_2$ + 2 F^- → $Ca_{10}(PO_4)_6F_2$ + 2 OH^-

General Questions and Problems

3.88 The hydride ion has the same electron configuration ($1s^2$) as the noble gas helium.

3.89 The H^- ion has a stable noble gas configuration, but the Li^- ion doesn't and is thus likely to be unstable. (Notice in Figure 3.1 that the electron affinity of Li is very small, indicating that Li is unlikely to gain an electron to form Li^-.)

3.90 (a) CrO_3 (b) VCl_5 (c) MnO_2 (d) MoS_2

3.91 H_3AsO_4

3.92 (a) A gluconate ion has one negative charge.
(b) Three gluconate ions are in one formula unit of iron(III) gluconate, and the formula is Fe(gluconate)$_3$.

3.93 (a) Cu_3PO_4 copper(I) phosphate   (b) Na_2SO_4 sodium sulfate
(c) MnO_2 manganese(IV) oxide   (d) $AuCl_3$ gold(III) chloride
(e) $Pb(CO_3)_2$ lead(IV) carbonate   (f) Ni_2S_3 nickel(III) sulfide

3.94 (a) $Co(CN)_2$ (b) UO_3 (c) $SnSO_4$ (d) MnO_2 (e) K_3PO_4 (f) Ca_3P_2
(g) $LiHSO_4$ (h) $Al(OH)_3$

3.95

Ion	Protons	Electrons	Neutrons
(a) $^{16}O^{2-}$	8	10	8
(b) $^{89}Y^{3+}$	39	36	50
(c) $^{133}Cs^+$	55	54	78
(d) $^{81}Br^-$	35	36	46

3.96 (a) X is likely to be a metal, because metals are more likely to form cations.
(b) Y is likely to be a nonmetal.
(c) The formula for the product is X_2Y_3.
(d) X is likely to be in Group 3A or Group 3B (or to be a transition metal) and Y is likely to be in Group 6A.

3.97 (a) Mn^{4+} (b) Cu^+ (c) Ti^{4+}

Self-Test for Chapter 3

Multiple Choice

1. How many atoms does a formula unit of Li_2CO_3 contain?
(a) 3   (b) 4   (c) 5   (d) 6

2. How many ions are produced when a formula unit of Li_2CO_3 is dissolved in water?
(a) 3   (b) 4   (c) 5   (d) 6

3. Which of the following is not a property of ionic compounds?
(a) crystalline   (b) conductor of electricity   (c) high melting   (d) 1:1 ratio of cations to anions

4. Which of the following is the correct name for $Fe(NO_3)_3$?
(a) ferrous nitrate   (b) iron nitrate   (c) iron(III) nitrate   (d) iron(II) nitrate

5. Bromine has a:
(a) large ionization energy and large electron affinity   (b) large ionization energy and small electron affinity   (c) small ionization energy and large electron affinity   (d) small ionization energy and small electron affinity

6. H_2CrO_4 is an acid that:
    (a) can provide one H^+ ion when dissolved   (b) can provide two H^+ ions when dissolved
    (c) can provide one OH^- when dissolved   (d) H_2CrO_4 is not an acid.

7. An element that loses three electrons to attain the electron configuration of argon is:
    (a) titanium   (b) scandium   (c) calcium   (d) potassium

8. The formula for gold(III) chloride is:
    (a) Au_3Cl (b) $AuCl$ (c) $AuCl_2$ (d) $AuCl_3$

9. Which of the following anions is not biologically important?
    (a) Cl^- (b) Br^- (c) HCO_3^- (d) HPO_4^-

10. The redness of rubies is due to which ion?
    (a) iron   (b) titanium   (c) aluminum   (d) chromium

Sentence Completion

1. _____ _____ measures the ease with which an atom gives up an electron.

2. The name of K_3PO_4 is _____ _____.

3. Radium (atomic number 88) loses _____ electrons to achieve a noble gas configuration.

4. NO_3^- is an example of a _____ ion.

5. The formulas of ionic compounds are _____ formulas.

6. Atoms of main group elements tend to combine in chemical compounds so that they attain _____ outer-shell electrons.

7. A _____ provides OH^- ions in water.

8. _____ is the principal mineral component of bone.

9. Ionic compounds are usually _____ solids.

10. The first three elements in group ____A form neither cations nor anions.

True or False

1. Zinc can form ions with different charges.

2. Na^+ and F^- have the same electron configuration.

3. Ionization energy measures the amount of energy released when an ion is formed from a neutral atom.

4. $Co(CO_3)_2$ is a possible compound.

5. A solution of H_3PO_4 contains only H^+ and $H_2PO_4^-$ ions.

6. Ionic crystals conduct electricity.

7. Cuprous ion is the same as copper(II) ion.

8. Many ionic compounds are not water-soluble.

9. Group 5A consists of metals and nonmetals.

10. Elements in group 7A have the largest ionization energies.

11. The octet rule is limited to main group elements.

12. Both men and women suffer the same percent bone loss over their lifetimes.

Match each entry on the left with its partner on the right.

1.	$FeBr_2$	(a)	Sulfite anion
2.	S^{2-}	(b)	Electron-dot symbol
3.	NH_4^+	(c)	Alkali metal
4.	SO_3^{2-}	(d)	Has the same electron configuration as Na^+
5.	Ca	(e)	Iron(II) bromide
6.	$FeBr_3$	(f)	Transition metal
7.	Ar	(g)	Sulfate anion
8.	·Be·	(h)	Alkaline earth metal
9.	Co	(i)	Has the same electron configuration as Cl^-
10.	SO_4^{2-}	(j)	Iron(III) bromide
11.	Ne	(k)	Polyatomic cation
12.	K	(l)	Sulfide anion

Chapter 4   Molecular Compounds

Chapter Outline

I. Covalent bonds (Sections 4.1–4.4).
   A Formation of covalent bonds (Section 4.1).
      1. Covalent bonds occur when two atoms share electrons.
      2. Electron sharing results from the overlap of orbitals of two atoms.
      3. The optimum distance between nuclei of two atoms is the bond length.
      4. Seven elements exist as diatomic molecules: H_2, N_2, O_2, F_2, Cl_2, Br_2, I_2.
   B. Covalent bonds and the periodic table (Section 4.2).
      1. Molecular compounds result when atoms form covalent bonds to another atom or to more than one atom.
      2   The octet rule states that each atom in a molecular compound shares the number of electrons necessary to achieve a noble-gas configuration.
      3   Most main group elements form from one to four covalent bonds and obey the octet rule.
         a. Boron forms only three bonds because it has only three valence electrons.
         b. Sulfur and phosphorus may form five or six bonds if they use d orbitals.
   C. Multiple covalent bonds (Section 4.3).
      1. Some atoms can share more than one electron pair to form multiple bonds.
         a. A double bond is formed when two pairs are shared.
         b. A triple bond is formed when three pairs are shared.
      2. Even when multiple bonds occur, the atoms still obey the octet rule.
   D. Coordinate bonds occur when one atom donates both of the shared electrons (Section 4.4).
II. Molecular compounds (Sections 4.5–4.8).
   A. Characteristics of molecular compounds (Section 4.5).
      1. Molecular compounds are electrically neutral and have no charged particles.
      2. Molecular compounds have low melting and boiling points.
      3. Molecular compounds may be solids, liquids, or gases.
      4. Molecular compounds are usually insoluble in water and do not conduct electricity.
   B. Molecular formulas (Section 4.6).
      1. Molecular formulas show the numbers and kinds of atoms in one molecule of a compound.
      2. Structural formulas show how atoms are connected.
      3. Lewis structures are structural formulas that show electron lone pairs (Section 4.7).
         a. One approach to drawing Lewis structures involves knowing common bonding patterns.
         b. The other approach is a general method.
            i. Find the number of valence electrons for all atoms.
            ii. Draw a line between each pair of connected atoms to represent an electron pair.
            iii. Place lone pairs around all peripheral atoms to give them octets.
            iv. Place remaining electrons around the central atom.
            v. If the central atom doesn't have an octet, use an electron pair from a neighboring atom to form a multiple bond to the central atom.
      4. Some larger organic molecules are written as condensed structures.
   C. Molecular shapes can be predicted by using the VSEPR model (Section 4.8).
      1. Draw a Lewis structure of the molecule, and identify the atom whose geometry you want to know.
      2. Count the number of charge clouds around the atom.

3. Predict shape by assuming that the charge clouds orient in space so that they are as far apart as possible.
    a. If there are two charge clouds, the geometry is linear.
    b. If there are three charge clouds, the geometry is trigonal planar or bent.
    c. If there are four charge clouds, the geometry is tetrahedral, trigonal pyramidal, or bent.
III. Polar covalent bonds (Sections 4.9–4.11).
    A. Polar covalent bonds occur when the electrons in a covalent bond are attracted more to one atom than another (Section 4.9).
        1. The ability of an atom to attract electrons is called electronegativity.
        2. Atoms with electronegativity differences between 0.5 and 1.9 form polar covalent bonds.
        3. Atoms with electronegativity differences > 1.9 form ionic bonds.
    B. Molecules containing polar covalent bonds can be polar (Section 4.10).
        1. Molecular polarity depends on both the presence of polar covalent bonds and on molecular shape.
        2. Polarity has a dramatic effect on molecular properties.
    C. Naming binary molecular compounds (Section 4.11).
        1. The less electronegative element is always written first.
        2. Name the first element in the compound, using a prefix if necessary.
        3. Name the second element, using an *-ide* ending and using a prefix if necessary.

Solutions to Chapter 4 Problems

4.1

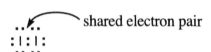 shared electron pair

Each iodine atom achieves the noble gas configuration of xenon.

4.2   (a) PH_3 hydrogen—one covalent bond;   phosphorus—three covalent bonds
            (b) H_2Se hydrogen—one covalent bond;   selenium—two covalent bonds
            (c) HCl   hydrogen—one covalent bond;   chlorine—one covalent bond
            (d) SiF_4 fluorine—one covalent bond;   silicon—four covalent bonds

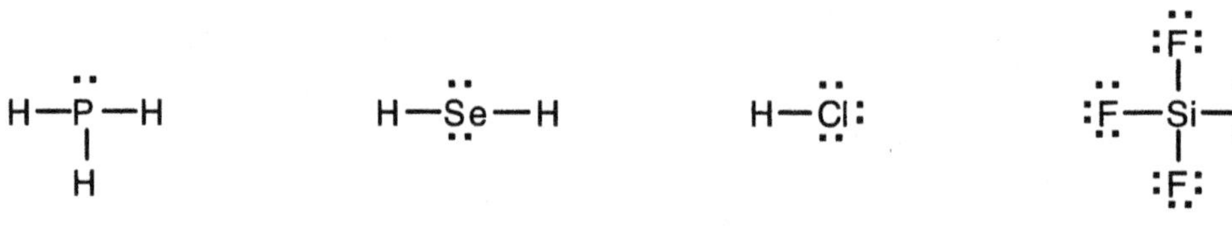

4.3   Lead is a member of group 4A and should form four covalent bonds, as do carbon and silicon. $PbCl_4$ is thus a more likely formula for a covalent compound, and $PbCl_2$ is the formula for an ionic compound.

4.4   (a) CH_2Cl_2. Carbon forms four covalent bonds. Two bonds form between carbon and hydrogen, and the other two form between carbon and chlorine.
            (b) BH_3. Boron forms three covalent bonds.
            (c) NI_3. Nitrogen forms three covalent bonds.
            (d) $SiCl_4$. Silicon, like carbon, forms four covalent bonds.

4.5   In acetic acid, all hydrogen atoms have two outer-shell electrons and all carbon and oxygen atoms have eight outer-shell electrons.

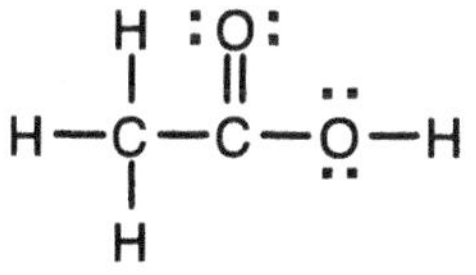

Acetic acid

4.6

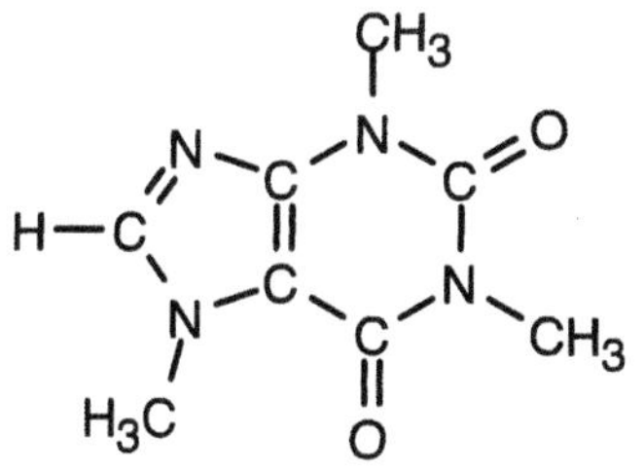

4.7 $AlCl_3$ is a covalent molecular compound, and Al_2O_3 is ionic.

4.8   C and N must be bonded to each other. After drawing the C—N bond and all bonds to hydrogens, two electrons remain; they are a lone pair on nitrogen. All atoms now have a noble gas configuration.

CH_5N: 14 valence electrons

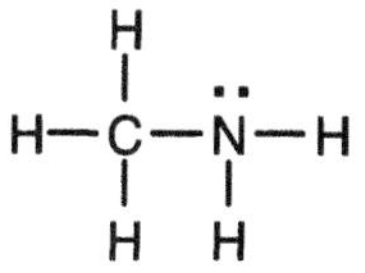

4.9

(a)

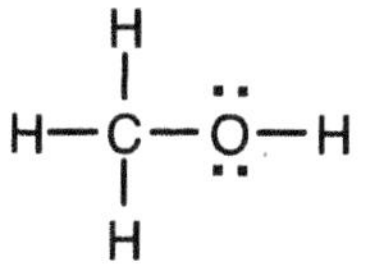

(b)

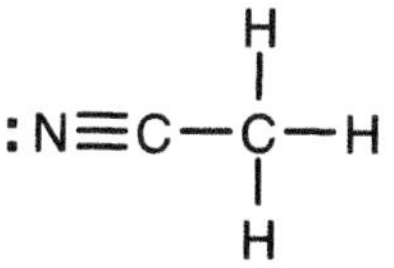

(c)

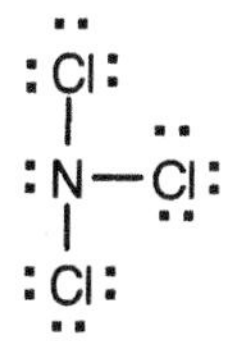

4.10   (a) For phosgene, $COCl_2$:

   Step 1:   Total valence electrons
   $4 \ e^-$ (from C) + $6 \ e^-$ (from O) + $2 \times 7 \ e^-$ (from Cl) = $24 \ e^-$

   Step 2:   Six electrons are involved in the covalent bonds.

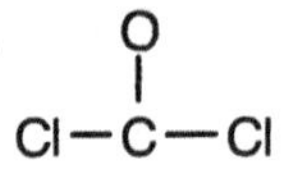

$$\begin{array}{c} O \\ | \\ Cl-C-Cl \end{array}$$

   Step 3:   The other 18 electrons are placed in nine lone pairs.

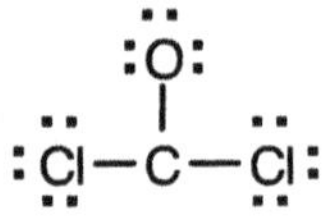

$$\begin{array}{c} :\ddot{O}: \\ | \\ :\ddot{C}l-C-\ddot{C}l: \end{array}$$

   Step 4:   All electrons are used up in the preceding structure, but carbon doesn't have an electron octet, so one electron pair must be moved from oxygen to form a carbon–oxygen double bond.

   Step 5:   The 24 electrons have been used up, and all atoms have a complete octet.

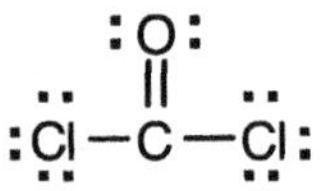

$$\begin{array}{c} :\ddot{O}: \\ \| \\ :\ddot{C}l-C-\ddot{C}l: \end{array}$$

(b) For OCl^-:

   Step 1:   Total valence electrons
   $6 \ e^-$ (from O) + $7 \ e^-$ (from Cl) + $1 \ e^-$ (negative charge) = $14 \ e^-$

   Step 2:   Two electrons used. O—Cl

   Step 3:   Twelve additional electrons used. $:\ddot{O}-\ddot{C}l:^-$

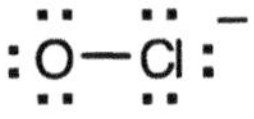

   Step 4:   The above structure uses 14 valence electrons, and all atoms have complete octets.

(c) For H_2O_2:

   Step 1: $2 \ e^-$ (from 2 H) + $2 \times 6 \ e^-$ (from O) = 14 electrons

   Step 2:   Six electrons are involved in covalent bonds.   H—O—O—H

   Step 3:   The other eight electrons are placed in four lone pairs. $H-\ddot{O}-\ddot{O}-H$

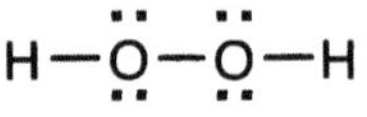

   Step 4:   The 14 electrons have been used up, and all atoms have complete octets.

(d) For SCl_2: 20 electrons

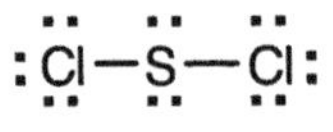

$$:\ddot{C}l-\ddot{S}-\ddot{C}l:$$

4.11

HNO$_3$:   24 electrons

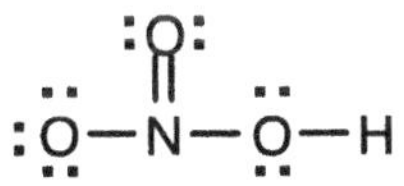

4.12   (a) The molecular formula for methyl methacrylate is C$_6$H$_{10}$O$_2$.
(b) Methyl methacrylate has two double bonds and four electron lone pairs.

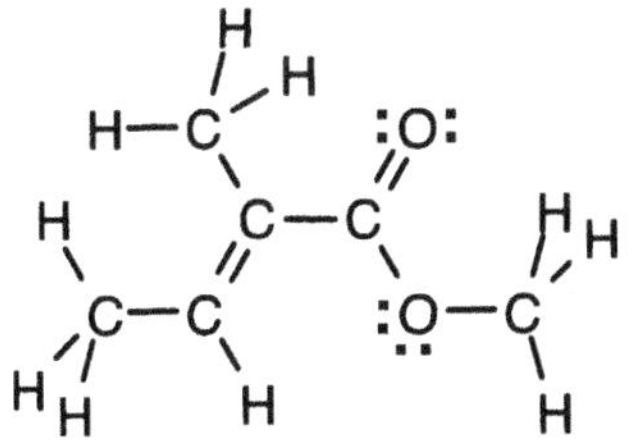

Methyl methacrylate

4.13

CO is reactive because it can form coordinate covalent bonds with compounds that can accept an electron pair. NO is reactive because it has an unpaired electron.

4.14

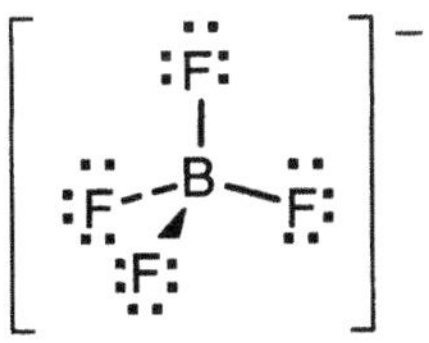

tetrahedral

4.15   Carbon, the central atom, is surrounded by four bonds. Referring to Table 4.2, we see that chloroform has tetrahedral geometry.

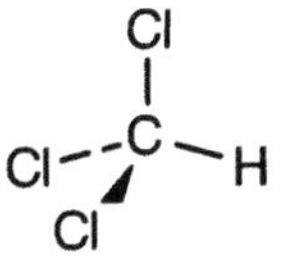

Chloroform

Each carbon of dichloroethylene is surrounded by three charge clouds. Dichloroethylene is planar, with 120° bond angles.

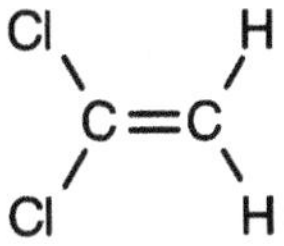

Dichloroethylene

4.16 The geometry at (a) is tetrahedral, and the geometry at (b) is trigonal planar.

4.17 Both molecules are bent and have bond angles of approximately 90°.

4.18

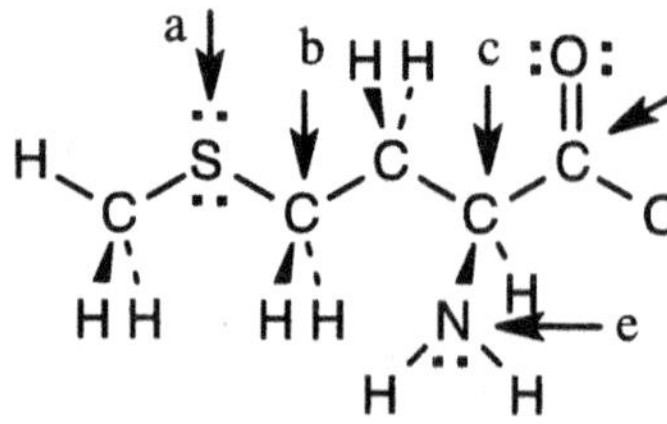

Methionine

a. bent
b. tetrahedral
c. tetrahedral
d. trigonal planar
e. pyramidal

4.19 Use Figure 4.6 to predict electronegativity:

Least electronegative – – – – – – – –> *Most electronegative*

H (2.1), P (2.1) < S (2.5) < N (3.0) < O (3.5)

4.20

Electronegativity	Difference	Type of Bond
(a) I (2.5), Cl (3.0)	0.5	polar covalent
(b) Li (1.0), O (3.5)	2.5	ionic
(c) Br (2.8), Br (2.8)	0	covalent
(d) P (2.1), Br (2.8)	0.7	polar covalent

(a) δ^+ δ^- (b)   (d) δ^+ δ^-
     I—Cl   Li$^+$ O$^-$ P —Br

The Br–Br bond (c) is nonpolar.

4.21

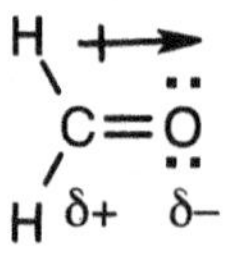

Formaldehyde is polar because of the polarity of the carbon–oxygen bond and because of the two electron lone pairs.

4.22 The —CH$_3$ portions of diethyl ether are tetrahedral. The C–O–C portion is bent and has a bond angle of 112°. The molecule has the indicated polarity because of the polar C–O bonds and because of the two lone pairs of electrons.

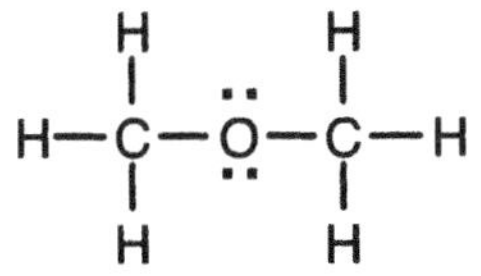

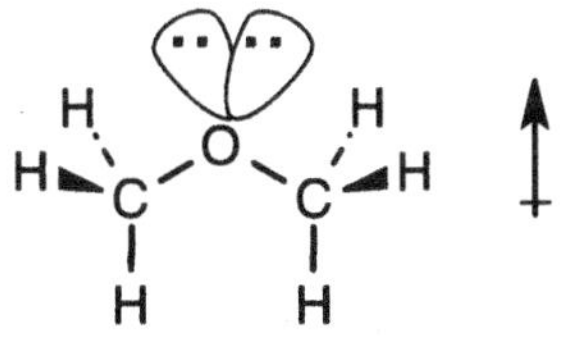

4.23

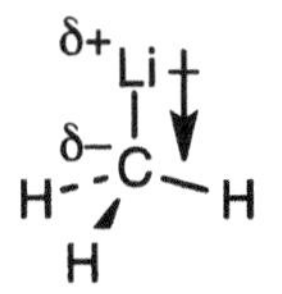

The difference in electronegativity between Li (1.0) and C (2.5) indicates that the bond between them is polar covalent, with carbon the more electronegative atom. The electrostatic potential map shows that carbon is electron-rich (red) and lithium is electron-poor (blue).

4.24 (a) S$_2$Cl$_2$ Disulfur dichloride   (b) ICl Iodine monochloride
(c) ICl$_3$ Iodine trichloride

4.25 (a) SeF$_4$ Selenium tetrafluoride   (b) P$_2$O$_5$ Diphosphorus pentoxide
(c) BrF$_3$ Bromine trifluoride

4.26

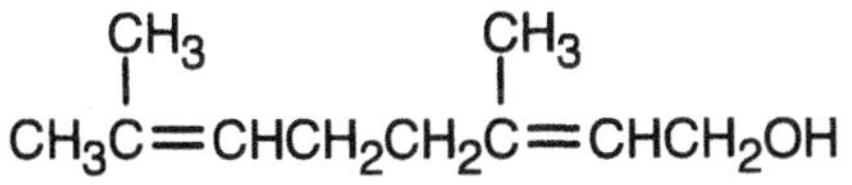

$$CH_3C{=}CHCH_2CH_2C{=}CHCH_2OH$$ Geraniol   C$_{10}$H$_{18}$O

(with CH$_3$ groups on the indicated carbons)

Understanding Key Concepts

4.27 (a) tetrahedral geometry   (b) pyramidal geometry   (c) trigonal planar geometry

4.28 All models except (c) represent a molecule with a tetrahedral central atom. In models (b) and (d), some atoms are hidden.

4.29

(a) (b)

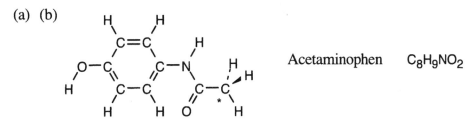

Acetaminophen   C$_8$H$_9$NO$_2$

(c) All carbons except for the starred carbon have trigonal planar geometry. The starred carbon has tetrahedral geometry. Nitrogen has pyramidal geometry.

4.30

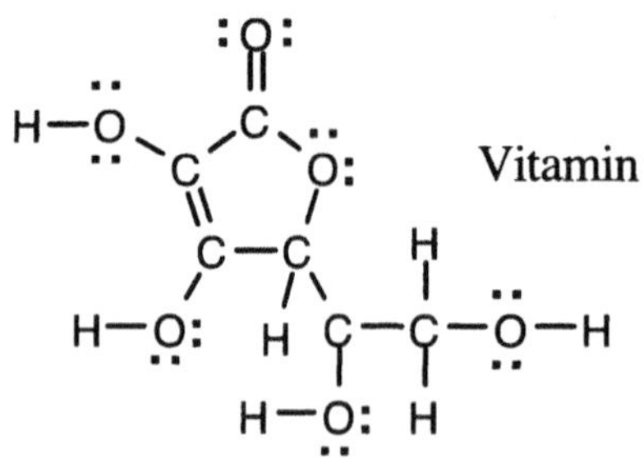

Vitamin C

4.31

(a) (b)

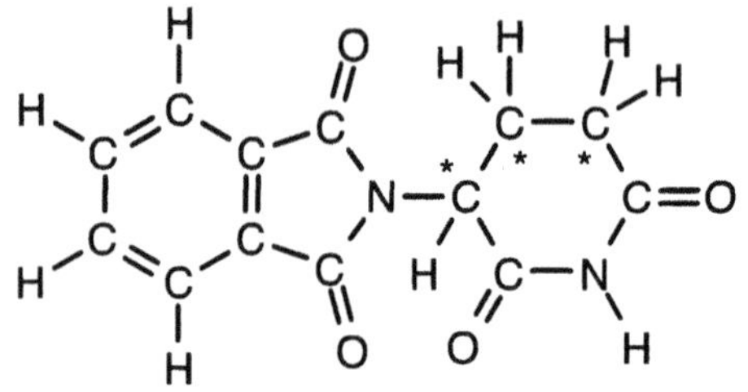

Thalidomide $C_{13}H_{10}N_2O_4$

(c) All carbons except for the starred carbons have trigonal planar geometry.
The starred carbons have tetrahedral geometry.
The nitrogens have pyramidal geometry.

4.32

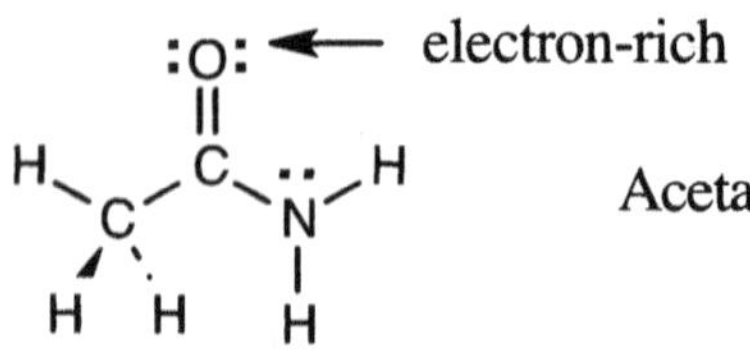

Acetamide

The electrostatic potential maps show that oxygen is the most electron-rich atom (red) in acetamide. The hydrogens are most electron-poor (blue).

Covalent Bonds

4.33 A covalent bond is a chemical bond in which two electrons are shared between two atoms. An ionic bond is formed by the attraction of a positively charged ion to a negatively charged ion. In an ionic bond, both electrons of the electron pair "belong" to the negatively charged ion.

4.34 In a covalent bond, each atom donates an electron to the bond. Both electrons in a coordinate covalent bond come from the same atom.

4.35 (a) oxygen: (i) (iv)   (b) potassium: (iii)   (c) phosphorus: (ii)
(d) iodine; (i) (iv)   (e) hydrogen: (i) (ii)   (f) cesium: (iii)

4.36 Form covalent bonds: (a) aluminum and bromine; (b) carbon and fluorine
Form ionic bonds: (c) cesium and iodine; (d) zinc and fluorine; (e) lithium and chlorine

4.37

4.38   Tellurium, a group 6A element, forms two covalent bonds, as do oxygen, sulfur, and other members of group 6A.

4.39   In the same group as nitrogen (5A), antimony is expected to form 3 covalent bonds. Thus, $SbCl_3$ is covalent, and $SbCl_5$ is ionic.

4.40   If the central atom is expected to form fewer bonds than appear in the formula, the compound probably contains a coordinate covalent bond.
Coordinate covalent bonds: (b) $Cu(NH_3)_4^{2+}$ (c) NH_4^+

4.41   Coordinate covalent bonds: (b) BF_4^- (c) H_3O^+

4.42   Since tin is a member of group 4A, it forms four covalent bonds. $SnCl_4$ is the most likely formula for a molecular compound of tin and chlorine.

4.43   A low-boiling, low-melting compound of gallium and chlorine is most likely covalent (ionic compounds are high-boiling and high-melting). Since gallium is a group 3A element, a likely formula is $GaCl_3$.

4.44   The indicated bond is coordinate covalent because both electrons in the bond come from nitrogen.

$$:N\equiv N-\overset{..}{\underset{..}{O}}:\quad\text{coordinate covalent}$$

4.45   The indicated bond is coordinate covalent because both electrons in the bond come from sulfur.

$$\begin{array}{c}:\overset{..}{O}:\\ |\longleftarrow\text{ coordinate covalent}\\ S\\ :\overset{..}{\underset{..}{Cl}}\qquad\overset{..}{\underset{..}{Cl}}:\end{array}$$

Structural Formulas

4.46   (a) A *molecular formula* shows the numbers and kinds of atoms in a molecule; a *structural formula* shows how the atoms in a molecule are bonded to one another.
(b) A *structural formula* shows the bonds between atoms; a *condensed structure* shows central atoms and the atoms connected to them written as groups but does not show bonds.
(c) A *lone pair* of valence electrons is a pair that is not shared; a *shared pair* of electrons is shared between two atoms as a covalent bond.

4.47   Two possible methods to distinguish between the compounds:
(a) Take the melting point of the two compounds. The covalent solid melts at a lower temperature.
(b) Try to dissolve the two solids in water. The ionic solid is more likely to be water-soluble than the covalent solid.

4.48   (a) N_2 10 valence electrons N_2 contains a triple bond.
          (b) NOCl   18 valence electrons   N and O are joined by a double bond.
          (c) CH_3CH_2CHO 24 valence electrons   C and O form a double bond.
          (d) OF_2 20 valence electrons

4.49

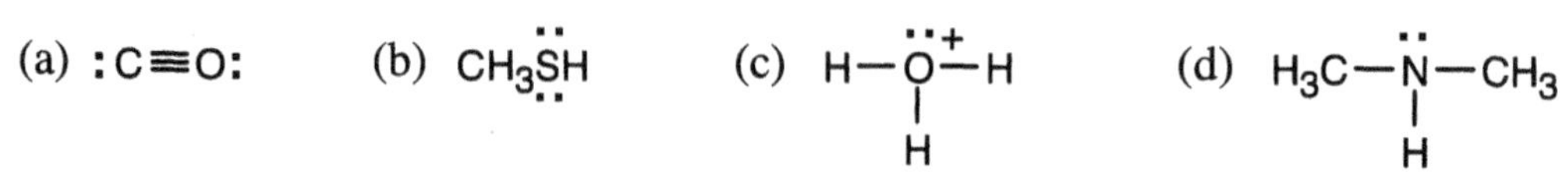

(a) :C≡O: (b) CH_3SH (c) H—O⁺—H   (d) H_3C—N—CH_3
                                    | |
                                    H   H

4.50   A compound with the formula C_2H_8 can't exist because any structure drawn would violate the rules of valence.

4.51   Structure (a) is reasonable. Structure (b) would be reasonable if there were a double bond between the two carbons bearing the –OH groups. Structure (c) would be reasonable if the hydrogen bonded to oxygen were moved to the carbon bearing the C=O double bond.

4.52

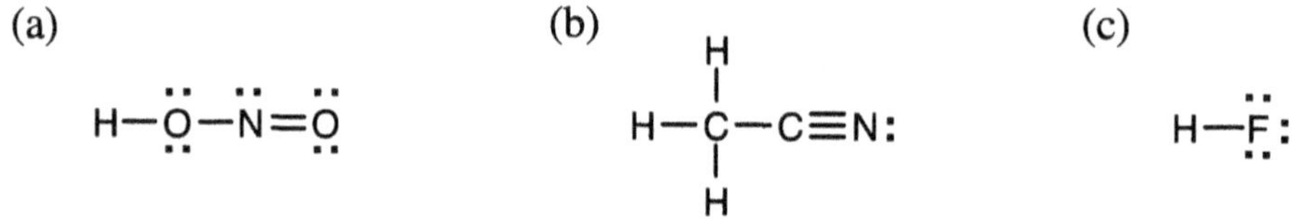

(a)   (b)   (c)

H—O—N=O   H—C—C≡N: H—F:
                                 |
                             H   H
                                 |
                                 H

4.53

$$\left[\begin{array}{c} :O: \\ \| \\ :O—N—O: \end{array} \right]^-$$

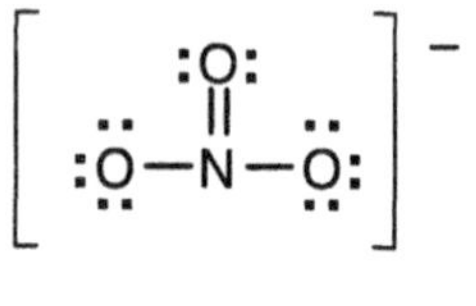

Three oxygen atoms and one nitrogen atom yield a total of 23 valence electrons. An additional electron is added so that the octet rule is satisfied for all atoms.

4.54   (a) $CH_3CH_2CH_3$ (b) $H_2C=CHCH_3$ (c) CH_3CH_2Cl

4.55

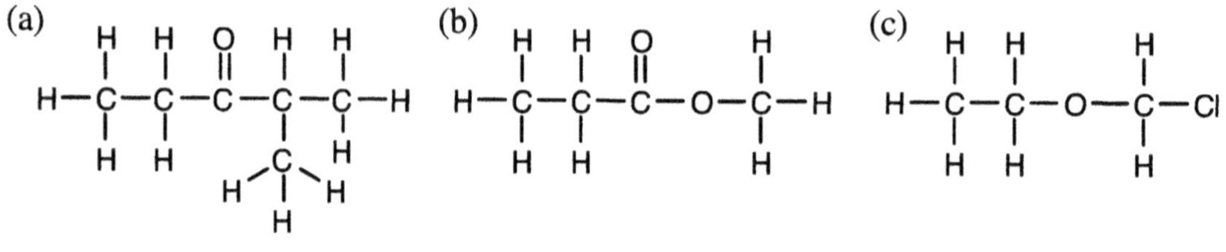

(a)   (b)   (c)

H H O H H   H H O   H   H H   H
| | ‖ | | | | ‖ | | | |
H—C—C—C—C—C—H   H—C—C—C—O—C—H   H—C—C—O—C—Cl
| | | | | | | | | |
H H   C H   H H   H   H H   H
        /|\
       H H H
         |
         H

4.56 CH_3COOH

Drawing Lewis Structures

4.57 Recall that in Section 4.2 it was stated that sulfur (and selenium) can form more than 4 covalent bonds.

(a)

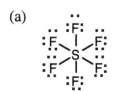

(b)

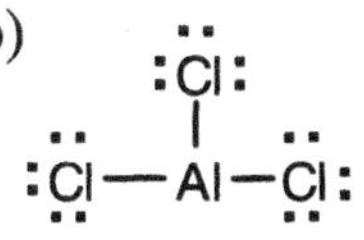

```
      ..
     :Cl:
      |    ..
:Cl — Al — Cl:
 ..          ..
```

(c)

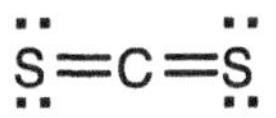

```
 ..          ..
 S = C = S
 ..          ..
```

(d)

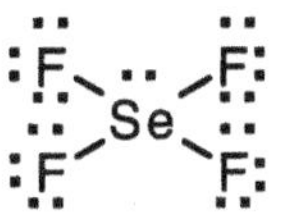

```
 ..           ..
:F     ..    F:
   \   ..   /
    Se
   /   ..   \
:F     ..    F:
 ..           ..
```

(e)

```
 ..              ..
:Cl — Be — Cl:
 ..              ..
```

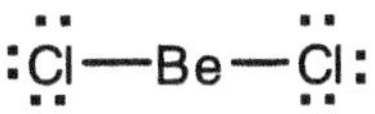

(f)

```
               :O:
                ||
         ..    ..    ..
  :O — N — N — O:
   ..    ..    ..
                ||
               :O:
```

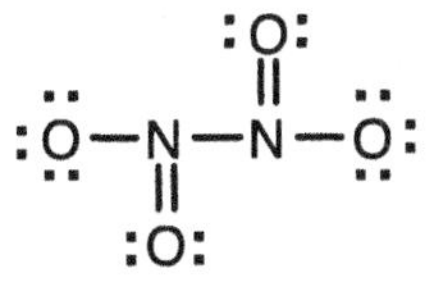

4.58

(a)

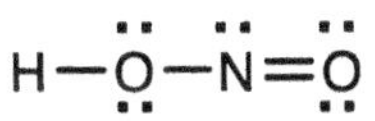

```
        ..    ..
H — O — N = O
        ..
```

(b)

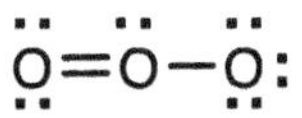

```
 ..    ..    ..
 O = O — O:
 ..    ..    ..
```

(c)

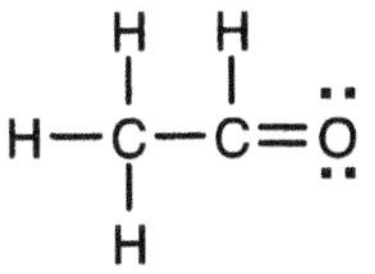

```
   H    H
   |    |    ..
H — C — C = O
   |         ..
   H
```

4.59

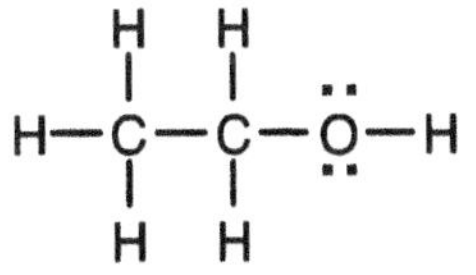

```
   H    H
   |    |   ..
H — C — C — O — H
   |    |   ..
   H    H
```

Ethanol

4.60

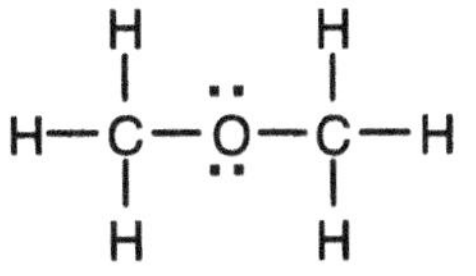

```
   H          H
   |          |
H — C — O — C — H
   |    ..    |
   H          H
```

Dimethyl ether

4.61

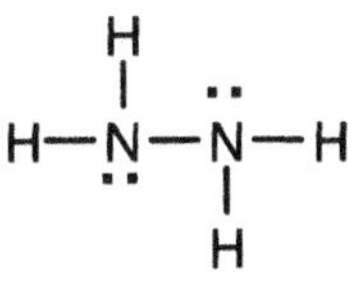

```
   H
   |    ..
H — N — N — H
   ..   |
        H
```

Hydrazine

4.62

```
 ..          ..
:Cl:        :Cl:
    \        /
     C = C
    /        \
:Cl:        :Cl:
 ..          ..
```

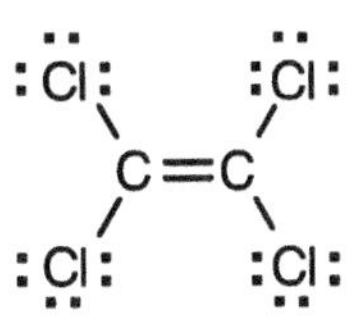

Tetrachloroethylene contains a double bond.

4.63

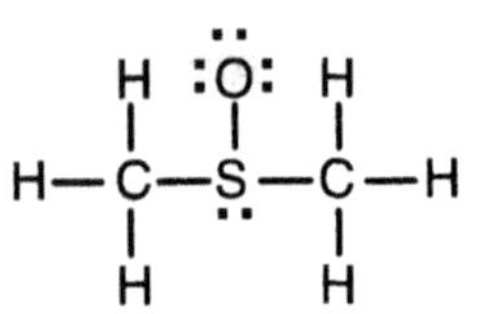

Dimethyl sulfoxide

4.64

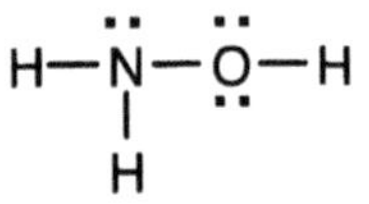

Hydroxylamine

4.65 Each atom of carbonate ion has 2 inner-shell electrons, plus the 24 electrons pictured, for a total of 32 electrons. Together, carbon and the three oxygens have 30 protons. Since there are two more electrons than protons, carbonate ion has a charge of –2.

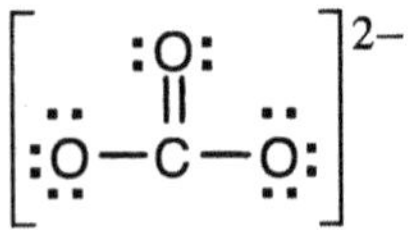

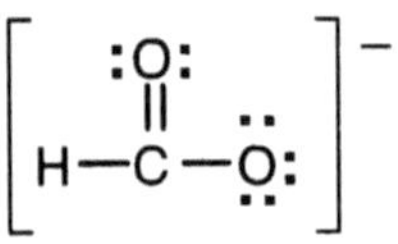

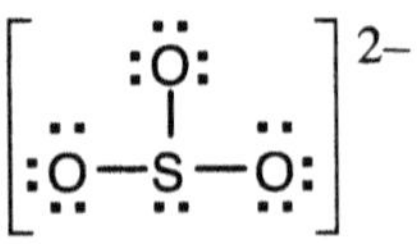

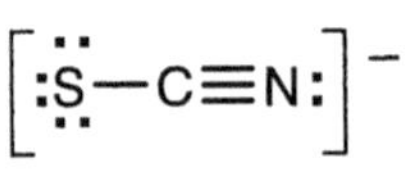

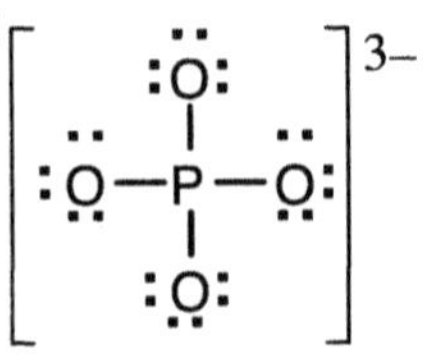

4.66

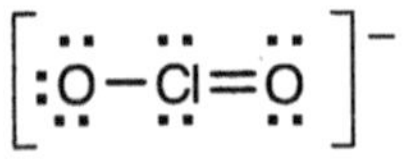

Molecular Geometry

4.67 Use Table 4.2 to predict molecular geometry. B equals the number of bonds, and E equals the number of electron lone pairs:

Molecule	Number of bonds	Number of Lone Pairs	Shape	Bond Angle
(a) AB_3	3	0	trigonal planar	120°
(b) AB_2E	2	1	bent	120°

4.68 As in the previous problem, use Table 4.2.

Molecule	Number of bonds	Number of Lone Pairs	Shape	Bond Angle
(a) AB_4	4	0	tetrahedral	109°
(b) AB_3E	3	1	pyramidal	109°
(c) AB_2E_2	2	2	bent	109°

4.69

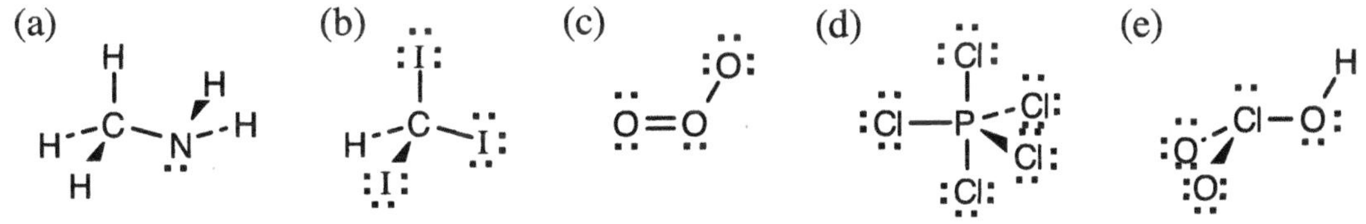

(a)   (b)   (c)   (d)   (e)

4.70

Molecule	Number of Bonding Pairs Around Central Atom	Number of Lone Pairs	Shape	Bond Angle
(a) SiF_4	4	0	tetrahedral	109°
(b) CF_2Cl_2	4	0	tetrahedral	109°
(c) SO_3	3*	0	trigonal planar	120°
(d) BBr_3	3	0	trigonal planar	120°
(e) NF_3	3	1	pyramidal	109°

* For determining shape, the double bond counts as one bond pair, and the number of bonds is three.

4.71

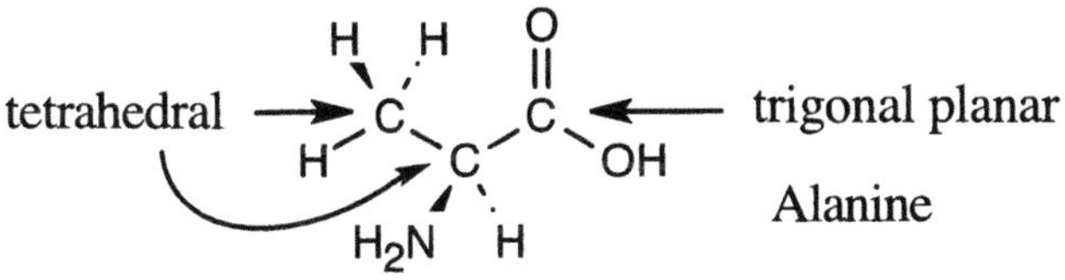

tetrahedral ⟶   ⟵ trigonal planar

Alanine

4.72

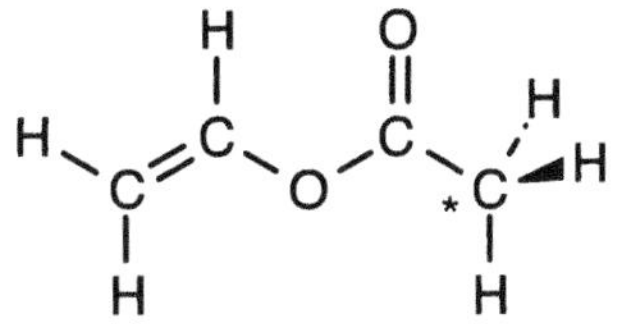

Vinyl acetate

All carbons are trigonal planar, except for the starred carbon, which is tetrahedral.

Polarity of Bonds and Molecules

4.73   The most electronegative elements are found on the upper right side of the periodic table. The least electronegative elements are found on the left side of the periodic table.

4.74   Using the periodic table, count up from element 114. Element 119 should occur under francium and accordingly should be one of the least electronegative elements, with an electronegativity of 0.8.

4.75   *Less electronegative   ———> More electronegative*
K < Be < Si < B < O

4.76   *More electronegative   ———> Less electronegative*
Cl > C > Cu > Ca > Cs

4.77

$\overset{\delta+\ \ \delta-}{\text{(a) I—Br}}$ $\overset{\delta-\ \ \delta+}{\text{(b) O—H}}$ $\overset{\delta+\ \ \delta-}{\text{(c) C—F}}$ $\overset{\delta-\ \ \delta+}{\text{(d) N—C}}$ (e) nonpolar

4.78   Bonds in (b), (c), and (d) are nonpolar.

$\overset{\delta-\ \ \delta+}{\text{(a) O—Cl}}$ $\overset{\delta+\ \ \delta-}{\text{(e) C—O}}$

4.79

Electronegativity		*Difference*	*Type of Bond*
(a) Be (1.5),	F (4.0)	2.5	ionic
(b) Ca (1.0),	Cl (3.0)	2.0	ionic
(c) O (3.5),	H (2.1)	1.4	polar covalent
(d) Be (1.5),	Br (2.8)	1.3	polar covalent

4.80   Use Figure 4.6 to determine bond polarities.

Least polar bonds   ———> Most polar bonds

PH_3 < HCl < H_2O < CF_4

4.81   Both compounds have dipole moments due to the lone pair electrons of the central atom. The dipole moment of NH_3 is greater because of the bond polarities of the three N–H bonds; the P–H bonds are nonpolar.

4.82

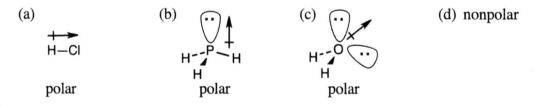

(a)   H–Cl   polar

(b)   H--P—H (with H below)   polar

(c)   H--O (with H below)   polar

(d) nonpolar

4.83

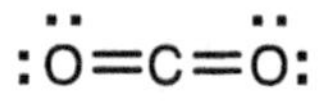

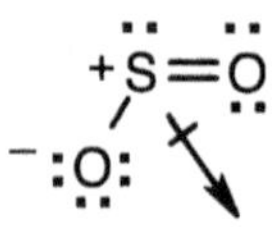

$:\overset{..}{O}=C=\overset{..}{O}:$ $^+S=\overset{..}{\underset{..}{O}}$, $^-:\overset{..}{\underset{..}{O}}:$

The bond polarities of the individual bonds cancel in CO_2, but bent geometry makes SO_2 polar.

4.84   Both molecules are polar because of the lone pair electrons. Water is more polar because the bonds between oxygen and hydrogen are polar covalent, but the bonds between sulfur and hydrogen are nonpolar.

Names and Formulas of Molecular Compounds

4.85 (a) PI_3 phosphorus triiodide   (b) $AsCl_3$ arsenic trichloride
(c) P_4S_3 tetraphosphorus trisulfide   (d) Al_2F_6 dialuminum hexafluoride
(e) N_2O_5 dinitrogen pentoxide   (f) $AsCl_5$ arsenic pentachloride

4.86 (a) SeO_2 selenium dioxide   (b) XeO_4 xenon tetroxide
(c) N_2S_5 dinitrogen pentasulfide   (d) P_3Se_4 triphosphorus tetraselenide

4.87 (a) NO_2 nitrogen dioxide   (b) SF_6 sulfur hexafluoride
(c) BrI_3 bromine triiodide   (d) N_2O_3 dinitrogen trioxide
(e) NI_3 nitrogen triiodide   (f) IF_7 iodine heptafluoride

4.88 (a) $SiCl_4$ silicon tetrachloride   (b) NaH sodium hydride
(c) SbF_5 antimony pentafluoride   (d) OsO_4 osmium tetroxide

Chemistry in Action

4.89 Carbon monoxide is reactive because its lone electron pair can form a coordinate covalent bond with another molecule.

4.90 A vasodilator is a chemical that relaxes arterial walls, causing a drop in blood pressure.

4.91 A polymer is formed of many repeating units contained in a long chain.

4.92 Carbohydrates, proteins, and DNA are all examples of polymers that occur in nature.

4.93 Chemical names are complicated because the name of each of the 20 million known chemicals must be unique and must contain enough information for chemists to identify the composition and structure of each chemical.

4.94 $(CH_3)_2C{=}CHCH_2CH_2CH(CH_3)CH_2CH_2OH$

General Questions and Problems

4.95 (a) It was thought that noble gases couldn't form bonds because they already had a full electron octet.

(b)

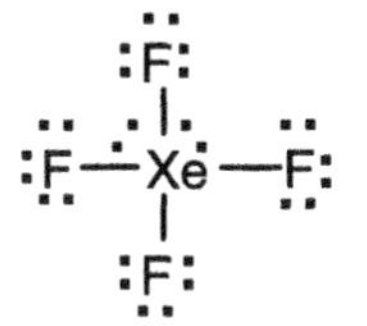

Xenon tetrafluoride

There are 6 electron clouds around the central atom.

(c) The Xe–F bonds are polar covalent. Each atom contributes one electron to the bond.

4.96

(a)

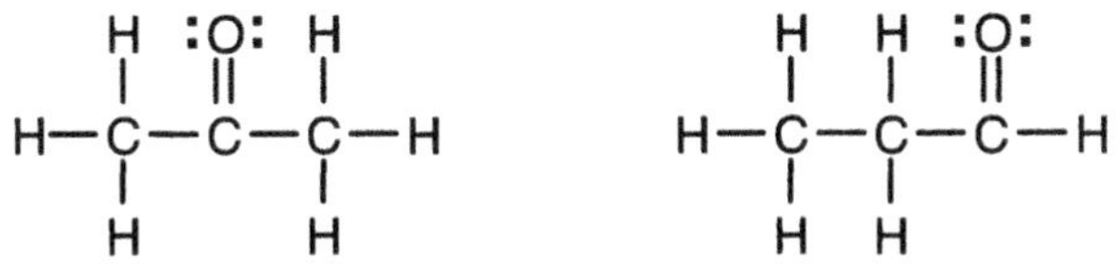

(b) The C=O carbon atoms have trigonal planar geometry, and the other carbons have tetrahedral geometry. (c) The C=O bonds are polar.

4.97

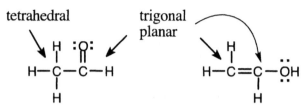

Both molecules are expected to be polar because of their C—O bonds.

4.98   Consult Figure 4.3 for help.

(a) Carbon forms four bonds. The correct formula is CCl_4.
(b) Nitrogen forms three bonds. The correct formula is N_2H_4.
(c) Sulfur forms two bonds. The correct formula is H_2S.
(d) C_2OS *could* actually be correct (S=C=C=O), but compounds with such adjacent double bonds are rare. More likely is the formula COS, a structural relative of carbon dioxide (S=C=O).

4.99   (a) $BaCl_2$ ionic bonds   (b) $Ca(NO_3)_2$ ionic and covalent bonds   (c) BCl_4^- covalent bonds and coordinate covalent bonds   (d) $TiBr_4$ covalent bonds

4.100

(a)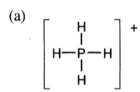

(b) Phosphonium ion is tetrahedral.

(c) Phosphorus donates its lone pair of electrons to H^+ to form a coordinate covalent bond.
(d) Number of electrons: 15 (from P) + 3 (from 3 H) = 18
    Number of protons: 15 (from P) + 4 (from 4 H) = 19
PH_4^+ is positive because the number of protons exceeds the number of electrons by one.

4.101 Both figures show that the halogens and the group 6A elements are the most electronegative. It is surprising to see in Figure 3.1 that group 5A elements have virtually zero electron affinity, whereas their electronegativities given in Figure 4.6 are significant.

4.102 *Compound*   *Name*

(a) $CaCl_2$ calcium chloride
(b) $TeCl_2$ tellurium dichloride
(c) BF_3 boron trifluoride
(d) $MgSO_4$ magnesium sulfate
(e) K_2O potassium oxide
(f) FeF_3 iron(III) fluoride
(g) PF_3 phosphorus trifluoride

4.103 $TiBr_4$ is a molecular compound, and TiO_2 is an ionic compound. The electronegativity difference between Ti and Br (approx. 1.4) indicates polar covalent bonds, whereas the electronegativity difference between Ti and O (approx. 2.1) indicates ionic bonds.

4.104

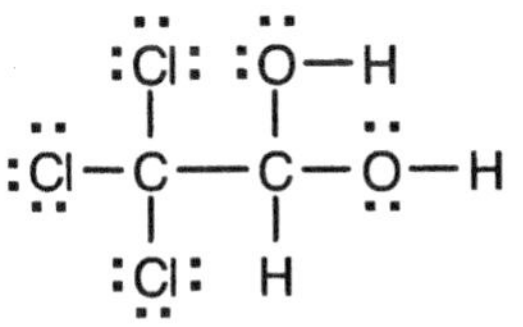

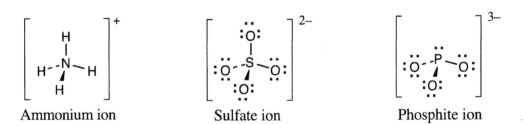

Chloral hydrate

4.105

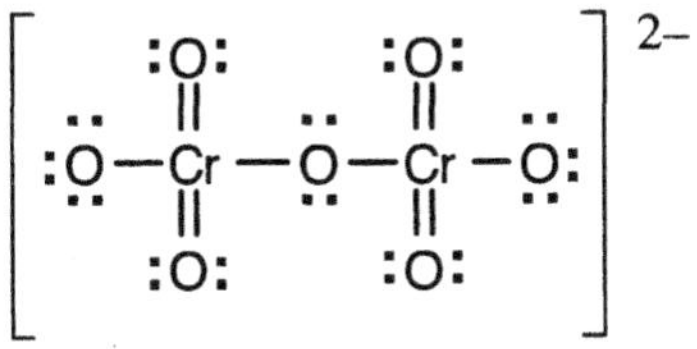

$$\left[\begin{array}{c} \ddot{O} \quad\quad \ddot{O} \\ \| \quad\quad \| \\ :\ddot{O}-Cr-\ddot{O}-Cr-\ddot{O}: \\ \| \quad\quad \| \\ \ddot{O}: \quad\quad \ddot{O}: \end{array}\right]^{2-}$$

Dichromate ion

4.106

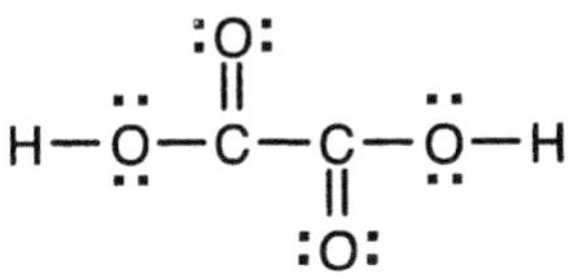

Oxalic acid

4.107

(a) O=Se=O

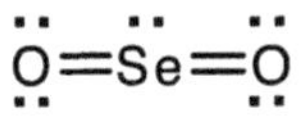

(b) :F, :, F: Kr

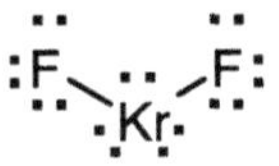

4.108

(a) :Cl—C—O—C—H

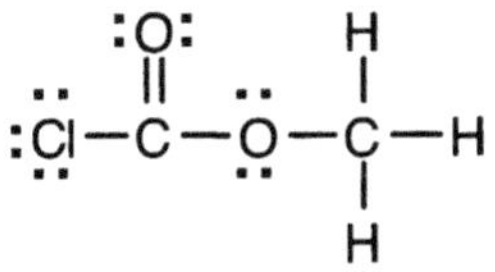

(b) H—C—C≡C—H

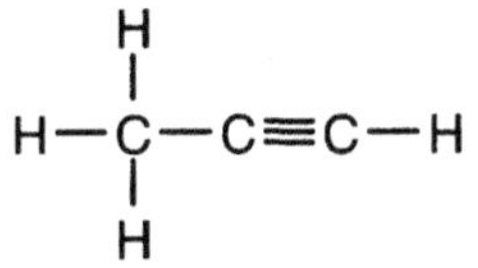

4.109 Ammonium ion and sulfate ion are tetrahedral. Phosphite ion is pyramidal.

Ammonium ion

Sulfate ion

Phosphite ion

Self-Test for Chapter 4

Multiple Choice

1. Which of these diatomic molecules contains a double bond?
    (a) H_2 (b) I_2 (c) O_2 (d) N_2

2. Which of these molecules is pyramidal?
    (a) CBr_4 (b) $AlCl_3$ (c) SF_6 (d) PH_3

3. Choose the element that forms three covalent bonds and has one lone pair of electrons.
    (a) C   (b) N   (c) O   (d) F

4. How many charge clouds does the molecule H_2S have?
    (a) 2   (b) 3   (c) 4   (d) can't tell

5. Which of the following double bonds is not likely to be found in organic molecules?
    (a) O=O   (b) C=C   (c) C=O   (d) C=N

6. All of the following are true about the polyatomic ion BF_4^- except:
    (a) All atoms don't have electron octets.   (b) It has polar covalent bonds.   (c) It contains a coordinate covalent bond.   (d) It has a tetrahedral shape.

7. One of these molecules doesn't contain a polar covalent bond. Which is it?
    (a) $BeBr_2$ (b) PCl_3 (c) CO_2 (d) CS_2

8. Which of the following compounds is polar?
    (a) $BeBr_2$ (b) PCl_3 (c) CO_2 (d) CS_2

9. A name for S_2F_2 is:
    (a) sulfur fluoride   (b) sulfur difluoride   (c) disulfur fluoride   (d) disulfur difluoride

10. Which of the following is not true for molecular compounds?
    (a) They are water-soluble.   (b) They can be solids, liquids, or gases.   (c) They are composed of nonmetals.   (d) They have low melting points.

Sentence Completion

1. An _____ element strongly attracts electrons.

2. A molecular compound that occurs in living organisms is called a _____ .

3. In Lewis structures, a line represents a _____ bond.

4. _____ and _____ are the most common triple bonds in chemical compounds.

5. The formula X_2 represents a _____ molecule.

6. A molecule whose central atom forms three bonds and has no lone pairs has a _____ _____ shape.

7. _____ orbitals in sulfur and phosphorus can be used for covalent bonds.

8. N_2 contains a _____ bond.

9.   _____ molecular compounds are formed from only two elements.

10. Many molecular compounds are soluble in _____ liquids.

11. Large organic molecules are often written as _____ structures.

True or False

1. Br_2 is a molecular compound.

2.   Six electrons are used to form a triple bond.

3.   Coordinate covalent bonds occur only in cations or anions, not in neutral compounds.

4.   The first step in drawing a Lewis structure is to find the total number of electrons in the combined atoms.

5. $AlCl_3$ is a pyramidal molecule.

6.   The shape of ionic compounds can be predicted by the VSEPR model.

7.   Electronegativity decreases in going down the periodic table.

8. CI_4 contains polar covalent bonds.

9.   Both planar and bent molecules have bond angles of 120°.

10. Group 7A elements can form more than one covalent bond.

11. Bent compounds may have either one or two lone pairs.

Match each entry on the left with its partner on the right.

1. BCl_3 (a) Contains a pure covalent bond

2. Planar molecule   (b) $BeCl_2$

3. Bent molecule   (c) Central atom has more than an electron octet

4. Cl_2 (d) NH_3

5. BCl_4^- (e) Contains a triple bond

6. NaI   (f) H_2O

7. $C{\equiv}O$ (g) Contains a double bond

8. SF_6 (h) Central atom doesn't have an electron octet

9. Linear molecule   (i) Contains an ionic bond

10. $O=C=O$ (j) $AlCl_3$

11. Pyramidal molecule   (k) Contains a coordinate covalent bond

12. CH_3Cl (l) Contains a polar covalent bond

Chapter Outline

I. Chemical equations (Sections 5.1–5.2).
   A. Writing chemical equations (Section 5.1).
     1. A chemical equation describes a chemical reaction.
       a. The reactants are written on the left.
       b. The products are written on the right.
       c. An arrow goes between them to indicate the chemical change.
     2. The number and kinds of atoms must be the same on both sides of the equation.
       a. This is known as the law of conservation of mass.
     3. Numbers that are placed in front of formulas are called coefficients.
     4. States of matter (s), (g), (l) are often placed after chemical formulas.
   B. Balancing chemical equations (Section 5.2).
     1. Write an unbalanced equation using the correct formulas for all substances.
     2. Add appropriate coefficients to balance the atoms of each type, one at a time.
     3. Check to make sure that the numbers and kinds of atoms are balanced.
     4. Make sure all coefficients are reduced to their lowest whole-number values.
II. Chemical reactions (Sections 5.3–5.8).
   A. Classes of chemical reactions (Section 5.3).
     1. Precipitation reactions occur when an insoluble solid is formed.
     2. Acid–base reactions occur when an acid and a base react to yield water and a salt.
     3. Redox reactions occur when electrons are transferred between reaction partners.
   B. Precipitation reactions (Section 5.4).
     1. To predict whether a precipitation reaction occurs, you must know the solubilities of the products.
     2. Table 5.1 gives general solubility rules to predict if a precipitation reaction will occur.
   C. Acid–base reactions (Section 5.5).
     1. Acid–base reactions are known as neutralization reactions because when the reaction is complete the solution is neither acidic nor basic.
     2. An example: $HA(aq) + MOH(aq) \longrightarrow H_2O(l) + MA(aq)$
     3. When a carbonate or bicarbonate is one of the reactants, CO_2 is also produced.
   D. Redox reactions (Sections 5.6–5.7).
     1. Definition of redox reactions (Section 5.6).
       a. A redox reaction occurs when electrons are transferred from one atom to another.
       b. The substance that loses electrons is oxidized and is known as the reducing agent.
       c. The substance that gains electrons is reduced and is known as the oxidizing agent.
       d. Oxidation and reduction always occur together.
         i. In the reaction of a metal with a nonmetal, the metal loses electrons, and the nonmetal gains electrons.
         ii. In the reaction of two nonmetals, the "more metallic" element loses electrons, and the "less metallic" element gains electrons.
       e. Redox reactions occur during corrosion, combustion, respiration, and photography.

2. Recognizing redox reactions (Section 5.7).
   a. With some substances, it isn't obvious if a redox reaction has occurred.
   b. In a neutral compound, oxidation numbers are assigned to each element to indicate electron ownership.
   c. To assign oxidation numbers:
      i.   An atom in its elemental state has an oxidation number of zero.
      ii. A monatomic ion has an oxidation number equal to its charge.
      iii. In a molecular compound, an atom usually has the same oxidation number that it would have if it were a monatomic ion.
      iv. The sum of the oxidation numbers in a neutral compound is zero.
      v.   The oxidation number of oxygen is usually –2; the oxidation number of hydrogen is usually +1.
E. Net ionic equations (Section 5.8).
   1. A molecular equation shows reactants and products as molecules and doesn't indicate if they are ions.
   2. An ionic equation is written if ions are involved and shows all ionic reactants and products.
   3. A net ionic equation includes only the ions that undergo change and deletes spectator ions.

Solutions to Chapter 5 Problems

5.1   (a) Solid cobalt(II) chloride plus gaseous hydrogen fluoride yield solid cobalt(II) fluoride plus gaseous hydrogen chloride.

(b) Aqueous lead(II) nitrate plus aqueous potassium iodide yield solid lead(II) iodide plus aqueous potassium nitrate.

5.2   An equation is balanced if the number and types of atoms on the left side equals the number and types of atoms on the right side.

(a) On the left: $2\,H + Cl + K + O$
    On the right: $2\,H + Cl + K + O$ The equation is balanced.
(b) On the left: $1\,C + 4\,H + 2\,Cl$
    On the right: $1\,C + 3\,H + 3\,Cl$ The equation is not balanced.
(c) Balanced
(d) Not balanced in H, O.

5.3   *Step 1*: Write the unbalanced equation.

$$O_2 \longrightarrow O_3$$

Step 2: Balance the atoms of each type, one by one.

$$3\,O_2 \longrightarrow 2\,O_3 \quad \text{The equation is balanced.}$$

5.4   (a) $Ca(OH)_2 + 2\,HCl \longrightarrow CaCl_2 + 2\,H_2O$

(b) $4\,Al + 3\,O_2 \longrightarrow 2\,Al_2O_3$

(c) $2\,CH_3CH_3 + 7\,O_2 \longrightarrow 4\,CO_2 + 6\,H_2O$

(d) $2\,AgNO_3 + MgCl_2 \longrightarrow 2\,AgCl + Mg(NO_3)_2$

5.5   *Step 1:* $A + B_2 \longrightarrow A_2B_2$

   Step 2: $2\,A + B_2 \longrightarrow A_2B_2$ The equation is balanced.

5.6   (a) $AgNO_3(aq) + KCl(aq) \longrightarrow AgCl(s) + KNO_3(aq)$
   Precipitation: Solid AgCl is formed.

   (b) $2\,Al(s) + 3\,Br_2(l) \longrightarrow 2\,AlBr_3(s)$
   Redox reaction: Al^{+3} is formed from Al, and Br^- is formed from Br_2.

   (c) $Ca(OH)_2(aq) + 2\,HNO_3(aq) \longrightarrow 2\,H_2O(l) + Ca(NO_3)_2(aq)$
   Acid–base neutralization.

5.7 $6\,CO_2(g) + 6\,H_2O(l) \longrightarrow C_6H_{12}O_6(s) + 6\,O_2(g)$

5.8   Use Table 5.1 for solubility guidelines.

   Insoluble   *Soluble*
   (a) $CdCO_3$ (most carbonates are insoluble)   (b) Na_2S
   (c) $PbSO_4$ (exception to the rule that sulfates are soluble)   (d) $(NH_4)_3PO_4$
   (e) Hg_2Cl_2 (exception to the rule that chlorides are soluble)

5.9   As in Worked Example 5.6, identify the products, and use Table 5.1 to predict their solubility. If the products are insoluble, a precipitation reaction will occur.

   (a) $NiCl_2(aq) + (NH_4)_2S(aq) \longrightarrow 2\,NH_4Cl(aq) + NiS(s)$
   A precipitation reaction will occur.

   (b) $2\,AgNO_3(aq) + CaBr_2(aq) \longrightarrow Ca(NO_3)_2(aq) + 2\,AgBr(s)$
   A precipitation reaction will occur.

5.10 $CaCl_2(aq) + Na_2C_2O_4(aq) \longrightarrow 2\,NaCl(aq) + CaC_2O_4(s)$

5.11   (a) $2\,CsOH(aq) + H_2SO_4(aq) \longrightarrow Cs_2SO_4(aq) + 2\,H_2O(l)$

   (b) $Ca(OH)_2(aq) + 2\,CH_3CO_2H(aq) \longrightarrow Ca(CH_3CO_2)_2(aq) + 2\,H_2O(l)$

   (c) $NaHCO_3(aq) + HBr(aq) \longrightarrow NaBr(aq) + CO_2(g) + H_2O(l)$

5.12

	Oxidized Reactant/ Reducing Agent	*Reduced Reactant/ Oxidizing Agent*
(a)	Fe	Cu^{2+}
(b)	Mg	Cl_2
(c)	Al	Cr_2O_3

   The oxidizing agent is the reduced reactant, and the reducing agent is the oxidized reactant.

5.13 $2\,K(s)$ + $Br_2(l) \longrightarrow 2\,KBr(s)$
   Reducing agent   *Oxidizing agent*

5.14   Lithium is oxidized, and iodine is reduced.

5.15

Compound	Oxidation Number of Metal	Name
(a) VCl_3	+3	vanadium(III) chloride
(b) $SnCl_4$	+4	tin(IV) chloride
(c) CrO_3	+6	chromium(VI) oxide
(d) $Cu(NO_3)_2$	+2	copper(II) nitrate
(e) $NiSO_4$	+2	nickel(II) sulfate

5.16 Oxidation numbers are written above the atoms.

(a) $\overset{+1\,-2}{Na_2S}(aq) + \overset{+2\,-1}{NiCl_2}(aq) \longrightarrow 2\,\overset{+1\,-1}{NaCl}(aq) + \overset{+2\,-2}{NiS}(s)$
This reaction is not a redox reaction because no atoms change oxidation numbers.

(b) $2\,\overset{0}{Na}(s) + 2\,\overset{+1\,-2}{H_2O}(l) \longrightarrow 2\,\overset{+1\,-2\,+1}{NaOH}(aq) + \overset{0}{H_2}(g)$
Sodium is oxidized and hydrogen is reduced in this reaction.

(c) $\overset{0}{C}(s) + \overset{0}{O_2}(g) \longrightarrow \overset{+4\,-2}{CO_2}(g)$
Carbon is oxidized and oxygen is reduced in this redox reaction.

(d) $\overset{+2\,-2}{CuO}(s) + 2\,\overset{+1\,-1}{HCl}(aq) \longrightarrow \overset{+2\,-1}{CuCl_2}(aq) + \overset{+1\,-2}{H_2O}(l)$
This is not a redox reaction because no atoms change oxidation number.

(e) $2\,\overset{+7\,-2}{MnO_4^-}(aq) + 5\,\overset{+4\,-2}{SO_2}(g) + 2\,\overset{+1\,-2}{H_2O}(l) \longrightarrow 2\,\overset{+2}{Mn^{2+}}(aq) + 5\,\overset{+6\,-2}{SO_4^{2-}}(aq) + 4\,\overset{+1}{H^+}(aq)$
In this redox reaction, the oxidation number of Mn changes from +7 to +2 and the oxidation number of S changes from +4 to +6.

5.17

Reducing agent	Oxidizing agent
(b) Na	H_2O
(c) C	O_2
(e) SO_2	MnO_4^-

5.18 (a) Write the equation, including all ions.

$Zn(s) + Pb^{2+} + 2\,NO_3^- \longrightarrow Zn^{2+} + 2\,NO_3^- + Pb(s)$
The nitrate ions on each side cancel.

$Zn(s) + Pb^{2+}(aq) \longrightarrow Zn^{2+}(aq) + Pb(s)$

(b) $OH^-(aq) + H^+(aq) \longrightarrow H_2O(l)$
K^+ and SO_4^{2-} cancel, and coefficients are reduced.

(c) $2\,Fe^{3+}(aq) + Sn^{2+}(aq) \longrightarrow 2\,Fe^{2+}(aq) + Sn^{4+}(aq)$
The chloride ions cancel.

5.19 Reactions (a) and (c) are redox reactions, and (b) is a neutralization reaction.

Understanding Key Concepts

5.20 Product mixture (d) is the only mixture that contains the same number of atoms as (a).

5.21 (c) $2A + B_2 \longrightarrow A_2B_2$

5.22 (d) $\longrightarrow$ (c)
reactants   products

5.23 (a) Mixing of sodium and carbonate ions produces outcome (1). No insoluble product is formed, and sodium and carbonate ions remain in solution.
(b) Mixing barium and chromate ions produces outcome (2). $BaCrO_4$ precipitate forms (one barium ion for each chromate ion), and the excess barium ions remain in solution.
(c) Mixing silver and sulfite ions yields outcome (3). Ag_2SO_3 precipitate forms (two silver ions for each sulfite ion), and no Ag^+ or SO_3^{2-} ions remain in solution.

5.24 The observed product is a precipitate that contains two cations per anion. From the list of cations, Ag^+ is the only one that forms precipitates and has a 2:1 cation/anion ratio with the anions listed. The anion can be either CO_3^{2-} or CrO_4^{2-}, since both form precipitates with Ag^+. Thus, the possible products are Ag_2CO_3 and Ag_2CrO_4.

5.25 (a) $CaCl_2$ is dissolved in beaker A. (PbI_2 has the same ratio of cations to anions but is insoluble in water.)
(b) Na_2SO_4 is dissolved in beaker B.
(c) $CaSO_4$ is the precipitate, and Na^+ and Cl^- are the spectator ions.

Balancing Chemical Equations

5.26 A balanced equation is an equation in which the number of atoms of each kind is the same on both sides of the reaction arrow.

5.27 Changing the subscripts on a substance to balance an equation changes the identity of the substance and makes the equation meaningless.

5.28 (a) $SO_2(g) + H_2O(g) \longrightarrow H_2SO_3(aq)$

(b) $2K(s) + Br_2(l) \longrightarrow 2KBr(s)$

(c) $C_3H_8(g) + 5O_2(g) \longrightarrow 3CO_2(g) + 4H_2O(g)$

5.29 $4NH_3(g) + Cl_2(g) \longrightarrow N_2H_4(l) + 2NH_4Cl(s)$

5.30 (a) $2C_2H_6(g) + 7O_2(g) \longrightarrow 4CO_2(g) + 6H_2O(l)$

(b) balanced

(c) $2Mg(s) + O_2(g) \longrightarrow 2MgO(s)$

(d) $2K(s) + 2H_2O(l) \longrightarrow 2KOH(aq) + H_2(g)$

5.31 (a) balanced

(b) $C_2H_8N_2 + 2\,N_2O_4 \longrightarrow 3\,N_2 + 2\,CO_2 + 4\,H_2O$

(c) balanced

(d) $2\,N_2O \longrightarrow 2\,N_2 + O_2$

5.32 (a) $Hg(NO_3)_2(aq) + 2\,LiI(aq) \longrightarrow 2\,LiNO_3(aq) + HgI_2(s)$

(b) $I_2(s) + 5\,Cl_2(g) \longrightarrow 2\,ICl_5(s)$

(c) $4\,Al(s) + 3\,O_2(g) \longrightarrow 2\,Al_2O_3(s)$

(d) $CuSO_4(aq) + 2\,AgNO_3(aq) \longrightarrow Ag_2SO_4(s) + Cu(NO_3)_2(aq)$

(e) $2\,Mn(NO_3)_3(aq) + 3\,Na_2S(aq) \longrightarrow Mn_2S_3(s) + 6\,NaNO_3(aq)$

5.33 (a) $4\,NO_2(g) + O_2(g) \longrightarrow 2\,N_2O_5(g)$

(b) $P_4O_{10}(s) + 6\,H_2O(l) \longrightarrow 4\,H_3PO_4(aq)$

(c) $B_2H_6(l) + 3\,O_2(g) \longrightarrow B_2O_3(s) + 3\,H_2O(l)$

(d) $Cr_2O_3(s) + 3\,CCl_4(l) \longrightarrow 2\,CrCl_3(s) + 3\,COCl_2(aq)$

(e) $4\,Fe_3O_4(s) + O_2(g) \longrightarrow 6\,Fe_2O_3(s)$

5.34 (a) $2\,C_4H_{10}(g) + 13\,O_2(g) \longrightarrow 8\,CO_2(g) + 10\,H_2O(l)$

(b) $C_2H_6O(g) + 3\,O_2(g) \longrightarrow 2\,CO_2(g) + 3\,H_2O(l)$

(c) $2\,C_8H_{18}(g) + 25\,O_2(g) \longrightarrow 16\,CO_2(g) + 18\,H_2O(l)$

5.35 (a) $2\,C_4H_{10}(g) + 9\,O_2(g) \longrightarrow 8\,CO(g) + 10\,H_2O(l)$

(b) $C_2H_6O(g) + 2\,O_2(g) \longrightarrow 2\,CO(g) + 3\,H_2O(l)$

(c) $2\,C_8H_{18}(g) + 17\,O_2(g) \longrightarrow 16\,CO(g) + 18\,H_2O(l)$

5.36 $4\,HF + SiO_2 \longrightarrow SiF_4 + 2\,H_2O$

5.37 $Na_2CO_3(aq) + 2\,HNO_3(aq) \longrightarrow CO_2(g) + 2\,NaNO_3(aq) + H_2O(l)$

Types of Chemical Reactions

5.38 (a) $Mg(s) + 2\,HCl(aq) \longrightarrow MgCl_2(aq) + H_2(g)$ redox reaction

(b) $KOH(aq) + HNO_3(aq) \longrightarrow KNO_3(aq) + H_2O(l)$ neutralization reaction

(c) $Pb(NO_3)_2(aq) + 2\,HBr(aq) \longrightarrow PbBr_2(s) + 2\,HNO_3(aq)$ precipitation reaction

(d) $Ca(OH)_2(aq) + 2\,H_2SO_4(aq) \longrightarrow 2\,H_2O(l) + CaSO_4(aq)$ neutralization reaction

5.39

(a) $2 H^+(aq) + SO_4^{2-}(aq) + 2 K^+(aq) + 2 OH^-(aq) \rightarrow 2 K^+(aq) + SO_4^{2-}(aq) + 2 H_2O(l)$
$H^+(aq) + OH^-(aq) \rightarrow H_2O(l)$

(b) $Mg^{2+}(aq) + 2 OH^-(aq) + 2 H^+(aq) + 2 Cl^-(aq) \rightarrow Mg^{2+}(aq) + 2 Cl^-(aq) + 2 H_2O(l)$
$H^+(aq) + OH^-(aq) \rightarrow H_2O(l)$

5.40

(a) $Ba^{2+}(aq) + 2 NO_3^-(aq) + 2 K^+(aq) + SO_4^{2-}(aq) \rightarrow BaSO_4(s) + 2 K^+(aq) + 2 NO_3^-(aq)$
$Ba^{2+}(aq) + SO_4^{2-}(aq) \rightarrow BaSO_4(s)$

(b) $Zn(s) + 2 H^+(aq) + SO_4^{2-}(aq) \rightarrow Zn^{2+}(aq) + H_2(g) + SO_4^{2-}(aq)$
$Zn(s) + 2 H^+(aq) \rightarrow Zn^{2+}(aq) + H_2(g)$

5.41   redox: (a), (c), (d); neutralization: (b)

5.42   redox: (b), (c); precipitation: (a), (d), (e)

5.43   Use Section 5.4 as a guide.
Only $ZnSO_4$ is soluble in water.

5.44   Use Section 5.4 as a guide.
Only $Ba(NO_3)_2$ is soluble in water.

5.45   A precipitation reaction occurs only in (b). A neutralization occurs with the reagents in (a).

(b) $FeCl_2(aq) + 2 KOH(aq) \longrightarrow Fe(OH)_2(s) + 2 KCl(aq)$

5.46   If the products consist of soluble ions, no reaction will occur. No reaction occurs in (b) and (c).

(a) $2 NaBr(aq) + Hg_2(NO_3)_2(aq) \longrightarrow Hg_2Br_2(s) + 2 NaNO_3(aq)$

(d) $(NH_4)_2CO_3(aq) + CaCl_2(aq) \longrightarrow CaCO_3(s) + 2 NH_4Cl(aq)$

(e) $2 KOH(aq) + MnBr_2(aq) \longrightarrow Mn(OH)_2(s) + 2 KBr(aq)$

(f) $3 Na_2S(aq) + 2 Al(NO_3)_3(aq) \longrightarrow Al_2S_3(s) + 6 NaNO_3(aq)$

5.47   In net ionic reactions, no spectator ions appear. Otherwise, the equations are balanced for number of atoms and charge, and coefficients are reduced to their lowest common denominators.

(a) $Mg(s) + Cu^{2+}(aq) \longrightarrow Mg^{2+}(aq) + Cu(s)$

(b) $2 Cl^-(aq) + Pb^{2+}(aq) \longrightarrow PbCl_2(s)$

(c) $2 Cr^{3+}(aq) + 3 S^{2-}(aq) \longrightarrow Cr_2S_3(s)$

5.48   (a) $2 Au^{3+}(aq) + 3 Sn(s) \longrightarrow 3 Sn^{2+}(aq) + 2 Au(s)$

(b) $2 I^-(aq) + Br_2(l) \longrightarrow 2 Br^-(aq) + I_2(s)$

(c) $2 Ag^+(aq) + Fe(s) \longrightarrow Fe^{2+}(aq) + 2 Ag(s)$

5.49 (a) $FeSO_4(aq) + Sr(OH)_2(aq) \longrightarrow Fe(OH)_2(s) + SrSO_4(s)$

(b) $Na_2S(aq) + ZnSO_4(aq) \longrightarrow Na_2SO_4(aq) + ZnS(s)$

5.50 (a) The net ionic equation is the same as 5.49 (a) because no ions are spectator ions.

(b) $S^{2-}(aq) + Zn^{2+}(aq) \longrightarrow ZnS(s)$

Redox Reactions and Oxidation Numbers

5.51 In general, the best reducing agents are metals. The most reactive reducing agents are in groups 1A and 2A. The most reactive oxidizing agents are in groups 6A and 7A.

5.52 The most easily reduced elements are found in groups 6A and 7A. The most easily oxidized elements are in groups 1A and 2A.

5.53 *Gains electrons:* (a) oxidizing agent, (d) substance undergoing reduction
Loses electrons: (b) reducing agent, (c) substance undergoing oxidation

5.54 Oxidation number increases: (b) reducing agent, (c) substance undergoing oxidation
Oxidation number decreases: (a) oxidizing agent, (d) substance undergoing reduction

5.55
$$\begin{array}{cccc} {\scriptstyle +5\ -2} & {\scriptstyle +4-2} & {\scriptstyle 0+1-2} & {\scriptstyle +1+5-2} \\ \text{(a) } N_2O_5 & \text{(b) } SO_3{}^{2-} & \text{(c) } CH_2O & \text{(d) } HClO_3 \end{array}$$

5.56 (a) Co: +3   (b) Fe: +2   (c) U: +6   (d) Cu: +2   (e) Ti: +4   (f) Sn: +2

5.57 The reduced element gains electrons, and the oxidized element loses electrons.

	(a)	(b)	(c)
Oxidized	Si	Br	Sb
Reduced	Cl	Cl	Cl

5.58

	(a)	(b)	(c)	(d)
Oxidized	S	Na	Zn	Cl
Reduced	O	Cl	Cu	F

5.59 (a) $2\ Al(s) + 3\ H_2SO_4(aq) \longrightarrow Al_2(SO_4)_3(aq) + 3\ H_2(g)$
(b) $2\ Fe(s) + 3\ Cl_2(g) \longrightarrow 2\ FeCl_3(s)$
(c) $5\ CO(g) + I_2O_5(s) \longrightarrow I_2(s) + 5\ CO_2(g)$

5.60 (a) $N_2O_4(l) + 2\ N_2H_4(l) \longrightarrow 3\ N_2(g) + 4\ H_2O(g)$
(b) $CaH_2(s) + 2\ H_2O(l) \longrightarrow Ca(OH)_2(aq) + 2\ H_2(l)$
(c) $2\ Al(s) + 6\ H_2O(l) \longrightarrow 2\ Al(OH)_3(s) + 3\ H_2(g)$

5.61

	Reducing agent	*Oxidizing agent*
(a)	Al	H_2SO_4
(b)	Fe	Cl_2
(c)	CO	I_2O_5

5.62 *Reducing agent*   *Oxidizing agent*
    (a) N_2H_4 N_2O_4
    (b) CaH_2 H_2O
    (c)   Al H_2O

Chemistry in Action

5.63

$$\frac{0.067 \text{ g}}{1 \text{ L}} \times 5.0 \text{ L} = 0.34 \text{ g}$$

5.64 (a) $2 C_5H_4N_4 + 3 O_2 \longrightarrow 2 C_5H_4N_4O_3$
    (b) This is a redox reaction in which purine is oxidized and O_2 is reduced.

5.65 Elemental cadmium is oxidized, and nickel [as $NiO(OH)$] is reduced.

5.66 Elemental zinc is the reducing agent and Mn^{+4} is the oxidizing agent.

General Questions and Problems

5.67 (a) $2 Al(s) + Fe_2O_3(s) \longrightarrow Al_2O_3(l) + 2 Fe(l)$

    (b) $2 NH_4NO_3(s) \longrightarrow 2 N_2(g) + O_2(g) + 4 H_2O(g)$

5.68 (a) $Li_2O(s) + H_2O(g) \longrightarrow 2 LiOH(s)$
    (b) This is not a redox reaction because the oxidation numbers of reactant and product atoms remain the same.

5.69 $CuCl_2(aq) + Na_2CO_3(aq) \longrightarrow CuCO_3(s) + 2 NaCl(aq)$
    A precipitate of $CuCO_3$ forms

    $Cu^{2+}(aq) + CO_3^{2-}(aq) \longrightarrow CuCO_3(s)$

5.70 (a) $Al(OH)_3(aq) + 3 HNO_3(aq) \longrightarrow Al(NO_3)_3(aq) + 3 H_2O(l)$ neutralization

    (b) $3 AgNO_3(aq) + FeCl_3(aq) \longrightarrow 3 AgCl(s) + Fe(NO_3)_3(aq)$ precipitation

    (c) $(NH_4)_2Cr_2O_7(s) \longrightarrow Cr_2O_3(s) + 4 H_2O(g) + N_2(g)$ redox

    (d) $Mn_2(CO_3)_3(s) \longrightarrow Mn_2O_3(s) + 3 CO_2(g)$ none

5.71 (a) $P_4 + 5 O_2 \longrightarrow 2 P_2O_5$

    (b) The reactants both have an oxidation number of zero. In the product, the oxidation number of oxygen is –2, and the oxidation number of phosphorus is +5. P_4 is the reducing agent, and O_2 is the oxidizing agent.

5.72 (a) $2 SO_2(g) + O_2(g) \longrightarrow 2 SO_3(g)$

    (b) $SO_3(g) + H_2O(g) \longrightarrow H_2SO_4(l)$

    (c) The oxidation number of sulfur is +4 in SO_2 and is +6 in both SO_3 and H_2SO_4.

5.73

Compound	Oxidation Number of Metal	Compound	Oxidation Number Of Metal
(a) MnO_2	+4	(b) CrO_2	+4
Mn_2O_3	+3	CrO_3	+6
$KMnO_4$	+7	Cr_2O_3	+3

5.74 (a) The oxidation number of chromium in dichromate is +6.
(b) The oxidation number of carbon in C_2H_5OH is –2; the oxidation number of carbon in CO_2 is +4.
(c) The oxidizing agent is dichromate, and the reducing agent is C_2H_5OH.

5.75 $Mg(OH)_2(s) + 2\,HCl(aq) \longrightarrow MgCl_2(aq) + H_2O(l)$

5.76 $Fe^{3+}(aq) + 3\,NaOH(aq) \longrightarrow Fe(OH)_3(s) + 3\,Na^+(aq)$

$Fe^{3+}(aq) + 3\,^-OH(aq) \longrightarrow Fe(OH)_3(s)$

5.77 $Mg^{2+}(aq) + CO_3{}^{2-}(aq) \longrightarrow MgCO_3(s)$

$Ca^{2+}(aq) + CO_3{}^{2-}(aq) \longrightarrow CaCO_3(s)$

5.78 $2\,Bi^{3+}(aq) + 3S^-(aq) \longrightarrow Bi_2S_3(s)$

5.79 (a) $Fe_2O_3(s) + 3\,CO(g) \longrightarrow 2\,Fe(s) + 3\,CO_2(g)$ (b) This is a redox reaction.

5.80 $CO_2(g) + 2\,NH_3(g) \longrightarrow NH_2CONH_2(s) + H_2O(l)$

5.81 (a) $MgCO_3(aq) + 2\,HCl(aq) \longrightarrow MgCl_2(aq) + CO_2(g) + H_2O(l)$

$CO_3{}^{2-}(aq) + 2\,H^+(aq) \longrightarrow CO_2(g) + H_2O(l)$

(b) This is a neutralization reaction.

5.82 (a) Reactants: Mn = +4, I = –1;   Products: Mn = +2, I = 0
(b) MnO_2 is the oxidizing agent, and I^- is the reducing agent.

Self-Test for Chapter 5

Multiple Choice

1.   Which of the following salts is soluble in water?
(a) $FeSO_4$ (b) $BaSO_4$ (c) $SrSO_4$ (d) $PbSO_4$

2.   Which of the following compounds has sulfur in a +1 oxidation state?
(a) S_2F_2 (b) H_2SO_4 (c) SO_2 (d) Na_2S

3.   Which of the following is a treatment for gout?
(a) oxalate (b) purine (c) allopurinol (d) urate

4.   Which of the following is not a component of a dry cell battery?
     (a) MnO_2 (b) I_2 (c) NH_4Cl (d) Zn

5.   When the equation $SiCl_4 + H_2O \longrightarrow SiO_2 + HCl$ is balanced, the coefficients are:
     (a) 1,1,1,1   (b) 1,1,1,2   (c) 1,2,1,2   (d) 1,2,1,4

6.   Which of the following is not a redox process?
     (a) respiration   (b) corrosion   (c) neutralization   (d) combustion

7.   If you wanted to remove Ba^{2+} from solution, which reagent would you add?
     (a) CH_3CO_2H (b) $NaOH$ (c) H_2SO_4 (d) HCl

8.   In the reaction $2 Ca + O_2 \longrightarrow 2 CaO$, calcium is:
     (a) reduced/oxidizing agent   (b) oxidized/reducing agent   (c) reduced/reducing agent
     (d) oxidized/oxidizing agent

9.   When HCl is added to a solution, bubbles of gas appear. Which compound is probably
     present in the solution?
     (a) $SrCO_3$ (b) $Ca(OH)_2$ (c) $AgBr$ (d) K_2SO_4

10.   Which lead-containing compound is probably soluble in water?
      (a) PbS (b) $PbSO_4$ (c) $PbCl_2$ (d) $Pb(NO_3)_2$

Sentence Completion

1.   The numbers placed in front of formulas to balance equations are called _____.

2.   A _____ is a solid that forms during a reaction.

3.   Ions that appear on both sides of the reaction arrow are _____ ions.

4.   The substances in a reaction can be solids, liquids, or gases, or they can be in _____

     solution.

5.   When acid is added to a solution, bubbles of gas are evolved if either _____ or _____ ions

     are present.

6.   _____ is the science of extracting and purifying metals.

7.   In a chemical equation, _____ are shown on the left of the reaction arrow.

8.   The oxidation state of gold in $AuCl_3$ is _____.

9.   In the reaction $2 Mg + O_2 \longrightarrow 2 MgO$, Mg is the _____ agent.

10.   A reaction between an acid and a base is a _____ reaction.

True or False

1. Lithium and iodine are the redox components of a dry cell battery

2. If the chloride of a cation is water-insoluble, the bromide and iodide of that cation are also insoluble.

3. Limestone ($CaCO_3$) can be dissolved by treatment with HNO_3.

4. In a redox equation, the oxidizing agent is oxidized and the reducing agent is reduced.

5. If all coefficients in a chemical equation are even numbers, the equation is not properly balanced.

6. In a redox reaction, a reducing agent becomes more negative

7. In the reaction between K and Cl_2, K is the oxidizing agent.

8. Increased urate concentration in urine leads to gout.

9. Most sodium salts are soluble in water.

10. The same compound can be both oxidized and reduced in a reaction.

Match each entry on the left with its partner on the right.

1. Zn   (a) Net ionic equation

2. $C_3H_8O + O_2 \longrightarrow C_3H_6O + H_2O$ (b) Deterioration of a metal by oxidation

3. Respiration   (c) Redox reaction

4. $H^+ + OH^- \longrightarrow H_2O$ (d) Precipitation reaction

5. $CoCO_3$ (e) Salt soluble in water

6. $S + O_2 \longrightarrow SO_2$ (f) Unbalanced equation

7. $HCl + NaOH \longrightarrow NaCl + H_2O$ (g) Manganese has an oxidation number of +7

8. Corrosion   (h) Oxidized in a battery

9. $KMnO_4$ (i) Salt insoluble in water

10. MnO_2 (j) Neutralization reaction

11. $AgNO_3 + NaCl \longrightarrow AgCl + NaNO_3$ (k) Biological redox reaction

12. $CoCl_2$ (l) Reduced in a battery

Chapter Outline

I.   The mole (Section 6.1).
   A. Molecular weight is the sum of the atomic weights of atoms in a molecule.
   B. Formula weight is the sum of the atomic weights of atoms in a formula unit.
   C. One mole of any pure substance has a mass equal to its molecular or formula weight in grams.
      1. Avogadro's number (6.022×10^{23}), known as the mole, represents the number of formula units that has a mass in grams equal to its weight in amu.
II. Mole–mass relationships (Section 6.2–6.4).
   A. Gram–mole conversions (Section 6.2).
      1. Molar mass is the mass in grams of one mole of any substance.
      2. Molar mass is a conversion factor that allows calculation of moles from grams and of grams from moles.
   B. Mole relationships and chemical equations (Section 6.3).
      1. The coefficients in an equation tell how many moles of reactant or product are involved in the reaction.
      2. The coefficients can be put in a mole ratio, which can be used as a conversion factor.
   C. Mass relationships and chemical equations (Section 6.4).
      1. Mole–mole conversions are made by using mole ratios.
      2. Mole–mass conversions are made by using molar mass as a conversion factor.
      3. Mass–mass conversions can be made by a mass–mole conversion of one substance, mole ratios, and a mole–mass conversion of the other substance.
   D. A summary of calculations using mole–mass relationships:
      1. Write the balanced equation.
      2. Choose mole–mass relationships and mole ratios to calculate the desired quantity.
      3. Set up the factor-label method to calculate the answer.
      4. Check the answer with a ballpark solution.
III. Limiting reagent and percent yield (Section 6.5).
   A. In a reaction, the reactant that is consumed first is the limiting reagent.
   B. Percent yield = actual yield/theoretical yield x 100%.
   C. Theoretical yield is found by using a mass–mass calculation.

Solutions to Chapter 6 Problems

6.1   (a) For ibuprofen, $C_{13}H_{18}O_2$:

At. wt of 13 C = 13 x 12.0 amu = 156.0 amu
At. wt of 18 H = 18 x 1.0 amu =   18.0 amu
At. wt of 2 O =   2 x 16.0 amu =   32.0 amu

MW of $C_{13}H_{18}O_2$ = 206.0 amu

(b) For phenobarbital, $C_{12}H_{12}N_2O_3$:

At. wt of 12 C = 12 x 12.0 amu = 144.0 amu
At. wt of 12 H = 12 x 1.0 amu = 12.0 amu
At. wt of 2 N = 2 x 14.0 amu = 28.0 amu
At. wt of 3 O = 3 x 16.0 amu = 48.0 amu

MW of $C_{12}H_{12}N_2O_3$ = 232.0 amu

6.2   At. wt of 6 C = 6 x 12.0 amu = 72.0 amu
At. wt of 8 H = 8 x 1.0 amu = 8.0 amu
At. wt of 6 O = 6 x 16.0 amu = 96.0 amu

MW of $C_6H_8O_6$ = 176.0 amu

Since the molecular weight of ascorbic acid is 176.0 amu, 6.022×10^{23} molecules have a mass of 176 g.

$$500 \text{ mg ascorbic acid } \times \frac{1 \text{ g}}{10^3 \text{ mg}} \times \frac{6.022 \times 10^{23} \text{ molecules}}{176 \text{ g}} = 1.71 \times 10^{21} \text{ molecules}$$

A 500 mg tablet contains 1.71×10^{21} molecules of ascorbic acid.

6.3   At. wt of 9 C = 9 x 12.0 amu = 108.0 amu
At. wt of 8 H = 8 x 1.0 amu = 8.0 amu
At. wt of 4 O = 4 x 16.0 amu = 64.0 amu

MW of $C_9H_8O_4$ = 180.0 amu

$$5.0 \times 10^{20} \text{ molecules } \times \frac{180.0 \text{ g}}{1 \text{ mol}} \times \frac{1 \text{ mol}}{6.022 \times 10^{23} \text{molecules}} = 0.15 \text{ g}$$

5.0×10^{20} molecules of aspirin weigh 0.15 g.

6.4

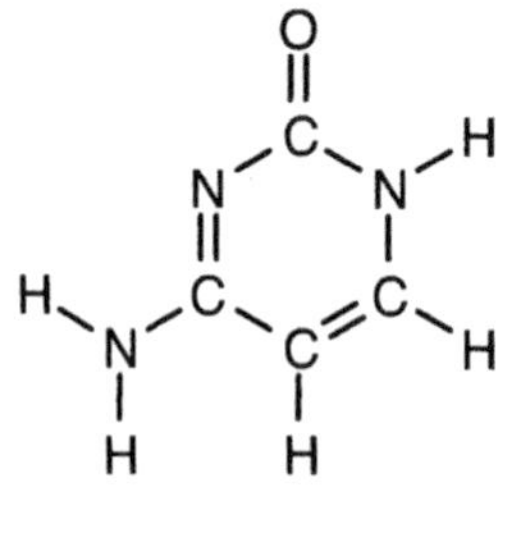

Cytosine $C_4H_5N_3O$

At. wt of 4 C = 4 x 12.0 amu = 48.0 amu
At. wt of 5 H = 5 x 1.0 amu = 5.0 amu
At. wt of 3 N = 3 x 14.0 amu = 42.0 amu
At. wt of 1 O = 1 x 16.0 amu = 16.0 amu

MW of $C_4H_5N_3O$ = 111.0 amu

6.5   Molar mass of C_2H_6O = 46.0 g/mol

$$10.0 \text{ g } \times \frac{1 \text{ mol}}{46.0 \text{ g}} = 0.217 \text{ mol in a } 10.0 \text{ g sample}$$

Ballpark check: The sample size, 10.0 g, is about 1/5 mol, or about 0.2 mol.

$$0.10 \text{ mol } \times \frac{46.0 \text{ g}}{1 \text{ mol}} = 4.6 \text{ g in a } 0.10 \text{ mol sample}$$

6.6   Molar mass of acetaminophen = 151 g

$$0.0225 \text{ mol } \times \frac{151 \text{ g}}{1 \text{ mol}} = 3.40 \text{ g}$$

5.00 g acetaminophen weighs more than 0.0225 mol.

6.7   The number of molecules in Step 2 would be greater because the value of l^2 is smaller for a sphere than for a cube. If the density were less, the mass in Step 3, and the number of moles in Step 4, would be less. The net result in Step 5 would be an increase in the value of Avogadro's number.

6.8   (a) $Ni(s) + 2\,HCl(aq) \longrightarrow NiCl_2(aq) + H_2(g)$

$$9.81 \text{ mol HCl } \times \frac{1 \text{ mol Ni}}{2 \text{ mol HCl}} = 4.91 \text{ mol Ni}$$

(b) $6.00 \text{ mol Ni } \times \dfrac{1 \text{ mol NiCl}_2}{1 \text{ mol Ni}} = 6.00 \text{ mol NiCl}_2 \text{ from } 6.00 \text{ mol Ni}$

$$12.00 \text{ mol HCl } \times \frac{1 \text{ mol NiCl}_2}{2 \text{ mol HCl}} = 6.00 \text{ mol NiCl}_2 \text{ from } 12.00 \text{ mol HCl}$$

6.00 mol $NiCl_2$ can be formed from 6.00 mol Ni and 12.00 mol HCl.

6.9 $6\,CO_2 + 6\,H_2O \longrightarrow C_6H_{12}O_6 + 6\,O_2$

$$15.0 \text{ mol glucose } \times \frac{6 \text{ mol CO}_2}{1 \text{ mol glucose}} = 90.0 \text{ mol CO}_2$$

6.10 (a) This is a mole-to-mole problem.

$$9.90 \text{ mol SiO}_2 \; \times \; \frac{4 \text{ mol HF}}{1 \text{ mol SiO}_2} \; = \; 39.6 \text{ mol HF}$$

(b) This is a mass-to-mass problem.

$$23.0 \text{ g SiO}_2 \; \times \; \frac{1 \text{ mol SiO}_2}{60.1 \text{ g SiO}_2} \; \times \; \frac{2 \text{ mol H}_2\text{O}}{1 \text{ mol SiO}_2} \; \times \; \frac{18.0 \text{ g H}_2\text{O}}{1 \text{ mol H}_2\text{O}} \; = \; 13.8 \text{ g H}_2\text{O}$$

Ballpark check: About 1/3 mol SiO_2 is used to produce 2/3 mol H_2O. Since the molar mass of H_2O is 18 g, we expect about 12 g H_2O, which is reasonably close to the calculated answer.

6.11 For WO_3:

$$5.00 \text{ g W} \; \times \; \frac{1 \text{ mol W}}{183.8 \text{ g W}} \; \times \; \frac{1 \text{ mol WO}_3}{1 \text{ mol W}} \; \times \; \frac{231.8 \text{ g WO}_3}{1 \text{ mol WO}_3} \; = \; 6.31 \text{ g WO}_3$$

For H_2:

$$5.00 \text{ g W} \; \times \; \frac{1 \text{ mol W}}{183.8 \text{ g W}} \; \times \; \frac{3 \text{ mol H}_2}{1 \text{ mol W}} \; \times \; \frac{2.02 \text{ g H}_2}{1 \text{ mol H}_2} \; = \; 0.165 \text{ g H}_2$$

6.31 g WO_3 and 0.165 g H_2 are needed to produce 5.00 g W.

Ballpark check: About 3/4 of the mass of WO_3 is composed of W. Thus, 5.00 g W comes from about 4/3 x 5.00 g W = 6.33 g WO_3, a result almost identical to the calculated result.

6.12 First, find the limiting reagent.

$$19.4 \text{ g C}_2\text{H}_4 \; \times \; \frac{1 \text{ mol C}_2\text{H}_4}{28.0 \text{ g C}_2\text{H}_4} \; = \; 0.693 \text{ mol C}_2\text{H}_4; \; \; 50 \text{ g HCl} \; \times \; \frac{1 \text{ mol HCl}}{36.5 \text{ g HCl}} \; = \; 1.4 \text{ mol HCl}$$

Ethylene is the limiting reagent.

$$19.4 \text{ g ethylene} \; \times \; \frac{1 \text{ mol ethylene}}{28.0 \text{ g ethylene}} \; \times \; \frac{1 \text{ mol ethyl chloride}}{1 \text{ mol ethylene}} \; \times \; \frac{64.5 \text{ g ethyl chloride}}{1 \text{ mol ethyl chloride}}$$

$$= \; 44.7 \text{ g ethyl chloride}$$

$$\frac{25.5 \text{ g ethyl chloride actually formed}}{44.7 \text{ g theoretical yield of ethyl chloride}} \; \times \; 100\% \; = \; 57.0\%$$

Ballpark check: The amount of ethylene reactant corresponds to about 2/3 mol. The theoretical yield of product is about 2/3 mol ethyl chloride (somewhat more than 40 g). Since the actual yield is 25.5 g, the percent yield should be around 60%.

6.13 Note: to save space, ethylene oxide will be represented as EO, and ethylene glycol as EG.

$$35.0 \text{ g EO } \times \frac{1 \text{ mol EO}}{44.0 \text{ g EO}} \times \frac{1 \text{ mol EG}}{1 \text{ mol EO}} \times \frac{62.0 \text{ g EG}}{1 \text{ mol EG}} = 49.3 \text{ g ethylene glycol}$$

This quantity represents the maximum possible amount of ethylene glycol that can be produced. If the reaction occurs in 96.0% yield, then 49.3 g EG x 0.960 = 47.3 g EG is actually formed.

Ballpark check: A bit more than 3/4 mol EO is used to produce the same number of mol of EG, corresponding to about 47 g EG, close to the calculated result. The percent yield is also in close agreement.

6.14

$$8.0 \text{ mg } \times \frac{1 \text{ g}}{10^3 \text{ mg}} \times \frac{1 \text{ mol}}{55.8 \text{ g}} = 1.4 \times 10^{-4} \text{ mol for adult males}$$

$$18 \text{ mg } \times \frac{1 \text{ g}}{10^3 \text{ mg}} \times \frac{1 \text{ mol}}{55.8 \text{ g}} = 3.2 \times 10^{-4} \text{ mol for premenopausal women}$$

6.15 According to the equation $A_2 + 2 B_2 \longrightarrow 2 AB_2$, two B_2 are needed for each A_2. In the illustration, there are seven A_2 and 17 B_2. Since the seven A_2 can consume only 14 B_2, A_2 is the limiting reagent.

Understanding Key Concepts

6.16 Methionine: $C_5H_{11}NO_2S$

At. wt of 5 C = 5 x 12.0 amu =	60.0 amu
At. wt of 11 H = 11 x 1.0 amu =	11.0 amu
At. wt of N =	14.0 amu
At. wt of 2 O = 2 x 16.0 amu =	32.0 amu
At. wt of S =	32.1 amu
MW of $C_5H_{11}NO_2S$	= 149.1 amu

6.17 (a) $A_2 + 3 B_2 \longrightarrow 2 AB_3$

(b) $1.0 \text{ mol } A_2 \times \dfrac{2 \text{ mol } AB_3}{1 \text{ mol } A_2} = 2.0 \text{ mol } AB_3$

$1.0 \text{ mol } B_2 \times \dfrac{2 \text{ mol } AB_3}{3 \text{ mol } B_2} = 0.67 \text{ mol } AB_3$

6.18 There are 10 molecules of A and 7 molecules of B_2. According to the equation, 10 molecules of AB can theoretically be formed, with two molecules of B_2 left over.

6.19 B_2 is the limiting reagent. Since there are 11 B_2 in (a) but only 8 AB_2 in (b), the percent yield is 8/11 x 100% = 73%.

6.20 *Note:* To save space, ethylene oxide will be represented as EO, and ethylene glycol as EG.

$$9.0 \text{ g H}_2\text{O} \times \frac{1 \text{ mol H}_2\text{O}}{18.0 \text{ g H}_2\text{O}} \times \frac{1 \text{ mol EO}}{1 \text{ mol H}_2\text{O}} \times \frac{44.0 \text{ g EO}}{1 \text{ mol EO}} = 22 \text{ g ethylene oxide}$$

$$9.0 \text{ g H}_2\text{O} \times \frac{1 \text{ mol H}_2\text{O}}{18.0 \text{ g H}_2\text{O}} \times \frac{1 \text{ mol EG}}{1 \text{ mol H}_2\text{O}} \times \frac{62.0 \text{ g EG}}{1 \text{ mol EG}} = 31 \text{ g ethylene glycol}$$

Molar Masses and Moles

6.21 One mole of a substance is an amount equal to its formula weight in grams. One mole of a molecular compound contains 6.022×10^{23} molecules.

6.22 Molecular weight is the sum of the atomic weights of the individual atoms in a molecule. Formula weight is the sum of the atomic weights of the individual atoms in a formula unit of any compound, whether molecular or ionic.
Molar mass is the mass in grams of 6.022×10^{23} molecules or formula units of any substance.

6.23

$$\frac{6.022 \times 10^{23} \text{ units Na}_2\text{SO}_4}{1 \text{ mol Na}_2\text{SO}_4} \times \frac{2 \text{ Na}^+ \text{ ions}}{1 \text{ unit Na}_2\text{SO}_4} = \frac{1.204 \times 10^{24} \text{ Na}^+ \text{ ions}}{1 \text{ mol Na}_2\text{SO}_4}$$

$$\frac{6.022 \times 10^{23} \text{ units Na}_2\text{SO}_4}{1 \text{ mol Na}_2\text{SO}_4} \times \frac{1 \text{ SO}_4^{2-} \text{ ion}}{1 \text{ unit Na}_2\text{SO}_4} = \frac{6.022 \times 10^{23} \text{ SO}_4^{2-} \text{ ions}}{1 \text{ mol Na}_2\text{SO}_4}$$

6.24 Each formula unit of K_2SO_4 contains three ions—two K^+ ions and one SO_4^{2-} ion. Thus, one mole of K_2SO_4 contains three moles of ions, and

$$1.75 \text{ mol K}_2\text{SO}_4 \times \frac{3 \text{ mol ions}}{1 \text{ mol K}_2\text{SO}_4} = 5.25 \text{ mol ions}$$

6.25

$$16.2 \text{ g Ca} \times \frac{1 \text{ mol}}{40.1 \text{ g Ca}} \times \frac{6.022 \times 10^{23} \text{ atoms}}{1 \text{ mol}} = 2.43 \times 10^{23} \text{ atoms}$$

6.26

$$2.68 \times 10^{22} \text{ atoms} \times \frac{1 \text{ mol}}{6.022 \times 10^{23} \text{ atoms}} \times \frac{238.0 \text{ g}}{1 \text{ mol}} = 10.6 \text{ g uranium}$$

6.27–6.29

Compound	Molar Mass	Moles C	Atoms C	Grams C
(a) $CaCO_3$	100.1 g	1	6.022×10^{23}	12.0
(b) $CO(NH_2)_2$	60.0	1	6.022×10^{23}	12.0
(c) $C_2H_6O_2$	62.0	2	1.204×10^{24}	24.0

6.30 Molar mass of caffeine = 194 g

$$125 \text{ mg caffeine} \times \frac{1 \text{ g}}{10^3 \text{ mg}} \times \frac{1 \text{ mol caffeine}}{194 \text{ g caffeine}} = 6.44 \times 10^{-4} \text{ mol caffeine}$$

6.31 Molar mass of aspirin = 180 g

$$500 \text{ mg aspirin } \times \frac{1 \text{ g}}{10^3 \text{ mg}} \times \frac{1 \text{ mol aspirin}}{180 \text{ g aspirin}} = 2.78 \times 10^{-3} \text{ mol aspirin}$$

6.32 Molar mass of $C_{16}H_{13}ClN_2O$:
(16 x 12.0 g) + (13 x 1.0 g) + (35.5 g) + (2 x 14.0 g) + 16.0 g = 284.5 g/ mol Valium

6.33, 6.34, 6.37

Compound	Molar Mass	Number of Moles in 4.50 g	Number of Grams in 0.075 mol
(a) $Al_2(SO_4)_3$	342.3 g	0.0131 mol	26 g
(b) $NaHCO_3$	84.0 g	0.0536 mol	6.3 g
(c) $C_4H_{10}O$	74.0 g	0.0608 mol	5.6 g
(d) $C_{16}H_{18}N_2O_5S$	350.1 g	0.0129 mol	26 g

Note: Slightly different values for molar mass result when exact atomic weights are used.

6.35 Note: For simplicity, calcium citrate is indicated by "C cit", and 1000 mg = 1.00 g

$$1.00 \text{ g Ca } \times \frac{1 \text{ mol Ca}}{40.1 \text{ g Ca}} \times \frac{1 \text{ mol C cit}}{3 \text{ mol Ca}} \times \frac{498.5 \text{ g C cit}}{1 \text{ mol C cit}} = 4.14 \text{ g calcium citrate}$$

6.36 Molar mass of aspirin = 180 g

$$0.0015 \text{ mol aspirin } \times \frac{180 \text{ g aspirin}}{1 \text{ mol aspirin}} = 0.27 \text{ g aspirin}$$

$$0.0015 \text{ mol } \times \frac{6.022 \times 10^{23} \text{ molecules}}{1 \text{ mol}} = 9.0 \times 10^{20} \text{ molecules aspirin}$$

6.38

$$8.5 \times 10^{20} \text{ formula units } \times \frac{1 \text{ mol}}{6.022 \times 10^{23} \text{ formula units}} = 1.4 \times 10^{-3} \text{ mol}$$

$$0.0014 \text{ mol } CaC_2O_4 \times \frac{128 \text{ g } CaC_2O_4}{1 \text{ mol } CaC_2O_4} = 0.18 \text{ g } CaC_2O_4$$

Mole and Mass Relationships from Chemical Equations

6.39 (a) $N_2(g) + O_2(g) \longrightarrow 2 NO(g)$

(b) 7.50 mol of N_2 are needed to react with 7.50 mol of O_2.

(c) $3.81 \text{ mol } N_2 \times \frac{2 \text{ mol NO}}{1 \text{ mol } N_2} = 7.62 \text{ mol NO}$

(d) $0.250 \text{ mol NO } \times \frac{1 \text{ mol } O_2}{2 \text{ mol NO}} = 0.125 \text{ mol } O_2$

6.40   (a) $C_4H_8O_2(l) + 2 H_2(g) \longrightarrow 2 C_2H_6O(l)$

(b) 3.0 mol of ethyl alcohol are produced from 1.5 mol of ethyl acetate.

(c) $1.5 \text{ mol } C_4H_8O_2 \times \dfrac{2 \text{ mol } C_2H_6O}{1 \text{ mol } C_4H_8O_2} \times \dfrac{46.0 \text{ g } C_2H_6O}{1 \text{ mol } C_2H_6O} = 138 \text{ g } C_2H_6O$

(d) $12.0 \text{ g } C_4H_8O_2 \times \dfrac{1 \text{ mol } C_4H_8O_2}{88.0 \text{ g } C_4H_8O_2} \times \dfrac{2 \text{ mol } C_2H_6O}{1 \text{ mol } C_4H_8O_2} \times \dfrac{46.0 \text{ g } C_2H_6O}{1 \text{ mol } C_2H_6O}$

$= 12.5 \text{ g } C_2H_6O$

(e) $12.0 \text{ g } C_4H_8O_2 \times \dfrac{1 \text{ mol } C_4H_8O_2}{88.0 \text{ g } C_4H_8O_2} \times \dfrac{2 \text{ mol } H_2}{1 \text{ mol } C_4H_8O_2} \times \dfrac{2.02 \text{ g } H_2}{1 \text{ mol } H_2} = 0.551 \text{ g } H_2$

6.41   (a) Molar mass of $Mg(OH)_2 = 24.3 \text{ g} + (2 \times 16.0 \text{ g}) + (2 \times 1.0 \text{ g}) = 58.3 \text{ g}$

(b) $1.2 \text{ g } Mg(OH)_2 \times \dfrac{1 \text{ mol } Mg(OH)_2}{58.3 \text{ g } Mg(OH)_2} = 0.021 \text{ mol } Mg(OH)_2$

Since there are 3 teaspoons in a tablespoon, the dose per teaspoon is 0.0070 mol.

6.42   (a) $N_2(g) + 3 H_2(g) \longrightarrow 2 NH_3(g)$

(b) $16.0 \text{ g } NH_3 \times \dfrac{1 \text{ mol } NH_3}{17.0 \text{ g } NH_3} \times \dfrac{1 \text{ mol } N_2}{2 \text{ mol } NH_3} = 0.471 \text{ mol } N_2$

(c) $75.0 \text{ g } N_2 \times \dfrac{1 \text{ mol } N_2}{28.0 \text{ g } N_2} \times \dfrac{3 \text{ mol } H_2}{1 \text{ mol } N_2} \times \dfrac{2.02 \text{ g } H_2}{1 \text{ mol } H_2} = 16.2 \text{ g } H_2$

6.43   (a) $N_2H_4(l) + 3 O_2(g) \longrightarrow 2 NO_2(g) + 2 H_2O(g)$

(b) $165 \text{ g } N_2H_4 \times \dfrac{1 \text{ mol } N_2H_4}{32.0 \text{ g } N_2H_4} \times \dfrac{3 \text{ mol } O_2}{1 \text{ mol } N_2H_4} = 15.5 \text{ mol } O_2$

(c) $15.5 \text{ mol } O_2 \times \dfrac{32.0 \text{ g } O_2}{1 \text{ mol } O_2} = 496 \text{ g } O_2$

6.44   (a) $Fe_2O_3(s) + 3 CO(g) \longrightarrow 2 Fe(s) + 3 CO_2(g)$

(b) $3.02 \text{ g } Fe_2O_3 \times \dfrac{1 \text{ mol } Fe_2O_3}{159.7 \text{ g } Fe_2O_3} \times \dfrac{3 \text{ mol } CO}{1 \text{ mol } Fe_2O_3} \times \dfrac{28.0 \text{ g } CO}{1 \text{ mol } CO} = 1.59 \text{ g } CO$

(c) $1.68 \text{ mol } Fe_2O_3 \times \dfrac{3 \text{ mol } CO}{1 \text{ mol } Fe_2O_3} \times \dfrac{28.0 \text{ g } CO}{1 \text{ mol } CO} = 141 \text{ g } CO$

6.45   (a) $2\,Mg(s) + O_2(g) \longrightarrow 2\,MgO(s)$

(b) $25.0\,g\,Mg \times \dfrac{1\,mol\,Mg}{24.3\,g\,Mg} \times \dfrac{1\,mol\,O_2}{2\,mol\,Mg} \times \dfrac{32.0\,g\,O_2}{1\,mol\,O_2} = 16.5\,g\,O_2$

41.5 g MgO will result from reaction of 25.0 g Mg and 16.5 g O_2.

(c) $25.0\,g\,O_2 \times \dfrac{1\,mol\,O_2}{32.0\,g\,O_2} \times \dfrac{2\,mol\,Mg}{1\,mol\,O_2} \times \dfrac{24.3\,g\,Mg}{1\,mol\,Mg} = 38.0\,g\,Mg$

63.0 g MgO will result from reaction of 25.0 g O_2 and 38.0 g Mg.

6.46 $TiO_2(s) \longrightarrow Ti(s) + O_2(g)$

$95\,kg\,Ti \times \dfrac{1\,mol\,Ti}{47.9\,g\,Ti} \times \dfrac{1\,mol\,TiO_2}{1\,mol\,Ti} \times \dfrac{79.9\,g\,TiO_2}{1\,mol\,TiO_2} = 158\,kg\,TiO_2$

6.47

$105\,kg\,Fe_2O_3 \times \dfrac{10^3\,g}{1\,kg} \times \dfrac{1\,mol\,Fe_2O_3}{159.7\,g\,Fe_2O_3} \times \dfrac{3\,mol\,CO}{1\,mol\,Fe_2O_3} = 1.97 \times 10^3\,mol\,CO$

6.48

$4 \times 10^8\,kg\,SO_2 \times \dfrac{10^3\,g}{1\,kg} \times \dfrac{1\,mol}{64\,g} = 6 \times 10^9\,mol$

$6 \times 10^9\,mol\,H_2SO_4 \times \dfrac{98\,g}{1\,mol} \times \dfrac{1\,kg}{1 \times 10^3\,g} = 6 \times 10^8\,kg\,H_2SO_4$

6.49

$1.5\,kg\,Fe_2O_3 \times \dfrac{10^3\,g}{1\,kg} \times \dfrac{1\,mol\,Fe_2O_3}{159.7\,g} \times \dfrac{2\,mol\,Fe}{1\,mol\,Fe_2O_3} = 19\,mol\,Fe$

6.50   Two moles of SO_2 are produced from each mole of pyrite.

$1.0\,kg\,FeS_2 \times \dfrac{10^3\,g}{1\,kg} \times \dfrac{1\,mol\,FeS_2}{119.7\,g} \times \dfrac{2\,mol\,SO_2}{1\,mol\,FeS_2} = 17\,mol\,SO_2$

6.51

$7.5\,mol\,O_2 \times \dfrac{1\,mol\,B_2H_6}{3\,mol\,O_2} \times \dfrac{27.67\,g\,B_2H_6}{1\,mol\,B_2H_6} = 69\,g\,B_2H_6$

Percent Yield

6.52

(a) $25.0\,g\,CO \times \dfrac{1\,mol\,CO}{28.0\,g\,CO} = 0.893\,mol\,CO$; $6.00\,g\,H_2 \times \dfrac{1\,mol\,H_2}{2.02\,g\,H_2} = 2.97\,mol\,H_2$

Carbon monoxide is the limiting reagent.

(b) $10.0\,g\,CO \times \dfrac{1\,mol\,CO}{28.0\,g\,CO} \times \dfrac{1\,mol\,CH_3OH}{1\,mol\,CO} \times \dfrac{32.0\,g\,CH_3OH}{1\,mol\,CH_3OH} = 11.4\,g\,CH_3OH$

(c) $\dfrac{9.55\,g}{11.4\,g} \times 100\% = 83.8\%$ yield

6.53

(a) $75.0 \text{ kg N}_2\text{H}_4 \text{ x } \dfrac{1 \text{ kmol N}_2\text{H}_4}{32.0 \text{ kg N}_2\text{H}_4} = 2.34 \text{ kmol N}_2\text{H}_4$

$75.0 \text{ kg O}_2 \text{ x } \dfrac{1 \text{ kmol O}_2}{32.0 \text{ kg O}_2} = 2.34 \text{ kmol O}_2$

Although the same number of moles of each are present, O_2 is the limiting reagent because three moles of O_2 are needed to react with each mole of hydrazine, according to the balanced equation.

(b) $75.0 \text{ kg O}_2 \text{ x } \dfrac{1 \text{ kmol O}_2}{32.0 \text{ kg O}_2} \text{ x } \dfrac{2 \text{ kmol NO}_2}{3 \text{ kmol O}_2} \text{ x } \dfrac{46.0 \text{ kg NO}_2}{1 \text{ kmol NO}_2} = 71.9 \text{ kg NO}_2$

(c) $\dfrac{59.3 \text{ g actually formed}}{71.9 \text{ g theoretical yield}} \text{ x } 100\% = 82.5\%$

6.54 (a) $CH_4(g) + 2 Cl_2(g) \longrightarrow CH_2Cl_2(l) + 2 HCl(g)$

(b) $50.0 \text{ g CH}_4 \text{ x } \dfrac{1 \text{ mol CH}_4}{16.0 \text{ g CH}_4} \text{ x } \dfrac{2 \text{ mol Cl}_2}{1 \text{ mol CH}_4} \text{ x } \dfrac{71.0 \text{ g Cl}_2}{1 \text{ mol Cl}_2} = 444 \text{ g Cl}_2$

(c) If the reaction occurred in 100% yield:

$50.0 \text{ g CH}_4 \text{ x } \dfrac{1 \text{ mol CH}_4}{16.0 \text{ g CH}_4} \text{ x } \dfrac{1 \text{ mol CH}_2\text{Cl}_2}{1 \text{ mol CH}_4} \text{ x } \dfrac{85.0 \text{ g CH}_2\text{Cl}_2}{1 \text{ mol CH}_2\text{Cl}_2} = 266 \text{ g CH}_2\text{Cl}_2$

Since the reaction occurs in 76% yield:

$266 \text{ g x } 0.76 = 202 \text{ g CH}_2\text{Cl}_2$ are actually formed.

6.55

(a) $55.8 \text{ g K}_2\text{PtCl}_4 \text{ x } \dfrac{1 \text{ mol K}_2\text{PtCl}_4}{415.3 \text{ g K}_2\text{PtCl}_4} \text{ x } \dfrac{2 \text{ mol NH}_3}{1 \text{ mol K}_2\text{PtCl}_4} \text{ x } \dfrac{17.0 \text{ g NH}_3}{1 \text{ mol NH}_3} = 4.57 \text{ g NH}_3$

(b) If the reaction occurred in 100% yield:

$55.8 \text{ g K}_2\text{PtCl}_4 \text{ x } \dfrac{1 \text{ mol K}_2\text{PtCl}_4}{415.3 \text{ g K}_2\text{PtCl}_4} \text{ x } \dfrac{1 \text{ mol cisplatin}}{1 \text{ mol K}_2\text{PtCl}_4} \text{ x } \dfrac{300.1 \text{ g cisplatin}}{1 \text{ mol cisplatin}}$

$= 40.3 \text{ g cisplatin}$

Since the reaction occurs in 95% yield, $40.3 \text{ g x } 0.95 = 38 \text{ g cisplatin}$ are actually formed.

6.56

(a) $75 \text{ g C}_6\text{H}_6 \text{ x } \dfrac{1 \text{ mol C}_6\text{H}_6}{78 \text{ g C}_6\text{H}_6} = 0.96 \text{ mol C}_6\text{H}_6$

$27.5 \text{ g HNO}_3 \text{ x } \dfrac{1 \text{ mol HNO}_3}{63.0 \text{ g HNO}_3} = 0.437 \text{ mol HNO}_3$

Nitric acid is the limiting reagent.

(b) $0.437 \text{ mol HNO}_3 \text{ x } \dfrac{1 \text{ mol C}_6\text{H}_5\text{NO}_2}{1 \text{ mol HNO}_3} \text{ x } \dfrac{123 \text{ g}}{1 \text{ mol C}_6\text{H}_5\text{NO}_2} = 53.8 \text{ g C}_6\text{H}_5\text{NO}_2$

6.57

$$\frac{48.2 \text{ g}}{53.8 \text{ g}} \times 100\% = 89.6\%$$

Chemistry in Action

6.58 The most serious error in calculating Avogadro's number by spreading oil on water is the estimate of the size of the area the oil covered. Some approximations that Franklin made, but that can be determined with reasonable precision, are the volume of oil, the mass of the oil, its density and its molar mass. Other assumptions, involving the thickness of the oil layer and the arrangement of oil molecules on the surface of the water, are also sources of error.

6.59

$$8 \text{ mg Fe} \times \frac{1 \text{ g}}{10^3 \text{ mg}} \times \frac{1 \text{ mol Fe}}{55.8 \text{ g Fe}} \times \frac{4 \text{ mol O}_2}{1 \text{ mol Fe}} = 6 \times 10^{-4} \text{ mol O}_2$$

6.60 The formula for ferrous sulfate is $FeSO_4$. Its molar mass is 151.9 g/mol.

$$250 \text{ mg FeSO}_4 \times \frac{55.8 \text{ g Fe}}{151.9 \text{ g FeSO}_4} = 91.8 \text{ mg Fe}$$

General Questions and Problems

6.61

(a) $15.0 \text{ g Zn} \times \dfrac{1 \text{ mol Zn}}{65.4 \text{ g Zn}} \times \dfrac{1 \text{ mol H}_2}{1 \text{ mol Zn}} \times \dfrac{2.02 \text{ g H}_2}{1 \text{ mol H}_2} = 0.463 \text{ g H}_2$

(b) In this redox reaction, H^+ is reduced (oxidizing agent) and Zn is oxidized (reducing agent).

6.62 Molar mass of batrachotoxin $(C_{31}H_{42}N_2O_6) = 538$ g/mol

$$0.05 \text{ μg} \times \frac{1 \text{ g}}{10^6 \text{ μg}} \times \frac{1 \text{ mol}}{538 \text{ g}} \times \frac{6.022 \times 10^{23} \text{ molecules}}{1 \text{ mol}} = 6 \times 10^{13} \text{ molecules}$$

6.63 (a) 24 C x (12.0 amu) + 36 H x (1.00 amu) + 5 O x (16 amu) = 404 amu
molar mass = 404 g/mol

(b) $10 \text{ mg lovastatin} \times \dfrac{1 \text{ g}}{10^3 \text{ mg}} \times \dfrac{1 \text{ mol}}{404 \text{ g}} = 2.5 \times 10^{-5} \text{ mol lovastatin}$

6.64 (a) $C_{12}H_{22}O_{11}(s) \longrightarrow 12\,C(s) + 11\,H_2O(l)$

(b) $60.0\text{ g sucrose} \times \dfrac{1\text{ mol sucrose}}{342\text{ g sucrose}} \times \dfrac{12\text{ mol C}}{1\text{ mol sucrose}} \times \dfrac{12.0\text{ g C}}{1\text{ mol C}} = 25.3\text{ g carbon}$

(c) $6.50\text{ g C} \times \dfrac{1\text{ mol C}}{12.0\text{ g C}} \times \dfrac{11\text{ mol }H_2O}{12\text{ mol C}} \times \dfrac{18.0\text{ g }H_2O}{1\text{ mol }H_2O} = 8.94\text{ g }H_2O$

6.65 (a) $Cu(s) + 4\,H^+(aq) + 2\,NO_3^-(aq) \longrightarrow Cu^{2+}(aq) + 2\,NO_2(g) + 2\,H_2O(l)$

(b) $35.0\text{ g }HNO_3 \times \dfrac{1\text{ mol }HNO_3}{63.0\text{ g }HNO_3} \times \dfrac{1\text{ mol Cu}}{4\text{ mol }HNO_3} \times \dfrac{63.5\text{ g Cu}}{1\text{ mol Cu}} = 8.82\text{ g Cu}$

$35.0\text{ g }HNO_3$ is more than enough to dissolve 5.00 g Cu.

6.66

(a) $1.50\text{ g }C_2H_6O \times \dfrac{1\text{ mol }C_2H_6O}{46.0\text{ g }C_2H_6O} \times \dfrac{2\text{ mol }K_2Cr_2O_7}{3\text{ mol }C_2H_6O} \times \dfrac{294.2\text{ g }K_2Cr_2O_7}{1\text{ mol }K_2Cr_2O_7}$

$= 6.40\text{ g }K_2Cr_2O_7$

(b) $80.0\text{ g }C_2H_6O \times \dfrac{1\text{ mol }C_2H_6O}{46.0\text{ g }C_2H_6O} \times \dfrac{3\text{ mol }C_2H_4O_2}{3\text{ mol }C_2H_6O} \times \dfrac{60.0\text{ g }C_2H_4O_2}{1\text{ mol }C_2H_4O_2}$

$= 104\text{ g }C_2H_4O_2$

6.67

$100.0\text{ lb }C_6H_{12}O_6 \times \dfrac{454\text{ g}}{1\text{ lb}} \times \dfrac{1\text{ mol }C_6H_{12}O_6}{180.0\text{ g }C_6H_{12}O_6} \times \dfrac{2\text{ mol }C_2H_6O}{1\text{ mol }C_6H_{12}O_6} \times \dfrac{46.0\text{ g }C_2H_6O}{1\text{ mol }C_2H_6O}$

$= 2.32 \times 10^4\text{ g }C_2H_6O$

$2.32 \times 10^4\text{ g ethanol} \times \dfrac{1\text{ mL ethanol}}{0.789\text{ g ethanol}} \times \dfrac{1\text{ qt}}{946.4\text{ mL}} = 31.1\text{ qt ethanol}$

6.68 (a) $4\,NH_3(g) + 5\,O_2(g) \longrightarrow 4\,NO(g) + 6\,H_2O(g)$

(b) $17.0\text{ g }NH_3 \times \dfrac{1\text{ mol }NH_3}{17.0\text{ g}} \times \dfrac{1\text{ mol NO}}{1\text{ mol }NH_3} \times \dfrac{30.0\text{ g NO}}{1\text{ mol NO}} = 30.0\text{ g NO}$

6.69 $2\,NaOH(aq) + Cl_2(g) \longrightarrow NaOCl(aq) + NaCl(aq) + H_2O(l)$

$32.5\text{ g NaOH} \times \dfrac{1\text{ mol NaOH}}{40.0\text{ g NaOH}} \times \dfrac{1\text{ mol NaOCl}}{2\text{ mol NaOH}} = 0.406\text{ mol NaOCl}$

6.70 (a) $BaCl_2(aq) + Na_2SO_4(aq) \longrightarrow BaSO_4(s) + 2\,NaCl(aq)$

(b) $27.4\text{ g }Na_2SO_4 \times \dfrac{1\text{ mol }Na_2SO_4}{142\text{ g }Na_2SO_4} \times \dfrac{1\text{ mol }BaSO_4}{1\text{ mol }Na_2SO_4} \times \dfrac{233\text{ g }BaSO_4}{1\text{ mol }BaSO_4}$

$= 45.0\text{ g }BaSO_4$

6.71 (a) $3 NO_2(g) + H_2O(l) \longrightarrow 2 HNO_3(aq) + NO(g)$

(b) $65.0 \text{ g } NO_2 \times \dfrac{1 \text{ mol } NO_2}{46.0 \text{ g } NO_2} \times \dfrac{2 \text{ mol } HNO_3}{3 \text{ mol } NO_2} \times \dfrac{63.0 \text{ g } HNO_3}{1 \text{ mol } HNO_3}$

$= 59.3 \text{ g } HNO_3$

(c) $\dfrac{43.8 \text{ g}}{59.3 \text{ g}} \times 100\% = 73.9\%$

6.72

(a) $47 \text{ g } C_7H_6O_3 \times \dfrac{1 \text{ mol } C_7H_6O_3}{138 \text{ g } C_7H_6O_3} = 0.34 \text{ mol } C_7H_6O_3$

$25 \text{ g } C_4H_6O_3 \times \dfrac{1 \text{ mol } C_4H_6O_3}{102 \text{ g } C_4H_6O_3} = 0.25 \text{ mol } C_4H_6O_3$

Acetic anhydride is the limiting reagent.

$0.25 \text{ mol } C_4H_6O_3 \times \dfrac{1 \text{ mol } C_9H_8O_4}{1 \text{ mol } C_4H_6O_3} \times \dfrac{180 \text{ g } C_9H_8O_4}{1 \text{ mol } C_9H_8O_4} = 45 \text{ g } C_9H_8O_4$

(b) $\dfrac{35 \text{ g}}{45 \text{ g}} \times 100\% = 78\%$

6.73

$15.2 \text{ g } Ag \times \dfrac{1 \text{ mol } Ag}{108 \text{ g } Ag} \times \dfrac{1 \text{ mol } AgNO_3}{1 \text{ mol } Ag} \times \dfrac{170 \text{ g } AgNO_3}{1 \text{ mol } AgNO_3} = 23.9 \text{ g } AgNO_3$

6.74 (a) $P_4(s) + 10 Cl_2(g) \longrightarrow 4 PCl_5(s)$

(b) $15.2 \text{ g } P_4 \times \dfrac{1 \text{ mol } P_4}{124 \text{ g } P_4} \times \dfrac{4 \text{ mol } PCl_5}{1 \text{ mol } P_4} \times \dfrac{208 \text{ g } PCl_5}{1 \text{ mol } PCl_5} = 102 \text{ g } PCl_5$

6.75

$80.0 \text{ kg } H_2O \times \dfrac{1 \text{ mol } H_2O}{18.0 \text{ g } H_2O} \times \dfrac{1 \text{ mol } Li_2O}{1 \text{ mol } H_2O} \times \dfrac{29.8 \text{ g } Li_2O}{1 \text{ mol } Li_2O} = 132 \text{ kg } Li_2O$

6.76 (a) $6 NH_4ClO_4(s) + 10 Al(s) \longrightarrow 4 Al_2O_3(s) + 2 AlCl_3(s) + 12 H_2O(g) + 3 N_2(g)$

(b) $14.5 \times 10^3 \text{ g } NH_4ClO_4 \times \dfrac{1 \text{ mol } NH_4ClO_4}{117 \text{ g } NH_4ClO_4} \times \dfrac{15 \text{ mol gases}}{6 \text{ mol } NH_4ClO_4} = 310 \text{ mol gases}$

Remember that both water and nitrogen are gases in this problem.

Self-Test for Chapter 6

Multiple Choice

1.   What mass of $CaCO_3$ has the same number of molecules as 21 g of NaF?
(a) 10 g   (b) 20 g   (c) 50 g   (d) 100 g

2.   Consider the following equation: $LiOH + CO_2 \longrightarrow LiHCO_3$. In which situation is LiOH the limiting reagent?
(a) 6 g $LiOH$ + 11 g CO_2 (b) 10 g $LiOH$ + 16 g CO_2
(c) 4 g $LiOH$ + 7 g CO_2 (d) 9 g $LiOH$ + 17 g CO_2

3.   In the equation $P_2O_5 + 3 H_2O \longrightarrow 2 H_3PO_4$ the mole ratio of product to H_2O is:
(a) 2:1   (b) 2:3   (c) 3:2   (d) 1:2

4.   In the reaction $2 Ca + O_2 \longrightarrow 2 CaO$, how many grams of CaO can be produced from 20 g of Ca? (a) 20 g   (b) 28 g   (c) 40 g   (d) 56 g

5. $3 NO_2 + H_2O \longrightarrow 2 HNO_3 + NO$

All the following statements about this reaction are true except:
(a) The starting material is both oxidized and reduced.
(b) NO_2 in the atmosphere might contribute to acid rain.
(c) At least 6 g of H_2O are needed to react completely with 46 g of NO_2.
(d) 92 g of NO_2 produces 28 g of NO.

True or False

1.   A mole of oxygen atoms has the same mass as a mole of nitrogen atoms.

2.   The coefficients in chemical reactions show the relative numbers of moles of reactants and

products.

3.   Percent yield is the amount of a substance that can theoretically be produced divided by the

amount actually produced.

4.   Mole ratios are used to convert between moles and grams of a compound.

5.   In the reaction $4 Al + 3 O_2 \longrightarrow 2 Al_2O_3$, the mole ratio of product to Al is 2.

Match each entry on the left with its partner on the right.

1.   42.0 amu   (a) Converts moles Na to grams Na

2.   23.0 g sodium / 1 mol   (b) Molar mass of NaF

3.   42.0 g   (c) Converts grams Na to moles Na

4.   1 mol / 23.0 g sodium   (d) Avogadro's number

5. 6.02×10^{23} (e) Formula weight of NaF

Chapter Outline

I. Energy (Sections 7.1–7.4).
  A. Energy and chemical bonds (Section 7.1).
    1. There are two kinds of energy.
      a. Potential energy is stored energy.
      b. Kinetic energy is the energy of motion.
    2. Chemical bonds are a form of potential energy.
    3. Whether a reaction occurs, and how much heat is associated, depends on the potential energy of reactants and products.
  B. Heat changes during chemical reactions (Section 7.2).
    1. Bond dissociation energies measure the strength of covalent bonds.
      a. Bond breaking requires heat and is endothermic.
      b. Bond formation releases heat and is exothermic.
    2. The reverse of an endothermic process is exothermic, and the reverse of an exothermic process is endothermic.
    3. The law of conservation of energy states that energy can neither be created nor destroyed during any physical or chemical change.
    4. The difference between the energy needed for breaking bonds and the energy released in forming bonds is the heat of reaction, also known as enthalpy (ΔH).
  C. Exothermic and endothermic reactions: ΔH (Section 7.3).
    1. In exothermic reactions, the bond dissociation energies of the products are greater than the bond dissociation energies of the reactants, and ΔH is negative.
    2. In endothermic reactions, the bond dissociation energies of the products are smaller than the bond dissociation energies of the reactants, and ΔH is positive.
    3. The amount of heat released in the reverse of a reaction is equal to that absorbed in the forward reaction, but ΔH has the opposite sign.
    4. The heat of reaction can be determined by the formula:
      $\Delta H = \Sigma$ (bond dissociation energies)$_{\text{reactants}}$ – Σ(bond dissociation energies)$_{\text{products}}$
  D. Free energy: ΔG (Section 7.4).
    1. Spontaneous processes.
      a. A spontaneous process proceeds without any external influence.
      b. A nonspontaneous process needs a constant external source of energy.
    2. Entropy (ΔS) measures the amount of disorder in a system.
      a. If disorder increases, ΔS is positive.
      b. If disorder decreases, ΔS is negative.
    3. The absorption of heat and the increase or decrease in disorder determine if a reaction is spontaneous.
      a. $\Delta G = \Delta H - T\Delta S$.
      b. If ΔG is negative, the process is spontaneous, and the reaction is exergonic.
      c. If ΔG is positive, the process isn't spontaneous, and the reaction is endergonic.
    4. ΔG for the reverse of a reaction is equal in value to ΔG for the forward reaction, but the sign is changed.
    5. Some nonspontaneous processes become spontaneous when temperature increases.
II. Reaction rates (Sections 7.5–7.6).
  A. How reactions occur (Section 7.5).
    1. In addition to the value of ΔG, other factors determine if a reaction will occur.
      a. Reactants must collide in the correct orientation.
      b. The energy of collision must be great enough to cause bond breaking.

      c. Many reactions with a favorable free energy don't occur at room temperature, and heat must be added to get them started.

   2. The energy changes during a reaction can be graphed on a reaction energy diagram.

   3. The amount of energy needed to produce favorable collisions is the activation energy E_{act}.

      a. E_{act} determines the reaction rate.

      b. The size of E_{act} is unrelated to the size of ΔH.

  B. Factors that affect reaction rate (Section 7.6).

   1. Increasing temperature increases reaction rate.

   2. Increasing the concentration of reactants increases reaction rate.

   3. Catalysts increase the reaction rate by lowering E_{act}.

III. Chemical equilibrium (Sections 7.7–7.9).

  A. Reversible reactions (Section 7.7).

   1. Some reactions proceed to virtual completion.

   2. Other reactions go to partial completion, at which point products begin to reform starting material.

      a. These reactions are reversible.

      b. The reaction from left to right is the forward reaction.

      c. The reaction from right to left is the reverse reaction.

   3. At some point the rate of the forward reaction equals the rate of the reverse reaction, and equilibrium is established.

   4. It is not necessary for the concentrations of products and reactants to be equal at equilibrium.

  B. Equilibrium (Section 7.8).

   1. Equilibrium equations.

      a. For the reaction $a\text{ A} + b\text{ B} \longrightarrow c\text{ C} + d\text{ D}$,

$$K = \frac{[C]^c[D]^d}{[A]^a[B]^b}$$

      b. K = equilibrium constant.

      c. Expression on the right = equilibrium constant expression.

      d. The concentrations of pure solids or liquids are omitted from the equilibrium expression.

   2. The value of K determines the position of equilibrium.

      a. When $K \gg 1$, reaction goes to completion.

      b. When $K > 1$, the forward reaction is favored.

      c. When K is of intermediate value, significant amounts of reactants and products are present at equilibrium.

      d. When $K < 1$, the reverse reaction is favored.

      e. When $K \ll 1$, there is essentially no reaction.

  C. Effect of changing reaction conditions (Section 7.9).

   1. Le Châtelier's principle: When a stress is applied to a system, the equilibrium shifts to remove the stress.

   2. Effect of changing concentration.

      a. Increasing the concentration of reactants favors the forward reaction.

      b. Increasing the concentration of products favors the reverse reaction.

   3. Effect of changing temperature.

      a. Decreasing temperature favors an exothermic reaction.

      b. Increasing temperature favors an endothermic reaction.

   4. Effect of changing pressure.

      a. There is no effect unless one of the reactants or products is a gas.

      b. Increasing pressure shifts the equilibrium in the direction that produces fewer gas molecules.

Solutions to Chapter 7 Problems

7.1   (a) Use the following expression to calculate ΔH:

$\Delta H = \Sigma$ (bond dissociation energies)$_{reactants} - \Sigma$(bond dissociation energies)$_{products}$

$$\begin{aligned}\Sigma \text{ (bond dissociation energies)}_{reactants} &= 12(C=O) + 12(O–H) \\ &= 12(191 \text{ kcal/mol}) + 12(112 \text{ kcal/mol}) \\ &= 3636 \text{ kcal/mol}\end{aligned}$$

$$\begin{aligned}\Sigma \text{(bond dissociation energies)}_{products} &= 5(C–C) + 7(C–H) + 7(C–O) + 5(O–H) + 6(O=O) \\ &= [5(83) + 7(99) + 7(86) + 5(112) + 6(119)] \text{ kcal/mol} \\ &= 2984 \text{ kcal/mol}\end{aligned}$$

$\Delta H = 3636 \text{ kcal/mol} - 2984 \text{ kcal/mol} = +652 \text{ kcal/mol}$
652 kcal/mol x 4.18 kJ/kcal = 2730 kJ/mol

(b) The reaction is endothermic because ΔH is positive.

7.2   (a) The reaction is endothermic because ΔH is positive.

(b) $\dfrac{801 \text{ kcal}}{4 \text{ mol Al}}$ x 1.00 mol Al = 200 kcal (836 kJ) required

(c) 10.0 g Al x $\dfrac{1 \text{ mol Al}}{27.0 \text{ g Al}}$ x $\dfrac{801 \text{ kcal}}{4 \text{ mol Al}}$ = 74.2 kcal (310 kJ) required

7.3

127 g NO x $\dfrac{1 \text{ mol}}{30.0 \text{ g NO}}$ x $\dfrac{43 \text{ kcal}}{2 \text{ mol NO}}$ = 91 kcal (380 kJ) absorbed

7.4 $\Delta H = \Sigma$ (bond dissociation energies)$_{reactants} - \Sigma$(bond dissociation energies)$_{products}$

$$\begin{aligned}\Sigma \text{ (bond dissociation energies)}_{reactants} &= (C–C) + 5(C–H) + (C–O) + (O–H) + 3(O=O) \\ &= [83 + 5(99) + 86 + 112 + 3(119)] \text{ kcal/mol} \\ &= 1133 \text{ kcal/mol}\end{aligned}$$

$$\begin{aligned}\Sigma \text{(bond dissociation energies)}_{products} &= 4(C=O) + 6(O–H) \\ &= [4(191) + 6(112)] \text{ kcal/mol} = 1436 \text{ kcal/mol}\end{aligned}$$

$\Delta H = 1133 \text{ kcal/mol} - 1436 \text{ kcal/mol} = -303 \text{ kcal/mol}$

$\dfrac{303 \text{ kcal}}{1 \text{ mol}}$ x $\dfrac{1 \text{ mol}}{46 \text{ g}}$ x $\dfrac{1 \text{ Cal}}{1 \text{ kcal}}$ = $\dfrac{6.59 \text{ Cal}}{1 \text{ g}}$

This value agrees fairly well with the caloric value of alcohol (7.1 Cal/g) shown in Table 7.1

7.5   (a) Entropy increases because the number of molecules increases.
(b) Entropy decreases because disorder decreases when gases condense.
(c) Entropy decreases because two moles of gaseous product are formed from three moles of gaseous reactants.

7.6   (a) $\Delta G = \Delta H - T\Delta S$: $\Delta H = +42.6\ kcal/mol$ $\Delta S = +38.6\ cal/(mol \cdot K)$ $T = 298\ K$
$\Delta G = +42.6\ kcal/mol - [298\ K \times 38.6\ cal/(mol \cdot K) \times 1\ kcal/10^3\ cal]$
     $= +42.6\ kcal/mol - 11.5\ kcal/mol = +31.1\ kcal/mol = 130\ kJ/mol$
The reaction is not spontaneous at 25 °C.

    (b) The reaction is spontaneous at higher temperatures. In the expression $\Delta G = \Delta H - T\Delta S$, the term $T\Delta S$ becomes larger at high temperature and causes ΔG to become negative.

7.7 $\Delta G = \Delta H - T\Delta S$: $\Delta H = +1.44\ kcal/mol$ $\Delta S = +5.26\ cal/(mol \cdot K)$
(a) If $T = 263\ K$,
$$T\Delta S = 263\ K \times \frac{5.26\ cal}{mol\ K} \times \frac{1\ kcal}{10^3\ cal} = \frac{1.38\ kcal}{mol}$$

$\Delta G = 1.44\ kcal/mol - 1.38\ kcal/mol = +0.06\ kcal/mol = +0.25\ kJ/mol$
At 263 K, melting is not spontaneous because ΔG is positive.

(b) If $T = 273\ K$,
$$T\Delta S = 273\ K \times \frac{5.26\ cal}{mol\ K} \times \frac{1\ kcal}{10^3\ cal} = \frac{1.44\ kcal}{mol}$$

$\Delta G = 1.44\ kcal/mol - 1.44\ kcal/mol = +0.00\ kcal/mol$
At 273 K, $\Delta G = 0$, and melting and freezing are in equilibrium.

(c) If $T = 283\ K$,
$$T\Delta S = 283\ K \times \frac{5.26\ cal}{mol\ K} \times \frac{1\ kcal}{10^3\ cal} = \frac{1.49\ kcal}{mol}$$

$\Delta G = 1.44\ kcal/mol - 1.49\ kcal/mol = -0.05\ kcal/mol = -0.21\ kJ/mol$
At 283 K, melting is spontaneous because ΔG is negative.

7.8   (a) The sign of ΔS is positive because disorder increases from reactant to products.
(b) In the expression $\Delta G = \Delta H - T\Delta S$, ΔH is a negative number. Because ΔS is positive, $(-T\Delta S)$ is negative at all temperatures. Thus, ΔG is negative at all temperatures, and the reaction is spontaneous at all temperatures.

7.9

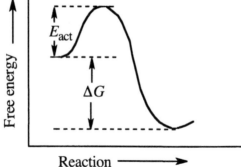

In this reaction, E_{act} is large, the reaction is slow, and the free-energy change is large and negative.

7.10

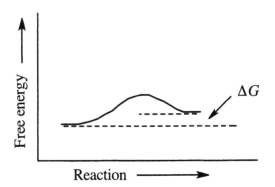

In this reaction, ΔG is small and positive. E_{act} can be small or large, but it is always larger than ΔG.

7.11

(a)

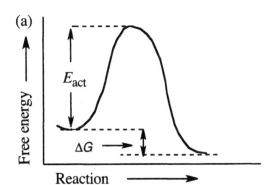

In this reaction, E_{act} is large, and ΔG is small and negative.

(b) The rate of reaction can be increased by either increasing concentration of reactants, increasing the temperature, or adding a catalyst.

7.12 Evaporation of 1.0 g sweat cools the body by 540 cal (0.540 kcal). Removing 678 kcal requires the evaporation of:

$$678 \text{ kcal } \times \frac{1.0 \text{ g}}{0.540 \text{ kcal}} = 1260 \text{ g sweat}$$

7.13

$$K = \frac{[\text{products}]}{[\text{reactants}]}$$

(a) $K = \dfrac{[NO_2]^2}{[N_2O_4]}$ (b) $K = \dfrac{[H_2O]^2}{[H_2S]^2[O_2]}$ (c) $K = \dfrac{[Br_2][F_2]^5}{[BrF_5]^2}$

Don't forget that the coefficients of the reactants and products appear as exponents in the equilibrium expression. In (b), the concentration of solid sulfur doesn't enter into the equation.

7.14 If K is greater than 1, the reaction favors products. If K is less than 1, the reaction favors reactants.
(a) Products are strongly favored.
(b) Reactants are strongly favored.
(c) Products are somewhat favored.

7.15   In the expression for the equilibrium constant, the concentration of the product HI is squared in the numerator. The concentrations of the reactants appear in the denominator. Substitute the given concentrations into the expression. The equilibrium favors products.

$$K = \frac{[HI]^2}{[H_2][I_2]} = \frac{[0.507]^2}{[0.0510][0.174]} = 29.0$$

7.16

(a) $K = \dfrac{[AB]^2}{[A_2][B_2]} \; ; K = \dfrac{[AB]^2}{[A_2][B]^2}$

(b) $K = \dfrac{[1]^2}{[3][3]} = 0.11 \; ; K = \dfrac{[4]^2}{[2][3]^2} = \dfrac{16}{18} = 0.89$

7.17   High pressure favors the production of SO_3 because increasing the pressure shifts the equilibrium in the direction that decreases the number of molecules in the gas phase. Low temperature favors the production of SO_3 because exothermic reactions are favored by lower temperatures.

7.18   (a) Increasing the temperature shifts the equilibrium to the left, favoring reactants.
(b) Increasing the pressure shifts the equilibrium to the right, favoring product.
(c) Removing CH_4 from the reaction vessel causes more CH_4 to be formed and shifts the equilibrium toward the right, favoring product.

7.19 $Cu_2O(s) + C(s) \longrightarrow 2\,Cu(s) + CO(g)$ $\Delta G = -3.8$ kJ $(-1.0$ kcal$)$

Understanding Key Concepts

7.20 ΔH is positive because energy must be supplied in order to break the attractive forces between molecules of the crystal. ΔS is also positive because the molecules of gas are more disordered than the molecules of solid. ΔG is negative because it is stated in the problem that the reaction is spontaneous.

7.21 ΔH is negative because energy is released when a liquid condenses. ΔS is negative because disorder decreases when a gas condenses. ΔG is negative because it is stated in the problem that the reaction is spontaneous.

7.22   (a) $2\,A_2 + B_2 \longrightarrow 2\,A_2B$

(b) ΔG is negative because the reaction is spontaneous. ΔS is negative because the product mixture has fewer gas molecules and less disorder than the reactant mixture. ΔH must be negative in order for ΔG to be negative since $(-T\,\Delta S)$ is positive.

7.23   (a) The blue curve represents the faster reaction, since less energy is needed to surmount the energy barrier leading to formation of products.
(b) The red curve represents a spontaneous reaction since the energy of its products is less than the energy of its reactants: ΔG is negative.

7.24

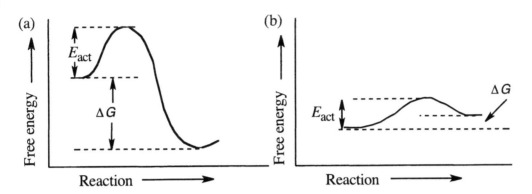

7.25   (a) ΔS is positive because the product has more disorder than the reactants.
(b) At low temperatures, the reaction is nonspontaneous because ΔH is positive and $T\Delta S$ is small. As the temperature rises, a certain temperature is reached at which $\Delta H = T\Delta S$. At this temperature, $\Delta G = 0$. Above this temperature, ΔG is negative and the reaction is spontaneous.

Enthalpy and Heat of Reaction

7.26   In an endothermic reaction, the total enthalpy of the reactants is greater than the total enthalpy of the products. In other words, the reactants have stronger bonds and are more stable, while the products have weaker bonds and are less stable. Energy must therefore be supplied for the reaction to take place.

7.27   In a chemical reaction, the difference in bond energies between products and reactants is known as the *heat of reaction*, or enthalpy change.

7.28   (a) ΔH is positive. $Br_2(l) + 7.4 \text{ kcal/mol} \longrightarrow Br_2(g)$

(b) $5.8 \text{ mol } Br_2 \times \dfrac{7.4 \text{ kcal}}{1 \text{ mol } Br_2} = 43 \text{ kcal needed}$

(c) $82 \text{ g } Br_2 \times \dfrac{1 \text{ mol } Br_2}{159.8 \text{ g } Br_2} \times \dfrac{31.0 \text{ kJ}}{1 \text{ mol } Br_2} = 15.9 \text{ kJ needed}$

7.29   (a) ΔH is negative. $H_2O(l) \longrightarrow H_2O(s) + 1.44 \text{ kcal}$

(b) $2.5 \text{ mol } H_2O \times \dfrac{-6.02 \text{ kJ}}{1 \text{ mol } H_2O} = -15.1 \text{ kJ}$

(c) $32 \text{ g } H_2O \times \dfrac{1 \text{ mol } H_2O}{18 \text{ g } H_2O} \times \dfrac{-1.44 \text{ kcal}}{1 \text{ mol } H_2O} = -2.6 \text{ kcal}$

(d) $+1.44 \text{ kcal/mol}$

7.30   (a) $2 C_2H_2(g) + 5 O_2(g) \longrightarrow 4 CO_2(g) + 2 H_2O(g)$

(b) $\Delta H = \Sigma$ (bond dissociation energies)$_{reactants} - \Sigma$(bond dissociation energies)$_{products}$

Σ (bond dissociation energies)$_{reactants}$ = 4(C–H) + 2(C≡C) + 5(O=O)
= [4(99) + 2(201) + 5(119)] kcal/mol
= 1393 kcal/mol (5820 kJ/mol)

Σ(bond dissociation energies)$_{products}$ = 8(C=O) + 4(O–H)
= [8(191) + 4(112)] kcal/mol
= 1976 kcal/mol (8260 kJ/mol)

ΔH = 1393 kcal/mol – 1976 kcal/mol = –583 kcal/mol = –2440 kJ/mol

(c)

$$\frac{2440 \text{ kJ}}{1 \text{ mol}} \times \frac{1 \text{ mol}}{2 \text{ mol } C_2H_2} \times \frac{1 \text{ mol } C_2H_2}{26 \text{ g } C_2H_2} = \frac{46.9 \text{ kJ}}{1 \text{ g } C_2H_2}$$

This value is similar to the energy values for gasoline and natural gas and indicates that acetylene is one of the best fuels.

7.31

(a) :N≡N: +   2 :O=O: $\longrightarrow$ 2 ·N=O
                                          /
                                       :O:

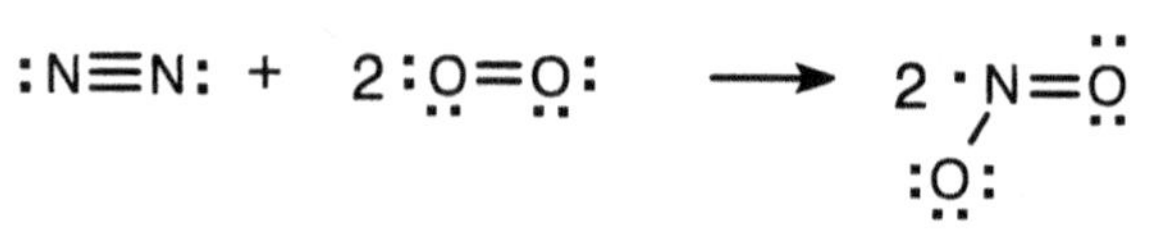

(b) Σ (bond dissociation energies)$_{reactants}$ = N≡N + 2(O=O)
= 226 kcal/mol + 2(119 kcal/mol)
= 464 kcal/mol (1940 kJ/mol)

Σ(bond dissociation energies)$_{products}$ = 2(N=O) + 2(N–O)
= 2(145 kcal/mol) + 2(48 kcal/mol)
= 386 kcal/mol (1610 kJ/mol)

ΔH = 464 kcal/mol – 386 kcal/mol = 78 kcal/mol (330 kJ/mol)

7.32   (a) $C_6H_{12}O_6 + 6 O_2 \longrightarrow 6 CO_2 + 6 H_2O$

(b) $\dfrac{-3.8 \text{ kcal}}{1 \text{ g glucose}} \times \dfrac{180 \text{ g glucose}}{1 \text{ mol glucose}} \times 1.50 \text{ mol glucose} = -1.0 \times 10^3 \text{ kcal} = -4.2 \times 10^3 \text{ kJ}$

(c) The production of glucose from CO_2 and H_2O is an endothermic process.

$\dfrac{3.8 \text{ kcal}}{1 \text{ g glucose}} \times 15.0 \text{ g glucose} = 57 \text{ kcal (238 kJ) needed to produce 15 g glucose}$

7.33 (a) $2\,C_8H_{18}\ +\ 25\,O_2\ \longrightarrow\ 16\,CO_2\ +\ 18\,H_2O\ +\ heat$

(b) ΔH is negative, because energy is released.

(c) $\dfrac{1002\ kJ}{5.00\ g\ C_8H_{18}}\ \times\ \dfrac{114\ g\ C_8H_{18}}{1\ mol\ C_8H_{18}}\ =\ \dfrac{2.28\times10^4\ kJ\ (5460\ kcal)}{1\ mol\ C_8H_{18}}$ released

(d) $450.0\ kcal\ \times\ \dfrac{1\ mol\ C_8H_{18}}{5460\ kcal}\ =\ 0.0824\ mol\ C_8H_{18}$

$0.0824\ mol\ \times\ \dfrac{114\ g}{1\ mol}\ =\ 9.39\ g\ C_8H_{18}$

(e) $17.0\ g\ C_8H_{18}\ \times\ \dfrac{1002\ kJ}{5.00\ g\ C_8H_{18}}\ =\ 3.40\times10^3\ kJ\ (814\ kcal)$ released

Entropy and Free Energy

7.34 Increase in entropy: (a)
Decrease in entropy: (b), (c)

7.35 (a) Entropy decreases because there is an increase in order.
(b) Entropy decreases because there are fewer moles of gaseous product than reactant.
(c), (f) Entropy decreases because formation of a precipitate decreases entropy.
(d), (e) Entropy increases because there are more moles of gaseous products than gaseous reactants.

7.36 The two factors that influence the spontaneity of a reaction are: (1) the release or absorption of heat, and (2) the increase or decrease in entropy.

7.37 An exothermic reaction releases heat (negative ΔH), whereas an exergonic reaction is spontaneous (negative ΔG).

7.38 The free-energy change (ΔG) of a chemical reaction shows whether or not a reaction is spontaneous. If the sign of ΔG is negative, the reaction is spontaneous. Of the two factors that contribute to ΔG (ΔH and ΔS), ΔH is usually larger at low temperatures. Thus if a reaction is spontaneous (negative ΔG) it is usually exothermic (negative ΔH).

7.39 If an endothermic reaction is accompanied by a large increase in entropy, the ($-T\Delta S$) term in the expression for ΔG becomes large and negative and outweighs the positive enthalpy term, resulting in a negative value for ΔG and indicating an exergonic reaction.

7.40 (a) Dissolution of NaCl is endothermic since ΔH is positive.
(b) Entropy increases because disorder increases.
(c) Since the dissolution of NaCl is spontaneous, ΔG for the reaction must be negative. Because we already know that ΔH is positive, it must be true that $T\Delta S$ is the major contributor to ΔG.

7.41 (a) Entropy decreases because two atoms of liquid and one molecule of gas react to yield two molecules of solid.
(b) Because ΔS is negative, $-T\Delta S$ is positive. The reaction is spontaneous up to the temperature at which $\Delta H\ =\ T\Delta S$; above this temperature, the reaction no longer is spontaneous.

7.42   (a) $H_2(g) + Br_2(l) \longrightarrow 2\, HBr(g)$

(b) Entropy increases because the number of gaseous product molecules is greater than the number of gaseous reactant molecules, and thus the sign of ΔS is positive.

(c) The process is spontaneous at all temperatures because ΔH is negative and ΔS is positive.

(d) $\Delta G = \Delta H - T\Delta S$; $\Delta H = -17.4$ kcal/mol; $\Delta S = 27.2$ cal/(mol·K); $T = 300$ K

$$T\Delta S = 300\ K\ \times\ \frac{27.2\ cal}{mol\ K}\ \times\ \frac{1\ kcal}{10^3\ cal} = \frac{8.16\ kcal}{mol}\left(\frac{34.1\ kJ}{mol}\right)$$

$$\Delta G = -17.4\ kcal/mol - 8.16\ kcal/mol = -25.6\ kcal/mol\ (-107\ kJ/mol)$$

7.43   (a) ΔS is negative because two molecules of a gas combine to form one molecule of liquid.

(b) This reaction is spontaneous only up to a certain temperature, above which $T\Delta S$ is greater than ΔH and the reaction becomes nonspontaneous.

Rates of Chemical Reactions

7.44   The *activation energy* of a reaction is the amount of energy needed for reactants to surmount the energy barrier to reaction.

7.45   A reaction with $E_{act} = +5$ kcal is faster than one with $E_{act} = +10$ kcal because less energy is needed to surmount the energy barrier.

7.46

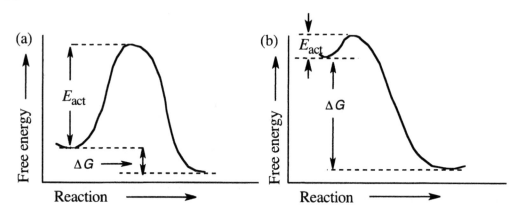

7.47   Increasing concentration increases the reaction rate because the increased crowding of reactants causes more collisions.

7.48   A catalyst is a substance that increases reaction rate by lowering the activation energy barrier, yet remains unchanged when the reaction is completed.

7.49   A catalyst that reduces the energy of activation of a forward reaction by 5.0 kcal/mol (from 28.0 kcal/mol to 23.0 kcal/mol) also reduces the energy of activation of the reverse reaction by 5.0 kcal/mol. Lowering the energy of activation of the reverse reaction, however, will not cause it to take place if it is not spontaneous.

7.50 (a) The negative value of ΔG indicates that diamonds spontaneously turn into graphite at 25°C.
(b) Because this behavior is not observed, the activation energy of the reaction must be extremely high and the reaction rate must be extremely slow.

7.51 (a) The reaction of hydrogen with carbon is not spontaneous at 25°C because ΔG is positive.
(b) It is not possible to find a catalyst for the reaction because it is not spontaneous at any temperature.

Chemical Equilibria

7.52 In a reversible reaction, chemical equilibrium is a state in which the rates of the forward reaction and the reverse reaction are equal. The amounts of reactants and products need not be equal at equilibrium.

7.53 Catalysts lower the height of the activation energy barrier for both forward and reverse reactions by the same amount but don't change the equilibrium constant.

7.54 Remember that solids and pure liquids don't appear in the equilibrium expression

(a) $K = \dfrac{[CO_2]^2}{[CO]^2[O_2]}$ (b) $K = \dfrac{[MgCl_2][H_2]}{[HCl]}$

(c) $K = \dfrac{[H_3O^+][F^-]}{[HF]}$ (d) $K = \dfrac{[SO_2]}{[O_2]}$

7.55

(a) $K = \dfrac{[H_2S]^2}{[S_2][H_2]^2}$ (b) $K = \dfrac{[HCl]^2}{[H_2S][Cl_2]}$

(c) $K = \dfrac{[BrCl]^2}{[Br_2][Cl_2]}$ (d) $K = \dfrac{[CO][H_2]}{[H_2O]}$

7.56

$$K = \frac{[NO_2]^2}{[N_2O_4]} = \frac{(0.0325 \text{ mol/L})^2}{(0.147 \text{ mol/L})} = 7.19 \times 10^{-3} \text{ Reactants are favored.}$$

7.57

$$K = \frac{[CO_2]^2}{[CO]^2[O_2]} = \frac{(0.11 \text{ mol/L})^2}{(0.025 \text{ mol/L})^2 (0.015 \text{ mol/L})} = 1.3 \times 10^3 \text{ Products are favored.}$$

7.58

(a) $K = 7.19 \times 10^{-3} = \dfrac{(0.0250 \text{ mol/L})^2}{[N_2O_4]}$; $[N_2O_4] = 0.0869 \text{ mol/L}$

(b) $K = 7.19 \times 10^{-3} = \dfrac{[NO_2]^2}{(0.0750 \text{ mol/L})}$; $[NO_2] = 0.0232 \text{ mol/L}$

7.59

(a) $1.3 \times 10^3 = \dfrac{(0.18 \text{ mol/L})^2}{(0.0200 \text{ mol/L})^2 [O_2]}$

$[O_2] = \dfrac{(0.18 \text{ mol/L})^2}{(0.0200 \text{ mol/L})^2 \times 1.3 \times 10^3} = 0.062 \text{ mol/L}$

(b) $[CO_2]^2 = K \times [CO]^2 \times [O_2] = 1.3 \times 10^3 \times (0.080 \text{ mol/L})^2 \times 0.520 \text{ mol/L}$
$= 4.3 \ (\text{mol/L})^2; [CO_2] = 2.1 \text{ mol/L}$

7.60 If the pressure is raised, relatively more reactants than products are found at equilibrium, because high pressure favors the reaction that produces fewer gas molecules.

7.61 If the pressure is lowered, a relatively greater concentration of reactants than products is found at equilibrium, because lower pressure favors the reaction that produces more gas molecules.

Le Châtelier's Principle

7.62 (a) The reaction is endothermic.
(b) Reactants are favored at equilibrium.
(c) (1) Increasing pressure favors formation of ozone, since increased pressure shifts the equilibrium in the direction of the reaction that produces fewer gas molecules.
(2) Increasing the O_2 concentration increases the amount of O_3 formed.
(3) Increasing the concentration of O_3 shifts the equilibrium to the left.
(4) A catalyst has no effect on the equilibrium.
(5) Increasing the temperature shifts the equilibrium to the right because the reaction is endothermic.

7.63 (a) This reaction is exothermic.
(b) Products are favored at equilibrium.
(c) (1) Increasing pressure has no effect on the equilibrium.
(2) Increasing the HCl concentration shifts the equilibrium to the left.
(3) Decreasing the Cl_2 concentration decreases the amount of HCl formed.
(4) Increasing the H_2 concentration increases the amount of HCl formed.
(5) A catalyst has no effect on the equilibrium.

7.64 According to Le Châtelier's principle, an increase in pressure shifts the equilibrium in the direction that decreases the number of molecules in the gas phase.
(a) The concentration of products decreases.
(b) The concentration of products remains the same.
(c) The concentration of products increases.

7.65 A decrease in volume increases the system pressure.
(a) The equilibrium shifts to favor reactants.
(b) The equilibrium shifts to favor products.
(c) The position of equilibrium remains the same.

7.66 $CO(g) + H_2O(g) \ \rightleftharpoons \ CO_2(g) + H_2(g) \quad \Delta H = -9.8 \text{ kcal/mol} \ (-41 \text{ kJ/mol})$
Because it has a negative value of ΔH, the reaction is exothermic, and the equilibrium favors products. Decreasing the temperature increases the amount of H_2.

7.67 $3 O_2(g) \rightleftharpoons 2 O_3(g)$ $\Delta H = +68$ kcal/mol (+285 kJ/mol)
Increasing the temperature of the reaction increases the equilibrium constant.

7.68 $H_2(g) + I_2(g) \rightleftharpoons 2 HI(g)$ $\Delta H = -2.2$ kcal/mol (−9.2 kJ/mol)
(a) Adding I_2 to the reaction mix increases the equilibrium concentration of HI.
(b) Removing H_2 causes the equilibrium concentration of HI to decrease.
(c) Addition of a catalyst does not change the equilibrium concentration of HI.
(d) Increasing the temperature decreases the concentration of HI.

7.69 $Fe^{3+}(aq) + Cl^-(aq) \rightleftharpoons FeCl^{2+}(aq)$
(a) Addition of $Fe(NO_3)_3$ increases the equilibrium concentration of $FeCl^{2+}$.
(b) Removal of Cl^- by precipitation decreases the concentration of $FeCl^{2+}$.
(c) Increasing the temperature of the endothermic reaction increases the equilibrium concentration of $FeCl^{2+}$.
(d) Addition of a catalyst does not change the equilibrium concentration of $FeCl^{2+}$.

Applications

7.70   A gram of fat contains more energy (9 kcal/g) than a gram of carbohydrate (4 kcal/g).

7.71   The chips contain 22.5 g carbohydrate and 22.5 g fat.

$$22.5 \text{ g carbohydrate} \times \frac{4.0 \text{ kcal}}{1 \text{ g carbohydrate}} = 90 \text{ kcal}; \quad 22.5 \text{ g fat} \times \frac{9.0 \text{ kcal}}{1 \text{ g fat}} = 200 \text{ kcal}$$

   A small bag of potato chips contains 290 Cal (kcal).

7.72   Body temperature is regulated by the thyroid gland and by the hypothalamus region of the brain.

7.73   Dilation of the blood vessels cools the body by allowing more blood to flow close to the surface of the body.

7.74   Add the two reactions, cancel all quantities common to both sides of the equation, and add the two values of ΔG to arrive at the value of ΔG for the coupled reactions.

$$ADP + HOPO_3^{2-} + PEP + H_2O \longrightarrow ATP + H_2O + \text{pyruvate} + HOPO_3^{2-}$$
$$ADP + \text{phosphoenolpyruvate} \longrightarrow ATP + \text{pyruvate} \quad \Delta G = -31.4 \text{ kJ/mol}$$

7.75   Reactions in the human body can only take place within a limited range of temperatures. In addition to coupling, other strategies include removal of products in further reactions that drive a reaction to completion, and increasing the concentration of reactants.

General Questions and Problems

7.76   (a) $C_2H_5OH + 3 O_2 \longrightarrow 2 CO_2 + 3 H_2O + 327$ kcal
(b) ΔH is negative because energy is released.

   (c) $5.00 \text{ g } C_2H_5OH \times \dfrac{1 \text{ mol } C_2H_5OH}{46.0 \text{ g } C_2H_5OH} \times \dfrac{327 \text{ cal}}{1 \text{ mol}} = 35.5 \text{ kcal}$

(d) Calories needed = specific heat of H_2O x mass (g) x temperature change (°C)
Specific heat of water = 1.00 cal /(g · °C); mass of 500 mL H_2O = 500 g;
Temperature change = 80.0 °C

$$\text{Calories} = \frac{1.00 \text{ cal}}{g \cdot °C} \times 500.0 \text{ g} \times 80.0 \text{ °C} = 4.00 \times 10^4 \text{ cal} = 40.0 \text{ kcal}$$

$$40.0 \text{ kcal} \times \frac{5.00 \text{ g } C_2H_5OH}{35.5 \text{ kcal}} = 5.63 \text{ g } C_2H_5OH$$

(e) $\dfrac{35.5 \text{ kcal}}{5.00 \text{ g } C_2H_5OH} \times \dfrac{0.789 \text{ g } C_2H_5OH}{1 \text{ mL } C_2H_5OH} = 5.60 \text{ kcal/mL}$

7.77 $\quad N_2(g) + 3 H_2(g) \longrightarrow 2 NH_3(g) \quad \Delta H = -22 \text{ kcal/mol} (-92 \text{ kJ/mol})$

(a) The production of ammonia from its elements is an exothermic process.

(b) $\dfrac{-22 \text{ kcal}}{2 \text{ mol } NH_3} \times 0.700 \text{ mol } NH_3 = -7.7 \text{ kcal} (-32 \text{ kJ})$

7.78 (a) $Fe_3O_4(s) + 4 H_2(g) \longrightarrow 3 Fe(s) + 4 H_2O(g) \quad \Delta H = +36 \text{ kcal/mol} (151 \text{ kJ/mol})$

(b) $55 \text{ g Fe} \times \dfrac{1 \text{ mol Fe}}{55.8 \text{ g Fe}} \times \dfrac{36 \text{ kcal}}{1 \text{ mol } Fe_3O_4} \times \dfrac{1 \text{ mol } Fe_3O_4}{3 \text{ mol Fe}} = 12 \text{ kcal} (50 \text{ kJ})$

(c) $75 \text{ g Fe} \times \dfrac{1 \text{ mol Fe}}{55.8 \text{ g Fe}} \times \dfrac{4 \text{ mol } H_2}{3 \text{ mol Fe}} \times \dfrac{2.0 \text{ g } H_2}{1 \text{ mol } H_2} = 3.6 \text{ g } H_2$

(d) Reactants are favored in this reaction.

7.79 (a) CO removes Hb from the bloodstream because the reaction of CO with Hb is more favorable than the reaction of O_2 with Hb. Less Hb is available to react with O_2, and less HbO_2 is available to the tissues.

(b) Administering high doses of O_2 to a victim of CO poisoning shifts the equilibrium in the following reaction to the right.

$$Hb(CO)(aq) + O_2(aq) \rightleftharpoons HbO_2(aq) + CO(aq)$$

This shift results in displacement of CO from Hb(CO) and in formation of HbO_2 to replenish body tissues with O_2.

7.80

(a)

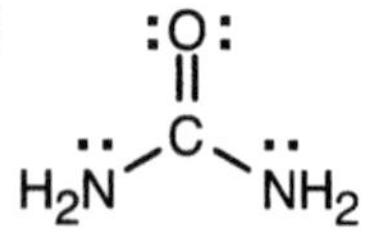

(b) Σ (bond dissociation energies)$_{reactants}$ = (C=O) + 2(C–N) + 4(N–H) + 2(O–H)
= [178 + 2(73) + 4(93) + 2(112)] kcal/mol
= 920 kcal/mol

Σ(bond dissociation energies)$_{products}$ = 2(C=O) + 4(N–H)
= [2(191) + 6(93)] kcal/mol = 940 kcal/mol

ΔH = 920 kcal/mol – 940 kcal/mol = –20 kcal/mol (–84 kJ/mol)

7.81

(a) $10.0 \text{ g H}_2\text{O} \times \dfrac{1 \text{ mol H}_2\text{O}}{18.0 \text{ g H}_2\text{O}} \times \dfrac{9.72 \text{ kcal}}{1 \text{ mol H}_2\text{O}} = 5.40 \text{ kcal needed}$

(b) 22.6 kJ are released.

7.82   (a) $4 \text{ NH}_3(g) + 5 \text{ O}_2(g) \rightleftharpoons 4 \text{ NO}(g) + 6 \text{ H}_2\text{O}(g) + \text{heat}$

(b) $K = \dfrac{[\text{NO}]^4 [\text{H}_2\text{O}]^6}{[\text{NH}_3]^4 [\text{O}_2]^5}$

(c) (1) Raising the pressure shifts the equilibrium to the left and favors reactants.
    (2) Adding NO(g) shifts the equilibrium to the left and favors reactants.
    (3) Decreasing NH$_3$ shifts the equilibrium to the left and favors reactants.
    (4) Lowering the temperature shifts the equilibrium to the right and favors products.

7.83   (a) $2 \text{ CH}_3\text{OH}(l) + 3 \text{ O}_2(g) \longrightarrow 2 \text{ CO}_2(g) + 4 \text{ H}_2\text{O}(g)$

(b) $1.85 \text{ mol CH}_3\text{OH} \times \dfrac{-174 \text{ kcal}}{1 \text{ mol CH}_3\text{OH}} = -322 \text{ kcal} \; (-1340 \text{ kJ})$

(c) $50.0 \text{ g CH}_3\text{OH} \times \dfrac{1 \text{ mol CH}_3\text{OH}}{32.0 \text{ g CH}_3\text{OH}} \times \dfrac{-728 \text{ kJ}}{1 \text{ mol CH}_3\text{OH}} = -1140 \text{ kJ} \; (-272 \text{ kcal})$

7.84

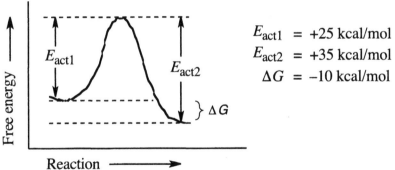

$E_{\text{act1}} = +25 \text{ kcal/mol}$
$E_{\text{act2}} = +35 \text{ kcal/mol}$
$\Delta G = -10 \text{ kcal/mol}$

(a) The forward process is exergonic.
(b) $\Delta G = -10 \text{ kcal/mol} \; (-4.2 \text{ kJ/mol})$

7.85

(a) $0.255 \text{ mol} \times \dfrac{-848.9 \text{ kJ}}{2 \text{ mol Al}} = -108 \text{ kJ} \; (-25.9 \text{ kcal})$

(b) $5.00 \text{ g} \times \dfrac{1 \text{ mol Al}}{27.0 \text{ g Al}} \times \dfrac{-202.9 \text{ kcal}}{2 \text{ mol Al}} = -18.8 \text{ kcal}$
18.8 kcal of heat is released.

7.86

$1.00 \text{ g} \times \dfrac{1 \text{ mol Na}}{23.0 \text{ g}} \times \dfrac{-88.0 \text{ kcal}}{2 \text{ mol Na}} = -1.91 \text{ kcal} \; (-7.99 \text{ kJ/mol})$

1.91 kcal of heat is evolved. The reaction is exothermic.

Self-Test for Chapter 7

Multiple Choice

1. In which of the following processes does entropy decrease?
   (a) $C_6H_{12}O_6(s) + 6\ O_2(g) \longrightarrow 6\ CO_2(g) + 6\ H_2O(l)$

   (b) $2\ Na(s) + 2\ H_2O(l) \longrightarrow 2\ NaOH(aq) + H_2(g)$

   (c) $2\ Mg(s) + O_2(g) \longrightarrow 2\ MgO(s)$

   (d) $Zn(s) + CuSO_4(aq) \longrightarrow Cu(s) + ZnSO_4(aq)$

2. The reaction that will proceed at any temperature has:
   (a) negative ΔH, negative ΔS (b) negative ΔH, positive ΔS (c) positive ΔH, positive ΔS
   (d) positive ΔH, negative ΔS

3. Which of the conditions in Problem 2 indicates the reaction with the largest positive value of ΔG?

4. In the reaction $CH_3CO_2H + CH_3OH \rightleftharpoons CH_3CO_2CH_3 + H_2O$, the yield of $CH_3CO_2CH_3$ can be improved by:
   (a) distilling off the $CH_3CO_2CH_3$ (b) removing the water   (c) using more CH_3CO_2H and CH_3OH (d) all of the above

5. The equilibrium expression for the reaction $C_6H_6 + 3\ H_2 \longrightarrow C_6H_{12}$ is:

   (a) $\dfrac{[C_6H_{12}]}{[C_6H_6]\,[H_2]}$ (b) $\dfrac{[C_6H_{12}]}{[C_6H_6]\,[H_2]^3}$ (c) $\dfrac{[C_6H_{12}]}{[C_6H_6]\,[3\ H_2]}$ (d) $\dfrac{[C_6H_6]\,[H_2]^3}{[C_6H_{12}]}$

6. A reaction with which of the following K values is most likely to go to completion at room temperature?
   (a) $K = 10^5$ (b) $K = 10^2$ (c) $K = 10^{-1}$ (d) $K = 10^{-4}$

7. In which of the following reactions will increasing the pressure decrease the yield of product?
   (a) $2\ Mg(s) + O_2(g) \longrightarrow 2\ MgO(s)$
   (b) $H_2C{=}CH_2(g) + H_2(g) \longrightarrow CH_3CH_3(g)$
   (c) $C(s) + H_2O(g) \longrightarrow CO(g) + H_2(g)$
   (d) $3\ O_2(g) \longrightarrow 2\ O_3(g)$

8. According to Le Châtelier's principle, which of the following changes also changes the value of K?
   (a) changing temperature   (b) changing concentration   (c) changing pressure   (d) all of the above

9. All of the following statements are true about the reaction $3\ O_2(g) \longrightarrow 2\ O_3(g)$ (heat of formation = +34 kcal/mol at 25°C) except :
   (a) The reaction is endothermic.   (b) ΔS is negative.   (c) ΔG is positive.   (d) The rate of the reverse reaction increases with temperature.

10. In the reaction $Si + O_2 \longrightarrow SiO_2$ ($\Delta H = -218$ kcal/mol at 25°C), what is ΔH in kcal when 80 g of O_2 reacts with 70 g of Si?
    (a) 218 kcal   (b) –218 kcal   (c) –436 kcal   (d) –545 kcal

Sentence Completion

1. A reaction that has equal amounts of reactants and products at equilibrium has $K =$ ____.

2. The law of ____ ____ ____ states that energy can be neither created nor destroyed.

3. Addition of a ____ increases the rate of a reaction.

4. A reaction that easily proceeds in either direction is ____.

5. A reaction that absorbs heat from the surroundings is an ____ reaction.

6. An ____ ____ ____ gives the relationship between the concentrations of products and reactants at equilibrium.

7. The rate of a reaction can be increased by increasing ____ or ____ or by adding a ____.

8. The reactions that continually take place in the body are known as ____.

9. ____ ____ is unrelated to reaction spontaneity.

10. For a chemical reaction to occur, reactant molecules must ____.

True or False

1. The caloric value of food tells how much energy is absorbed when food is burned in oxygen.

2. In a chemical equilibrium, both product and reactant concentrations remain constant.

3. According to Le Châtelier's principle, changing pressure only affects equilibrium if gaseous reactants or products are involved.

4. In an exothermic reaction, the bond dissociation energies of the products are greater than the bond dissociation energies of the reactants.

5. A reaction with a large E_{act} will probably have a large heat of reaction.

6. Raising the temperature of a reaction always increases the rate of reaction.

7. A very unfavorable reaction may take place if the temperature is high enough.

8. Catalysts increase the rate of a reaction by increasing the number of collisions between reactants.

9. At chemical equilibrium, all chemical reaction stops.

10. At low temperatures, the spontaneity of a reaction is determined by ΔH.

Match each entry on the left with its partner on the right.

1. Enzyme

2. Exergonic reaction

3. K

4. Enthalpy

5. Reaction energy diagram

6. Free energy

7. Exothermic reaction

8. Endergonic reaction

9. E_{act}

10. Entropy

11. Reversible reaction

12. Endothermic reaction

(a) Shows energy relationships in a reaction

(b) A reaction that gives off heat

(c) Reduces the size of E_{act}

(d) Energy needed for a reaction to occur

(e) Measure of the amount of disorder in a reaction.

(f) Reaction that is not spontaneous

(g) Reaction that can go in either direction

(h) Reaction that absorbs heat

(i) Difference in energy of products and reactants

(j) Reaction that is spontaneous

(k) Determines if a reaction is spontaneous

(l) Measures the ratio of products to reactants

Chapter 8   Gases, Liquids, and Solids

Chapter Outline

I. Introduction to gases, liquids, and solids (Section 8.1).
  A. Phases of matter are determined by the attractive forces between molecules.
    1. In gases, attractive forces are very weak.
    2. In liquids, attractive forces are strong.
    3. In solids, forces are so strong that atoms are held in place.
  B. During changes of phase, also known as changes of state, heat is either absorbed or released.
    1. Every change of state is characterized by a free-energy change, ΔG.
      a. ΔG consists of an enthalpy term and an entropy term.
      b. The enthalpy term is a measure of the heat absorbed or released during a phase change.
      c. The entropy change is a measure of the change in molecular disorder.
    2. At the temperature where a change of phase occurs, two states are in equilibrium.
    3. At the change from solid to liquid, two phases are at equilibrium at the melting point.
    4. At the change from liquid to gas, two phases are at equilibrium at the boiling point.
II. Intermolecular forces (Section 8.2).
  A. Intermolecular forces are the forces that act between molecules.
  B. In an ideal gas, intermolecular forces are unimportant.
  C. Three types of intermolecular forces are important in liquids and solids.
    1. Dipole–dipole forces occur when the positive end of a polar molecule is attracted to the negative end of a second molecule.
    2. London forces.
      a. Short-lived polarity in molecules causes a temporary attraction between molecules.
      b. London forces increase with increasing molecular weight and vary with molecular shape.
    3. Hydrogen bonding.
      a. Hydrogen bonds occur between a hydrogen atom bonded to an electronegative atom (O, N, F) and an unshared electron pair of a second electronegative atom.
      b. In hydrogen bonds, the hydrogen atom is partially bonded to two different electronegative atoms.
      c. Hydrogen bonds can be quite strong, and hydrogen bonding is responsible for elevated boiling points.
III. Gases (Sections 8.3–8.11).
  A. The kinetic–molecular theory explains the behavior of gases (Section 8.3).
    1. A gas consists of a great many molecules moving about with no attractive forces.
    2. The amount of space that molecules occupy is much smaller than the space between molecules.
    3. The energy of the molecules is related to Kelvin temperature.
    4. When molecules collide, their total kinetic energy is conserved.
    5. A gas that obeys all these behaviors is an ideal gas.
  B. Pressure (Sections 8.4).
    1. Pressure is defined as force per unit area.
    2. Units of pressure are mmHg, Pascal (in the SI system), atmosphere, and pounds per square inch (psi).
    3. Gas pressure can be measured by using a barometer or a manometer.

C. Gas laws (Sections 8.5–8.11).
   1. Boyle's law (for a fixed amount of gas at constant T) (Section 8.5).
      a. The pressure of a gas is inversely proportional to its volume.
      b. $P_1V_1 = P_2V_2$.
   2. Charles's law (for a fixed amount of gas at constant P) (Section 8.6).
      a. The volume of a gas is directly proportional to its temperature in K.
      b. $V_1/T_1 = V_2/T_2$.
   3. Gay-Lussac's law (for a fixed amount of gas at constant V) (Section 8.7).
      a. Pressure is directly proportional to temperature in K.
      b. $P_1/T_1 = P_2/T_2$.
   4. Combined gas law (Section 8.8).
      a. $P_1V_1/T_1 = P_2V_2/T_2$ for a fixed amount of gas.
   5. Avogadro's law (at constant T and P) (Section 8.9).
      a. The volume of a gas is directly proportional to its molar amount at constant T and P.
      b. $V_1/n_1 = V_2/n_2$.
      c. Standard temperature and pressure = 273.15 K and 1 atm.
      d. Standard molar volume of a gas = 22.4 L.
   6. Ideal gas law (Section 8.10).
      a. $PV = nRT$, where R is a gas constant.
   7. Dalton's law of partial pressure (Section 8.11).
      a. Mixtures of gases behave the same as a pure gas.
      b. The partial pressure of a gas in a mixture is the same as the gas would have if it were alone.
IV. Liquids and solids (Sections 8.12–8.15).
  A. Liquids (Section 8.12–8.13).
    1. Evaporation occurs when molecules near the surface of a liquid escape into the gaseous state.
      a. When molecules are in the gaseous state, they obey gas laws.
    2. The contribution of the partial pressure of the escaped gas to the total pressure is known as vapor pressure.
      a. Vapor pressure rises with increasing temperature.
    3. The normal boiling point of a liquid is at 760 mmHg.
      a. The boiling point rises or falls with atmospheric pressure.
    4. Viscosity and surface tension are properties of liquids.
      a. Viscosity is a liquid's resistance to flow.
      b. Surface tension is the resistance of a liquid to spread out.
    5. Water is a unique liquid (Section 8.13).
      a. Water has very high specific heat, high heat of vaporization, and strong hydrogen bonding.
      b. Solid water is less dense than liquid water.
  B. Solids (Section 8.14).
    1. A crystalline solid has atoms, molecules, or ions rigidly held in an orderly arrangement.
      a. Categories of crystalline solids include ionic solids, molecular solids, covalent network solids, and metallic solids.
    2. Particles in an amorphous solid do not have an orderly arrangement.
  C. Changes of phase (Section 8.15).
    1. The heat needed to completely melt a solid is the heat of fusion.
    2. The heat needed to completely vaporize a liquid is the heat of vaporization.

Solutions to Chapter 8 Problems

8.1 (a) The change of state from liquid to gas is disfavored by ΔH (positive sign) but is favored by ΔS (large positive value).

(b) $\Delta G = \Delta H - T\Delta S : \Delta H = +9.72$ kcal/mol; $\Delta S = +26.1$ cal/(mol · K); $T = 373$ K

$$T\Delta S = 373 \text{ K} \times \frac{26.1 \text{ cal}}{\text{mol K}} \times \frac{1 \text{ kcal}}{10^3 \text{ cal}} = \frac{9.74 \text{ kcal}}{\text{mol}} = \frac{40.7 \text{ kJ}}{\text{mol}}$$

$\Delta G = 9.72$ kcal/mol $- 9.74$ kcal/mol $= -0.02$ kcal/mol $= 0.08$ kJ/mol

(c) For the change from gas to liquid, $\Delta H = -9.72$ kcal/mol (-40.1 kJ/mol) and $\Delta S = -26.1$ cal/mol·K (-109 kJ/mol·K).

8.2 Boiling points generally increase with increasing molecular (or atomic) weight because of London dispersion forces.

(a) Kr, Ar, Ne. This series is arranged in order of decreasing boiling point.
(b) Cl_2, Br_2, I_2. This series is arranged in order of increasing boiling point.

8.3 Methyl alcohol (a) and methylamine (c) are capable of hydrogen bonding because each contains a hydrogen atom bonded to an electronegative atom. Ethylene (b) does not form hydrogen bonds.

8.4 (a) *London forces* are the only intermolecular forces between nonpolar ethane molecules, and thus ethane has a low boiling point.

(b) The major intermolecular force between ethyl alcohol molecules is *hydrogen bonding*, which causes ethyl alcohol to be high boiling. Dipole–dipole interactions and London forces are also present but are weaker than hydrogen bonding.

(c) *Dipole–dipole* interactions are the principal forces between ethyl chloride molecules and cause the boiling point of ethyl chloride to be higher than that of ethane. London forces are also present.

8.5 Use the appropriate conversion factor from Section 8.4.

$$0.289 \text{ atm} \times \frac{760 \text{ mmHg}}{1 \text{ atm}} = 220 \text{ mmHg}$$

$$0.289 \text{ atm} \times \frac{14.7 \text{ psi}}{1 \text{ atm}} = 4.25 \text{ psi}$$

$$0.289 \text{ atm} \times \frac{101,325 \text{ Pa}}{1 \text{ atm}} = 2.93 \times 10^4 \text{ Pa}$$

8.6 Shifting to biomass-based fuels would decrease dependence on fossil fuels but would have little effect on current atmospheric CO_2 levels. However, biosynthesis of biomass fuels would consume CO_2, which would later be burned and released back into the atmosphere, setting up an equilibrium in which CO_2 levels would remain constant.

8.7 The pressure of the gas inside the manometer is greater than atmospheric pressure because the mercury level is higher in the open arm of the manometer than in the closed end. Since atmospheric pressure is 750 mmHg and since the difference in mercury levels in the manometer arm is 250 mmHg, the pressure of the gas inside the manometer is 750 mm + 250 mm = 1000 mmHg.

8.8   If the variables in the problem are pressure and volume, Boyle's law must be used.

Solution: $P_1 \times V_1 = P_2 \times V_2$

$$V_2 = \frac{P_1 \times V_1}{P_2} = \frac{(90 \text{ atm})(5.0 \text{ L})}{(1.0 \text{ atm})} = 450 \text{ L}$$

Ballpark check: Since the pressure is reduced by almost 100 times, the volume must increase by almost 100 times, from 5 L to 500 L.

The ballpark solution and the detailed solution agree.

8.9   *Solution:* $P_1 \times V_1 = P_2 \times V_2$

$$V_2 = \frac{P_1 \times V_1}{P_2} = \frac{(4.0 \text{ atm})(3.2 \text{ L})}{(10.0 \text{ atm})} = 1.3 \text{ L}$$

Ballpark check: Since the pressure increases by three times, the volume must decrease by the same amount, from 4.0 L to 1.3 L.

At a pressure of 0.70 atm: $V_2 = \frac{P_1 \times V_1}{P_2} = \frac{(4.0 \text{ atm})(3.2 \text{ L})}{(0.70 \text{ atm})} = 18 \text{ L}$

8.10

$$112 \text{ mmHg} \times \frac{14.7 \text{ psi}}{760 \text{ mmHg}} = 2.17 \text{ psi}; \quad 75 \text{ mmHg} \times \frac{14.7 \text{ psi}}{760 \text{ mmHg}} = 1.45 \text{ psi}$$

Blood pressure would be recorded as 2.17/1.45.

8.11   Charles's law is used to calculate volume or temperature changes when pressure and quantity remain constant.

Solution:

$$\frac{V_1}{T_1} = \frac{V_2}{T_2}$$

$$T_2 = \frac{V_2 \times T_1}{V_1} = \frac{(1.0 \text{ L})(273 \text{ K})}{0.30 \text{ L}} = 910 \text{ K } (637 \text{ °C})$$

Ballpark check: Since the volume increases threefold, the temperature must also increase threefold, from 273 K to around 900 K.

If $V_2 = 0.20$ L: $T_2 = \frac{V_2 \times T_1}{V_1} = \frac{(0.20 \text{ L})(273 \text{ K})}{0.30 \text{ L}} = 182 \text{ K } (-91 \text{ °C})$

8.12 Use Gay-Lussac's law when pressure and temperature vary, and volume and quantity are unchanged. Don't forget to change temperature from °C to K.

Solution:

$$\frac{P_1}{T_1} = \frac{P_2}{T_2}$$

$$P_2 = \frac{P_1 \times T_2}{T_1} = 30 \text{ psi} \times \frac{318 \text{ K}}{288 \text{ K}} = 33 \text{ psi}$$

Ballpark check: Since the temperature increase is about 10%, the pressure increase is also expected to be approximately 10%.

8.13 In this problem, P, V, and T vary.

$$\frac{P_1 V_1}{T_1} = \frac{P_2 V_2}{T_2}; \qquad P_1 = 752 \text{ mmHg}; \ T_1 = 295 \text{ K}; \ V_1 = 275 \text{ L}$$

$$P_2 = 480 \text{ mmHg}; \ T_2 = 241 \text{ K}; \ V_2 = \text{?}$$

$$V_2 = \frac{P_1 V_1 T_2}{P_2 T_1} = \frac{(752 \text{ mmHg})(275 \text{ L})(241 \text{ K})}{(480 \text{ mmHg})(295 \text{ K})} = 352 \text{ L}$$

8.14 The temperature increase [from 18 °C (291 K) to 50 °C (323 K)] increases the volume by about 10%. The pressure increase (from 1 atm to 2 atm) decreases the volume by half. The resulting balloon volume should be somewhat more than half the original volume, as represented by balloon (a).

8.15 Use Avogadro's Law; the quantity on the left side of the equation is the standard molar volume of a gas, 22.4 L/mol.

$$\frac{V_1}{n_1} = \frac{V_2}{n_2}$$

$$n_2 = \frac{V_2 \times n_1}{V_1} = 1.00 \times 10^5 \text{ L CH}_4 \times \frac{1.0 \text{ mol}}{22.4 \text{ L}} = 4.46 \times 10^3 \text{ mol CH}_4$$

The same container could also hold 4.46×10^3 moles of CO_2.

$$4.46 \times 10^3 \text{ mol CH}_4 \times \frac{16.0 \text{ g CH}_4}{1 \text{ mol CH}_4} = 7.14 \times 10^4 \text{ g CH}_4$$

$$4.46 \times 10^3 \text{ mol CO}_2 \times \frac{44.0 \text{ g CO}_2}{1 \text{ mol CO}_2} = 1.96 \times 10^5 \text{ g CO}_2$$

Ballpark Check: Since one mole of a gas occupies 22.4 L at STP, a 100,000 L container holds 100,000/22.4 moles, or about 4500 moles. Thus, the ballpark solution and the exact solution agree.

8.16 $PV = nRT$; $P = nRT/V$

$n = 3.2 \text{ g} \times \dfrac{1 \text{ mol}}{44.0 \text{ g}} = 0.073 \text{ mol};$ $R = 0.0821 \dfrac{\text{L} \cdot \text{atm}}{\text{mol} \cdot \text{K}}$

$T = 20°C = 293 \text{ K};$ $V = 350 \text{ mL} = 0.35 \text{ L}$

$P = \dfrac{0.073 \text{ mol} \times \dfrac{0.0821 \text{ L} \cdot \text{atm}}{\text{mol} \cdot \text{K}} \times 293 \text{ K}}{0.35 \text{ L}} = 5.0 \text{ atm}$

8.17 $PV = nRT$; $n = PV/RT$

$P = 150 \text{ atm};$ $V = 180 \text{ L He};$ $R = 0.0821 \dfrac{\text{L} \cdot \text{atm}}{\text{mol} \cdot \text{K}};$ $T = 25°C = 298 \text{ K}$

$n = \dfrac{150 \text{ atm} \times 180 \text{ L He}}{0.0821 \dfrac{\text{L} \cdot \text{atm}}{\text{mol} \cdot \text{K}} \times 298 \text{ K}} = 1.1 \times 10^3 \text{ mol He}$

$1.1 \times 10^3 \text{ mol He} \times \dfrac{4.0 \text{ g}}{1 \text{ mol He}} = 4.4 \times 10^3 \text{ g He}$

8.18 We can use the ideal gas law to compare the volumes of two gases: Since the piston is moveable, $P = 1$ atm in all cases.

(a) The increase in temperature increases the volume to 450/300 = 3/2 of the original volume, and the decrease in amount decreases the volume to 0.200/0.300 = 2/3 of the original value. Since 3/2 x 2/3 = 1, the two changes exactly cancel, and the final volume is the same as the original volume.

$T_1 = 300 \text{ K};$ $n_1 = 0.300 \text{ mol};$ $T_2 = 450 \text{ K};$ $n_2 = 0.200 \text{ mol};$ $V_1/V_2 = ?$

$\dfrac{V_1}{V_2} = \dfrac{n_1 T_1 P_2}{n_2 T_2 P_1} = \dfrac{n_1 T_1}{n_2 T_2};$ $\dfrac{V_1}{V_2} = \dfrac{(0.300 \text{ mol})(300 \text{ K})}{(0.200 \text{ mol})(450 \text{ K})} = 1$

(b) The decrease in temperature decreases the volume to 200/300 = 2/3 of the original, and the increase in amount increases the volume to 0.400/0.300 = 4/3 of the original volume. Since 2/3 x 4/3 = 8/9, the final volume is a bit less than the original volume.

$T_1 = 300 \text{ K};$ $n_1 = 0.300 \text{ mol};$ $T_2 = 200 \text{ K};$ $n_2 = 0.400 \text{ mol};$ $V_1/V_2 = ?$

$\dfrac{V_1}{V_2} = \dfrac{(0.300 \text{ mol})(300 \text{ K})}{(0.400 \text{ mol})(200 \text{ K})} = \dfrac{9}{8}$ The volume in (b) is 8/9 of the original volume.

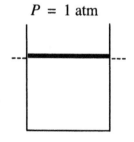

$P = 1$ atm

$T = 300$ K
$n = 0.300$ mol

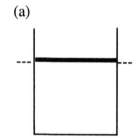

(a)

$T = 450$ K
$n = 0.200$ mol

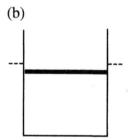

(b)

$T = 200$ K
$n = 0.400$ mol

8.19 0.98 x 9.5 atm = 9.3 atm He
0.020 x 9.5 atm = 0.19 atm O_2

The partial pressure of oxygen in diving gas (0.19 atm) is approximately equal to the partial pressure of oxygen in air (0.21 atm).

8.20

$$\frac{573 \text{ mmHg}}{760 \text{ mmHg}} \times 100\% = 75.4\% \text{ N}_2; \qquad \frac{100 \text{ mmHg}}{760 \text{ mmHg}} \times 100\% = 13.2\% \text{ O}_2$$

$$\frac{40 \text{ mmHg}}{760 \text{ mmHg}} \times 100\% = 5.3\% \text{ CO}_2; \qquad \frac{47 \text{ mmHg}}{760 \text{ mmHg}} \times 100\% = 6.2\% \text{ H}_2\text{O}$$

8.21 We know from the previous problem that the partial pressure of O_2 in the lungs at atmospheric pressure is 13.2%. Thus, at 265 mmHg,

265 mmHg x 0.132 = 35.0 mmHg

8.22 The ratio of He molecules/ Xe molecules is 8/4 or 2/1. Since 2/3 of the molecules are He, P_{He} = 2/3(750 mmHg) = 500 mmHg. P_{Xe} = 250 mmHg.

8.23 To melt isopropyl alcohol:

$$1.50 \text{ mol} \times \frac{60.0 \text{ g}}{1 \text{ mol}} \times \frac{21.4 \text{ cal}}{1 \text{ g}} \times \frac{1 \text{ kcal}}{10^3 \text{ cal}} = 1.93 \text{ kcal}$$

To boil isopropyl alcohol:

$$1.50 \text{ mol} \times \frac{60.0 \text{ g}}{1 \text{ mol}} \times \frac{159 \text{ cal}}{1 \text{ g}} \times \frac{1 \text{ kcal}}{10^3 \text{ cal}} = 14.3 \text{ kcal}$$

8.24

$$2.50 \text{ mol H}_2\text{O} \times \frac{18.0 \text{ g}}{1 \text{ mol H}_2\text{O}} \times \frac{2260 \text{ J}}{1 \text{ g}} \times \frac{1 \text{ kJ}}{10^3 \text{ J}} = 102 \text{ kJ}$$

8.25 At 25 °C and 50 atm, CO_2 is probably close to a gas/liquid phase equilibrium (solid line on graph).

Understanding Key Concepts

8.26

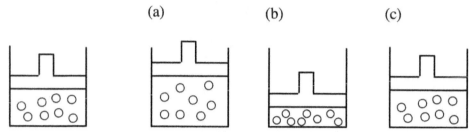

(a)   (b)   (c)

(a) According to Charles's law, the volume of a gas at fixed pressure is directly proportional to its temperature. Since the temperature increases by 50% (from 300 K to 450 K), volume also increases by 50%.

(b) Boyle's law states that the volume of a gas is inversely proportional to its pressure. Doubling the pressure halves the volume.

(c) For changes in both pressure and temperature, the combined gas law states that PV/T is constant. Thus, reducing both the pressure and the temperature by one-third leaves the volume unchanged.

8.27   Drawing (b) represents the situation at 150 K if the boiling point of the gas is 200 K; at this temperature, the gas is a liquid. Drawing (c) represents the gas in a sealed container after the temperature has been lowered from 350 K to 150 K if the boiling point is 100 K. The gas remains a gas, and its volume is unchanged; only pressure is reduced because the molecules are moving slower.

8.28   Drawing (a) shows the sample of water as a solid, its state at 200 K. At 300 K, water is a liquid with a very low vapor pressure (as shown in Figure 8.20), represented by (c).

8.29   At equilibrium, the gases are totally mixed.

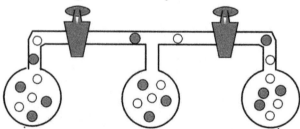

8.30   Both sides of the manometer have equal heights because both sides have equal pressure.

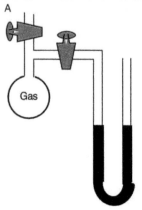

8.31   The horizontal parts of the curve represent phase changes.
(a) Melting point: 10 °C
(b) Boiling point: 75 °C
(c) Heat of fusion: 1.3 kcal/mol (the distance between the two points of the curve at the melting point)
(d) Heat of vaporization: 7.5 kcal/mol (the distance between the two points of the curve at the boiling point)

8.32   Refer to Problem 8.18 for an approach to solving this problem. Note the quantities that change and those that remain constant; these differ in each part of the problem. Be sure to convert temperature to kelvins.

(a) $\dfrac{V_2}{V_1} = \dfrac{n_2 T_2 P_1}{n_1 T_1 P_2} = \dfrac{T_2}{T_1}$; $\dfrac{V_2}{V_1} = \dfrac{(323\ \text{K})}{(298\ \text{K})} = 1.08$

(b) $\dfrac{V_2}{V_1} = \dfrac{n_2 T_2 P_1}{n_1 T_1 P_2} = \dfrac{T_2 P_1}{T_1 P_2}$; $\dfrac{V_2}{V_1} = \dfrac{(448\ \text{K})(0.92\ \text{atm})}{(298\ \text{K})(2.7\ \text{atm})} = 0.51$

(c) $\dfrac{V_2}{V_1} = \dfrac{n_2 T_2 P_1}{n_1 T_1 P_2} = \dfrac{n_2 P_1}{n_1 P_2}$; $\dfrac{V_2}{V_1} = \dfrac{(0.22\ \text{mol})(0.92\ \text{atm})}{(0.075\ \text{mol})(2.7\ \text{atm})} = 1.0$

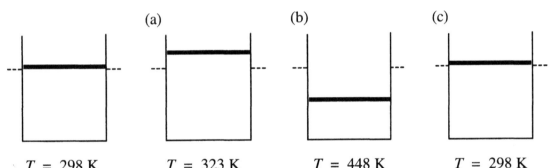

| (a) | (b) | (c) |

$T = 298$ K $T = 323$ K $T = 448$ K $T = 298$ K
$n = 0.075$ mol $n = 0.075$ mol $n = 0.075$ mol $n = 0.22$ mol
$P = 0.92$ atm $P = 0.92$ atm $P = 2.7$ atm $P = 2.7$ atm

8.33   There are 12 molecules of gas in the container, and 4 are green (partial pressure = 240 mmHg.) The total pressure is 3 x 240 mmHg = 720 mmHg.
$P_{\text{red}} + P_{\text{yellow}} + P_{\text{green}} = 720$ mm:
   red = 6/12 = 1/2;   yellow = 2/12 = 1/6;   green = 4/12 = 1/3
$P_{\text{red}} = 1/2 \times 720$ mmHg = 360 mmHg;
$P_{\text{yellow}} = 1/6 \times 720$ mmHg = 120 mmHg;
$P_{\text{green}} = 1/3 \times 720$ mmHg = 240 mmHg

Intermolecular Forces

8.34   (a) All molecules exhibit London forces, which increase in strength with increasing molecular weight.
(b) Dipole–dipole interactions are important for molecules that are polar.
(c) Hydrogen bonding occurs between an unshared electron pair on an electronegative atom (O, N, or F) and a hydrogen atom bonded to a second electronegative atom (O, N, F).

8.35   Hydrogen bonding takes place between molecules having an electron lone pair and a hydrogen bonded to an electronegative atom, such as NH_3 (d) or CH_3CO_2H (f). Dipole–dipole interactions are the most important interactions between molecules that have polar covalent bonds, such as HCN (b) or CH_3Cl (e). London dispersion forces are most important for molecules that do not experience other types of forces, such as N_2 (a) or CCl_4 (c). Notice that CCl_4 contains polar covalent bonds, but their dipole moments cancel because of symmetry.

8.36   Ethanol is higher boiling than dimethyl ether because of hydrogen bonding. Since molecules of ethanol are strongly attracted to each other, the boiling point of ethanol is higher than that of dimethyl ether, whose molecules are held together by weaker dipole–dipole interactions.

8.37   London forces are the major attractive forces for Br_2 and I_2 molecules. Since London forces become stronger with increasing molar mass, the melting point of I_2 is higher than the melting point of Br_2.

Gases and Pressure

8.38   One atmosphere is the amount of pressure needed to hold a column of mercury 760 mm high.

8.39   Four common units for measuring pressure: atmosphere (atm), mmHg, pounds per square inch (psi), Pascal (Pa).
   $$1 \text{ atm} = 760 \text{ mmHg} = 14.7 \text{ psi} = 101,325 \text{ Pa}$$

8.40   (1) A gas consists of many tiny particles moving about at random with no attractive forces between particles.
   (2) The amount of space occupied by gas molecules is much smaller than the amount of space between molecules.
   (3) The average kinetic energy of gas particles is proportional to Kelvin temperature.
   (4) When molecules collide, they spring apart elastically, and their total energy is constant.

8.41   According to the kinetic–molecular theory of gases, gas pressure is due to collisions with the walls of the container. The more collisions, the higher the pressure.

8.42

(a) $1 \text{ atm} \times \dfrac{760 \text{ mmHg}}{1 \text{ atm}} = 760 \text{ mmHg}$

(b) $25.3 \text{ psi} \times \dfrac{760 \text{ mmHg}}{14.7 \text{ psi}} = 1310 \text{ mmHg}$

(c) $7.5 \text{ atm} \times \dfrac{760 \text{ mmHg}}{1 \text{ atm}} = 5.7 \times 10^3 \text{ mmHg}$

(d) $28.0 \text{ in.Hg} \times \dfrac{25.4 \text{mm}}{1 \text{ in.}} = 711 \text{ mmHg}$

(e) $41.8 \text{ Pa} \times \dfrac{760 \text{ mmHg}}{101,325 \text{ Pa}} = 0.314 \text{ mmHg}$

8.43

    (a) $440 \text{ mmHg} \times \dfrac{1 \text{ atm}}{760 \text{ mmHg}} = 0.58 \text{ atm}$

    (b) $440 \text{ mmHg} \times \dfrac{133.3224 \text{ Pa}}{1 \text{ mmHg}} = 59{,}000 \text{ Pa}$

8.44   When the level in the arm connected to the container is 176 mm (17.6 cm) lower than the level open to the atmosphere, the pressure in the gas container is greater than atmospheric pressure.

     $754.3 \text{ mmHg} + 176 \text{ mmHg} = 930 \text{ mmHg} = 1.22 \text{ atm}$

8.45   When the level in the arm connected to the container is 283 mm (28.3 cm) higher than the level open to the atmosphere, the pressure in the gas container is less than atmospheric pressure.

     $283 \text{ mmHg} \times \dfrac{1 \text{ atm}}{760 \text{ mmHg}} = 0.372 \text{ atm}$ $1.021 \text{ atm} - 0.372 \text{ atm} = 0.649 \text{ atm}$

     $0.649 \text{ atm} \times \dfrac{760 \text{ mmHg}}{1 \text{ atm}} = 493 \text{ mmHg}$

Boyle's Law

8.46   Boyle's law: Volume varies inversely with pressure at constant temperature and number of moles, that is, $P_1V_1 = P_2V_2$.

8.47   Two assumptions of the KMT explain the behavior of gases described by Boyle's Law. (1) The amount of space occupied by gas particles is much smaller than the space between particles. This allows compression of a gas without interactions between gas molecules. (2) Collisions between gas molecules and between molecules and the wall of a container are elastic. This means that all of the kinetic energy results in gas pressure.

     Boyle's law involves an inverse proportionality: Pressure and volume change in opposite directions.

8.48 $P_1V_1 = P_2V_2$; $P_1 = 65.0 \text{ mmHg}$; $P_2 = 385 \text{ mmHg}$; $V_1 = 600.0 \text{ mL} = 0.600 \text{ L}$; $V_2 = ?$

     $V_2 = \dfrac{P_1V_1}{P_2} = \dfrac{65.0 \text{ mmHg} \times 0.600 \text{ L}}{385 \text{ mmHg}} = 0.101 \text{ L} = 101 \text{ mL}$

8.49 $P_1V_1 = P_2V_2$; $P_1 = 1.00 \text{ atm}$; $P_2 = ?$; $V_1 = 2.85 \text{ L}$; $V_2 = 1.70 \text{ L}$

     $P_2 = \dfrac{P_1V_1}{V_2} = \dfrac{1.00 \text{ atm} \times 2.85 \text{ L}}{1.70 \text{ L}} = 1.68 \text{ atm}$

8.50 $P_1V_1 = P_2V_2$; $P_1 = 5.0 \text{ atm}$; $P_2 = 1.0 \text{ atm}$; $V_1 = 0.350 \text{ L}$; $V_2 = ?$

     $V_2 = \dfrac{P_1V_1}{P_2} = \dfrac{5.00 \text{ atm} \times 0.350 \text{ L}}{1.00 \text{ atm}} = 1.75 \text{ L}$

8.51 $P_1V_1 = P_2V_2$; $P_1 = 1$ atm $= 760$ mmHg; $V_1 = 1.25$ L; $P_2 = 220$ mmHg $V_2 = ?$;

$$V_2 = \frac{P_1V_1}{P_2} = \frac{760 \text{ mmHg} \times 1.25 \text{ L}}{220 \text{ mmHg}} = 4.32 \text{ L}$$

Charles's Law

8.52 Charles's law: Volume varies directly with temperature at constant pressure and number of moles; that is, $V_1/T_1 = V_2/T_2$.

8.53 An important assumption of the KMT relates to the behavior of gases described by Charles's Law: The average kinetic energy of gas particles is proportional to the Kelvin temperature. This means that the relationship of temperature and volume is linear.

Charles's law involves a direct proportionality: Volume and temperature change in the same direction.

8.54

$$\frac{V_1}{T_1} = \frac{V_2}{T_2};   V_1 = 960 \text{ L}; \ V_2 = 1200 \text{ L}; \ T_1 = 291 \text{ K}; \ T_2 = ?$$

$$T_2 = \frac{V_2T_1}{V_1} = \frac{1200 \text{ L} \times 291 \text{ K}}{960 \text{ L}} = 364 \text{ K} = 91°\text{C}$$

8.55

$$\frac{V_1}{T_1} = \frac{V_2}{T_2};   V_1 = 875 \text{ L}; \ V_2 = 955 \text{ L}; \ T_1 = ? \ ; \ T_2 = 56 °\text{C} = 329 \text{ K}$$

$$T_1 = \frac{V_1T_2}{V_2} = \frac{875 \text{ L} \times 329 \text{ K}}{955 \text{ L}} = 301 \text{ K} = 28 °\text{C}$$

8.56

$$\frac{V_1}{T_1} = \frac{V_2}{T_2};   V_1 = 185 \text{ mL}; \ V_2 = ?; \ T_1 = 38 °\text{C} = 311 \text{ K}; \ T_2 = 97 °\text{C} = 370 \text{ K}$$

$$V_2 = \frac{V_1T_2}{T_1} = \frac{185 \text{ mL} \times 370 \text{ K}}{311 \text{ K}} = 220 \text{ mL}$$

8.57

$$\frac{V_1}{T_1} = \frac{V_2}{T_2};   V_1 = 43.0 \text{ L}; \ V_2 = ?; \ T_1 = 25 °\text{C} = 298 \text{ K}; \ T_2 = -8 °\text{C} = 265 \text{ K}$$

$$V_2 = \frac{V_1T_2}{T_1} = \frac{43.0 \text{ L} \times 265 \text{ K}}{298 \text{ K}} = 38.2 \text{ L}$$

Gay-Lussac's Law

8.58 Gay-Lussac's law: Pressure varies directly with temperature at constant volume and number of moles; that is, $P_1/T_1 = P_2/T_2$.

8.59 The assumptions explained for Boyle's Law and Charles's Law explain the behavior of gases under Gay-Lussac's law.

Gay-Lussac's law involves a direct proportionality: Pressure and temperature change in the same direction.

8.60

$$\frac{P_1}{T_1} = \frac{P_2}{T_2}; \quad P_1 = 0.95 \text{ atm}; \ P_2 = ?; \ T_1 = 25\,°C = 298 \text{ K}; \ T_2 = 117\,°C = 390 \text{ K}$$

$$P_2 = \frac{P_1 T_2}{T_1} = \frac{0.95 \text{ atm x } 390 \text{ K}}{298 \text{ K}} = 1.2 \text{ atm}$$

8.61

$$\frac{P_1}{T_1} = \frac{P_2}{T_2}; \quad P_1 = 3.85 \text{ atm}; \ P_2 = 18.0 \text{ atm}; \ T_1 = 25\,°C = 298 \text{ K}; \ T_2 = ?$$

$$T_2 = \frac{P_2 T_1}{P_1} = \frac{18.0 \text{ atm x } 298 \text{ K}}{3.85 \text{ atm}} = 1390 \text{ K} = 1120\,°C$$

Combined Gas Law

8.62

$$\frac{P_1 V_1}{T_1} = \frac{P_2 V_2}{T_2}; \quad P_1 = 760 \text{ mmHg}; \ V_1 = 2.84 \text{ L}; \ T_1 = 273 \text{ K}$$
$$P_2 = 520 \text{ mmHg}; \ V_2 = 7.50 \text{ L}; \ T_2 = ?$$

$$T_2 = \frac{P_2 V_2 T_1}{P_1 V_1} = \frac{520 \text{ mmHg x } 7.50 \text{ L x } 273 \text{ K}}{760 \text{ mmHg x } 2.84 \text{ L}} = 493 \text{ K} = 220\,°C$$

8.63

$$\frac{P_1 V_1}{T_1} = \frac{P_2 V_2}{T_2}; \quad P_1 = 120 \text{ atm}; \ V_1 = 6.80 \text{ L}; \ T_1 = 20\,°C = 293 \text{ K}$$

$$P_2 = 1.00 \text{ atm}; \ V_2 = ?; \ T_2 = 273 \text{ K}$$

$$V_2 = \frac{P_1 V_1 T_2}{T_1 P_2} = \frac{120 \text{ atm x } 6.80 \text{ L x } 273 \text{ K}}{293 \text{ K x } 1.00 \text{ atm}} = 760 \text{ L}$$

8.64

$$\frac{P_1 V_1}{T_1} = \frac{P_2 V_2}{T_2}; \quad P_1 = 748 \text{ mmHg}; \ V_1 = 75.4 \text{ mL}; \ T_1 = 23\,°C = 296 \text{ K}$$
$$P_2 = 760 \text{ mmHg}; \ V_2 = ?; \ T_2 = 0\,°C = 273 \text{ K}$$

$$V_2 = \frac{P_1 V_1 T_2}{T_1 P_2} = \frac{748 \text{ mmHg x } 75.4 \text{ mL x } 273 \text{ K}}{296 \text{ K x } 760 \text{ mmHg}} = 68.4 \text{ mL}$$

8.65 (a) For one mole of gas, the combined gas law states that V is proportional to T/P, or $V \propto T/P$. Thus, if the pressure is halved and the temperature is doubled, the new volume is four times greater than the original volume.

$$\frac{P_1 V_1}{T_1} = \frac{P_2 V_2}{T_2}; \quad P_2 = 0.5 P_1; \ T_2 = 2T_1; \ V_2 = ?$$

$$V_2 = \frac{P_1 V_1 T_2}{T_1 P_2} = \frac{P_1 V_1 \text{ x } 2T_1}{T_1 \text{ x } 0.5 P_1} = 4V_1$$

(b) If both the pressure and the temperature are doubled, the volume remains the same.

$$\frac{P_1V_1}{T_1} = \frac{P_2V_2}{T_2}; \quad P_2 = 2P_1; T_2 = 2T_1; V_2 = \,?$$

$$V_2 = \frac{P_1V_1T_2}{T_1P_2} = \frac{P_1V_1 \times 2T_1}{T_1 \times 2P_1} = V_1$$

8.66 (a) For one mole of gas, the combined gas law states that P is proportional to T/V, or $P \propto T/V$. Thus, if the temperature doubles and the volume is halved, the new pressure is four times greater than the original pressure:

$$\frac{P_1V_1}{T_1} = \frac{P_2V_2}{T_2}; \quad V_2 = 0.5V_1; T_2 = 2T_1; P_2 = \,?$$

$$P_2 = \frac{P_1V_1T_2}{T_1V_2} = \frac{P_1V_1 \times 2T_1}{T_1 \times 0.5V_1} = 4\,P_1$$

(b) If the temperature is halved and the volume is doubled, the new pressure is one-fourth the original pressure:

$$\frac{P_1V_1}{T_1} = \frac{P_2V_2}{T_2}; \quad V_2 = 2V_1; T_2 = 0.5T_1; P_2 = \,?$$

$$P_2 = \frac{P_1V_1T_2}{T_1V_2} = \frac{P_1V_1 \times 0.5T_1}{T_1 \times 2V_1} = 0.25P_1$$

8.67 In this problem, temperature is constant. First, we find the volume of gas at 1.25 atm and 25 °C.
$P_1V_1 = P_2V_2; P_1 = 1850$ atm; $P_2 = 1.25$ atm; $V_1 = 2.30$ L; $V_2 = \,?$

$$V_2 = \frac{P_1V_1}{P_2} = \frac{1850 \text{ atm} \times 2.30 \text{ L}}{1.25 \text{ atm}} = 3400 \text{ L}$$

If the cylinder holds 3400 L of helium at 1.25 atm and 25 °C, it can be used to fill 3400 L/1.50 L = 2270 balloons.

Avogadro's Law and Standard Molar Volume

8.68 Avogadro's law states that equal volumes of gases at the same temperature and pressure contain equal numbers of molecules. Since the volume of space taken up by gas molecules is so much smaller than the amount of space between molecules, Avogadro's law is true regardless of the chemical identity of the gas.

8.69 The conditions of STP are 760 mmHg (1 atm) pressure and 273 K temperature.

8.70

$$1.0 \text{ L} \times \frac{1 \text{ mol}}{22.4 \text{ L}} \times \frac{6.02 \times 10^{23} \text{ molecules}}{1 \text{ mol}} = 2.7 \times 10^{22} \text{ molecules}$$

$$1.0 \text{ L} \times \frac{1 \text{ mol}}{22.4 \text{ L}} \times \frac{32.0 \text{ g}}{1 \text{ mol}} = 1.4 \text{ g } O_2$$

8.71

$$n_2 = \frac{V_2 \times n_1}{V_1} = 48.6 \text{ L} \times \frac{1.0 \text{ mol}}{22.4 \text{ L}} = 2.17 \text{ mol}$$

8.72

$$16.5 \text{ L} \times \frac{1 \text{ mol}}{22.4 \text{ L}} \times \frac{16.0 \text{ g CH}_4}{1 \text{ mol CH}_4} = 11.8 \text{ g CH}_4$$

8.73

$$1.75 \text{ g HCN} \times \frac{1 \text{ mol}}{27.0 \text{ g HCN}} \times \frac{22.4 \text{ L}}{1 \text{ mol HCN}} = 1.45 \text{ L HCN at STP}$$

8.74

$$V = 4.0 \text{ m} \times 5.0 \text{ m} \times 2.5 \text{ m} = 50 \text{ m}^3; \quad 50 \text{ m}^3 \times \frac{10^3 \text{ L}}{1 \text{ m}^3} = 5.0 \times 10^4 \text{ L}$$

$$\frac{1 \text{ mol}}{22.4 \text{ L}} \times 5.0 \times 10^4 \text{ L} = 2230 \text{ mol gas}$$

$$\frac{0.21 \text{ mol O}_2}{1 \text{ mol gas}} \times 2230 \text{ mol gas} = 470 \text{ mol O}_2$$

$$470 \text{ mol O}_2 \times \frac{32.0 \text{ g O}_2}{1 \text{ mol O}_2} = 15{,}000 \text{ g O}_2 = 15 \text{ kg O}_2$$

8.75

$$\frac{0.79 \text{ mol N}_2}{1 \text{ mol gas}} \times 2230 \text{ mol gas} = 1.8 \times 10^3 \text{ mol N}_2$$

$$1760 \text{ mol N}_2 \times \frac{28.0 \text{ g N}_2}{1 \text{ mol N}_2} = 49{,}000 \text{ g N}_2 = 49 \text{ kg N}_2$$

The Ideal Gas Law

8.76 The ideal gas law: $PV = nRT$

8.77 The combined gas law can be used to calculate changes in P, V, and T when the amount of gas is fixed. The ideal gas law is valid for any number of moles and uses the ideal gas constant R to calculate any one of the variables P, V, T, and n if the other three are known.

8.78 $PV = nRT$; $n = PV/RT$

For Cl_2: $P = 1.0 \text{ atm}$; $V = 2.0 \text{ L}$; $R = 0.082 \dfrac{\text{L} \cdot \text{atm}}{\text{mol} \cdot \text{K}}$; $T = 273 \text{ K}$

$$n = \frac{1.0 \text{ atm} \times 2.0 \text{ L}}{0.082 \dfrac{\text{L} \cdot \text{atm}}{\text{mol} \cdot \text{K}} \times 273 \text{ K}} = 0.089 \text{ mol Cl}_2$$

$$0.089 \text{ mol Cl}_2 \times \frac{71 \text{ g}}{1 \text{ mol Cl}_2} = 6.3 \text{ g Cl}_2$$

For CH_4: $P = 1150$ mmHg $= 1.5$ atm; $V = 3.0$ L; $R = 0.082 \dfrac{L \cdot atm}{mol \cdot K}$; $T = 300$ K

$$n = \frac{1.5 \text{ atm} \times 3.0 \text{ L}}{0.082 \dfrac{L \cdot atm}{mol \cdot K} \times 300 \text{ K}} = 0.18 \text{ mol } CH_4$$

$$0.18 \text{ mol } CH_4 \times \frac{16 \text{ g}}{1 \text{ mol } CH_4} = 2.9 \text{ g } CH_4$$

There are more molecules in the CH_4 sample than in the Cl_2 sample. The Cl_2 sample, however, weighs more because the molar mass of Cl_2 is much greater than the molar mass of CH_4.

8.79 As in the preceding problem, use the relationship $n = PV/RT$.

For CO_2: $\quad n = \dfrac{500 \text{ mmHg} \times 2.0 \text{ L } CO_2}{62.4 \dfrac{mmHg \cdot L}{mol \cdot K} \times 300 \text{ K}} = 0.053 \text{ mol } CO_2$

For N_2: $\quad n = \dfrac{760 \text{ mmHg} \times 1.5 \text{ L } N_2}{62.4 \dfrac{mmHg \cdot L}{mol \cdot K} \times 330 \text{ K}} = 0.055 \text{ mol } N_2$

The CO_2 sample has somewhat fewer molecules. Since the molar mass of CO_2 is much greater than the molar mass of N_2, however, the CO_2 sample weighs more (2.3 g) than the N_2 sample (1.5 g).

8.80

$n = 2.3$ mol He; $\quad T = 294$ K; $\quad V = 0.15$ L

$$P = \frac{nRT}{V} = \frac{2.3 \text{ mol He} \times 0.082 \dfrac{L \cdot atm}{mol \cdot K} \times 294 \text{ K}}{0.15 \text{ L}} = 370 \text{ atm}$$

$$370 \text{ atm} \times \frac{14.7 \text{ psi}}{1 \text{ atm}} = 5.40 \times 10^3 \text{ psi}$$

8.81

$n = 3.5$ mol O_2; $\quad P = 1.6$ atm; $\quad V = 27$ L

$$T = \frac{PV}{nR} = \frac{1.6 \text{ atm} \times 27 \text{ L}}{3.5 \text{ mol} \times 0.0821 \dfrac{L \cdot atm}{mol \cdot K}} = 150 \text{ K} = -123 \text{ °C}$$

8.82

$$n = 15.0 \text{ g } CO_2 \times \frac{1 \text{ mol}}{44 \text{ g}} = 0.341 \text{ mol } CO_2; \quad T = 310 \text{ K}; \quad V = 0.30 \text{ L}$$

$$P = \frac{nRT}{V} = \frac{0.341 \text{ mol } CO_2 \times 62.4 \dfrac{mmHg \cdot L}{mol \cdot K} \times 310 \text{ K}}{0.30 \text{ L}} = 2.2 \times 10^4 \text{ mmHg}$$

8.83

$$PV = nRT; \quad n = 20.0 \text{ g N}_2 \times \frac{1 \text{ mol}}{28.0 \text{ g}} = 0.714 \text{ mol N}_2; \quad V = 4.00 \text{ L}; \quad P = 6.00 \text{ atm}$$

$$T = \frac{PV}{nR} = \frac{6.00 \text{ atm} \times 4.00 \text{ L}}{0.714 \text{ mol} \times 0.0821 \dfrac{\text{L} \cdot \text{atm}}{\text{mol} \cdot \text{K}}} = 409 \text{ K} = 136 \, ^{\circ}\text{C}$$

8.84

$$n = 18.0 \text{ g O}_2 \times \frac{1 \text{ mol}}{32.0 \text{ g}} = 0.563 \text{ mol O}_2; \quad T = 350 \text{ K}; \quad P = 550 \text{ mmHg}$$

$$V = \frac{nRT}{P} = \frac{0.562 \text{ mol O}_2 \times 62.4 \dfrac{\text{mmHg} \cdot \text{L}}{\text{mol} \cdot \text{K}} \times 350 \text{ K}}{550 \text{ mmHg}} = 22.4 \text{ L O}_2$$

8.85

$$n = \frac{PV}{RT}; \quad P = 2.5 \text{ atm}; \quad V = 0.55 \text{ L}; \quad T = 347 \text{ K}$$

$$= \frac{2.5 \text{ atm} \times 0.55 \text{ L}}{0.082 \dfrac{\text{L} \cdot \text{atm}}{\text{mol} \cdot \text{K}} \times 347 \text{ K}} = 0.048 \text{ moles}$$

Dalton's Law and Partial Pressure

8.86 Partial pressure is the pressure contribution of one component of a mixture of gases to the total pressure.

8.87 Dalton's law of partial pressure says that the total pressure exerted by a gas mixture is the sum of the individual pressures of the components in the mixture.

8.88

$$440 \text{ mmHg} \times \frac{1 \text{ atm}}{760 \text{ mmHg}} \times \frac{160 \text{ mmHg}}{1.0 \text{ atm}} = 93 \text{ mmHg}$$

8.89

$$120 \text{ psi} \times \frac{760 \text{ mmHg}}{14.7 \text{ psi}} \times 0.21 = 1300 \text{ mmHg}$$

Liquids

8.90 The vapor pressure of a liquid is the partial pressure of the vapor above the liquid.

8.91 A liquid's heat of vaporization is the amount of heat needed to vaporize one gram of the liquid at its boiling point.

8.92 Increased pressure raises a liquid's boiling point; decreased pressure lowers a liquid's boiling point.

8.93 CH_3Cl has a higher vapor pressure because its intermolecular forces (dipole–dipole) are weaker than the intermolecular forces of CH_3OH (hydrogen bonds).

8.94

(a) $\dfrac{9.72 \text{ kcal}}{1 \text{ mol } H_2O}$ x 3.00 mol H_2O = 29.2 kcal of heat required.

(b) $\dfrac{9.72 \text{ kcal}}{1 \text{ mol } H_2O}$ x $\dfrac{1 \text{ mol } H_2O}{18.0 \text{ g}}$ x 320 g = 173 kcal of heat is released.

8.95

$\dfrac{159 \text{ cal}}{1 \text{ g isopropyl alcohol}}$ x 190.0 g isopropyl alcohol = 3.02×10^4 cal = 30.2 kcal

Solids

8.96   The atoms in a crystalline solid are arranged in a regular, orderly network. The atoms in an amorphous solid have no regular arrangement.

8.97   *Type of Solid*   *Example*

Ionic solid $NaCl$, $MgBr_2$
Molecular solid   Ice, sucrose
Covalent network solid   Diamond
Metallic solid   Cu, Fe

8.98

$\dfrac{45.9 \text{ cal}}{1 \text{ g}}$ x $\dfrac{1 \text{ kcal}}{1000 \text{ cal}}$ x $\dfrac{60.0 \text{ g}}{1 \text{ mol}}$ x 1.75 mol = 4.82 kcal

8.99

$\dfrac{630 \text{ cal}}{1 \text{ mol Na}}$ x $\dfrac{1 \text{ kcal}}{1000 \text{ cal}}$ x $\dfrac{1 \text{ mol Na}}{23.0 \text{ g Na}}$ x 262 g Na = 7.18 kcal

Chemistry in Action

8.100 Increased concentrations of CO_2 in the atmosphere, coupled with an increase in the average global temperature, are evidence for global warming.

8.101 The three most important greenhouse gases are carbon dioxide, water vapor, and methane.

8.102 *Systolic pressure* (the higher number) is the maximum blood pressure developed in the artery just after contraction. *Diastolic pressure* (the lower number) is the minimum pressure that occurs at the end of the heartbeat cycle. A blood pressure reading of 180/110 is an indication of high blood pressure.

8.103

180 mmHg x $\dfrac{1 \text{ atm}}{760 \text{ mmHg}}$ = 0.24 atm; 110 mmHg x $\dfrac{1 \text{ atm}}{760 \text{ mmHg}}$ = 0.14 atm

Blood pressure would be reported as 0.24/0.14.

8.104 The supercritical state of matter is a condition intermediate between liquid and gas, in which there is some space between molecules yet they are too close together to be truly a gas.

8.105 Supercritical CO_2 is nontoxic and nonflammable and can be continuously recycled.

General Questions and Problems

8.106 As the temperature increases, the kinetic energy of gas molecules increases, and the force per unit area that they exert in colliding against the walls of a container increases, thus increasing pressure.

8.107 Two moles of hydrogen react with one mole of oxygen according to the balanced equation. Since equal volumes of gases have equal numbers of moles at STP, 2.5 L of O_2 reacts with 5.0 L of H_2.

8.108 3.0 L of H_2 and 1.5 L of O_2 react completely. At STP, one mole of H_2 occupies 22.4 L. Thus, 3.0 L of hydrogen = 3.0/22.4 or 0.13 mol. This is also the number of moles of H_2O formed.

$$n = 0.13 \text{ mol } H_2O; \quad T = 373 \text{ K}; \quad P = 1.0 \text{ atm}$$

$$V = \frac{nRT}{P} = \frac{0.13 \text{ mol } H_2O \times 0.0821 \frac{L \cdot atm}{mol \cdot K} \times 373 \text{ K}}{1.0 \text{ atm}} = 4.0 \text{ L } H_2O$$

8.109 $PV = nRT$; $P = 1.0$ atm; $V = 0.24$ L; $T = 310$ K

$$n = \frac{PV}{RT} = \frac{1.0 \text{ atm} \times 0.24 \text{ L}}{0.0821 \frac{L \cdot atm}{mol \cdot K} \times 310 \text{ K}} = 0.0094 \text{ mol} = 9.4 \text{ mmol } CO_2$$

8.110

$$0.0094 \text{ mol } CO_2 \times \frac{44.0 \text{ g } CO_2}{1 \text{ mol } CO_2} = 0.41 \text{ g } CO_2$$

$$\frac{0.41 \text{ g } CO_2}{1 \text{ min}} \times \frac{60 \text{ min}}{1 \text{ hr}} \times \frac{24 \text{ hr}}{1 \text{ day}} = \frac{590 \text{ g } CO_2}{\text{day}}$$

8.111 At STP, equal volumes of gases have an equal number of moles. However, O_2 has a greater molecular weight than H_2, and the vessel containing O_2 is heavier.

8.112 $P = 0.975$ atm; $V = 1.6 \times 10^5$ L; $T = 375$ K

$$n = \frac{PV}{RT} = \frac{0.975 \text{ atm} \times 1.6 \times 10^5 \text{ L}}{0.0821 \frac{L \cdot atm}{mol \cdot K} \times 375 \text{ K}} = 5.07 \times 10^3 \text{ mol}$$

$$\text{Density} = \frac{5.07 \times 10^3 \text{ mol}}{1.6 \times 10^5 \text{ L}} \times \frac{29 \text{ g}}{\text{mol}} = \frac{0.92 \text{ g}}{\text{L}}$$

The air in the balloon is less dense than air at STP (density = 1.3 g/L).

8.113

$$n = \frac{745 \text{ mmHg} \times 14.7 \text{ L}}{62.4 \dfrac{\text{mmHg} \cdot \text{L}}{\text{mol} \cdot \text{K}} \times 298 \text{ K}} = 0.589 \text{ mol}; \quad \frac{10.0 \text{ g}}{0.589 \text{ mol}} = 17.0 \text{ g/mol}$$

8.114 Divide the molar mass (molecular weight in grams) by 22.4 L to find the density in grams per liter.

Gas	Molecular Weight	Density (g/L) at STP
(a) CH_4	16.0 g/mol	0.714
(b) CO_2	44.0 g/mol	1.96
(c) O_2	32.0 g/mol	1.43

8.115 $n = 1 \text{ mol}; \quad T = 1 \text{ K}; \quad P = 1 \times 10^{-14} \text{ mmHg}$

$$V = \frac{nRT}{P} = \frac{1 \text{ mol} \times 62.4 \dfrac{\text{mmHg} \cdot \text{L}}{\text{mol} \cdot \text{K}} \times 1 \text{ K}}{1 \times 10^{-14} \text{ mmHg}} = 6 \times 10^{15} \text{ L}$$

$$\text{Density} = \frac{6.022 \times 10^{23} \text{ atoms}}{6 \times 10^{15} \text{ L}} = \frac{1 \times 10^{8} \text{ atoms}}{\text{L}}$$

8.116

(a)

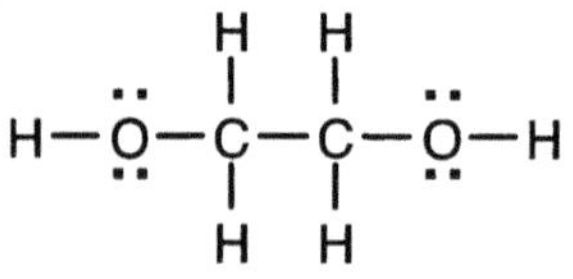

```
        H   H
        |   |
H — O — C — C — O — H
        |   |
        H   H
```

Ethylene glycol

(b)

```
    H   H
    |   |
H — C — C — Cl:
    |   |
    H   H
```

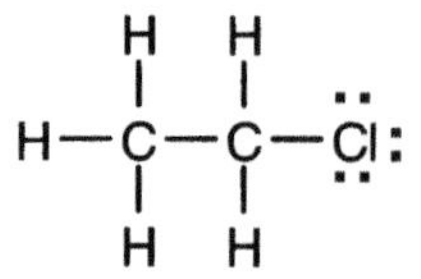

Chloroethane

(c) Ethylene glycol has a higher boiling point than chloroethane because it forms hydrogen bonds.

8.117 Since the pressure at sea level is 1 atm, the external pressure increases by 1 atm for every 10 m of depth.

(a) $\dfrac{1.0 \text{ atm}}{10 \text{ m}} \times 25 \text{ m} = 2.5 \text{ atm}; \; 2.5 \text{ atm} + 1.0 \text{ atm} = 3.5 \text{ atm}$

(b) For O_2: $0.20 \times 3.5 \text{ atm} = 0.7 \text{ atm}$

   For N_2: $0.80 \times 3.5 \text{ atm} = 2.8 \text{ atm}$

8.118 (a) Since the size of a Rankine degree is the same as a Fahrenheit degree, we can use the same conversion factor as we use for °F/°C conversions.

$$\frac{9\,°R}{5\,°C} \times 273.15\,°C = 491.67\,°R$$

(b) To calculate the gas constant R, use the ideal gas law at standard temperature and pressure.

$$R = \frac{PV}{nT};\quad P = 1\text{ atm};\ V = 22.4\text{ L};\ n = 1\text{ mol};\ T = 491.67\,°R$$

$$R = \frac{1\text{ atm} \times 22.4\text{ L}}{1\text{ mol} \times 492\,°R} = 0.0455\ \frac{\text{L}\cdot\text{atm}}{\text{mol}\cdot°R}$$

8.119 (a) $2\,C_8H_{18} + 25\,O_2 \longrightarrow 16\,CO_2 + 18\,H_2O$

(b) $4.6 \times 10^{10}\text{ L }C_8H_{18} \times \dfrac{0.792\text{ g}}{1\text{ mL}} \times \dfrac{10^3\text{ mL}}{1\text{ L}} = 3.6 \times 10^{13}\text{ g }C_8H_{18}$

$$= 3.6 \times 10^{10}\text{ kg }C_8H_{18}$$

$$3.6 \times 10^{13}\text{g }C_8H_{18} \times \frac{1\text{ mol }C_8H_{18}}{114\text{ g }C_8H_{18}} \times \frac{16\text{ mol }CO_2}{2\text{ mol }C_8H_{18}} \times \frac{44.0\text{ g }CO_2}{1\text{ mol }CO_2} = 1.1 \times 10^{14}\text{ g }CO_2$$

$$= 1.1 \times 10^{11}\text{ kg }CO_2$$

(c) To find the volume of CO_2, use the ideal gas law at STP; n can be calculated from the mass of CO_2 that was found in part (b).

$$n = 1.1 \times 10^{14}\text{ g }CO_2 \times \frac{1\text{ mol }CO_2}{44\text{ g }CO_2} = 2.5 \times 10^{12}\text{ mol }CO_2$$

$$V = \frac{nRT}{P} = \frac{2.5 \times 10^{12}\text{ mol }CO_2 \times 0.0821\ \frac{\text{L}\cdot\text{atm}}{\text{mol}\cdot\text{K}} \times 273\text{ K}}{1.0\text{ atm}} = 5.6 \times 10^{13}\text{ L }CO_2$$

Self-Test for Chapter 8

Multiple Choice

1. Which of the following units would you be least likely to use in a chemical laboratory?
   (a) pascal   (b) pounds per square inch   (c) mmHg   (d) atmosphere

2. A fixed amount of a gas has its temperature and volume doubled. What happens to its pressure?
   (a) increases fourfold   (b) doubles   (c) stays the same   (d) is halved

3. In which of the gas laws is the amount of gas not fixed?
   (a) Boyle's law   (b) Charles's law   (c) Gay-Lussac's law   (d) Avogadro's law

4. Which of the following compounds does not exhibit hydrogen bonding?
   (a) CH_3OCH_3 (b) CH_3OH (c) HF (d) CH_3NH_2

5. Which of the following compounds is the lowest melting?
   (a) NaI (b) Au (c) SiO_2 (d) sugar

6. Which term describes the change of state that occurs when a gas changes to a solid?
   (a) fusion (b) condensation (c) deposition (d) sublimation

7. When does a gas obey ideal behavior?
   (a) at low density (b) at high pressure (c) at low temperature (d) in a large container

8. If 22.0 g of CO_2 has a pressure of 1.00 atm at 300 K, what is its volume?
   (a) 22.4 L (b) 12.3 L (c) 11.2 L (d) 9.5 L

9. What volume does the amount of gas in Problem 8 occupy at STP?
   (a) 22.4 L (b) 12.3 L (c) 11.2 L (d) 9.5 L

10. What is the density of CO_2 gas in g/L at STP if one mole of gas has a volume of 22.4 L?
    (a) 44.0 g/L (b) 11.0 g/L (c) 6.4 g/L (d) 1.96 g/L

Sentence Completion

1. In Boyle's law, the _____ of a gas is inversely proportional to its _____.

2. A liquid has _____ volume and _____ shape.

3. _____ law states that the total pressure of a gas mixture is the sum of the individual pressure of the components in the mixture.

4. A pressure of 760 mmHg and a temperature of 273 K are known as ___ ___ ___ .

5. _____ law says that equal volumes of gases at the same temperature and pressure contain equal numbers of molecules.

6. In a closed container, liquid and vapor are at _____.

7. Units for measuring pressure include _____, _____, _____, _____, and _____.

8. The _____ __ _____ is the heat necessary to melt one gram of a solid at its melting point.

9. In Charles's law, _____ and _____ are kept constant.

10. Gas particles move in straight lines, with energy proportional to _____.

11. The transformation of a substance from one phase to another is known as a _____ ___ _____.

12. A liquid that evaporates readily is said to be _____.

True or False

1. Molecules of ethyl alcohol exhibit hydrogen bonding.

2. All gases are similar in their physical behavior.

3. Molecules of CH_3Cl experience both dipole–dipole interactions and London forces.

4. Doubling the pressure of a gas at constant temperature doubles the volume.

5. $R = 0.082$ L atm/(mol · K) is a value for the gas constant.

6. Atoms in solids have an orderly arrangement.

7. Standard temperature and pressure are 760 mmHg and 273°C.

8. All substances become solids if the temperature is low enough.

9. The atmospheric pressure in Death Valley (282 ft below sea level) is lower than the atmospheric pressure at sea level.

10. The more liquid there is in a closed container, the higher the vapor pressure.

11. Surface tension is a liquid's resistance to flow.

Match each entry on the left with its partner on the right. Use each answer once.

1. $P_1V_1 = P_2V_2$ (a) Avogadro's law

2. Dipole–dipole attraction   (b) Gas constant

3. $P_{total} = P_{gas\ 1} + P_{gas\ 2} + ...$ (c) Force per unit area

4. 760 mmHg at 273 K   (d) Charles's law

5. Hydrogen bonding   (e) Occurs between molecules of CH_3Br

6. $V_1/n_1 = V_2/n_2$ (f) STP

7. 0.007500 mmHg   (g) Boyle's law

8. London forces   (h) Occurs between molecules of CH_3OH

9. 62.4 mmHg L/mol K   (i) Ideal gas law

10. $V_1/T_1 = V_2/T_2$ (j) Pascal

11. Pressure   (k) Dalton's law of partial pressure

12. $PV = nRT$ (l) Occurs between molecules of N_2

Chapter 9   Solutions

Chapter Outline

I. Characteristics of solutions (Sections 9.1–9.6).
   A. Mixtures and solutions (Section 9.1).
     1. Mixtures are either heterogeneous or homogeneous.
       a. Heterogeneous mixtures have nonuniform mixing.
       b. Homogeneous mixtures have uniform mixing.
     2. Homogeneous mixtures can be classified by particle size.
       a. In solutions, particles range in size from 0.1 to 2 nm.
       b. In colloids, particles range in size from 2 to 1000 nm.
     3. When a solid is dissolved in a liquid, the liquid is the solvent and the solid is the solute.
   B. The solution process (Sections 9.2–9.3).
     1. Solubility depends on the strength of attraction between solute particles and solvent, relative to the attractions in the pure substances.
     2. In predicting solubility, polar solvents dissolve polar substances, and nonpolar solvents dissolve nonpolar substances.
     3. Solvation can be either an exothermic or an endothermic process.
     4. Some ionic compounds attract water to form solid hydrates (Section 9.3).
   C. Solubility (Sections 9.4–9.6).
     1. Solubility is a dynamic process (Section 9.4).
       a. When no more of an added solute will dissolve, the solution is said to be saturated.
       b. In a saturated solution, an equilibrium is established between dissolving and crystallizing.
     2. The solubility of a substance is the maximum amount of the substance that will dissolve in a solvent.
     3. Effect of temperature on solubility (Section 9.5).
       a. The effect of temperature on the solubility of a solid solute is unpredictable.
       b. A gas is always less soluble as temperature increases.
       c. A solid that is more soluble at high temperature than at low temperature may form a supersaturated solution.
     4. Effect of pressure on solubility (Section 9.6).
       a. Increased pressure makes gas molecules more soluble in a liquid.
       b. Henry's law: $C = kP_{gas}$.
         i. The solubility of a gas in a liquid is proportional to its partial pressure over the liquid at constant T.
       c. When the partial pressure of a gas changes:

$$\frac{C_1}{P_1} = \frac{C_2}{P_2} = k \,(\text{at constant T})$$

II. Quantitative relationships in solutions (Sections 9.7–9.10).
   A. Concentration (Section 9.7).
     1. Percent concentrations.
       a. (m/m) % concentration $= \dfrac{\text{Mass of solute (g)}}{\text{Mass of solution (g)}} \times 100\%$.
       b. (v/v) % concentration $= \dfrac{\text{Volume of solute (mL)}}{\text{Volume of solution (mL)}} \times 100\%$.
       c. (m/v) % concentration $= \dfrac{\text{Mass of solute (g)}}{\text{Volume of solution (mL)}} \times 100\%$.

2. parts per million (ppm) $= \dfrac{\text{Mass of solute (g)}}{\text{Mass of solution (g)}} \times 10^6.$

$= \dfrac{\text{Volume of solute (mL)}}{\text{Volume of solution (mL)}} \times 10^6.$

3. parts per billion (ppb) $= \dfrac{\text{Mass of solute (g)}}{\text{Mass of solution (g)}} \times 10^9.$

$= \dfrac{\text{Volume of solute (mL)}}{\text{Volume of solution (mL)}} \times 10^9.$

4. Molarity $= \dfrac{\text{Moles of solute}}{\text{Volume of solution (L)}}.$

    a. Molarity can be used as a conversion factor.

B. Dilution (Section 9.8).

  1. During dilution, the number of moles of solute remains constant, while volume changes.

  2. $M_1 \times V_1 = M_2 \times V_2.$

  3. V_1/V_2 is known as a dilution factor.

C. Equivalents and milliequivalents (Sections 9.9–9.10).

  1. Electrolytes (Section 9.9).

    a. Substances that dissociate completely are strong electrolytes.

    b. Substances that dissociate partially are weak electrolytes.

    c. Molecular substances that don't produce ions are nonelectrolytes.

  2. The concentration of electrolytes is expressed in equivalents (Section 9.10).

    a. 1 gram-equivalent of an ion $= \dfrac{\text{molar mass of the ion}}{\text{number of charges on the ion}}.$

    b. Milliequivalents are useful when measuring ion concentrations in body fluids.

III. Properties of solutions (Sections 9.11–9.13).

A. Effects of particles in solution—colligative properties (Section 9.11).

  1. Lowering of vapor pressure.

  2. Boiling point elevation.

  3. Freezing point depression.

  4. These effects don't depend on the identity of the particles.

B. Osmosis (Section 9.12–9.13).

  1. When two solutions of different concentrations are separated by a semipermeable membrane, water passes through to the more concentrated side. This is known as osmosis.

  2. Osmotic pressure can be applied to establish an equilibrium between the rates of forward and reverse passage of water across the membrane.

  3. The osmotic pressure of a solution depends only on the number of particles in solution.

  4. Osmolarity = molarity × number of particles per formula unit.

  5. Two solutions that are isotonic have the same osmolarity.

    a. In cells, a hypotonic solution causes hemolysis.

    b. A hypertonic solution causes crenation.

  6. Dialysis is a process similar to osmosis except that the pores in the membrane allow small solute molecules to pass (Section 9.13).

    a. Hemodialysis is used to cleanse the blood of people whose kidneys malfunction.

    b. Colloidal particles are too large to pass through semipermeable membranes.

Solutions to Chapter 9 Problems

9.1 Orange juice is heterogeneous, and all of the other mixtures are homogeneous, although hand lotion might be heterogeneous in some cases. Apple juice and tea are solutions because they are nonfilterable and transparent to light. Hand lotion is a colloid.

9.2 Remember the rule "like dissolves like."
(a) CCl_4 and H_2O don't form solutions because CCl_4 is nonpolar and H_2O is polar.
(b) Benzene and $MgSO_4$ don't form solutions because $MgSO_4$ is ionic and benzene is nonpolar.
(c), (d) These two pairs of substances form solutions because they are chemically similar.

9.3 Glauber's salt: $Na_2SO_4 \cdot 10H_2O$

9.4 Molar mass of Glauber's salt: 322 g/mol. 322 g of Glauber's salt provides 1.00 mol of sodium sulfate.

9.5 A solution of 12.5 g KBr in 20 mL H_2O is equivalent to a solution of 62.5 g KBr in 100 mL H_2O. According to Figure 9.3, the solution is unsaturated at 60 °C. Cooling the solution to 10 °C makes the solution supersaturated.

9.6

$$\frac{C_1}{P_1} = \frac{C_2}{P_2}; P_1 = 760 \text{ mmHg}; C_1 = 0.169 \text{ g/100 mL}; P_2 = 2.5 \times 10^4 \text{ mmHg}; C_2 = ?$$

$$C_2 = \frac{C_1 P_2}{P_1} = \frac{\left(\dfrac{0.169 \text{ g}}{100 \text{ mL}}\right) \times 2.5 \times 10^4 \text{ mmHg}}{760 \text{ mmHg}} = 5.6 \text{ g } CO_2/100 \text{ mL}$$

9.7

$$\frac{C_1}{P_1} = \frac{C_2}{P_2}; P_1 = 1.00 \text{ atm}; C_1 = 0.169 \text{ g/100 mL}; P_2 = 4.0 \times 10^{-4} \text{ atm}; C_2 = ?$$

$$C_2 = \frac{C_1 P_2}{P_1} = \frac{\left(\dfrac{0.169 \text{ g}}{100 \text{ mL}}\right) \times 4.0 \times 10^{-4} \text{ atm}}{1.00 \text{ atm}} = 6.8 \times 10^{-5} \text{ g } CO_2/100 \text{ mL}$$

9.8 According to Dalton's Law (Section 8.11), the total pressure exerted by a gas is the sum of the partial pressures of the gases in the mixture. Thus the partial pressure of oxygen at a total pressure of 265 mmHg is 0.21 x 265 mmHg = 56 mmHg. The oxygen-carrying curve shows that hemoglobin is approximately 90% saturated at this partial pressure.

9.9 This is a (mass/mass) % concentration problem in which a mass of 100 g of alloy contains 15.8 g Ni. To find the mass of the alloy that contains 36.5 g Ni:
$$\text{Mass of alloy} = 36.5 \text{ g Ni} \times \frac{100 \text{ g alloy}}{15.8 \text{ g Ni}} = 231 \text{ g alloy}$$

9.10 A 7.5% (v/v) solution contains 7.5 mL of solute per 100 mL of solution.

$$500 \text{ mL solution} \times \frac{7.5 \text{ mL acetic acid}}{100 \text{ mL solution}} = 38 \text{ mL acetic acid}$$

To prepare the desired solution, measure 38 mL of acetic acid into a 500.0 mL volumetric flask and add water to the 500.0 mL mark.

9.11 1 dL = 100 mL

$$\frac{8.6 \text{ mg}}{100 \text{ mL}} \text{ x } \frac{1 \text{ g}}{1000 \text{ mg}} \text{ x } 100\% = 0.0086\% \text{ (m/v) Ca}^{2+}$$

Remember: (m/v)% specifies that the mass of solute be expressed in grams.

9.12 (a) A 16% (m/v) solution contains 16 g of solute per 100 mL of solution.

$$125 \text{ mL x } \frac{16 \text{ g glucose}}{100 \text{ mL}} = 20 \text{ g glucose}$$

(b) A 2.0% (m/v) solution contains 2.0 g of solute per 100 mL of solution.

$$1.2 \text{ g KCl x } \frac{100 \text{ mL H}_2\text{O}}{2.0 \text{ g KCl}} = 60 \text{ mL H}_2\text{O}$$

9.13

$$\frac{32 \text{ mg NaF}}{20 \text{ kg solution}} \text{ x } \frac{1 \text{ kg}}{10^6 \text{ mg}} \text{ x } 10^6 = 1.6 \text{ ppm}$$

9.14 For lead:

$$\frac{0.015 \text{ mg Pb}}{1 \text{ kg solution}} \text{ x } \frac{1 \text{ kg}}{10^6 \text{ mg}} \text{ x } 10^6 = 0.015 \text{ ppm}$$

$$\frac{0.015 \text{ mg Pb}}{1 \text{ kg solution}} \text{ x } \frac{1 \text{ kg}}{10^3 \text{ g}} \text{ x } 100 \text{ g} = 0.0015 \text{ mg Pb}$$

For copper:

$$\frac{1.3 \text{ mg Cu}}{1 \text{ kg solution}} \text{ x } \frac{1 \text{ kg}}{10^6 \text{ mg}} \text{ x } 10^6 = 1.3 \text{ ppm}$$

$$\frac{1.3 \text{ mg Cu}}{1 \text{ kg solution}} \text{ x } \frac{1 \text{ kg}}{10^3 \text{ g}} \text{ x } 100 \text{ g} = 0.13 \text{ mg Cu}$$

9.15

$$\frac{50.0 \text{ g}}{0.160 \text{ L}} \text{ x } \frac{1 \text{ mol}}{337 \text{ g}} = 0.927 \text{ M}$$

9.16

moles of solute = molarity (M) x volume = $\frac{\text{mol}}{\text{L}}$ x L

(a) M = $\frac{0.35 \text{ mol NaNO}_3}{1 \text{ L}}$; V = 175 mL = 0.175 L

moles = $\frac{0.35 \text{ mol}}{1 \text{ L}}$ x 0.175 L = 0.061 mol NaNO$_3$

(b) M = $\frac{1.4 \text{ mol HNO}_3}{1 \text{ L}}$; V = 480 mL = 0.48 L

moles = $\frac{1.4 \text{ mol}}{1 \text{ L}}$ x 0.48 L = 0.67 mol HNO$_3$

9.17 First, find the number of moles of cholesterol in 250 mL of blood:

$$250 \text{ mL} \times \frac{0.0050 \text{ mol cholesterol}}{1000 \text{ mL}} = 0.001\ 25 \text{ mol cholesterol}$$

Next, find the molar mass of cholesterol:

$$(27 \times 12.0 \text{ g/mol C}) + (46 \times 1.0 \text{ g/mol H}) + (16.0 \text{ g/mol O}) = 386.0 \text{ g/mol}$$

Now, convert moles into grams:

$$0.001\ 25 \text{ mol cholesterol} \times \frac{386.0 \text{ g}}{1 \text{ mol}} = 0.48 \text{ g cholesterol}$$

9.18

(a) $0.065 \text{ L} \times \dfrac{0.12 \text{ mol HCl}}{1 \text{ L}} = 0.0078 \text{ mol HCl}$

(b) $0.0078 \text{ mol HCl} \times \dfrac{1 \text{ mol CaCO}_3}{2 \text{ mol HCl}} \times \dfrac{100.0 \text{ g CaCO}_3}{1 \text{ mol CaCO}_3} = 0.39 \text{ g CaCO}_3$

9.19 $V_2 = 500.0 \text{ mL}; \quad M_2 = 1.25 \text{ M}; \quad M_1 = 16.0 \text{ M}; \quad V_1 = ?$

$$V_1 = V_2 \times \frac{M_2}{M_1} = 500.0 \text{ mL} \times \frac{1.25 \text{ M}}{16.0 \text{ M}} = 39.1 \text{ mL}$$

Ballpark check: Since the final molarity is about 1/12 the initial molarity, the initial volume is about 1/12 the final volume, or about 40 mL.

9.20 $C_1 = 5.0 \text{ ppm}; \quad V_1 = 1.5 \text{ L}; \quad C_2 = 0.010 \text{ ppm}; \quad V_2 = ?$

$$V_2 = V_1 \times \frac{C_2}{C_1} = 1.5 \text{ L} \times \frac{5.0 \text{ ppm}}{0.01 \text{ ppm}} = 750 \text{ L}$$

9.21

One equivalent = molar mass of ion (g) ÷ number of charges on ion.

Ion	Molar Mass	Charge	Gram-Equivalent	Milligram-Equivalent
(a) K^+	39.1 g	+1	39.1 g	39.1 mg, or 3.91×10^{-2} g
(b) Br^-	79.9 g	−1	79.9 g	79.9 mg, or 7.99×10^{-2} g
(c) Mg^{2+}	24.3 g	+2	12.2 g	12.2 mg, or 1.22×10^{-2} g
(d) $SO_4{}^{2-}$	96.0 g	−2	48.0 g	48.0 mg, or 4.80×10^{-2} g
(e) Al^{3+}	27.0 g	+3	9.0 g	9.0 mg, or 9.0×10^{-3} g
(f) $PO_4{}^{3-}$	95.0 g	−3	31.7 g	31.7 mg, or 31.7×10^{-2} g

9.22 One gram-equivalent of Mg^{2+} = 12.2 g [Problem 9.21(c)].

$$\frac{g\,Mg^{2+}}{1\,L} = \frac{12\,g\,Mg^{2+}}{1\,Eq} \times \frac{1\,Eq}{1000\,mEq} \times \frac{3.0\,mEq}{1\,L} = \frac{0.036\,g\,Mg^{2+}}{1\,L}$$

$$\frac{0.036\,g\,Mg^{2+}}{L} \times \frac{1000\,mg}{1\,g} \times \frac{1\,L}{1000\,mL} \times 250\,mL = 9.0\,mg\,Mg^{2+}$$

9.23 For Na^+:

$$\frac{20\,mEq\,Na^+}{1.0\,L} \times \frac{23\,mg\,Na^+}{1\,mEq} \times \frac{1\,g}{1000\,mg} \times \frac{1.0\,L}{1000\,mL} \times 100\,mL = 0.046\,(m/v)\%\,Na^+$$

For K^+:

$$\frac{10\,mEq\,K^+}{1.0\,L} \times \frac{39\,mg\,K^+}{1\,mEq} \times \frac{1\,g}{1000\,mg} \times \frac{1.0\,L}{1000\,mL} \times 100\,mL = 0.039\,(m/v)\%\,K^+$$

9.24 (a) 0.67 mol of $MgCl_2$ in 0.5 kg H_2O yields 2.0 mol ions.
(b) 2.0 mol ions in 0.5 kg H_2O is equivalent to 4.0 mol ions in 1.0 kg H_2O, which raise the boiling point by 4.0 x 0.51 °C = 2.0 °C.

Boiling point = 100.0 °C + 2.0 °C = 102.0 °C

9.25 If HF were a strong electrolyte it would dissociate completely, and a solution of 1.0 mol HF would yield 2.0 mol ions, which would elevate the boiling point of water by 2.0 x 0.51 °C = 1.02 °C. Since the observed boiling point elevation is only 0.5 °C, HF must be a weak electrolyte that is only slightly dissociated.

9.26 (a) The red curve represents the pure solvent, because the solvent boils at a lower temperature than the solution.
(b) A liquid boils when its vapor pressure equals atmospheric pressure. The solvent boils at 62 °C, and the solution boils at 69 °C, an approximately 7° boiling point elevation.
(c) One mole of solute raises the boiling point approximately 3.5 °C, and the observed boiling point elevation is approximately 7 °C. Thus, the concentration of the solute is about 2 M.

9.27 Glucose is not an electrolyte. Thus 1.0 mol glucose lowers the freezing point of 1.0 kg H_2O by 1.9 °C.
Freezing point = 0.0 °C – 1.9 °C = –1.9 °C

9.28 A freezing point depression of 1.86 °C is produced by 1 mol of ions in 1 kg of water. Thus, a freezing point depression of 2.8 °C must be produced by 2.8 ÷ 1.86 = 1.5 mol of ions. Since 0.5 mol of the ionic substance produces the freezing point depression expected for 1.5 mol ions, the substance gives three ions when it dissolves.

9.29 Osmolarity = molarity x number of particles.
(a) For 0.35 M KBr, osmolarity = 0.35 M x 2 = 0.70 osmol, since KBr yields two ions (K^+ and Br^-) in solution.
(b) For 0.15 M glucose, osmolarity = 0.15 M x 1 = 0.15 osmol, since glucose yields only one particle in solution. For K_2SO_4, osmolarity = 0.05 M x 3 = 0.15 osmol, since K_2SO_4 provides three particles per mole in solution. Total osmolarity = 0.30 osmol.

9.30   (a) For the oral rehydration solution, osmolarity is equal to the sum of the osmolarities of the individual components. For each of the ionic components, the number of millimoles = the number of mEq, since each ion has one charge. Thus,

$$90 \text{ mM Na}^+ + 20 \text{ mM K}^+ + 110 \text{ mM Cl}^- = 220 \text{ mM ions}$$
$$0.090 \text{ M Na}^+ + 0.020 \text{ M K}^+ + 0.110 \text{ M Cl}^- = 0.220 \text{ M ions}$$

For glucose:

$$\frac{2.0 \text{ g glucose}}{100 \text{ mL}} \times \frac{1000 \text{ mL}}{1 \text{ L}} \times \frac{1 \text{ mol}}{180 \text{ g glucose}} = 0.11 \text{ M glucose}$$

(b) Osmolarity = molarity × number of particles. In this problem, all components yield one particle in solution.
Osmolarity = 0.22 M + 0.11 M = 0.33 osmol

Understanding Key Concepts

9.31

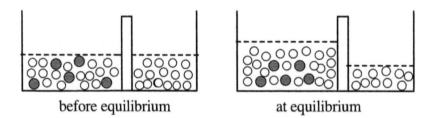

before equilibrium   at equilibrium

The membrane is permeable to the unshaded spheres but impermeable to the shaded spheres. Solvent (unshaded spheres) passes through the membrane until equilibrium is reached.

9.32   The boiling point of water is elevated by 0.5 °C for every mole of dissolved particles. 1 mol HCl dissolves to form 2 mol particles, which elevate the boiling point of water by 1 °C. Acetic acid exists in solution almost completely as CH_3CO_2H, and 1 mol acetic acid dissolves to form 1 mol particles, which elevate the boiling point of water by only 0.5 °C.

9.33   The same reasoning used in the previous problem applies here. The boiling point of water is elevated by 0.5 °C for every mole of dissolved particles. 1 mol HBr dissociates to form 2 mol ions, which raise the boiling point of water by 1.0 °C, but 1 mol HF is only slightly dissociated and raises the boiling point by 0.5 °C. Thus, the upper curve (red) represents 1 M HF, and the lower curve (blue) represents 1 M HBr.

9.34

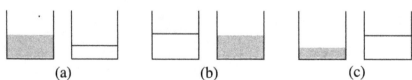

(a)   (b)   (c)

When a beaker of glucose solution (shaded) and a beaker of pure water (unshaded) stand for several days, the liquid levels appear as those pictured in (a). The dissolved glucose particles lower the vapor pressure of water and make evaporation slower.

9.35   Drawing (d) represents the solution that results when 50.0 mL of (a) is withdrawn and diluted by a factor of 4.

Solutions and Solubility

9.36   In a homogeneous mixture (such as tea), mixing is uniform throughout because the particle size is small. In a heterogeneous mixture (such as chicken soup), mixing is nonuniform because particle size is larger.

9.37   A solution is transparent to light; a colloid usually appears murky or opaque.

9.38   The polarity of water enables it to dissolve many ionic solids.

9.39   Water doesn't dissolve motor oil because oil is nonpolar and water is polar.

9.40   Rubbing alcohol (b) and black coffee (d) are solutions.

9.41   The pairs in (a), (b), and (d) are miscible.

9.42

$$C_2 = \frac{C_1 P_2}{P_1}; \quad C_1 = 51.8 \text{ g/100 mL}; \quad P_1 = 760.0 \text{ mmHg}; \quad P_2 = 225.0 \text{ mmHg}$$

$$= \frac{(51.8 \text{ g/100 mL}) \times 225.0 \text{ mmHg}}{760.0 \text{ mmHg}} = 15.3 \text{ g/100 mL}$$

9.43

$$C_2 = \frac{C_1 P_2}{P_1}; \quad C_1 = 0.15 \text{ g/100 mL}; \quad P_1 = 760.0 \text{ mmHg} = 1.0 \text{ atm}; \quad P_2 = 4.5 \text{ atm}$$

$$= \frac{(0.15 \text{ g/100 mL}) \times 4.5 \text{ atm}}{1.0 \text{ atm}} = 0.68 \text{ g/100 mL}$$

Concentration and Dilution of Solutions

9.44   Depending on the solubility of the solute in the solvent, a saturated solution may be either dilute or concentrated. If a solute is only slightly soluble in a solvent, a saturated solution will be dilute. If the solute is very soluble in the solvent, a saturated solution will be concentrated. For a highly soluble solute, even a highly concentrated solution may be unsaturated.

9.45   Mass/volume percent concentration [(m/v)]% is defined as the mass in grams of solute per 100 mL of solution and is used to describe the solution of a solid in a liquid.

9.46   Molarity (M) is defined as the number of moles of solute per liter of solution.

9.47   Volume/volume percent concentration [(v/v)%] is defined as the volume of solute in 100 mL of solution and is used for solutions in which both the solute and the solvent are liquids.

9.48

$$\frac{6.0 \text{ mL ethyl alcohol}}{100.0 \text{ mL solution}} \times 750.0 \text{ mL solution} = 45.0 \text{ mL ethyl alcohol}$$

Add water to 45.0 mL of ethyl alcohol to make a final volume of 750.0 mL.

9.49

$$500.0 \text{ mL solution} \times \frac{0.50 \text{ g B(OH)}_3}{100 \text{ mL solution}} = 2.5 \text{ g B(OH)}_3$$

Dissolve 2.5 g B(OH)$_3$ in water to a final volume of 500.0 mL.

9.50

$$250 \text{ mL solution} \times \frac{0.10 \text{ mol NaCl}}{1000 \text{ mL solution}} \times \frac{58.5 \text{ g NaCl}}{1 \text{ mol NaCl}} = 1.5 \text{ g NaCl}$$

Dissolve 1.5 g NaCl in water to a final volume of 250 mL.

9.51

$$1.50 \text{ L} \times \frac{1000 \text{ mL}}{1 \text{ L}} \times \frac{7.50 \text{ g Mg(NO}_3)_2}{100 \text{ mL solution}} = 113 \text{ g Mg(NO}_3)_2$$

Dissolve 113 g Mg(NO$_3$)$_2$ in water and dilute to 1.50 L.

9.52

(a) $0.078 \text{ mol KCl} \times \dfrac{74.6 \text{ g KCl}}{1 \text{ mol KCl}} = 5.8 \text{ g KCl}$

$\dfrac{5.8 \text{ g KCl}}{75 \text{ mL}} \times 100 \text{ mL} = 7.7 \text{ g KCl}; \dfrac{7.7 \text{ g KCl}}{100 \text{ mL}} \times 100\% = 7.7\% \text{ (m/v) KCl}$

(b) $0.044 \text{ mol sucrose} \times \dfrac{342 \text{ g sucrose}}{1 \text{ mol sucrose}} = 15 \text{ g sucrose}$

$\dfrac{15 \text{ g sucrose}}{380 \text{ mL}} \times 100 \text{ mL} = 3.9 \text{ g sucrose}; \dfrac{3.9 \text{ g}}{100 \text{ mL}} \times 100\% = 3.9\% \text{ (m/v) sucrose}$

9.53

$$\frac{90 \text{ mg glucose}}{100 \text{ mL}} \times \frac{1 \text{ g}}{1000 \text{ mg}} = \frac{0.090 \text{ g glucose}}{100 \text{ mL}}; \quad 0.090\% \text{ (m/v) glucose}$$

$$\frac{0.090 \text{ g glucose}}{100 \text{ mL}} \times \frac{1000 \text{ mL}}{1 \text{ L}} \times \frac{1 \text{ mol}}{180 \text{ g glucose}} = 0.0050 \text{ M}$$

9.54

(a) $50.0 \text{ mL} \times \dfrac{8.0 \text{ g KCl}}{100 \text{ mL}} = 4.0 \text{ g KCl}; 4.0 \text{ g KCl} \times \dfrac{1 \text{ mol KCl}}{74.6 \text{ g KCl}} = 0.054 \text{ mol KCl}$

(b) $200.0 \text{ mL} \times \dfrac{7.5 \text{ g acetic acid}}{100 \text{ mL}} = 15 \text{ g acetic acid}$

$15 \text{ g acetic acid} \times \dfrac{1 \text{ mol acetic acid}}{60 \text{ g acetic acid}} = 0.25 \text{ mol acetic acid}$

9.55

(a) For 0.50 M KCl: $\dfrac{0.50 \text{ mol KCl}}{1 \text{ L}} \times \dfrac{74.6 \text{ g}}{1 \text{ mol}} = \dfrac{37 \text{ g KCl}}{1 \text{ L}} = \dfrac{3.7 \text{ g KCl}}{100 \text{ mL}}$

For 5% (m/v) KCl: $\dfrac{5.0 \text{ g KCl}}{100 \text{ mL}}$

The 5% (m/v) solution is more concentrated.

(b) 2.5% (m/v) $NaHSO_4 = \dfrac{2.5 \text{ g } NaHSO_4}{100 \text{ mL solution}}$

$\dfrac{0.025 \text{ mol } NaHSO_4}{1 \text{ L}} \times \dfrac{120 \text{ g}}{1 \text{ mol}} = \dfrac{3.0 \text{ g } NaHSO_4}{1 \text{ L}} = \dfrac{0.30 \text{ g } NaHSO_4}{100 \text{ mL}}$

The 2.5% (m/v) solution is more concentrated.

9.56

$23 \text{ g KOH} \times \dfrac{100 \text{ mL}}{10.0 \text{ g KOH}} = 230 \text{ mL of a } 10.0\% \text{ (m/v) solution}$

$23 \text{ g KOH} \times \dfrac{1 \text{ mol}}{56.1 \text{ g KOH}} = 0.41 \text{ mol KOH}$

$0.41 \text{ mol KOH} \times \dfrac{1000 \text{ mL}}{0.25 \text{ mol KOH}} = 1600 \text{ mL of } 0.25 \text{ M solution}$

9.57

$\dfrac{3 \text{ g}}{100 \text{ mL}} \times \dfrac{1000 \text{ mL}}{1 \text{ L}} \times \dfrac{1 \text{ mol}}{34 \text{ g}} = 0.9 \text{ M}$

9.58

$\dfrac{10 \text{ mg KCN}}{1 \text{ kg body weight}} \times \dfrac{1 \text{ kg}}{10^6 \text{ mg}} \times 10^6 = 10 \text{ ppm}$

9.59 From Section 9.7 we know that 1 ppb = 1 μg solute/1 L solution. Thus, 15 ppb = 15 μg/L.

(a) $\dfrac{15 \text{ μg}}{1 \text{ L}} \times \dfrac{1 \text{ mg}}{10^3 \text{ μg}} = \dfrac{1.5 \times 10^{-2} \text{ mg}}{1 \text{ L}}$

(b) $1.0 \text{ μg} \times \dfrac{1 \text{ L}}{15 \text{ μg}} = 0.067 \text{ L}$

9.60

(a) $\dfrac{12.5 \text{ g } NaHCO_3}{0.350 \text{ L}} \times \dfrac{1 \text{ mol}}{84.0 \text{ g}} = 0.425 \text{ M}$

(b) $\dfrac{45.0 \text{ g } H_2SO_4}{0.300 \text{ L}} \times \dfrac{1 \text{ mol}}{98.1 \text{ g}} = 1.53 \text{ M}$

(c) $\dfrac{30.0 \text{ g NaCl}}{0.500 \text{ L}} \times \dfrac{1 \text{ mol}}{58.5 \text{ g}} = 1.03 \text{ M}$

9.61

(a) $0.200 \text{ L} \times \dfrac{0.30 \text{ mol acetic acid}}{1 \text{ L}} \times \dfrac{60.0 \text{ g acetic acid}}{1 \text{ mol acetic acid}} = 3.6 \text{ g acetic acid}$

(b) $1.50 \text{ L} \times \dfrac{0.25 \text{ mol NaOH}}{1 \text{ L}} \times \dfrac{40.0 \text{ g NaOH}}{1 \text{ mol NaOH}} = 15 \text{ g NaOH}$

(c) $0.750 \text{ L} \times \dfrac{2.5 \text{ mol HNO}_3}{1 \text{ L}} \times \dfrac{63.0 \text{ g HNO}_3}{1 \text{ mol HNO}_3} = 120 \text{ g HNO}_3$

9.62

$0.0040 \text{ mol HCl} \times \dfrac{1000 \text{ mL}}{0.75 \text{ mol}} = 5.3 \text{ mL HCl}$

9.63

$1.5 \text{ mg} \times \dfrac{1 \text{ g}}{1000 \text{ mg}} \times \dfrac{100 \text{ mL}}{0.40 \text{ g}} = 0.38 \text{ mL}$

9.64 First, calculate the number of moles of H_2SO_4 spilled:

$0.450 \text{ L} \times \dfrac{0.50 \text{ mol H}_2\text{SO}_4}{1 \text{ L}} = 0.23 \text{ mol H}_2\text{SO}_4$

According to the equation given in the problem, each mole of H_2SO_4 reacts with two moles of $NaHCO_3$. Thus, the 0.23 mol of H_2SO_4 spilled need to be neutralized with 0.46 mol of $NaHCO_3$.

$0.46 \text{ mol NaHCO}_3 \times \dfrac{84 \text{ g}}{1 \text{ mol}} = 39 \text{ g NaHCO}_3$

9.65

(a) $0.450 \text{ g AgBr} \times \dfrac{1 \text{ mol AgBr}}{187.8 \text{ g}} = 2.40 \times 10^{-3} \text{ mol AgBr}$

According to the equation given, 1 mole of AgBr reacts with 2 moles of $Na_2S_2O_3$. Thus, 2.40×10^{-3} mol AgBr reacts with 4.80×10^{-3} mol $Na_2S_2O_3$.

(b) To calculate the volume of 0.0200 M $Na_2S_2O_3$:

$4.80 \times 10^{-3} \text{ mol} \times \dfrac{1000 \text{ mL}}{0.0200 \text{ mol}} = 240 \text{ mL of } 0.0200 \text{ M Na}_2\text{S}_2\text{O}_3$

9.66

20.0% (v/v) means $\dfrac{20.0 \text{ mL concentrate}}{100.0 \text{ mL juice}}$

Thus, $100.0 \text{ mL concentrate} \times \dfrac{100.0 \text{ mL juice}}{20.0 \text{ mL concentrate}} = 500.0 \text{ mL juice}$

Since the final volume of the diluted juice is 500.0 mL, you would need to add 400.0 mL water to the original 100.0 mL of concentrate.

9.67

$$V_2 = V_1 \times \frac{M_1}{M_2}; \ V_1 = 100.0 \text{ mL}; \ M_1 = 0.500 \text{ M}; \ M_2 = 0.150 \text{ M}$$

$$= 100.0 \text{ mL} \times \frac{0.500 \text{ M}}{0.150 \text{ M}} = 333 \text{ mL of } 0.150 \text{ M NaOH solution}$$

100.0 mL of 0.500 M NaOH is diluted with 233 mL water to give 333 mL of 0.150 M NaOH solution.

9.68

$$V_1 = V_2 \times \frac{C_2}{C_1}; \ V_2 = 2.0 \text{ L}; \ C_2 = 75 \text{ ppm}; \ C_1 = 285 \text{ ppm}$$

$$= 2.0 \text{ L} \times \frac{75 \text{ ppm}}{285 \text{ ppm}} = 0.53 \text{ L of } 285 \text{ ppm } KNO_3 \text{ solution}$$

9.69

$$C_2 = C_1 \times \frac{V_1}{V_2}; \ C_1 = 37\% \text{ (m/v)}; \ V_1 = 65 \text{ mL}; \ V_2 = 480 \text{ mL}$$

$$= 37\% \text{ (m/v)} \times \frac{65 \text{ mL}}{480 \text{ mL}} = 5.0\% \text{ (m/v) NaCl}$$

9.70

$$V_2 = V_1 \times \frac{M_1}{M_2}; \ V_1 = 25.0 \text{ mL}; \ M_1 = 12.0 \text{ M}; \ M_2 = 0.500 \text{ M}$$

$$= 25.0 \text{ mL} \times \frac{12.0 \text{ M}}{0.500 \text{ M}} = 600 \text{ mL of } 0.500 \text{ M HCl solution}$$

9.71

$$V_1 = V_2 \times \frac{M_2}{M_1}; \ V_2 = 750.0 \text{ mL}; \ M_1 = 0.100 \text{ M}; \ M_2 = 0.0500 \text{ M}$$

$$= 750.0 \text{ mL} \times \frac{0.0500 \text{ M}}{0.100 \text{ M}} = 375 \text{ mL of } 0.100 \text{ M } NaHCO_3$$

Electrolytes

9.72 An electrolyte is a substance that conducts electricity when dissolved in water.

9.73 Sodium chloride is an example of a strong electrolyte. Glucose is an example of a nonelectrolyte.

9.74 If the concentration of Ca^{2+} is 3.0 mEq/L, there are 3.0 mmol of charges due to calcium per liter of blood. Since calcium has a charge of +2, there are 1.5 mmol of calcium per liter of blood.

9.75   The total anion concentration in the solution must equal the total cation concentration in order to conserve charge. Thus:

[Cations] = [Anions] = 5.0 mEq/L Na^+ + 12.0 mEq/L Ca^{2+} + 2.0 mEq/L K^+ = 19 mEq/L

9.76

$$10\% \ (m/v) = \frac{10 \ g \ KCl}{100 \ mL}; \quad 30 \ mL \ x \ \frac{10 \ g \ KCl}{100 \ mL} = 3.0 \ g \ KCl$$

The molar mass of KCl is 74.6 g/mol. Thus:

$$3.0 \ g \ KCl \ x \ \frac{1 \ mol}{74.6 \ g} = 0.040 \ mol \ KCl$$

Since one equivalent equals one mole when an ion has only one charge, there are 0.040 Eq, or 40 mEq, of K^+ in a 30 mL dose.

9.77   One gram-equivalent = molar mass of ion(g) divided by # of charges on ion:

Ion	Molar mass	Charge	Gram-equivalent
(a) Ca^{2+}	40.1 g	2+	20.1 g
(b) K^+	39.1 g	1+	39.1 g
(c) SO_4^{2-}	96.1 g	2–	48.1 g
(d) PO_4^{3-}	95.0 g	3–	31.7 g

9.78   Use the value 100 mEq/L for the concentration of Cl^- in blood:
For Cl^- ion, 100 mEq = 100 mmol = 0.100 mol.

$$1.0 \ g \ Cl^- \ x \ \frac{1 \ mol}{35.5 \ g} \ x \ \frac{1 \ L}{0.100 \ mol} \ x \ \frac{1000 \ mL}{1 \ L} = 280 \ mL$$

9.79   For Mg^{2+}, with a molar mass of 24.3 g and a charge of +2, the mass of one equivalent is 24.3 g/2 = 12.2 g, and the mass of 1 milliequivalent is 12.2 mg.

$$\frac{3 \ mEq \ Mg^{2+}}{1 \ L} \ x \ \frac{12 \ mg \ Mg^{2+}}{1 \ mEq \ Mg^{2+}} \ x \ \frac{1 \ L}{1000 \ mL} \ x \ 150.0 \ mL = 5 \ mg \ Mg^{2+}$$

Properties of Solutions

9.80   0.20 mol NaOH contains 0.40 mol solute particles, and 0.20 mol $Ba(OH)_2$ contains 0.60 mol solute particles. Since $Ba(OH)_2$ produces more solute particles, it produces greater lowering of the freezing point when dissolved in 2.0 kg of water.

9.81   When 0.300 mol KCl dissolves, it produces 0.600 mol particles; when 0.500 mol glucose dissolves, it produces 0.500 mol particles. The solution with more dissolved particles (0.300 mol KCl) has the higher boiling point.

9.82 Methanol has a molar mass of 32.0 g and provides one mole of solute particles per mole of methanol.

$$10.0\ °C \times \frac{1\ mol}{1.86\ °C \times 1\ kg} \times 5.00\ kg = 26.9\ mol\ methanol$$

$$26.9\ mol \times \frac{32.0\ g}{1\ mol} = 861\ g\ of\ methanol\ needed$$

9.83 Cane sugar provides one mole of solute particles per mole. The boiling point elevation:

$$\frac{650\ g\ sugar}{1.5\ kg\ H_2O} \times \frac{1\ mol}{342\ g} \times \frac{0.51\ °C \times 1\ kg}{1\ mol} = 0.65\ °C$$

The boiling point of the resulting solution is $100.0\ °C + 0.65\ °C = 100.65\ °C$.

Osmosis

9.84 The inside of a red blood cell contains dissolved substances and therefore has a higher osmolarity than pure water. Water thus passes through the cell membrane to dilute the cell contents until pressure builds up and the cell eventually bursts.

9.85 If a 0.15 M NaCl solution is isotonic with blood, then the NaCl solution has the same osmolarity as blood. If distilled water is hypotonic with blood, then the water has a lower osmolarity than blood.

9.86

Solution	Molarity	Number of Particles	Osmolarity
(a) 0.25 M KBr	0.25 M	2	0.50 osmol
0.20 M Na₂SO₄	0.20 M	3	0.60 osmol (greater)
(b) 0.30 M NaOH	0.30 M	2	0.60 osmol
3% (m/v) NaOH	0.75 M	2	1.5 osmol (greater)

9.87 The solution with the higher osmolarity gives rise to the greater osmotic pressure at equilibrium.

For NaCl: $\dfrac{5.0\ g}{0.350\ L} \times \dfrac{1\ mol}{58.5\ g} \times 2\ particles = 0.49\ osmol$

For glucose: $\dfrac{35.0\ g}{0.400\ L} \times \dfrac{1\ mol}{180\ g} \times 1\ particle = 0.49\ osmol$

Both solutions give rise to the same osmotic pressure.

9.88 The molar mass of NaCl is 58.5 g, and each mole of NaCl yields two moles of particles.

$$\frac{270\ g}{3.8\ L} \times \frac{1\ mol}{58.5\ g} \times 2\ particles = 2.4\ osmol$$

9.89 A solution that contains 0.30 osmol KCl is 0.15 M, since KCl produces two particles when dissolved.

$$\frac{74.5 \text{ g}}{1 \text{ mol}} \times \frac{0.15 \text{ mol}}{1 \text{ L}} \times \frac{1 \text{ L}}{1000 \text{ mL}} \times 175 \text{ mL} = 2.0 \text{ g KCl}$$

Approximately 2.0 g KCl are needed.

Chemistry in Action

9.90 At high altitude, P_{O2} is low, and not enough oxygen is available to cause 100% saturation of hemoglobin. In order to deliver enough oxygen to body tissues, the body compensates by manufacturing more hemoglobin, which drives the hemoglobin equilibrium to the right.

9.91 The major electrolytes in sweat are sodium ion (30–40 mEq/L), potassium ion (5–10 mEq/L), small amounts of metals such as magnesium, and chloride to balance charge (35–50 mEq/L).

9.92 In addition to fluid replacement, sports drinks provide electrolytes to replenish those lost during exercise, they furnish soluble complex carbohydrates for slow-release energy, and they may contain vitamins to protect cells from damage.

9.93 An enteric coating on a medication is a polymeric material that isn't digested by stomach acid but passes into the intestine, where it dissolves in the more basic intestinal environment and releases the medication.

General Questions and Problems

9.94

(a) $0.18 \times 5.0 \text{ atm} \times \dfrac{760 \text{ mmHg}}{1.0 \text{ atm}} = 680 \text{ mmHg}$

(b) $\dfrac{C_1}{P_1} = \dfrac{C_2}{P_2}$; $P_1 = 760 \text{ mmHg}$; $C_1 = 2.1 \text{ g}/100 \text{ mL}$; $P_2 = 680 \text{ mmHg}$; $C_2 = ?$

$= \dfrac{(2.1 \text{ g}/100 \text{ mL}) \times 680 \text{ mmHg}}{760 \text{ mmHg}} = 1.9 \text{ g}/100 \text{ mL}$

9.95

$$\frac{2.1 \text{ g}}{100 \text{ mL}} \times \frac{1 \text{ mol}}{32 \text{ g}} \times \frac{1000 \text{ mL}}{1 \text{ L}} = 0.66 \text{ M at } 1.0 \text{ atm}$$

Solubility = 0.59 M at 680 mmHg

9.96 Molar mass of uric acid ($C_5H_4N_4O_3$) = 168 g.

(a) (m/v)%: $\dfrac{0.067 \text{ g}}{1 \text{ L}} = \dfrac{0.0067 \text{ g}}{100 \text{ mL}}$; $\dfrac{0.0067 \text{ g}}{100 \text{ mL}} \times 100\% = 0.0067\% \text{ (m/v)}$

(b) ppm: One L of water weighs 1 kg. Thus

$$\frac{0.067 \text{ g}}{1 \text{ L}} = \frac{0.067 \text{ g}}{1 \text{ kg}} \times \frac{1 \text{ kg}}{1000 \text{ g}}; \frac{0.067 \text{ g}}{1000 \text{ g}} \times 10^6 = 67 \text{ ppm}$$

(c) $\dfrac{0.067\ g}{1\ L}$ x $\dfrac{1\ mol}{168\ g}$ = 0.000 40 M = 4.0 x 10^{-4} M

9.97

5.0% (m/v) = $\dfrac{5.0\ g\ CaCl_2}{100\ mL}$; $\dfrac{5.0\ g\ CaCl_2}{100\ mL}$ x 5.0 mL = 0.25 g $CaCl_2$

0.25 g $CaCl_2$ x $\dfrac{1\ mol}{111\ g}$ = 0.0023 mol $CaCl_2$ = 0.0023 mol Ca^{2+}

0.0023 mol Ca^{2+} x $\dfrac{2\ Eq}{1\ mol}$ = 0.0046 Eq Ca^{2+} = 4.6 mEq Ca^{2+}

9.98 (a) The volume of concentrated HNO_3 that contains 0.150 mol is:

$V_2 = V_1$ x $\dfrac{moles_2}{moles_1}$ = 1.0 L x $\dfrac{0.15\ mol}{16\ mol}$ = 0.0094 L HNO_3 = 9.4 mL HNO_3

(b) The volume of a 0.20 M solution that contains 0.15 moles:

$V_2 = V_1$ x $\dfrac{moles_2}{moles_1}$ = 1.0 L x $\dfrac{0.15\ mol}{0.20\ mol}$ = 0.75 L

9.99

(a) 13.0 mL x $\dfrac{0.0100\ mol}{1000\ mL}$ = 1.30 x 10^{-4} mol I_2

According to the equation, one mole of I_2 reacts with one mole of $C_6H_8O_6$. Thus, the 25.0 mL sample contains 1.30 x 10^{-4} mol $C_6H_8O_6$.

(b) $\dfrac{1.30\ x\ 10^{-4}\ mol}{25.0\ mL}$ x $\dfrac{1000\ mL}{1\ L}$ = 0.005 20 M = 5.20 mM

(c) Molar mass of $C_6H_8O_6$ = 176 g.

$\dfrac{176\ g}{1\ mol}$ x $\dfrac{0.005\ 20\ mol}{1\ L}$ x $\dfrac{1000\ mg}{1\ g}$ = $\dfrac{915\ mg\ ascorbic\ acid}{1\ L}$

60 mg x $\dfrac{1\ L}{915\ mg\ ascorbic\ acid}$ x $\dfrac{1000\ mL}{1\ L}$ = 66 mL juice

9.100–9.101

Component	Mass	Molar Mass	Molarity	Osmolarity
(a) NaCl	8.6 g	58.5 g	0.147 M	0.294 osmol
(b) KCl	0.30 g	74.6 g	0.0040 M	0.0080 osmol
(c) $CaCl_2$	0.33 g	111 g	0.0030 M	0.0090 osmol
			Total:	0.31 osmol

Ringer's solution (0.31 osmol) is approximately isotonic with blood plasma (0.30 osmol).

9.102

$$\frac{10 \text{ mg}}{5.0 \text{ L}} \times \frac{1 \text{ L}}{1000 \text{ mL}} \times \frac{1 \text{ g}}{1000 \text{ mg}} \times 100\% = 0.0002\% \text{ (m/v)}$$

9.103 For quantities expressed in parts per million, both the solute and solvent must be expressed in the same units. In this problem, both quantities are expressed in grams. The mass of statin drug is 10 mg = 10×10^{-3} g. The density of blood is 1.05 g/mL.

$$\frac{1.05 \text{ g}}{1 \text{ mL}} \times \frac{1000 \text{ mL}}{1 \text{ L}} \times 5.0 \text{ L} = 5.2 \times 10^3 \text{ g}$$

$$ppm = \frac{\text{mass of solute (g)}}{\text{mass of solvent (g)}} \times 10^6 = \frac{10 \times 10^{-3} \text{ g}}{5.2 \times 10^3 \text{ g}} \times 10^6 = 1.9 \text{ ppm}$$

9.104

$$0.080\% \text{ (v/v)} = \frac{0.080 \text{ mL}}{100 \text{ mL}} = \frac{0.80 \text{ mL}}{1 \text{ L}}; \frac{0.80 \text{ mL}}{1 \text{ L}} \times 5.0 \text{ L} = 4.0 \text{ mL alcohol}$$

9.105

(a)

(b) $\dfrac{51.8 \text{ g}}{1 \text{ L}} \times \dfrac{1 \text{ mol}}{17.0 \text{ g}} = 3.05 \text{ mol/L}$

9.106 (a) $CoCl_2(s) + 6 H_2O(g) \rightleftharpoons CoCl_2 \cdot 6H_2O(s)$

(b) Molar mass of $CoCl_2 \cdot 6H_2O$ = 238 g

$$2.50 \text{ g CoCl}_2 \times \frac{1 \text{ mol CoCl}_2 \cdot 6 \text{ H}_2\text{O}}{238 \text{ g}} \times \frac{6 \text{ mol H}_2\text{O}}{1 \text{ mol CoCl}_2 \cdot 6 \text{ H}_2\text{O}} \times \frac{18.0 \text{ g H}_2\text{O}}{1 \text{ mol H}_2\text{O}} = 1.13 \text{ g H}_2\text{O}$$

9.107 $BaCl_2(aq) + Na_2SO_4(aq) \longrightarrow BaSO_4(s) + 2 NaCl(aq)$

According to the balanced equation, one mole of $BaCl_2$ reacts with one mole of Na_2SO_4.

$$\# \text{ moles Na}_2\text{SO}_4 = \frac{0.200 \text{ mol}}{1 \text{ L}} \times 0.0350 \text{ L} = 0.007\,00 \text{ mol} = \# \text{ moles BaCl}_2$$

$$0.007\,00 \text{ mol BaCl}_2 \times \frac{1 \text{ L}}{0.150 \text{ mol}} = 0.0467 \text{ L} = 46.7 \text{ mL BaCl}_2$$

$$0.007\,00 \text{ mol} \times \frac{233.3 \text{ g}}{1 \text{ mol}} = 1.63 \text{ g BaSO}_4$$

9.108 (a) If 36.0 % of TCA is dissociated, the solution consists of 0.360 mol TCA anions, 0.360 mol H^+ cations, and 0.640 mol undissociated TCA, for a total of 1.360 mol ions and molecules in 1 kg water.

(b) The freezing point of water is depressed by 2.53 °C, resulting in a final temperature of –2.53 °C.

$$1.36 \text{ mol} \times \frac{1.86 \,^\circ C}{1 \text{ mol}} = 2.53 \,^\circ C$$

Self-Test for Chapter 9

Multiple Choice

1. 50 mL of a 1.0 M NaOH solution is diluted to 1.0 L. What is the dilution factor?
   (a) 1/50   (b) 1/20   (c) 1/10   (d) 1/2

2. Which of the following will not speed up the rate of solution of a solid?
   (a) stirring   (b) heating   (c) grinding the solid into powder   (d) increasing pressure on the solution

3. To make up 500 mL of a 5% (v/v) solution of methanol (CH_3OH; molar mass = 32 g) in water:
   (a) Dilute 25 mL of CH_3OH with water to a volume of 500 mL.
   (b) Dilute 5 mL of CH_3OH with water to a volume of 500 mL.
   (c) Add 32 g of CH_3OH to 500 g of water.
   (d) Add 25 mL of CH_3OH to 500 mL of water.

4. Which solution has the greatest osmolarity?
   (a) 0.2 M $CaCl_2$ (b) 0.3 M Na_3PO_4 (c) 0.5 M NaCl   (d) 0.8 M glucose

5. Which of the following is a colloid?
   (a) wine   (b) maple syrup   (c) milkshake   (d) salad oil

6. How many mL of a 12.0 M HCl solution are needed to make 1.0 L of 0.10 M HCl?
   (a) 120 mL   (b) 83 mL   (c) 50 mL   (d) 8.3 mL

7. Which of the following properties do not depend on the number of particles in solution?
   (a) boiling point elevation   (b) osmotic pressure   (c) heat of solution   (d) freezing point depression

8. How many grams of NaOH are needed to make 300 mL of a 0.3 M solution?
   (a) 40 g   (b) 12 g   (c) 3.6 g   (d) 1.0 g

9. How many moles of glucose are present in 250 mL of a 0.25 M solution?
   (a) 0.0625 mol   (b) 0.1 mol   (c) 0.25 mol   (d) 1.0 mol

10. How many mL of a 0.20 M solution of NaF contain 2.1 g of NaF?
    (a) 500 mL   (b) 250 mL   (c) 100 mL   (d) 50 mL

Sentence Completion

1. Two liquids soluble in each other are said to be _____.

2. An ___ ____ is the amount of an ion in grams that contains Avogadro's number of charges.

3. A weight/volume solution can be made up in a piece of glassware called a _____ _____.

4. According to Henry's law, the _____ of a gas varies with its _____ _____.

5. Two solutions that have the same osmolarity are _____.

6. Compounds that attract water from the atmosphere are called _____.

7. The formula used for calculating dilutions is _____.

8. Milk is an example of a _____.

9. _____ and _____ _____ _____ can pass through a dialysis membrane.

10. A solution that has reached its solubility limit is said to be _____.

11. An example of a nonelectrolyte is _____.

12. A solution that is hypotonic with respect to blood has a _____ osmolarity than blood plasma.

True or False

1. A solute is the liquid used to dissolve a substance.

2. It is possible to have a solution of a solid in a solid.

3. In making a volume/volume percent solution, one liquid is added to 100 mL of the other liquid.

4. All ionic compounds are soluble in water.

5. A solution of 0.10 M Na_3PO_4 has a greater osmolarity than a solution of 0.15 M NaCl.

6. Weight/weight percent is a useful way to express concentration.

7. In carrying out a dilution, the number of moles of solute remains constant.

8. The solubility of most substances increases with temperature.

9. A colloid differs from a solution in its ability to transmit light.

10. A blood cell undergoes crenation when placed in distilled water.

11. Particles dissolved in water lower the boiling point of water.

12. The amount of gas dissolved in a liquid increases with increasing pressure.

Match each entry on the left with its partner on the right.

1. Osmotic membrane

2. V_1/V_2

3. Solution

4. Equivalent

5. Suspension

6. Dialysis membrane

7. Osmolarity

8. Hypotonic

9. Colloid

10. Crenation

11. Hydrate

12. Electrolyte

(a) Muddy water

(b) Molarity x number of particles

(c) Conducts electricity in water

(d) Vinegar

(e) Crystalline compound that holds water

(f) Dilution factor

(g) Butter

(h) Permeable only to water

(i) A solution of lower osmolarity than another

(j) Formula weight/number of charges

(k) Permeable to water and small molecules

(l) Happens to cell in hypertonic solution

Chapter 10 – Acids and Bases

Chapter Outline

I. Introduction to acids and bases (Sections 10.1–10.3).
  A. Definition of acids and bases (Sections 10.1, 10.3).
    1. Arrhenius definition (Section 10.1).
      a. Acids donate H^+ ions in solution.
      b. Bases donate OH^- ions in solution.
      c. Acid + base —> salt + H_2O.
    2. Brønsted–Lowry definition (Section 10.3).
      a. A Brønsted–Lowry acid is a proton donor (an H_3O^+ donor).
        i. Some acids can donate more than one proton.
      b. A Brønsted–Lowry base is a proton acceptor.
        i. The base may be negatively charged or neutral.
      c. An acid–base reaction is one in which a proton is transferred.
      d. Products of acid–base reactions are also acids and bases.
      In the reaction HA + B: —> A^- + BH^+:
        i. HA and A^- are an acid–conjugate base pair.
        ii. B: and BH^+ are a base–conjugate acid pair.
  B. Many common substances are acids or bases (Section 10.2).
II. Acid/base strength (Sections 10.4–10.9).
  A. Strong/weak acids and bases (Section 10.4).
    1. Strong acids and bases are 100% dissociated in water.
    2. Weak acids and bases are less than 100% dissociated in solution.
    3. The stronger the acid, the weaker the conjugate base.
    The weaker the acid, the stronger the conjugate base.
    4. An acid–base proton transfer always favors formation of the weaker acid.
  B. Acid dissociation constants (Section 10.5).
    1. K_a is a measure of the degree to which an acid HA dissociates to H_3O^+ and A^-.
    2. K_a values for weak acids are much less than 1.
    3. Donation of each successive H^+ ion from a polyprotic acid becomes successively more difficult.
    4. Most organic acids have K_a near 10^{-5}.
  C. Water as an acid and a base (Section 10.6).
    1. Water can act both as an acid and a base.
    2. Substances that can act as both acids and bases are amphoteric.
    3. Dissociation of H_2O.
      a. $K_w = [H_3O^+][OH^-] = 1.00 \times 10^{-14}$ at 25 °C.
      b. This relationship is true for any aqueous solution.
      c. Thus, we can calculate $[H_3O^+]$ or $[OH^-]$ for any aqueous solution.
  D. Measuring acidity (Sections 10.7–10.9).
    1. pH (Sections 10.7–10.8).
      a. A pH of < 7 indicates acidity; a pH of > 7 indicates basicity.
      b. pH is the negative logarithm of $[H_3O^+]$.
      c. The pH scale is logarithmic.
      d. pH can be computed with a calculator.
    2. In the laboratory, pH can be measured with indicators or a pH meter (Section 10.9).

III. Buffers (Section 10.10).
   A. Characteristics of buffers.
      1. A buffer is the solution of a weak acid and its salt (or a weak base and its salt) at similar concentration.
      2. When a small amount of acid or base is added to a buffered solution, pH changes very little.
      3. The effective pH range of a buffer solution is determined by the K_a of the acid or base.
         a. A buffer solution works best when [HA] is close in value to [A⁻].
         b. A buffer solution works best when [HA] and [A⁻] are approximately ten times greater than the amount of acid or base added.
      4. The Henderson–Hasselbalch equation (pH = pK_a + log ([A⁻]/[HA]) is useful in buffer calculations. (pK_a = –log K_a)
      5. The carbonate/bicarbonate buffer system is the major regulator of the pH of body fluids.
         a. The phosphate system and proteins are two other buffer systems in the body.

IV. Equivalents of acids and bases (Sections 10.11–10.13).
   A. Normality (Section 10.11).
      1. A gram-equivalent of acid or base $= \dfrac{\text{molar mass}}{\text{number of H}^+ \text{ or OH}^- \text{ produced}}$.
      2. One equivalent of acid neutralizes one equivalent of base.
      3. Normality $= \dfrac{\text{equivalents of acid or base}}{\text{liters of solution}}$.
      4. Normality = (molarity of acid or base) × (number of H⁺ or OH⁻ produced).
   B. Common acid–base reactions (Section 10.12).
      1. Acid + hydroxide ion —> water + salt.
      2. Acid + carbonate or bicarbonate —> water + salt + CO_2.
      3. Acid + ammonia —> ammonium salt.
   C. Titration (Section 10.13).
      1. Titration is used to determine the acid or base concentration of a solution.
      2. In titration, a known volume of a solution of unknown acid or base concentration completely reacts with a solution of known concentration.
      3. The volume of solution of known concentration is measured, and the concentration of the unknown is calculated.

V. Acidity and basicity of salt solutions (Section 10.14).
   A. The salt of a strong base and a strong acid is neutral in solution.
   B. The salt of a strong base and a weak acid is basic in solution.
   C. The salt of a weak base and a strong acid is acidic in solution.
   D. The pH of the salt of a weak base and a weak acid can be predicted only if K_a values are known.

Solutions to Chapter 10 Problems

10.1 HCO_2H (a) and H_2S (b) are Brønsted–Lowry acids because they have protons to donate.

10.2 SO_3^{2-} (a) and F^- (c) are Brønsted–Lowry bases because they can be proton acceptors.

10.3   (a) The conjugate acid of HS^- is H_2S.
(b) The conjugate acid of PO_4^{3-} is HPO_4^{2-}.
(c) The conjugate base of H_2CO_3 is HCO_3^-.
(d) The conjugate base of NH_4^+ is NH_3.

10.4

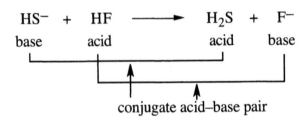

$$HS^- \; + \; HF \longrightarrow H_2S \; + \; F^-$$
base   acid   acid   base

conjugate acid–base pair

10.5   In Table 10.1, the stronger acid is listed *higher* in the table than the weaker acid.

Stronger acids: (a) NH_4^+ (b) H_2SO_4 (c) H_2CO_3

10.6   In Table 10.1, the stronger base is listed *lower* in the table than the weaker base.

Stronger bases: (a) F^- (b) OH^-

10.7

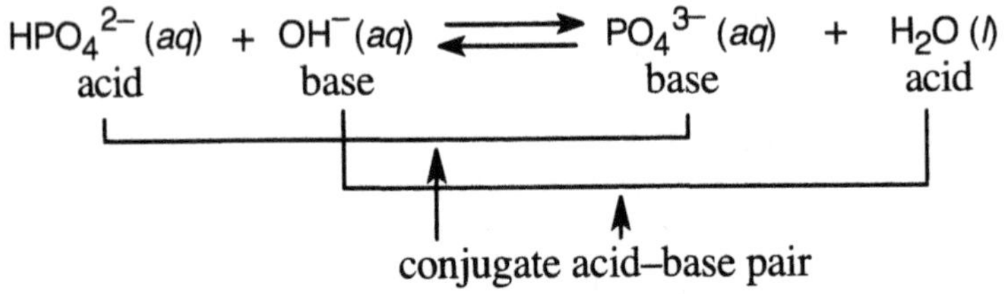

$$HPO_4^{2-} \, (aq) \; + \; OH^- \, (aq) \; \rightleftarrows \; PO_4^{3-} \, (aq) \; + \; H_2O \, (l)$$
acid   base   base   acid

conjugate acid–base pair

From Table 10.1, we see that OH^- is a stronger base than PO_4^{3-} and that HPO_4^{2-} is a stronger acid than H_2O. Thus, the forward direction of the equilibrium is favored.

$$HPO_4^{2-}(aq) \; + \; OH^-(aq) \; \rightleftarrows \; PO_4^{3-}(aq) \; + \; H_2O(l)$$
stronger acid   stronger base   weaker base   weaker acid

10.8

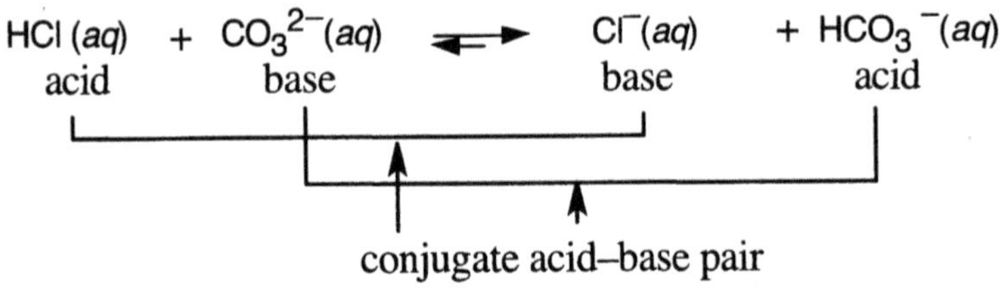

$$HCl \, (aq) \; + \; CO_3^{2-}(aq) \; \rightleftarrows \; Cl^-(aq) \; + \; HCO_3^{\,-}(aq)$$
acid   base   base   acid

conjugate acid–base pair

10.9 Remember that an electrostatic potential map shows the most electron-rich area of the molecule as red and the least electron-rich area as blue. In alanine, the $-NH_3^+$ group is the most electron-poor, and thus its hydrogens are the most acidic.

10.10 The value for K_a of benzoic acid is smaller than the value for citrate, indicating that benzoic acid is a weaker acid. Benzoate is thus a stronger base than citrate.

10.11 (a) Ammonia is basic.

$$[OH^-] = \frac{K_w}{[H_3O^+]} = \frac{1.0 \times 10^{-14}}{3.1 \times 10^{-12}} = 3.2 \times 10^{-3} \text{ M}$$

(b) Vinegar is acidic. Since $1 \times 10^{-14} = [H_3O^+][OH^-]$,

$$[OH^-] = \frac{K_w}{[H_3O^+]} = \frac{1.0 \times 10^{-14}}{4.0 \times 10^{-3}} = 2.5 \times 10^{-12} \text{ M}$$

10.12 (a) $pH = -\log [H^+] = -\log [3.1 \times 10^{-12}] = 11.51$
(b) $pH = -\log [H^+] = -\log [4.0 \times 10^{-3}] = 2.40$

10.13 (a) For pH = 13, $[H_3O^+] = 1 \times 10^{-13}$ M; $[OH^-] = 0.1$ M
(b) For pH = 3, $[H_3O^+] = 1 \times 10^{-3}$ M; $[OH^-] = 1 \times 10^{-11}$ M
(c) For pH = 8, $[H_3O^+] = 1 \times 10^{-8}$ M; $[OH^-] = 1 \times 10^{-6}$ M

The solution of pH = 3 is most acidic, and the solution of pH = 13 is most basic.

10.14 A solution of 0.01 M HNO_2 has a higher pH because HNO_2 is a weaker acid, and its $[H^+]$ is lower.

10.15

Solution	pH	Acidic/Basic	$[H_3O^+]$	$[OH^-]$
(a) Saliva	6.5	acidic	3×10^{-7} M	3×10^{-8} M
(b) Pancreatic juice	7.9	basic	1×10^{-8} M	1×10^{-6} M
(c) Orange juice	3.7	acidic	2×10^{-4} M	5×10^{-11} M
(d) Wine	3.5	acidic	3×10^{-4} M	3×10^{-11} M

Least acidic → Pancreatic juice Saliva Orange juice Wine → Most acidic

10.16 Use a calculator to determine pH. Remember that the significant figures in the answer are the digits to the right of the decimal point.

(a) $[H_3O^+] = 5.3 \times 10^{-9}$ mol/L: pH = 8.28
(b) $[H_3O^+] = 8.9 \times 10^{-6}$ mol/L: pH = 5.05

10.17 $[H_3O^+] = 2.5 \times 10^{-3}$, since HCl is a strong acid. As in the previous problem, use the EE key and the log key on your calculator, and take the negative value of the log.
$[H_3O^+] = 2.5 \times 10^{-3}$; $pH = -\log (2.5 \times 10^{-3}) = -(-2.60) = 2.60$

10.18 Refer to Worked Examples 10.13 and 10.14 in the text.
When 0.020 mol of HNO_3 is added, the HF concentration increases from 0.100 M to 0.120 M, and the F^- decreases from 0.120 M to 0.100 M because of the reaction:

$$F^-(aq) + HNO_3(aq) \longrightarrow HF(aq) + NO_3^-(aq)$$

$$pH = pK_a + \log\frac{[A^-]}{[HA]} = 3.46 + \log\frac{[0.100]}{[0.120]} = 3.46 - 0.08 = 3.38$$

10.19

$$NH_4^+(aq) + H_2O(aq) \rightleftharpoons H_3O^+(aq) + NH_3(aq)$$

$$pH = pK_a + \log\frac{[NH_3]}{[NH_4^+]} = 9.25 + \log\frac{[0.080]}{[0.050]} = 9.25 + 0.20 = 9.45$$

10.20

$$pH = pK_a + \log\frac{[HCO_3^-]}{[H_2CO_3]}; \ 7.40 = 6.37 + \log\frac{[HCO_3^-]}{[H_2CO_3]}$$

$$\log\frac{[HCO_3^-]}{[H_2CO_3]} = 1.03; \ \frac{[HCO_3^-]}{[H_2CO_3]} = 10.7$$

The ratio of bicarbonate ion to carbonic acid is 10.7, indicating that more than 90% of dissolved CO_2 exists as bicarbonate at pH = 7.4

10.21 You can see that there are nine HCN molecules and six CN^- molecules in the figure.

$$pH = pK_a + \log\frac{[CN^-]}{[HCN]} = 9.31 + \log\frac{[6]}{[9]} = 9.31 - 0.18 = 9.13$$

10.22, 10.23

Sample	Mass	Molar Mass	# of ions*	Gram Equivalent	# of g-Eq	Normality of 300.0 mL
(a) HNO_3	5.0 g	63.0 g	1	63.0 g	0.079	0.26 N
(b) $Ca(OH)_2$	12.5 g	74.1 g	2	37.0 g	0.338	1.13 N
(c) H_3PO_4	4.5 g	98.0 g	3	32.7 g	0.14	0.47 N

*The "number of ions" refers to the number of H^+ or OH^- ions produced for each mole of acid or base in solution.

10.24 $3\,HCl(aq) + Al(OH)_3(aq) \longrightarrow 3\,H_2O(l) + AlCl_3(aq)$

$2\,HCl(aq) + Mg(OH)_2(aq) \longrightarrow 2\,H_2O(l) + MgCl_2(aq)$

10.25 (a) $2\,HCO_3^-(aq) + H_2SO_4(aq) \longrightarrow 2\,H_2O(l) + 2\,CO_2(g) + SO_4^{2-}(aq)$

(b) $CO_3^{2-}(aq) + 2\,HNO_3(aq) \longrightarrow H_2O(l) + CO_2(g) + 2\,NO_3^-(aq)$

10.26 $2\,NH_3(aq)\ +\ H_2SO_4(aq)\ \longrightarrow\ (NH_4)_2SO_4(aq)$

10.27

10.28 First, write the balanced equation for the neutralization reaction:

$$HCl(aq)\ +\ NaOH(aq)\ \longrightarrow\ H_2O(l)\ +\ NaCl(aq)$$

We see from this equation that one mole of base is needed to neutralize each mole of acid.

$$\text{Moles HCl}\ =\ 58.4\ \text{mL}\ \times\ \frac{1\ L}{1000\ \text{mL}}\ \times\ \frac{0.250\ \text{mol NaOH}}{1\ L}\ \times\ \frac{1\ \text{mol HCl}}{1\ \text{mol NaOH}}$$

$$=\ 0.0146\ \text{mol HCl}$$

$$\frac{0.0146\ \text{mol HCl}}{20.0\ \text{mL}}\ \times\ \frac{1000\ \text{mL}}{1\ L}\ =\ 0.730\ \text{M HCl}$$

10.29 $2\,NaOH(aq)\ +\ H_2SO_4(aq)\ \longrightarrow\ 2\,H_2O(l)\ +\ Na_2SO_4(aq)$

Notice that two moles of base are needed to neutralize one mole of acid.

$$\text{Moles NaOH}\ =\ 50.0\ \text{mL}\ \times\ \frac{1\ L}{1000\ \text{mL}}\ \times\ \frac{0.200\ \text{mol H}_2SO_4}{1\ L}\ \times\ \frac{2\ \text{mol NaOH}}{1\ \text{mol H}_2SO_4}$$

$$=\ 0.0200\ \text{mol NaOH}$$

$$0.0200\ \text{mol NaOH}\ \times\ \frac{1\ L}{0.150\ \text{mol}}\ =\ 0.133\ \text{L NaOH}\ =\ 133\ \text{mL NaOH}$$

10.30 $2\,KOH(aq)\ +\ H_2SO_4(aq)\ \longrightarrow\ 2\,H_2O(l)\ +\ Na_2SO_4(aq)$

(a) $\text{Moles H}_2SO_4\ =\ 16.1\ \text{mL}\ \times\ \frac{1\ L}{1000\ \text{mL}}\ \times\ \frac{0.150\ \text{mol H}_2SO_4}{1\ L}\ =\ 2.42\ \times\ 10^{-3}\ \text{mol}$

$$2.42\ \times\ 10^{-3}\ \text{mol}\ H_2SO_4\ \times\ \frac{2\ \text{Eq H}_2SO_4}{1\ \text{mol H}_2SO_4}\ =\ 4.84\ \times\ 10^{-3}\ \text{Eq H}_2SO_4$$

(b) $\dfrac{0.004\,84\ \text{mol KOH}}{0.0215\ L}\ =\ 0.225\ \text{M KOH}$

10.31

$$\text{Moles NaOH} = 9.30 \text{ mL} \times \frac{1 \text{ L}}{1000 \text{ mL}} \times \frac{0.0012 \text{ mol NaOH}}{1 \text{ L}} = 1.1 \times 10^{-5} \text{ mol NaOH}$$

$$\frac{1.1 \times 10^{-5} \text{ mol NaOH}}{0.050 \text{ L}} = 2.2 \times 10^{-4} \text{ M KOH} = 2.2 \times 10^{-4} \text{ M H}_3\text{O}^+; \text{ pH} = 3.66$$

10.32 The salt of a weak acid and a strong base produces a basic solution, the salt of a strong acid and a weak base produces an acidic solution, and the salt of a strong acid and a strong base is neutral.

Salt	Cation is from:	Anion is from:	Solution is:
(a) K_2SO_4	strong base (KOH)	strong acid(H_2SO_4)	neutral
(b) Na_2HPO_4	strong base (NaOH)	weak acid ($H_2PO_4^-$)	basic
(c) MgF_2	strong base ($Mg(OH)_2$)	weak acid (HF)	basic
(d) NH_4Br	weak base (NH_3)	strong acid (HBr)	acidic

Understanding Key Concepts

10.33 (a) The reaction of HF with OH^- is represented by outcome (2). One OH^- reacts with each HF to produce three F^- anions, and nine OH^- anions are left over.

(b) The reaction of H_2SO_3 with OH^- is represented by outcome (3). Two OH^- ions react with each H_2SO_3 molecule to produce three SO_3^{2-} anions, and six OH^- anions are left over.

(c) The reaction of H_3PO_4 with OH^- is represented by outcome (1). Three OH^- anions react with each H_3PO_4 molecule to produce three PO_4^{3-} anions, and three OH^- anions are left over.

10.34 In both molecules, the most acidic hydrogen (deepest blue) is bonded to oxygen. Acetic acid is more acidic because its hydrogen is more positively polarized and less tightly held.

10.35 (a) The acid in the first picture (1) is the weakest because it is the least dissociated.

(b) The acid in the second picture (2) is the strongest acid because all molecules of the acid are dissociated

(c) The acid in the first picture (1) has the smallest value of K_a because it is the weakest acid.

10.36 (a) Picture (3) represents a weak diprotic acid, which has dissociated slightly to form the HA^- anion.

(b) Picture (1) represents an impossible situation. H_2A dissociates stepwise to form HA^-. Only when virtually all H_2A has dissociated to form HA^- is A^{2-} formed by dissociation of HA^-.

10.37 The titration reaction uses up 2/3 of the 1.0 M solution in the buret. Since the solution in the buret is 1.0 M, the solution in the flask must be 0.67 M.

Acids and Bases

10.38 In water, HBr dissociates almost completely. Water acts as a base to accept a proton, and a solution of H_3O^+ and Br^- results.

10.39 In water, CH_3CO_2H dissociates only to the extent of about 1%. Water acts as a base, yielding a solution of CH_3CO_2H, along with smaller amounts of H_3O^+ and $CH_3CO_2^-$.

10.40 In water, KOH dissociates completely to yield K^+ and OH^- ions.

10.41 In water, NH_3 remains largely unreacted, but a small amount acts as a base and accepts a proton from water to yield NH_4^+ and OH^- ions.

10.42 A monoprotic acid, such as HCl, has only one proton to donate, whereas a diprotic acid, such as H_2SO_4, has two protons to donate.

10.43 H^+ represents a proton, but the species H^+ is too reactive to exist in solution. Instead, the proton reacts with water to form H_3O^+.

10.44 Strong acids: (a) $HClO_4$; (e) HI

10.45 Weak bases: (a) NH_3; (c) HPO_4^{2-}; (e) CN^-

Brønsted–Lowry Acids and Bases

10.46 Brønsted–Lowry acids: (a) HCN; (d) H_2CO_3; (f) $CH_3NH_3^+$
Brønsted–Lowry base: (b) $CH_3CO_2^-$
Neither: (c) $AlCl_3$; (e) Mg^{2+}

10.47 Base and conjugate acid are pairs, as are acid and conjugate base.

(a) $CO_3^{2-}(aq)$ + $HCl(aq)$ $\longrightarrow$ $HCO_3^-(aq)$ + $Cl^-(aq)$
    base   acid   conjugate acid conjugate base

(b) $H_3PO_4(aq)$ + $NH_3(aq)$ $\longrightarrow$ $H_2PO_4^-(aq)$ + $NH_4^+(aq)$
    acid   base   conjugate base conjugate acid

(c) $NH_4^+(aq)$ + $CN^-(aq)$ $\rightleftharpoons$ $NH_3(aq)$ + $HCN(aq)$
    acid   base   conjugate base conjugate acid

(d) $HBr(aq)$ + $OH^-(aq)$ $\longrightarrow$ $H_2O(l)$ + $Br^-(aq)$
    acid   base   conjugate acid conjugate base

(e) $H_2PO_4^-(aq)$ + $N_2H_4(aq)$ $\rightleftharpoons$ $HPO_4^{2-}(aq)$ + $N_2H_5^+(aq)$
    acid   base   conjugate base conjugate acid

10.48

	(a)	(b)	(c)	(d)
Base	$ClCH_2CO_2^-$	C_5H_5N	SeO_4^{2-}	$(CH_3)_3N$
Conjugate acid	$ClCH_2CO_2H$	$C_5H_5NH^+$	$HSeO_4^-$	$(CH_3)_3NH^+$

10.49

	(a)	(b)	(c)	(d)
Acid	HCN	$(CH_3)_2NH_2^+$	H_3PO_4	$HSeO_3^-$
Conjugate base	CN^-	$(CH_3)_2NH$	$H_2PO_4^-$	SeO_3^{2-}

10.50 $HCO_3^-(aq) + HCl(aq) \longrightarrow H_2O(l) + CO_2(g) + Cl^-(aq)$

       $HCO_3^-(aq) + NaOH(aq) \longrightarrow H_2O(l) + Na^+(aq) + CO_3^{2-}(aq)$

       $H_2PO_4^-(aq) + HCl(aq) \longrightarrow H_3PO_4(aq) + Cl^-(aq)$

       $H_2PO_4^-(aq) + NaOH(aq) \longrightarrow HPO_4^{2-}(aq) + H_2O(l) + Na^+(aq)$

10.51 The stronger acid and weaker base are conjugate pairs, as are the stronger base and weaker acid. The reaction to form weaker base and weaker acid is favored.

(a) $HCl(aq) + PO_4^{3-}(aq) \rightleftharpoons HPO_4^{2-}(aq) + Cl^-(aq)$
stronger acid   stronger base   weaker acid   weaker base

(b) $CN^-(aq) + HSO_4^-(aq) \rightleftharpoons HCN(aq) + SO_4^{2-}(aq)$
stronger base   stronger acid   weaker acid   weaker base

(c) $HClO_4(aq) + NO_2^-(aq) \rightleftharpoons HNO_2(aq) + ClO_4^-(aq)$
stronger acid   stronger base   weaker acid   weaker base

(d) $HF(aq) + CH_3O^-(aq) \rightleftharpoons CH_3OH(aq) + F^-(aq)$
stronger acid   stronger base   weaker acid   weaker base

10.52 (a) $HCl(aq) + NaHCO_3(s) \longrightarrow H_2O(l) + CO_2(g) + NaCl(aq)$

       (b) $H_2SO_4(aq) + 2\,NaHCO_3(s) \longrightarrow 2\,H_2O(l) + 2\,CO_2(g) + Na_2SO_4(aq)$

10.53 (a) $LiOH(aq) + HNO_3(aq) \longrightarrow H_2O(l) + LiNO_3(aq)$

       (b) $BaCO_3(aq) + 2\,HI(aq) \longrightarrow H_2O(l) + CO_2(g) + BaI_2(aq)$

       (c) $H_3PO_4(aq) + 3\,KOH(aq) \longrightarrow 3\,H_2O(l) + K_3PO_4(aq)$

       (d) $Ca(HCO_3)_2(aq) + 2\,HCl(aq) \longrightarrow 2\,H_2O(l) + 2\,CO_2(g) + CaCl_2(aq)$

       (e) $Ba(OH)_2(aq) + H_2SO_4(aq) \longrightarrow 2\,H_2O(l) + BaSO_4(s)$

Acid and Base Strength: K_a and pH

10.54 For the reaction: $HA(aq) + H_2O(l) \rightleftharpoons H_3O^+(l) + A^-(aq)$

$$K = \frac{[H_3O^+][A^-]}{[HA][H_2O]}$$

Since $[H_2O]$ has no effect on the equilibrium, we define a new constant:

$$K_a = K[H_2O] = \frac{[H_3O^+][A^-]}{[HA]}$$

10.55

$$[H_3O^+] = \frac{K_a[HA]}{[A^-]}$$

10.56 K_w is the product of the molar concentrations of H_3O^+ and OH^- in any aqueous solution and is numerically equal to 1.0×10^{-14} at 25°C.

$$K_a = \frac{[H_3O^+][OH^-]}{[H_2O]}; \quad K_a[H_2O] = K_w = [H_3O^+][OH^-]$$

10.57 The quantity pH is defined as the negative logarithm of the molar H_3O^+ concentration. For example, if $[H_3O^+] = 1.0 \times 10^{-3}$ M, then pH = 3.

10.58 A solution of 0.10 M HCl is 100% dissociated; $[H^+] = [HCl] = 0.10$, and pH = 1. A solution of 0.10 M CH_3COOH is only partially dissociated, and its pH is expected to be higher than 1.0.

10.59 $CH_3COOH(aq) + H_2O(l) \rightleftharpoons CH_3COO^-(g) + H_3O^+(aq)$

$[H_3O^+]$ = antilog (−2.88) = 1.3×10^{-3}. 1.3% of acetic acid is dissociated.

10.60 $H_3PO_4(aq) + H_2O(l) \rightleftharpoons H_2PO_4^-(aq) + H_3O^+(aq)$

$$K_a = \frac{[H_2PO_4^-][H_3O^+]}{[H_3PO_4]}$$

$H_2PO_4^-(aq) + H_2O(l) \rightleftharpoons HPO_4^{2-}(aq) + H_3O^+(aq)$

$$K_a = \frac{[HPO_4^{2-}][H_3O^+]}{[H_2PO_4^-]}$$

$HPO_4^{2-}(aq) + H_2O(l) \rightleftharpoons PO_4^{3-}(aq) + H_3O^+(aq)$

$$K_a = \frac{[PO_4^{3-}][H_3O^+]}{[HPO_4^{2-}]}$$

10.61 The most acidic solution (see Table 10.2) has the lowest pH.
Lowest pH   *Highest pH*
HSO_4^- < HF < HCOOH < H_2CO_3 < NH_4^+

10.62 Urine (pH = 7.9) is weakly basic, since solutions with pH greater than 7.0 are basic. The $[H_3O^+] = 1 \times 10^{-8}$

10.63 Because the pH of a 0.10 M HCN solution is lower than 7.0, the solution is acidic. $[H_3O^+]$ = antilog (−5.2) = 6×10^{-6}

10.64 The $[H_3O^+]$ of sweat ranges from 1×10^{-4} to 2×10^{-7} — a range of three orders of magnitude.

10.65 The $[H_3O^+]$ of saliva ranges from 2×10^{-6} to 8×10^{-8}.

10.66 The pH of an 0.02 M solution of a strong monoprotic acid is 1.7. The pH of a 0.02 M solution of a strong base is $14 - 1.7 = 12.3$

10.67	**10.62**	**10.63**	**10.64**	**10.65**	**10.66**
pOH	6.1	8.8	7.2–10.0	6.9–8.2	12.3; 1.7

10.68, 10.69

	$[H_3O^+]$	pH	$[OH^-]$	pOH
(a) Egg white	2.5×10^{-8} M	7.60 (iv)	4×10^{-7}	6.40
(b) Apple cider	5.0×10^{-4} M	3.30 (i)	2.0×10^{-11}	10.70
(c) Ammonia	2.3×10^{-12} M	11.64 (iii)	4.3×10^{-3}	2.36
(d) Vinegar	4.0×10^{-3} M	2.40 (ii)	2.5×10^{-12}	11.60

Most acidic: vinegar, apple cider, egg white, ammonia   *Least acidic*

10.70 (a) pH = 4; $[H_3O^+] = 1 \times 10^{-4}$ M $\qquad$ $[OH^-] = 1 \times 10^{-10}$ M
$\qquad$ (b) pH = 11; $[H_3O^+] = 1 \times 10^{-11}$ M $\qquad$ $[OH^-] = 1 \times 10^{-3}$ M
$\qquad$ (c) pH = 0; $[H_3O^+] = 1$ M $\qquad$ $[OH^-] = 1 \times 10^{-14}$ M
$\qquad$ (d) pH = 1.38; $[H_3O^+] = 4.2 \times 10^{-2}$ M $\qquad$ $[OH^-] = 2.4 \times 10^{-13}$ M
$\qquad$ (e) pH = 7.96; $[H_3O^+] = 1.1 \times 10^{-8}$ M $\qquad$ $[OH^-] = 9.1 \times 10^{-7}$ M

10.71 0.12×0.10 M $= 0.012$ M H_3O^+; $[H_3O^+] = 1.2 \times 10^{-2}$

$$[OH^-] = \frac{K_w}{[H_3O^+]} = \frac{1.0 \times 10^{-14}}{1.2 \times 10^{-2}} = 8.3 \times 10^{-13} \text{ M}$$

pH = 1.92

Buffers

10.72 A buffer is composed of a weak acid and its conjugate base. Any added H_3O^+ can react with the conjugate base and be neutralized, and any added OH^- can react with the acid. In either case, the ratio of acid to conjugate base changes only slightly, and the pH of a buffered solution remains nearly constant.

10.73 $CH_3CO_2H + CH_3CO_2^- Na^+$ is a better buffer than $HNO_3 + NaNO_3$ because acetic acid is a weak acid and acetate ion is its conjugate base. Nitric acid is a strong acid, and nitrate ion is nonbasic. Thus, the nitric acid/sodium nitrate mixture is not a buffer and can't control pH.

10.74

(a) $pH = pK_a + \log\dfrac{[CH_3CO_2^-]}{[CH_3CO_2H]} = 4.74 + \log\dfrac{[0.100]}{[0.100]} = 4.74$

(b) $CH_3CO_2^- Na^+(aq) + HNO_3(aq) \longrightarrow CH_3CO_2H(aq) + NaNO_3(aq)$.
The added acid is neutralized by sodium acetate.

$\quad CH_3CO_2H(aq) + OH^-(aq) \longrightarrow CH_3CO_2^-(aq) + H_2O(l)$
The added base is neutralized by acetic acid.

10.75 At a specific pH, the most effective buffer is composed of a solution of an acid whose K_a is close to the desired $[H_3O^+]$ and the salt of that acid. Buffer system (b), whose acid (NH_4^+) has a $K_a = 5.6 \times 10^{-10}$, is the best buffer to use.

10.76

$$pH = pK_a + \log \frac{[CN^-]}{[HCN]} = 9.31 + \log \frac{[0.150]}{[0.200]} = 9.31 - 0.12 = 9.19$$

10.77 Use the formula in the previous problem. Adding 0.020 mol HCl to 1.00 L of the solution in Problem 10.76 changes the value of [HCN] to 0.220 M and the value of [CN⁻] to 0.130 M.

$$pH = pK_a + \log \frac{[CN^-]}{[HCN]} = 9.31 + \log \frac{[0.130]}{[0.220]} = 9.31 - 0.23 = 9.08$$

If 0.020 mol NaOH is added to 1.00 L of the HCN/NaCN buffer system, the concentrations change to [HCN] = 0.180 M and [CN⁻] = 0.170 M.

$$pH = pK_a + \log \frac{[CN^-]}{[HCN]} = 9.31 + \log \frac{[0.170]}{[0.180]} = 9.31 - 0.02 = 9.29$$

10.78

$$pH = pK_a + \log \frac{[NH_3]}{[NH_4^+]} = 9.25 + \log \frac{[0.10]}{[0.15]} = 9.25 - 0.18 = 9.07$$

10.79 A solution with equal amounts of NH_4^+ and NH_3 has a pH of 9.25. If 0.025 moles of NaOH are added to the solution in the previous problem, $[NH_4^+]$ decreases to 0.125 M, $[NH_3]$ increases to 0.125, the base/acid ratio is 1.00, and the solution has pH = 9.25.

Concentrations of Acid and Base Solutions

10.80 An equivalent of an acid or base is its formula weight in grams divided by the number of H_3O^+ or OH⁻ ions it produces.

10.81 The normality of an acid is equal to its molarity when the acid is monoprotic. For a diprotic or triprotic acid, normality is equivalent to molarity times the number of acidic protons.

10.82, 10.83

Grams needed for 500 mL of 0.15 N solution are found by multiplying the gram equivalent by 0.075 (0.500 L x 0.15 N).

Sample	Molar Mass	# of H⁺ or OH⁻	Gram Equivalent	Grams needed for 500 mL of 0.15 N soln.
(a) HNO_3	63.0 g	1	63.0 g	4.73 g
(b) H_3PO_4	98.0 g	3	32.7 g	2.45 g
(c) KOH	56.1 g	1	56.1 g	4.21 g
(d) $Mg(OH)_2$	58.3 g	2	29.2 g	2.19 g

10.84 Since a 0.0050 N solution of any acid has 0.0050 equivalents per liter, 25 mL of a 0.0050 N KOH solution is needed to neutralize 25 mL of a 0.0050 N H_2SO_4. 50 mL of a 0.005 M NaOH solution is needed to neutralize 25 mL of a 0.005 M H_2SO_4 since each H_2SO_4 molecule yields two hydrogens.

10.85

(a) $\dfrac{0.12 \text{ mol } H_2SO_2}{1 \text{ L}}$ x $\dfrac{2 \text{ Eq}}{1 \text{ mol}}$ x 0.0750 L = 0.018 Eq

(b) $\dfrac{0.12 \text{ mol } H_3PO_2}{1 \text{ L}}$ x $\dfrac{3 \text{ Eq}}{1 \text{ mol}}$ x 0.0750 L = 0.027 Eq

10.86 (a) 0.25 mol $Mg(OH)_2$ x 2 Eq/mol = 0.50 Eq $Mg(OH)_2$

(b) Molar mass of $Mg(OH)_2$ = 58.3 g;   1 Eq $Mg(OH)_2$ = 29.2 g

2.5 g $Mg(OH)_2$ x $\dfrac{1 \text{ Eq}}{29.2 \text{ g}}$ = 0.086 Eq $Mg(OH)_2$

(c) Molar mass of CH_3CO_2H = 60.0 g;   1 Eq CH_3CO_2H = 60.0 g

15 g CH_3CO_2H x $\dfrac{1 \text{ Eq}}{60 \text{ g}}$ = 0.25 Eq CH_3CO_2H

10.87

Molar mass of $C_6H_5O_7H_3$ = 192.0 g; 1 Eq $C_6H_5O_7H_3$ = $\dfrac{192.0 \text{ g}}{1 \text{ mol}}$ x $\dfrac{1 \text{ mol}}{3 \text{ Eq}}$ = 64.0 g

$\dfrac{64.0 \text{ g}}{1 \text{ Eq}}$ x $\dfrac{1 \text{ Eq}}{1000 \text{ mEq}}$ x 152 mEq = 9.73 g

10.88 Molar mass of $Ca(OH)_2$ = 74.1 g; 1 Eq $Ca(OH)_2$ = 37.1 g

$\dfrac{5.0 \text{ g}}{0.500 \text{ L}}$ x $\dfrac{1 \text{ mol}}{74.1 \text{ g}}$ = 0.13 M; $\dfrac{0.13 \text{ mol}}{1 \text{ L}}$ x $\dfrac{2 \text{ Eq}}{1 \text{ mol}}$ = $\dfrac{0.26 \text{ Eq}}{1 \text{ L}}$ = 0.26 N

10.89 Molar mass of $C_6H_5O_7H_3$ = 192 g; 1 Eq $C_6H_5O_7H_3$ = 64.0 g

$\dfrac{25 \text{ g}}{0.800 \text{ L}}$ x $\dfrac{1 \text{ mol}}{192 \text{ g}}$ = 0.16 M; $\dfrac{0.16 \text{ mol}}{1 \text{ L}}$ x $\dfrac{3 \text{ Eq}}{1 \text{ mol}}$ = $\dfrac{0.48 \text{ Eq}}{1 \text{ L}}$ = 0.48 N

10.90 $HCl(aq) + NaOH(aq) \longrightarrow H_2O(l) + NaCl(aq)$

One mole of HCl is needed to neutralize one mole of NaOH.

Moles HCl = 22.4 mL x $\dfrac{0.12 \text{ mol NaOH}}{1 \text{ L}}$ x $\dfrac{1 \text{ L}}{1000 \text{ mL}}$ x $\dfrac{1 \text{ mol HCl}}{1 \text{ mol NaOH}}$

= 0.0027 mol HCl

$\dfrac{0.0027 \text{ mol HCl}}{12 \text{ mL}}$ x $\dfrac{1000 \text{ mL}}{1 \text{ L}}$ = 0.23 M HCl

10.91 $Ba(OH)_2(aq) + 2 HNO_3(aq) \longrightarrow 2 H_2O(l) + Ba(NO_3)_2(aq)$

Equivalents $Ba(OH)_2 = 15.0 \text{ mL} \times \dfrac{0.12 \text{ mol Ba(OH)}_2}{1 \text{ L}} \times \dfrac{1 \text{ L}}{1000 \text{ mL}} \times \dfrac{2 \text{ Eq Ba(OH)}_2}{1 \text{ mol Ba(OH)}_2}$

$= 0.0036 \text{ Eq Ba(OH)}_2 = 0.0036 \text{ Eq HNO}_3$

$0.0036 \text{ Eq HNO}_3 \times \dfrac{1 \text{ mol HNO}_3}{1 \text{ Eq HNO}_3} \times \dfrac{1 \text{ L}}{0.085 \text{ mol}} \times \dfrac{1000 \text{ mL}}{1 \text{ L}} = 42 \text{ mL HNO}_3$

10.92 $2 KOH(aq) + H_2SO_4(aq) \longrightarrow 2 H_2O(l) + K_2SO_4(aq)$

$0.0150 \text{ L H}_2SO_4 \times \dfrac{0.0250 \text{ mol H}_2SO_4}{1 \text{ L H}_2SO_4} \times \dfrac{2 \text{ mol KOH}}{1 \text{ mol H}_2SO_4} = 0.000750 \text{ mol KOH}$

$\dfrac{0.000750 \text{ mol NaOH}}{0.0100 \text{ L NaOH}} = 0.0750 \text{ M}$

10.93 $V_1 \times N_1 = V_2 \times N_2; \; V_1 = 35.0 \text{ mL}; \; N_1 = 0.100 \text{ N}; \; V_2 = 21.5 \text{ mL}$

$N_2 = \dfrac{V_1 \times N_1}{V_2} = \dfrac{35.0 \text{ mL} \times 0.100 \text{ N}}{21.5 \text{ mL}} = 0.163 \text{ N}$

Chemistry in Action

10.94 (a) The pH of stomach acid ranges from 2 to 3.

(b) $NaHCO_3(aq) + HCl(aq) \longrightarrow CO_2(g) + H_2O(l) + NaCl(aq)$

(c) Molarity of acid at pH 1.8 = 0.016 M

$\dfrac{0.016 \text{ mol HCl}}{1 \text{ L}} \times 0.0150 \text{ L} = 0.000\,24 \text{ mol HCl}$

$0.000\,24 \text{ mol HCl} \times \dfrac{1 \text{ mol antacid}}{1 \text{ mol HCl}} \times \dfrac{84.0 \text{ g}}{1 \text{ mol antacid}} = 0.020 \text{ g} = 20 \text{ mg}$

10.95 Stomach acid is needed for the digestion of proteins in the diet, for the absorption of micronutrients, and for providing a sterile environment by killing bacteria and yeasts.

10.96 Bicarbonate reacts with excess H_3O^+ to form H_2CO_3, which goes on to produce H_2O and CO_2 (which is exhaled). This reaction removes H_3O^+ from the blood stream and lowers the serum $[H^+]$, raising pH.

10.97 Gastric juice is the most acidic body fluid, and pancreatic juice is the most basic.

10.98 pH of rain = 5.6; $[H_3O^+] = 3 \times 10^{-6} \text{ M}$

10.99 (a) $[H_3O^+] = 0.03$ M

(b) 25 L $\times \dfrac{0.03 \text{ mol}}{1 \text{ L}} \times \dfrac{63 \text{ g}}{1 \text{ mol}} = 47$ g, or approximately 50 g HNO_3

General Questions and Problems

10.100

(a) The ideal gas law (Chapter 8): $PV = nRT$; $n = PV/RT$

$P = 1.0$ atm; $V = 15$ L HCl; $R = 0.0821 \dfrac{\text{L} \cdot \text{atm}}{\text{mol} \cdot \text{K}}$; $T = 25\,°C = 298$ K

$n = \dfrac{1 \text{ atm} \times 15.0 \text{ L HCl}}{0.0821 \dfrac{\text{L} \cdot \text{atm}}{\text{mol} \cdot \text{K}} \times 298 \text{ K}} = 0.613$ mol HCl

(b) $\dfrac{0.613 \text{ mol HCl}}{0.250 \text{ L}} = 2.45$ M; pH $= -0.39$

10.101

(a) pH at $0\,°C = 7.47$ pH at $50\,°C = 6.63$

(b) $K_w = [H_3O^+][OH^-] = [H_3O^+]^2$ since $[H_3O^+] = [OH^-]$

at $0\,°C$: $K_w = (3.38 \times 10^{-8})^2 = 1.14 \times 10^{-15}$;

at $50\,°C$: $K_w = (2.34 \times 10^{-7})^2 = 5.48 \times 10^{-14}$

(c) The reaction is endothermic since heat increases the ratio of products to reactants.

10.102 Citric acid reacts with sodium bicarbonate to release CO_2 bubbles:

$$C_6H_5O_7H_3(aq) + 3\,NaHCO_3(aq) \longrightarrow C_6H_5O_7Na_3(aq) + 3\,H_2O(l) + 3\,CO_2(g)$$

Sodium bicarbonate is the antacid.

10.103 $2\,NaOH(aq) + H_2SO_4(aq) \longrightarrow 2\,H_2O(l) + Na_2SO_4(aq)$

0.040 L $H_2SO_4 \times \dfrac{0.10 \text{ mol } H_2SO_4}{1 \text{ L } H_2SO_4} \times \dfrac{2 \text{ mol NaOH}}{1 \text{ mol } H_2SO_4} = 0.0080$ mol NaOH

0.0080 mol NaOH $\times \dfrac{1000 \text{ mL NaOH}}{0.50 \text{ mol NaOH}} = 16$ mL NaOH

10.104

Both 50 mL of a 0.20 N HCl solution and 50 mL of a 0.20 acetic acid solution contain the same number of moles of acid – 0.010 moles. Because HCl is a strong acid, it is almost completely dissociated in water, and the H_3O^+ concentration approaches 0.20 M. Acetic acid, however, is a weak acid that is only slightly dissociated, and the H_3O^+ concentration is much lower – around 0.002 M. Since the HCl solution has a higher H_3O^+ concentration, it has a lower pH.

10.105

(a) $pH = pK_a - \log \dfrac{[H_2PO_4^-]}{[HPO_4^{2-}]}$ or $pH = pK_a + \log \dfrac{[HPO_4^{2-}]}{[H_2PO_4^-]}$

(b) Using the second of the above expressions:

$7.40 = 7.21 + \log \dfrac{[HPO_4^{2-}]}{[H_2PO_4^-]}$; $0.19 = \log \dfrac{[HPO_4^{2-}]}{[H_2PO_4^-]}$; $\dfrac{[HPO_4^{2-}]}{[H_2PO_4^-]} = 1.55$

An approximately 3/2 ratio of $HPO_4^{2-}/H_2PO_4^-$ maintains the optimum blood pH.

10.106 $2\ HCl(aq) + Ca(OH)_2(aq) \longrightarrow 2\ H_2O(l) + CaCl_2(aq)$

$0.140\ L\ HCl\ \times\ \dfrac{0.150\ mol\ HCl}{1\ L\ HCl}\ \times\ \dfrac{1\ mol\ Ca(OH)_2}{2\ mol\ HCl} = 0.0105\ mol\ Ca(OH)_2$

$\dfrac{0.0105\ mol\ Ca(OH)_2}{30.0\ mL\ Ca(OH)_2}\ \times\ \dfrac{1000 mL}{1\ L} = 0.35\ M\ Ca(OH)_2 = 0.70\ N\ Ca(OH)_2$

10.107

Both (a), NaF and HF, and (c), NH_4Cl and NH_3 are effective buffer systems. The NaF/HF system is a solution of a weak acid and the salt of its anion. The NH_4Cl/NH_3 system is a solution of a weak base and the salt of its cation. Neither (b) nor (d) are buffer systems because $HClO_4$ and HBr are both strong acids.

The pH of each buffer solution, when the acid and its conjugate base (or the base and its conjugate acid) are of equal concentration, equals the pK_a of the acid. For (a), pH = 3.46; for (c), pH = 9.25.

10.108

(a) $\underset{\text{acid}}{NH_4^+(aq)} + \underset{\text{base}}{OH^-(aq)} \longrightarrow \underset{\text{conjugate base}}{NH_3(g)} + \underset{\text{conjugate acid}}{H_2O(l)}$

(b) $PV = nRT$; $P = 755\ mmHg$; $V = 2.86\ L$; $T = 333\ K$; $R = \dfrac{62.4\ mmHg \cdot L}{mol \cdot K}$

$n = \dfrac{PV}{RT} = \dfrac{755\ mmHg\ \times\ 2.86\ L}{\dfrac{62.4\ mmHg \cdot L}{mol \cdot K}\ \times\ 333\ K} = 0.104\ mol\ NH_3$

$0.104\ mol\ \times\ \dfrac{53.5\ g}{1\ mol} = 5.56\ g\ NH_4Cl$

10.109

$CaO(aq) + SO_2(g) \longrightarrow CaSO_3(s)$

(a) 1 mol CaO (56 g) reacts with 1 mol SO_2.

(b) $1\ kg\ SO_2\ \times\ \dfrac{1\ mol\ SO_2}{64\ g\ SO_2}\ \times\ \dfrac{1\ mol\ SO_2}{1\ mol\ CaO}\ \times\ \dfrac{56\ g\ CaO}{1\ mol\ CaO} = 0.9\ kg\ CaO$

10.110

(a) $Na_2O(aq) + H_2O(l) \longrightarrow 2\,NaOH(aq)$

(b) $1.55\ g\ Na_2O \times \dfrac{1\ mol\ Na_2O}{62.0\ g\ Na_2O} \times \dfrac{2\ mol\ NaOH}{1\ mol\ Na_2O} = 0.0500\ mol\ NaOH$

$\dfrac{0.0500\ mol\ NaOH}{500.0\ mL} \times \dfrac{1000\ mL}{1\ L} = 0.100\ M\ NaOH;\ pH = 13.00$

(c) $0.0500\ mol\ NaOH \times \dfrac{1\ mol\ HCl}{1\ mol\ NaOH} \times \dfrac{1\ L}{0.0100\ mol\ HCl} = 5.00\ L\ HCl$

$5.00\ L\ HCl = 5.00 \times 10^3\ mL\ HCl$

Self-Test for Chapter 10

Multiple Choice

1. What volume of 0.10 M H_2SO_4 will neutralize 30 mL of 0.05 M $Ca(OH)_2$?
    (a) 30 mL   (b) 15 mL   (c) 10 mL   (d) 6.0 mL

2. Which of the following salts is acidic in solution?
    (a) NH_4Br (b) $NaBr$ (c) NH_4CN (d) $NaCN$

3. KCN is the salt of a:
    (a) strong acid and strong base   (b) strong acid and weak base   (c) weak acid and strong base
    (d) weak acid and weak base

4. A solution has a pH of 9. What is the value of $[OH^-]$?
    (a) 5   (b) 10^{-9} (c) 9   (d) 10^{-5}

5. Which of the following is a diprotic acid?
    (a) CH_3CO_2H (b) $Ba(OH)_2$ (c) H_2SO_3 (d) H_3PO_4

6. Look at Table 10.2 and decide which base is a weaker base than F^-:
    (a) $H_2PO_4^-$ (b) HCO_3^- (c) CN^- (d) NH_3

7. Which of the following substances turns phenolphthalein red?
    (a) urine   (b) milk of magnesia   (c) blood   (d) coffee

8. Which of the following bases is an Arrhenius base?
    (a) $NaOH$ (b) $Ca_3(PO_4)_2$ (c) NH_3 (d) LiF

9. In the reaction $Mg(OH)_2(aq) + 2\,HBr(aq) \longrightarrow 2\,H_2O(l) + MgBr_2(aq)$, what is the conjugate acid of $Mg(OH)_2$?
    (a) HBr (b) H_2O (c) $MgBr_2$ (d) can't tell

10. How many water molecules are produced in the balanced neutralization reaction of $H_3PO_4 + Mg(OH)_2$?
    (a) 2   (b) 3   (c) 4   (d) 6

Sentence Completion

1. One _____ of an acid reacts with one _____ of a base.

2. Phenolphthalein turns _____ in basic solution.

3. H_2CO_3 is a _____ acid.

4. The anion of a weak acid is a _____ base.

5. _____ is the splitting apart of an acid into a proton and an anion.

6. An Arrhenius base yields _____ when dissolved in water.

7. _____ is the reaction of an acid with a base.

8. _____ is the measure of a solution's acidity.

9. To completely neutralize 10.0 mL of 1.0 M H_3PO_4, you need _____ mL of 1.0 M NaOH.

10. CH_3CO_2H and $CH_3CO_2^-$ are known as a _____ acid–base pair.

11. The buffer system of blood is the _____ / _____ system.

12. Substances that can act as either acids or bases are _____.

True or False

1. 30.0 mL of 0.10 M H_2SO_4 is neutralized by 30.0 mL of 0.10 M NaOH.

2. A change of one pH unit is a tenfold change in $[H_3O^+]$.

3. H_2SO_4 / HSO_4^- is a good buffer system.

4. All bases are negatively charged.

5. Bicarbonate ion neutralizes more acid than carbonate ion.

6. If the pH of a solution is 7.0, $[OH^-] = 10^{-7}$.

7. Water can act as both an acid and a base.

8. According to the Brønsted definition, an acid is a substance that dissolves in water to give H_3O^+ ions.

9. Ammonia reacts with an acid to yield ammonium hydroxide.

10. Whether an acid or a base is strong or weak depends on its percent dissociation in water.

11. The reaction $H_2O + H_2PO_4^- —> H_3O^+ + HPO_4^{2-}$ proceeds in the direction written.

12. One equivalent of $Ca(OH)_2$ equals 37 g.

Match each entry on the left with its partner on the right.

1. Strong acid

2. 1 M HCl

3. $[H_3O^+] = 10^{-8}$

4. Alkalosis

5. K_w

6. Weak base

7. Strong base

8. Salt

9. $[H_3O^+] = 10^{-6}$

10. Weak acid

11. 1 M H$_3$PO$_4$

12. Acidosis

(a) $[H_3O^+]\ [OH^-]$

(b) Cl^-

(c) pH = 6

(d) HCl

(e) 1 N acid

(f) CH_3CO_2H

(g) $[OH^-] = 10^{-6}$

(h) Blood pH lower than 7.35

(i) $CH_3CO_2^-$

(j) Na_2SO_4

(k) 3 N acid

(l) Blood pH higher than 7.35

Chapter Outline

I. Introduction to radioactivity (Sections 11.1–11.3).
   A Nuclear reactions (Section 11.1).
      1. A nuclear reaction occurs when a nuclide spontaneously changes to a different nuclide.
      2. Nuclear reactions differ from chemical reactions in several ways.
         a. Nuclear reactions produce different elements.
         b. Different isotopes have the same behavior in chemical reactions but different behavior in nuclear reactions.
         c. The rate of a nuclear reaction is unaffected by a change in temperature.
         d. A nuclear reaction is the same whether an atom is in a compound or is elemental.
         e. The energy change in a nuclear reaction is immense.
   B. The discovery and nature of radioactivity (Section 11.2).
      1. Radioactivity was discovered by Becquerel and the Curies.
      2. Three types of radiation may be emitted:
         a. α radiation: He^{2+} nuclei with low penetrating power.
         b. β radiation: electrons (e^-) with medium penetrating power.
         c γ radiation: high-energy light waves with very high penetrating power.
   C. Stable and unstable isotopes (Section 11.3).
      1. All elements have radioactive isotopes.
      2. Most radioisotopes are made in particle accelerators: These are known as artificial radioisotopes.
      3. Radioisotopes have the same chemical properties as their nonradioactive isotopes.
II. Nuclear decay (Sections 11.4–11.7).
   A. Nuclear emissions (Section 11.4).
      1. Alpha emission.
         a. After α emission, the atomic number of the resulting isotope decreases by 2, and the mass number decreases by 4.
      2. Beta emission.
         a. In β emission, a neutron decomposes to a proton and an electron.
         b. The electron is emitted, and the proton is retained.
         c. The atomic number of the resulting isotope increases by 1, and the mass number is unchanged.
      3. Gamma (γ) emission.
         a. Gamma (γ) emission usually accompanies α or β emission and doesn't affect either mass number or atomic number.
      4. Positron emission.
         a. Positron emission occurs when a proton is converted to a neutron and an ejected positron (positive electron).
         b. The mass number of the nucleus is unchanged, but the atomic number decreases by 1.
      5. Electron capture (EC).
         a. EC occurs when a nucleus captures an electron from the surrounding electron cloud, converting a proton into a neutron.
         b. The mass number of the nucleus is unchanged, but the atomic number decreases by 1.

B. Half-life (Section 11.5).
  1. Half-life is the amount of time it takes for half of a sample of a radioisotope to decay.
  2. Half-life doesn't depend on the amount of sample or on temperature.
  3. Each half-life sees the decay of half of what remains of the sample.
  4. Radiocarbon dating uses the decay of carbon-14 to determine the age of archeological artifacts.
C. Radioactive decay series (Section 11.6).
  1. Some heavy radioisotopes undergo a series of disintegrations until a nonradioactive product is reached.
D. Ionizing radiation (Section 11.7).
  1. Ionizing radiation is any high-energy radiation that can create reactive ions when it collides with a chemical compound.
  2. Ionizing radiation converts molecules into highly reactive ions.
  3. Ionizing radiation can injure the body.
    a. Gamma and X radiation are more harmful when radiation comes from outside the body.
    b. Alpha and β radiation are more dangerous when emitted from within the body.
  4. The intensity of radiation decreases with the square of the distance from the source.
III. Detecting radiation (Sections 11.8–11.9).
A. Devices for detecting radiation (Section 11.8).
  1. Photographic film badges.
  2. Geiger counter.
  3. Scintillation counter.
B. Units of radiation (Section 11.9).
  1. The *curie*(Ci) measures the number of disintegrations per second.
  2. The *roentgen* (R) measures the intensity of radiation.
  3. The *rad* (gray in SI units) measures the energy absorbed per gram of tissue.
  4. The *rem* and the *sievert* (SI) measure tissue damage.
IV. Artificial transmutation (Section 11.10).
A. Artificial transmutation occurs when nuclei are bombarded with high-energy particles.
B. After bombardment, a new nucleus is produced.
C. The transuranium elements were all produced via artificial transmutation.
V. Nuclear fission and nuclear fusion (Section 11.11).
A. Nuclear fission.
  1. Nuclear fission occurs when a heavy nucleus fragments after bombardment by a small particle, such as a neutron.
  2. The large amounts of energy released are due to mass-to-energy conversions and are measured by $E = mc^2$.
  3. Many different fission products can result from one bombardment.
  4. In some cases, bombardment with one neutron can cause production of more than one neutron, in addition to fragmentation.
    a. This is called a chain reaction.
    b. If the bombarded sample weighs more than a critical mass, a nuclear explosion can result.
    c. A controlled fission reaction can be used to produce energy.
B. Nuclear fusion.
  1. If two light nuclei are made to collide, a nuclear fusion reaction occurs that produces a combined nucleus plus energy.
  2. Nuclear fusion reactions occur in stars.

Solutions to Chapter 11 Problems

11.1 For α emission, subtract 2 from the atomic number of radon and 4 from the mass number:

$$^{222}_{86}Rn \rightarrow \, ^4_2He \, + \, ^{218}_{84}?$$

Then look in the periodic table for the element with atomic number 84:

$$^{222}_{86}Rn \rightarrow \, ^4_2He \, + \, ^{218}_{84}Po$$

11.2 Add 4 to the mass number of radon-222 to calculate the isotope of radium:

$$^{226}_{88}Ra \rightarrow \, ^4_2He \, + \, ^{222}_{86}Rn$$

11.3

$$^{89}_{38}Sr \rightarrow \, ^0_{-1}e \, + \, ?$$

The mass number of the product element stays the same, but the atomic number increases by 1, to 7. Looking in the periodic table, we find that ^{89}Y is the element formed:

$$^{89}_{38}Sr \rightarrow \, ^0_{-1}e \, + \, ^{89}_{39}Y$$

11.4

(a) $^3_1H \rightarrow \, ^0_{-1}e \, + \, ^3_2He$ (b) $^{210}_{82}Pb \rightarrow \, ^0_{-1}e \, + \, ^{210}_{83}Bi$ (c) $^{20}_9F \rightarrow \, ^0_{-1}e \, + \, ^{20}_{10}Ne$

11.5 For positron emission, the atomic number decreases by 1, but the mass number stays the same.

(a) $^{38}_{20}Ca \rightarrow \, ^0_1e \, + \, ^{38}_{19}K$ (b) $^{118}_{54}Xe \rightarrow \, ^0_1e \, + \, ^{118}_{53}I$ (c) $^{79}_{37}Rb \rightarrow \, ^0_1e \, + \, ^{79}_{36}Kr$

11.6 As in positron emission, the atomic number decreases by 1 and the mass number stays unchanged in electron capture.

(a) $^{62}_{30}Zn \, + \, ^0_{-1}e \rightarrow \, ^{62}_{29}Cu$ (b) $^{110}_{50}Sn \, + \, ^0_{-1}e \rightarrow \, ^{110}_{49}In$ (c) $^{81}_{36}Kr \, + \, ^0_{-1}e \rightarrow \, ^{81}_{35}Br$

11.7 Table 11.2 shows the changes brought about by various radioactive decay patterns. Only β emission produces a change of +1 to the atomic number and a decrease in the number of neutrons. The original element was indium ($Z = 49$), and tin ($Z = 50$) is the decay product.

$$^{120}_{49}In \rightarrow \, ^0_{-1}e \, + \, ^{120}_{50}Sn$$

11.8 $17,000 \div 5730 = 2.97$, or approximately 3 half-lives.

The percentage of $^{14}_6C$ is (1/2) x (1/2) x (1/2) x 100% = 12.5% of the original sample.

11.9 To determine blood volume, use the formula:

$$R_{\text{sample}} = R_{\text{tracer}}\left(\frac{V_{\text{sample}}}{V_{\text{system}} + V_{\text{tracer}}}\right)$$

Where $R_{\text{sample}} = 0.10\%$, $R_{\text{tracer}} = 100\%$, $V_{\text{sample}} = 5.00$ mL, and $V_{\text{tracer}} = 1.00$ mL
As an approximation, ignore the volume of the tracer, and rearrange the formula:

$$V_{\text{system}} = (R_{\text{tracer}} \times V_{\text{sample}}) / R_{\text{sample}} = (100\% \times 5.00 \text{ mL}) / 0.10\% = 5000 \text{ mL} = 5.0 \text{ L}$$

It is apparent that the volume of the tracer is very small, relative to the volume of the system.

11.10 Find the point on the graph that represents 50% of the sample remaining. Locate the time that corresponds to this point; this is the half-life – 3 days.

11.11

$$\frac{I_1}{I_2} = \frac{d_2^2}{d_1^2} : I_1 = 250 \text{ units}; I_2 = 25 \text{ units}; d_1^2 = (4.0 \text{ m})^2 = 16 \text{ m}^2; d_2^2 = ?$$

$$d_2^2 = \frac{d_1^2 \times I_1}{I_2} = \frac{16 \text{ m}^2 \times 250 \text{ units}}{25 \text{ units}} = 160 \text{ m}^2$$

$$d_2 = 13 \text{ m}$$

11.12

$$\frac{5 \text{ mrem}}{270 \text{ mrem}} \times 100\% = 1.9\%$$

The annual dose of radiation for most people will increase by approximately 2%.

11.13

$$\frac{44 \ \mu\text{Ci}}{1 \text{ mL}} \times 3.98 \text{ mL} = 175 \ \mu\text{Ci}$$

11.14 In Section 11.9, we learned that 1 Gray = 100 rad.

$$0.20 \text{ kGy} \times \frac{1000 \text{ Gy}}{1 \text{ kGy}} \times \frac{100 \text{ rad}}{1 \text{ Gy}} = 2.0 \times 10^4 \text{ rad}$$

To convert the dose to rem, use the formula rem = rad x RBE, where RBE = relative biological effectiveness factor.

The dose is 2.0×10^4 rem if the radiation is primarily γ rays (RBE = 1). Since α radiation (RBE = 20) is 20 times more penetrating than γ radiation, the dose is $20 \times 2.0 \times 10^4$ rad = 4×10^5 rem for α radiation

11.15

$$^{241}_{95}\text{Am} \rightarrow ^{4}_{2}\text{He} + ^{237}_{93}\text{Np}$$

11.16

$$^{241}_{95}\text{Am} + ^{4}_{2}\text{He} \rightarrow 2 \ ^{1}_{0}\text{n} + ^{243}_{97}\text{Bk}$$

11.17

$$^{40}_{18}\text{Ar} + ^{1}_{1}\text{H} \rightarrow ^{1}_{0}\text{n} + ^{40}_{19}\text{K}$$

11.18 Try to estimate the value of n in the expression $0.1\% = 100\% \times (0.5)^n = 100\% \times 1/2^n$. This expression shows that the amount of radiation decreases to $1/1000$ of its initial value. A table of powers of two shows that after 10 half-lives ($n = 10$) the intensity of radiation will have dropped to approximately $1/1000$ of its initial activity. If a half-life is 6 hours, it will take 60 hours for the activity of the radiation to reach this level.

11.19

$$^{235}_{92}\text{U} + {}^{1}_{0}\text{n} \rightarrow 2\,{}^{1}_{0}\text{n} + {}^{137}_{52}\text{Te} + {}^{97}_{40}\text{Zr}$$

11.20

$$^{2}_{1}\text{H} + {}^{2}_{1}\text{H} \rightarrow {}^{1}_{0}n + {}^{3}_{2}\text{He}$$

Understanding Key Concepts

11.21 After one half-life, the sample would consist of eight ${}^{28}_{13}\text{Al}$ atoms and eight ${}^{28}_{12}\text{Mg}$ atoms.

After two half-lives, the remaining eight ${}^{28}_{12}\text{Mg}$ atoms would have decayed to four ${}^{28}_{13}\text{Al}$ atoms, producing the outcome shown in the picture.

11.22

$$^{28}_{12}\text{Mg} \rightarrow {}^{0}_{-1}\text{e} + {}^{28}_{13}\text{Al}$$

11.23

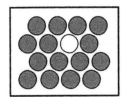

⬤ Aluminum-28

◯ Magnesum-28

11.24 The illustrated isotope, with six protons and eight neutrons, is ${}^{14}_{6}\text{C}$.

11.25 The shorter arrows represent β emission because they show the decomposition of a neutron with an accompanying one-unit increase in atomic number.
The longer arrows represent α emission because they indicate a decay that results in the loss of two protons and two neutrons (α particle).

11.26

$$^{241}_{94}\text{Pu} \rightarrow {}^{241}_{95}\text{Am} \rightarrow {}^{237}_{93}\text{Np} \rightarrow {}^{233}_{91}\text{Pa} \rightarrow {}^{233}_{92}\text{U}$$

11.27 The isotope can decay by either positron emission or electron capture since the atomic number decreases by 1 and the mass number remains the same.

$$^{148}_{69}\text{Tm} \rightarrow {}^{0}_{1}\text{e} + {}^{148}_{68}\text{Er} \quad \text{or} \quad {}^{148}_{69}\text{Tm} + {}^{0}_{-1}\text{e} \rightarrow {}^{148}_{68}\text{Er}$$

11.28 The half-life is approximately 3.5 years.

11.29 The curve doesn't represent nuclear decay. According to the curve, half of the sample has decayed after 5 days. Half of the remaining sample should have decayed after 10 days, but on this curve the second half-life is shown at 13 days. A decay curve should approach zero after six half-lives, but this curve shows 10% activity remaining at that time.

Radioactivity

11.30 A substance is said to be radioactive if it emits radiation by decay of an unstable nucleus.

11.31

Radiation	Particle Produced	Atomic Number	Mass Number	Penetrating Power
α emission	^4_2He	decreases by 2	decreases by 4	low
β emission	$^{0}_{-1}\text{e}$	increases by 1	unchanged	medium
γ emission	none	unchanged	unchanged	high
positron emission	$^{0}_{1}\text{e}$	decreases by 1	unchanged	medium
electron capture	$^{0}_{-1}\text{e}$ (captured, not emitted)	decreases by 1	unchanged	high

11.32

Nuclear Reaction	Chemical Reaction
Involves change in an atom's nucleus	Involves change in an atom's outer-shell electrons
Usually produces a different element	Never produces a different element
Different isotopes have different behavior in a nuclear reaction	Different isotopes have the same behavior in a chemical reaction
Rate is unaffected by a change in temperature or by a catalyst	Rate changes with a change in temperature or by using a catalyst
Rate is the same, whether the atom is in a compound or uncombined	
Energy change is millions of times larger for a nuclear reaction	

11.33 When ionizing radiation strikes a molecule, a high-energy reactive ion with an odd number of electrons is produced. This reactive ion immediately reacts with other chemical compounds, creating other reactive fragments that can cause further reactions.

11.34 Ionizing radiation causes cell damage by breaking bonds in DNA. The resulting damage may lead to mutation, cancer, or cell death.

11.35 Background radiation may arise from naturally occurring radioactive isotopes or from cosmic rays.

11.36 A neutron in the nucleus decomposes to a proton and an electron, which is emitted as a β particle.

11.37 An α particle is a helium nucleus, ^4_2He; a helium atom is a helium nucleus plus two electrons.

Nuclear Decay and Transmutation

11.38 A nuclear equation is balanced if the number of nucleons is the same on both sides and if the sums of the charges on the nuclei and on any other elementary particles are the same on both sides.

11.39 A transuranium element is an element with an atomic number greater than 92. It is produced by bombardment of an element of slightly smaller mass with high-energy particles.

11.40 For an atom emitting an α particle, the atomic number decreases by 2, and the mass number decreases by 4.
For an atom emitting a β particle, the atomic number increases by 1, and the mass number is unchanged.

11.41 For an atom emitting a γ ray, both atomic number and mass number are unchanged.
For an atom emitting a positron, the atomic number decreases by 1, and the mass number is unchanged

11.42 In nuclear fission, bombardment of a nucleus causes fragmentation in many different ways to yield a large number of smaller fragments. Normal radioactive decay of a nucleus produces an atom with a similar mass and yields a predictable product.

11.43 Bombardment of a $^{235}_{92}U$ nucleus with one neutron produces three neutrons, which, on collision with three more $^{235}_{92}U$ nuclei yield nine neutrons, and so on. Because the reaction is self-sustaining, it is known as a chain reaction.

11.44

(a) $^{35}_{16}S \rightarrow {}^{0}_{-1}e + {}^{35}_{17}Cl$ 　　　　(b) $^{24}_{10}Ne \rightarrow {}^{0}_{-1}e + {}^{24}_{11}Na$

(c) $^{90}_{38}Sr \rightarrow {}^{0}_{-1}e + {}^{90}_{39}Y$

11.45

(a) $^{190}_{78}Pt \rightarrow {}^{4}_{2}He + {}^{186}_{76}Os$ 　　　(b) $^{208}_{87}Fr \rightarrow {}^{4}_{2}He + {}^{204}_{85}At$

(c) $^{245}_{96}Cm \rightarrow {}^{4}_{2}He + {}^{241}_{94}Pu$

11.46

(a) $^{109}_{47}Ag + {}^{4}_{2}He \rightarrow {}^{113}_{49}In$ 　　　(b) $^{10}_{5}B + {}^{4}_{2}He \rightarrow {}^{13}_{7}N + {}^{1}_{0}n$

11.47

(a) $^{26}_{11}Na \rightarrow {}^{0}_{-1}e + {}^{26}_{12}Mg$ 　　　(b) $^{212}_{83}Bi \rightarrow {}^{4}_{2}He + {}^{208}_{81}Tl$

11.48

(a) $^{235}_{92}U + {}^{1}_{0}n \rightarrow {}^{160}_{62}Sm + {}^{72}_{30}Zn + 4\,{}^{1}_{0}n$

(b) $^{235}_{92}U + {}^{1}_{0}n \rightarrow {}^{87}_{35}Br + {}^{146}_{57}La + 3\,{}^{1}_{0}n$

11.49

(a) $^{126}_{50}Sn \rightarrow ^{0}_{-1}e + ^{126}_{51}Sb$ β decay   (b) $^{210}_{88}Ra \rightarrow ^{4}_{2}He + ^{206}_{86}Rn$ α decay

(c) $^{76}_{36}Kr + ^{0}_{-1}e \rightarrow ^{76}_{35}Br$ electron capture

11.50

$$^{198}_{80}Hg + ^{1}_{0}n \rightarrow ^{198}_{79}Au + ^{1}_{1}H$$

A proton is produced in addition to gold-198.

11.51

$$^{59}_{27}Co + ^{1}_{0}n \rightarrow ^{60}_{27}Co$$

$$^{60}_{27}Co \rightarrow ^{0}_{-1}e + ^{60}_{28}Ni$$

11.52 The four α decays result in a loss of 16 nucleons from the mass number and a reduction of 8 in atomic number. The β decay results in a gain of 1 in atomic number and no change in mass number. The parent isotope, which has seven more protons and a mass 16 units greater than bismuth-212, is thorium-228.

11.53

$$^{209}_{83}Bi + ^{58}_{26}Fe \rightarrow ^{266}_{109}Mt + ^{1}_{0}n$$ A neutron is also produced.

Half-Life

11.54 If strontium-90 has a half-life of 28.8 years, half of a given quantity of strontium-90 will have decayed after 28.8 years.

11.55 Use Figure 11.4, which shows a radioactive decay curve. After 1.5 half-lives, about 35% of a radioactive sample remains. After 3.2 half-lives, 10% remains.

11.56 (a) An 80% decrease in activity takes place in 2.3 half-lives (Figure 11.4). For selenium-75, this is equivalent to 2.3 x 120 days = 280 days.

(b) 365 ÷ 120 = 3.04, or approximately 3 half-lives.

0.050 g x $(0.5)^3$ = 0.050 x 0.125 = 0.0063 g

Approximately 0.0063 grams of $^{75}_{34}Se$ will remain after a year.

11.57 (a) A 75% loss of activity takes place in 2 half-lives (240 days).

(b) After 7 half-lives, 99% of any sample will have decayed. Since the half-life of $^{75}_{34}Se$ is approximately 0.33 year, 99% of the sample will have disintegrated in 7 x 0.33 = 2.3 years.

11.58 If the half-life of mercury-97 is 64.1 hours:

7 days = 168 hours ; 168/64.1 = 2.6, or approximately 3 half-lives

30 days = 720 hours ; 720/64.1 = approximately 11 half-lives

5.0 ng x $(0.5)^3$ = approx. 1 ng of mercury-197 remains after 7 days.

5.0 ng x $(0.5)^{11}$ = approx. 2 x 10^{-3} ng of mercury-197 remains after 30 days.

11.59

(a) $^{198}_{79}Au \rightarrow {}^{0}_{-1}e + {}^{198}_{80}Hg$

(b) $\dfrac{3.75\ mCi}{30.0\ mCi}$ = 0.125 = 3.00 half lives; 3.00 x 2.695 days = 8.09 days

(c) $\dfrac{1.0\ mCi}{1\ kg}$ x 70.0 kg = 70 mCi

Measuring Radioactivity

11.60 The inside walls of a Geiger counter tube are negatively charged, and a wire in the center is positively charged. Radiation ionizes argon gas inside the tube, which creates a conducting path for current between the wall and the wire. The current is detected, and the Geiger counter makes a clicking sound.

11.61 A film badge is protected from light exposure, but exposure to other radiation causes the film to get cloudy. Photographic development of the film and comparison with a standard allows the amount of exposure to be calculated.

11.62 In a scintillation counter, a phosphor emits a flash of light when struck by radiation. The number of flashes are counted and converted to an electrical signal.

11.63 Rems indicate the amount of tissue damage from any type of radiation, and allow comparisons between equivalent doses of different types of radiation to be made.

11.64 According to Table 11.6, any amount of radiation above 25 rems produces detectable effects in humans.

11.65 (1) curie   (c) Number of disintegrations per second
       (2) rem   (b) Amount of tissue damage
       (3) rad   (d) Amount of radiation per gram of tissue
       (4) roentgen   (a) Ionizing intensity of radiation

11.66

28 mCi x $\dfrac{1\ mL}{15\ mCi}$ = 1.9 mL

11.67

(a) 68 kg x $\dfrac{180\ \mu Ci}{1\ kg}$ x $\dfrac{1\ mCi}{10^3\ \mu Ci}$ = 12 mCi

(b) 12 mCi x $\dfrac{1\ mL}{6.5\ mCi}$ = 1.8 mL

11.68

(a) $\dfrac{I_1}{I_2} = \dfrac{d_2^2}{d_1^2}$; $I_1 = 300$ rem; $d_1^2 = (2.0 \text{ m})^2 = 4.0 \text{ m}^2$; $d_2^2 = (16.0 \text{ m})^2 = 256 \text{ m}^2$; $I_2 = ?$

$I_2 = \dfrac{d_1^2 \times I_1}{d_2^2} = \dfrac{4.0 \text{ m}^2 \times 300 \text{ rem}}{256 \text{ m}^2} = 4.7 \text{ rem}$

(b) $\dfrac{I_1}{I_2} = \dfrac{d_2^2}{d_1^2}$; $I_1 = 300$ rem; $d_1^2 = (2.0 \text{ m})^2 = 4.0 \text{ m}^2$; $d_2^2 = (25.0 \text{ m})^2 = 625 \text{ m}^2$; $I_2 = ?$

$I_2 = \dfrac{d_1^2 \times I_1}{d_2^2} = \dfrac{4.0 \text{ m}^2 \times 300 \text{ rem}}{625 \text{ m}^2} = 1.9 \text{ rem}$

11.69

$\dfrac{I_1}{I_2} = \dfrac{d_2^2}{d_1^2}$; $I_1 = 650$ rem; $I_2 = 25$ rem; $d_1^2 = 1.0 \text{ m}^2$; $d_2^2 = ?$

$d_2^2 = \dfrac{d_1^2 \times I_1}{I_2} = \dfrac{1.0 \text{ m}^2 \times 650.0 \text{ rem}}{25 \text{ rem}} = 26 \text{ m}^2$

$d_2 = 5.1 \text{ m}$

Chemistry in Action

11.70 (1) *In vivo procedures* take place inside the body and assess the functioning of organs or body systems. Determination of whole-blood volume using chromium-51 is an example.

(2) *Therapeutic procedures* are used to kill diseased tissue. For example, irradiation of a tumor with cobalt-60 is a treatment for cancer.

(3) In *boron neutron capture therapy (BNCT)*, boron-containing drugs are administered to a cancer patient and are concentrated in the tumor, which is then irradiated with a neutron beam. The boron captures a neutron and undergoes transmutation to produce a lithium nucleus and an alpha particle, which kills the tumor.

11.71 The total sample dose is 2.0 mL x 1.25 μCi = 2.5 μCi. The calculated blood volume:

$2.5 \text{ μCi} \times \dfrac{1.0 \text{ mL}}{2.6 \times 10^{-4} \text{ μCi}} \times \dfrac{1 \text{ L}}{1000 \text{ mL}} = 9.6 \text{ L}$

11.72 The purpose of food irradiation is to kill harmful microorganisms by exposing food to ionizing radiation, which destroys the genetic material of the microorganisms.

11.73 Gamma rays from cobalt-60 are used to treat food.

11.74 The body-imaging techniques CT and PET are noninvasive and yield a large array of images that can be processed by computer to produce a three-dimensional image of an organ.

11.75 MRI imaging does not involve radiation and produces images that have greater contrast than those from CT and PET scans.

General Questions and Problems

11.76 The region with no filter monitors α radiation, the region with a plastic filter monitors β radiation, and the region with a tinfoil filter monitors γ radiation. This type of badge filters the types of radiation by penetrating power.

11.77 It takes 3 half-lives for radiation to decay to one-eighth of its original value.
3 x 5730 years = 17,200 years old.

11.78 Nuclear reactions occur spontaneously, and no substance can "react with" radioactive emissions to neutralize them.

11.79 A film badge is more useful for measuring radiation exposure over a period of time. Scintillation counters and Geiger counters are more useful for measuring a current source of radiation.

11.80

$$\frac{I_1}{I_2} = \frac{d_2^2}{d_1^2}; I_1 = 28 \text{ cpm}; d_1^2 = (10 \text{ m})^2 = 100 \text{ m}^2; d_2^2 = (5.0 \text{ m})^2 = 25 \text{ m}^2; I_2 = ?$$

$$I_2 = \frac{d_1^2 \times I_1}{d_2^2} = \frac{100 \text{ m}^2 \times 28 \text{ cpm}}{25 \text{ m}^2} = 110 \text{ cpm}$$

11.81 If an isotope has more protons than neutrons, either electron capture or positron emission is the most likely decay route because they both reduce the number of protons and increases the number of neutrons. If an isotope has more neutrons than protons, β emission is the most likely decay route because it both decreases the number of neutrons and increases the number of protons.

11.82

(a) $^{99}_{42}\text{Mo} \rightarrow ^{0}_{-1}\text{e} + ^{99}_{43}\text{Tc}$ ^{99}Mo decays to Tc-99m by β emission.

(b) $^{98}_{42}\text{Mo} + ^{1}_{0}\text{n} \rightarrow ^{99}_{42}\text{Mo}$

11.83 24 hours ÷ 6.01 hours = approx. 4 half-lives. 15 μCi x $(0.5)^4$ = 0.94 μCi

11.84

(a) $^{238}_{94}\text{Pu} \rightarrow ^{4}_{2}\text{He} + ^{234}_{92}\text{U}$
(b) The metal case serves as a shield to protect the wearer from α radiation.

11.85

(a) $^{24}_{11}\text{Na} \rightarrow ^{0}_{-1}\text{e} + ^{24}_{12}\text{Mg}$

(b) 50 hr ÷ 15 hr = 3.3 half-lives. $(0.5)^3$ = 0.125. Somewhat less than 12.5% of the original sodium-24 remains after 50 hrs.

11.86 Embryos and fetuses are particularly susceptible to the effects of radiation because their rate of cell division is high.

11.87 This question illustrates the relative dangers of internal radiation and external radiation. Alpha and beta radiation, because of their short penetrating distance, are dangerous inside the body. You can put the alpha cookie in your pocket, but don't try this with the beta cookie, which might damage sensitive genetic material; hold it your hand (wearing gloves). The gamma cookie, with a large penetrating distance, can probably be eaten because the radiation will pass through the body before it can cause damage. Throw away the neutron cookie.

11.88 Nuclear fission does not require high temperatures or holding materials long enough for nuclei to react. Drawbacks of fission include disposal of radioactive waste and issues of safety.

11.89

$$^{197}_{79}\text{Au} + 7\,^{1}_{0}\text{n} \rightarrow 3\,^{0}_{-1}\text{e} + {}^{204}_{82}\text{Pb}$$

Gold-197 is bombarded by 7 neutrons and yields lead-204 plus 3 β particles

11.90

(a) $^{253}_{99}\text{Es} + {}^{4}_{2}\text{He} \rightarrow {}^{256}_{101}\text{Md} + {}^{1}_{0}\text{n}$ (b) $^{250}_{98}\text{Cf} + {}^{11}_{5}\text{B} \rightarrow {}^{257}_{103}\text{Lr} + 4\,^{1}_{0}\text{n}$

11.91

$$^{238}_{92}\text{U} + {}^{1}_{0}\text{n} \rightarrow 2\,^{0}_{-1}\text{e} + {}^{239}_{94}\text{Pu}$$

11.92

$$^{10}_{5}\text{B} + {}^{1}_{0}\text{n} \rightarrow {}^{7}_{3}\text{Li} + {}^{4}_{2}\text{He}$$

11.93

$$^{232}_{90}\text{Th} \rightarrow {}^{208}_{82}\text{Pb} + 6\,^{4}_{2}\text{He} + 4\,^{0}_{-1}\text{e}$$

The 24-amu loss in mass in going from $^{232}_{90}\text{Th}$ to $^{208}_{82}\text{Pb}$ is due to the emission of six α particles, which also account for a reduction in atomic number from 90 to 78. The

emission of four β particles increases the atomic number from 78 to 82 and yields $^{208}_{82}\text{Pb}$.

11.94 Alpha particles are used for the bombardment.
$$^{238}_{92}\text{U} + 3\,^{4}_{2}\text{He} \rightarrow {}^{246}_{98}\text{Cf} + 4\,^{1}_{0}\text{n}$$

11.95

$$^{48}_{20}\text{Ca} + {}^{249}_{97}\text{Bk} \rightarrow {}^{294}_{117}\text{Uus} + 3\,^{1}_{0}\text{n}$$
$$^{48}_{20}\text{Ca} + {}^{249}_{97}\text{Bk} \rightarrow {}^{293}_{117}\text{Uus} + 4\,^{1}_{0}\text{n}$$

Self-Test for Chapter 11

Multiple Choice

1. Bombardment of a uranium-235 atom with a neutron produces three neutrons, which can go on to bombard three more U-235 atoms. How many neutrons are produced after the fourth cycle?
    (a) 12 (b) 36 (c) 81 (d) 108

2. The product of the α emission of $^{146}_{62}Sm$ is:
    (a) $^{146}_{63}Eu$ (b) $^{144}_{61}Pm$ (c) $^{144}_{60}Nd$ (d) $^{142}_{60}Nd$

3. A half-inch-thick piece of plastic blocks 50% of radiation. How much radiation passes through a one-inch-thick piece of plastic?
    (a) 50% (b) 25% (c) 12% (d) 0%

4. The *curie* measures:
    (a) amount of radioactivity (b) ionizing intensity of radiation (c) amount of radiation absorbed (d) tissue damage

5. A sample of a radionuclide has a half-life of 40 days. How much radioactivity remains after 160 days?
    (a) 25% (b) 12.5% (c) 6.25% (d) 0%

6. How many disintegrations per second does one microcurie of a sample emit?
    (a) 3.7×10^{10} (b) 3.7×10^{7} (c) 3.7×10^{6} (d) 3.7×10^{4}

7. If a person standing 100 m from a radiation source approaches to within 10 m of the source, how much does the intensity of the radiation change?
    (a) increases by a hundredfold (b) increases tenfold (c) stays the same (d) decreases tenfold

8. Artificial transmutation was probably used to produce which one of the following radionuclides?
    (a) $^{238}_{92}U$ (b) $^{210}_{82}Pb$ (c) $^{60}_{27}Co$ (d) $^{239}_{94}Pu$

9. Which of the following radioisotopes is not medically useful?
    (a) $^{131}_{53}I$ (b) $^{14}_{6}C$ (c) $^{24}_{11}Na$ (d) $^{60}_{27}Co$

10. In an experiment by the Curies, aluminum-27 was bombarded with α particles. If each aluminum-27 atom captured one α particle and emitted one neutron, what other atom was produced?
    (a) $^{29}_{13}Al$ (b) $^{28}_{14}Si$ (c) $^{30}_{15}P$ (d) $^{31}_{15}P$

Sentence Completion

1. The change of one element to another is called _____.

2. _____ _____ causes the most tissue damage.

3. A chemical compound tagged with a radioactive atom can be used as a _____.

4. All people are exposed to _____ radiation.

5. A nuclear equation is balanced when the number of _____ is the same on both sides of the equation.

6. The age of a sample can be determined by measuring the amount of _____ it contains.

7. The _____ is a unit for measuring the number of radioactive disintegrations per second.

8. In _____ _____, an atom is split apart by neutron bombardment to give small fragments.

9. People who work around radiation sources wear _____ _____ for detection of radiation.

10. PET and CT are techniques for _____ _____.

11. Very light elements release large amounts of energy when they undergo _____ _____.

12. The _____ _____ is the size of a radioactive sample that is needed for a nuclear reaction to be self-sustaining.

True or False

1. If a sample has a half-life of 12 days, it will have decayed completely in 24 days.

2. X rays are considered to be ionizing radiation.

3. The ratio of carbon-14 to carbon-12 in the atmosphere is constant.

4. Pierre and Marie Curie discovered radioactivity.

5. A β particle travels at nearly the speed of light.

6. An α particle travels at nearly the speed of light.

7. The product of β emission has an atomic number 1 amu smaller than the starting material.

8. A nuclear power plant can undergo a nuclear explosion in an accident.

9. The rad is the unit most commonly used in medicine to measure radiation dosage.

10. Radiation causes injury by ionizing molecules.

11. Most of the known radioisotopes are naturally occurring.

12. Many isotopes undergo nuclear fission.

Match each entry on the left with its partner on the right.

1. Rutherford   (a) α particle

2. $^{245}_{96}Cm$ (b) Used in cancer therapy

3. $t_{1/2}$ (c) Discovered radioactivity

4. $^{0}_{-1}e$ (d) Neutron

5. Becquerel   (e) Used for archeological dating

6. $^{90}_{38}Sr$ (f) Discovered α and β particles

7. $^{1}_{0}n$ (g) Natural radioactive element that undergoes fission

8. P. and M. Curie   (h) Discovered radium

9. $^{60}_{27}Co$ (i) Transuranium element

10. $^{4}_{2}He$ (j) Component of radioactive waste

11. $^{14}_{6}C$ (k) β particle

12. $^{235}_{92}U$ (l) Half-life

Chapter 12   Introduction to Organic Chemistry: Alkanes

Chapter Outline

I. Introduction to organic chemistry (Sections 12.1–12.5).
 A. The nature of organic molecules (Section 12.1).
  1. Carbon always forms four bonds.
  2. Almost all of the bonds in organic molecules are covalent.
   a. These bonds are polar covalent bonds when carbon forms a bond to an element on the far left of the periodic table.
   b. Carbon can form multiple bonds by sharing more than two electrons.
  3. Organic molecules have specific three-dimensional shapes.
  4. In addition to hydrogen, oxygen and nitrogen are often present in organic molecules.
  5. Organic molecules are low-melting and low-boiling, relative to inorganic compounds.
  6. Organic molecules are usually insoluble in water and don't conduct electricity.
 B. Functional groups (Section 12.2).
  1. A functional group is an atom or group of atoms that has a characteristic reactivity.
  2. The chemistry of organic molecules is determined by functional groups.
  3. Functional groups fall into three categories.
   a. Hydrocarbons.
   b. Compounds with C–X single bonds, where X is electronegative.
   c. Compounds with C=O double bonds.
 C. Structures of organic molecules: alkane isomers (Sections 12.3–12.4).
  1. When hydrocarbons contain more than three carbons, there is more than one way to arrange the carbon atoms (Section 12.3).
   a. Some alkanes are straight-chain alkanes.
   b. Other alkanes are branched.
  2. Compounds with the same formula but different orders of connecting the carbon atoms are called constitutional isomers.
   a. Constitutional isomers have different structures and different properties.
  3. Drawing structures (Section 12.4).
   a. Condensed structures are simpler to draw than structural formulas.
    i. In condensed structures, C—H and C—C single bonds are implied rather than drawn.
    ii. Vertical bonds are often shown for clarity.
    iii. Occasionally, parentheses are used to show a row of —CH_2— groups.
   b. In line structures C and H don't appear.
    i   Each C–C bond is represented as a line
    ii. The beginning or end of a line represents a carbon atom.
    iii. Any atom other than C or H must be shown.
 D. The shapes of organic molecules (Section 12.5).
  1. The groups around a C—C bond are free to assume an infinite number of conformations.
  2. Molecules adopt the least crowded conformation.
  3. Two structures with identical connections between atoms are identical, no matter how they are drawn.
II. Alkanes (Sections 12.6–12.8).
 A. Naming alkanes (Section 12.6).
  1. Straight-chain alkanes.
   a. Count the carbons.
   b. Find the root name.
   c. Add -ane to the root name.

2. Alkyl groups.
   a. Remove a hydrogen from an alkane and replace -ane with -yl.
   b. More than one alkyl group can be formed from some alkanes.
      i. Isopropyl and propyl are the two groups that can be formed from propane.
      ii. Four groups can be formed from butane.
      iii. Alkyl groups can be substituents on a straight chain.
3. Substitution patterns.
   a. Primary carbon: $R-CH_3$.
   b. Secondary carbon: $R-CH_2-R'$.
   c. Tertiary carbon:

$$R-\overset{\overset{\displaystyle R'}{|}}{C}H-R$$

   d. Quaternary carbon:

$$R-\overset{\overset{\displaystyle R'}{|}}{\underset{\underset{\displaystyle R''}{|}}{C}}-R'$$

4. Naming branched-chain alkanes.
   a. Name the main chain by finding the longest continuous chain of carbons and naming it.
   b. Number the carbons in the main chain, starting from the end nearer the first branch point.
   c. Identify and number each branching substituent according to its point of attachment to the main chain.
   d. Write the name as a single word.
B. Properties of alkanes (Section 12.7).
   1. The boiling points and melting points of alkanes increase with the number of carbons.
   2. Alkanes are insoluble in water but are soluble in nonpolar organic solvents.
   3. Alkanes are colorless and odorless.
   4. Alkanes are flammable.
   5. Alkanes with four or fewer carbons are gases, those from C_5 to C_{15} are liquids, and those with more than 15 carbons are solids.
C. Reactivity of alkanes (Section 12.8).
   1. Alkanes are very unreactive.
   2. Reactions that alkanes undergo:
      a. Combustion: alkane + $O_2 \longrightarrow CO_2 + H_2O$.
      b. Halogenation: alkane + $X_2 \longrightarrow$ halogenated alkane + HCl.
III. Cycloalkanes (Sections 12.9–12.10).
   A. Properties of cycloalkanes (Section 12.9).
      1. Cycloalkanes contain rings of carbon atoms.
      2. Cyclopropane and cyclobutane are more reactive than other cycloalkanes.
      3. Cyclohexane exists in a chairlike conformation.
      4. Cycloalkanes have properties similar to those of acyclic alkanes.
      5. Free rotation is not possible around the carbon–carbon bonds of a cycloalkane ring.
   B. Drawing and naming cycloalkanes (Section 12.10).
      1. Drawing cycloalkanes.
         a. The cycloalkane ring is represented as a polygon.
      2. Naming cycloalkanes.
         a. Use the cycloalkane as the parent.
         b. Number the substituents.
            i. Start numbering at the group that has alphabetical priority.
            ii. Proceed around the ring to give to the second group the lowest possible number.

Solutions to Chapter 12 Problems

12.1

(a)

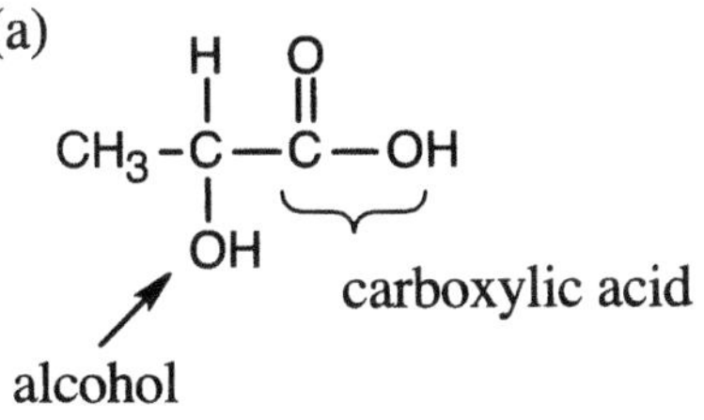

Lactic acid

(b)

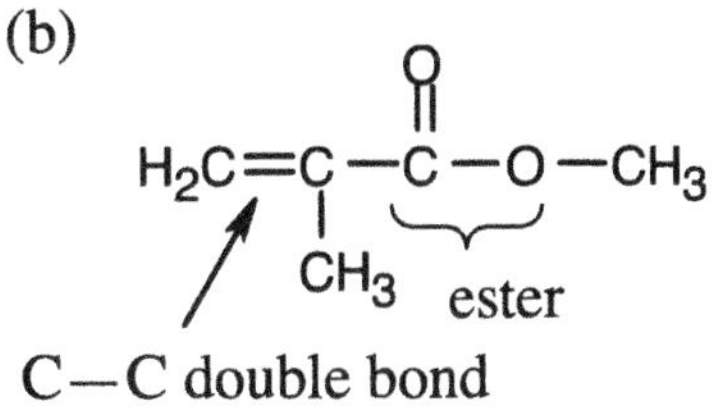

Methyl methacrylate

(c)

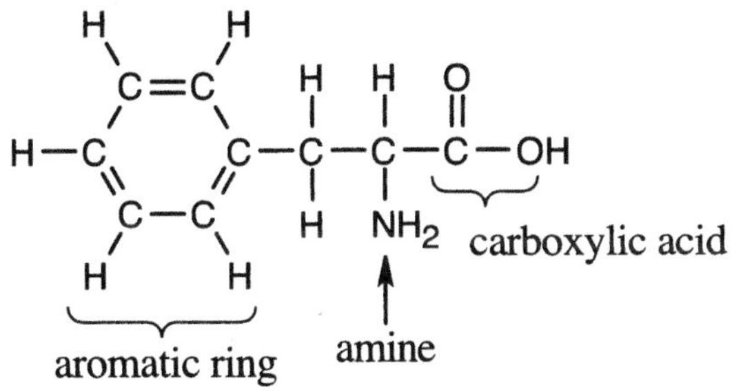

Phenylalanine

12.2

(a)

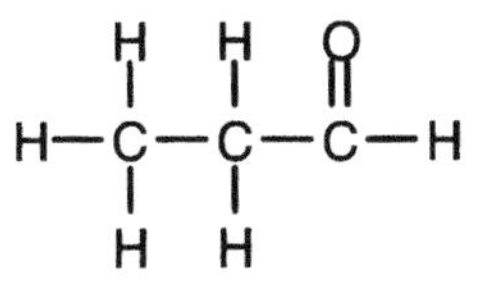

an aldehyde

(b)

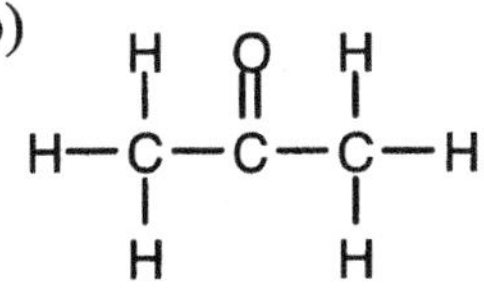

a ketone

(c)

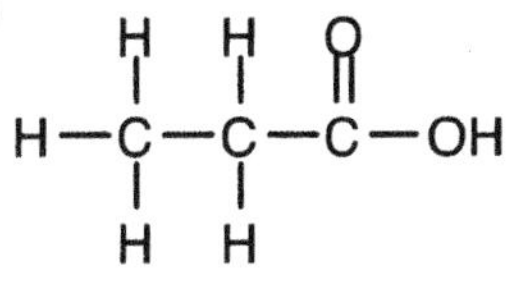

a carboxylic acid

12.3

(a)

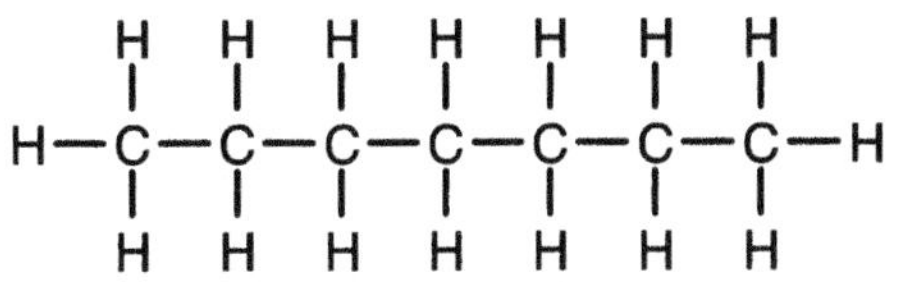

C_7H_{16} Heptane

(b)

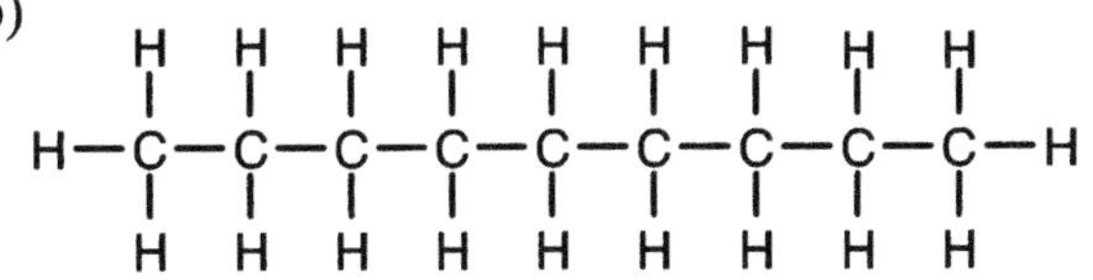

C_9H_{20} Nonane

12.4

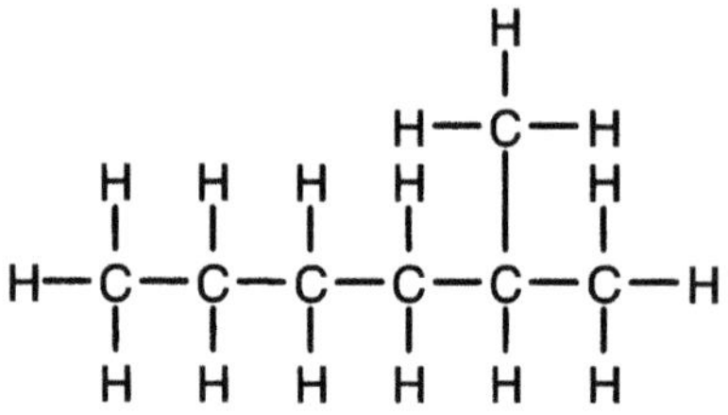

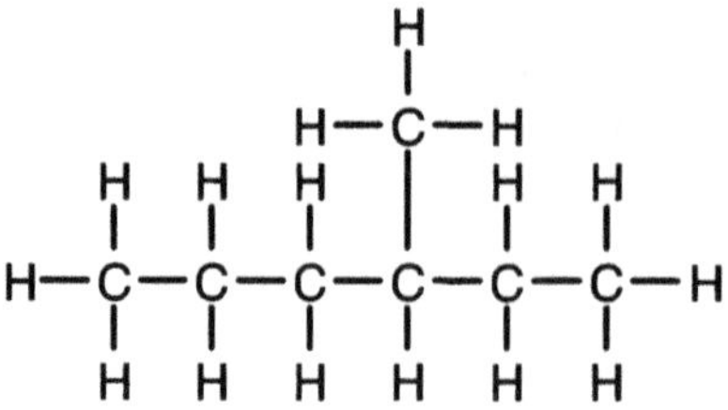

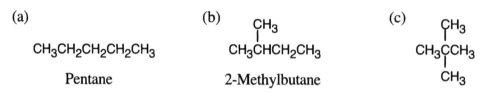

12.5

(a)

CH₃CH₂CH₂CH₂CH₃

Pentane

(b)

$$\underset{\displaystyle \text{CH}_3}{\overset{\displaystyle \text{CH}_3}{\text{CH}_3\text{CHCH}_2\text{CH}_3}}$$

2-Methylbutane

(c)

$$\begin{array}{c}\text{CH}_3\\ |\\ \text{CH}_3\text{CCH}_3\\ |\\ \text{CH}_3\end{array}$$

2,2-Dimethylpropane

12.6   *Step 1:* Find a straight carbon chain and draw it as a zigzag line.
Step 2: Add groups to the appropriate carbons, remembering that atoms other than carbon
and hydrogen must be indicated.

	Condensed Structure	*Straight-chain Backbone*	*Line-bond Structure*

(a)

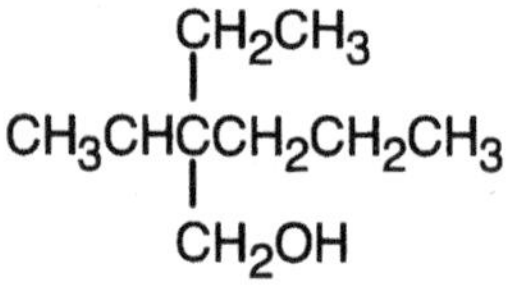

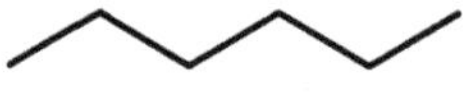

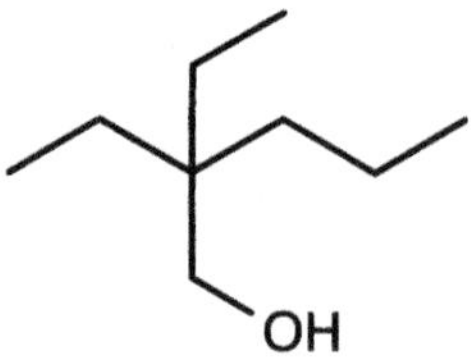

CH₂CH₃
|
CH₃CHCCH₂CH₂CH₃
|
CH₂OH

(b)

CH₂CH₃   CH₃
| |
CH₃CHCHCH₂CHCH₃
|
CH₃CHCH₂CH₃

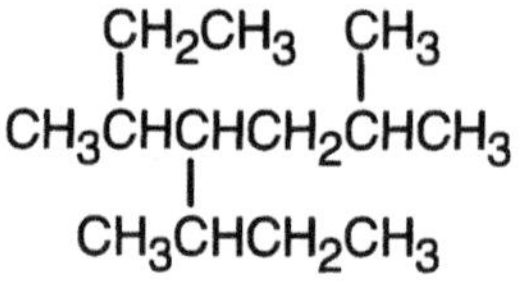

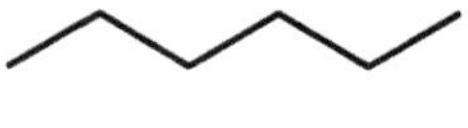

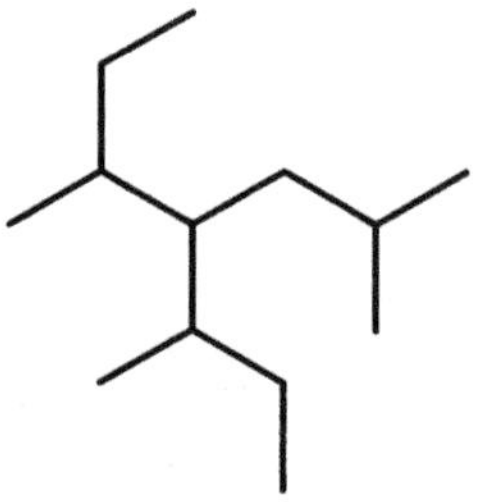

(c)

Br   Cl
| |
CH₃C—CHCH₂CH₂CHCH₂CH₃
|
H₃C   CH₂CH₂CH₃

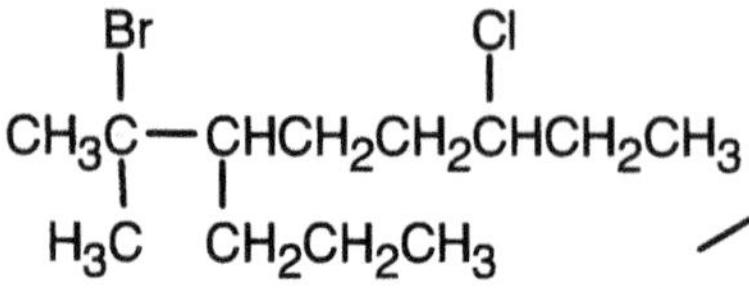

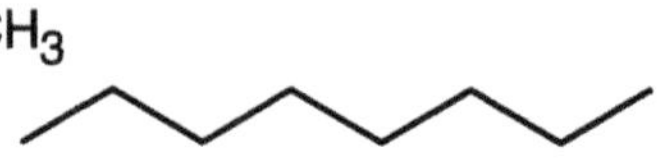

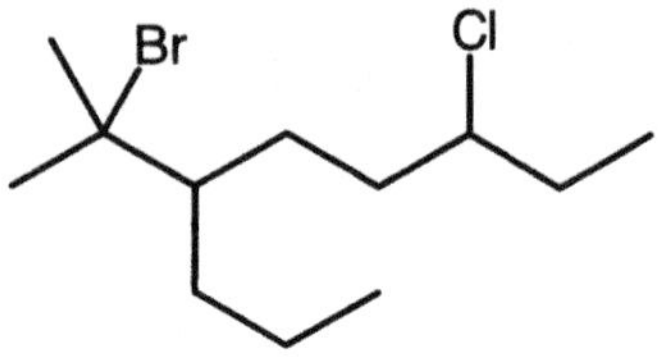

Notice that it is sometimes necessary to change the direction of a group to keep two groups
from bumping into each other.

12.7   Reverse the steps in the previous problem.
*Step 1:*Draw a chain of carbons that is the same length as the longest chain in the line structure.
Step 2: Add condensed groups to the condensed backbone.

	Line Structure	*Condensed Backbone*	*Condensed Structure*

(a)

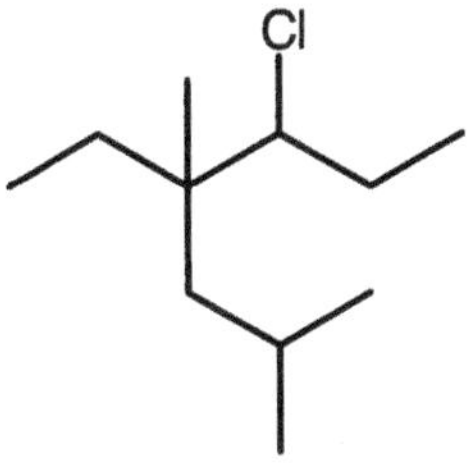

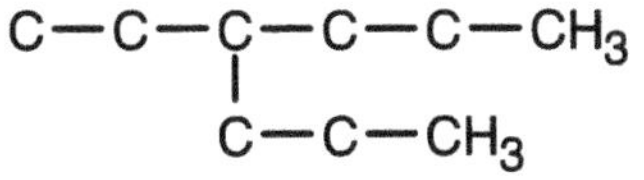

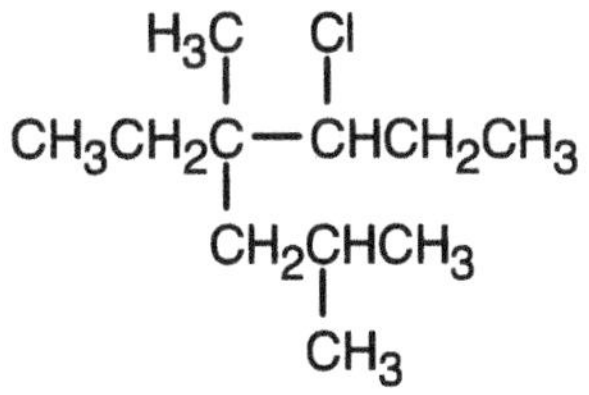

C—C—C—C—C—CH$_3$,
      |
     C—C—CH$_3$

     H$_3$C Cl
      | |
CH$_3$CH$_2$C—CHCH$_2$CH$_3$
      |
    CH$_2$CHCH$_3$
        |
       CH$_3$

(b)

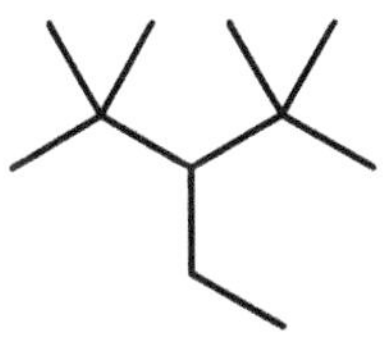

CH$_3$C—C—CCH$_3$

  H$_3$C CH$_3$ H$_3$C CH$_3$
   \/   \/
CH$_3$C—CH—CCH$_3$
       |
     CH$_2$CH$_3$

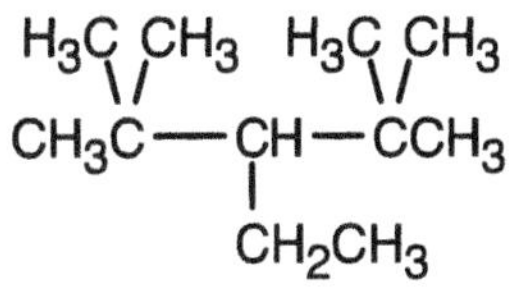

12.8

(a)   CH$_3$CH$_2$CHO

(b)   CH$_3$COCH$_3$

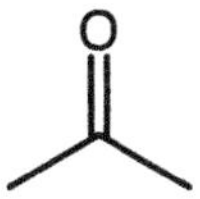

(c)   CH$_3$CH$_2$CO$_2$H

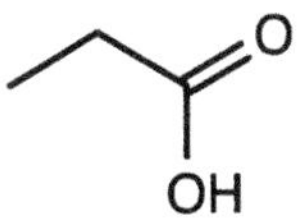

12.9   All three structures have the same molecular formula (C$_7$H$_{16}$). Structures (a) and (c) are conformers.

12.10 To solve this problem in a systematic way, use the following method:

(a) Draw the C$_7$H$_{16}$ isomer having no branches, and replace one of the —CH$_2$— hydrogens with a —CH$_3$. There are three different isomers:

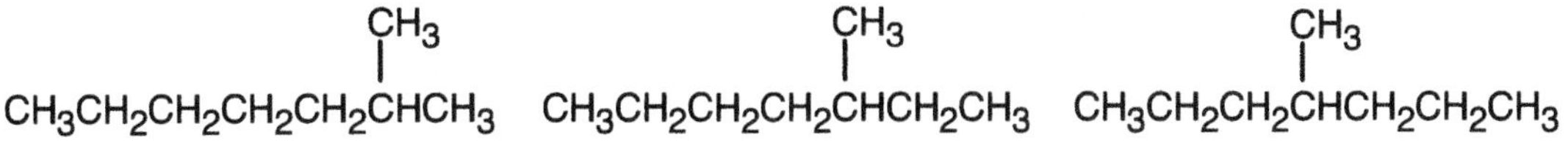

           CH$_3$ CH$_3$ CH$_3$
            | | |
CH$_3$CH$_2$CH$_2$CH$_2$CH$_2$CHCH$_3$ CH$_3$CH$_2$CH$_2$CH$_2$CHCH$_2$CH$_3$ CH$_3$CH$_2$CH$_2$CHCH$_2$CH$_2$CH$_3$

(b) Continue with the C_6 isomer having no branches, and replace the different kinds of hydrogens with $-CH_3$ groups, making sure that you don't draw the same isomer.

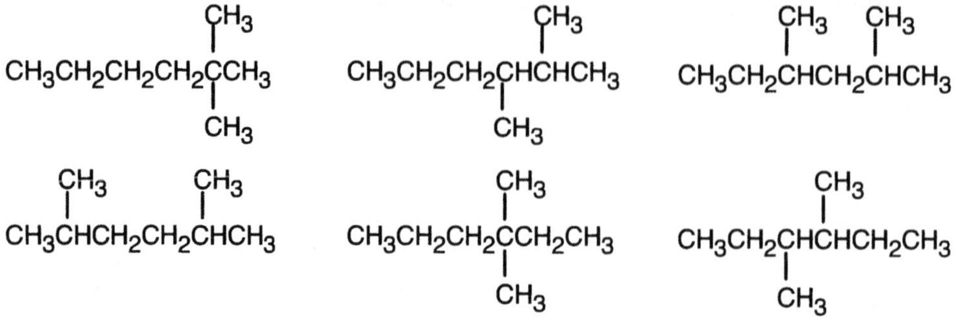

$$\begin{array}{c} CH_3 \\ | \\ CH_3CH_2CH_2CH_2CCH_3 \\ | \\ CH_3 \end{array}$$

$$\begin{array}{c} CH_3 \\ | \\ CH_3CH_2CH_2CHCHCH_3 \\ | \\ CH_3 \end{array}$$

$$\begin{array}{cc} CH_3 \quad CH_3 \\ | \qquad | \\ CH_3CH_2CHCH_2CHCH_3 \end{array}$$

$$\begin{array}{cc} CH_3 \qquad CH_3 \\ | \qquad\quad | \\ CH_3CHCH_2CH_2CHCH_3 \end{array}$$

$$\begin{array}{c} CH_3 \\ | \\ CH_3CH_2CH_2CCH_2CH_3 \\ | \\ CH_3 \end{array}$$

$$\begin{array}{c} CH_3 \\ | \\ CH_3CH_2CHCHCH_2CH_3 \\ | \\ CH_3 \end{array}$$

Line structures:

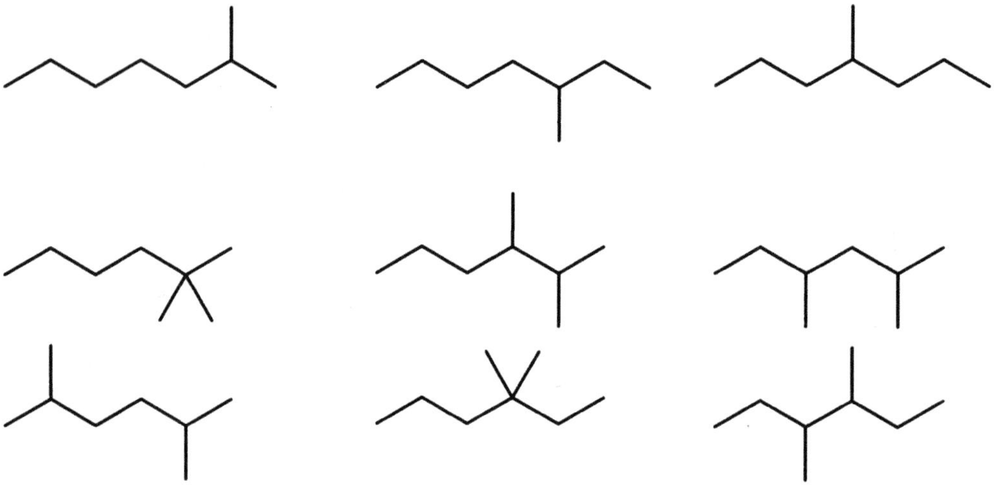

12.11

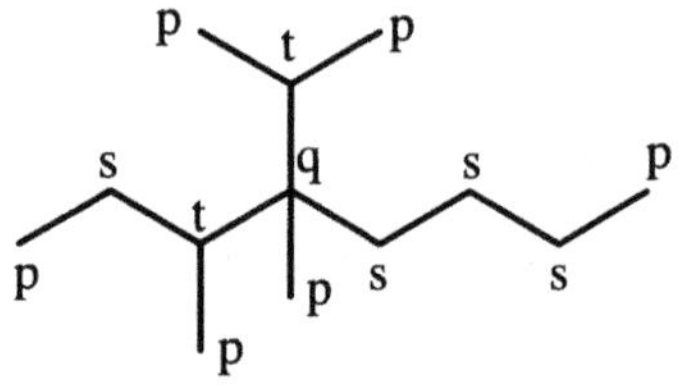

12.12

(a)

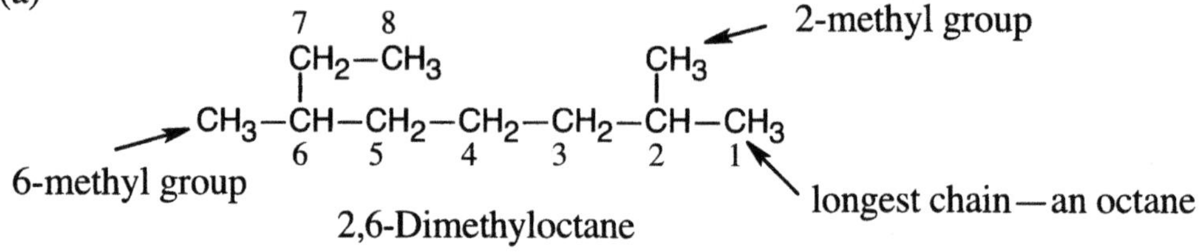

6-methyl group

2-methyl group

longest chain—an octane

2,6-Dimethyloctane

(b)

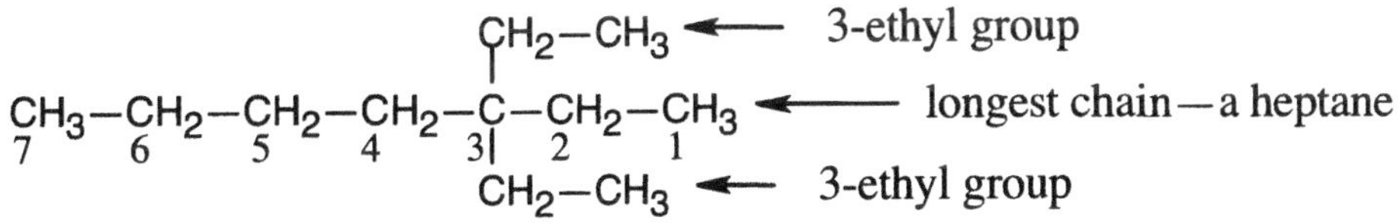

$$CH_2—CH_3 \longleftarrow \text{ 3-ethyl group}$$

$$\underset{7}{CH_3}—\underset{6}{CH_2}—\underset{5}{CH_2}—\underset{4}{CH_2}—\underset{3}{C}—\underset{2}{CH_2}—\underset{1}{CH_3} \longleftarrow \text{ longest chain — a heptane}$$

$$CH_2—CH_3 \longleftarrow \text{ 3-ethyl group}$$

3,3-Diethylheptane

12.13 To answer this problem, draw the straight-chain hydrocarbon corresponding to the parent name, and replace —H's with the groups indicated.

(a)

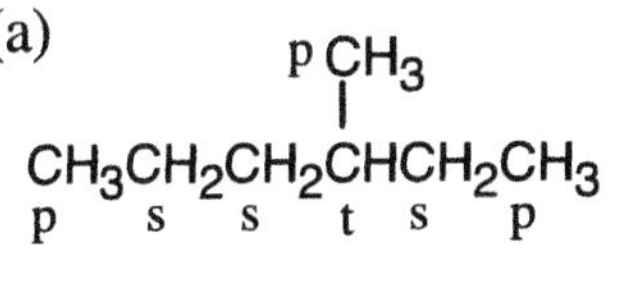

$$\overset{P \; CH_3}{\underset{p \quad s \quad s \quad t \quad s \quad p}{CH_3CH_2CH_2CHCH_2CH_3}}$$

3-Methylhexane

(b)

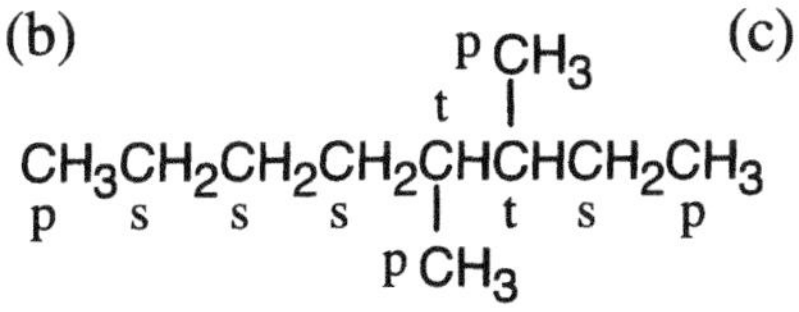

$$\overset{P \; CH_3}{\overset{t}{\underset{p \quad s \quad s \quad s \quad | \quad t \quad s \quad p}{CH_3CH_2CH_2CH_2CHCHCH_2CH_3}}}$$
$$P \; CH_3$$

3,4-Dimethyloctane

(c)

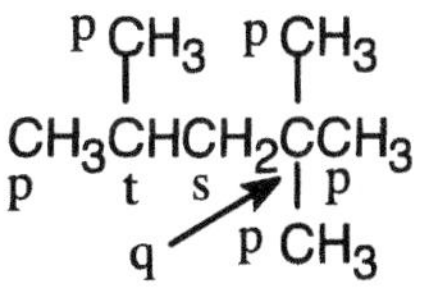

$$\overset{P \; CH_3 \; P \; CH_3}{\underset{p \quad t \quad s \quad | \; p}{CH_3CHCH_2CCH_3}}$$
$$\underset{q}{} \; P \; CH_3$$

2,2,4-Trimethylpentane

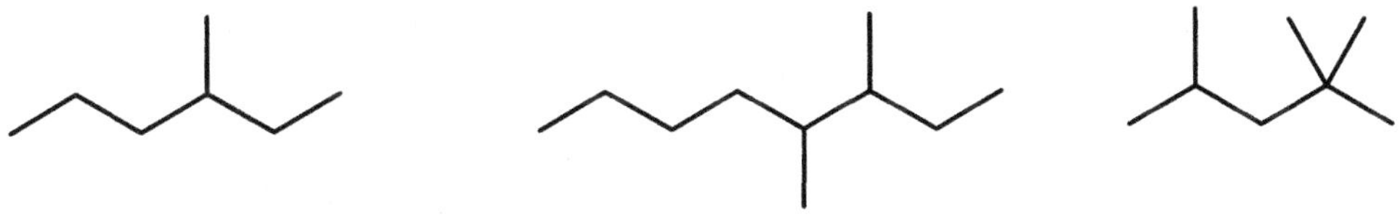

Where p = primary, s = secondary, t = tertiary, and q = quaternary

12.14 There are many answers to this question. For example,

(a)

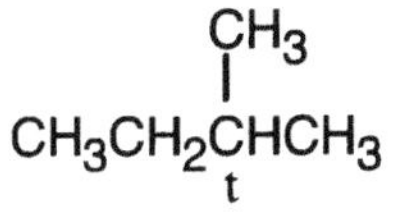

$$\overset{CH_3}{\underset{t}{CH_3CH_2CHCH_3}}$$

2-Methylbutane

(b)

$$\overset{H_3C \; \; CH_3}{\underset{t \quad | \; q}{CH_3CHCCH_3}}$$
$$CH_3$$

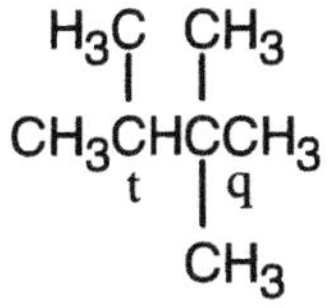

2,2,3-Trimethylbutane

12.15

(a)

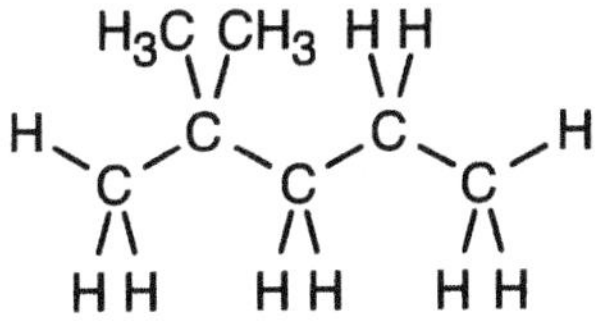

2,2-Dimethylpentane

(b)

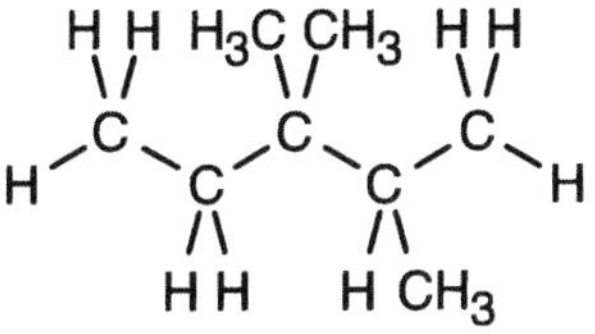

2,3,3-Trimethylpentane

12.16

$$2 \; CH_3CH_3 \; + \; 7 \; O_2 \longrightarrow 4 \; CO_2 \; + \; 6 \; H_2O$$

12.17

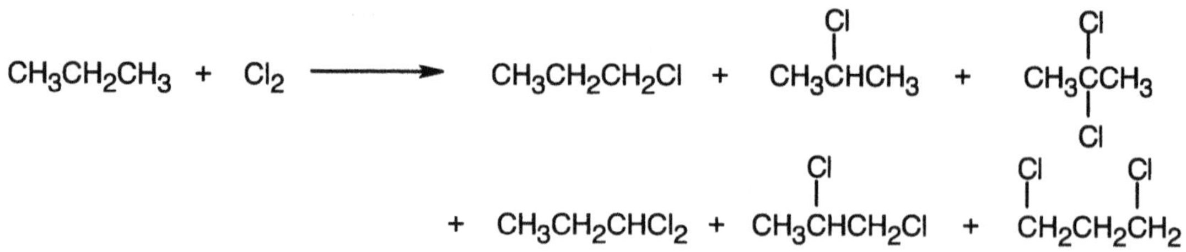

$$CH_3CH_2CH_3 + Cl_2 \longrightarrow CH_3CH_2CH_2Cl + CH_3\underset{\underset{Cl}{|}}{CH}CH_3 + CH_3\underset{\underset{Cl}{|}}{\overset{\overset{Cl}{|}}{C}}CH_3$$

$$+ CH_3CH_2CHCl_2 + CH_3\underset{\overset{|}{Cl}}{CH}CH_2Cl + \underset{\overset{|}{Cl}}{CH_2}CH_2\underset{\overset{|}{Cl}}{CH_2}$$

Six different mono- and disubstitution products can be formed from the reaction of propane with chlorine.

12.18

(a)

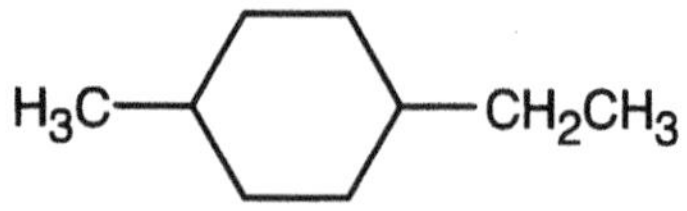

H_3C—⬡—CH_2CH_3

1-Ethyl-4-methylcyclohexane

The parent ring is a cyclohexane. The two substituents are an ethyl group and a methyl group. The ethyl group receives the smaller number because it has alphabetical priority.

(b)

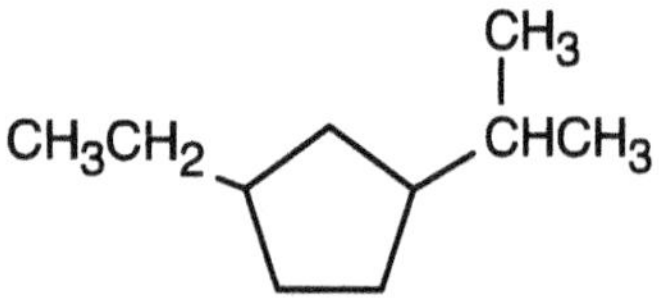

CH_3CH_2—⬠—CHCH_3 with CH_3 on top

1-Ethyl-3-isopropylcyclopentane

The parent ring is a cyclopentane. The two substituents are an ethyl group and an isopropyl group. The ethyl group receives the smaller number because it has alphabetical priority.

12.19

(a)

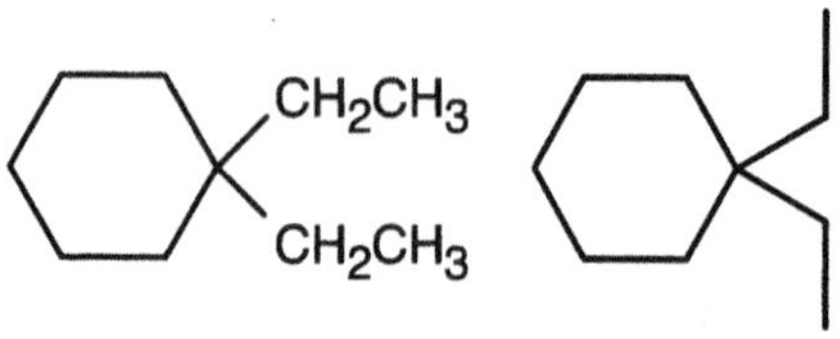

CH_2CH_3 / CH_2CH_3 on cyclohexane

1,1-Diethylcyclohexane

(b)

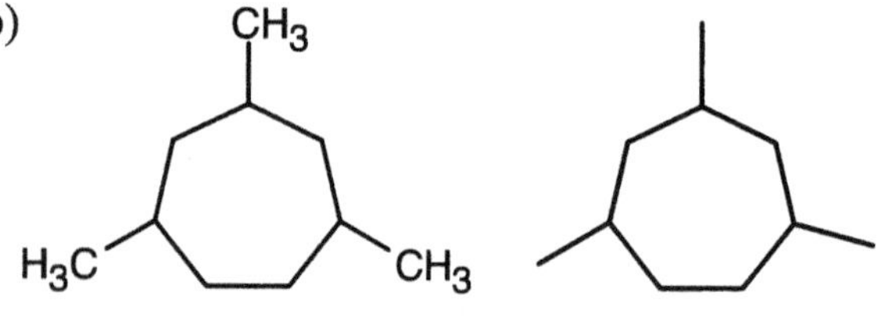

CH_3, H_3C, CH_3 on cycloheptane

1,3,5-Trimethylcycloheptane

12.20

(a) Ethylene and propylene are the starting materials for industrial chemicals and plastics.

(b) Synthetic rubber is less sticky and safer for driving than natural rubber.

12.21

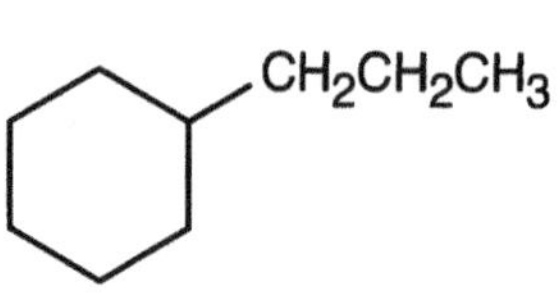

⬡—CH_2CH_2CH_3

Propylcyclohexane

Understanding Key Concepts

12.22

(a)

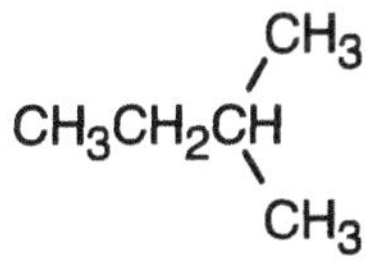

CH₃CH₂CH
with CH₃ (top) and CH₃ (bottom)

12 hydrogens

(b)

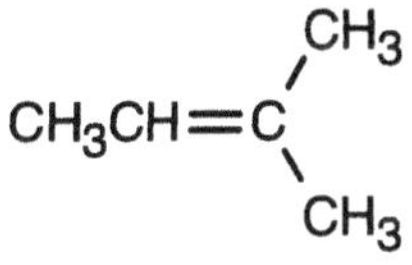

CH₃CH=C
with CH₃ (top) and CH₃ (bottom)

10 hydrogens

(c)

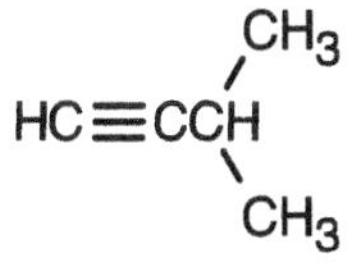

HC≡CCH
with CH₃ (top) and CH₃ (bottom)

8 hydrogens

12.23

(a)

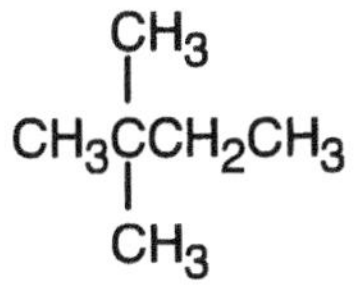

CH₃CCH₂CH₃
with CH₃ (top) and CH₃ (bottom)

(b)

CH₃CHCHCH₃
with CH₃ (top) and OH (bottom)

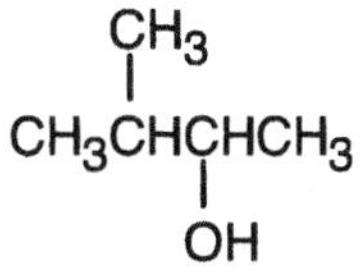

12.24 In a line drawing, a carbon is assumed to be at the intersection of lines.

(a)

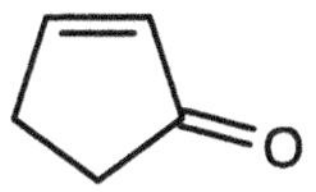

(b)

12.25

(a)

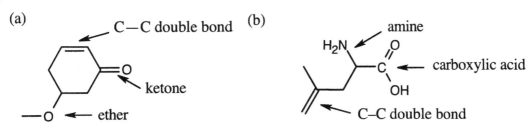

C—C double bond

ketone

—O ← ether

(b)

H₂N ← amine

C ← carboxylic acid

OH

C–C double bond

12.26

(a)

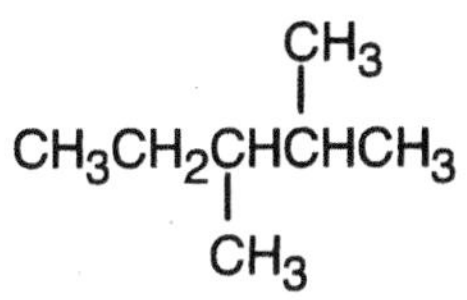

CH₃CH₂CHCHCH₃
with CH₃ (top) and CH₃ (bottom)

2,3-Dimethylpentane

(b)

CH₃CHCH₂CH₂CHCH₃
with CH₃ (top) and CH₃ (bottom)

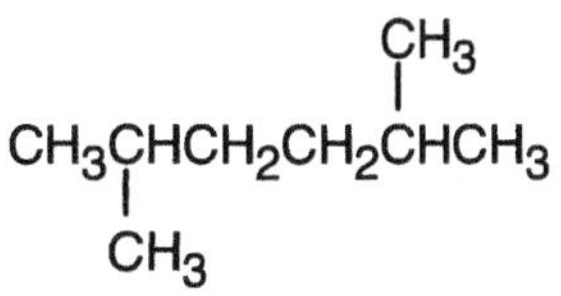

2,5-Dimethylhexane

12.27

(a)

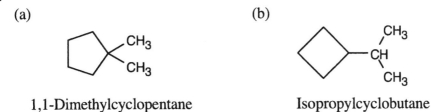

CH₃
CH₃

1,1-Dimethylcyclopentane

(b)

CH₃
CH
CH₃

Isopropylcyclobutane

12.28 In one of the isomers (b), the methyl groups are on the same side of the ring, and in the other isomer (a), they are on opposite sides.

(a)

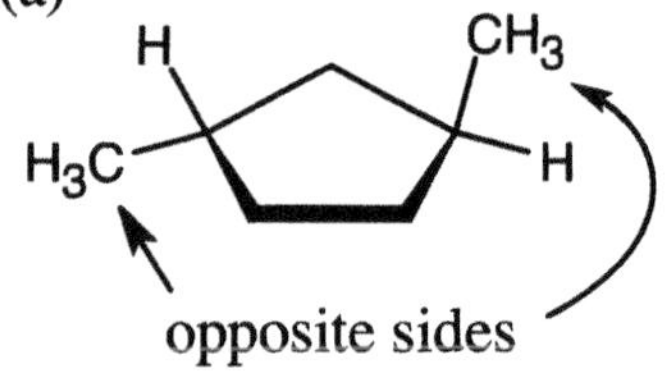

opposite sides

(b)

same side

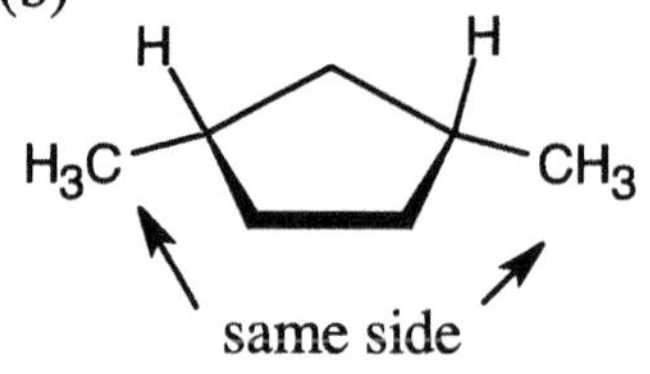

Organic Molecules and Functional Groups

12.29 If you look at the periodic table you will see that carbon belongs to group 4A, whose elements can form four bonds. Because carbon is in the middle of the periodic table, these bonds are covalent, and because it is in period 2, these bonds are strong. Consequently, carbon is unique in that it can form four strong bonds to other elements and to other carbon atoms, making possible a great many different compounds.

12.30 Functional groups are groups of atoms within a molecule that have a characteristic chemical behavior. They are important because most of the chemistry of organic compounds is determined by functional groups. The reactivity of a functional group is similar in all compounds in which it occurs.

12.31 Most organic compounds don't dissolve in water because they are nonpolar. They don't conduct electricity because they are covalent, not ionic.

12.32 A polar covalent bond is a covalent bond in which electrons are shared unequally, being more attracted to one atom than the other. For example, the electrons in the C—Br bond of bromomethane are attracted more strongly to the electronegative bromine than to carbon.

12.33 There are many possible answers to this question. For example,

(a)

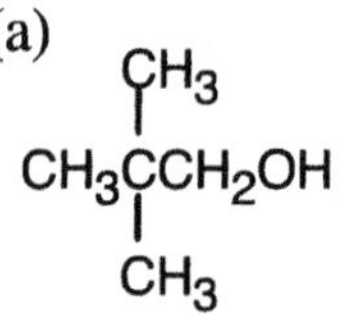

(b)

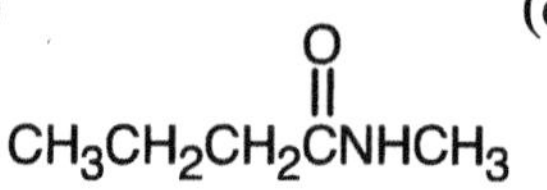

(c)

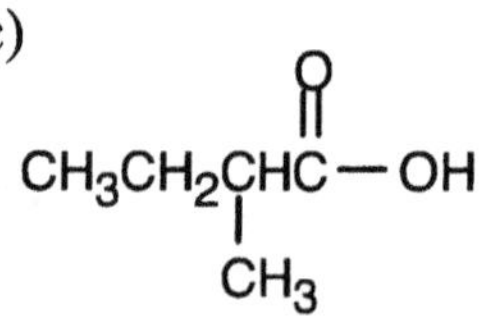

(d)

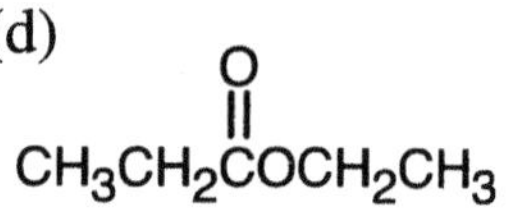

12.34

(a)

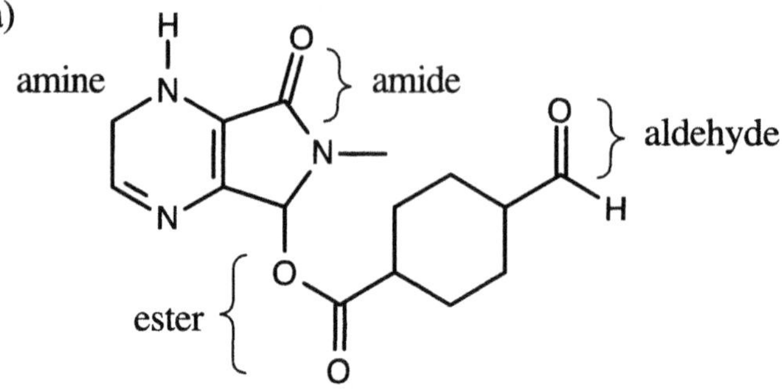

(b)

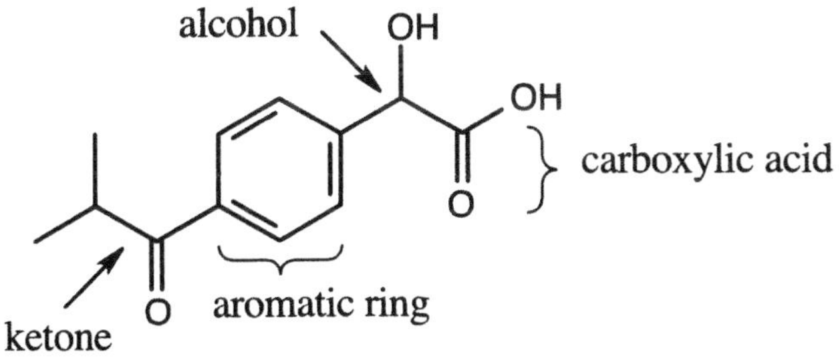

alcohol

OH

OH

} carboxylic acid

O

aromatic ring

ketone

12.35

(a)

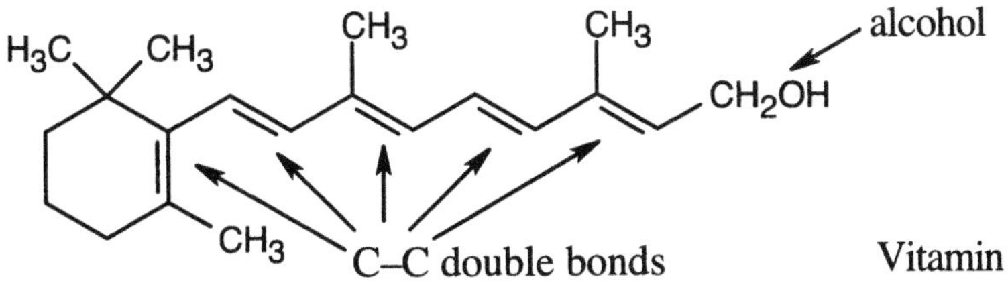

H₃C CH₃

CH₃

CH₃

alcohol

CH₂OH

CH₃

C–C double bonds

Vitamin A

(b) carboxylic acid

amine

OH

H

O

} ester

O

N

N

OCH₂CH₃

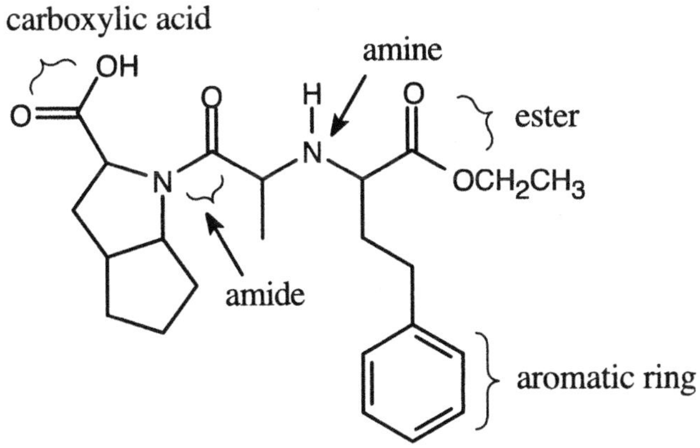

Ramipril

amide

aromatic ring

12.36 There are many possible answers to each of these questions. For example,

(a)

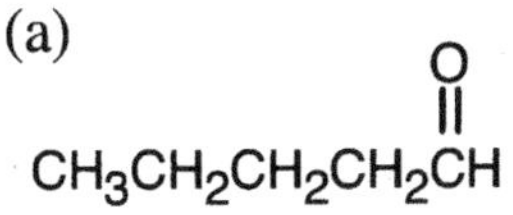

CH₃CH₂CH₂CH₂CH

aldehyde

(b)

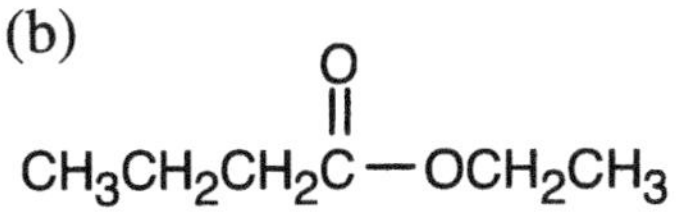

CH₃CH₂CH₂C—OCH₂CH₃

ester

(c)

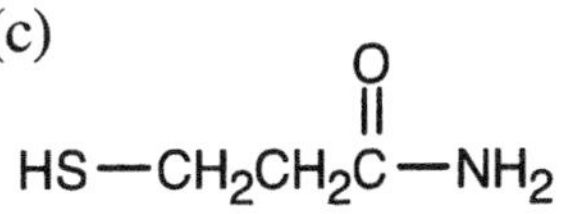

HS—CH₂CH₂C—NH₂

amide
thiol

12.37

(a)

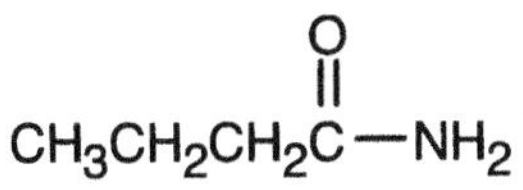

CH₃CH₂CH₂C—NH₂

amide

(b)

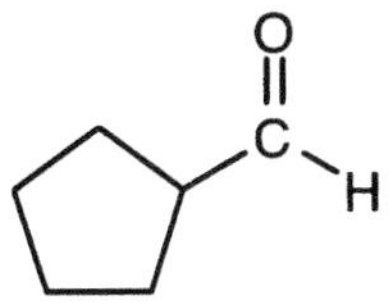

aldehyde

(c)

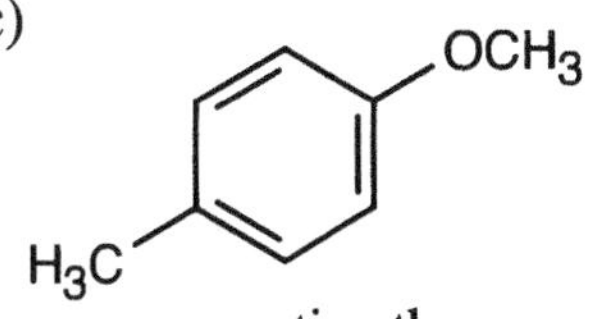

OCH₃

H₃C

aromatic ether

Alkanes and Isomers

12.38 For two compounds to be isomers, they must have the same molecular formula but different structures.

12.39 Compounds with the formulas C_5H_{10} and C_4H_{10} are not isomers because they don't have the same molecular formulas.

12.40 A primary carbon is bonded to one other carbon; a secondary carbon is bonded to two other carbons; a tertiary carbon is bonded to three other carbons; and a quaternary carbon is bonded to four other carbons.

12.41 A compound can't have a quintary carbon because carbon forms only four bonds, not five.

12.42 There are many possible answers to this question and the following question. For example:

(a)

$$
\begin{array}{c}
CH_3 \\
t\ \ | \\
CH_3\overset{}{C}H\overset{}{C}HCH_3 \\
|\ \ t \\
CH_3
\end{array}
$$

2,3-Dimethylbutane

(b)

Cyclopentane

12.43

(a)

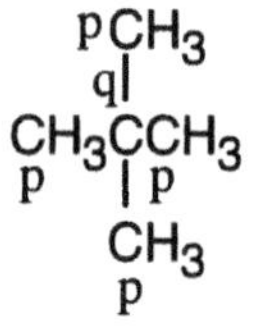

$$
\begin{array}{c}
p\,CH_3 \\
q| \\
CH_3\overset{}{C}CH_3 \\
p\ \ |\ p \\
CH_3 \\
p
\end{array}
$$

2,2-Dimethylpropane

(b)

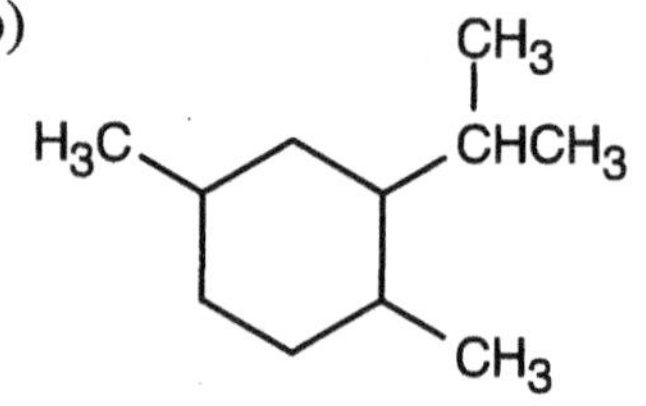

2-Isopropyl-1,4-dimethylcyclohexane

12.44

(a)

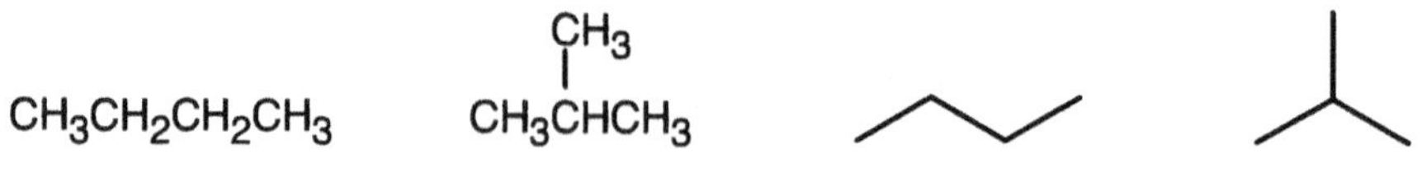

$CH_3CH_2CH_2CH_3$

$$
\begin{array}{c}
CH_3 \\
| \\
CH_3CHCH_3
\end{array}
$$

(b)

$CH_3CH_2CH_2CH_2OH$

$$
\begin{array}{c}
OH \\
| \\
CH_3CH_2CHCH_3
\end{array}
$$

$$
\begin{array}{c}
CH_3 \\
| \\
CH_3CHCH_2OH
\end{array}
$$

$$
\begin{array}{c}
CH_3 \\
| \\
CH_3CHCH_2OH
\end{array}
$$

(c)

$CH_3CH_2OCH_2CH_3$

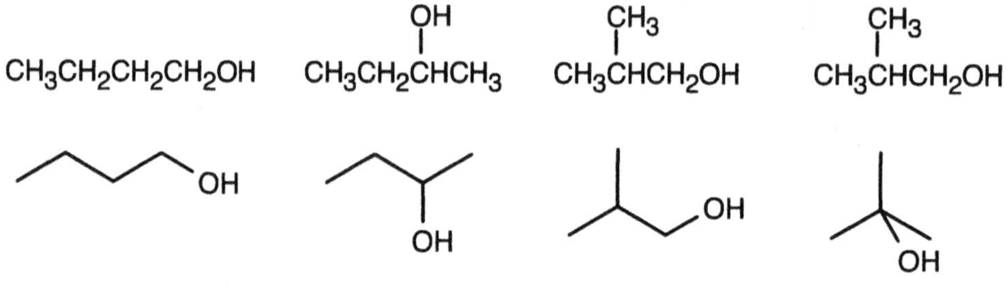

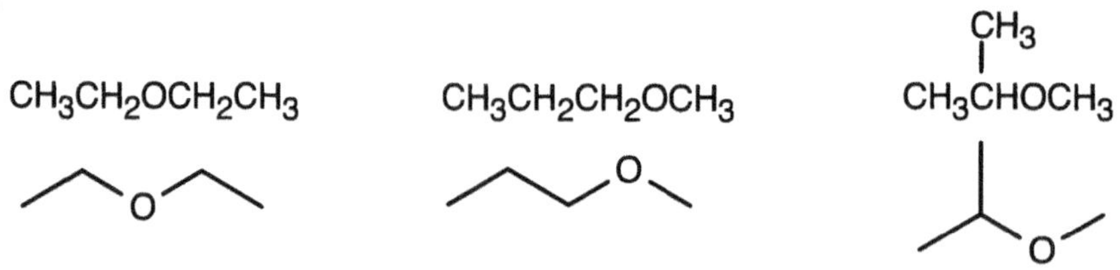

$CH_3CH_2CH_2OCH_3$

$$
\begin{array}{c}
CH_3 \\
| \\
CH_3CHOCH_3
\end{array}
$$

12.45 There are several possible answers to this question. For example,

(a)

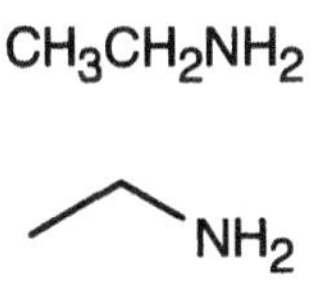

$CH_3CH_2NH_2$

(b)

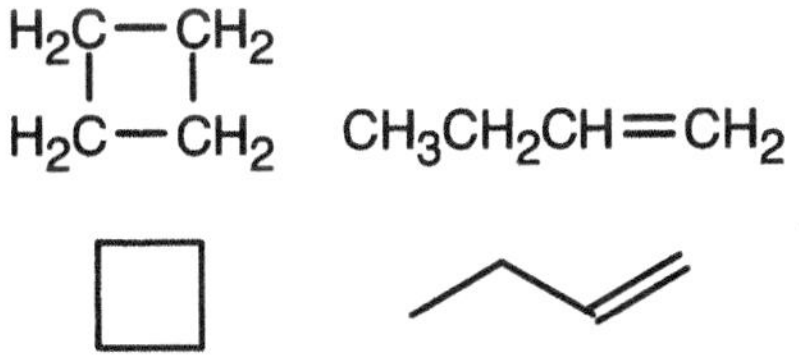

H_2C—CH_2
H_2C—CH_2 CH_3CH_2CH=CH_2

(c)

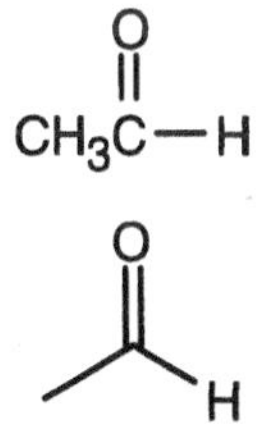

$CH_3\overset{\overset{O}{\|}}{C}$—$H$

(d)

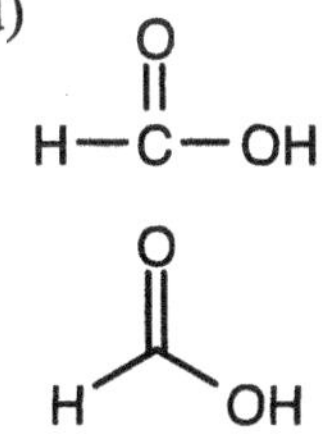

H—$\overset{\overset{O}{\|}}{C}$—$OH$

12.46

(a)

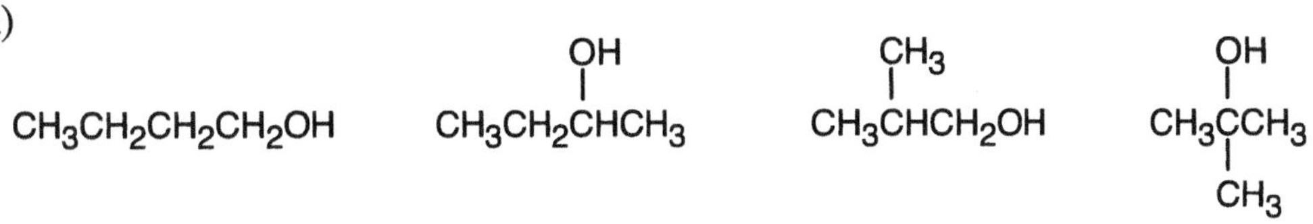

$CH_3CH_2CH_2CH_2OH$ $CH_3CH_2\overset{\overset{OH}{|}}{C}HCH_3$ $CH_3\overset{\overset{CH_3}{|}}{C}HCH_2OH$ $CH_3\overset{\overset{OH}{|}}{\underset{\underset{CH_3}{|}}{C}}CH_3$

(b)

$CH_3CH_2CH_2NH_2$ $CH_3\overset{\overset{NH_2}{|}}{C}HCH_3$ $CH_3CH_2\overset{\overset{H}{|}}{N}CH_3$ $CH_3\overset{\overset{CH_3}{|}}{N}CH_3$

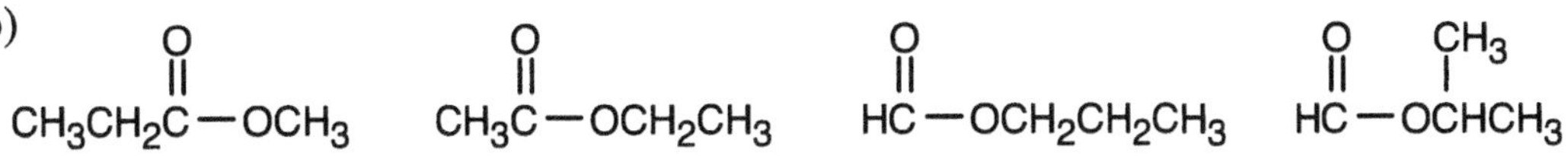

(c)

$CH_3CH_2CH_2\overset{\overset{O}{\|}}{C}CH_3$ $CH_3CH_2\overset{\overset{O}{\|}}{C}CH_2CH_3$ $CH_3\overset{\overset{O}{\|}}{C}H\underset{\underset{CH_3}{|}}{C}CH_3$

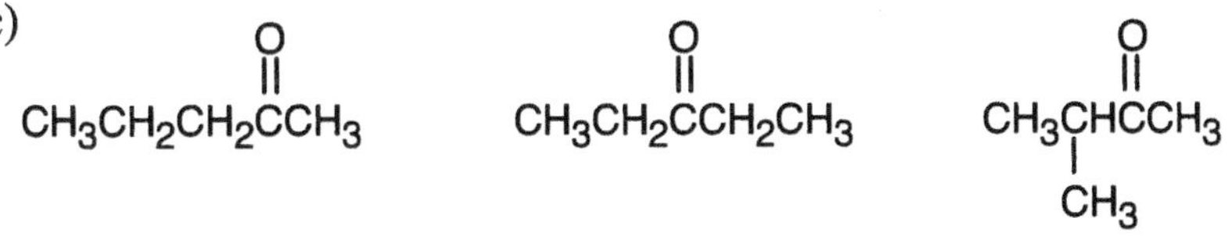

12.47

(a)

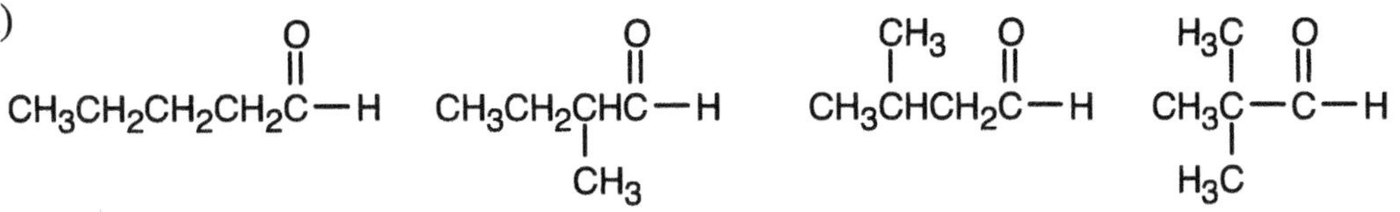

$CH_3CH_2CH_2CH_2\overset{\overset{O}{\|}}{C}$—$H$ $CH_3CH_2\overset{\overset{O}{\|}}{\underset{\underset{CH_3}{|}}{C}}H\overset{}{C}$—$H$ $CH_3\overset{\overset{CH_3}{|}}{C}HCH_2\overset{\overset{O}{\|}}{C}$—$H$ $CH_3\overset{\overset{H_3C}{|}}{\underset{\underset{H_3C}{|}}{C}}\overset{\overset{O}{\|}}{C}$—$H$

(b)

$CH_3CH_2\overset{\overset{O}{\|}}{C}$—$OCH_3$ $CH_3\overset{\overset{O}{\|}}{C}$—$OCH_2CH_3$ $HC\overset{\overset{O}{\|}}{}$—$OCH_2CH_2CH_3$ $HC\overset{\overset{O}{\|}}{}$—$O\overset{\overset{CH_3}{|}}{C}HCH_3$

(c)

$CH_3CH_2CH_2\overset{\overset{O}{\|}}{C}$—$OH$ $CH_3\overset{\overset{O}{\|}}{\underset{\underset{CH_3}{|}}{C}}H\overset{}{C}$—$OH$

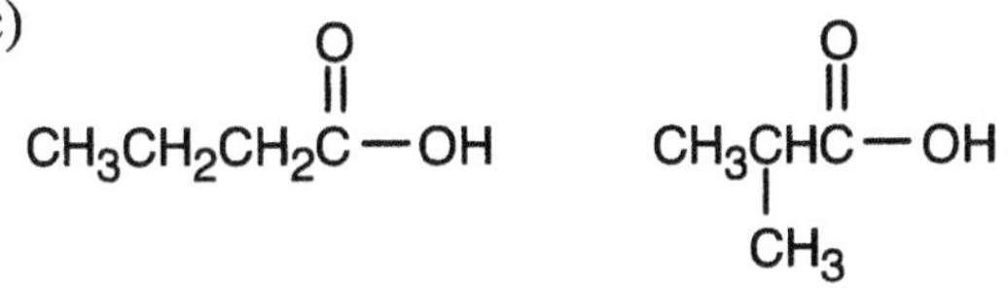

Remember that the C=O group of an aldehyde is found only at the end of a chain, and the C=O group of a ketone must occur in the middle.

12.48

(a)

CH$_3$CH$_2$CH$_3$ and   CH$_3$CH$_2$ are identical.
|
CH$_3$

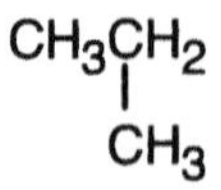

(b)

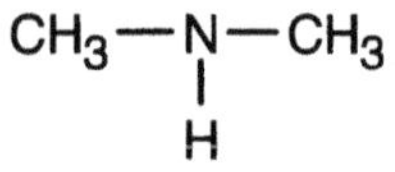

CH$_3$—N—CH$_3$ and   CH$_3$CH$_2$—N—H   are isomers.
| |
H   H

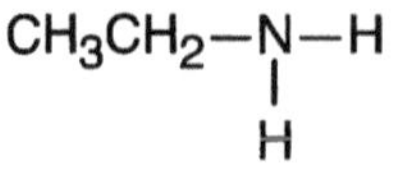

(c)

CH$_3$CH$_2$CH$_2$—O—CH$_3$ and   CH$_3$CH$_2$CH$_2$—C—CH$_3$ are unrelated.
(with O double-bonded to C)

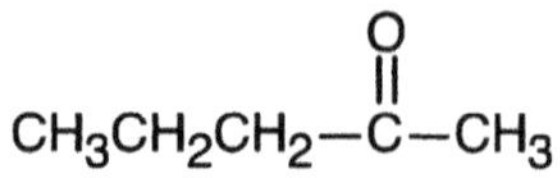

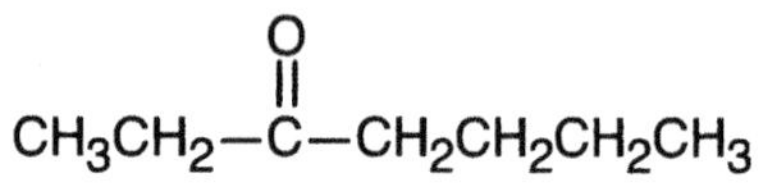

(d)

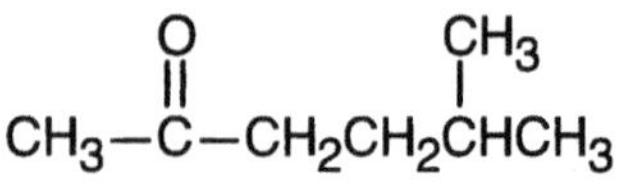

CH$_3$—C—CH$_2$CH$_2$CHCH$_3$ and   CH$_3$CH$_2$—C—CH$_2$CH$_2$CH$_2$CH$_3$ are isomers.
(left with O double bond on C and CH$_3$ branch; right with O double bond on C)

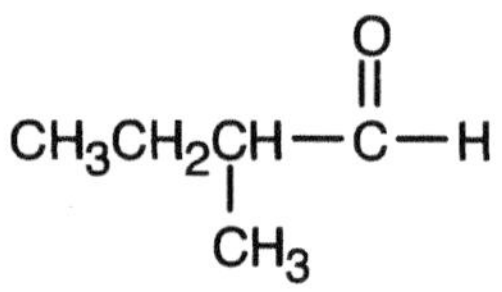

(e)

CH$_3$CH=CHCH$_2$CH$_2$—O—H   and   CH$_3$CH$_2$CH—C—H   are isomers.
(right with O double bond on C and CH$_3$ branch)

12.49

(a)

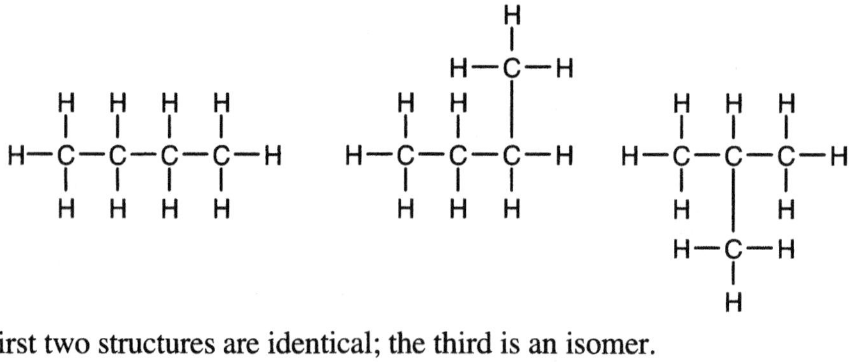

The first two structures are identical; the third is an isomer.

(b)

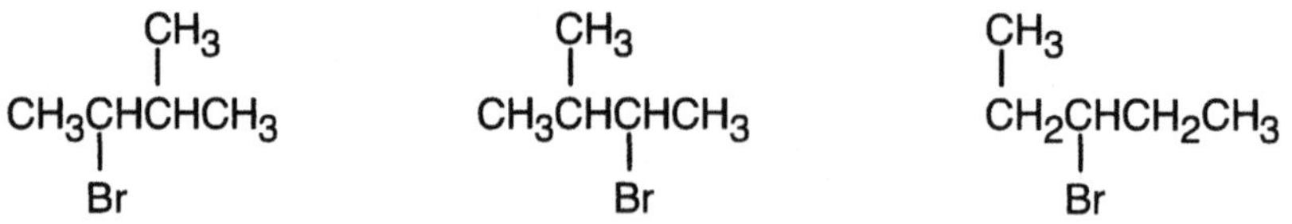

CH$_3$ CH$_3$ CH$_3$
| | |
CH$_3$CHCHCH$_3$ CH$_3$CHCHCH$_3$ CH$_2$CHCH$_2$CH$_3$
| | |
Br   Br   Br

The first two structures are identical; the third is an isomer.

(c)

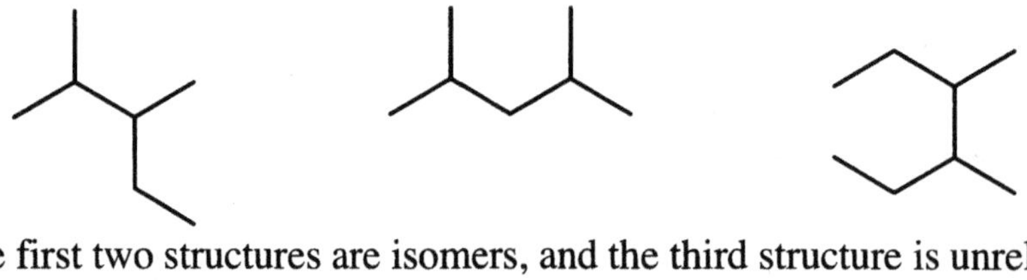

The first two structures are isomers, and the third structure is unrelated to them.

12.50 All three structures have a carbon atom with five bonds.

(a)

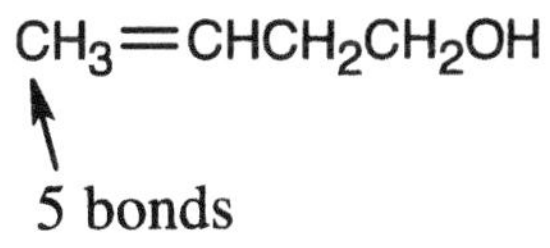
CH3=CHCH2CH2OH
5 bonds

(b)

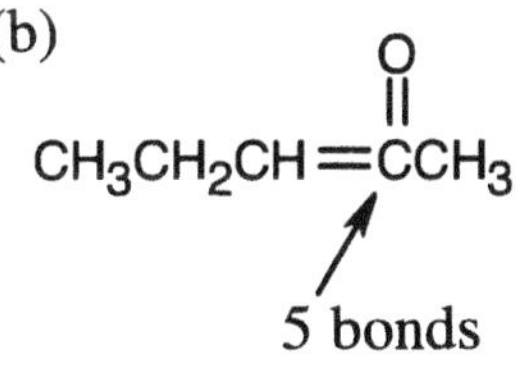
O
CH3CH2CH=CCH3
5 bonds

(c)

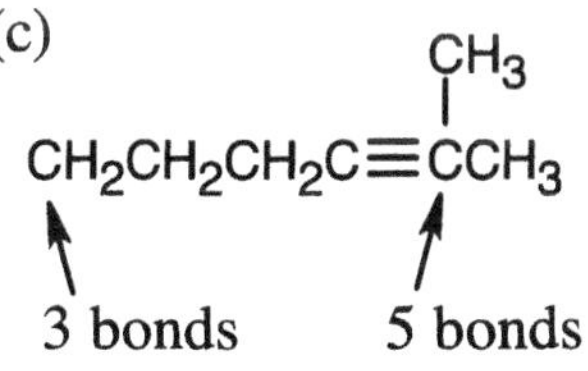
CH3
CH2CH2CH2C≡CCH3
3 bonds
5 bonds

12.51

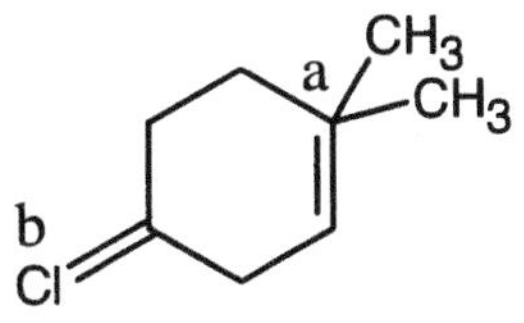
CH3
a
CH3
b
Cl

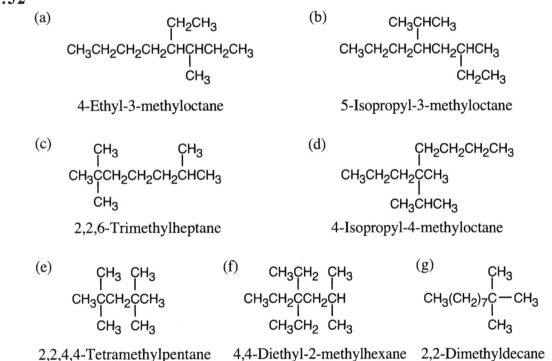

a. The carbon lettered "a" has five bonds.
b. The chlorine–carbon bond should be a single bond.

Alkane Nomenclature

12.52

(a)

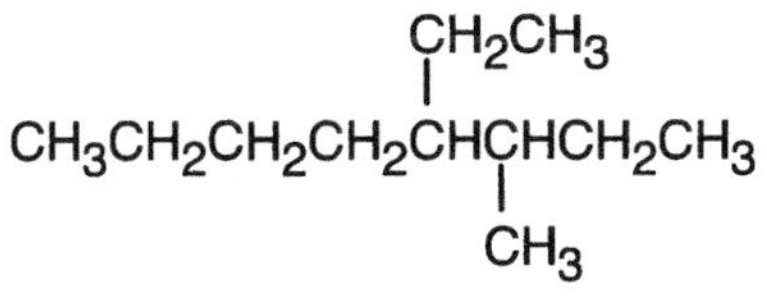

4-Ethyl-3-methyloctane

(b)

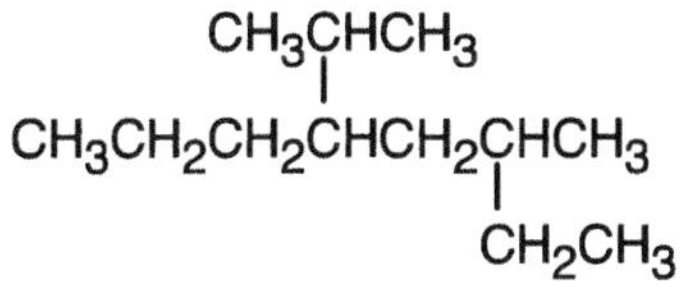

5-Isopropyl-3-methyloctane

(c)

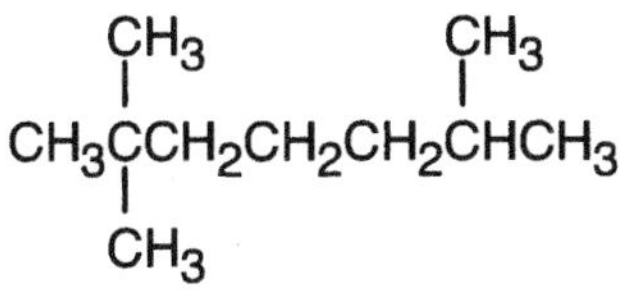

2,2,6-Trimethylheptane

(d)

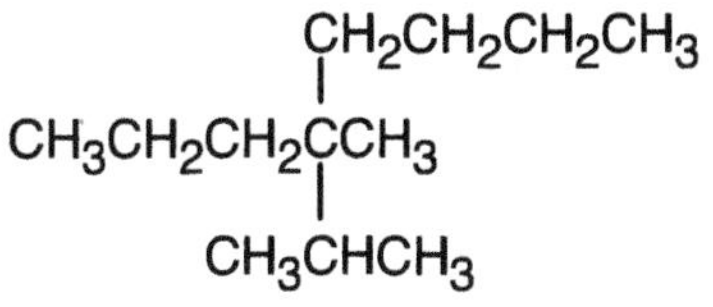

4-Isopropyl-4-methyloctane

(e)

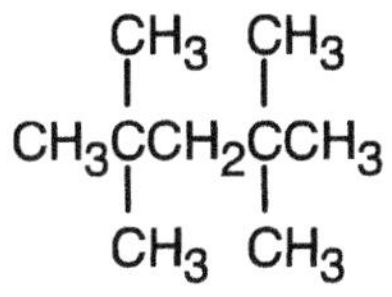

2,2,4,4-Tetramethylpentane

(f)

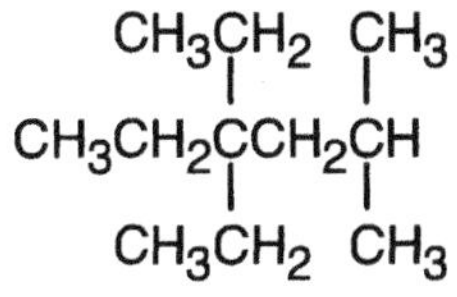

4,4-Diethyl-2-methylhexane

(g)

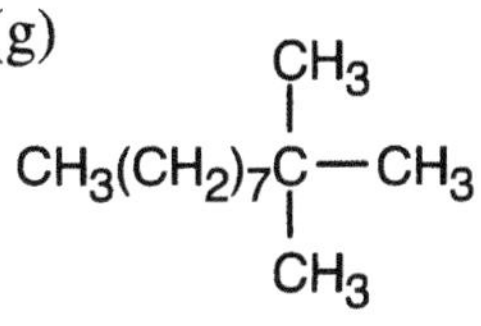

2,2-Dimethyldecane

12.53

CH₃CH₂CH₂CH₂CH₂CH₃
Hexane

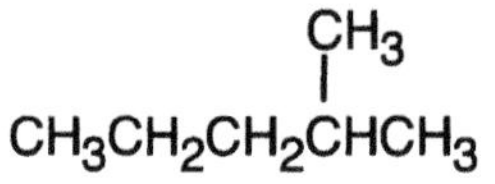

$$CH_3CH_2CH_2\overset{\overset{\displaystyle CH_3}{|}}{CH}CH_3$$
2-Methylpentane

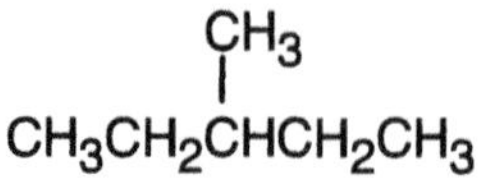

$$CH_3CH_2\overset{\overset{\displaystyle CH_3}{|}}{CH}CH_2CH_3$$
3-Methylpentane

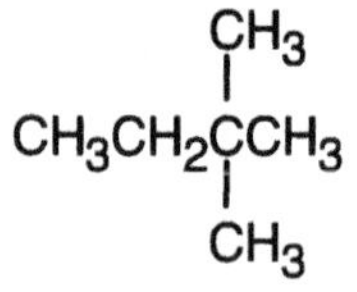

$$CH_3CH_2\overset{\overset{\displaystyle CH_3}{|}}{\underset{\underset{\displaystyle CH_3}{|}}{C}}CH_3$$
2,2-Dimethylbutane

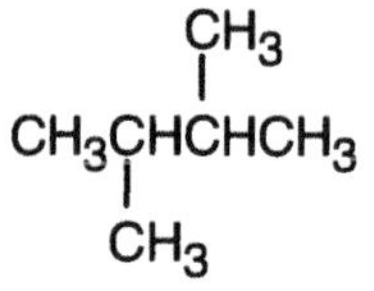

$$CH_3\overset{\overset{\displaystyle CH_3}{|}}{CH}\overset{\overset{\displaystyle CH_3}{|}}{CH}CH_3$$
2,3-Dimethylbutane

12.54

(a) 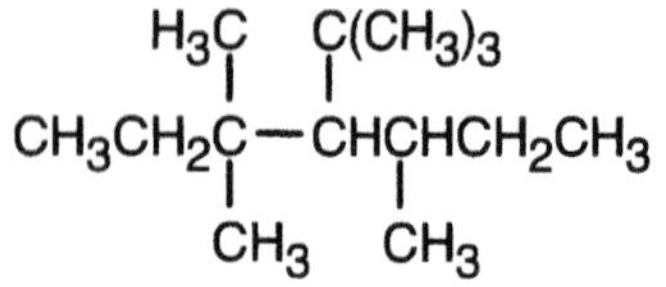
$$CH_3CH_2\overset{\overset{\displaystyle H_3C}{|}}{\underset{\underset{\displaystyle CH_3}{|}}{C}}{-}\overset{\overset{\displaystyle C(CH_3)_3}{|}}{CH}\overset{}{\underset{\underset{\displaystyle CH_3}{|}}{CH}}CH_2CH_3$$
4-*tert*-Butyl-3,3,5-trimethylheptane

(b) 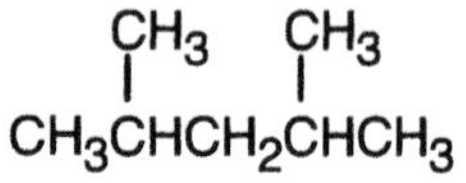
$$CH_3\overset{\overset{\displaystyle CH_3}{|}}{CH}CH_2\overset{\overset{\displaystyle CH_3}{|}}{CH}CH_3$$
2,4-Dimethylpentane

(c) 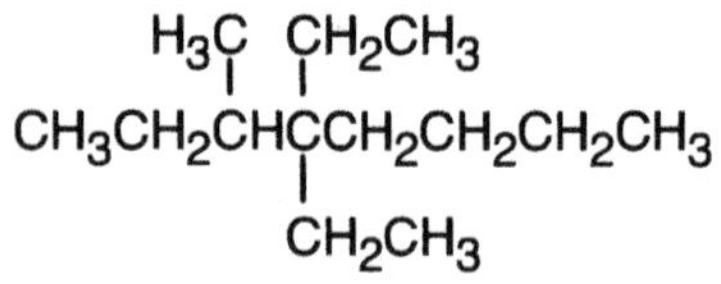
$$CH_3CH_2\overset{\overset{\displaystyle H_3C}{|}}{CH}\overset{\overset{\displaystyle CH_2CH_3}{|}}{\underset{\underset{\displaystyle CH_2CH_3}{|}}{C}}CH_2CH_2CH_2CH_3$$
4,4-Diethyl-3-methyloctane

(d) 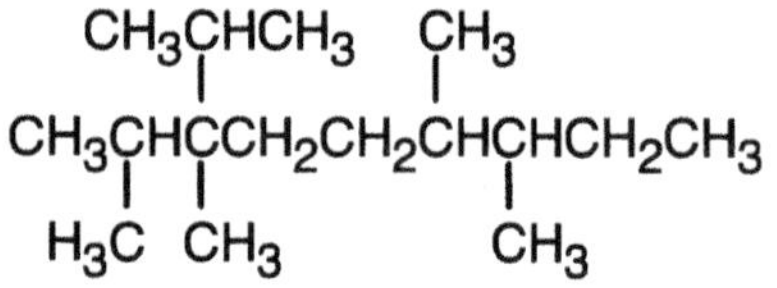
$$CH_3\overset{\overset{\displaystyle CH_3CHCH_3}{|}}{\underset{\underset{\displaystyle H_3C}{|}}{CH}}\overset{}{\underset{\underset{\displaystyle CH_3}{|}}{C}}CH_2CH_2\overset{\overset{\displaystyle CH_3}{|}}{CH}\overset{}{\underset{\underset{\displaystyle CH_3}{|}}{CH}}CH_2CH_3$$
3-Isopropyl-2,3,6,7-tetramethylnonane

(e)
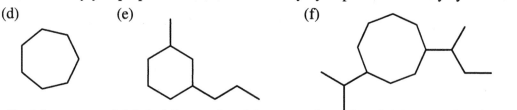

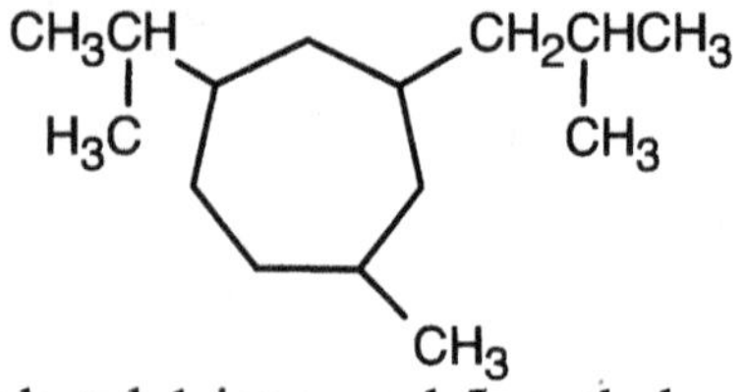

3-Isobutyl-1-isopropyl-5-methylcycloheptane

(f)

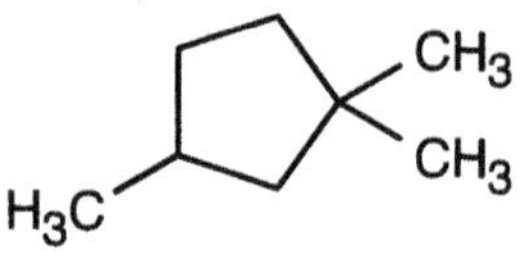

1,1,3-Trimethylcyclopentane

12.55

(a)

1,1-Dimethylclopropane

(b)

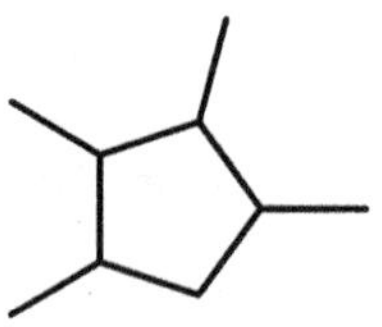

1,2,3,4-Tetramethylcyclopentane

(c)

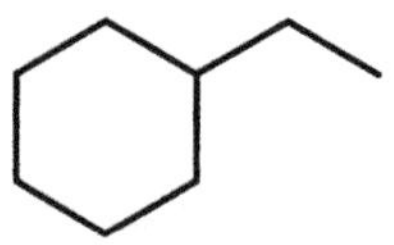

Ethylcyclohexane

(d)

Cycloheptane

(e)

1-Methyl-3-propylcyclohexane

(f)

1-*sec*-butyl-4-isopropylcyclooctane

12.56

(a)

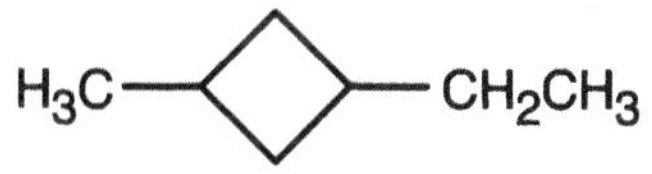

H3C
CH2CH3

1-Ethyl-3-methylcyclobutane

(b)

H3C
CH3
H3C
CH3

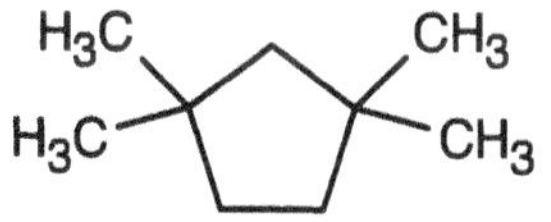

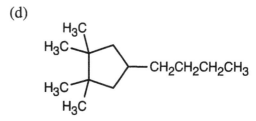

1,1,3,3-Tetramethylcyclopentane

(c)

CH2CH2CH3
CH2CH3

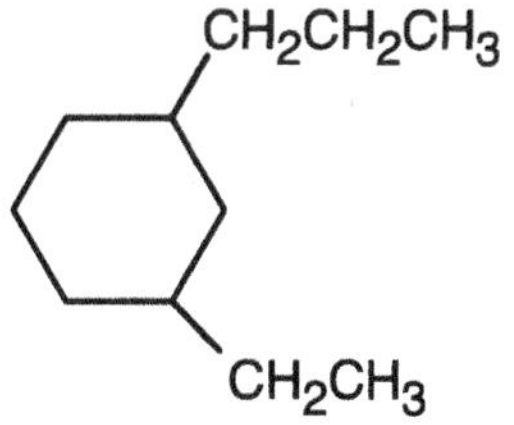

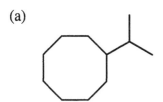

1-Ethyl 3-propylcyclohexane

(d)

H3C
H3C
CH2CH2CH2CH3
H3C
H3C

4-Butyl-1,1,2,2-tetramethylcyclopentane

12.57

(a)

Isopropylcyclooctane

(b)

CH2CH3
CH2CH3

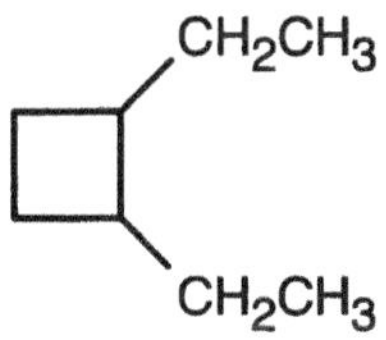

1,2-Diethylcyclobutane

(c)

H3C
CH3

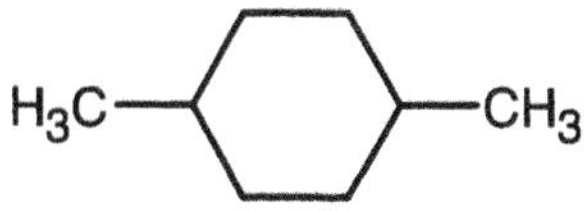

1,4-Dimethylcyclohexane

12.58 *Structure* *Error*

(a)

CH3
CH3CCH2CH2CH3
CH3

2,2-Dimethylpentane

The prefix *di-* must appear when two substituents are the same.

(b)

CH3 CH3
CH3CHCH2CHCH3

2,4-Dimethylpentane

You must choose the longest carbon chain as the parent name.

(c)

CH3
CH3CHCH2

Isobutylcyclobutane

This compound is an alkyl-substituted cycloalkane. Choose the cycloalkane as the parent name.

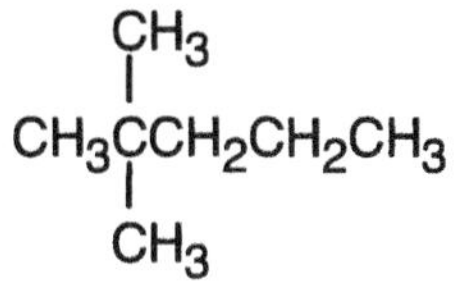

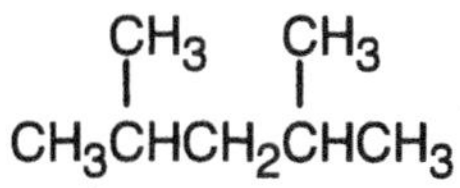

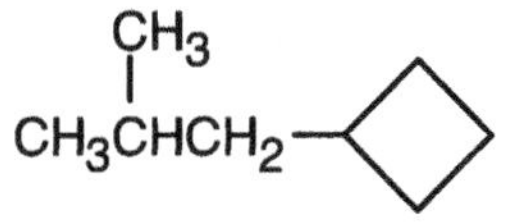

12.59

	Structure	*Error*

(a)

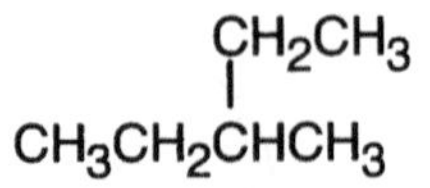

$$CH_2CH_3$$
$$|$$
$$CH_3CH_2CHCH_3$$

3-Methylpentane

The longest carbon chain is a pentane and should be used as the root name.

(b)

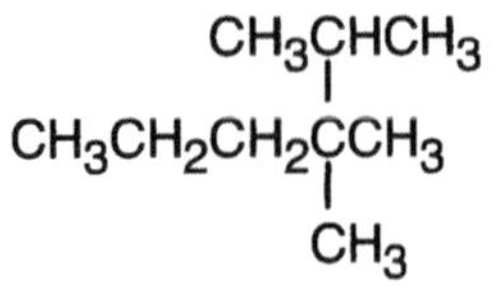

$$CH_3CHCH_3$$
$$|$$
$$CH_3CH_2CH_2CCH_3$$
$$|$$
$$CH_3$$

2,3,3-Trimethylhexane

The longest carbon chain is a hexane and should be used as the root name.

(c)

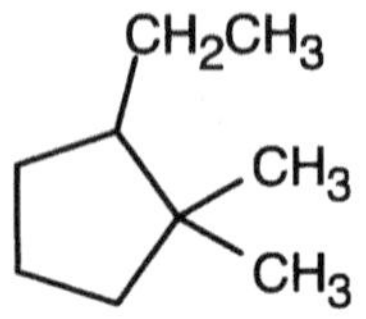

2-Ethyl-1,1-dimethylcyclopentane

The substituents should be given the lowest possible numbers. The prefix *di-* should be used when two substituents are the same.

(d)

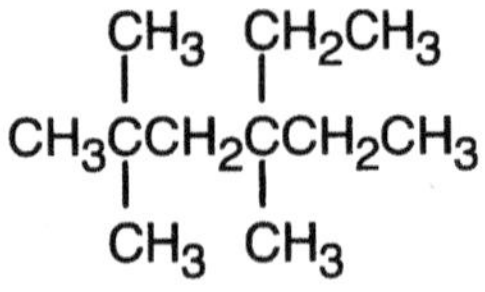

$$CH_3 \quad CH_2CH_3$$
$$| \qquad |$$
$$CH_3CCH_2CCH_2CH_3$$
$$| \qquad |$$
$$CH_3 \quad CH_3$$

4-Ethyl-2,2,4-trimethylhexane

Numbering must start from the end nearer the first substituent.

(e)

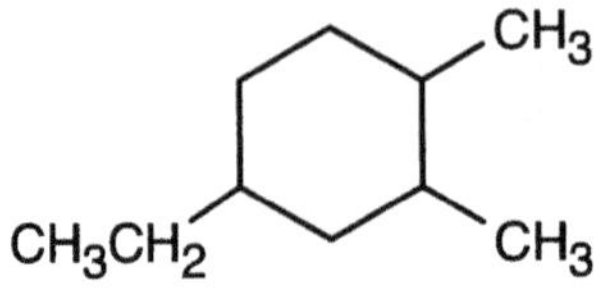

4-Ethyl-1,2-dimethylcyclohexane

Substituents must be cited in alphabetical order (prefixes are not used for alphabetizing).

(f)

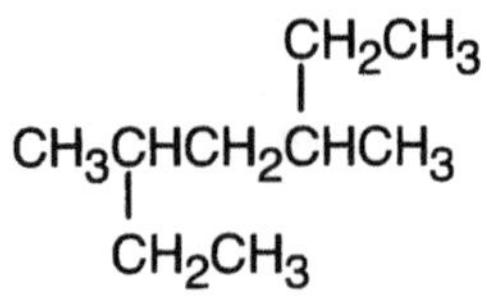

$$CH_2CH_3$$
$$|$$
$$CH_3CHCH_2CHCH_3$$
$$|$$
$$CH_2CH_3$$

3,5-Dimethylheptane

The longest carbon chain is a heptane and should be used as the root name.

(g)

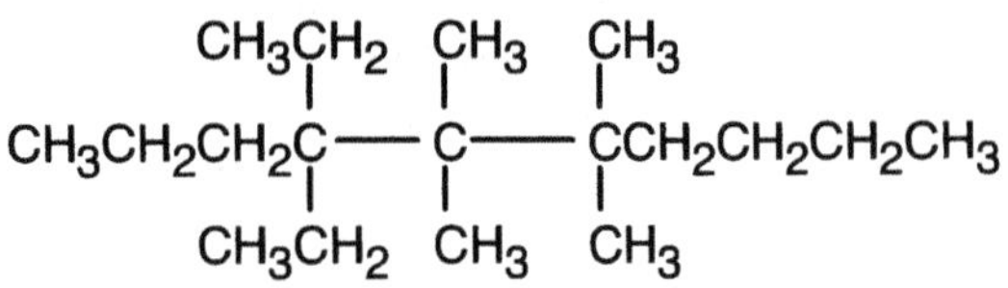

$$CH_3CH_2 \quad CH_3 \quad CH_3$$
$$| \qquad\quad | \qquad |$$
$$CH_3CH_2CH_2C{-}C{-}CCH_2CH_2CH_2CH_3$$
$$| \qquad\quad | \qquad |$$
$$CH_3CH_2 \quad CH_3 \quad CH_3$$

4,4-Diethyl-5,5,6,6-tetramethyldecane

The prefixes *tetra-* and *di-* must be included in the name. Substituents must be cited in alphabetical order. Numbering must start from the end nearer to the first substituent.

12.60

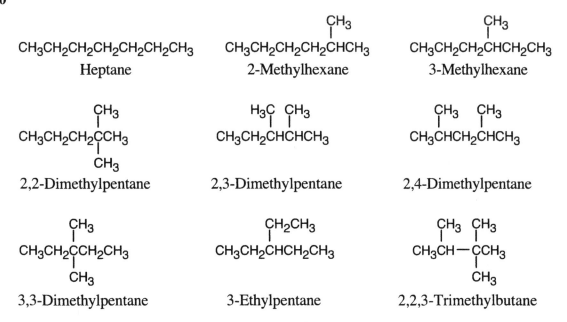

$$CH_3CH_2CH_2CH_2CH_2CH_3$$
Heptane

$$CH_3CH_2CH_2CH_2\overset{\overset{\displaystyle CH_3}{|}}{C}HCH_3$$
2-Methylhexane

$$CH_3CH_2CH_2\overset{\overset{\displaystyle CH_3}{|}}{C}HCH_2CH_3$$
3-Methylhexane

$$CH_3CH_2CH_2\overset{\overset{\displaystyle CH_3}{|}}{\underset{\underset{\displaystyle CH_3}{|}}{C}}CH_3$$
2,2-Dimethylpentane

$$CH_3CH_2\overset{\overset{\displaystyle H_3C}{|}}{C}H\overset{\overset{\displaystyle CH_3}{|}}{C}HCH_3$$
2,3-Dimethylpentane

$$CH_3\overset{\overset{\displaystyle CH_3}{|}}{C}HCH_2\overset{\overset{\displaystyle CH_3}{|}}{C}HCH_3$$
2,4-Dimethylpentane

$$CH_3CH_2\overset{\overset{\displaystyle CH_3}{|}}{\underset{\underset{\displaystyle CH_3}{|}}{C}}CH_2CH_3$$
3,3-Dimethylpentane

$$CH_3CH_2\overset{\overset{\displaystyle CH_2CH_3}{|}}{C}HCH_2CH_3$$
3-Ethylpentane

$$CH_3\overset{\overset{\displaystyle CH_3}{|}}{C}H-\overset{\overset{\displaystyle CH_3}{|}}{\underset{\underset{\displaystyle CH_3}{|}}{C}}CH_3$$
2,2,3-Trimethylbutane

12.61

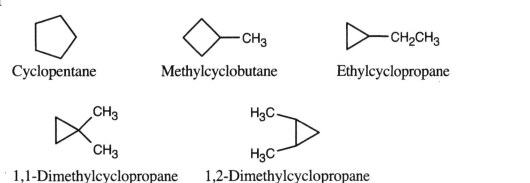

Cyclopentane

Methylcyclobutane

Ethylcyclopropane

1,1-Dimethylcyclopropane

1,2-Dimethylcyclopropane

Reactions of Alkanes

12.62

$$CH_3CH_2CH_3 + 5\ O_2 \longrightarrow 3\ CO_2 + 4\ H_2O$$

12.63

$$2\ C_8H_{18} + 25\ O_2 \longrightarrow 16\ CO_2 + 18\ H_2O$$

12.64

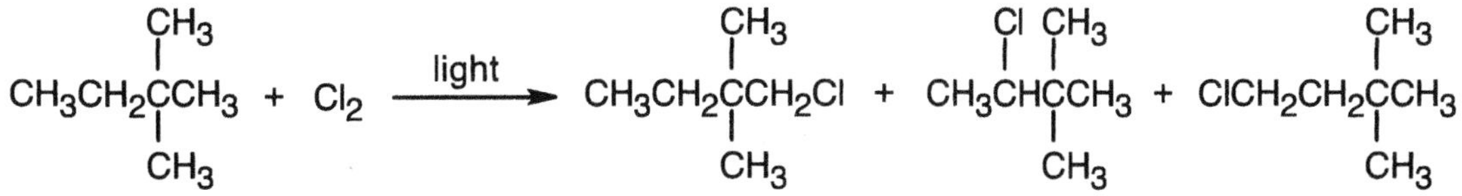

$$CH_3CH_2\overset{\overset{\displaystyle CH_3}{|}}{\underset{\underset{\displaystyle CH_3}{|}}{C}}CH_3 + Cl_2 \xrightarrow{light} CH_3CH_2\overset{\overset{\displaystyle CH_3}{|}}{\underset{\underset{\displaystyle CH_3}{|}}{C}}CH_2Cl + CH_3\overset{\overset{\displaystyle Cl}{|}}{C}H\overset{\overset{\displaystyle CH_3}{|}}{C}CH_3 + ClCH_2CH_2\overset{\overset{\displaystyle CH_3}{|}}{\underset{\underset{\displaystyle CH_3}{|}}{C}}CH_3$$

12.65

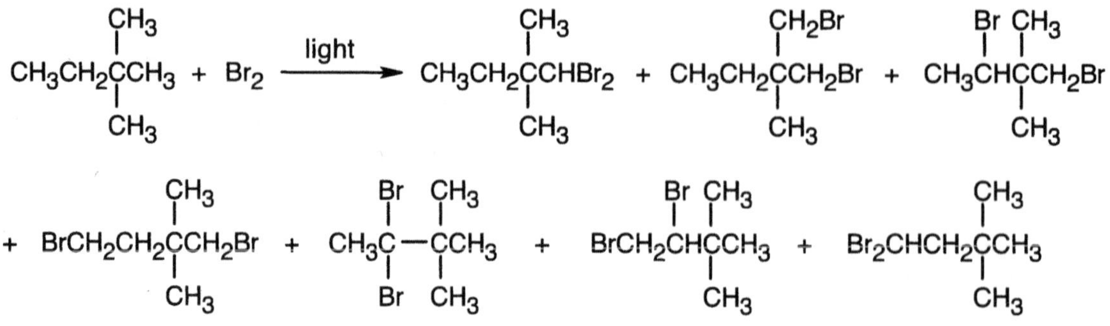

$$CH_3CH_2\underset{\underset{CH_3}{|}}{\overset{\overset{CH_3}{|}}{C}}CH_3 + Br_2 \xrightarrow{light} CH_3CH_2\underset{\underset{CH_3}{|}}{\overset{\overset{CH_3}{|}}{C}}CHBr_2 + CH_3CH_2\underset{\underset{CH_3}{|}}{\overset{\overset{CH_2Br}{|}}{C}}CH_2Br + CH_3\overset{\overset{Br}{|}}{C}H\overset{\overset{CH_3}{|}}{C}CH_2Br$$

$$+ \ BrCH_2CH_2\underset{\underset{CH_3}{|}}{\overset{\overset{CH_3}{|}}{C}}CH_2Br + CH_3\overset{\overset{Br}{|}}{\underset{\underset{Br}{|}}{C}}\overset{\overset{CH_3}{|}}{\underset{\underset{CH_3}{|}}{C}}CH_3 + BrCH_2\overset{\overset{Br}{|}}{C}H\overset{\overset{CH_3}{|}}{\underset{\underset{CH_3}{|}}{C}}CH_3 + Br_2CHCH_2\underset{\underset{CH_3}{|}}{\overset{\overset{CH_3}{|}}{C}}CH_3$$

General Questions and Problems

12.66

(a)

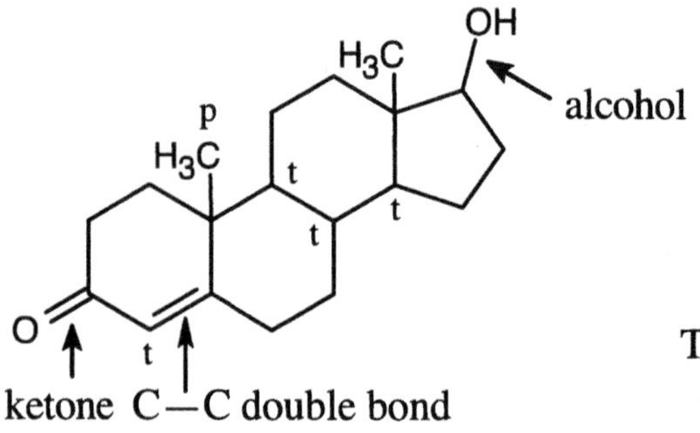

Testosterone

(b)

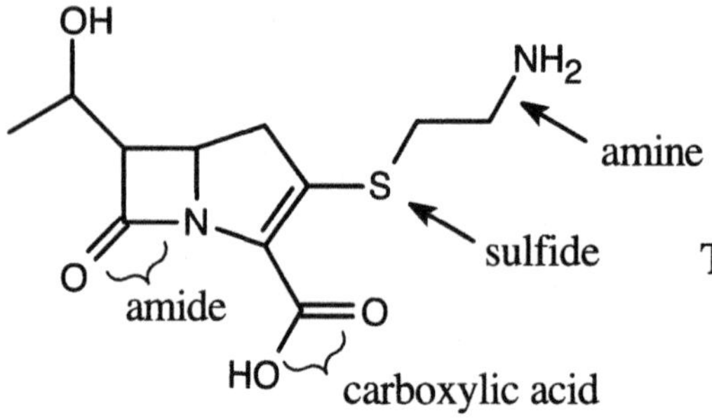

Thienamycin

12.67

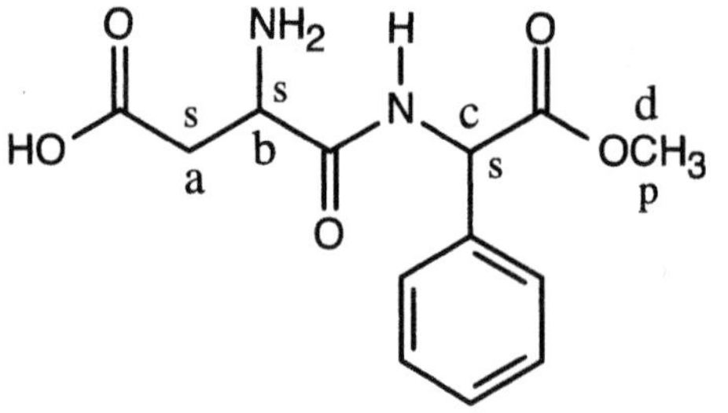

p = primary
s = secondary
t = tertiary
q = quaternary

12.68 Testosterone has 4 tertiary carbons, indicated on the structure shown in Problem 12.66(a).

12.69 Because carbon forms only four bonds, the largest number of hydrogens that can be bonded to three carbons is eight.

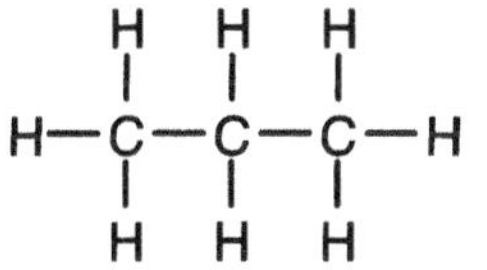

C_3H_8

12.70 Since "like dissolves like," lipstick, which is composed primarily of hydrocarbons, is more soluble in the hydrocarbon petroleum jelly than in water.

12.71

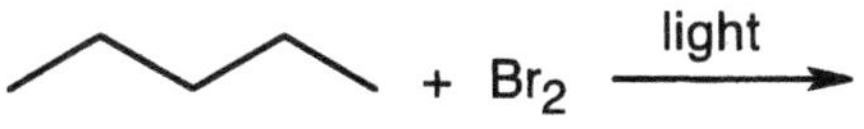

(a)

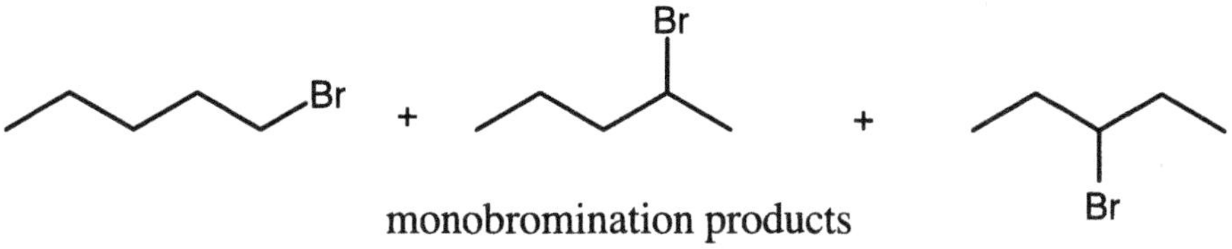

monobromination products

(b)

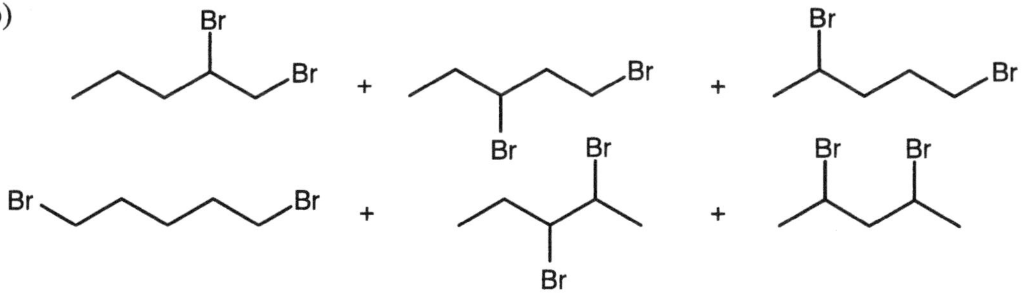

dibromination products

12.72 Pentane has a higher boiling point than neopentane because London forces, which must be overcome in boiling, are greater for linear than for more spherical or nonlinear compounds with the same number of carbons.

12.73 Other structures are also possible.

(a)

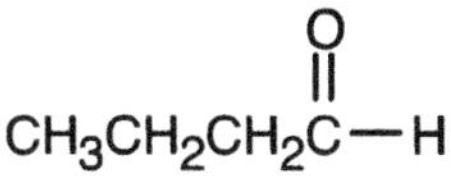

(b)

$CH_3CH_2CH=CHCH_2I$

(c)

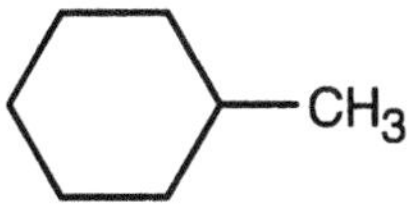

(d)

$CH_3CH=CHCH=CH_2$

Chemistry in Action

12.74 A chemical feedstock is a simple organic chemical used as the starting material in many organic reactions.

12.75 Synthetic rubber is more flexible and behaves better in extreme temperatures than natural rubber.

Mastering Reactions

12.76

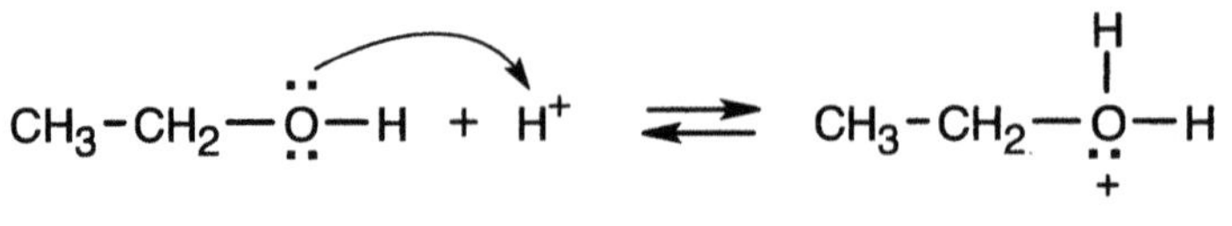

$$CH_3-CH_2-\overset{..}{\underset{..}{O}}-H \; + \; H^+ \; \rightleftharpoons \; CH_3-CH_2-\overset{\overset{\displaystyle H}{|}}{\underset{..}{\underset{+}{O}}}-H$$

12.77

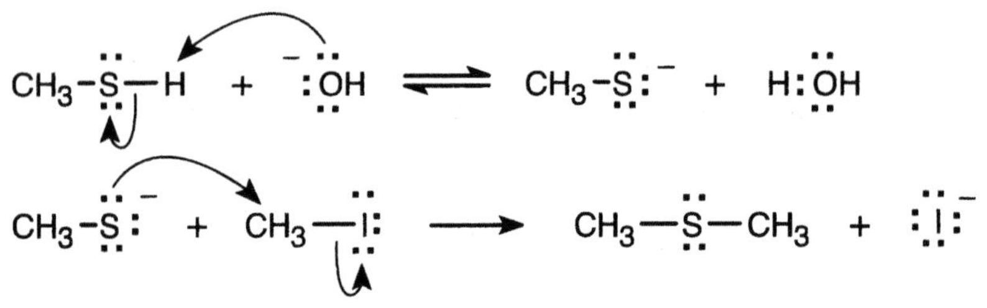

$$CH_3-\overset{..}{\underset{..}{S}}-H \; + \; \overset{-}{}\!:\!\overset{..}{O}H \; \rightleftharpoons \; CH_3-\overset{..}{\underset{..}{S}}\!:^- \; + \; H\!:\!\overset{..}{\underset{..}{O}}H$$

$$CH_3-\overset{..}{\underset{..}{S}}\!:^- \; + \; CH_3-\overset{..}{\underset{..}{I}}\!: \; \longrightarrow \; CH_3-\overset{..}{\underset{..}{S}}-CH_3 \; + \; :\!\overset{..}{\underset{..}{I}}\!:^-$$

Self-Test for Chapter 12

Multiple Choice

1. Which of the following functional groups doesn't contain a carbon–oxygen double bond?
   (a) ether   (b) aldehyde   (c) ketone   (d) ester

2. In which of the following alkanes are carbons not tetrahedral?
   (a) ethane   (b) propane   (c) cyclopropane   (d) cyclohexane

3. How many products can result from chlorination of ethane? (Include products with more than one chlorine.)
   (a) 2   (b) 4   (c) 6   (d) 9

4. How many branched-chain isomers of C_6H_{14} are there?
   (a) 2   (b) 3   (c) 4   (d) 5

5. Which of the following condensed structures doesn't represent a cycloalkane?
   (a) C_3H_6 (b) C_4H_{10} (c) C_5H_{10} (d) C_6H_{12}

6.

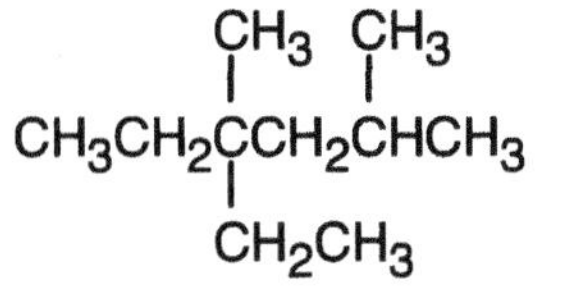

$$
\begin{array}{c}
\text{CH}_3 \quad \text{CH}_3 \\
| \qquad | \\
\text{CH}_3\text{CH}_2\text{CCH}_2\text{CHCH}_3 \\
| \\
\text{CH}_2\text{CH}_3
\end{array}
$$

   The correct name for the above structure is:
   (a) 3-ethyl-3,5-dimethylhexane   (b) 3-methyl-3-*sec*-butylpentane
   (c) 2,4-dimethyl-4-ethylhexane   (d) 4-ethyl-2,4-dimethylhexane

7. How many secondary carbons are in the structure shown in Problem 6?
   (a) 1   (b) 2   (c) 3   (d) 4

8. Which of the following structures is incorrectly drawn?

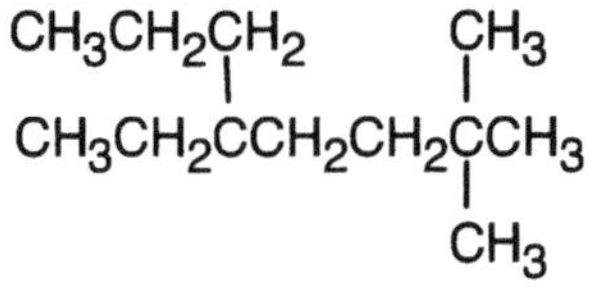

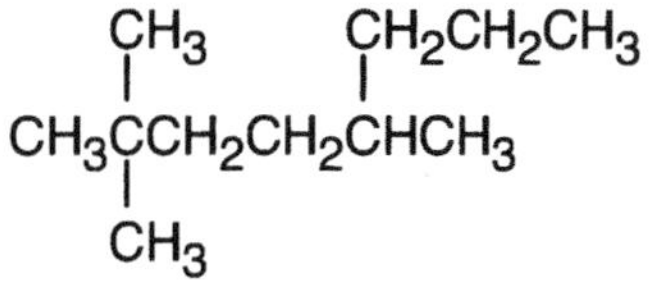

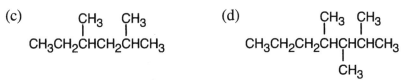

9. How many moles of O_2 are necessary for the complete combustion of one mole of C_6H_{12}?
   (a) 4   (b) 6   (c) 9   (d) 10

10. Which alkyl group has a quaternary carbon when part of a hydrocarbon?
    (a) *tert*-butyl   (b) isobutyl   (c) *sec*-butyl   (d) butyl

Sentence Completion

1. C_{20} to C_{36} alkanes are known as _____.

2.   Alkynes are compounds that contain _____ bonds.

3.   Alcohols and ethers are functional groups that contain _____.

4.   Mixtures of hydrocarbons can be separated by _____.

5.   A _____ _____ is a shorthand way of drawing a chemical structure.

6.   A _____ carbon is bonded to four other carbons.

7.   Organic compounds generally have _____ melting points than inorganic compounds.

8.   Cycloalkanes are compounds that contain carbon atoms joined in a _____.

9.   Organic molecules are named by the _____ system.

10.   Compounds with the same formula but different structures are called _____.

11.   _____ is the reaction of an alkane with oxygen.

12.   A straight-chain alkane is _____ boiling than a branched-chain alkane.

True or False

1.   Cyclohexane and hexane are isomers.

2.   A molecule with the formula C_5H_{12} can have the root name pentane, butane, or propane.

3.   A cyclohexane ring is flat.

4.   The correct name of the following alkane is 1,3-dimethylpentane.

$$\begin{array}{cc} CH_3 & CH_3 \\ | & | \\ \end{array}$$
$$CH_3CH_2CHCH_2CH_2$$

5.   The compound 2,3-dimethylbutane has only primary and tertiary carbons.

6.   Acyclic alkanes and cycloalkanes have similar chemical reactivity.

7.   The $C-Cl$ bond in CH_3Cl is ionic.

8.   The compound 1,4-dimethylcyclohexane is correctly named.

9.   Alkanes with one to four carbons exist as gases at room temperature.

10.   Compounds with many functional groups are more reactive than compounds with few functional groups.

11. 2-Methylpentane and 3-methylpentane have nearly identical boiling points.

12. At room temperature, an alkane exists in a single conformation.

Match each entry on the left with its partner on the right.

1. $RCH=O$ (a) Contains polar covalent bonds

2. C_5H_{12} (b) Butyl group

3. $CH_3CH(CH_3)_2$ (c) Ketone

4. $CH_3CH_2CH_2CH_3$ (d) Natural gas

5. $CH_3CH_2CH_2-$ (e) Formula of methylcyclobutane

6. $R_2C=O$ (f) Branched-chain alkane

7. CH_2Cl_2 (g) An alkene

8. $C_{30}H_{62}$ (h) Propyl group

9. C_5H_{10} (i) Aldehyde

10. $CH_3CH_2CH_2CH_2-$ (j) Formula of 2-methylbutane

11. $CH_3CH=CH_2$ (k) A solid

12. CH_4 (l) Straight-chain alkane

Functional Groups of Importance in Biochemical Molecules

Functional Group	Structure	Type of Biomolecule
Amino group	$-NH_3^+,\ -NH_2$	Alkaloids and neurotransmitters; amino acids and proteins (Sections 15.1, 15.3, 15.6, 18.3, 18.7, 28.6)
Hydroxyl group	$-OH$	Monosaccharides (carbohydrates) and glycerol: a component of triacylglycerols (lipids) (Sections 17.4, 21.4, 23.2)
Carbonyl group	$-\overset{\displaystyle O}{\overset{\|}{C}}-$	Monosaccharides (carbohydrates); in acetyl group (CH_3CO) used to transfer carbon atoms during catabolism (Sections 16.1, 17.4, 20.4, 20.8, 21.4)
Carboxyl group	$-\overset{\displaystyle O}{\overset{\|}{C}}-OH,\ -\overset{\displaystyle O}{\overset{\|}{C}}-O^-$	Amino acids, proteins, and fatty acids (lipids) (Sections 17.1, 18.3, 18.7, 23.2)
Amide group	$-\overset{\displaystyle O}{\overset{\|}{C}}-N-$	Links amino acids in proteins; formed by reaction of amino group and carboxyl group (Sections 17.1, 17.4, 18.7)
Carboxylic acid ester	$-\overset{\displaystyle O}{\overset{\|}{C}}-O-R$	Triacylglycerols (and other lipids); formed by reaction of carboxyl group and hydroxyl group (Sections 17.1, 17.4, 23.2)
Phosphates: mono-, di-, tri-	$-\overset{\|}{\underset{\|}{C}}-O-\overset{\displaystyle O}{\underset{\displaystyle O^-}{\overset{\|}{P}}}-O^-$ $-\overset{\|}{\underset{\|}{C}}-O-\overset{\displaystyle O}{\underset{\displaystyle O^-}{\overset{\|}{P}}}-O-\overset{\displaystyle O}{\underset{\displaystyle O^-}{\overset{\|}{P}}}-O^-$ $-\overset{\|}{\underset{\|}{C}}-O-\overset{\displaystyle O}{\underset{\displaystyle O^-}{\overset{\|}{P}}}-O-\overset{\displaystyle O}{\underset{\displaystyle O^-}{\overset{\|}{P}}}-O-\overset{\displaystyle O}{\underset{\displaystyle O^-}{\overset{\|}{P}}}-O^-$	ATP and many metabolism intermediates (Sections 17.8, 20.5, and throughout metabolism sections)
Hemiacetal group	$-\overset{\displaystyle OR}{\underset{\displaystyle OR}{\overset{\|}{C}}}-OH$	Cyclic forms of monosaccharides; formed by a reaction of carbonyl group with hydroxyl group (Sections 16.7, 21.4)
Acetal group	$-\overset{\displaystyle \|}{\underset{\displaystyle OR}{C}}-OR$	Connects monosaccharides in disaccharides and larger carbohydrates; formed by reaction of carbonyl group with hydroxyl group (Sections 16.7, 21.7, 21.9)
Thiols	$-SH$	Found in amino acids cysteine, methionine; structural components of proteins (Sections 14.9, 18.3, 18.8, 18.10)
Sulfides	$-S-$	
Disulfides	$-S-S-$	

The San Francisco
Bay Area

MEL SCOTT

The San Francisco Bay Area

A METROPOLIS IN PERSPECTIVE

UNIVERSITY OF CALIFORNIA PRESS

BERKELEY AND LOS ANGELES   1959

UNIVERSITY OF CALIFORNIA PRESS
BERKELEY AND LOS ANGELES

CAMBRIDGE UNIVERSITY PRESS
LONDON, ENGLAND

© COPYRIGHT, 1959, BY
THE REGENTS OF THE UNIVERSITY OF CALIFORNIA

LIBRARY OF CONGRESS CATALOG CARD NUMBER: 59-12537

PRINTED IN THE UNITED STATES OF AMERICA

To Gerrie

Preface

Perhaps it is fitting that the preface to a book which views the San Francisco Bay Area in the perspective of its one hundred and ninety years of growth and its numberless years of future development should be written in Venice, a city whose history spans more than fifteen hundred years and whose legend, ever renewed by the enduring evidence of its great glory, promises to fire the imaginations of men for still more centuries. By comparison with the city at the head of the Adriatic, the urban complex surrounding San Francisco Bay is only in its infancy; yet almost from the beginning it, too, has enjoyed a legendary fame and is known throughout the world as a place of especial beauty and fascinating history. The contemplation of the past, present, and future of the San Francisco Bay Area amid the splendors of Venice cannot but make one wonder whether the people of the Bay Area, in their eagerness to build new skyscrapers, freeways, and subdivisions and to rebuild older districts that have become blighted, will be able to achieve, in the decades and centuries ahead, a civic magnificence comparable, in a wholly different society, to that of Venice at the peak of its power. For Venice is, as Catherine Bauer says, "still the greatest civic show on earth"—the product of intense pride in one's mother city, and of passionate loyalty to its people and its institutions. Hardly another city in the world can equal it as an expression of the devotion of a people to their local culture.

To be great in the same way that Venice is great, the San Francisco Bay Area must now and in the future have residents who identify themselves with their metropolitan regional environment as closely as generations of Venetians have with theirs. In the slowly unwinding centuries of the past, when men traveled by sail and on horseback, when knowledge of the world and its wonders and problems had not so far increased as to overawe the most brilliant mind, perhaps it was easy for the citizens of Venice to concentrate their energies on the enrichment and ennoblement of their city, and to do so with a singleness of purpose not possible for the citizens of any present-day metropolis. And yet if American metropolitan communities are to become worthy of the love of their citizens, something of the unifying purpose that inspired the Venetians must be applied in their development. In the San Francisco Bay Area, as well as in every other metropolitan region, great or small, there must be a vision of magnificent possibilities, for no country has greater material resources for civic accomplishment than ours.

Vision is, however, the growth of time. It comes from decades of shared experiences; and in metropolitan regions which are continually adding new residents to their populations the development of common goals becomes a problem in itself. Moreover, in our age, when the swift augmentation of the means of attaining goals causes relatively rapid shifts in the goals themselves, consensus becomes all the more difficult. Should we conclude, then, that it is well-nigh impossible for the people of the metropolitan region to agree on what that region can become and to work toward a common goal? To accept such a conclusion would be to deny the capacity of Americans in general and Californians in particular for dealing with the formidable but invigorating challenges of their times.

There has been no lack of vision among the business and professional men, scholars, and political leaders of the San Francisco Bay Area. Even a superficial investigation of official records, city and county histories, newspaper files, and planning reports would convince anyone that the most perceptive residents of the Bay cities and counties have shared a conception of the area as a galaxy of interdependent communities. And from this view of the area as an organization of interrelated communities has sprung a remarkable variety of proposals for federating it politically; for linking its cities with highways, transportation systems, and utilities; and for providing it with a system of regional parks. That the proposals have sometimes been in conflict and have even created enmities between communities does not detract from their essential significance: all have emphasized the underlying unity of the San Francisco Bay Area. But this conception of the area as a single entity has never been assimilated by the whole population of the area. The vision of the few has never become the goal of the many. Indeed, most residents of the area have remained ignorant of the proposals that have been made from time to time for establishing area-wide services and facilities.

The development of a shared vision of the possibilities of the San Francisco Bay Area surely must begin with the dissemination of knowledge of the way in which that area has become a metropolitan regional community. And in telling the story of that evolution it is especially important to emphasize that the more thoughtful or daring men of the area have time and again suggested that it be organized physically, socially, or politically as a single urban region. If history demonstrates anything, it demonstrates that great achievement, civic or national, is possible only when all elements of a society are conscious of a common heritage and enjoy the prospects of individual benefit in a future to which all contribute. I have addressed myself to the problem of presenting the common heritage—a rich store of ideas for the development of the metropolitan region—because no one else has attempted to document the way in which the growth of the San Francisco Bay Area has inspired, for more than half a century or perhaps even longer, plans and proposals for welding it into a cohesive urban community. Ever since the 'seventies and 'eighties of the last century, authors have been producing histories of the cities and counties of the Bay Area. Only two works, one published in 1892 and the other in the 1920's, have dealt with the area as a geographical entity, and these have done so only sketchily. A study of the growth and development of the entire area has therefore long been needed. Although this volume provides much of the detail that a reader may wish to have, it is by no means a definitive work. Much else can and should be done by others to increase knowledge of the common heritage, so that in time there will be established among the people of the San Francisco Bay Area a metropolitan regional fealty.

I am grateful to Professor T. J. Kent, Jr., former chairman of the Department of City and Regional Planning on the Berkeley campus of the University of California, to Professor H. L. Vaughan, chairman of the Department of Landscape Architecture, and to Dean William Wurster of the College of Architecture for sponsoring the study on which this work is based. Thanks to their interest, the Columbia Foundation generously provided a grant to finance the initial work on the study. Throughout the period of research and during the many years that the writing of this book was in progress Professor Kent served as counselor, critic, and "fan." His encouragement was invaluable.

My other colleagues in the Department of City and Regional Planning—Francis Violich, chairman, Donald L. Foley, Melvin Webber, and Catherine Bauer—have also offered welcome criticism, all the more appreciated in view of the busy lives they lead.

For much of the research material required in the preparation of the manuscript and for the greater part of the graphic work on the handsome maps showing the historical development of the San Francisco Bay Area I wish to thank Charles Richard Dunann. David Arbegast has earned my deepest gratitude for completing these maps during my absence in Europe; and I am grateful to Stephen King for helping him on technical matters.

Those who graciously assisted by providing information for some of the maps include Jacob N. Bowman, H. L. McMasters, J. A. Bennyhoff, and Professors Robert F. Heizer, John B. Leighly, Perry Byerly, and the late Professor George D. Louderback. A formal expression of indebtedness can scarcely repay them for their contributions.

So many persons have participated in the development of the text by providing information or giving their critical judgment on certain sections that I fear to list names lest I inadvertently fail to include those of some to whom I am indebted. I plead a poor memory if there are regrettable omissions. I recall appreciatively the aid of Professor John Bollens, Helen Giffen, Guy Wilfrid Hayler, Russel Van Nest Black, Fred E. Reed, the late Frederick Law Olmsted, Laura Wood Roper, John Reber, Paul Oppermann, James McCarthy, Robert Williams, Norman Lind, Corwin Mocine, George A. Scott, R. C. Kennedy, John S. Carpenter, and William Stokes.

The staff of the Bancroft Library deserve special thanks for their assistance in making available the resources of that treasury of historic lore; the following were at all times helpful in suggesting sources of material: Dr. George P. Hammond, the late Eleanor Bancroft, John Barr Tompkins, Julia H. Macleod, Helen H. Bretnor, Robert H. Becker, and Richard F. Bernard. Anne H. Reed, head of the newspaper room in the University Library, also cheerfully aided me in ferreting out needed information.

I gratefully acknowledge permission to make direct quotations from several published works. The board of governors of the Commonwealth Club of California authorized my use of many passages from the *Transactions* of the club. Charles Scribner's Sons permitted me to quote a sentence about the San Francisco Civic Center from Christopher Tunnard's *The City of Man*. The University of Chicago Press consented to my using a paragraph from the second edition of Robert A. Walker's *The Planning Function in Urban Government;* and the Houghton Mifflin Company and MacAllaster Moore were glad to let me make use of various parts of Charles Moore's *Daniel H. Burnham, Architect, Planner of Cities*. Ida Belle Hegemann was pleased that I wished to quote extensively from her husband's *Report on a City Plan for the Municipalities of Oakland and Berkeley*.

In addition to members of the faculty of the Department of City and Regional Planning, several other persons whose judgment I value read and commented on parts of the book. I appreciate counsel from Bruce Bliven, Henry Fagin, Nathan Glazer, William Doebele, Holway Jones, and Professors Josephine Miles, Victor Jones, George Belknap, and Walton Bean.

To August Frugé, Director of the University of California Press, and Lucie E. N. Dobbie, Executive Editor, my thanks for their patience in awaiting completion of the final manuscript and for many kindnesses during the process of publication. My gratitude to my editor, Dorothy Huggins, cannot adequately be expressed in words. No writer, I am sure, ever had a more helpful or more capable editor. I am grateful, indeed, to John B. Goetz, who also gave me much valuable advice and help with the illustrative materials.

Venice, November 29, 1958   MEL SCOTT

Contents

The San Francisco
Bay Area

CHAPTER ONE

Heritage

Imagine, if you can, the San Francisco Bay Area without the bay. Geologists tell us that there was a time, fifteen to twenty-five thousand years ago, when the vast area now occupied by the bay was a long coastal valley. To the northeast a deep canyon connected this valley with the Central Valley, and through this canyon, which is now Carquinez Strait, flowed a great trunk river, carrying the runoff of the entire interior of California.

As the mighty current emerged from the canyon, it swung westward toward the Marin hills, passed through the narrow part of the valley now submerged beneath the waters of San Pablo Strait, curved southward round a hill known today as Angel Island, and finally flowed through the precipitous walls of Golden Gate Canyon into the Pacific Ocean. The depth of this river may have been as much as thirty feet.

Somewhere near the hill that we call Angel Island another river joined this one. A smaller stream, it coursed through the southern part of the elongated valley, collecting the runoff from what is now the Santa Clara Valley and from the slopes and mountains that enclose the southern arm of present San Francisco Bay.

Exactly what caused the inundation of the long trough valley by the waters of the Pacific no one knows. Drowned valleys can be produced by depression or subsidence of the land. But a theory now rather widely accepted attributes the formation of San Francisco Bay to the rise of the ocean level from the melting of the great ice sheet of the last glacial period. As the waters crept through the gorge at the mouth of the trunk river, they gradually covered not only the coastal valley but also a low area east of Carquinez Canyon, filled today by Suisun Bay. In all, more than four hundred and fifty square miles of valley lands disappeared beneath the invading flood.

How different the metropolitan scene would now be if the waters of the Pacific Ocean had remained outside the Golden Gate! The center of the valley, between Angel Island and Yerba Buena Island and about opposite the end of the abandoned Berkeley Pier, might be the heart of an enormous metropolis, discernible from the distant hills as a cluster of skyscrapers. And in the shadows of these tall buildings ships might be loading at docks along the trunk river. To the north, to the south, to the east, and to the west the metropolis would cover mile after square mile of the valley, its pattern of streets broken here and there by the hills we see as islands—Alcatraz, Angel, Yerba Buena, Brooks, and many smaller islands. But the mosaic of blocks and structures would be recognizably a single urban form. Even though it might be divided politically into many municipalities, as is the sprawling urban complex of the Los Angeles basin, its underlying physical unity would be apparent to the dullest eye.

Because a bay now fills the valley, many residents of the San Francisco Bay Area are scarcely aware that they live in what is essentially a single metropolis. The bay splits the urban pattern into several parts, and there is not one center but two: San Francisco on the west side of the bay and Oakland on the east side. Yet the cities, some eighty in all, are so interdependent, economically and socially, and the problems they face—air pollution, vanishing open space, bay pollution, inadequate transit, uncoördinated planning—are so pervasive that the oneness of the area cannot be denied. Smog respects no city and county boundaries, and the people in six of the nine counties bordering on the bay have already acknowledged that they must deal with it collectively. The air pollution control district they formed in 1955 does not yet include the three northern counties of the Bay Area (Sonoma, Napa, and Solano); but some political scientists regard this district, which has on its governing board representatives of both cities and counties, as the beginning of metropolitan government. Perhaps it is only a matter of time until population growth and mounting problems will force recognition of the actual regional city or regional metropolis. And when that time comes, undoubtedly the voters of the regional metropolis will devise some appropriate form of metropolitan government.

In the meantime, the cities only occasionally act in concert. The jealousies and rivalries of more than a century of urban growth and development in the San Francisco Bay Area plague them. The bay at times seems a sinister element, encouraging competition between ports, political bickering over the location of additional bridges, and endless arguments over whether industries discharging wastes into its waters are being properly regulated. Yet the bay is also a unifying force. The people who live around its shore are one in their pride in its universally attested magnificence. It is an incomparable harbor, a huge recreation area for fishermen and yachtsmen, the one great open space that will never be entirely lost to metropolitan dwellers, no matter how many tideland reclamation projects reduce the area of its surface.

The history of the regional metropolis encircling this great bay is a paradoxical one, in which, as in a kind of morality play, the forces of division struggle with the forces of unity. One can understand the present difficulties in solving area-wide problems only if he knows this complex history. One can take hope only if he sees what has already been accomplished. Physically the area is well on the way toward integration. The principal problems now are political, not technical. History is not lacking in suggestions for solving them. Even an account dealing primarily with the physical growth and development of the Bay Area, as this one does, must accord the prophets of metropolitan planning and metropolitan federation special notice, in the hope that their dreams will come true.

The First Inhabitants

The story of man's occupancy of this area begins, of course, with the Indians. Each of the various tribes living in what is now the San Francisco Bay Area had its roughly defined territory. The Costanoans inhabited the San Francisco Peninsula and most of present-day Santa Clara, Alameda, and Contra Costa counties. The Coast Miwok occupied the Marin Peninsula and the southern part of Sonoma County. The Pomo held the upper part of Sonoma County and the territory to the north. The Wappo regarded themselves as having proprietary rights to the Napa Valley. Solano and Yolo counties were the home of the southern Wintun. The Yokuts dwelt in eastern Contra Costa County and San Joaquin County. Natural barriers such as mountain ranges and the bay thus tended to define the areas belonging to each tribe, although the divisions of territory were not exactly what one might expect from a study of the topography. The pattern of Indian occupancy does suggest, however, that any human beings living in the Bay Area would be inclined to think of it as being composed of several divisions. And certainly the Europeans and Americans who none too gradually ousted the Indians after their thirty-five hundred years or more of occupancy did tend to think of it in this way, even though they recognized an over-all unity in the area.

Confused Explorers

The discoverers of San Francisco Bay, Don Gaspar de Portolá and his band of some sixty soldiers, priests, Christian Indians, muleteers, and servants, at first thought of their find as an immense estuary that blocked their way to the only Bay of San Francisco that they had heard of, the little bay near Point Reyes now known as Drakes Bay which had been given the name *Bahia de San Francisco* by the mariner Sebastian Rodríguez Cermeño in 1595. Joseph González Cabrera Bueno, pilot of one of the Manila galleons that annually made the perilous voyage from the Philippines to Acapulco, had described this small bay in some detail in a book on navigation published in Madrid in 1734, and this description the members of the Portolá expedition had with them.

The entire episode of discovery is one of confusion compounded by confusion. In the first place, Portolá and his followers were not trying to reach any Bay of San Francisco but to rediscover the port of Monterey, which the seventeenth-century adventurer Sebastian Vizcaíno had visited in 1602 and had extolled as a superlative haven—exactly the place for the richly laden Manila galleons to take on fresh water and supplies after months of beating across the north Pacific. For more than one hundred and sixty-five years Spain had not bothered to follow up Vizcaíno's explorations by colonizing Alta California or by making provision for a refreshing break

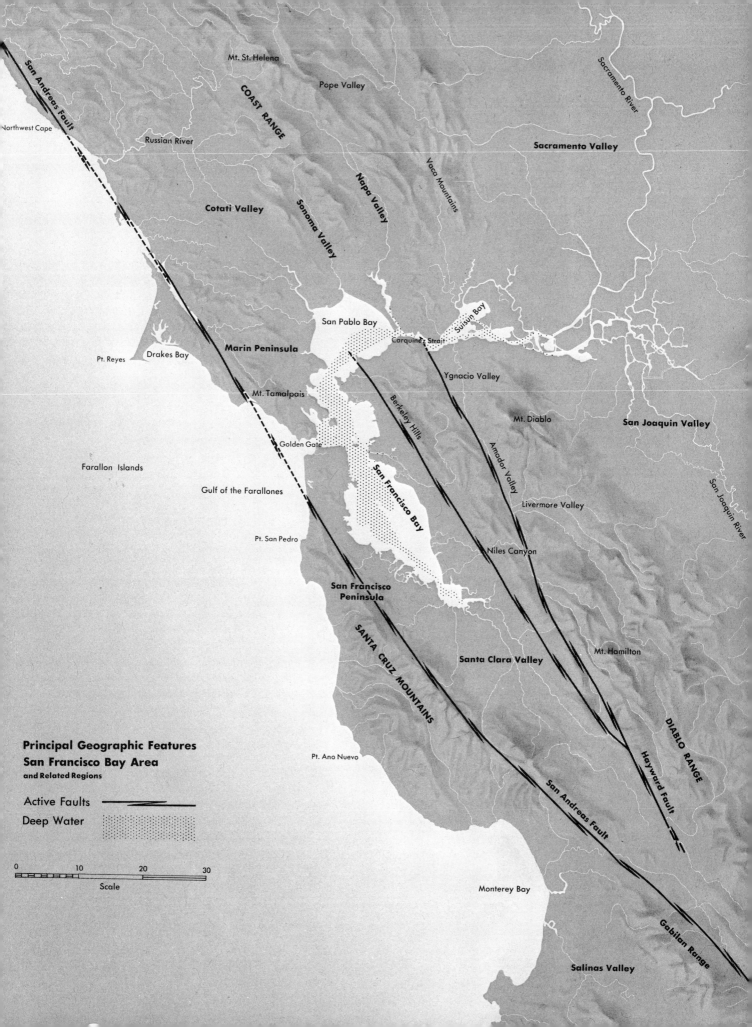

**Principal Geographic Features
San Francisco Bay Area
and Related Regions**

Active Faults

Deep Water

0   10   20   30
Scale

San Andreas Fault

Northwest Cape

Russian River

Mt. St. Helena

Pope Valley

COAST RANGE

Napa Valley

Vaca Mountains

Sacramento River

Sacramento Valley

Cotati Valley

Sonoma Valley

Pt. Reyes

Drakes Bay

Marin Peninsula

San Pablo Bay

Carquinez Strait

Suisun Bay

Ygnacio Valley

Mt. Tamalpais

Berkeley Hills

Mt. Diablo

San Joaquin Valley

Golden Gate

San Francisco Bay

Amador Valley

Farallon Islands

Gulf of the Farallones

San Francisco Peninsula

Livermore Valley

Niles Canyon

San Joaquin River

Pt. San Pedro

SANTA CRUZ MOUNTAINS

Santa Clara Valley

Mt. Hamilton

DIABLO RANGE

Pt. Ano Nuevo

Hayward Fault

San Andreas Fault

Monterey Bay

Gabilan Range

Salinas Valley

in the tedious journeys of the galleons at Monterey. But in 1769 uneasiness over possible Russian interest in this most remote of lands to which Spain claimed sovereignty moved Charles III to approve a program for its occupation. Marching wearily north from the first settlement at San Diego, Portolá and his followers reached Monterey Bay near the mouth of the Salinas River. Failing to recognize any of the landmarks mentioned in Vizcaíno's account of the area, the captain and his men pressed on up the coast, still searching for the long-lost port.

They were far up the San Francisco Peninsula when they found their progress arrested by the great bulk of Montara Mountain. Dispirited, half-starved, and soaked by an early rain, they decided to camp beside a creek near the base of the mountain. The next day, October 31, 1769, was fair, and the sea sparkled as they climbed a westward flank of the mountain to survey the coast ahead. To the west were several small islands. Forty miles to the north a long headland jutted into the sea. Not far from it rose some white cliffs. From the maps of Vizcaíno and from the description of Cabrera Bueno they at length recognized the headland as Point Reyes, the islands as the Farallones, and the flashing waters before them as the Gulf of the Farallones. They now knew that they had passed Monterey, but Portolá decided that he would not turn back without making a reconnaissance of Point Reyes and Cermeño's Bahia de San Francisco.

This is the little bay in which Francis Drake is believed to have reconditioned the *Golden Hind* in 1579 before sailing across the Pacific on his celebrated piratical voyage round the world. Thirty-seven years before Drake's visit, the explorer Juan Rodríguez Cabrillo, the first European to chart the coast of California, had noted the harbor but had been unable to land there because of a storm. He had sailed on southward past the Golden Gate without realizing that an enormous anchorage lay behind the hills. Cermeño, a Portuguese commissioned by the Viceroy of New Spain to make a search for safe ports on the California coast where the Manila galleons could allow their scurvy-ridden crews to recuperate, brought his *San Agustín* to anchor under the headland of Point Reyes sixteen years after Drake's sojourn on the coast. Cermeño's ship, carrying a fabulous cargo of silk, wax, porcelain, and spices, was totally wrecked by a sudden storm. Fortunately the crew had already put ashore a launch, more or less dismantled, on which they were working when the vessel foundered. In this craft, the *San Buenaventura*, they had intended to make careful explorations close to shore. Had they done so, they might have come upon the entrance to the great body of water now known as San Francisco Bay. But in their anxiety to return to Mexico before the winter grew worse, they provisioned the launch as best they could, headed toward the Farallones, and made their way down the coast, having given the small bay in the lee of Point Reyes the name that was to confuse historians and later explorers, among them Portolá.

Discovery of the Bay

In the faint hope that a packet named the *San José*, dispatched from San Blas in Mexico with supplies for the Alta California colonists, might by some remote chance be awaiting him in this little harbor, Portolá ordered Sergeant José Francisco de Ortega and some scouts to proceed to Point Reyes and return within three days. They set out after Mass on Wednesday morning, November 1, following the coast.

Portolá remembered what the Visitor General of New Spain, José de Gálvez, had promised Father Junípero Serra when the two were discussing plans for the first three missions that the Franciscan was to establish in Alta California. In reply to Serra's hurt remonstrance that none of the three was to be named for St. Francis, Gálvez had remarked: "If St. Francis wants a mission, let him cause his port to be discovered, and it will be placed there."[1] Should Ortega reach the Bahia de San Francisco, Gálvez would have no choice but to authorize the president of the missions to build an establishment on its shore dedicated to Francis of Assisi.

The day after Ortega departed, some of the soldiers in the camp begged permission to go into the near-by mountains to hunt for deer. Returning after dark, they reported having seen from the crest of the Santa Cruz Mountains "an immense arm of the sea, or an estuary, which penetrated into the land as far as the eye could reach, extending to the southeast."[2]

Puzzled, Father Juan Crespi, one of the two priests in the expedition, consulted the description of the Bahia de San Francisco by Cabrera Bueno and concluded that the waters seen by the hunters must be the estuary mentioned as leading inland from the main bay under Point Reyes. There is such an inner bay, known today as Drakes Estero.

Toward evening on Friday, November 3, Ortega and his scouts returned to the base camp on San Pedro Creek, bringing some extraordinary news. They had found their route along the coast intercepted by an immense "estuary" that penetrated far inland and branched to the north and to the south. Indians they met in their march had signified, they thought, that there was a port or a ship at the head of the *estero*.

The band of hunters and Ortega's group had both

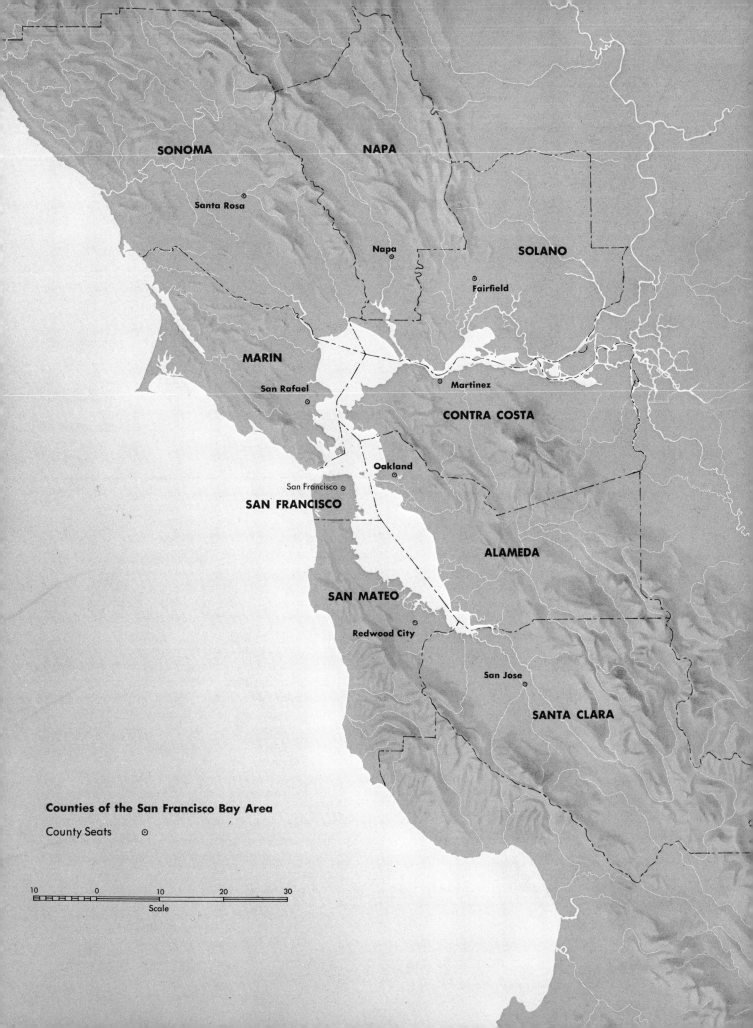

SONOMA

NAPA

Santa Rosa ⊙

Napa ⊙

SOLANO

Fairfield ⊙

MARIN

San Rafael ⊙

Martinez ⊙

CONTRA COSTA

Oakland ⊙

San Francisco ⊙

SAN FRANCISCO

ALAMEDA

SAN MATEO

Redwood City ⊙

San Jose ⊙

SANTA CLARA

Counties of the San Francisco Bay Area

County Seats   ⊙

10   0   10   20   30

Scale

discovered the greatest natural harbor on the Pacific Coast, but the import of the discovery entirely escaped them at the moment. The expedition was single-mindedly intent on reaching the bay near Point Reyes. This meant that they had to circumvent the *estero*.

Discouragement and Retreat

Portolá and the whole force crossed the mountains on the east, traveled southeastward through the San Andreas Valley, and on November 6 camped on San Francisquito Creek near the future site of Stanford University. The captain then began to doubt the wisdom of proceeding round the southern arm of the *estero* without knowing more about what to expect. He again sent out Ortega and his scouts, who turned the southern end of the bay and journeyed northward "eight or ten leagues" before being forced by hostile Indians to retrace their steps. Ortega's estimate that the *estero* "extended inland more than eighteen leagues"[3] (47.64 miles) indicates that he arrived at some point from which he could see the full length of the bay; but Portolá bitterly wrote in his diary that his scouts "had found nothing."[4]

The captain and his men had concluded, in their confusion, that Cabrera Bueno's description of the Bahia de San Francisco applied to the whole open Gulf of the Farallones and that the newly discovered great bay was the diminutive estuary today known as Drakes Estero. This misunderstanding was to continue for some years, until the unique nature of the new-found bay was realized and it ceased to be an *estero* and became instead the *Gran Puerto de San Francisco*, or San Francisco Bay.

The wanderers returned to San Diego, pausing en route at Monterey a second time without identifying it as the object of their search. Their unintended explorations north of that point had accomplished much more than Portolá appreciated. The expedition had raised the curtain on an area that within six or seven decades was increasingly to become the focus of the expansionist ambitions of the nation that was about to be formed on the east coast of America—the United States. An early consequence of the discovery of San Francisco Bay was to be the founding of a mission named for St. Francis and the establishment of a presidio, or military outpost. But since Portolá had not actually reached the supposed port of St. Francis, he left that task to others, thereby setting the stage for further discoveries.

Discovery of Interior Valleys

Young Pedro Fages, who succeeded Portolá as governor of Alta California, was the next to attempt to bypass San Francisco Bay on the east in order to reach Cermeño's Bahia de San Francisco. In the fall of 1770, some months after Monterey Bay had finally been rediscovered, Fages blazed a new trail to the San Francisco Bay Area through the Salinas and Santa Clara valleys. From the southern tip of the bay he made his way along the *contra costa*, or eastern side, through the sites of the present-day cities of Oakland, Berkeley, and Richmond. But when scouts who had been sent ahead reported that the *estero* continued indefinitely, he decided to turn back, for he feared to be too long away from Monterey and his regular responsibilities.

In the spring of 1772 Fages returned to the Bay Area with official instructions to explore the "Port of San Francisco"—that is, what is now called Drakes Bay— and look for a suitable site for a mission. Accompanied by Father Juan Crespi and a small company of soldiers, he again marched through the Salinas and Santa Clara valleys, along the route that was to become the regular line of travel between the provincial capital at Monterey and Bay Area settlements. As before, he proceeded up the eastern side of San Francisco Bay. He saw the Farallones through the Golden Gate from the slopes of the Berkeley Hills and continued northward along San Pablo Bay. Still following the shoreline, he swung eastward along Carquinez Strait and Suisin Bay until marshlands forced him inland to Willow Pass, in the hills between present-day Concord and Pittsburg. From the summit of the pass an amazing prospect greeted him and his companions—the vast interior valley of California and the snow-crowned Sierra far in the distance. Flowing into Suisun Bay from the east was the broad San Joaquin River, which Fages christened the *Rio Grande de San Francisco*. To the north he could also see the Sacramento River. In the vicinity of present-day Antioch, Fages concluded that there was no possibility of getting across or around the waters and marshes at the eastern end of Suisun Bay. He turned back, having discovered an inland domain so extensive and seemingly so remote that both Spain and Mexico were to leave it largely untouched during their years of rule in California.

On the return to Monterey the explorers opened another new route, later to be much used by gold seekers hurrying from Monterey and San Jose to Carquinez Strait and the river routes to the Mother Lode country. Moving southward, Fages and his men followed a series of valleys on the eastern side of the Berkeley Hills. They traversed in succession the Ygnacio, San Ramon, Livermore, and Sunol valleys until they came to Niles Canyon and marched west. As they passed through these warm, pleasant vales, Mount Diablo was on their left, a lonely peak only a little more than thirty-eight hundred feet high

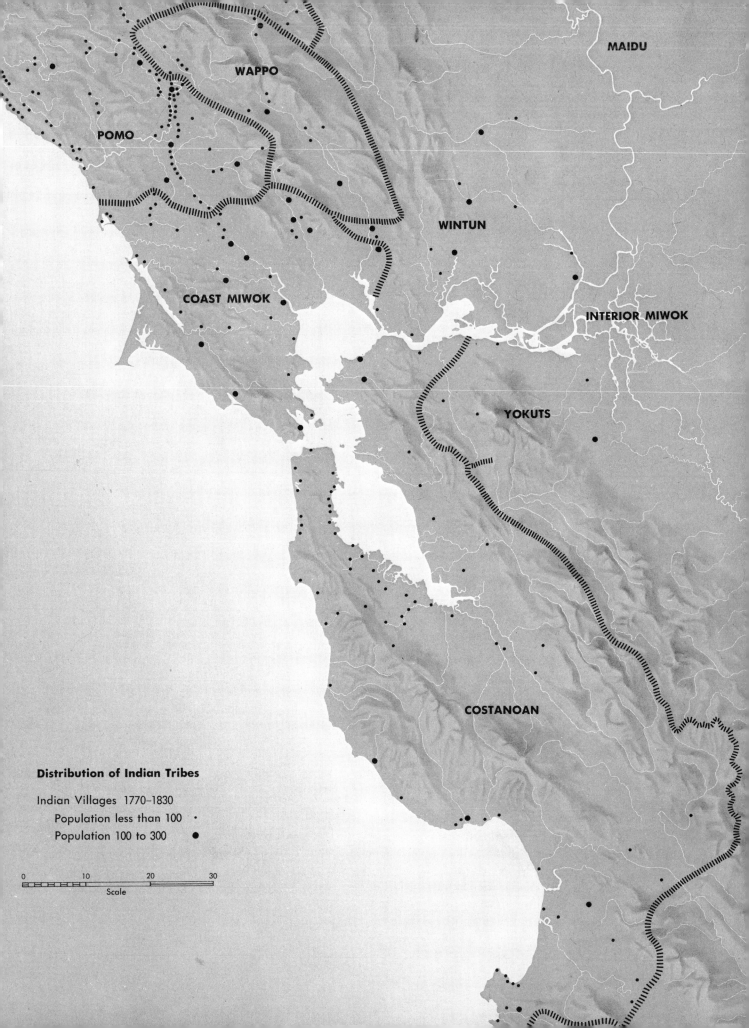

MAIDU

WAPPO

POMO

WINTUN

COAST MIWOK

INTERIOR MIWOK

YOKUTS

COSTANOAN

Distribution of Indian Tribes

Indian Villages 1770–1830

Population less than 100 ·

Population 100 to 300 ●

0   10   20   30

Scale

but with a majesty belying its actual height. From its summit the governor and his soldiers could have surveyed the entire Bay Area and the greater part of the Central Valley. Perhaps they wondered how much one could see from this serene landmark. But, homeward bound and eager to report their discoveries, they indulged in no side excursions. Emerging from Niles Canyon, they went southward past the future site of Mission San Jose on the gently rolling lands overlooking the southern shores of the bay, and then down the Santa Clara Valley again to Monterey.

Survey of the Bay

The Spanish colonists now began to appreciate that the so-called Estuary of San Francisco was indeed an extraordinary body of water. Yet it was not until 1775, when preparations were at last under way for the founding of San Francisco, that a detailed survey of the bay was undertaken—this time by boat. At twilight on August 5 of that year the first vessel ever to enter San Francisco Bay sailed slowly through the Golden Gate against the strong, outflowing tide. She was the supply ship *San Carlos*, under the command of Juan Manuel de Ayala, who had orders not only to take soundings and make observations throughout the bay but also to assist an overland party from Monterey in the construction of houses for settlers whom Juan Bautista de Anza, a frontier captain, was then gathering together on the west coast of what is now Mexico and in the outpost of Tubac, near the site of present-day Tucson.

Ayala himself was unable to participate in the exploration of the bay because he had been wounded in the foot by the accidental discharge of a double-barreled pistol. He entrusted the actual reconnaissance to José de Cañizares, first pilot, and to Juan Bautista Aguirre, second pilot. In the forty-four days that the *San Carlos* remained in the bay, anchored most of the time off Angel Island, Cañizares made three voyages in the ship's boat to the northern parts of the bay, exploring San Pablo Bay, Carquinez Strait, and Suisun Bay to the mouth of the San Joaquin River. Aguirre surveyed the southern arm of the bay. From information collected by the two, Cañizares prepared a report and a chart showing the great bay as a separate entity, in no way connected with the Bahia de San Francisco (Drakes Bay). Thus at last the importance of San Francisco Bay was recognized. In his report Cañizares said that it was "not one harbor, but many."[5]

Cañizares' map, known officially as Ayala's map, was somewhat vague about the northern shore of San Pablo Bay and left unanswered a question raised that year by the mariner Juan Francisco de la Bodega y Cuadra, who on his return from a voyage to northern waters had discovered Bodega Bay in what is now Sonoma County: Was this coastal bay in some way connected with San Francisco Bay? That it was not was proved the following year when Cañizares and others reëxamined San Pablo Bay and rowed up Petaluma Creek.

On September 18, 1775, Ayala in the *San Carlos* sailed back to Monterey, having seen nothing of the overland party that was to assist his crew in building houses for Anza's colonists. When, somewhat later, Father Francisco Palóu and others arrived from Monterey, they, too, were disappointed to find no one to aid them in preparing shelters for the prospective settlers. The work of creating a presidio and a mission at San Francisco remained for the colonists who were at the time more than eleven hundred miles away, about to begin their long trek across blazing deserts and high, cold mountains.

Colonists for San Francisco

The recruitment of settlers for San Francisco in the northern provinces of New Spain was part of an ambitious plan to open and maintain an overland supply route to Alta California from Sonora. The precarious condition of the establishments in the new province suggested that some means more dependable and faster than the two supply ships *San Carlos* and *San Antonio* should be found for transporting provisions to them. Time and again these vessels were long delayed on the dangerous voyage from San Blas, in what is now the Mexican state of Nayarit, while the colonists at San Diego, Monterey, San Antonio, San Luis Obispo, and San Gabriel all but starved. The newcomers had as yet made little progress in cultivating the soil, and the Indian neophytes at the missions had scarcely learned even the rudiments of farming. Practically everything required for subsistence had to be brought by sea. So difficult was the problem of sustaining the little settlements on the distant periphery of civilization that officials in New Spain more than once talked of abandoning the Alta California venture. But at the moment when the future of the province appeared blackest, Anza had come forth with a proposal to the viceroy, Antonio Bucareli, that he be commissioned to explore a route from the frontier in Sonora to Monterey. This hazardous route the hardy captain had opened in 1774, and over it he led the 240 colonists for San Francisco in the fall of 1775 and the winter of 1775–76.

The wayfarers arrived in Monterey on March 10, 1776, after a journey from Tubac of 130 days. They were the first and last large party to travel the overland route. The unenlightened policy of the commandant general of the frontier provinces, Teodoro de Croix, fanned the flames of resentment among the Indians of the Gila-Colorado region until the Yumas, roused to savage fury, massacred the Spaniards in two settlements on the west bank of the Colorado River in 1781 and exterminated the soldiers accompanying a party of colonists on their way to California. Thereafter the overland route to the coast remained closed except to small military groups. Upon his arrival in Monterey, Anza fully believed that he had started an immigration movement that would make Alta California more populous and prosperous, as well as permanently Spanish. Had it not been for the indifference and temporizing of one official, California might indeed have become deeply rooted in Latin culture—and perhaps it would have been a good deal more difficult for Americans later to incorporate into a republic with a predominantly Anglo-Saxon political and social heritage.

While the future residents of San Francisco remained at Monterey, Anza set off to select sites for the presidio and mission they were to build. His instructions from Viceroy Bucareli also bade him select a site somewhere else in the Bay Area for a second mission and explore further the Rio Grande de San Francisco that Fages had discovered. Anza was accompanied by ten soldiers and by Father Pedro Font and Lieutenant José Joaquín Moraga, who had made the arduous trek from Tubac with him. Among the soldiers was one who had journeyed with Fages to the Rio de San Francisco four years earlier, and another to whom the trip up the San Francisco Peninsula was familiar, for he had been over the same ground in 1774 when Father Palóu and Fernando de Rivera y Moncada, successor of Fages, were also prospecting for mission sites. This veteran of the reconnaissance of 1774 guided Anza to the tip of the peninsula by way of the San Andreas Valley, the west flank of the San Bruno Mountains, and Lake Merced. The march from Monterey took four days.

Sites for Presidio and Mission

The party camped on the banks of Mountain Lake, now on the southern edge of the San Francisco Presidio. After a day spent in intensive exploration of the terrain in the area, Anza was satisfied that the mesa "a gunshot away" from the lake was an excellent site for a fort settlement. From this high point "one sees a large part of the port and its islands, as far as the other side, the mouth of the harbor, and of the sea all that the sight can take in as far as beyond the farallones," Father Font wrote.[6] Anza's decision designating this area as a military reservation has never been reversed. Until airplanes and nuclear weapons were invented, it was one of the most strategic

locations to be found in the San Francisco Bay Area.

On the third day of exploration, Anza, Font, and Moraga reached "a beautiful arroyo which, because it was Friday of Sorrows, we called the Arroyo de los Dolores."[7] A little stream emerging from the hills impressed Father Font as being adequate for irrigation and for operation of a small mill. To test the soil, Moraga planted a little maize and some chick-peas. All three agreed that here the mission of St. Francis should be built, near the head of a slope that stretched gently down to the little bay now known as Mission Bay. The site was about three miles from that chosen for the presidio.

Father Font and other priests thought that the Arroyo de San Mateo, farther down the peninsula, would be an appropriate site for the second mission planned by the viceroy; but as matters turned out, that mission was built on a site near Guadalupe Creek in the northern part of the Santa Clara Valley. As Anza and his cohorts rounded the southern end of the bay on their way to explore the Rio Grande de San Francisco, the soldier who had accompanied Rivera and Father Palóu in 1774 pointed out the location that had pleased them. Anza noted the advantages of the valley for settlement: the level terrain, the rich soil, and streams which would supply the needed water.

But the leader of the San Francisco colonists learned no more than Fages about the San Joaquin River. The tule marshes blocked his progress, and besides, Father Font convinced him, after much argument, that the Rio Grande was not a river at all, but a fresh-water sea. The excursion to the river was noteworthy chiefly because on the return trip to Monterey Anza crossed the Diablo Range from the east and emerged at the southern end of the Santa Clara Valley in the vicinity of Gilroy. No earlier expedition had traversed this route.

The territory north of the great bay remained for the most part *terra incognita*. The bay itself constituted a formidable barrier to exploration in this early period when not a single settlement had yet been established in the Bay Area. By contrast, the San Francisco Peninsula and the country on the east side of the bay were fairly well known. Various expeditions had blazed the principal routes in use today in these areas and had traversed the sites now occupied by the major cities of the region.

Time and Place

From time to time variously interested persons have contended that the logical place for a metropolitan center in the Bay Area would be on the east or mainland side of the bay, at the terminus of transcontinental railroads and at the ends of canyons and mountain passes affording direct access to the raw materials of a whole continent.

But the historical circumstances under which the Bay Area was settled and gained the impetus for its early development clearly explain why San Francisco, though surrounded on three sides by water, and though it has from time to time been crippled by earthquakes and fires, has continued as a metropolitan focal point despite the competition of other cities in the area, and despite the metropolitan dispersion of recent decades.

Between Spanish Alta California and the British colonies on the Atlantic seaboard lay a continental wilderness. The settlements on both sides faced outward across the seas rather than inland. For Alta California the resources of civilization were at the ends of the sea lanes, even though the colonists briefly had hopes of maintaining an overland route to New Spain. The sea lanes were to continue for a century or more to be the vital links with the sources from which flowed manufactured goods, books, music and art, many of the delicacies of the table, fashions, news of critical political developments, and, most important, the majority of newcomers who swelled the population. In the early days of Alta California the sea lanes extended chiefly to San Blas, and the Pacific was almost exclusively a Spanish ocean. But it did not long remain so. In the very year that San Francisco was founded, word reached Mexico City that the English were sending Captain James Cook to explore the Pacific, and of course Spain was already fearful of Russian designs on the west coast of North America. The sea was an open road to any ambitious nation. A sovereign power anxious to hold a newly discovered harbor large enough to accommodate all the fleets in the world would naturally establish a settlement at the entrance to that harbor; and as long as the sea remained the easiest and fastest means of importing and exporting goods, that port could reasonably be expected to attract trade, population, and economic and political influence more readily than other settlements less advantageously situated in relation to the sea. So it was with San Francisco, which for a century was not so much at the edge of a continent as it was at the edge of an immense ocean that was connected with all the other great seas of the world. The early growth—slow during Spanish and Mexican days, lightning-like during the gold rush, slow for a decade or more after that, then rapid again during the Nevada silver boom—gave the city the deep roots it needed to sustain itself and flourish at a later time when the sea was no longer so important as it had been.

Founding of San Francisco

The beginnings of the metropolis were crude but picturesque. Anza did not participate in the founding—he had departed for his outpost in Sonora some two months earlier. It was Moraga who conducted the colonists to their new home. The journey from Monterey consumed

Mission Dolores, San Francisco, in 1856. Drawing from Henry Miller's "Journal of a Sketching Tour of the California Missions." Courtesy of Bancroft Library, University of California.

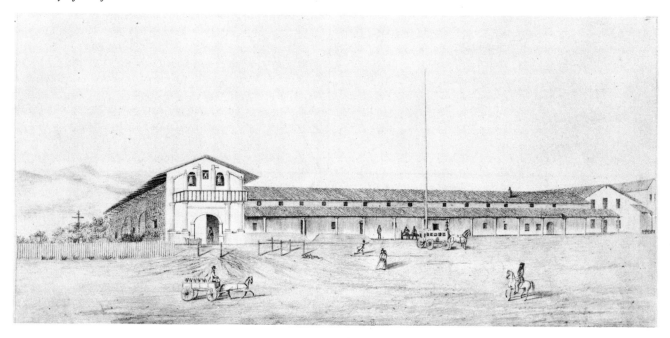

all of ten days because the women and children had to rest often and the herds of cattle and horses and the mule train also moved slowly. On June 27, 1776, the colony at last reached the Laguna de los Dolores, where the mission was to be erected. The next day a shelter of branches was made, in which on the following day Fathers Palóu and Cambon celebrated the first Mass. Then ensued a long period of waiting for the supply ship *San Carlos*, which carried essential equipment and had among its crew skilled carpenters who were to assist in the construction of the presidio and the mission. It was August 18 before the vessel sailed through the Golden Gate, after spending almost two months at sea and being blown about so much that it had sailed more than two thousand miles just going from Monterey to San Francisco Bay. The settlers had not been idle during the long wait, however. They had cut supplies of logs with which to build the presidio and the mission, and they now set to work building the military establishment. When completed in the middle of September it included a chapel, a warehouse, and flat-roofed log houses for the soldiers. The temporary mission church, also of logs, was blessed on October 3 and was formally dedicated on October 9. San Francisco at last was on the map. The colonists celebrated the joyous event in typical early California style: they killed two beeves and held a barbecue.

One of the most interesting facts about the birth of this city is that it coincided with the proclamation of the Declaration of Independence and the birth of the United States of America. Mass was said in the rude shelter on the banks of the Laguna de los Dolores just five days before the Continental Congress formally adopted the great document penned by Thomas Jefferson. But all during the time that the settlement was being planned, restless and adventurous Americans were moving over the Allegheny Mountains into the Ohio Valley, initiating the westward migration that was to surge all the way to the Pacific and engulf the fringe of Spanish-speaking communities in California. Just seventy years after the new nation was founded three thousand miles from San Francisco Bay, that nation's flag flew over the Presidio of San Francisco.

Founding of Mission Santa Clara

In the month following the dedication of the mission at San Francisco the governor of the province, Rivera, again inspected the place on the Guadalupe River in the Santa Clara Valley that he and Father Palóu had favored in 1774 as a site for the second mission to be established in the San Francisco Bay Area. But it was January before he ordered Moraga, who was now *comandante* of the

Presidio in San Francisco, to proceed with the founding of Mission Santa Clara, dedicated to Clare of Assisi, founder of the Franciscan Order of Poor Clares.

Moraga, accompanied by Father Tomás de la Peña and some soldiers who were to assist in building the new ecclesiastical establishment, encamped on the banks of the Guadalupe on January 7, 1777, preparatory to selecting the exact spot for the mission. In a country rainless the greater part of the year, water to irrigate crops was a prime consideration. About eight miles up the river from the shore of the bay, the group discovered a little creek that emptied into the Guadalupe. The flow of this creek, they saw, could easily be diverted to irrigate the mission gardens. On the west bank of the river near the confluence of the two streams and just north of the present Bayshore Highway, the soldiers some days later cleared a plot of land for the mission building, not without certain misgivings that the site selected might be subject to flooding. As later events proved, their fears were well founded.

The Town of San José

Before long the priests and soldiers at the mission received an important visitor, Felipe de Neve, the new governor of the province. Rivera had been transferred to Loreto in Baja California as lieutenant governor, Monterey had become the capital of the two Californias, and now the new administrator was on his way to visit the port of San Francisco. He turned a sharp eye on the broad expanse of the Santa Clara Valley, because he was looking for a site for a new type of settlement, neither military nor ecclesiastical but primarily for the production of food and the propagation of more Spaniards to populate Alta California.

At the time he had assumed office, months earlier in Loreto, Neve had received instructions from the viceroy to establish agricultural settlements that would supply the missions and presidios with foodstuffs and perhaps eventually relieve the viceroyalty of the responsibility and expense of shipping provisions from San Blas. One such community Neve already had in mind, the future Los Angeles on the Rio de Porciuncula not far from Mission San Gabriel. Still another civil settlement, or *pueblo* (town), should be located in the Santa Clara Valley, he decided as he surveyed the virgin land through which the Guadalupe serpentined to the bay.

The Pueblo de San José came into being on November 29, 1777, with Moraga for the third time serving as a kind of colonial accoucheur. At the direction of Neve he assembled in the Presidio at San Francisco early in November the sixty-six hopeful souls who were to form the pioneer agricultural colony of the province: nine soldiers of "known agricultural skill" from the garrisons of Monterey and San Francisco and five *pobladores*, or settlers, together with their wives and children. At the head of this company Moraga marched to a place on the eastern bank of the Guadalupe roughly two miles from Mission Santa Clara and approximately a mile and a quarter north of the present center of San Jose.

To each of the settlers the *comandante* assigned provisionally a lot upon which to erect a dwelling, and a field large enough for the sowing of a fanega (approximately two bushels) of grain. Each man also received the necessary farming implements and two cows, a yoke of oxen, two horses, two beeves, two sheep, two goats, and a mule. The settlers were to pay for both goods and animals in products of the soil within five years. In addition, as an assurance of security during the possible tribulations of a new venture, the government granted each colonist a soldier's pay of ten dollars a month and daily rations for three years.

How wise Neve was in thus bolstering morale against discouragement and unforeseen miseries was soon demonstrated. Moraga, unhappily, had chosen a low-lying site for the town. In the spring of 1778, and again the following winter, the unruly Guadalupe inundated the fields of the settlers and flooded their houses, as well as the near-by mission. In the spring of 1779 the people of San José built new homes on higher ground, and in 1781 the mission fathers began construction of new buildings a little more than two miles south of their first establishment (at what is now the intersection of Campbell Avenue and Franklin Street in the city of Santa Clara).

Interdependent Settlements

Within a few years both settlements demonstrated the desirability of the Santa Clara Valley as an agricultural area. The produce and livestock of the San José residents was more than enough to supply their own needs and those of the presidios in Monterey and San Francisco. On a visit to Mission Santa Clara in 1792, George Vancouver, captain of the first foreign vessel to put in at San Francisco Bay, marveled at the abundant harvests of wheat, maize, peas, and beans, "which had been obtained with little labour and without manure."[8] In the mission gardens he noted peach, apricot, apple, pear, and fig trees flourishing—a sight prophetic of the thousands of acres of orchards eventually to be planted in the valley. Only in the cultivation of the grape did the Franciscans appear to have no success, owing perhaps, Vancouver thought, to "a want of knowledge in their culture" since the soil and the climate were "well adapted to most sorts of fruit."[9] On the fertile plains surrounding the mission he observed black cattle "in large herds . . . in a sort of wild state."[10]

Although they were more than forty-five miles apart, the settlements at San Francisco and in the Santa Clara Valley enjoyed a close relationship from the very beginning. As the only establishments in the Bay Area, they naturally depended upon one another for social contacts. The visit of one of the fathers from Mission Santa Clara to Mission Dolores was an event; and the appearance of a foreigner such as Vancouver at Mission Santa Clara under an escort from the Presidio of San Francisco was an occasion calling for an exhibition of roping and slaughtering, a feast, and much other festivity. But it was the economic tie between San Francisco and the Santa Clara Valley that was particularly significant. The people in the settlements at the port needed foodstuffs from San José and Mission Santa Clara and could obtain them as they were needed. San Francisco was thus an outlet for the producers in the valley, whereas the valley itself was to become one of the chief sources of supply for the lusty young metropolis born of the gold rush. Indeed, the first important railroad in the Bay Area would be built chiefly as a means of transporting foodstuffs from the valley to markets in San Francisco. The early interdependence of San Francisco and the Santa Clara Valley was the basis for the metropolitan relationships that exist today.

Mission San José

After twenty years the ties binding together the first four little establishments in the Bay Area were lengthened to entwine a fifth—a new mission on the southeastern side of the bay. The original intention of mission authorities had been to select a site for this mission on the San Francisco Peninsula about midway between Mission Santa Clara and San Francisco; but since a large Indian population on the opposite side of the bay offered a more promising field for missionary endeavor, a site in what is now southern Alameda County was chosen. It was fifteen miles from Mission Santa Clara and twelve miles from the town of San José. Behind the site rose Mission Peak, and near by flowed the small stream now known as Mission Creek. The soil in the area was especially fertile. In only a few years Mission San José was to become one of the most prosperous establishments in the entire mission chain and was to be known far and wide for its grain, its fruits and wine, and its hides and tallow.

The founding took place on June 11, 1797, with Mass sung by Father President Fermín de Lasuén in a shelter of boughs. For the next ten years construction was under way. The neophytes made bricks from the clay at hand,

Mission San José in 1856. Drawing from Henry Miller's "Journal of a Sketching Tour of the California Missions." Courtesy of Bancroft Library.

but they carried redwood timbers for the church all the way from the hills overlooking the site of present-day Oakland—a distance of thirty miles. Years later, sweating crews of Americans were to cut down redwoods in the same groves to build the crude city of San Francisco.

A New Site for San José

The year 1797 also witnessed the removal of the Pueblo de San José to its third and final site, approximately a mile and a quarter south of the second. The Guadalupe River had overflowed its banks so many times that life was neither healthful nor comfortable in the location selected in 1779. The intersection of Market and West San Fernando streets in present-day San Jose marks the approximate center of the third town, from which almost half a century later the modern city began to develop.

Two years after the third start was made, Father Magín Catalá of Mission Santa Clara, with the help of Indian neophytes, began transforming the road that connected the mission and the town into a beautiful, willow-lined avenue. This road is today The Alameda, one of the principal east-west arteries of San Jose.

Communication among the five establishments in the Bay Area was entirely by land during the early period, although the bay offered an alternative means of travel. The failure of the Spaniards even to provide themselves with small boats that could be used for voyages on the bay greatly surprised G. H. von Langsdorff, the physician who accompanied Count Nikolai Rezanov on his famous visit to the Presidio of San Francisco in 1806 to obtain food for the starving Russian colony in Alaska. When Langsdorff and two companions sailed down the bay in a ship's boat to landing places near Missions San José and Santa Clara, he showed that water routes of communication could be established among the settlements and introduced the means of local travel that became common when foreign vessels in increasing numbers came into the bay.

Fort Ross, Russian Colony

The long isolation of Alta California from contact with people of other nations was swiftly ending, thanks to the presence along the California coast of swarms of sea otters. Langsdorff noted in his diary that San Francisco

Bay was "full" of these lustrous, brown-black creatures, which American ships under contract to the Russian American Fur Company of Alaska had been hunting on the islands off the coast and even on the forbidden mainland itself since 1803. The pursuit of the otter not only served to acquaint New England ship captains and their crews with a land that had more potentialities than the Spaniards seemed to be aware of, but it also aroused in the Russians a desire for a base on the California shore from which they could hunt independently of their American partners.

In the fall of 1811 the "Little Czar" of the Alaska colony, Alexander Baranov, finally took the step he had long contemplated. He sent an agent named Ivan Kuskoff to establish two permanent settlements north of the Golden Gate—a small one in Salmon Creek Valley six miles inland from Bodega Head, and a larger one at Fort Ross on the high bluffs twelve miles north of the mouth of the Russian River. The latter was dedicated in the spring of 1812. Baranov had decided that since intensified Spanish vigilance made clandestine hunting in San Francisco Bay and on the coast to the south well-nigh im-

possible, he would restrict his pursuit of the otter to the region north of the Spanish settlements. By avoiding conflict with the Spaniards, he hoped sooner or later to obtain a much-desired concession for hunting privileges in their territory. As for his relations with American ship captains, he now dispensed with the services of the Yankee ships and relied entirely upon his own vessels.

In an earlier period the Spaniards doubtless would have made a supreme effort to prevent colonization by the foreign power that they most feared. But New Spain was aflame with the revolution begun by the obscure parish priest Miguel Hidalgo in 1810, and the troops of the viceroy were engaged in battle after battle with the equally militant successor of Hidalgo, José María Morelos. The still loyal Spaniards in Alta California could expect no expeditionary force to arrive to dislodge the Russians, who continued to occupy the new outpost until 1841, when they voluntarily abandoned it because it was no longer useful to them either as a hunting base or as an agricultural colony. After 1810 no ships reached the province from San Blas with the usual supplies, mail, government decrees, and money to pay the presidio garri-

Fort Ross as Seen from the Hill. On the left is the sandy beach; on the right, the landing. Drawing from Historical Atlas Map of Sonoma County, 1877.

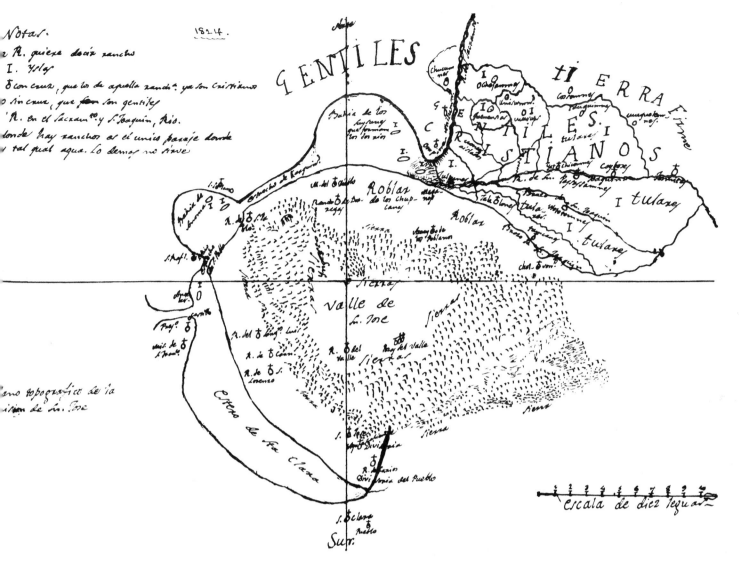

Map of the San Francisco Bay Area about 1824. Found among records of Mission San José. Photograph courtesy of Bancroft Library.

sons. Alta California, cut off from New Spain, was obliged to tolerate the planting of a Russian fort on soil claimed by Spain, however bitter acceptance of the situation might be.

Missions in the North Bay

The presence of this unwelcome foreign colony directed Spanish attention to the country north of San Francisco Bay and probably spurred expansion into that area. Gabriel Moraga, son of José Joaquín Moraga, at the direction of the provincial authorities, made three trips to Fort Ross and the Bodega settlement between 1812 and 1814 to learn what he could regarding Russian intentions and activities. These expeditions served to acquaint him with the trails and valleys of what are now Marin and Sonoma counties and to suggest possible sites for new settlements.

Moraga is believed to have recommended the site on the sheltered bay side of the Marin Peninsula for the auxiliary mission, or *asistencia*, of San Rafael, founded in 1817. This establishment, the nucleus of the present county seat of Marin County, was built as a kind of rancho sanatorium for the Indians of Mission Dolores, who for several years had been dying at an alarming rate from the ravages of venereal disease and from general weakening of their constitutions by the change from a roving, outdoor life to a confined, regulated existence within the mission compound. Transfer of a small number of the ailing neophytes to the sunnier, drier climate of San Rafael on an experimental basis a few months earlier had so improved their health that the decision was made to create a permanent establishment there. There was probably still another reason for founding this new Spanish settlement, and that was to bulwark Spain's claim to the inviting but little-known country north of San Francisco Bay with an actual establishment.

As the Russians showed no disposition to expand, provincial fears of their intentions gradually abated, and a good deal of stealthy trade developed between Bay Area settlements and Fort Ross. By the time the news that Mexico had won its independence from Spain reached Alta California, in 1822, the exchange between Russian traders and families living in the bay settlements was being carried on in the open, to the mutual satisfaction of both groups. The Russians had such exotic goods as laces, jewels, china, and silks to barter for hides and tallow, wheat, and pelts of deer, bears, and foxes trapped by the Indians.

San Francisco Solano, the last of the twenty-one California missions, came into being in the Sonoma Valley less as a barrier to Russian expansion than as a scheme to suppress both Mission Dolores and Mission San Rafael. With the apparent encouragement of Luis Ar-

güello, the first governor under the Mexican regime, young Father José Altimira, a newcomer to Mission Dolores, urged the first territorial *Diputación*, or legislative assembly, to transfer the "unhealthful" Mission Dolores to a locality north of San Rafael. The six legislators not only approved the proposed change, they also decreed that the establishment at San Rafael, which had recently been made independent of Mission Dolores, likewise should be consolidated with a new mission in the country of the Petalumas, or Canicaimos. Before Church authorities could act upon the protests of Father Juan Amorós of San Rafael, the audacious Father Altimira and a party of soldiers were tramping through the Petaluma, Sonoma, Napa, and Suisin valleys in quest of a site for the proposed mission. They settled on the valley known to the Indians as Sonoma, and on July 4, 1823, dedicated a site that recommended itself to them because of its fine climate, timber, stone, and water.

Great was the displeasure of the father president of the

Map of the Ranchos of Vicente and Domingo Peralta, about 1857. Note the intersection of Broadway, Fourteenth Street, and the County Road, now San Pablo Avenue, in Oakland. Photograph of map courtesy of Bancroft Library.

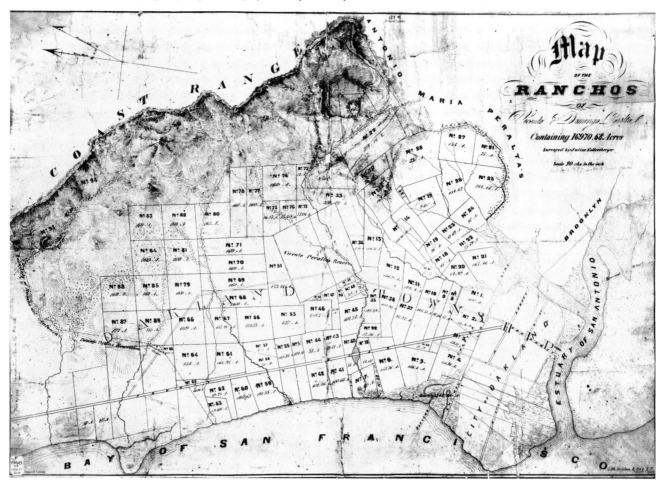

mission and the other fathers when they learned of the unauthorized actions of Father Altimira. Nevertheless, late in August, work began on a granary, irrigation ditch, corral, and other necessary structures at New San Francisco. At length the controversy precipitated by Father Altimira's unprecedented course ended in a compromise; he was appointed priest of the new mission, but neither Mission Dolores nor Mission San Rafael was abandoned.

Mexican Ranchos

Under the new Mexican regime there was a gradual increase in a type of landholding that was to cause endless complications for the energetic Americans when they gained possession of California. This was the rancho, of vast acreage, indefinite as to boundaries, held by a single family, and ideally suited to an economy producing chiefly hides and tallow for export, but highly frustrating to later-day American settlers bent on acquiring lands of their own, building homes, platting cities, and subdividing

the valleys into family-sized farms and orchards. Only about thirty grants of land for ranchos were made in Alta California in the Spanish period, and relatively few in the first decade of Mexican rule. Most of the allocation of the rich valleys and tawny hills of coastal California to land-hungry Mexicans and to a few foreigners who had become Mexican citizens followed decrees of the Mexican Congress in 1833 and 1834 secularizing the missions and placing spiritual jurisdiction of the churches in the hands of parish priests. Many ranchos in the San Francisco Bay Area were created from lands formerly occupied and used by the missions, although thousands of acres in the area had never been used by these establishments. These vacant public lands, as well as the mission lands, were disposed of in accordance with a colonization law of 1824 and supplementary regulations of 1828. The law of 1824, intended to encourage permanent settlement in the more sparsely populated territories of the republic, such as Alta California, provided that Mexican nationals and

The Intersection of Broadway, Fourteenth Street, and San Pablo Avenue, Oakland, 1941. Aerial photograph courtesy of Mike Roberts.

foreigners wishing to settle in Mexican territory might petition for as much as eleven square leagues of land (approximately 48,700 acres), but not more. The law stipulated, however, that no person should receive more than one square league of irrigable land, four leagues of land dependent on rain, or six leagues of grazing land. Very few grants in the San Francisco Bay Area were of the maximum size allowed under the law; most of those in the Santa Clara Valley, for instance, contained from one to three square leagues, and only a few were as large as six or more leagues.

Don Luis Peralta, who had come to San Francisco as a boy of seventeen with the Anza expedition and had later served as a soldier in the Presidio garrison, acquired one of the most famous of the ranchos in the last years of Spanish control and the first years of Mexican rule. Known as Rancho San Antonio, his feudal holding stretched from San Leandro Creek in what is now central Alameda County northward to the Cerrito de San Antonio (little hill of St. Anthony), a landmark now surmounted by a mane of tall eucalyptus trees and commonly called Albany Hill. On the land later divided among his four sons now stand the cities of Oakland, Berkeley, Alameda, Piedmont, Emeryville, Albany, and San Leandro. The boundary separating the Peralta rancho from the Rancho San Pablo of the Castro family was eventually to become part of the boundary between Alameda and Contra Costa counties.

Yankee Trade and a New Town

Almost from the beginning of the Mexican period, rancho and mission became linked with an economic system that stretched all the way round the Horn to soap, candle, and shoe factories in Massachusetts, Rhode Island, Connecticut, and other Atlantic seaboard states. Republican Mexico reversed the centuries-old monopolistic trade policies of Spain and opened California ports to ships of all nations. Through the Golden Gate sailed Yankee vessels seeking chiefly hides for the New England leather industry. English and occasionally Peruvian and Russian ships also sought anchorage in the lee of the *Alta Loma* (high hill), as Telegraph Hill was then called; but for the most part the ships that entered San Francisco Bay were registered out of Boston, Providence, and other down-East ports.

From the San Francisco anchorage the crewmen set out in their launches to rancho and mission *embarcaderos*, or landing places, on sloughs and creeks around the bay, seeking "California bank notes," as hides were called because rancheros used them in lieu of currency to pay for goods bought from the ships. To the anchored vessels came schooners owned by the missions and built by the Indians according to plans drawn by the mission fathers. The bay thus served as a unifying element for the entire territory surrounding it, and the anchorage at San Francisco became the focus of commercial activity.

In 1834 the increase in the number of vessels trafficking in San Francisco Bay for hides and tallow suggested to Governor José Figueroa and the territorial *Diputación* the possibility of establishing a commercial town or trading post on Yerba Buena Cove (now the area between Montgomery Street and the Embarcadero in San Francisco), so called because the fragrant "good herb" (*Micromeria chamissonis*) was found growing on the surrounding slopes. The decision to center importing and exporting activities in the cove coincided with a three-part plan which contemplated the secularization of Mission Dolores, the shifting of the garrison of the Presidio to a new town to be developed in the Sonoma Valley as secularization of Mission San Francisco Solano was carried out, and recognition of the Presidio of San Francisco as a town, with an area of four square leagues of land (27 square miles), as provided by Spanish and Mexican law.

In a letter to Mariano Guadalupe Vallejo, *comandante* of the Presidio of San Francisco, the *Diputación* designated the boundaries of the new town as a line running from the south side of Rincon Point on the bay (Fourth and Berry streets) to the *Divisadero* (Lone Mountain) and thence to the south side of Point Lobos, on the ocean. These boundaries were to be cited years later by the City of San Francisco when it was growing rapidly and had to prove its title to lands needed for urban expansion, including the thousand or more acres embraced by Golden Gate Park.

In the protracted legal battle over the pueblo lands the city also was required to prove that the Presidio, which the *Diputación* recognized as a town, had actually functioned as a civil settlement. The *Diputación's* order in November, 1834, for the election of an *ayuntamiento*, or town council, was therefore extremely significant for the city that was to develop from the town of Yerba Buena. The territorial assembly included territory on both sides of the bay in the jurisdiction of the town. This action brought a protest to the governor from Antonio María Peralta and twenty-six other rancheros of the *contra costa*, who complained that "to be obliged to go to the port by land, we are under the necessity of traveling forty leagues, going and coming back; and to go by sea, we are exposed to the danger of being wrecked."[11] But His Excellency the Governor was not moved by the suggestion that the *contra costa* be included in the jurisdiction of the Pueblo de San José. The town council of Yerba Buena was duly elected in December, 1834, and was installed in January, 1835, with four rancheros of the East Bay among its nine members. The council was regularly renewed each year until 1839, when it was superseded by an alcalde, a kind of mayor and petty justice combined. Its existence during those four years was of crucial importance, however, in establishing San Francisco's claim to its pueblo lands.

The protest of the rancho owners of the East Bay against being obliged to participate in decisions affecting the new trading town bears early and eloquent testimony to the obstacles placed in the way of regional action by the great bay. Bridges, telephone and telegraph cables, radio, and television today have overcome the physical barrier, yet sectional feeling persists.

First Town Plans

William A. Richardson, an Englishman who had jumped ship and lived at the Presidio, became the first settler in the port village of Yerba Buena, which developed in the general area marked today by Portsmouth Square. Initially he carried on a small retail business with ships' crews and Indians, from a tent stretched over pine posts, and in 1837 he built his *Casa Grande*, a large adobe, on the one street in the town, the *Calle de la Fundación*. This street, shown on a "plan" of the townsite made by Richardson in 1835, ran at an angle to the beach and connected at the north with a road to the Presidio and at the south with a road to Mission Dolores. The government retained title to a strip of land about two hundred yards wide between the beach and the street.

By 1839 several lots in the town had been granted without regard to any street system, except for the Calle de la Fundacion, and it became necessary to establish some orderly arrangement of streets in the growing community. At the order of Alcalde Francisco de Haro, a Swiss newcomer named Jean Vioget devised a town plan to be used in granting additional lots. In preparing his plan, Vioget sought to include within near-rectangular blocks all the houses and fences already erected. In an area bounded by California Street, Montgomery Street, Pacific Avenue, and Grant Avenue—occupied today by part of Chinatown and part of the financial district—he indicated twelve blocks and parts of blocks more or less conforming to a rectilinear arrangement, though these were never actually laid out on the ground. No street names appear on extant copies of the Vioget map, but present-day San Franciscans can identify Kearny Street and Grant Avenue as the north-south streets and Jackson, Washington, Clay, and Sacramento streets as the east-west streets. Richardson's Calle de la Fundacion is shown intersecting at an angle the street now called Grant

Avenue. Vioget's north later proved to be eleven degrees too far east, and his north-south streets intersected the parallel east-west streets at two and one-half degrees from a right angle.

The most significant feature of the plan was its division of the townsite into more or less rectangular blocks. Vioget later testified that his original map included dotted lines indicating possible extensions of the streets, but he probably never thought of the town as expanding beyond the gently sloping land bordering the cove. He could hardly have foreseen that Yerba Buena would become a great city stretching far to the south, west, and north over steep hills and through valleys. The projection of his parallel streets up forbidding gradients and over crests to terrifying descents was the work of later surveyors, but he initiated the pattern that they elected to extend with total disregard for topography.

The Town of Sonoma

While the trading village was being established at the Port of St. Francis, the territorial government proceeded with its plan for a town at Mission San Francisco Solano in the Sonoma Valley. It also undertook to start small settlements on the sites of present-day Santa Rosa and Petaluma. But Indian hostility and trouble with settlers brought an end to both schemes. The order to Mariano Guadalupe Vallejo to found the pueblo that is now the town of Sonoma was dated June 23, 1835. All efforts were concentrated on making the new town a success.

Using a pocket compass, the young officer, with the assistance of William Richardson and Indian laborers, staked out a typical Spanish-Mexican town. A square, eight-acre plaza in the center of the town was surrounded by rectangular blocks. Extending southward from the plaza was an avenue 110 feet wide, which connected with a road to an *embarcadero* four miles away. In the block at the northeast corner of the plaza stood the mission, in which Vallejo and his family took up quarters, and on Battery Hill, just north of the pueblo, the *comandante* mounted cannon.

Sonoma in time became the trading center for the North Bay area. Some two hundred settlers lived within its jurisdiction by 1840.

In more than a century the plaza and the streets conceived by Vallejo have not changed, and though each generation has left its contribution of buildings in the town, Sonoma even now retains some of the unhurried atmosphere of its early days.

San José, though larger in population, was by contrast a straggling, formless community. In 1841, Nicholas ("Cheyenne") Dawson, of the Bidwell-Bartleson party, the first group of emigrants from the United States to reach the Mexican territory by the overland route, described San José as "a sleepy village of perhaps one hundred and fifty inhabitants, with no regular streets."[12] With one or two exceptions the houses were of adobe, "resembling unburnt brick kilns, with no floors, no chimneys, and with the openings for doors and windows closed by shutters instead of glass."[13] Dawson found "no farms around, but a few gardens; very few stores, and very little in them; no vehicles but carts, made entirely of wood; very little money, but plenty of hides and tallow."[14]

The End of Mexican Rule

The unprepossessing appearance of the few little towns and the run-down state of the missions and the presidios evoked the ill-concealed disdain of American immigrants who came overland in good-sized parties in 1843, 1844, and 1845. They referred contemptuously to the Mexican population as indolent "greasers" and waited for the day when the United States would take over the country. Some even dreamed of creating a new, independent nation on the Pacific Coast.

Official American interest in California dated from the declaration of the Monroe Doctrine, which, among other things, served notice on the Czar of Russia that he was not to use Fort Ross as a springboard for further colonization on the Pacific Coast. The first attempt of the United States actually to acquire territory on the Pacific was Andrew Jackson's offer of $3,500,000 to Mexico in 1835 for that part of California lying north of the thirty-eighth parallel. This proposed transfer of territory would have given the United States control of San Francisco Bay. Though Jackson's efforts were unsuccessful, the visit of Lieutenant Charles Wilkes, of the United States Navy, to the bay in 1841 as head of a scientific expedition plainly indicated to the Mexicans that the United States had not ceased to covet the magnificent harbor. And the abortive seizure of Monterey by Commodore Thomas Ap Catesby Jones, commander of the United States Pacific Squadron, in 1842 as a move to forestall a rumored British plan to occupy California, perhaps made unmistakingly clear the ultimate fate of the territory. By the time James K. Polk, a resolute expansionist, moved into the White House in March, 1845, the annexation of California was one of the main items on the national agenda.

Polk wanted the transfer of California to the United States to take place without bloodshed; but his careful plans, implemented in California by Thomas Oliver Larkin, confidential agent of the State Department, were disrupted by the provocative maneuvers of Captain John Charles Frémont, by the Bear Flag revolt staged by Amer-

ican settlers in the North Bay area and the Sacramento Valley, and by the outbreak of war with Mexico. Even so, all the ports in California were occupied without opposition, including San Francisco, over which Captain John Montgomery, of the United States Navy, raised the American flag on July 9, 1846. It was mainly the arrogant behavior of the commander of the American occupation force in Los Angeles that touched off resistance by the native Californians and precipitated a series of engagements in southern California. As far as the San Francisco Bay Area was concerned, American control was effective months before the capitulation of the Californians in January, 1847.

Heritage from Spain and Mexico

The Spanish-Mexican population of the San Francisco Bay Area and the few score foreigners who more or less adopted their customs and religion upon settling among them bequeathed to the Americans a potentially rich area the resources of which had scarcely been touched, although the promise of things to come had been indicated.

The mission fathers, with the help of Indian neophytes, had amply demonstrated that the lands in the fertile valleys were suitable for growing various grains, fruits, and vegetables. And both the padres and the rancheros had shown that the entire country was suitable for stock raising, though little or no effort had been made to breed superior cattle.

The few valuable redwood forests of the area—on the Marin Peninsula, in the Russian River country, in the Santa Cruz Mountains on the San Francisco Peninsula, and in the Berkeley Hills—were known; some of them had been lumbered for many years, but to an insignificant extent.

In 1845 Andrés Castillero, a visitor from Mexico, while staying at Mission Santa Clara had discovered that mineral deposits which had been known to the Indians for centuries contained quicksilver. Soon the New Almaden Company was formed, and the New Almaden Mine became famous as one of the greatest quicksilver mines in the world.

The great bay was already famous around the world. Seamen from Latin America, from Europe, and from the United States had described its magnificence in waterfront taverns from Copenhagen to Valparaiso. Once the magic word "gold" was spoken, the sea lanes were filled with vessels bound for the celebrated harbor.

Nor was there lack of roads to lead the gold seekers to the "diggings," serve the stagecoaches, and much later provide the framework for a twentieth-century regional circulation system. These roads, often the merest ruts,

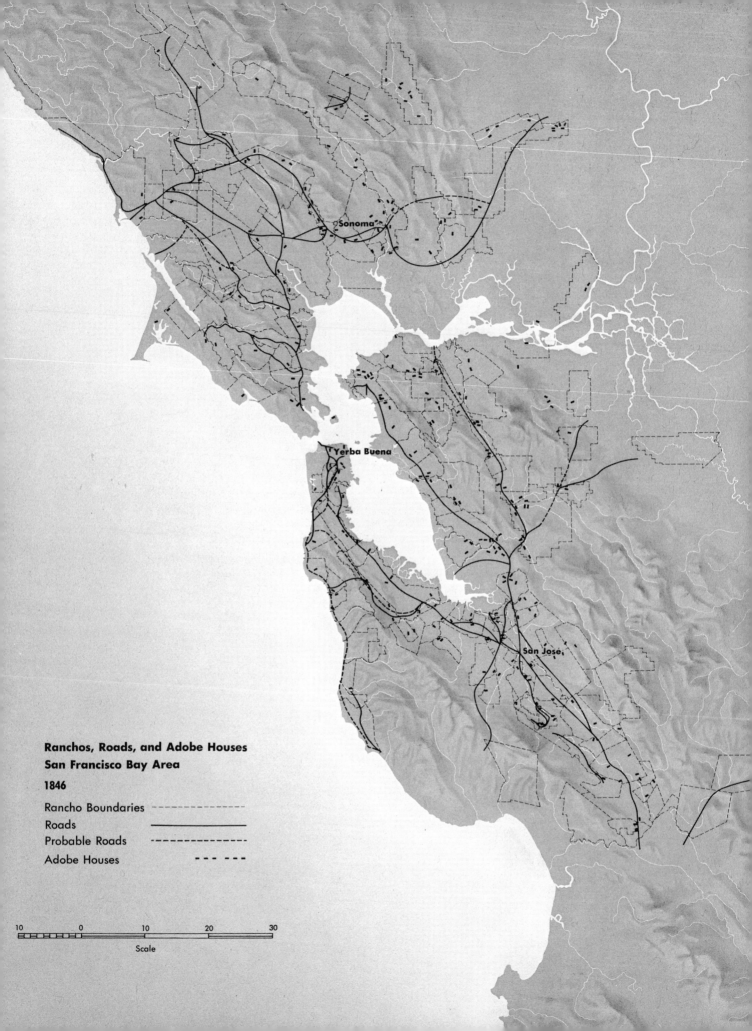

**Ranchos, Roads, and Adobe Houses
San Francisco Bay Area**

1846

Rancho Boundaries
Roads
Probable Roads
Adobe Houses

Sonoma

Yerba Buena

San Jose

10   0   10   20   30

Scale

acknowledged the logic of topography. They avoided, wherever possible, steep grades, marshes, deep sand, and boulder-strewn washes. They threaded the valleys and the natural passes; they crossed the well-known fords in the streams that flowed from the hills to the bay. Where they were indirect, their very indirection was purposeful and was no irritation to those who traveled over them in ox carts or astride handsome mounts.

From Monterey a highroad ran to Mission San Juan Bautista and thence through the Santa Clara Valley to San José, following virtually the same route through the valley as Highway 101 today. A second road penetrated the valley from the west, coming from Santa Cruz through the mountains to the site of present-day Los Gatos and continuing to Santa Clara. The road from Santa Clara to Yerba Buena was that known today as El Camino Real, though in Spanish and Mexican times that term was used for any main road and did not denote this particular road as a "King's Highway" or "royal road." From San José a well-traveled route swung northeast to Mission San José and continued from there all the way to Ignacio Martinez' adobe on Pinole Creek. From Mission San José a traveler could reach the valleys east of the Berkeley Hills by going through Mission Pass or through Niles Canyon. At the eastern end of the pass one road led across the Livermore Valley and through the hills to the San Joaquin Valley and Sutter's Fort near the Sacramento River; another turned north through the Amador, San Ramon, and Ygnacio valleys to Carquinez Strait. In the North Bay area there were roads from Mission San Rafael to the grist mill of Stephen Smith at Bodega and from Smith's mill to the Cotati, Sonoma, and Napa valleys, to say nothing of many shorter roads.

All the main routes, with the exception of the one along the *contra costa*, are shown on the topographical sketch of "the gold and quicksilver district of California" that Lieutenant Edward Otho Cresap Ord prepared to accompany President Polk's message to Congress of December 5, 1848, announcing the discovery of gold in the newly acquired territory.

Seventy years of Spanish-Mexican occupation of the San Francisco Bay Area had set the stage for a drama that electrified the world. So swiftly did that drama unfold and so numerous and polyglot were the actors who crowded upon the scene that the easygoing folk who first held the spotlight were all but shoved aside; yet their culture has not completely vanished. Most of the names they gave the bays and promontories, the mountains, the rivers, the valleys, canyons, and settlements remain. Countless land titles throughout the area can be traced directly to rancho grants, and some rancho boundaries are perpetuated in the boundaries of counties, cities, and modern subdivisions. Most of the adobes of the pastoral age have crumbled, but some of the customs of those who built them have survived—the barbecue, the fiesta, the rodeo—and, though modernized and Anglicized, serve as reminders of the vanished dons, vaqueros, and padres. Traditions and legends have a vitality that defies time, and though it seems indisputable that the greatest heritage from the first white settlers of the Bay Area is the record of their heroic trek from northern Mexico under Anza and their pioneer struggles to make a home in exile, their contribution to the physical form of the vast metropolitan region of today must be acknowledged.

CHAPTER TWO

Mother of Cities

Residents of the town of Yerba Buena had scarcely become accustomed to seeing the Stars and Stripes fluttering from the staff in front of the customhouse on Portsmouth Plaza when, on July 31, 1846, the ship *Brooklyn* arrived with approximately two hundred Mormons under the leadership of Elder Samuel Brannan. The unheralded advent of these wayfarers more than doubled the population of the settlement, then estimated at 150.

Merchants and traders of the town were profoundly impressed by the arrival of this numerous company of Americans. True, they were sectarians who had been persecuted and were anxious to begin life anew in a far country; but other citizens of the United States would surely follow, now that their flag had been planted on the Pacific shore. The residents of Yerba Buena talked of its becoming a great city.

William Heath Davis, a shrewd American-born merchant who knew the bay and all coastal California as only a man who had spent years in the hide and tallow trade could know it, thought that there was reason to believe that wholly new towns could be established. He invited his old friend Don Vicente Peralta to dinner and offered him $5,000 in cash for a part of his rancho on the *contra costa*. On that part of the rancho known as the Encinal de Temescal, where the skyscrapers of downtown Oakland now rise, Davis proposed to lay out a town that would be a kind of Brooklyn to the metropolis a-borning on the San Francisco Peninsula—a picturesque retreat for overworked businessmen. It would include all the land from the bay to what is now Lake Merritt and from the Estuary of San Antonio to the present Fifteenth Street. Davis outlined his plans to construct a wharf on the estuary and to inaugurate a ferryboat service between his new town and Yerba Buena.

Alas for the dream! After taking the matter "under advisement" for some days, Don Vicente refused to part with any of his acres. To no avail did Davis prophesy, correctly, that if the ranchero did not himself open a tract to legitimate settlement, eventually squatters would wrest his land from him, slaughter his cattle, and sell the meat in the port across the bay.

A Rival City

Unlike the land-loving Vicente Peralta, Mariano Guadalupe Vallejo was eager to increase the value of land in his Rancho Suscol by inviting settlement. He willingly deeded to his friends Thomas O. Larkin and Robert Semple, a participant in the Bear Flag Revolt, a townsite on the north side of Carquinez Strait. There, on deep water about midway between the Golden Gate and the vast interior valleys of California, promoters Larkin and Semple envisaged the rise of the great metropolis of the West Coast. In Semple's view, Yerba Buena, on its windy peninsula, was off the direct route of communication between Monterey, the territorial capital, and the huge, promising interior, in which John Sutter, at New Helvetia, was raising wheat and cattle. From Monterey, travelers could proceed by way of San Jose, Mission San Jose,

Mission Pass, and the warm valleys on the east side of the Berkeley Hills to a crossing at the strait. A city on the north side of this waterway could dominate the trade of all northern California, Semple asserted.

"Francisca" was the name chosen for the city-to-be, in honor of Vallejo's wife, María Francisca Felipa Benicia Carrillo Vallejo. Semple began advertising the prospective city under this name in the first newspaper in the territory, *The Californian*, which he and Walter Colton had begun to publish in Monterey.

So effectively did the former Kentuckian ballyhoo his and Larkin's dream city that the residents of Yerba Buena became alarmed, then indignant. A city with a name so closely resembling that of San Francisco Bay would easily become known throughout the world, cheating Yerba Buena of recognition. The first alcalde under the American regime, Lieutenant Washington Allen Bartlett of the United States Navy, decided to forestall the infringement. On January 23, 1847, he proclaimed that "San Francisco was the official name," of the first settlement, and he ordained that it should thereafter "be used in all official communications and public documents, or records appertaining to the town [of Yerba Buena]."[1]

Compelled to change the name of their projected city, Larkin and Semple substituted the fourth of Señora Vallejo's many names for the one originally chosen. The columns of *The Californian* on June 19, 1847, notified the world that Francisca had become Benicia City. To impress the villagers of San Francisco with the strength of his conviction that their town had no chance in competition with Benicia, Semple ostentatiously gave away a lot in San Francisco on the Fourth of July.

By September, Benicia was beginning to develop. Semple, on the site daily, showed lots to twenty or thirty visitors a day and made a good many sales. In fact, his success encouraged him to raise the price of lots from twenty to fifty dollars. San Franciscans were frankly troubled by this real-estate venture. Larkin, living in their midst, missed no opportunity to make them wonder if they ought not to invest in Benicia.

Surveys in San Francisco

Actually, San Francisco itself had been in a flurry of land speculation all summer and had little reason to be perturbed by the activities of Larkin and Semple. In anticipation of a rapid increase in population and a demand for additional lots, Alcalde Bartlett, at the urging of a citizens' committee, had ordered a survey made that enlarged the town on all sides, and then had acceded to pleas for the laying out and selling of lots on the mud flats of Yerba Buena Cove. This area, partly submerged except at low tide, was of immense potential value because eventually it was certain to be filled to deep water. Town officials favored the proposed sale as a means of obtaining funds to supply an inadequate treasury; speculators saw an opportunity to enrich themselves.

Both the general survey and the survey of the waterfront lots were made by a Dublin Irishman named Jasper O'Farrell, who had come to Yerba Buena in 1843. He is said to have tried to introduce streets adapted to the hilly terrain; but landowners would tolerate no deviation from the gridiron street system shown on Vioget's map of the town, because they considered this pattern most convenient for the subdivision of lots. O'Farrell therefore realigned the streets platted by his predecessor and extended them, even though continuance of the rigid rectilinear system would eventually necessitate cutting streets through dunes and lofty hills to the north, west, and south of the settled area. He used his own judgment concerning Market Street, however. That thoroughfare he surveyed as a diagonal artery 110 feet wide, following the direction of the old road to Mission Dolores. South of Market Street, O'Farrell laid out blocks at right angles to it and made them four times the size of those on the north side of the street, because he deemed small lots undesirable. Downtown San Francisco, consequently, consists of two different gridiron patterns spliced together at an acute angle at Market Street, with a series of triangular blocks and several dead-end intersections along the north side of the thoroughfare.

O'Farrell's survey, including the water lots, covered some eight hundred acres and extended approximately three-quarters of a mile from north to south and two miles from east to west. North of Market Street it included the area bounded by Post, Leavenworth, and Francisco streets and the waterfront. South of Market Street were four full blocks fronting on Fourth Street and eleven full blocks on Second Street.

Even though California had not yet become a part of the United States by treaty with Mexico, and no representative of either nation could give valid title to land, General Stephen W. Kearny, military governor of California, released the waterfront lots to the town and decreed that they should be sold at auction for the benefit of the community. More than half of the 450 parcels into which O'Farrell had divided the submerged area were snapped up in four days in late July, 1847. Beach lots measuring 45 by 137½ feet sold for as much as $600, while submerged lots of the same dimensions brought from $50 to $400. By contrast, lots 100 varas wide in the big blocks south of Market Street sold for only $29, including fees. (A vara was about 33 inches.)

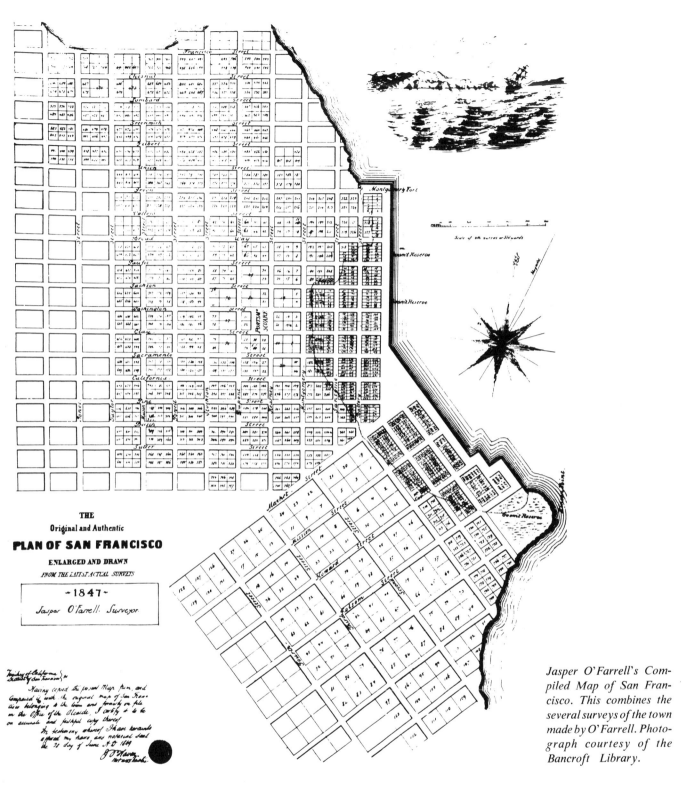

THE
Original and Authentic
PLAN OF SAN FRANCISCO
ENLARGED AND DRAWN
FROM THE LATEST ACTUAL SURVEYS

~1847~

Jasper O'Farrell. Surveyor.

Jasper O'Farrell's Compiled Map of San Francisco. This combines the several surveys of the town made by O'Farrell. Photograph courtesy of the Bancroft Library.

The population of San Francisco was then estimated at approximately 460, exclusive of Colonel Jonathan D. Stevenson's Seventh New York Volunteers, who had arrived on three transports in March. Although the prospects of the town impressed Army and Navy officers favorably and encouraged them in all manner of land speculation, William Tecumseh Sherman was one West Point man who would not invest in San Francisco real estate. The future hero of the march through Georgia "felt actually insulted" at being thought "such a fool as to pay money for property in such a horrid place as Yerba Buena."[2]

The Ubiquitous Gridiron

So far as land platting was concerned, the rival city of Benicia was no better than San Francisco. O'Farrell laid out that community, too, with a pattern as uncompromisingly rectangular as the one fastened upon San Francisco. His town survey contains not the slightest indication that the site on Carquinez Strait is characterized by gently rolling hills. With complete disregard of the irregularities of the shoreline, he platted the blocks into the offshore area. On paper Benicia is a mechanical arrangement of more than four hundred blocks divided uniformly into eight lots measuring 100 by 150 feet, with alleys 25 feet wide running lengthwise through the blocks. All streets are 85 feet wide, as Semple and Larkin had agreed they should be. The only concessions to urban amenity in this monotonous scheme for vending land are four public squares, each equal to two of the rectangular blocks, a centrally situated park four blocks in extent, and a cemetery of the same size, also occupying a focal position in the layout.

Gridiron platting was everywhere identified with urban order and progress under the new American regime in California. In San Jose, first one surveyor and then another imposed the rectitude of straight streets upon the meandering roadways of the old pueblo. In Sonoma, O'Farrell and an associate named J. M. Hudspeth augmented Vallejo's simple design for a plaza into a gridiron town plan, to the evident satisfaction of the American alcalde, Lilburn W. Boggs, an appointee of the military governor. And in the spring of 1848 when Nathan Coombs founded a fifth town in the Bay Area, it too was staked out according to a rectilinear plan.

This new town was called Napa, a name derived from an Indian word. Coombs, having received eighty acres from Nicolas Higuera in payment for work on the latter's new adobe house, decided to start a town at the confluence of the Napa River and Napa Creek. Since the river was navigable to this junction, the founder foresaw a good future for the community as the natural shipping point for farmers in the Napa Valley, which was even then fairly well settled by American and Spanish-Mexican families.

Before the first building in the town was completed, the owner heard momentous news that sent him flying to the foothills of the Sierra Nevada, there to be joined by most of the residents of San Francisco, San Jose, Sonoma, Benicia, Monterey, San Juan Bautista, and every other town and crossroads settlement in northern California.

Gold Fever

Rumors that gold had been found at Sutter's sawmill at Coloma and at Mormon Bar on the American River had been circulating since mid-February, 1848; but Californians remained skeptical until Samuel Brannan made a trip to the areas of discovery in April and May and returned to San Francisco with glittering particles of the precious metal. Then, seeing him dash up and down the streets shouting "Gold, gold, gold from the American River!," the Doubting Thomases believed.

By early summer, gold fever struck the populace of southern California and the northwestern provinces of Mexico. In late summer, fortune seekers from Hawaii joined the rush to the placers. By early fall, American settlers from the Willamette Valley in Oregon were invading the Mother Lode country. Still later came Chileans, Australians, and some Chinese. With shovel, pan, basket, and bowl, prospectors ranged from the eastern tributaries of the Sacramento River southward to the tributaries of the San Joaquin. They numbered not more than eight or ten thousand by the end of the year, however, and were but the vanguard of the hordes of gold-lusting migrants yet to come.

Winter rains and snows drove large numbers of miners from the placer regions to the bay towns, where they filled every available shelter to overflowing. Carpenters earning from $16 to $20 a day hastily clapped together more buildings in Benicia, which had had only fifteen or twenty structures before the stampede to the gold country began. San Francisco, a town of some two hundred buildings at the beginning of the summer, expanded on all sides as the prices of lots recently thought almost worthless soared fantastically. Speculators gladly paid $10,000 for certain choice corners. In San Jose, Sonoma, and Napa both substantial and flimsy structures augmented the supply of housing.

On December 5, 1848, President Polk spoke the word that dissolved the last lingering doubts entertained by Easterners concerning the fabulous stories of California that they had been reading in their newspapers since mid-September, or earlier. In a message to Congress based on communications from Larkin and Colonel Richard B. Mason, the Chief Executive proclaimed: "The accounts of the abundance of gold in that territory are of such an extraordinary character as would scarcely command belief were they not corroborated by the authentic reports of officers in the public service, who have visited the mineral district, and derived the facts which they detail from personal observation."[3]

The Great Migration

Not only were tens of thousands of more than usually energetic and adventurous Americans immediately impelled toward the sparsely settled territory that Mexico had formally ceded to the United States just nine days after the discovery of gold; thousands of impoverished or persecuted Europeans were also provided a haven where every man was as good as the next one and the capabilities of all were needed to develop a country practically untouched. Restless veterans of the war with Mexico, destitute survivors of the potato famine of 1846–1847 in Ireland, and libertarians who had defied autocracy in the revolutions of 1848 in France and central Europe alike responded to the sudden opportunity to begin life anew in El Dorado. Still later, in 1850, thousands of farmers uprooted by the Taiping rebellion in southeastern China embarked for the golden sanctuary. The nuggets in the stream beds were lodestars of hope to the distressed, beacon fires of temptation to the unscrupulous and the greedy.

Throughout 1849 and on into the next year and the next the great migration continued, by way of the steaming Isthmus of Panama, across Nicaragua, through the Strait of Magellan, and round Cape Horn, across the plains from Missouri, across the southern deserts, over the plateaus and through the bandit-infested barrancas of Mexico. Along the way thousands died of cholera and tropical diseases, of thirst, of hardship, privation, and exposure. Ships disappeared at sea and were never heard of again. But large numbers of the Argonauts reached their destination. Hubert Howe Bancroft, the historian, estimated that forty-two thousand emigrants came overland to California in 1849, of whom nine thousand were from Mexico.[4] The authors of *The Annals of San Francisco* placed the number of sea-borne arrivals at forty thousand,

San Francisco in 1849, as Seen from Broadway near Kearny Street. Long Wharf and the storeship Apollo are the most prominent features in Yerba Buena Cove. Happy Valley lies in the low sand hills south of the town. From an engraving in Gazlay's American Biography, 1861.

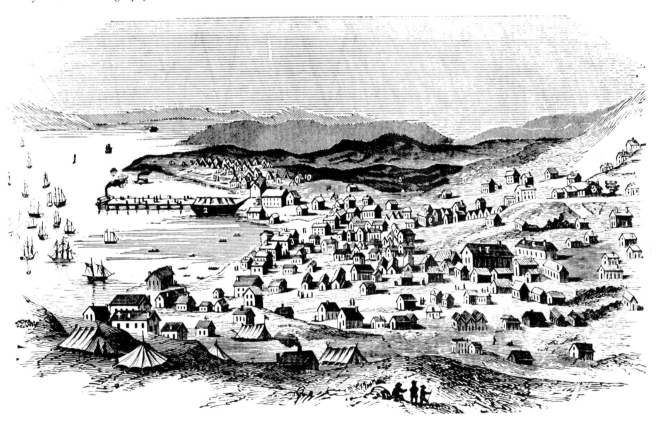

not including the three or four thousand seamen who deserted from hundreds of ships after reaching San Francisco Bay.[5]

Bay and River Routes

Overland parties headed directly for the mining regions. Probably two-thirds or more of the passengers of incoming ships struck out for the gold fields as soon as they could procure horses and wagons or buy passage on sloops and steamboats destined for Sacramento or Stockton. The water route to the interior was by far the easier, since roads were little more than ruts and the land journey from San Francisco involved a long, slow trip down the Peninsula and round the southern arm of the bay or an equally roundabout peregrination through the North Bay country, after a crossing to Sausalito or Mission San Rafael.

The bay in 1849 and 1850 was the equivalent of a network of highways and rail lines. Together with the Sacramento and San Joaquin rivers, it afforded easy access to the mines, and it united all the surrounding country with the port at San Francisco. With few exceptions the towns established in the Bay Area just before the gold rush and during it were situated on the bay or on navigable sloughs and creeks tributary to it—Benicia, Napa, New York of the Pacific (now Pittsburg), Martinez, Alviso, Vallejo, San Antonio, Clinton, Mezesville (Redwood City), San Rafael (as a platted town), Antioch, Suisun, Union City, Petaluma, Oakland, and Alameda. Communities in the fertile valleys represented a secondary ring of settlement, which developed as the gold fever abated and tired or disillusioned miners realized that the common soil held for the ordinary man riches at least as great as those in the gravel of the Mother Lode country.

San Francisco Waterfront

San Francisco, the metropolis suddenly brought into being by the gold rush, virtually rose from the bay, or at least in part on the bay, for the immediate endeavor of her residents, aside from devising temporary shelter for the hordes of newcomers, was to extend wharves into the bay and then begin the process of filling Yerba Buena Cove to deep water. Nature favored the city by making the western side of the bay deep and the eastern or continental side shallow. But the motley parade of steamers, brigs, whalers, colliers, barks, schooners, and bottoms of every sort that swept in through the Golden Gate in the spring and summer of 1849 had to drop anchor at arm's length from the bustling shore, and passengers and cargoes had to be lightered across the mud flats to the waterfront on Montgomery Street.

The most impressive of the piers built to eliminate this inconvenient and bothersome little journey was Central Wharf, or Long Wharf, in a location now marked by Commercial Street. It extended two thousand feet into the bay, to a point where the water was deep enough to permit Pacific Mail steamers to lie alongside. So profitable was this wharf to the men who financed it that other groups quickly followed their example. Before long the shore of the cove was spiked with piers. Sacramento, Clay, Washington, California, and other streets grew bayward on pilings. Many smaller piers, some built by the municipality, also sprang up between the longer ones.

On both sides of the wharves arose a ramshackle assortment of buildings perched on piles—commission houses, groceries, saloons, cheap-John shops, and mock auction rooms. Plank walks laid on piles linked the wharves, and here and there a crosswalk enclosed an unseaworthy hulk that had been converted into a warehouse, store, hotel, or office. By 1850 more than a thousand people were living on these old ships and in the buildings constructed on piles. Along the crosswalks, as along the wharves, merchants and shipping companies constructed more warehouses and shops resting on piles, little realizing that these built-up crosswalks would become, in the not distant future, the cross streets of the lower business district, such as Sansome, Battery, and Drum streets. The port of entry to El Dorado thus presented to the arriving voyager the appearance of a rickety Venice, hemmed in by a forest of masts.

Cities on the Strait

More than the desire to make a fortune in wharf charges spurred the businessmen of San Francisco to action along the waterfront. Their chronic fear that Benicia, a city on deep water, might really become the metropolis of which Larkin and Semple had dreamed was kept alive by the interest of the Army and Navy in Benicia. General Persifer Smith, who relieved Colonel Mason in the territorial command, established a general depot for his division there and made no secret of his hearty dislike for San Francisco. It was, he informed the Adjutant General in Washington, D.C., "in no way fitted for military or commercial purposes; there is no harbor, a bad landing place, bad water, no supplies of provisions, and inclement climate, and it is cut off from the rest of the country except by a long circuit around the southern extremity of the bay."[6] Benicia, on the other hand, appealed to the general as a place "open to the whole country in the rear and accessible without difficulty to ships of the largest class."[7] It was also "above the influence of . . . fogs."

Others shared the general's opinion that the country in

the vicinity of Carquinez Strait had the advantage of superior geographical location. Colonel William M. Smith, agent for Ignacio Martinez, owner of the huge Rancho El Pinole, determined to give Larkin and Semple some near-by competition by building a town directly opposite Benicia on the south side of the strait. There, at the terminus of the road coming up from San Jose through the San Ramon and Ygnacio valleys, Smith had a surveyor divide 120 acres into blocks and lots. The town was named Martinez, after the ranchero on whose land it stood. Lots sold readily, and houses and two or three stores began to rise almost immediately.

Speculative Ventures

A less successful promotional effort was that of Colonel Jonathan D. Stevenson, late of the New York Volunteers, who engaged William T. Sherman and some of his cohorts to lay out New York of the Pacific on Suisun Bay near the mouth of the San Joaquin River. The city languished for many decades as one of the abortive ventures of the gold rush era, though time was to prove Sherman wrong in the statement made in his memoirs that " 'New York of the Pacific' never came to anything."[8] Eventually, after various changes of name, it became Pittsburg, today a thriving industrial city.

At the extreme southern end of San Francisco Bay still another get-rich-quick town appeared in the winter of 1849–50. Jacob D. Hoppe and other leading residents of San Jose obtained a tract of land not far from the old *embarcadero* of Mission Santa Clara on the lower Guadalupe River and employed Chester S. Lyman to lay out the city of Alviso. To stir up interest in what they hoped would become the port for the Santa Clara Valley, they talked of a canal to San Jose. Lots went on sale at $600, and the city founders braced themselves for a rush of business.

They were disappointed. At the end of two years Alviso had two hotels, several stores, a tavern, a blacksmith shop, and a handful of dwellings. Thereafter the sound of the hammer was heard only occasionally in the town. The price of lots tobogganed. For two decades or more there was, however, a considerable movement of grain, fruits, and vegetables from the docks of Alviso to San Francisco. Then the town sank into a lethargy from which it has never roused itself. It was the victim of progress, in the form of a railroad on the Peninsula.

Agitation for the railroad began the very winter that Alviso was founded, and it continued, off an on, for more than a decade, through various unsuccessful attempts to finance the enterprise, until the line was finally started in the 'sixties.

Growth of San Francisco

In the meantime, in San Francisco the unceasing arrival of voyagers and the winter retreat of miners from the gold fields to the city stimulated an orgy of land speculation that made the promotional activities of the founders of Benicia, Martinez, New York of the Pacific, and Alviso appear trivial. Few lots were sold in the city's first suburb, the Potrero Nuevo, laid out by Dr. John Townsend and Cornelius de Boom on the south bank of Mission Bay in 1849; but the failure of the Potrero Nuevo as a subdivision was due more to its then seemingly remote and inaccessible location than to any lack of market for real estate. In the city proper the firm of Finley, Johnson and Company sold for $300,000 property that had cost them only $23,000 the year before. A lot on Portsmouth Square, bought in the spring for $6,000, sold in the fall for $45,000. The lot which Semple had given away two years earlier to demonstrate his faith in Benicia now commanded a small fortune.

Because the last of the lots surveyed in 1847 by Jasper O'Farrell had been sold early in 1849, the town council in October ordered William Eddy, the city surveyor, to survey additional lands as far west as Leavenworth and Eighth streets, in the vicinity of the present Civic Center. More than three thousand lots in this newly platted area were sold by January, 1850. Together they contained nearly two square miles of territory, exclusive of streets.

The built-up area of the city extended from Clark's Point to the Rincon, overflowed through the little gap known as the *portezuela*, between the hills at Pacific and Jones streets, and surged west over the sand hills far beyond the original confines of the village of Yerba Buena. Tents spread around the base of Telegraph Hill toward the north. South of Market Street, in an area protected by high sand hills and supplied by a good spring of water, more tents, perhaps a thousand, stood side by side. This was "Happy Valley," which became anything but happy as torrential rains descended during the winter of 1849–50. Here, at approximately the present intersection of First and Mission streets, Peter and James Donahue, pioneer industrialists, established a small foundry to produce picks and shovels for miners, and here began to develop the city's first manufacturing district. Still farther south, near what is now Howard Street, was "Pleasant Valley."

Approximately twenty thousand people inhabited this city of tents, shanties, and flimsy houses with walls covered by muslin in lieu of plaster. It had sprung up with weedlike rapidity, to the utter amazement of miners who had left it in the early spring when it was a town of perhaps two thousand residents.

First State Legislature

Many of the inhabitants of this boom town considered themselves merely temporary residents of California. When their luck ran out or the going got tough, they would leave. But there was another class, in Sacramento, Stockton, and other towns as well as in San Francisco, who had come to stay. The men of this class were eager to assume civic responsibilities and to establish democratic self-government in place of the military authority that was proving inadequate to protect life and property in California's fast-growing communities.

This better element was represented by the men who began convening at San Jose on December 15, 1849, as members of California's first state legislature under American rule. Their coming together in the temporary state capital was irregular, to say the least, but so had been an earlier gathering in Monterey at which a state constitution had been drafted. The people of California had ratified the constitution and had elected a civil governor, lieutenant governor, state legislators, and two representatives to Congress; and now the lawmakers of the audacious, self-created commonwealth were going to organize a state government even though Congress had not yet admitted California to the Union. Both Missouri and Michigan had done the same thing before admission, setting a precedent for California.

Once the lawmakers had overcome the initial difficulties of an unfinished state house (originally planned as a hotel) and the lack of such essential equipment as paper, pens, ink, and writing desks, or even the funds with which to purchase these articles, they elected John C. Frémont and William M. Gwin to the United States Senate, drafted civil and criminal codes, created tax and judicial structures, and provided for the organization of counties, cities, and towns.

The senate committee on county boundaries at first suggested creation of eighteen counties, but the legislators finally agreed upon a total of twenty-seven, seven of which bordered on San Francisco Bay: San Francisco, Santa Clara, Contra Costa, Marin, Sonoma, Solano, and Napa. Both Sonoma and Napa counties extended considerably farther north than they do today, and Sonoma County had only a short coastline, compared with its present rather long boundary on the Pacific. San Francisco County included most of what is now San Mateo County. Contra Costa County and Santa Clara County each included parts of what is now Alameda County. Since no accurate surveys of the state had yet been made and the legislature lacked reliable maps, the boundaries of Sonoma, Napa, and Solano counties were left indefinite,

subject to more precise delineation at a later time.

County seats designated by the legislature were: San Francisco, for the county of that name; San Jose, for Santa Clara County; Martinez, for Contra Costa County; San Rafael, for Marin County; Sonoma, for the county of that name; Benicia, for Solano County; and Napa, for the county of that name.

Among the first cities incorporated as self-governing municipalities were four in the Bay Area—San Francisco, San Jose, Benicia, and Sonoma.

The New City of Vallejo

Toward the close of the session, the legislature turned its attention to the subject of the permanent location of the state capital. Various citizens of San Jose offered tracts of land for a capitol and other public structures. The municipal authorities of Monterey offered Colton Hall, in which the state constitution had been drafted, and all the land needed for public buildings. San Francisco was willing to contribute such buildings and grounds as the legislature might select, providing the whole did not cost more than $100,000. Senator Mariano G. Vallejo, of Sonoma, topped all these propositions in a "memorial" in which he offered, if the legislature would establish the capital on land which he owned "upon the straits of Carquinez and Napa river," to lay out a city to be called "Eureka or such other name as the legislature might suggest."[9] Further, he proposed to give to the state, as soon as the legislature accepted his offer, 156 acres for building sites and a total of $370,000 in grants for specific purposes, including $125,000 for a capitol.

The permanent location for the capital proved to be a controversial issue that the legislature decided to sidestep, preferring to schedule an election in which the people of the state should choose among the cities competing for the honor. The voters, not being politicians, found the choice easy: they enthusiastically endorsed Vallejo's offer.

At the time the senator from Sonoma presented his memorial, the site of what was to become not Eureka but the city of Vallejo was marked by two small sheet-iron buildings, one of them called, somewhat pretentiously, the Union House. Here travelers to and from the mines found lodging. On this site Vallejo and his associates laid out a town of rectangular blocks south of present Georgia Street. Several interested persons were induced to erect buildings in 1850, but the town was far from being equipped to function as the seat of government when the lawmakers assembled there in 1851. After a few days they adjourned to San Jose, which was still the legal capital since no act had been passed changing the location.

Anticipating that the city of Vallejo would be ready to accommodate them properly a year later, the legislators on February 4, 1851, enacted a measure making the new city the permanent seat of government. But in 1852 they were to be disappointed in Senator Vallejo's ability to produce the statehouse that he had promised. In 1853 the legislators shifted the capital to Benicia, and in 1854 to Sacramento.

Señor Vallejo lacked business experience of a type that could rally his associates to support his magnificent project. The city that he had envisaged as a state capital owed its growth to the Navy Yard established on Mare Island in 1854 and to its selection somewhat later as the bay terminus of a railroad to the Sacramento Valley. Both in its unique origin and in its development under the stimulus of military activity it differed from other Bay Area towns, the majority of which owed their existence directly or indirectly to the mushroom growth of San Francisco.

Mother of Cities

The city on the Peninsula was literally a metropolis, a mother of cities. Although it grew from about twenty thousand in the winter of 1849–50 to not more than fifty thousand in the winter of 1854–55 (when the boom ushered in by the gold rush collapsed), San Francisco was of sufficient size, in an almost totally undeveloped country, to stimulate the birth and growth of settlements throughout the territory surrounding the bay. The people of this port city at first were dependent upon distant sources for practically everything they ate, wore, slept on, rode in, read, and bought and sold. Alternately, the wharves in Yerba Buena Cove were glutted with imports or were almost empty, depending upon whether several ships arrived within a few days of one another or a week or more went by without the arrival of a single large cargo. With an entire urban population thus at the mercy of unreliable sources of supply and deprived of many of the more delectable articles of the table, such as fresh fruits and vegetables, opportunities were wide open for men who had not succumbed to the lure of gold to start farms, to set up sawmills or grist mills, to manufacture salt from the waters of the bay, to build sloops and schooners for the transportation of lumber and farm produce, to develop toll roads, and to engage in every type of enterprise that would aid in supplying the market. At the landing places around the bay, from which raw materials and foodstuffs were shipped to the city, there were opportunities for still other men to lay out towns and sell real estate. The development of a good-sized port city in a few short years not surprisingly brought into being a whole complex of towns that were socially and economically linked to it.

Two of the basic needs, food and shelter, provided the stimulus for most of the villages and towns formed in this nascent period of the metropolitan region. The ranchos, particularly those in southern California, supplied the ever-expanding demand for beef; hunters of wild game provided a small part of the fresh meat consumed; and ships brought in nearly everything else required for sustenance during the first two or three years of the gold rush. But little shelter could have been provided if the hastily improvised city had had to depend on remote sources for lumber. A few precut houses were shipped all the way from Massachusetts, but it was the primeval redwood forests of the San Francisco Bay Area that supplied most of the boards, two-by-fours, and shingles needed for building shanties, hotels, and gambling houses in San Francisco. The first nonspeculative communities spawned by the metropolis were small lumber settlements, most of them only temporary. One or two that survived the period of ruthless exploitation of the ancient redwood groves did so because they enjoyed additional locational advantages. The assault on the virgin stands of timber was so unrelenting that by the end of the 1850's most of the early lumber settlements were surrounded by stumps and devastation. Six terrible fires in San Francisco between December 24, 1849, and May 4, 1851, also contributed to the exhaustion of the forests. The timber operators moved ever farther from the scene of their first endeavors— northward from the Marin Peninsula into the Russian River country, and over the mountains from the bay side of the San Francisco Peninsula into the more inaccessible canyons on the coastal side.

Lumber Towns

A hamlet on Redwood Slough, some twenty miles south of San Francisco on the bay side of the Peninsula, was one of the few settlements associated with lumber operations to achieve permanence. In 1853, when fifteen sawmills were going full blast in the Cañada de Raymundo, a few miles inland, the little settlement on the slough boasted wharves, stores, and boat works in which lumber schooners were built. Schooners piled high with milled lumber twisted down the slough to the bay, and logs were rafted on the ebb tide up the bay to San Francisco. What more natural than that S. M. Mezes, an attorney who had received a large tract of land in Rancho de las Pulgas from the Argüello family in payment for his work in protecting their title from squatters and other encroachers, should conceive the idea, in 1854, of laying out a typical gridiron town near the landing place? A busy *embarcadero* invariably suggested the possibility of attracting trade and permanent settlers. Mezesville, now Redwood City, had the further advantage of being at the junction of El Camino Real with a road from the lumbering area, the site of the present city of Woodside. Before another decade the town would also be a railroad stop.

The village of San Antonio, on upper San Antonio Creek, as the Oakland Estuary was then called, owed its existence in part to lumbering operations in the hills above the present Fruitvale section of Oakland, but other developments also contributed to its prosperity. Even before 1851, when James Larue built the wharf and store that became the nucleus of the village, the *embarcadero* of San Antonio was a busy place. Three sawmills were operating in the redwoods on the hills above the landing by the end of 1850, and lumber was being shipped from the landing to San Francisco. Captain Thomas Gray's propeller steamer *Kangaroo* began making semiweekly trips from the city to the *embarcadero* that same year, inaugurating the first transbay ferry service. Stages first ran to Stockton and to San Jose from the landing about the same time. Miners, too, set out on horseback from the *embarcadero* for the gold country, taking a route through Niles Canyon and Livermore Valley. San Antonio thus sprang up at a break in transportation routes and had not only lumber shipping but also travel to encourage its development. It was one of two small communities that were the progenitors of East Oakland. The other was Clinton, a promotional venture on the east side of the slough that has since become Lake Merritt. Both towns later merged to form Brooklyn, which in turn was absorbed by Oakland in 1872.

Pressure on the Ranchos

The collective appetite of the rapidly growing city near the Golden Gate was a much more potent force in spurring the formation of new settlements than was the need for shelter. Relatively few men could engage in the lumber operations, because, for one thing, the forests grew only in certain areas. But since all the valleys that drained into the bay offered good land for farming, as soon as the novelty of placer mining wore off or the vicissitudes of mining became discouraging, many of those who had been farmers elsewhere naturally turned to the soil to make a living.

At first the California rancho system tended to be a deterrent to widespread settlement. Would-be agriculturists found some of the choicest acres in the possession of Mexican rancheros. When the rancheros refused to sell, as they often did, the land-hungry Americans had the choice of moving on, becoming squatters, or resorting to legal trickery to get possession of the land. For years,

relations between the earlier Californians and the newcomers were marked by struggles on the ranchos and in the courts. Presumably the rancho system was protected by a clear-cut provision of the Treaty of Guadalupe Hidalgo stating that the United States would recognize "legitimate titles to every description of property, personal and real, existing in the ceded territories" formerly belonging to Mexico. But a Congress not unsympathetic to the desires of Americans who were eager to obtain land enacted a measure in 1851 that required all holders of land grants to establish the validity of their titles, thereby encouraging a certain amount of squatting on the ranchos of families whose grants were suspected of being fraudulent, though squatting of course was not confined to dubious grants. Some of the old families whose records were in good order had as much trouble with squatters as landholders who had grabbed large tracts in highly irregular fashion in the last days of the Mexican regime. Protracted legal battles, in which the rancheros sought to establish the validity of their titles, however, probably did more to break up the coveted grants than did the invasions of squatters. Many rancheros were forced into bankruptcy by the cost of defending their titles; some forfeited their grants because they were unable to bear the cost of presenting their claims; and still others, lacking cash, paid their attorneys with huge tracts of land. Thus the rancho system gradually yielded to the pressure of the newcomers, and acres once given over exclusively to cattle raising passed into the hands of men who sowed grain, set out fruit orchards, and planted potatoes, cabbages, and other vegetables.

Shipping Points

Just as some of the lumber shipping points became permanent towns, so did many of the produce shipping points. Antioch (originally Smith's Landing), Union City, Petaluma, and Suisun all developed at landings from which small craft transported agricultural products to San Francisco; and all four served as trading centers for the fertile agricultural areas in which the products were grown. Smith's Landing, renamed for the Biblical city by a group of pious folk who settled there in 1850 at the invitation of the Reverend J. H. Smith, was at the mouth of the San Joaquin River. Union City, founded in 1851 by J. M. Horner, occupied a site at the junction of Alameda Creek with a navigable slough and took its name from a small steamer called *The Union*, used by Horner to transport the vegetables and flour of his friends and neighbors to "the city." Petaluma, sixteen miles upstream on meandering Petaluma Creek, was surveyed as a town in January, 1852, and soon flourished as a shipping outlet for not only the Cotati Valley but also for settlements as far away as Mendocino County. The town of Suisun, at the head of Suisun Slough in Solano County, was laid out in 1854, after the landing first used by Captain Josiah Wing for the loading of wild grain had become a shipping point for farmers in the vicinity.

A platted town at the *embarcadero* of San Rafael in Marin County preceded several of these agricultural outlets but is in the same general category of subregional shipping and trade centers. The export of firewood and beef from the ranchos in the vicinity of the old mission settlement encouraged speculators by the name of Myers and McCullough to lay out a town in blocks three hundred feet square in 1850.

Interior towns that developed as population fanned out into the valleys around the bay were Vacaville, in Solano County, Santa Rosa, in the upper Cotati Valley, and San Jose and Santa Clara, in the Santa Clara Valley. The discovery of artesian water in San Jose and its vicinity early in 1854 immediately stimulated many new agricultural ventures and brought about further growth of both San Jose and Santa Clara. The latter town also had the distinction of being the seat of one of the first institutions of higher learning in the Bay Area, the College of Santa Clara, opened in 1851 in the dilapidated buildings of the old Mission Santa Clara.

The significant thing about most of the towns at the water's edge and in the valleys was that they were marked off into blocks and lots only after various kinds of economic activity indicated that an urban community on the site might enjoy some degree of permanence. Some of the towns, such as Antioch and Suisun, were slow in achieving importance, and one, Union City, later faded away as the near-by towns of New Haven and Alvarado developed; but the majority rested on solid if not spectacular economic foundations. The appearance of the promoter and the surveyor tended to confirm the geographical and economic advantages of the fledgling settlements.

East Bay Towns

At least two towns, Oakland and Alameda, differed from the others in origin. Neither started as an agricultural outlet, as a meeting point of transportation routes, or as a trading post. Both were akin to Benicia in that they were launched by men who were more interested in selling real estate and making money than in anything else.

From the day that William Heath Davis dreamed of laying out a town on the rancho of Vicente Peralta, the Encinal de Temescal seems to have been destined for some kind of speculative venture. Its very location directly opposite San Francisco made it especially tempting to land merchandizers. Next to attempt a town-planning scheme on the site now occupied by Oakland was Colonel Henry S. Fitch, a real-estate auctioneer, who persuaded Don Vicente to agree to sell him 2,400 acres for $8,000 if Fitch could raise that amount within fifteen days. But the colonel's deal fell through when his backer discovered a stranger living on the land and became fearful that the purchasers would be unable to get clear title to the property. The city that Fitch was unable to start by legitimate means a less scrupulous trio had no difficulty in launching by "all the devious ways of chicanery."[10] Oakland is the classic example of the shady real-estate operation, brought off at a time when rancho owners seemed rather helpless in the face of trespassers, squatters, and conniving attorneys.

In the summer of 1850, Horace W. Carpentier, a recent graduate of Columbia College in New York (now Columbia University), Edson Adams, a Yankee trader, and Alexander Moon, a much older man with a varied career, deliberately squatted on Vicente Peralta's land, each grabbing 160 acres. When Don Vicente, accompanied by forty of his vaqueros and a deputy sheriff with a writ of ejectment, sought to oust them, either Moon or Adams won the day by calm and conciliatory talk and protestations of innocence of any intention to deprive the ranchero of his land. But the three partners did not depart. Some time later, backed by a gang of Americans, they returned the call, at Peralta's own home, and "persuaded" him to grant them a lease, presumably with the promise that if his claim should be upheld by the United States Land Commission, they would leave peaceably. Having thus bullied Peralta, they proceeded to employ Julius Kellersberger to map a townsite, so that they could get on with their plan to sell lots on land that belonged to Peralta.

The surveyor drew up a typical gridiron platting scheme for the area extending from First to Fourteenth streets and from a line 300 feet west of West Street to Oak Street. The blocks were uniformly 200 by 300 feet, and the streets were all 80 feet wide with the exception of Main Street (now Broadway), which was 110 feet wide. Kellersberger has been praised for the width of his streets; he also deserves credit for allocating seven blocks, or squares, for parks. These are today the much-appreciated breathing spaces in the older part of Oakland.

In the meantime, Vicente Peralta received an honest offer for his land and in March, 1852, sold all the property south of what was known as the Encinal Line (roughly between what are now Eighteenth and Twentieth streets) to six men who were willing to pay him $10,000 for it. Among them was John C. Hays, who eventually acquired title to practically all the holdings of his associates. Far from deterring Carpentier and his unprincipled partners from proceeding with their scheme, the legitimate transaction merely spurred them to bolder acts. Carpentier obtained through his friend State Senator David C. Broderick the position of enrolling clerk of the senate and used the office to engineer the passage of a bill incorporating the town of Oakland. The act was signed by the governor on May 4, 1852, and became effective immediately.

Before the few souls living within the area of the town knew what was happening, the Carpentier-Adams-Moon triumvirate had set up a town government and put through an ordinance making Carpentier sole owner of the entire waterfront, comprising ten thousand acres of overflowed land, and giving him exclusive right to build wharves, piers, and docks for a period of thirty-seven years, with the privilege also of collecting wharfage and dockage. In return for this grant, Carpentier agreed to build three small wharves and a schoolhouse and to pay the town 2 per cent of the wharfage receipts. This, shorn of details, was the astonishing transaction that raised the

Julius Kellersberger's Map of Oakland, 1853

curtain on a bitter legal drama that was to continue until 1911, when at last Oakland regained the waterfront lost at its inception.

As for the conflicting claims of the Hays group and of Carpentier and his partners, these kept Oakland embroiled in disputes over land titles all through the 'fifties and 'sixties.

While Oakland was being conceived in iniquity and nurtured on corruption, W. W. Chipman, a lawyer and schoolteacher from Ohio, and Gideon Aughinbaugh, a Pennsylvania carpenter, laid out the town of Alameda at the eastern end of the oak-shaded peninsula known as the Encinal de San Antonio. The partners had purchased the entire *encinal* from Antonio Peralta at a time when the ever-active Colonel Fitch was dickering for a portion of it. By way of adjusting the breach of contract between Antonio and Fitch, Chipman and Aughinbaugh offered the colonel a minor interest in their new town, asked him to make the plan for it, and employed his auctioneering skill to dispose of lots. To lure prospective buyers from San Francisco, the promoters resorted to ballyhoo. They purchased two small ferryboats, the *Bonita* and the *Ranger*, and inaugurated their famed "watermelon excursions"—free boat trips and lunches, complete with watermelons and the perfervid oratory of Fitch.

A New County

One result of the growth of towns and farming settlements along the eastern side of the bay was a major change in political boundary lines in the Bay Area. The residents of Oakland, Alameda, Clinton, San Antonio, the unplatted community of Squatterville (on the site of present-day San Lorenzo), New Haven, and other small communities on the bay plain joined forces to create a new county, composed of parts of Contra Costa County and Santa Clara County. Henry C. Smith, who lived in New Haven and was Assemblyman for Santa Clara County, spearheaded the drive for the establishment of Alameda County. His petition to the state legislature pointed out, among other things, that Martinez, the county seat of Contra Costa County, was inconveniently situated to serve such towns as Oakland and Alameda, because it was at least twenty-five miles away and was separated from the bayside communities by a range of hills.

Horace Carpentier, Assemblyman for Contra Costa County, as well as owner of the Oakland waterfront and operator of the ferry service known as the Contra Costa Navigation Company, fought to make Oakland the seat of justice of this eighth Bay Area county; but for once he met his superior in political maneuvering. Smith, who is appropriately remembered as the "father of Alameda

County," succeeded in winning for New Haven, or Alvarado, the honor of being designated the first county seat.

Besides surveyed towns and unplatted but well-recognized little settlements, there appeared between 1849 and 1854 many roadside inns and crossroads taverns around which towns were later to develop. These mere beginnings of communities were found along the stage routes that linked the Bay Area towns. Between San Francisco and San Jose, Thorp's Place opened for business in 1849 at the site of present-day San Bruno, and in 1850 or 1851 the Angelo House was erected on the site of present Belmont, where a road leading to the San Andreas Valley joined El Camino Real. On the East Bay road between San Antonio and San Jose one of the first stage stations stood where the town of San Leandro later sprang up; and another, operated by William Hayward, marked the place where the town of Hayward was to develop.

Expanding Metropolis

The port metropolis toward which the people in all these wayside stops, rural settlements, bayside outlets, and valley towns looked for news of the distant world beyond the seas increased in population with each passing year. Its population was estimated at approximately thirty thousand at the end of 1851. In 1852 almost 77,000 newcomers arrived by ship—more than double the number who had disembarked the previous year; and only 23,000 homesick or disheartened people booked passage on departing vessels. As usual, thousands of the newcomers hurried on to the mines; yet the population of San Francisco rose to between 36,000 and 42,000.

The streets became more crowded; the wharves stretched farther into the bay, as if to welcome the pageant of ships; the sides of Telegraph Hill came tumbling down under the concussions of blasting powder and were dumped into the bay to create more land for buildings. Steam excavators cut Market Street through from Kearny to Battery Street, leveled the mound of sand that had obstructed Bush Street, and made way westward for California, Sacramento, and other streets. Horse-drawn carts dumped the sand into Yerba Buena Cove, and wagons on temporary rails also rolled to the water's edge with their freight of sand, until little by little the city pushed the bay many blocks from the original beach.

Between the post office at Kearny and Clay streets and Mission Dolores, a new omnibus line, the first regular transportation in the city, began operating on a thirty-minute schedule. This was the famous "Yellow Line," which charged a fare of fifty cents on week days and one dollar on Sundays. Just as the plank road to the Mission, when first completed, had proved a stimulus to real-estate

A Design by an Artist Named Stewart for the Improvement of Portsmouth Plaza, San Francisco, 1853. Estimated to cost $100,000, this proposed scheme was never carried out. Photograph courtesy of the San Francisco Public Library.

and building activities, so did the new omnibus line. The pattern of growth in San Francisco, westward and southward and up the slopes of many hills, was to be shaped largely by transit lines—and these would be extended not in response to any plan of development but, as in other American cities, wherever the opportunity for private gain appeared or the mere whim of a tycoon dictated.

Portents of Disaster

Immigration during 1853 was described as "spectacular"; yet there were signs that the boom days of the gold rush would sooner or later come to an end. A great many adventurers departed for Australia, said to be the scene of gold discoveries more promising than those in California. The weekly *Golden Era* observed in July that "our city is filling up with disappointed and disheartened miners, who say that a scarcity of gold and water in the diggings has made it necessary to seek employment in the city."[11]

Despite these portents, the wave of speculation that rose higher and higher with the arrival of each new ship-load of immigrants surged to fantastic heights. On the day after Christmas, bidders outshouted one another in their frenzy to purchase 120 small water lots that were covered by water of an average depth of eight feet. Only at great expense could these lots be filled for building, but the bewitched purchasers eagerly paid a total of $1,193,500 to possess them.

Two months later, creeping paralysis attacked the real-estate market and unimproved town lots were "almost unsalable at any price."[12]

A dream of animated newcomers forever crowding down gangplanks into the port of gold had sustained the saturnalia of speculation. Now immigration unexpectedly fell off and the city found itself appallingly overbuilt. Of one thousand commercial buildings available, only three hundred were occupied in the middle of 1854. Rents dropped 20 to 30 per cent. Several real-estate firms went bankrupt.

With clothing, household furnishings, imported foods, and luxuries of all kinds the city also was oversupplied.

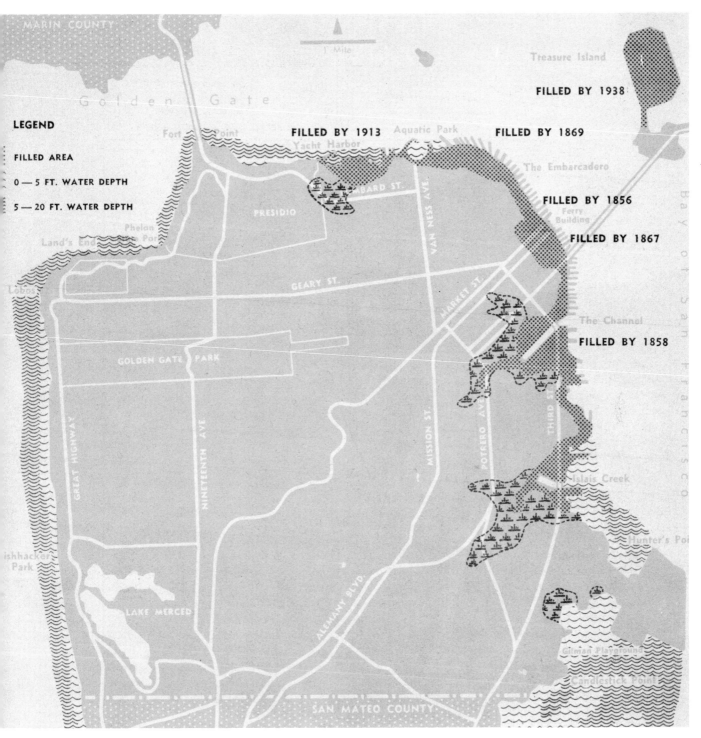

The Changing Shoreline of San Francisco

Now there were forced sales to ease the glutted market. Prices fell day by day. Business failures increased. Clerks lost their jobs and joined discouraged miners in a fruitless search for work.

As the depression grew steadily worse, forceclosures increased, the value of real estate diminished to half what it had been, and credit dried up. The once mercurial inhabitants of San Francisco were borne ineluctably toward the Black Friday of February 23, 1855, when the banking and express firm of Adams and Company failed to open

its doors and general panic seized depositors and investors, bringing about the downfall of many banks and
business houses and wiping out personal fortunes.

The Marvel of California

In a little more than eight years from the time of the
American occupation San Francisco had been transformed from an obscure village to a world-famous city.
To all Californians it was *the* city; for even San Jose,
Stockton, Sacramento, and Marysville were hardly more
than good-sized towns. From the new San Francisco
Mint, opened in April, 1854, standardized coins flowed
into the arteries of trade and finance, replacing the curious
assortment of foreign coins, gold slugs, and pinches of
gold dust previously used as money. In San Francisco's
principal business streets the first gas lamps on the Pacific
Coast lighted the way of the night reveler. The hills were
"dotted with new cottages of all styles of architecture,
ancient and modern,"[13] and at least one real-estate firm,
that of the unctuous Henry Fitch, advertised that it could
"transact business in the English, French, German, Spanish, and Italian languages."[14] San Francisco was the
marvel of California, a city that the whole race of man-
kind had had a hand in fashioning—but it was, as yet,
no breath-taking symbol of human brotherhood.

As Bancroft described it: "It was a straggling city . . .
with its dumps and blotches of hills and hillocks, of bleak
spots of vacancy and ugly cuts and raised lines. The architecture was no less patchy, for in the centre prison-like
and graceful structures alternated, interspersed with frail
wooden frames and zinc and corrugated iron walls, and
occasionally the hull of some hauled-up vessel; while
beyond rude cabins and ungainly superimposed stories of
lodging-houses in neglected grounds varied with tasteful
villas embowered in foliage, and curious houses perched
high on square-cut mounds."[15]

The gridiron street pattern, perpetuated and extended
through the surveys of O'Farrell and Eddy, involved the
municipality and individual citizens in endless expenditures for the adjustment of street grades. "If the great
thoroughfares had been adapted to the natural configuration of the tract of country upon which the city stands,"
the authors of the *Annals of San Francisco* pointed out,
"there might have been some apparent irregularity in the
plan, and some, perhaps some little ground available for
building purposes lost, yet many millions of dollars would
have been saved to the community at large, which, as
matters stand, have already been unprofitably expended,
while millions more must still be spent in overcoming the
obstacles wilfully placed in the way by the originally
defective plans," or, more precisely, by the "absurd
mathematical notions" of Francisco de Haro and Vioget.[16]

CHAPTER THREE

The Plow,
the Iron Horse, and New Towns

As thousands awakened from the gold rush dream of sudden wealth and began to regard California as something more than a Far Western treasure house stocked by an indiscreet nature especially for them to loot, they came soberly to the conclusion that the destiny of the area around San Francisco Bay lay principally in the development of agriculture, manufacturing, and transportation.

San Francisco, though shaken by the failure of two hundred firms in 1855, maintained its position as *the* commercial, financial, and shipping center of California. In addition, it became a center for the manufacture of the new and expensive mining machinery required to extract gold from the veins of quartz in which it was now chiefly to be found. Quartz mining, in fact, fathered a whole series of California industries, the plants of some of which formed the nuclei of new towns in the San Francisco Bay Area. But in the period 1855–1870, agricultural rather than manufacturing developments were of primary significance in shaping the future metropolitan region.

Farming and New Towns

The foundations for agricultural enterprises long associated with the various counties in the Bay Area were laid during the years of readjustment following the financial crisis of 1855. Louis Pellier introduced *la petite prune d'Agen* at San Jose in 1856–1857, giving Santa Clara County the fruit that was to make it famous throughout the world. Colonel Agoston Haraszthy, the Hungarian nobleman who later introduced 315 named varieties of

wine grapes to California, settled in Sonoma in 1856, founded a horticultural society, and began importing vines from abroad. First to advocate the growing of grapes without irrigation, he wrote a treatise on the culture of the vine and the manufacture of wine that was published in 1858 by the state for gratuitous distribution. That same year Charles Krug started the Napa Valley wine industry, producing twelve hundred gallons of wine, on the John Patchet place near the city of Napa, by processes new to early residents. In the Point Reyes area of Marin County, three brothers named Steele and a number of other farmers in 1856 began developing the dairying interests for which the northern part of the county is well known. In Contra Costa County, which was to become a great wheat-producing area, many farmers in the 1850's followed the example set by Elam Brown, of Acalanes, in 1848 when he planted a rather large area to wheat and discovered that the yield was prodigious. By 1858 nearly seventeen thousand acres in the county were rippling with the golden grain.

A natural consequence of the accelerated development of farming was the establishment of new towns in the fertile valleys—Saint Helena in the upper Napa Valley; Sebastopol on the west side of the Cotati Valley, and Bloomfield on the road between the valley and Bodega Bay; Healdsburg on the main wagon road through the Russian River country to Mendocino County; Rio Vista on the Sacramento River in eastern Solano County; Fairfield on the same slough that served its near neighbor,

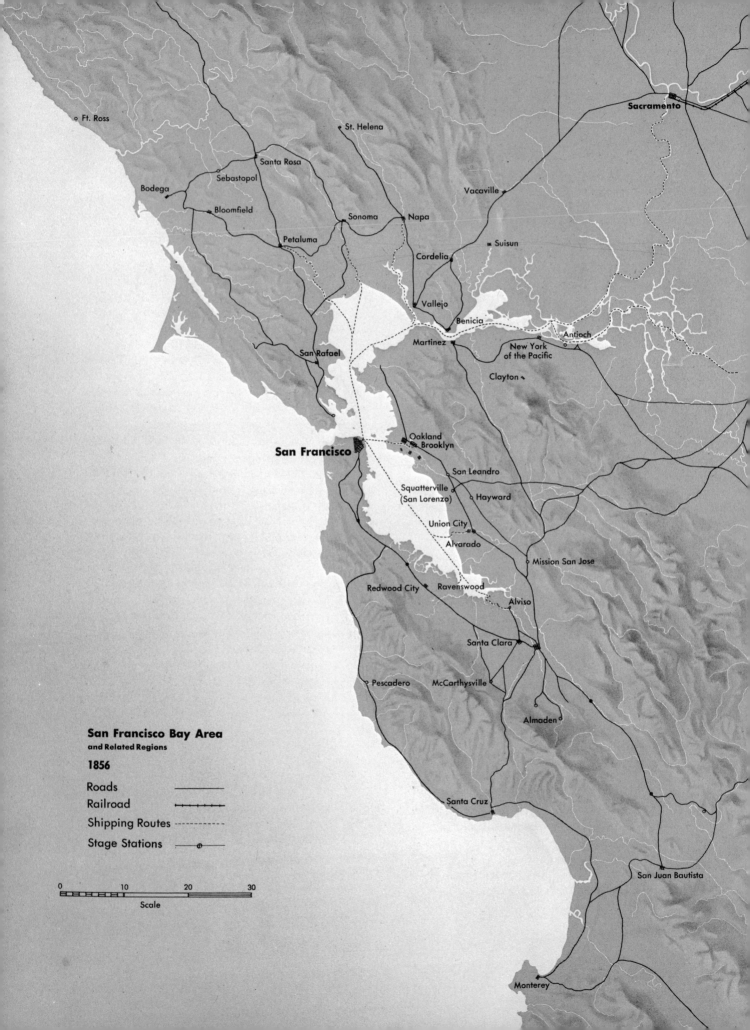

Ft. Ross

St. Helena

Santa Rosa
Sebastopol
Bodega
Bloomfield
Petaluma
Sonoma
Napa

Vacaville

Cordelia
Suisun

Vallejo
Benicia
San Rafael
Martinez
Antioch
New York
of the Pacific

Clayton

Sacramento

San Francisco

Oakland
Brooklyn

San Leandro
Squatterville
(San Lorenzo)
Hayward

Union City
Alvarado

Mission San Jose

Redwood City
Ravenswood
Alviso

Santa Clara

Pescadero
McCarthysville

Almaden

Santa Cruz

San Juan Bautista

Monterey

San Francisco Bay Area
and Related Regions

1856

Roads ————————
Railroad ╟┼┼┼┼┼┼┤
Shipping Routes - - - - - - -
Stage Stations ——◻——

0   10   20   30
Scale

Suisun; and Pacheco and Walnut Creek in the Ygnacio Valley of central Contra Costa County. In addition to these towns, all founded between 1855 and 1860, the town of Clayton was laid out at the foot of Mount Diablo in 1856 by Joel Clayton when the discovery of veins of coal on the northern slopes of the mountain gave promise of large-scale coal mining operations.

Two of this group of towns, Rio Vista and Pacheco, later proved to be subject to flooding. Rio Vista was removed to higher ground after the disastrous floods of the winter of 1861–62. Salvio and Fernando Pacheco and their friend Francisco Galindo started a new town in 1869 two miles east of Pacheco and named it Todos Santos (All Saints). Some Americans disrespectfully tagged it Drunken Indian, but others soon made amends by calling it Concord, by which name it is now known.

Fairfield got off to a good start, thanks to an ambitious founder, Captain R. H. Waterman. At a county-seat convention in 1858, the very year in which the town was platted, Waterman aggressively undertook to transfer the seat of justice from Benicia. His inducement to the voters to accept Fairfield as a county seat was an offer to deed to the county "a certain piece of land containing about sixteen acres, known upon the plat of the town of Fairfield as 'Union Park,'" and certain other properties.[1] In the battle of the ballots waged on September 2, 1858, the sometime state capital was further shorn of glory, and the county records were immediately moved to a temporary courthouse in Fairfield.

Industrial Growth

With few exceptions, industries in the San Francisco Bay Area in the 1850's developed *with* the towns and did not give rise to new communities. Perhaps one of the exceptions is in Contra Costa County where warehouses and a flour mill on Nueces (Walnut) Creek prompted the laying out of the town of Pacheco. Flour mills, however, were usually among the first structures erected in new towns, because in every county bordering on the bay the growing of grains was attempted. San Francisco, San Jose, and the larger communities each had several mills by the end of the 'fifties, some of which dated from the beginning of the gold rush.

Breweries, too, were established very early. One was in operation in San Francisco in 1850. Others were started in Oakland in 1852, in San Jose in 1853, and in other towns in subsequent years.

Wagon shops, blacksmith shops, saddle shops, small foundries, small planing mills, bakeries, soda works, confectionery shops, and similar establishments supplying home needs all helped to provide employment and stimu-late the growth of towns; but there was no appreciable manufacturing other than the production of mining machinery until the 'sixties, when the Civil War made importation difficult and Californians seized their opportunity to launch new industries.

The making of jellies from California fruit by Daniel Prevost in San Francisco in 1856 is worthy of note as marking the beginning of the fruit-processing industry, which would eventually account for the growth of many communities.

Road Building

A wider distribution of population and the gradual growth of towns stimulated not only an increase in staging and in transbay travel but extensive road building as well, particularly in the North Bay counties. The Napa County Board of Supervisors levied a tax in 1858 for the construction of a road from the city of Napa to the Russian River Valley by way of Knight's Valley, and for the construction of another road up the east side of Napa Creek to Clear Lake by way of Chiles Canyon. In Sonoma County a network of roads from Petaluma to other points in the county was authorized. Begun in 1859, these roads soon linked the shipping outlet on Petaluma Creek with Sonoma, San Rafael, Bodega, Two Rock Valley, and near-by Lakeville, on Petaluma Slough.

In Alameda County there were no less than thirteen road districts by 1858, with a road supervisor for each. Citizens of Oakland "felt more free and travelled more frequently" because the county board of supervisors the year before had paid Horace Carpentier $6,000 for his toll bridge across the arm of the estuary between Oakland and Brooklyn (the present Lake Merritt) and had abolished the restrictive charge.[2] Vicente Peralta added another footnote to county history when he petitioned the board in November, 1858, to have Telegraph Road, now one of the main thoroughfares between Oakland and Berkeley, extended around his property on Temescal Creek rather than through it. The request was denied, however, and Telegraph Avenue today runs straight as a ruler.

Improvements in local transit in the latter half of the 'fifties consisted chiefly of the establishment of several new omnibus lines in San Francisco and one between San Jose and Santa Clara in 1856. The new lines in San Francisco extended from the business district to Meiggs' Wharf in North Beach, to the Presidio, to Mission Dolores, and to Third and Townsend streets. Unfortunately, the competitive paralleling of routes tended to concentrate population unduly in certain areas, thereby preventing a distribution that would have contributed to a more open

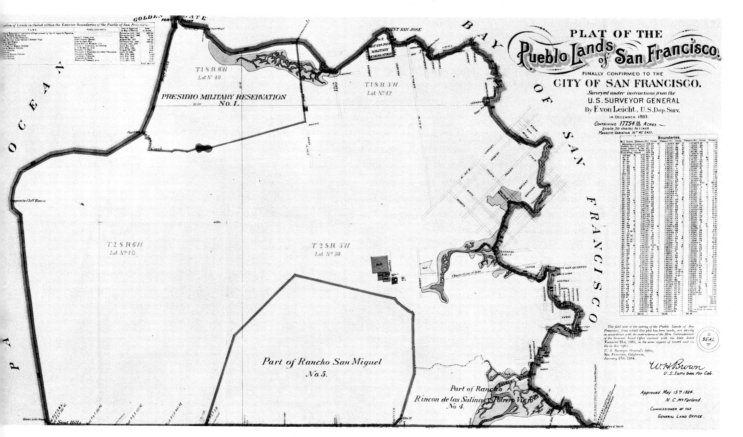

The Pueblo Lands of San Francisco as Surveyed in December, 1883. Of the 17,754.36 acres finally confirmed to the city as successor to the pueblo of Yerba Buena, all but approximately 4,000 were in federal or private ownership at the time of Judge Stephen J. Field's decision in 1864. The survey shows the shoreline of the bay as it was at the time of the American conquest in 1846. Filled lands beyond this shoreline were not included in the confirmation.

and more desirable type of urban development.

Expiration of the toll-collecting privilege on two plank roads to Mission Dolores and the construction of the San Bruno Turnpike from the mission to the site of present-day San Bruno in 1858 stimulated the movement of population toward the Mission Valley. The town of San Bruno developed around the San Bruno House on the turnpike.

Squatters and Land Titles

The influence of omnibus routes and toll-free roads in shaping the physical growth of the metropolis, though significant, was not so great as that of decisions reached in the political arena in the critical years following the end of the gold rush. Land commissioners, judges, squatters, venal local politicians, racketeers, reformers, and state legislators all had a hand in determining the manner in which the city developed. Two major problems faced the

city: the unsettled state of land titles, which retarded development of certain areas; and the corruption and extravagance of local officials at a time when the inhabitants were still suffering from the shock of the depression brought on by overspeculation.

In 1852 the City of San Francisco, as successor to the Pueblo of Yerba Buena, had filed a claim before the United States Land Commission for four square leagues of land, to which every pueblo was entitled under the laws of Spain and of Mexico. By this procedure the city sought not only to extend its corporate boundaries to the Pacific Ocean but also perhaps to get increased tax revenue from lands occupied by squatters. In December, 1854, the commission confirmed to the city all the land north of the so-called Vallejo Line, approved by the territorial *Diputación* in 1834 as the limits of the pueblo. This line, running from what is now known as Steamboat Point (Fourth and Berry streets) to the Divisadero (Lone

Mountain) and thence to the south side of Point Lobos, embraced only about three leagues of land instead of four. The city, therefore, appealed from the decision, asserting its claim to a larger quantity of land; while the United States government also appealed, on the ground that the city had no title to any land.

In the meantime, reasonably certain that its title to a good part of the lands within its 1851 charter limits would be upheld, the city sought to come to terms with the squatters. There were many of these in the unsurveyed area between Larkin and Johnson (Ninth) streets and the western boundary as established by the legislature in 1851 at Divisadero Street. Disputes between squatters, many of whom were hired representatives of some of San Francisco's wealthiest citizens, flared from time to time into open warfare and often resulted in bloodshed and loss of life. In the hope of putting an end to this violence by clarifying questions of ownership, the city enacted an ordinance giving title to those who had been in actual possession of lands west of Larkin and Johnson streets from January 1, 1855, to June 30, 1855. Titles to lands east of Larkin and Johnson streets obtained through grants made by the alcaldes, or municipal authorities, of the former pueblo likewise were recognized. But the ordinance provided that title to all disputed lands which were not actually held by bona fide property holders should be relinquished to the city.

As a plan for ending the disputes, the ordinance, signed by Mayor James Van Ness and cited as the Van Ness Ordinance, was for some years a failure, even after it was ratified by the state legislature in 1858. The squatter warfare continued, and it was not until the United States District Court, then the Circuit Court, and finally the Congress of the United States acted on the city's claim to the pueblo lands that the thorny issue of land titles was settled, in the 1860's.

The Van Ness Ordinance is important from the standpoint of city planning, however, because it determined the pattern of streets and public squares in the area known as the Western Addition. Actually, what is now called the Van Ness Ordinance was three separate ordinances—one dealing with land titles (No. 822), one with the reservation of lands for public purposes (No. 845), and one approving a map showing a plan for the area between Larkin and Johnson streets and the Divisadero (No. 846). This map, referred to as the Van Ness Map, extended the monotonous gridiron westward without regard to topography and designated certain areas as public squares: Jefferson Square, Alamo Square, Hamilton Square, and the so-called Hospital Lot, now in part Duboce Park. The width of Van Ness Avenue also was determined by this map.

The Ninth County

The Van Ness Ordinance affected only the citizens of San Francisco; but another enactment of this turbulent period, the Consolidation Act of 1856, which united the City of San Francisco and San Francisco County as a single political entity, affected residents of the San Francisco Peninsula as well. Originally San Francisco County extended southward to San Francisquito Creek, the present boundary between Santa Clara and San Mateo counties, and the city occupied only a small area on the northeast tip of the Peninsula. Through the years the criminal element and the big and little grafters had discovered that a system of dual authority, with one administration for the county and another for the city, was ideally suited for the protection of evildoers. Since corruption permeated both administrations, a malefactor could always find friends somewhere to connive with him in his shady operations and shield him from punishment. Popular indignation against the rampant abuses of local government eventually expressed itself in the second Vigilance uprising; but even before the murder of the crusading editor of the San Francisco *Bulletin*, James King of William, unleashed the thunderbolts, the tempest of reform was sweeping through the metropolis. Horace Hawes, San Francisco's representative in the state legislature, wrote and introduced a bill to restrict the area of the county, make the city and county boundaries coterminous, and establish a single governing body of twelve members, whose "powers were so carefully defined that they were almost nonexistent," as one historian remarked.[3] The bill was passed by the legislature and was approved by the governor on April 9, 1856, three weeks before the organization of the second Vigilance Committee.

Curiously, the title and enacting clause of the bill did not even mention that the measure provided for the creation of an entirely new county, San Mateo, the ninth and last of the Bay Area counties. Hawes apparently saw no way to consolidate the city and county governments of San Francisco without drastically reducing the size of the county. A story current at the time said that in order to get enough votes for his bill he was obliged to provide a haven for the crooked element—a new county. It is true that an undesirable element did try to organize San Mateo County, but fortunately the decent people of the area thwarted the attempt.

In working out his scheme for unification of city and county governments in San Francisco, Hawes had, of course, no example of a city embracing huge areas of farmland, as Los Angeles, for instance, did until fairly recently. A city in the 1850's was thought of as a compact,

Map of the City and County of San Francisco, 1861. Besides the areas surveyed by Jasper O'Farrell and William Eddy, the map shows three later additions to the city —the Potrero Nuevo, Horner's Addition, and the Western Addition. In the early 'sixties the city occupied some two thousand acres of the peninsula.

densely settled place. Hawes may have fancied himself daring, indeed, to propose sudden expansion of San Francisco to an area of forty-two square miles, or nearly twenty-seven thousand acres, for the city proper, even in 1860, occupied only two thousand acres. Within the new city limits were thousands of acres of pasture, cultivated farmland, and wildernesses of drifting sand.

The balloting in San Mateo County's first election was not without irregularities, as might have been predicted from the preëlection activities of the vicious element driven from San Francisco. Suspecting that there had been some padding of the returns, wary citizens challenged the votes in three precincts and succeeded in having them thrown out. The elimination of these votes denied the village of Belmont the honor of becoming the county seat and gave it to Redwood City. Afterward the State Supreme Court held that the entire election had been scheduled before the act creating the county went into effect, and a second election was therefore held in May, 1857. This second election did not, however, affect the location of the county seat.

Political developments also influenced the growth of a small community in Alameda County in 1856. The legislature passed a special act in February of that year authorizing the removal of the county seat from Alvarado to San Leandro, thus stimulating the growth of the latter town.

The Problem of Isolation

Like all the rest of California, the San Francisco Bay Area suffered increasingly from lack of rapid overland communication with the eastern United States and from lack of railroad transportation to the populous states east of the great deserts and mountains. Had San Francisco offices of certain important eastern banking institutions been able to communicate more readily with their home offices in early February, 1855, they might not have closed their doors and the city might not have been engulfed in financial panic. In the late 'fifties, when farms were beginning to produce abundantly, agriculturists realized that the problem of surpluses might be eased considerably if they could ship some of their products east by rail.

The possibility of a transcontinental railroad perennially engrossed the press, public speakers, and crackerbarrel philosophers; but all through the 'fifties the hopes of Bay Area residents and other northern Californians for a central route across the continent were alternately raised and dashed by the acrimonious debates in Congress between Southern and Northern senators over the location of the route and the parts to be played by the federal government and by private enterprise, respectively. The problem of overland communication was more readily solved—at first by the semiweekly Butterfield Stage, then by the Pony Express, and from 1861 on by the transcontinental telegraph. But not until the Civil War broke out and Congress became uneasy lest California support the Confederacy, or fall prey to foreign intervention, or become the nucleus of an independent Pacific republic was a railroad through the heart of the continent at last authorized—on July 1, 1862.

Rails on the Peninsula

More than a year before President Lincoln signed the Pacific Railroad Act, work had begun on a railroad between San Francisco and San Jose that prominent citizens of both communities hoped might become the last link in the transcontinental line. This was the railroad that farmers in the Santa Clara Valley had been talking about since 1849. The first and second companies organized to finance the line had taken the grandiose name The Pacific and Atlantic Rail Road Company and had proposed building eastward in some shining future. The third company modestly called itself The San Francisco and San Jose Rail Road Company; but it, too, failed to solve the problem of financing the project. The fourth company, formed in 1860, took the same name. It won the support of the state legislature and the press and was able to convince the voters of San Francisco, San Mateo, and Santa Clara counties that they should approve county subsidies for the railroad.

Ground was broken at San Francisquito Creek on the San Francisco Peninsula on May 1, 1861, for construction of the railroad, and by July grading of the route was well under way in both San Mateo and Santa Clara counties. The plan worked out in 1851 by William Lewis, the chief engineer, for a line running into San Francisco on a pile bridge east of the San Bruno Mountains had been abandoned in favor of a route west of the mountains and through the Mission Valley. With an eye on the county-aid elections, the officials of the line concluded that more San Franciscans would vote for financial assistance from the county if the railroad went through the more densely populated areas. Furthermore, the cost of construction through the Mission district would be less than along the bay shore.

No sooner was the railroad a certainty than large property owners along the route saw their opportunity to market land. Timothy Guy Phelps and some of his friends filed a map of a subdivision west of the County Road (El Camino Real) at Redwood City, convenient to the right of way of the new line. In September, 1862, C. B. Polhemus, one of the directors of the railroad, had William Lewis plat the town of San Mateo at the point where the right of way crossed San Mateo Creek. In the vicinity were the first of the great country estates for which the Peninsula was to be famous in the latter part of the century. In 1863 when the railroad was nearing completion between San Francisco and Mayfield, or what is now the southern part of Palo Alto, the Menlo Park Villa Association advertised five-acre "villa lots" in a tract of more than eight hundred acres. The name "Menlo Park" derived from Menlough on Lough Corrib, County Galway, Ireland, the former home of two brothers-in-law who had purchased a piece of Rancho de las Pulgas in 1854.

At ceremonies in San Jose on January 16, 1864, marking completion of the entire line, Judge Timothy Dame, president of the company, thrilled everyone by announcing that the Central Pacific Railroad had assigned to his company and to the Western Pacific Railroad (which is

San Francisco as Seen from Russian Hill, 1863. Reproduction courtesy of Bancroft Library.

not to be confused with the present-day railroad of the same name) the right to construct that section of the transcontinental railroad from San Francisco to Sacramento. As Dame was also president of the Western Pacific, which had been organized in 1862 to construct a railroad from San Jose to Sacramento via Stockton, the celebrants had little reason to doubt that the new line on the Peninsula would indeed become part of the great transcontinental railroad begun at Sacramento on February 22, 1863. But the distinction of being the last link in the great overland railroad was reserved by the fates for a four-mile local line that had been in operation in Oakland for some months.[4]

East Bay Railroads

The San Francisco and Oakland Ferry Railroad, extending from Seventh and Broadway in Oakland to the Oakland Wharf at Gibbon's Point, on the mud flats west of the city, was the first railroad completed in the Bay Area. Opened on September 2, 1863, it connected at Oakland Wharf with the transbay ferry *Contra Costa*. A year later it was extended across the arm of the estuary now known as Lake Merritt, and in 1865 it was linked with another small railroad known as the "Encinal Road."

The real name of this latter railroad was the San Francisco and Alameda Railroad. Built by Alfred A. Cohen, who participated in many Bay Area developments of the 'sixties, this line originally ran from High Street in Alameda to the Alameda Wharf, where passengers transferred to ferries to San Francisco. Cohen extended it southward to San Leandro in May, 1865, and to Hayward in August of that year. Although he was ambitious to join it at Niles Canyon with the Western Pacific Railroad, then building between San Jose and Stockton, he was unable to finance construction beyond Hayward. There the rails ended—until the day in 1869 when the "Big Four" of the Central Pacific (Leland Stanford, Charles Crocker, Collis P. Huntington, and Mark Hopkins) joined them to the transcontinental line and made Oakland rather than San Francisco the terminus.

Railroad Fever

The years preceding completion of the Pacific railroad were years of railroad fever in the San Francisco Bay Area. There was as much talk of stock subscriptions, county railroad bonds, public and private donations of land for depots, and of new subdivisions and new towns along railroad rights of way as there was of freeways,

fringe-area tract developments, and new shopping centers in the decade following World War II. At one time or another the residents of every major valley in the Bay Area furiously debated the merits of schemes for introducing the railroad to the local scene; and not a few of these schemes were successful. By the time the first overland train of the Central Pacific reached its destination, small engines with huge smokestacks were trailing plumes of black smoke up and down the Napa Valley and the Santa Clara Valley and between Vallejo and Sacramento, while a small railroad was under construction between San Rafael and Point San Quentin in Marin County. Voters in Contra Costa County had, however, decisively defeated a proposal that the county issue bonds for the construction of a railroad from Martinez to Danville, in the San Ramon Valley; and residents of the Cotati Valley had witnessed the failure of four successive companies that sought to finance a railroad in that area.

The Napa Valley Railroad, forty-one miles in length, extended from Soscol to Calistoga, where Samuel Brannan, treasurer of the line, had a hot springs resort which he hoped to make as fashionable as Saratoga in New York State. At Soscol the line connected with a ferry to San Francisco. The railroad provided Napa Valley farmers with the kind of fast transportation that they needed, and it aided A. Y. Easterby, vice-president of the company, in marketing land in a new subdivision near Napa called Holly Oak Park. "This property is within two hours of San Francisco and is comparatively as near as Menlo Park," an advertisement of Easterby and Company proclaimed in 1869.[5]

The railroad through the Santa Clara Valley from San Jose to Gilroy, at the southern end of the valley, was constructed by the controlling interests of the San Francisco and San Jose Rail Road under a contract with a company chartered in 1865 as the Southern Pacific Railroad. Gilroy citizens who welcomed the iron horse with a brass band, shouts, and waving handkerchiefs believed that the railroad eventually would be extended down the state to a connection at the Colorado River with a railroad from Missouri. In anticipation of big things, they had voted to incorporate their town and to have the townsite surveyed some months before the first train actually pulled in.

The California Pacific, as the railroad from Vallejo to Sacramento was called, was linked with San Francisco by the ferryboat *New World*, which made the bay crossing in an hour and twenty minutes, bringing Vallejo as close to the metropolis in time as Redwood City on the San Francisco Peninsula and San Leandro in Alameda County. A branch of the line extended from Davis to Woodland, in Yolo County. Significantly, the first freight hauled over the tracks of the California Pacific was wheat, for the great wheat era of the state was beginning. The Starr Mills, erected at Vallejo in 1869 about the time the railroad was completed, were soon producing one thousand barrels of flour a day and shipping more than eighteen hundred tons monthly to Europe.

Like Alfred A. Cohen's railroads in the East Bay, the Napa Valley Railroad, and the California Pacific, the little line completed in March, 1870, between San Rafael and Point San Quentin also connected with a ferry providing service to San Francisco. And when Peter Donahue, founder of the famous Union Iron Works in San Francisco, built a railroad in the Cotati Valley to Santa Rosa, completed later that same year, its southern terminus at Donahue, eight miles below Petaluma on Petaluma Creek, likewise was beside a slip used by ferries plying to and from "the city."

In a single decade, then, combination rail and ferry services united the metropolis near the Golden Gate with almost the whole surrounding region and with an important section of the Central Valley as well, making towns from fifty to seventy-five or a hundred miles away fairly accessible.

San Franciscans were bitterly disappointed, however, that their city was not chosen as the terminus of the transcontinental railroad. "Almost sure" that the titans of the Central Pacific would build a railroad bridge across Dumbarton Strait near the lower end of the bay and bring their trains up the Peninsula to San Francisco, one real-estate firm had put on an intensive campaign in 1868 to sell villa lots of ten to twenty acres at Menlo Park and Fair Oaks (Atherton).[6] But any spurt that may have been given to the real-estate market in San Mateo County and San Francisco by talk of a railroad bridge to the Peninsula was quickly ended by the announcement of a major business deal in Oakland.

Oakland: Railroad Terminus

On March 31, 1868, Horace Carpentier, still sole possessor of the Oakland waterfront, deeded to a four-day-old corporation known as the Oakland Water-front Company almost the entire Oakland waterfront. The next day this company deeded five hundred acres to the Western Pacific Railroad, an affiliate of the Central Pacific, to be used for a terminal for the transcontinental line, with the stipulation that the railroad might select the land it wanted. In addition, the Oakland Water-front Company

ceded to the railroad two strips of land, each not more than a hundred feet wide, for a right of way. In return for these grants, the Western Pacific agreed to complete its railroad from Niles into Oakland and to spend not less than $500,000 on terminal facilities within the next three years.

These swift developments climaxed a series of discussions that Carpentier had initiated with Leland Stanford. The Oakland Water-front Company was Carpentier's device for associating himself with the builders of the Central Pacific and benefiting by the potentially most profitable railroad venture in the West. Of the $5,000,000 worth of capital stock of the new company, Carpentier, as director, held 46 per cent, while his brother, Edward R. Carpentier, and Lloyd Tevis together held 9 per cent. Stanford, treasurer of the new company, owned 35 per cent, and attorney John B. Felton held 10 per cent. One share went to Dr. Samuel Merritt, Mayor of Oakland—and thereby hangs a tale.

The Waterfront "Compromise"

Although Oakland had struggled throughout its municipal history to regain the waterfront that Carpentier had grabbed in early days, the city now quickly arrived at a "compromise" with Carpentier. On the same day that the Oakland Water-front Company ceded land to the Western Pacific, it also regranted to the City of Oakland the parcel of land situated at the foot of Broadway—land also claimed by the San Francisco and Oakland Railway Company—and the arm of the Oakland Estuary known today as Lake Merritt. The Oakland City Council, for its part, ratified and confirmed the ordinances of 1852 and 1853 that had given Carpentier control of the waterfront. In other words, the city fathers, presumably on the urging of Dr. Merritt, released and abandoned all claims of the city to the waterfront and provided, by ordinance, that Carpentier should reconvey the waterfront properties in accordance with the terms of the contract between the Oakland Water-front Company, the Western Pacific, and other parties.

Although some scurrilous comment greeted this so-called "compromise," most Oakland residents were so jubilant over the selection of the city as the western terminus of the transcontinental railroad that they chose to overlook the "highly suspicious character" of the agreement. Generally, it was believed that real-estate values would increase and that Oakland's prospects for becoming a great commercial city were indeed roseate. Carpentier, formerly the "monster whose blighting influence had retarded the city's prosperity,"[7] now appeared to be a public benefactor.

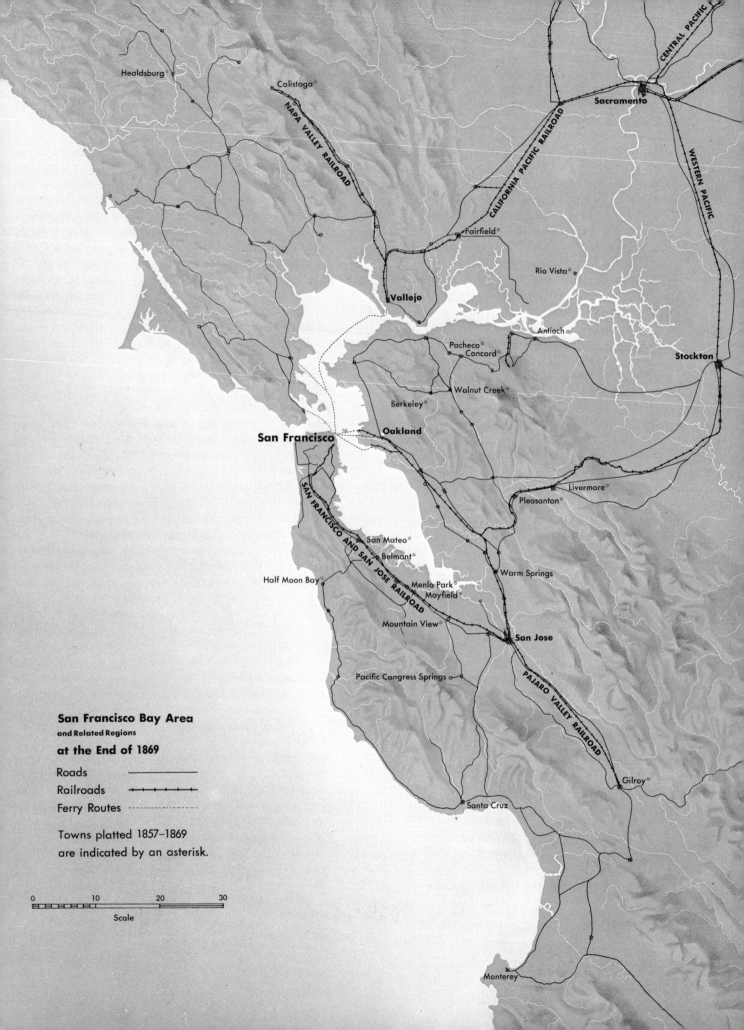

Healdsburg*

Calistoga*

NAPA VALLEY RAILROAD

CENTRAL PACIFIC

CALIFORNIA PACIFIC RAILROAD

Sacramento

WESTERN PACIFIC

Fairfield*

Rio Vista*

Vallejo

Antioch

Pacheco*
Concord*

Stockton

Walnut Creek*

Berkeley*

San Francisco

Oakland

Livermore*

Pleasanton*

SAN FRANCISCO AND SAN JOSE RAILROAD

San Mateo*

Belmont*

Warm Springs

Half Moon Bay*

Menlo Park*
Mayfield*

Mountain View*

San Jose

Pacific Congress Springs

PAJARO VALLEY RAILROAD

Gilroy*

San Francisco Bay Area
and Related Regions

at the End of 1869

Roads ————

Railroads +++++++

Ferry Routes ----------

Towns platted 1857–1869
are indicated by an asterisk.

Santa Cruz

Monterey

0   10   20   30
Scale

First Overland Train

On September 6, 1869, the first overland train rolled through Niles Canyon and headed north toward Alameda, cheered by crowds at San Leandro and grade crossings en route. Although Oakland was to be the permanent terminus, this first train had as its destination Alameda Wharf, which it reached by way of the local line of the San Francisco and Alameda Railroad. On November 8 the main-line trains were routed to Oakland Wharf along the Seventh Street line of the Oakland-Alameda system that the Central Pacific had acquired from A. A. Cohen prior to the opening of the transcontinental line. In the following year, tracks were laid on First Street in Oakland for use of main-line trains, so that Seventh Street might be reserved exclusively for local service.

In the boom days before and after the arrival of the first overland train, real-estate activities rose to a high pitch and several new towns were platted. William M. Mendenhall, who owned a large tract near the village of Laddsville in the Livermore Valley, gave twenty acres to the Western Pacific for a depot and in July, 1869, laid out a new town named in honor of Robert Livermore, the pioneer settler in that part of Alameda County. Laddsville, which had grown up a few years earlier around the old Livermore house half a mile or more from the tracks, declined as the new town developed. Only six days after the opening of the railroad, the sale of lots started in the newly platted town of Pleasanton, at the place in the Livermore Valley formerly called Alisal. A year or more later the Central Pacific itself formed the Decoto Land Company, purchased 284 acres on the bay plain in southern Alameda County from Ezra Decoto and his brothers, and laid out the town of Decoto. The settlement, however, grew very slowly until recent decades.

Economic Expansion

Speeches and editorials on the completion of the transcontinental railroad hailed the end of California's isolation as the dawn of a new era of development in the state, but in reality the new era of economic expansion had begun about the time the "Big Four" broke ground at Sacramento for the Central Pacific. The discovery of the fabulous Comstock Lode in Nevada in 1859, the opening of copper mines in Arizona, and the decreased flow of manufactured goods from the East as a result of the Civil War all contributed to the establishment of new home industries and to the growth of many already in existence. In rapid succession appeared carriage-manufacturing enterprises, boot and shoe factories in San Francisco, tanneries throughout the Bay Area, woolen mills in San Francisco and San Jose, the Spreckels sugar refinery in San Francisco and a beet sugar refinery at the town of Alvarado in Alameda County, blasting powder plants in Marin and Contra Costa counties, and a large smelter erected by Thomas H. Selby, a hardware merchant, in the North Beach District of San Francisco. By the end of the 'sixties the new boot and shoe industry was manufacturing one-fourth of all the shoes sold on the Pacific Coast. Mining and railroad building created so great a demand for explosives that by 1870 California manufacturers were producing nine-tenths of the powder used west of the Rocky Mountains. As for Selby's smelter, in five years it was processing twice as much ore as the next largest reduction works in the United States, at Newark, New Jersey.

The increase in population in the nine counties bordering on San Francisco Bay reflected the swift economic upsurge. Total population in the area rose from 114,074 in 1860 to 265,808 in 1870—a gain of 133 per cent, compared with 47 per cent in the entire state. The census of 1870 showed that nearly half the people of California lived in the territory bordering on the bay. More than one-fourth lived in San Francisco alone, for the population of the metropolis nearly tripled in the ten-year period. Residents of the city had been disgruntled in 1860 because the census of that year reported no more than 56,835 inhabitants; but they were duly impressed by the figure of 149,473 in 1870, and the San Francisco *Evening Bulletin* boldly predicted on May 24, 1870, that in another ten years the city would have 300,000 inhabitants. J. Ross Brown, of Oakland, former United States Minister to China, was so optimistic that he thought it "safe to say" thay by 1880 San Francisco would be a metropolis of half a million souls.[8]

Urban Problems

Population growth in cities large and small created all kinds of problems and needs that enterprising men were quick to turn into opportunities. In those days, when municipal governments left such matters as the provision of adequate water supplies to private initiative, aggressive water companies began the search for sources of supply that would be more dependable and more ample than the wells, springs, and little local streams tapped in the 'fifties. Anthony Chabot went no farther than Temescal Creek, four miles from Oakland, to find a site where he could build a dam and create a storage reservoir to supply the growing number of water users in the East Bay city. But the Spring Valley Water Company of San Francisco reached out thirty-two miles to get an adequate supply for San Francisco. By flume it brought the waters of Pilarcitos Creek, in San Mateo County, to the metropolis, and later built a dam and created Pilarcitos Lake. In 1870 it constructed a second storage reservoir by building San Andreas Dam in the San Andreas Valley. Lobos Creek, Islais Creek, and springs on which the city had previously depended continued to supply some of its water needs, but these local sources were to become increasingly insignificant as the Spring Valley Company added more and more distant sources to its system.

Through Chabot and his associates, San Jose and Vallejo also acquired new sources of supply. The San Jose Water Company, headed by Chabot, obtained rights to the waters of Los Gatos Creek. The people of Vallejo in 1871 began using water from a reservoir known as Lake Chabot, three miles northeast of the city.

Progress in urban transit was as marked as that in water supply. In 1860 the horsecar made its appearance in San Francisco, and toward the end of the decade it became a feature of the local scene in San Jose and Vallejo, though its advent in the last-named city was premature. With only six thousand inhabitants, Vallejo was just not large enough to support a horsecar line. One by one the omnibus lines in San Francisco converted to the newer form of transportation; new transit companies were organized; and the city grew westward as horsecar lines were extended beyond Van Ness Avenue into the Hayes Valley and the Western Addition. The area at the foot of Twin Peaks also began to develop when a steam-dummy line of the Market Street Railroad was opened to Castro Street. Still another area opened to settlement was the Bay View district near Hunters Point, though the costly line to the Bay View racecourse was not profitable.

While private companies continued to influence the physical development of Bay Area communities through their control, under very limited regulation, of essential water supply and transit services, private speculative interests, operating under franchises, lost control over the port of San Francisco, and with them the City of San Francisco itself surrendered to the state the administration of its waterfront. The transfer of the port to a State Board of Harbor Commissioners in 1863 climaxed years of corruption and mismanagement in port affairs, during which city officials had used harbor revenues for the payment of old debts and for meeting current expenses, even though piers and wharves were disintegrating and filled land was constantly slipping into the bay and preventing ships from berthing and discharging their cargoes. Some wharves even operated without proper authorization and yielded no income to the city.

Within two years the new state board repaired several wharves, built a new one, did considerable dredging, and

employed an engineer to survey for a sea wall. By the end of 1869 the sea wall had been constructed along the old zigzag waterfront line on East Street from the foot of Mission Street to the foot of Pacific Street and on Front Street from Vallejo Street to Union Street.

New Wealth; Civic Poverty

San Francisco at the end of the 'sixties dominated an economic empire that stretched from the Pacific Coast to the Rockies. The financial heart of this empire was Montgomery Street, from which flowed the capital to finance new mines, orchards, large-scale grain farms, and countless other enterprises. In the early days of the Comstock Lode excitement the San Francisco Stock Exchange had been organized, and soon thereafter powerful banks, such as the Bank of California and the Wells Fargo Bank, had come into existence. The Bank of California, founded by William C. Ralson and Darius O. Mills in 1864, not only aided the "Big Four" in their struggle to finance the Central Pacific; it also invested in a wide variety of industrial and agricultural ventures, thanks mainly to the energy, daring, and imagination of Ralston, after whose name might well be written "the Magnificent," because he was indubitably the most spectacular member of a new, self-created aristocracy of wealth.

The rise of this new class signified that the West, or at least the area bordering on San Francisco Bay, was entering a new cultural and social phase. From the gold rush emerged comparatively few men of wealth: Thomas Larkin, Samuel Brannan, Peter Donahue, James Lick—a mere handful. The period marked by the opening of the Comstock Lode and the development of important new industrial enterprises and railroads produced the first of a rather numerous order of men of large fortune. Their ostentatious, not to say vulgar, spending habits; their cultivation of a taste for luxuries in dress, household furnishings, food, and carriages; their quests for rare plants with which to ornament their estates; and the efforts of their wives and daughters to establish an exclusive social set—all exerted a profound influence on public thinking. These men enjoyed a type of living popularly associated with older, more affluent, and more stratified societies, such as had developed in Paris, London, and even New York. In a way, their opulence raised San Francisco to a new level of urbanity and reflected the general improvement in material well-being.

Yet San Francisco by comparison with other world cities was sadly lacking in the physical attributes of metropolitan greatness. It had no large public parks, no splendid boulevards, no art museums and monumental civic buildings. Frederick Law Olmsted, the designer of New York's

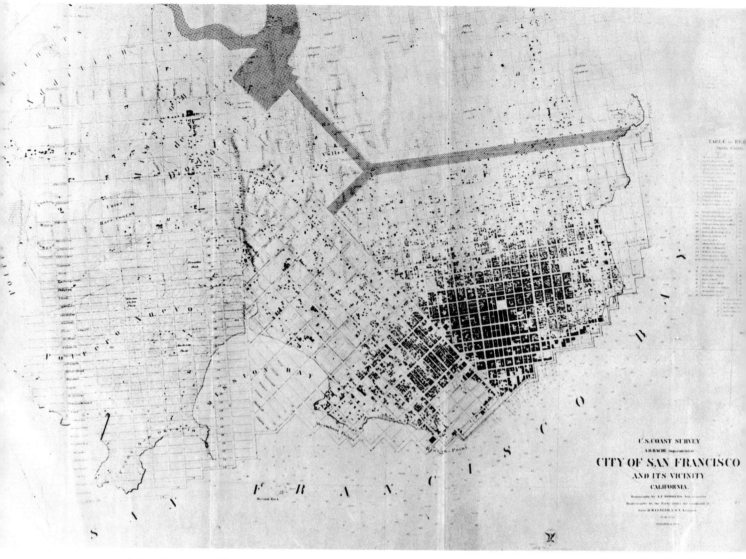

Map of San Francisco Showing Location of Proposed Park and Promenade.
Courtesy of Harvard University Library.

Central Park, observed in 1865 that the only open space San Francisco offered those who would go picnicking on a holiday was "a burial ground on a high elevation, scourged by the wind, laid out only with regard to the convenience of funerals, with no trees or turf, and with but stunted verdure of any kind, and this with difficulty kept alive."[9]

Agitation for a Park

Fortunately, about the time that San Franciscans became embarrassed by the shortcomings of their city, the opportunity to set aside land for an extensive park presented itself. Judge Stephen J. Field of the United States Circuit Court for the Northern District of California entered a decree on October 31, 1864, confirming the claim of the city "to a tract of land . . . embracing so much of the peninsula upon which the city is located as will contain an area equal to four square leagues as described in the petition [of the city],"[10] excepting lands previously reserved by the federal government or already privately owned, such as Rancho San Miguel and the Bernal rancho. These federal and private lands amounted to all but four thousand of the seventeen thousand acres affected by the decision. The decree stated that the confirmation of the residue of four thousand acres would be "in trust for the use and benefit of all the inhabitants."[11] Although this language of the court became the subject of precise judicial interpretation a few years later, most people immediately realized that it did not preclude the city from conveying title to individual citizens under some properly approved program. While various plans for disposal of the "outside lands" were being discussed, the San Francisco *Evening Bulletin* on September 8, 1865, published a lead editorial headed "The Need for a Great Park for San Francisco."

"To establish such an improvement to San Francisco at the present time would be an easy matter, but if it be left until our outside lands shall be divided and occupied, it will be a more difficult task, besides the cost of such an undertaking will be then very much increased," the newspaper urged. It suggested a park of three or four thousand acres "amongst the hills back of the city, south of Lone Mountain."

Talk of the desirability of creating a large park doubtless had been fairly widespread in leading circles for some time before this editorial appeared, for a letter written by Olmsted to his partner, Calvert Vaux, only three weeks later indicates that several prominent citizens, including the tireless Samuel Brannan, had already persuaded him to prepare plans for a park, on the assumption that the San Francisco Board of Supervisors could be induced to pay for his services.[12] Olmsted was then temporarily in the San Francisco Bay Area, doing preliminary work on plans for a new Berkeley campus of the College of California, predecessor of the University of California. For two years he had been manager of Frémont's mining estate in Mariposa County, but he was soon to leave for New York to resume work on Central Park.

The Olmsted Plan

The park plan for San Francisco that Olmsted was officially authorized to prepare after he had already set sail for the East was in some ways less ambitious than the proposals made by the press, in other ways far more imaginative and concerned with the long-term needs of the city. Olmsted projected the beginnings of a park system rather than a single park. At what is now Aquatic Park he planned a sea gate and parade ground. From this landing place for visiting dignitaries a depressed parkway, or promenade, was to run along the line of Van Ness Avenue to Eddy Street and there fork into two branches, one going to Market Street, the other to his main park in the general location of present-day Duboce Park. Though this recreation area, a pleasure ground of approximately one hundred and twenty acres, now seems unduly modest in view of Olmsted's recommendation that the contemplated park should be "conceived on a thoroughly liberal scale,"[13] his suggestion that the roads in the park would lend themselves to "indefinite extension"

throughout the western part of the city as parkways was very advanced for the times. Such costly features as the depressed parkway, which Olmsted thought necessary to afford pleasure seekers protection from the strong summer winds, probably doomed the plan to abandonment; yet this first great American landscape architect did make a contribution to the San Francisco of later generations. He succeeded in transmitting to Supervisors Monroe Ashbury, Charles H. Stanyan, and other officials his own deep conviction that the city should seize its now-or-never opportunity to create "a pleasure ground second to none in the world" and should plan it "with reference to the convenience not merely of the present population, or even of their immediate successors, but of many millions of people."[14]

Site for a Park

When, in 1866, Congress by special act terminated efforts of the federal government to upset Judge Field's confirmation of the city's title to the pueblo lands, and when, finally, the supervisors got down to the business of reaching agreement with land occupants and selecting reservations for public use, they displayed the kind of vision that Olmsted had hoped they would exhibit. Among the public areas recommended by a second Committee on Outside Lands was a park of more than one thousand acres.

San Francisco was not so fortunate, however, as to have its supervisors heed Olmsted's advice on the layout for streets in the unplanned section of the city. Instead of a system of streets ascending the hills diagonally, "in such a way as to secure sufficiently easy grades,"[15] the area west of Divisadero Street was committed to the same rigid gridiron pattern as the older areas.

The selection of the site for Golden Gate Park "was made in the face of bitter opposition," according to William Hammond Hall, the first park engineer. "It was generally believed and repeatedly urged by a good portion of the local press, that any attempt to build and maintain a Park on the dry sands and brush-covered hillocks which composed the site, would prove a costly failure," he wrote in 1886. "Powerful and winning pens, whose ink has within the past decade flowed in gratulation at the results attained and to be expected in Golden Gate Park, were within the ten years before busily engaged in denouncing the selection of the place for the purpose—declaring that no Park could be built there, and no verdure maintained, at any cost which the city could afford."[16]

"The Growth of Time"

The plan for the new campus of the College of California, the other important project that engaged Olmsted during

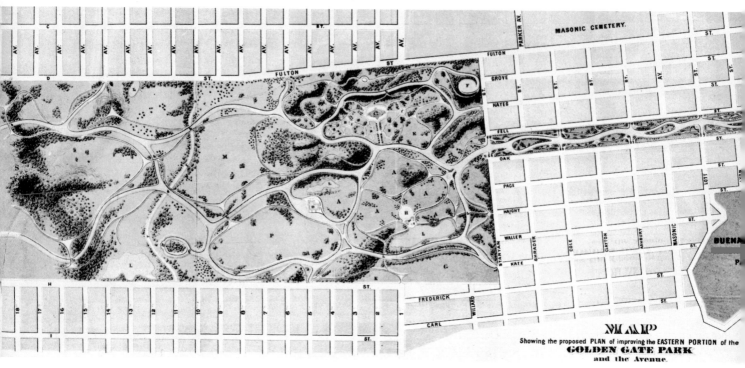

William Hammond Hall's Plan for the Development of the Eastern Part of Golden Gate Park and "the Avenue," Now Known as the Panhandle, 1870–1871. The eastern end of the park site included 270 acres of good arable land; the rest of the site was "a waste of drifting sand" that was reclaimed only after many years of patient labor.

his brief sojourn in the Bay Area in the summer of 1865, fared only a little better than his plan for parks in San Francisco. Aside from a main axis established by Olmsted "in the line of the Golden Gate,"[17] almost nothing about the campus of the university in Berkeley bears the imprint of his genius. The tenuous connection of the landscape architect with the private institution that was to be transformed into a state university is of minor significance beside the fact that in the late 'sixties the desire of certain farsighted leaders for an institution of higher learning supported by public funds was at last fulfilled. This, more than anything else, signified that California was indeed emerging from the pioneer stage.

The beginnings of this institution can be traced to conversations at Monterey in the spring of 1849 between Thomas O. Larkin and the Reverend Samuel H. Willey concerning the desirability of founding a college in California. The clergyman discovered that Larkin had a relative in Boston, the Reverend Doctor William M. Rogers, who was one of the overseers of Harvard University. At Larkin's suggestion the young divine wrote to Dr. Rogers, and in due time received a letter endorsing the idea that a college or university should be established, first of all, because California was too remote from the Atlantic seaboard to depend on eastern institutions for higher education, and second, because the well-being of the people of California would depend, "as it has depended in New England, on the educated men of the country."[18] Dr. Rogers urged a "country location" for the proposed college and pointed out that since a university "must be the growth of time," the benefactors of the new institution should be content, at the outset, with "what will equal a New England high school."[19]

Thus encouraged, Dr. Willey sought the earliest opportunity to advance substantially the cause of higher education in California. It came to him when delegates to the first state constitutional convention assembled at Monterey in September, 1849. Although there was at that time "no near prospect of a youthful population to need a college,"[20] he found among the delegates a sufficient number who could appreciate the wisdom of laying the foundations for a state university. The constitution as finally drafted included a section contemplating the eventual establishment of a "university with such branches as the public convenience may demand, for the promotion of literature, the arts and sciences."[21]

A "Country Location"

Through the years the Reverend Dr. Willey never lost sight of this goal; and he remembered Dr. Rogers' advice about selecting a "country location" for any college that might in time become a university. When the Reverend Henry Durant, a Congregationalist, arrived in San Francisco in 1853 with the intention of founding a college, Dr. Willey was among those who helped him start the enterprise, and it was he who selected Oakland as a "country location" for the fledgling establishment, at first called the Contra Costa Academy. The academy had no sooner acquired an eight-acre site and received a charter as the nonsectarian College of California, however, than the trustees and faculty realized that it was in the heart of a growing business district and would have to be moved to a new location that genuinely qualified as "country."

The search for a suitably rural location included the entire Bay Area and finally ended with the selection, in 1858, of farm property some miles north of Oakland—"accessible and yet sufficiently removed from the disturbance of the city," Trustee Willey wrote nearly thirty years later.[22]

The fact that the trustees of the College of California had selected what is now Berkeley as the site for a new campus caused a board of directors for a proposed state agricultural and mechanic arts college to look favorably upon a near-by site in 1867. At this point, Governor F. F. Low, long a contributor to the impecunious College of California, suggested that a real university might be created if the state should contribute the money that would otherwise be used for the agricultural and mechanic arts college, and if the College of California should give for the purpose its new campus, its library, and its buildings in Oakland. Such, briefly, is the story of the genesis of the University of California and of the decision to build it on an East Bay site opposite the Golden Gate.

The Town of Berkeley

In the natural course of events a town would have grown up around the university. Samuel H. Willey was responsible for laying out the nucleus of one while the campus site still belonged to the College of California. Forced by the owner of the site to purchase more land than they could really afford or thought they needed, the trustees of the college were in a formidable financial predicament until the always resourceful Dr. Willey conceived the idea of paying for the property by the sale of lots in a homestead association, a new and popular method of marketing land on the installment plan. The trustees formed the College Homestead Association on September 1, 1864, made Dr. Willey the financial manager, and proceeded to lay out a gridiron pattern of streets on part of the college land and to divide the blocks into one-acre lots.

Two years later, the trustees learned how lacking in originality their town planning was. The plan for the campus completed by Olmsted in 1866 showed, in addition to a site for the college buildings, a well-defined and thoughtfully planned "Berkeley neighborhood" that was in sharp contrast to the rectilinear scheme of the homestead tract. Although the "neighborhood" proposal was never carried out, it deserves a brief description because it embodied several important principles of present-day planning for residential areas. No cross-town streets invaded Olmsted's Berkeley neighborhood of winding, tree-shaded roads. These roads were designed to serve no purpose "beyond the mere supplying of the wants of the neighborhood itself" and were intended to be safe and quiet.[23] The lots were grouped in five subareas around a central open space to be used as a recreation area and social gathering place. In planning smaller units within the neighborhood, Olmsted was more realistic than some twentieth-century planners who have failed to recognize the natural tendency of any residential population to break down into minor social groupings in which face-to-face relationships can be readily maintained. He anticipated by many decades the "modern" emphasis on close relationships between house and garden, suggesting that dwellings in the neighborhood should have "attractive open-air apartments, so formed that they can be often occupied for hours at a time, with convenience and ease in every respect, without the interruption of ordinary occupations or difficulty of conversation."[24]

Other Institutions

The 'sixties and the early years of the 'seventies saw the founding of other educational institutions and the growth of those established in the 'fifties, though none of these other institutions brought into existence new communities. The State Normal School, founded in San Francisco in 1862, was moved to Washington Square in San Jose by act of the legislature in 1870. Later the school became San Jose State College. Dr. and Mrs. Cyrus Taggart Mills, who had begun operating the Young Ladies Seminary at Benicia in 1865, sold their interest in this school in 1870, purchased a tract of 140 acres at the base of the San Leandro Hills about five miles from Oakland, and erected thereon a large building containing both dormitories and classrooms. Patterned after Mount Holyoke Seminary in Massachusetts, Mills Seminary—now Mills College—has become a leading women's college of the West. The University of the Pacific, which was called the California Wesleyan College when it was chartered in 1851 at Santa Clara, moved to a new campus about half way between

San Jose and Santa Clara in 1871. Property not required by the institution was sold by the trustees as the University Tract.

The increasing sophistication and affluence of certain elements of the Bay Area population also encouraged the development of health resorts and recreation places in the 'sixties. Brannan's spa at Calistoga has already been mentioned. Far more popular than this Napa Valley resort was Pacific Congress Springs, which Darius O. Mills, president of the Bank of California, and other capitalists opened in 1866 on Campbell Creek one mile from the town of Saratoga in Santa Clara County. The waters that bubbled from the ground on the upper reaches of Campbell Creek were thought to taste like those at Congress Springs in the eastern Saratoga. Wealthy San Franciscans also began to frequent San Rafael during summer months and to speak of it as a health resort. But city people who journeyed to the picturesque beaches near the new town of Half Moon Bay (established in 1863) in San Mateo County did so purely for fun and not to rid themselves of liver complaint.

At an earlier time the physical beauties of the San Francisco Bay Area no doubt were appreciated and mentioned with pleasure, but in the late 'sixties they were studied with a discriminating eye and for the first time were commercially exploited. The completion of the transcontinental railroad began to turn a small stream of promotional "literature" into a flood of guidebooks, brochures, and travel accounts extolling the area.

New County Boundaries

There was as yet, however, no reference in popular magazines or newspapers to a specific Bay Area composed of the nine counties now commonly regarded as political units in the metropolitan region; but it should be noted that in the 'sixties some revisions in county boundaries brought the area to approximately its present political configuration. These revisions might be classed as adjustments to the facts of geography. Napa County, expanded in 1852 to include half of Clear Lake and in 1855 to include the entire lake and the territory surrounding it, was reduced to about its present size in 1861 when Lake County was created. The new northern boundary more nearly coincided with the mountains enclosing the upper part of Napa Valley and recognized that the territory to the north constituted another physiographic area. An even more striking example of readjustment in accordance with topography was the detachment of the northern part of Santa Cruz County and its transfer by the state legislature to San Mateo County in 1868. Twice before, in 1861 and again in 1866, residents of the Pescadero area had sought this change, because they were forty miles north of the county seat of Santa Cruz County and were cut off by an intervening mountain range, whereas they were but twenty miles from Redwood City, the county seat of San Mateo County, and were served by daily stages to that town.

From time to time in later years minor changes were made, as in the realignment of the northern boundary of Sonoma County in 1917 to conform to the nearest United States survey lines. But for all practical purposes the counties bordering on San Francisco Bay achieved permanent boundaries within a little more than eighteen years after the first legislature organized the state into counties. No one would contend, though, that these political boundaries define a precise physiographic area.

CHAPTER FOUR

Urban Rivalries

Outside the San Francisco Bay Area the economic development of California had scarcely begun at the time the transcontinental railroad was completed. The upper Sacramento Valley, almost the entire San Joaquin Valley, the coastal valleys south of Monterey, and the timberlands of the northern coast all awaited further settlement and further exploitation of their natural resources. These huge areas of the state were, in effect, untapped economic provinces that would enrich and increase in prestige the cities that could establish transportation links and trade connections with them. They were the grand prizes in a new cycle of railroad building that began in 1870.

Two things appeared indispensable in the contest for the riches of these regions: direct access by rail and a deep-water port. San Francisco had a port but was cut off from the interior valleys by the bay. Oakland enjoyed the advantage of being the terminus of the overland railroad and could easily be linked to other areas of the state by branches of the main line, but Oakland had as yet no port facilities. Vallejo, smaller than either San Francisco or Oakland, had both a deep-water harbor and a railroad —the California Pacific—providing access to the lower Sacramento Valley. Extension of this road into other areas of the state and into other states could make Vallejo the rival of either San Francisco or Oakland, or of both.

Not the cities but the Big Four—Leland Stanford, Collis P. Huntington, Mark Hopkins, and Charles Crocker— actually held the trump cards in the game that started as soon as the transcontinental railroad was completed,

though the fact did not immediately become clear. San Francisco, Oakland, and Vallejo found themselves contestants in a struggle in which each was handicapped in some way by its geographic situation. All three were also pawns in the hands of the owners of the Central Pacific.

Gloom in San Francisco

Only a few months after the first overland train completed its historic run, San Franciscans began to realize that the transcontinental rails were no unmixed blessing to their city. The Pacific railroad permitted eastern concerns, especially those in Chicago, to sell their products in areas theretofore served exclusively by the western metropolis. It carried East many products formerly shipped to the Atlantic seaboard from the wharves of San Francisco. Business at the port declined.

To make matters worse, production in the Nevada silver mines fell off because of floods, poor ventilation, and disastrous fires. And as always, depressed conditions were reflected in a slump in real estate in San Francisco.

Oakland, on the other hand, was enjoying a boom. "One only need take a walk or drive around and about Oakland, outside of the principal streets, to be perfectly astounded at the immense number of buildings in course of construction on every hand," the Oakland *Daily Transcript* reported on April 18, 1870. Scores of applicants for houses to rent were being turned away daily from real-estate offices, according to the newspaper.

So much gloom filled the spirits of certain business

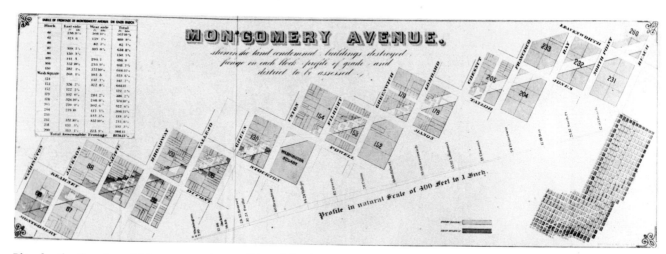

Plan for the Creation of Montgomery Avenue (Now Columbus Avenue). As presented in the San Francisco Municipal Reports for 1872–1873.

groups in San Francisco that the *Evening Bulletin* felt compelled to counteract "all the croaking one hears." "People talk of dull times, and compared to the days of high prices, when the interior consumed what the city imported or made and produced nothing but gold, the times are dull; judged by the standard of healthy business and progress they are not, and those who croak most now will be the most surprised five years hence at the rapid strides the city will have made," the newspaper editorialized on May 24, 1870.

The journal pointed to the "hundreds of modest dwellings" being constructed in areas that three or four years earlier had been "blank spaces." It cited improvements "of the most substantial and handsome character" in the thickly settled districts of the city: "The fine hotel on Market Street [William C. Ralston's Grand Hotel], the splendid book warehouse of Bancroft & Co.—the largest edifice of its kind west of New York—the elegant banking and store-houses on California, Sansome and Front streets, the numerous fine churches and school houses in progress, the new Mint, and the many handsome private residences, are among recent evidences of improved growth. Then the city is about to erect a City Hall at a point which five years ago was considered out of town, and is about to commence the work of laying out a great Park, stretching from its western charter line to the Ocean, which will be the signal for many private improvements in that direction. A magnificent new Avenue [now Columbus Avenue] is soon to be opened from the upper end of

Montgomery Street to North Beach, more than a mile through the built up portion of the city. Several new manufactures have been added to the city's industrial resources, and others will soon follow."

Struggle for a Terminus

In spite of such optimistic reassurances, many San Franciscans were troubled by the same sort of uneasiness that had taken possession of the fainthearted during the Benicia boom of earlier days. In increasing numbers they believed that somehow the metropolis must become the terminus of a transcontinental railroad, if not of the Central Pacific through its Western Pacific subsidiary, then of the Southern Pacific, originally chartered in 1865 to build southward from the Santa Clara Valley to a connection at the Colorado River with a railroad from the Mississippi Valley. Early in 1870 there were reports that Leland Stanford and his associates had consolidated this company, the San Francisco and San Jose Rail Road, and the extension between San Jose and Gilroy known as the Santa Clara and Pajaro Valley Railroad. If the line through the Santa Clara Valley were, indeed, to be built southward and then eastward, San Francisco possibly could become the terminus of a new southern transcontinental line; but the intentions of the Big Four were only to be guessed at. It was equally possible that the railroad being built down the San Joaquin Valley would be connected with a southern transcontinental line and would have its terminus in Oakland. For that matter, a southern transcontinental line routed through the Santa Clara Valley could just as easily be terminated at Oakland as at San Francisco. Nevertheless, the Big Four had the audacity to ask San Francisco to contribute a subsidy of $1,000,000 toward the building of a railroad southward from Gilroy, on the tacit understanding—but not the firm promise—that the terminus would be a thirty-acre site on Mission Bay granted by the state legislature in 1868.

The defeat of the subsidy by a narrow margin at an election in June, 1870, showed that a majority of San Franciscans either distrusted Stanford and his associates or were unconvinced that direct rail connections with the East and with remoter parts of the state were essential to the economic well-being of the city.

"The public saw a company of rich men, already the recipients of valuable subsidies, asking for more, but silent in their canvass as to their own purposes, and only 9,000 of our 25,000 voters were enough interested to go to the polls," the *Daily Evening Bulletin* pointed out on June 17, 1870. "This policy of coquetting with various towns, coaxing and threatening by turns, as if to get as much as possible from each, always holding in reserve an unavowed ulterior object, is hardly the best one to win confidence anywhere."

Ruin of a Grand Scheme

The election was scarcely over when San Franciscans became aware that there was still danger that Congress might enact a pending bill granting Yerba Buena Island to the Big Four for a terminal. The prospect of having transcontinental and San Joaquin Valley trains loading and unloading at docks on Yerba Buena Island, within sight of the waning port of San Francisco, was too much for citizens who were concerned about the shipping interests of the metropolis. Opposition to the proposal became vociferous; and the demand was renewed that San Francisco be made the western terminus of the transcontinental railroad. But the Big Four did not appear to be making a strenuous effort to secure passage of the pending bill. They were about to complete their famous Long Wharf at Oakland, extending two miles into the bay. The public outcry against the Yerba Buena Island proposal subsided, temporarily.

In the spring of 1871 San Francisco found itself threatened from another quarter—Vallejo. The California Pa-

Waterfront of the United States Navy Yard, Mare Island, 1870. The city of Vallejo appears in the distance. Photograph courtesy of Vallejo Chamber of Commerce.

cific Railroad Company, partly financed by British and German capital, bought the Petaluma Valley railroad of Peter Donahue and also the California Steam Navigation Company, which dominated commerce on the inland waterways of California. These additions to its system gave it complete control of all existing rail approaches to the bay from the north. But these mergers were merely the prelude to a grand scheme of the directors. They next announced plans for a line 950 miles in length from Woodland, on the Davisville-Marysville branch, to Christmas Lake in Oregon and thence to Salt Lake City.

"Vallejo will be an important railway center as well as a considerable shipping point," the San Francisco *Evening Bulletin* observed on May 22, 1871. And a few days later the San Francisco *News Letter* concluded that "so far as there is any rivalry between Vallejo and Oakland for commercial position, the latter may as well give up the contest."[1]

Oakland's lack of a harbor also led Lieutenant Colonel of Engineers B. S. Alexander to think that the Alameda County city was now out of the running in the struggle for dominance of the hinterland. Writing to General John B. Frisbie, vice-president of the California Pacific, he suggested: "... let there be a combination of the Central Pacific and California Pacific Railroads, which is highly probable at an early date, for the interests of both of these roads point in this direction, and then another combination with the China steamers, and Vallejo would be at once converted into the great railway centre of the State; the proposed great harbor at Oakland would probably never be excavated, and Vallejo from that time forward would contend with San Francisco alone for commercial supremacy."[2]

This was indeed a dazzling prospect for Vallejo, and Collis P. Huntington, Leland Stanford, and Mark Hopkins soon were in a position to fulfill the city's dream of becoming a great center, or to shatter it. Between July 13 and September 1, 1871, Huntington and his associates negotiated various contracts and agreements with the California Pacific that gave them undisputed control of this ambitious but financially weak railroad. They had watched with growing resentment the expansion of the California Pacific and had felt the pinch of competition from its operations, for its shorter route between San Francisco and Sacramento (87 miles) attracted more local passengers than their own circuitous line from Oakland via Stockton (137½ miles). To demonstrate that they meant to crush this potential rival, they had resorted to the well-worn stratagem of arranging to construct a branch from Sacramento paralleling its tracks. And so the directors of the debt-burdened California Pacific had

agreed to sell the greater part of their stock and to become parties to a series of involved transactions all greatly to the advantage of the Central Pacific.

Having gained control of the California Pacific, the titans of the Central Pacific were now masters of the railroad traffic of the entire San Francisco Bay Area and all northern California. And as if to leave no doubt of their monopoly, they immediately transferred the offices of the California Pacific from San Francisco to Sacramento, the seat of their railroad empire.

Panic in the Metropolis

In San Francisco many leading citizens were in a state of panic, clamoring for a railroad bridge to connect the metropolis with the Alameda shore. "San Francisco has quietly waited for the cars to bring themselves to her ships, until she finds the railroad transportation of the state, from the south, the east, and the north, fast concentrating on the eastern shore of the bay, and her ships passing themselves over to the cars," the *Daily Evening Bulletin* editorialized on October 26, 1871. "The fate of Venice awaits her if they are not brought back; and they can be brought back only by stretching the rails across the bay, and laying their ends upon our wharves."

The *Daily Morning Call*, which earlier had asserted that "Oakland is a part of San Francisco, so far as those influences are concerned which result from the aggregation of population and wealth,"[3] now reversed itself completely and acknowledged that "the necessity for some such medium of communication between San Francisco and Alameda shores of the Bay other than by vessel has long been felt and discussed by our citizens, but never with so much earnestness nor so much firm belief in its practicability as at the present time."[4]

The *Daily Alta California* alone opposed a transbay bridge as impracticable and urged San Francisco to save itself by providing superior harbor facilities and cheaper accommodations than any rival city could supply.

The Oakland *Daily Transcript* presented estimates by civil engineer George F. Allardt indicating that the cost of a low bridge five miles in length would be not less than $16,608,900. The "benefits" to San Francisco of such an expenditure, the Oakland newspaper predicted, would be an increase in the value of Alameda County property and "an exodus of families from San Francisco who object to steamboat travel," the continued exportation of grain from Oakland, and the refusal of the railroad companies to consider running through trains across a bridge because "open draws" would constantly disrupt schedules.[5]

"Nobody doubts that San Francisco must continue to be the metropolis of the Pacific Coast; and the shallow

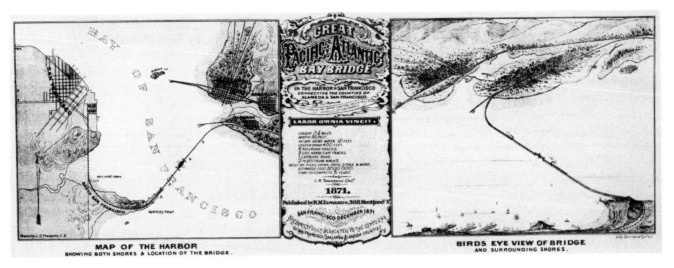

*The Proposed Pacific and Atlantic Bay Bridge from Hunters Point to Alameda,
1871. Photograph courtesy of Wells Fargo Bank.*

efforts of a few speculators to frighten San Franciscans into committing an outrage against themselves, and their posterity, is highly reprehensible," the *Transcript* scolded, concluding with the conciliatory thought that "Oakland is an invaluable adjunct to the commerce of San Francisco; and far-seeing San Franciscans are proud, not jealous, of Oakland."

But many San Franciscans *were* jealous of Oakland, and extremely apprehensive, especially when they learned that twenty-two members of the state legislature had forwarded a communication to Congress urging passage of the pending bill providing for establishment of a railroad terminal on Yerba Buena Island. In March, 1872, the San Francisco Chamber of Commerce sent a memorial to the President and Vice-President of the United States and to Congress attacking the proposed cession of part of the island; a citizens' meeting passed resolutions denouncing the grant; a committee visited the state legislature in an attempt to change the minds of the legislators; and finally, another committee hastened to Washington to request the President to veto the pending bill if Congress should pass it.

Futile Efforts

At this juncture San Francisco officials decided to attempt statesmanlike negotiations with the Big Four. The city offered to build a bridge across Dumbarton Strait in the southern arm of the bay, to construct a harbor belt line, and to fill in tidelands and grant a right of way to the Central Pacific if it would abandon all claim to Yerba Buena Island. The city insisted, however, that all rail-

roads should be permitted to use the bridge and should be granted occupancy of filled lands, and that no charge should be made for either privilege. The railroad magnates countered with a proposal that they would build the bridge and the harbor belt line, provided the people of the city would approve a subsidy of $2,500,000 and grant them a part of China Basin for commercial purposes. City officials were inclined to favor the proposed subsidy but reserved the right to confer upon any other company the privilege of laying track on land granted for a right of way, again insisting that any and all railroads should have the right to use the bridge. The arrogant monopolists then practically invited a mayoral veto of a supervisorial order for an election on the subsidy by demanding the option to shift the terminus from San Francisco if the growth of business elsewhere warranted a change. And a veto is exactly what they got from Mayor William Alvord, though it is doubtful that this perturbed them overmuch.

In the meantime, San Francisco capitalists toyed with two other railroad propositions—one to associate themselves with the Atlantic and Pacific Company (predecessor of the Atchison, Topeka, and Santa Fe Railway) in building a transcontinental railroad to San Francisco, the other to finance a railroad to connect with Thomas A. Scott's projected line from Fort Worth, Texas, to San Diego.

Both proposals were rejected in favor of a railroad to be built and owned entirely by California capitalists and to be known as the San Francisco and Colorado River Railroad Company. Like other ambitious railroad schemes of the times, this one depended upon approval by the voters of a large subsidy—$10,000,000. But long before the election on the subsidy could be held, a majority of San Francisco newspapers became suspicious of the directors of the new company and began attacking them as tricksters bent on obtaining the subsidy and then selling out to "Stanford & Company." On October 18, 1872, two weeks before the election, the directors announced in an advertisement in the *Daily Alta California* that they were abandoning, "for the present," all further efforts to obtain public aid. Thus virtually ended the movement to make San Francisco the terminus of an overland railroad.

New Developments

Once the local threat—if it were a threat—to their rapidly expanding railroad empire was eliminated, the Sacramento titans were free to concentrate on fighting Thomas Scott and on preventing entrance of the Union Pacific or the Northern Pacific into California from Oregon. In 1873 they built two branches of the Southern Pacific only far enough down the coast to block the approach of any rivals—one into the San Benito Valley to Tres Pinos, the other to Soledad in Monterey County. Their chief interest was in completing the line through the San Joaquin Valley and pushing their rails as rapidly as possible to the southeastern border of the state, acquiring large land grants from the federal government as they built. The only railroad in the Bay Area which the Big Four did not control was the Cotati Valley road built by Peter Donahue. They had added this to their holdings when they took over the California Pacific, but they later released it to Donahue to satisfy debts owed to him.

In January, 1873, the Board of United States Engineers for the Pacific Coast quieted San Francisco's fear that Yerba Buena Island would become the meeting place of rails and ships. The board suggested that a good harbor could be developed for Oakland in San Antonio Creek (now the Oakland Estuary) "for one-half the cost of a bridge from Oakland to Yerba Buena Island."[6] Congress authorized an investigation of the possibilities of dredging the shallow waters and, upon presentation of a report favoring the project, made the first of a series of appropriations for harbor improvements. For many years, however, the Long Wharf of the Big Four handled most of the cargo moving in and out of Oakland.

The port of San Francisco, meanwhile, was further improved, and its wharves again bustled with activity. Although it had become evident that the major railroad terminal of the Bay Area would be on the mainland side of the bay, San Francisco was no longer perturbed about the potential rivalry of Oakland. The metropolis was already so large that it attracted to itself, in spite of its peninsular location, the majority of newcomers and the lion's share of the new wealth of the state. Moreover, as time passed, San Franciscans observed that the Big Four themselves did little to build up Oakland but much to enhance the importance of the city by the Golden Gate.

A Torrent of Newcomers

An estimated seventy thousand people arrived in San Francisco by sea in 1873, compared with only twenty thousand in 1870. In 1874, eighty-five thousand disembarked at the metropolis, and although departures numbered in the thousands, the net inflow through the port brought smiles to the faces of those who had been lamenting its recent decline. Nothing like so many came by the overland train. Until 1873 the arrivals by train fluctuated between thirty and thirty-four thousand, then rose to forty-four thousand in 1873, and increased to fifty-six thousand in 1874. Not until 1875 did they approximate the number of arrivals by sea. In that year seventy-five thousand people made the long, tedious, dusty journey across the plains, the deserts, and the Sierra Nevada— and far more of them settled in San Francisco than in Oakland and other East Bay towns.[7]

The torrent of newcomers was impelled westward by financial panic in the East, by political convulsions in Europe, and by the strenuous efforts of the Big Four and the steamship companies to promote immigration. Stories of the big new bonanza that had been opened in the Comstock Lode at Virginia City in March, 1873, and of the stream of riches that was pouring into San Francisco from the mines also helped to increase the tide of immigration. Nor can one overlook, in seeking the causes of this new mass movement, the effect upon Easterners and Middle Western folk of the purple passages in letters penned by enthusiastic new arrivals in California.

Large numbers of Irish, Germans, and English, and a lesser number of French, Italians, Mexicans, Portuguese, and other foreign-born people swelled the influx into the state. Including the Chinese, the foreign-born accounted for two-thirds of the population increase in California during the 'seventies.[8] San Francisco, cosmopolitan from the time of the American occupation, became more than ever a city of many tongues, an international city in the true sense of the word. Not all the foreign-born came directly to California from other countries, however; a large proportion had lived for a time in Eastern or Midwestern states before moving to the Bay Area and other parts of the state. They were thus a part of the deep undercurrent of westward movement noted in American history even before the founding of the republic.

The Silver Boom

San Francisco, the great reception center for the influx of the 'seventies, became a city of shifting population, of new real-estate speculations, of feverish building activity. The old section around Portsmouth Plaza and the triangle bounded by Market, Kearny, and California streets became mainly commercial and lost population, while the section between California and Washington streets became more densely inhabited as people adopted the custom of living over shops. For three decades, or until the catastrophic earthquake and fire of 1906, the custom of living above commercial establishments was to be one of the characteristic features of San Francisco life, commented on by every visitor.

South of Market Street the growth of wholesale and industrial enterprises in the crowded Seventh Ward sent the fashionable scurrying from Rincon Hill and South Park to Stockton, Bush, Pine, Powell, and Mason streets, and to the southern slope of Russian Hill. Working-class families shifted westward along Mission, Howard, Folsom, and Harrison streets in the direction of Mission Dolores. In this South-of-Market area the congestion became so great that there was a demand for the creation of new streets parallel to Market Street in the large blocks created by Jasper O'Farrell in 1847.

The North Beach area, the lower slopes of Nob Hill, the area between Post and Market streets west of Kearny, and the homestead tracts and filled-in marshlands in the southern part of the city all attracted thousands of new inhabitants. Tracts west of Van Ness Avenue also vibrated with the sound of the hammer and saw as new dwellings rose.

In this westward and southward expansion of the city the horsecar lines played a major role. But it was not the picturesque and gaudy "bobtail" cars and bulbous "balloon" cars of the horsecar lines that excited San Franciscans in the period of the great silver boom; it was the cable car, the invention of Andrew S. Hallidie, a local manufacturer. A public demonstration of Hallidie's new

San Francisco in the late 1870's, with William C. Ralston's Palace Hotel in the distance. Photograph courtesy of Bancroft Library.

mode of transit on Clay Street between Kearny and Jones streets on the afternoon of August 2, 1873, presaged a boom in view lots and the conquest of once formidable barriers to city expansion, such as Nob Hill and Russian Hill. Steep grades that no horsecar line could surmount—grades resulting from the mechanical application of the gridiron street pattern to hilly terrain—were but an invitation to the smooth flight of the cable car; and wild was the scramble for hilltop lots and for cable franchises.

On the crest of Nob Hill arose grandiose residences that proclaimed the wealth and power of California's *nouveaux riches*, the railroad and mining kings. Among these ornate piles stood Leland Stanford's two-million-dollar show place, on the corner later occupied by the Stanford Court Apartments. In the fashion of the times, the house contained rooms in a variety of styles—Chinese, Pompeian, Italian, Indian, and plushy Victorian. Even more costly was the palace of Charles Crocker, which occupied the site on which Grace Cathedral now stands. But none could equal in vulgar pretentiousness the three-million-dollar gingerbread fantasy created by Mrs. Mark Hopkins on the property today occupied by the hotel that perpetuates her husband's name.

Of all these expressions of the ego of the self-made, only the brownstone mansion of James C. Flood, the sometime copartner with William S. O'Brien of the Auction Lunch Rooms, triumphed over the fire of 1906 and endures today, though its interior was gutted in the holocaust. As the exclusive Pacific Union Club, the old structure is a reminder of the kind of bonanza elegance that awed San Franciscans in the days when bartenders became millionaires almost overnight and chambermaids became mistresses of opulent households.

Leland Stanford headed the group that put into operation the historic California Street cable line, nowadays a delightful anachronism ding-donging up and down the slopes of Nob Hill and through a man-made canyon of the central business district. The immediate popularity of the new road forced the older Clay Street cable into a grim rivalry for the patronage of the social upper crust on the hill.

In the zestful mid-seventies tongues wagged not only over the splendor on "Nabob Hill" but also over the sumptuous Palace Hotel that the irrepressible William C. Ralston was building on Market and Montgomery streets. Himself the owner of a Belmont country house that was every bit as resplendent as the hilltop edifices, Ralston in 1874 set out to give San Francisco a hotel more luxurious than any other in America and twice as large as his earlier four-hundred-room Grand Hotel. If calculated in the inflated currency of the present, its cost would

be several times the $5,000,000 that the spectacular financier poured into it. Unfortunately, he did not live to hear the famous Palm Court echo to the clatter of four-in-hand teams hitched to shining landaus. He suffered financial reverses in 1875 and soon afterward was found dead in the waters off North Beach, perhaps a suicide.

Water Projects

Ralston was only one of the many who relished the bold and the colossal in the era when torrents of silver flowed from the Comstock. No project was too audacious to seem possible, not even a scheme of the Mount Gregory Water and Mining Company to conduct the waters of the Rubicon River, in El Dorado County, to San Francisco through 183 miles of iron pipes. San Francisco had visions of becoming a city of a million inhabitants; and whereas a few years earlier Professor George Davidson, of the United States Coast Survey, had derided Colonel A. W. Von Schmidt's scheme of tunneling five miles through the dividing ridge of the Sierra to bring the waters of Lake Tahoe to San Francisco, people were now willing to concede that it might be possible, though costly. In 1874 an official San Francisco Water Commission actually went to the Sierra to investigate the practicability of obtaining water from the lakes and streams near the sources of the Mokelumne River; but the following year the city turned from such distant sources and considered acquiring water rights on Calaveras Creek, a branch of Alameda Creek in northern Santa Clara and southern Alameda counties. The Spring Valley Water Company forestalled the move by purchasing riparian rights on Alameda Creek and its tributaries. A proposal to buy out the company failed at the polls, and San Francisco was content for almost a quarter of a century to let the private utility develop additional water resources on the San Francisco Peninsula and in southern Alameda County.

On the opposite side of the bay the Oakland *Daily Transcript* expressed the belief, however, that San Francisco sooner or later would have to build an aqueduct from the Sierra, and that it would be to Oakland's advantage to join in the project. Oakland, too, wrestled with the issue of municipal ownership of its water supply at this time and, like the metropolis, concluded that for the time being it might as well let private enterprise—Anthony Chabot and the Contra Costa Water Company—provide for its needs. However, the outgoing mayor of Oakland, Mack Webber, said in 1876 that if the city waited a few years the San Francisco supply would prove inadequate and Oakland could then join in building a great aqueduct from the Sierra to serve Sacramento, Stockton, Oakland, and San Francisco. Farsighted residents of the Bay Area

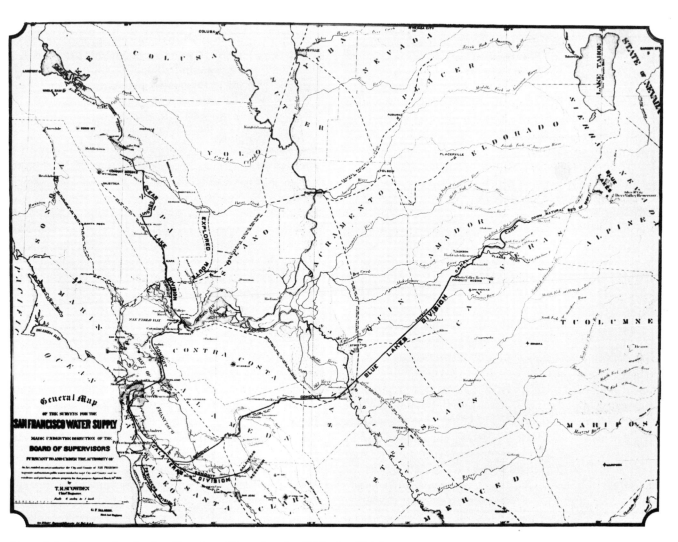

Map of the Surveys for the San Francisco Water Supply, 1874. An official water commission investigated Bay Area as well as distant sources of water supply. The proposed conduit marked "Blue Lakes Division" follows approximately the route of the present-day Mokelumne Aqueduct of the East Bay Municipal Utility District.

thus realized a long time ago that eventually the water deficiencies of the area would have to be met by importations from the streams that flow into the great Central Valley.

Speculation in Oakland

Chabot's new San Leandro Reservoir, impounding the waters of San Leandro Creek, added enough water to the supplies already in use to assure Oakland of an adequate supply for a good many years. The city was growing steadily, though not nearly so rapidly as some people had

expected when the transcontinental railroad was completed. In 1872 it had absorbed near-by Brooklyn and had annexed territory stretching as far north as present Thirty-sixth Street, thereby increasing its area from five to more than eleven square miles. It was linked with Alameda by the Webster Street drawbridge, and to the University of California campus at Berkeley by a "bobtail" horsecar line. Other lines, most of them built in 1875 and 1876, when there was much real-estate speculation and San Francisco capital was being invested in East Bay properties, extended to Temescal, Emeryville, West Oakland,

East Oakland, Mills Seminary, and Mountain View Cemetery, an extensive burial ground, designed by Frederick Law Olmsted, in the hills just north of the present city of Piedmont. Since many of these horsecar lines were built to open up new tracts rather than to serve already populated areas, the city toward the end of the decade tended to be overextended. Even in 1875, gas and water companies complained that they had been induced to spend large sums to provide service in areas only sparsely settled. In West Oakland, particularly, many whole blocks contained but a single house. Elsewhere houses built on speculation exceeded the demand.

Horace Carpentier, ever ambitious for the city that he had founded, advocated annexation of Berkeley to Oakland; but his proposal aroused the opposition of Judge J. W. Dwinelle, who declared that Oakland was in debt and that it would be well for Berkeley to keep out of her jaws. Berkeley succeeded in becoming a self-governing municipality in 1878, with its southern boundary five hundred feet south of Dwight Way. On the north the city extended to the county line, and in West Berkeley to Codornices Creek. Between the settlements near the University campus and the settlement of Ocean View, near San Pablo Road, lay vast fields. The total population in the built-up areas was only about two thousand.

Berkeley, Oakland, and Alameda had chiefly the status of "bedroom" communities during this period. Their attractiveness as places of residence for people who worked in San Francisco is indicated in part by the remarkable gain in transbay travel. Between 1873 and 1877 the number of passengers carried by ferryboats operating between San Francisco and Oakland more than doubled, increasing from 2,655,671 to 5,570,555.[9] The opening of a new ferry building at the foot of Market Street in San Francisco in September, 1875, facilitated the daily movement of commuters back and forth across the bay.

In passing, it should be noted that population gains and new construction did not contribute to the happiness of all the citizens of Oakland, because many of the beautiful oaks for which the city was named were sacrificed to "progress." "At almost every meeting of the Council there are petitions for the removal of trees, and if all these requests were complied with, Oakland would very soon be as windy and disagreeable as San Francisco," a citizen complained to the Oakland *News* as early as 1873.[10]

Politics and Rails

Another cause for discontent in Oakland was the domination of the Big Four, manifested by the defeat in the Oakland City Council of an attempt by a group of Oakland and Nevada capitalists to obtain a franchise for a railroad from Oakland to central and eastern Contra Costa County by way of Berkeley and a tunnel through the Berkeley Hills. The unequal struggle between the promoters of the Oakland, Berkeley, and Contra Costa Railroad Company and Charles Crocker, of the Big Four, occurred in 1876 some months before the monopolists completed their Southern Pacific line to Los Angeles through the San Joaquin Valley and made Oakland the Bay Area terminus. Immediately after the city council denied the backers of the little local road a franchise to lay tracks on Oakland streets, it submissively granted Crocker and his associates a franchise to build a new tentacle of the "octopus" that was tightening its hold on California. Known as the Northern Railroad, the new link ran from Oakland northward along the shoreline to Carquinez Strait and to Tracy in the San Joaquin Valley.

When the road was opened, in 1878, it provided a nearly level route from Oakland to the Valley and eliminated use by Southern Pacific trains of the more difficult route through Livermore Pass and Niles Canyon, with its heavy grades. At Port Costa, on Carquinez Strait, trains bound for Sacramento and points east and north made connection with the car-transfer steamer *Solano*. This train ferry, the largest of its kind in the world, began operating in 1879 and transported trains to Benicia, from whence they proceeded on a new cutoff to Suisin and the tracks formerly belonging to the California Pacific.

New Narrow-Gauge Line

No such tiger-like ferocity as was shown toward the capitalists who wanted to build the local railroad through the Berkeley Hills was displayed by the Big Four toward another railroad venture of the time, the South Pacific Coast Railroad. Yet this line, which stimulated the growth of Alameda, was potentially, at least, a competitor of the Southern Pacific and was eventually to become a property of the gigantic corporation formed by the Big Four.

The South Pacific Coast Railroad was an achievement of the ambitions of James G. Fair and James L. Flood, who had had the exhilarating experience of suddenly becoming Comstock millionaires. So pervasive was the talk of railroads in the ever-expanding, distance-conscious West that they, like other rich men with a desire to be known as empire builders, turned almost instinctively to a railroad scheme. They planned the South Pacific Coast Railroad as a narrow-gauge line that would run from the mainland side of San Francisco Bay to Santa Cruz and southward into the Salinas Valley. They thought of eventually extending it through the Coast Range and eastward to a connection with the Denver and Rio Grande Railroad, at that time a narrow-gauge line building westward.

Construction on the South Pacific Coast Railroad began at Dumbarton Point, in southern Alameda County, in May, 1876. From this location at the narrows in the southern arm of the bay the bonanza kings built their road to near-by Newark, a town founded in 1875 by the Newark Land Association and named for the manufacturing city in New Jersey. In the latter part of 1877, tracks were completed to San Jose via Alviso and Santa Clara. While construction was being pushed toward the village of Los Gatos, at the foot of the Santa Cruz Mountains, other crews were building southward from Alameda. Service between Alameda Point and Los Gatos (travel time: two and a half hours) was opened in June, 1878, and by 1880 the road had reached Santa Cruz. In 1881 it was extended to Oakland via the Webster Street Bridge. From Alameda Point a ferry service operated to San Francisco.

This narrow-gauge road triggered a real-estate boom in the southern and middle sections of Alameda, mainly because of the new rail-ferry service to San Francisco. As a commuter town, Alameda enjoyed an increase in population from 1,500 in 1870 to 5,700 in 1880. It was almost as large as Vallejo.

Metropolitan Hierarchy

A cloud hung over the city on Mare Island Strait. Vallejo was by-passed by through trains and had been hopelessly outdistanced by Oakland, its former rival. It had lost to Sacramento the railroad shops that the California Pacific once operated; it had failed in 1874 to wrest the county seat of Solano County from Fairfield; and it had reeled under an unexpected blow when the United States Navy drastically curtailed activities at Mare Island in the mid-seventies. The census of 1880 showed that its population had decreased to a little less than 6,000. Oakland, by contrast, had a population of 34,555 in 1880.

San Francisco, of course, overshadowed all other California cities, though its total population in 1880 (233,959) was considerably less than some of the forecasts made a decade earlier.

From the standpoint of metropolitan regional development, the 'seventies were significant for the accelerated growth of the East Bay and for the establishment of a San Francisco–Oakland axis in the Bay Area, with San Francisco as the major port and Oakland as the major railroad terminus. The population of Alameda County increased from 24,237 to approximately 63,000—a gain of 160 per cent. As the East Bay and San Francisco became more and more interdependent and began to complement each other's development, counties in the southern and northern sections of the Bay Area included relatively smaller proportions of the total population of the area. Santa Clara County gained less than 10,000 and slipped from second to third place among the counties in the area. Its residents numbered only a little more than 35,000 in 1880, compared with 26,246 ten years earlier. The four North Bay counties of Marin, Sonoma, Napa, and Solano together included only about 6,000 more inhabitants than Alameda County alone and among them had but 16.3 per cent of the total in the area, whereas ten years earlier nearly one-fifth of the population of the nine counties had lived in the North Bay. The proportion living in the two central counties of San Francisco and Alameda rose from 65 to 70 per cent, and for the next fifty years it remained about the same, though the percentage living in San Francisco declined steadily and the percentage living in Alameda County similarly increased. Not until the opening of transbay bridges and the construction of three-lane automobile highways throughout the Bay Area in the 1930's was the proportion concentrated in the two central counties to be reduced.

Outlying Counties

The growth that did take place in the North Bay was stimulated in large measure by the building of new railroads, the opening of new lumbering areas, and the further development of agriculture. Logging activities along the lower reaches of the Russian River in Sonoma County were fairly minor until Peter Donahue constructed a sixteen-mile branch of his San Francisco and North Pacific Railroad from Fulton to Guerneville in 1876, and the North Pacific Coast Railroad completed its narrow-gauge line to Duncan's Mills near the mouth of the river in 1877. The latter line had been opened between Sausalito and Tomales in 1875, providing an easy way for farmers in the coastal area of Marin County to ship their potatoes, butter, and oats to San Francisco; but its extension to the redwood forests of the Russian River had awaited the construction of a seventeen-hundred-foot tunnel through the mountains north of Tomales. On the line of the railroad in the San Geronimo–Nicasio Area of Marin County, three large new sawmills began operating; and in Sonoma County the towns of Valley Ford and Occidental made gains as local shipping points for agricultural products.

Not a little of the lumber produced around Guerneville was used for new structures in the thriving town of Santa Rosa, which increased in population during the 'seventies, while its rival, Petaluma, declined. (Santa Rosa in 1880: 3,616; Petaluma: 3,326.) Petaluma in that period gained an important new resident—a Canadian named Lyman C. Byce, who laid the foundations for the later fame of the city as a poultry and egg production center.

The Mill and Lumberyard of Heald and Guerne at Guerneville, Sonoma County.
From a lithograph in Historical Atlas Map of Sonoma County, 1877.

Besides building a branch of his San Francisco and North Pacific Railroad to Guerneville, Peter Donahue in the 'seventies built a railroad in the Sonoma Valley (Sears Point to Sonoma) and extended his Petaluma–Cloverdale main line to San Rafael in Marin County. When he laid rails of the last-mentioned line to Point Tiburon in 1882, the tip of the Marin Peninsula had two railroad terminals only half an hour by ferry from San Francisco. But even with the improved communication between the metropolis and the North Bay, developments in the northern counties were to progress slowly for many decades.

At the southern end of the bay, in Santa Clara County, a shift in production from grains to fruit began in the 'seventies; a similar change did not take place to any considerable extent in other Bay Area counties until the 'eighties. By 1875, San Jose had two large canneries, forerunners of many other processing plants later established there. In other respects this oldest of civil settlements in the Bay Area continued to be like Santa Rosa, Petaluma, and Napa, primarily a trading center and shipping point for an agricultural territory.

Dawn of the Electric Age

The introduction of a new invention especially associated, in the early days of its use, with urban living emphasized the difference in tempo between these outlying cities and San Francisco and Oakland. This technological wonder was the telephone. In February, 1878, the American Speaking Telephone Company began regular service in San Francisco with eighteen subscribers; and two months later the American District Telegraph Company installed the first switchboard for a telephone system in Oakland, serving a dozen or more subscribers.

At first the wires were strung over boards nailed to roofs, but it was not long before telephone poles and overhead wires became one more means of distinguishing a large city from a small one.

"The city," as San Francisco was always called, also led the way in the use of a new source of illumination—electricity. The Reverend Father Joseph M. Neri, professor of physics and other sciences at St. Ignatius College, gave the populace their first experience with the new marvel when, using a French dynamo, he installed three large arc floodlights on the roof of the college to illuminate the 1876 Centennial Exposition parade on Market Street.

Three years later, George H. Roe organized the California Electric Light Company and built the first central generating station in the United States, at the rear of a small lot near the corner of Fourth and Market streets. When the original station was destroyed by fire the following year, Roe moved to a new location and resumed service.

Still unknown was the secret of long-distance transmission of electricity, the use of electric power in the operation of transit vehicles, and the use of electricity industrially. But the electric age had dawned, presaging great new developments in the Bay Area and California—new developments that would contribute to the industrial growth of a state lacking in significant coal resources and as yet unaware of the extent of its petroleum deposits.

Social Turmoil

The social turmoil of the late 'seventies demonstrated how urgently the state, and the bay counties in particular, needed expansion of manufacturing and diversification of agriculture. The discontented mobs who gathered on the sand lots opposite the San Francisco City Hall in 1877 and 1878 to hear the vituperative Irish demagogue Denis Kearney berate the monopolists and the Chinese found what every mob wants—scapegoats. But the Number One enemy of these idle, frustrated men was an economy still in the early stages of development. Not that the railroad titans, the grain kings, and the land barons who had encouraged heavy in-migration could escape culpability for

Poplar City. A subdivision "connecting the cities of San Jose and Santa Clara . . . with orchards on the rear of each lot and poplar trees enclosing each block." From a lithograph in Historical Atlas Map of Santa Clara County, 1876.

the social ills of the times. This fraternity had created a huge labor force before there were crops and factories enough to provide jobs for all, and they had retarded economic development by charging excessive freight rates, stifling competition, and demanding high prices for land. But California was not fully awakened to the potentialities of its soils and the opportunities for agricultural diversification; nor did the West yet offer extensive markets for manufactured products. California was the land of grain, and the fields gave employment to labor only during the summer. In winter thousands of those who had sweated in the sun joined bread lines. But with the development of orchards in the Santa Clara Valley and vineyards in the Napa and Sonoma valleys came a new era of increased employment, for vine and orchard crops required a greater number of hands the year round. And as employment in agriculture expanded and became more stable, the market for products manufactured in the Bay Area also grew.

In spite of the ups and downs of the decade—the depression in the opening years, the silver orgy of 1873–1875, the slump of 1876, the turbulence and near insurrection of 1877–1878, and the political clashes leading to the adoption of a new State Constitution in 1879—the Bay Area made great gains. By the end of the decade every county in the area enjoyed railroad facilities. In remoter sections of the state, towns that were not even

on the map in 1870 looked to the metropolis for goods and services. To bay ports and bay cities they shipped their grain and wine, their wool and lumber and potatoes.

The Bay Area had begun to develop an oceanic hinterland and to attract through the Golden Gate the tramp steamers of the world, the Alaska whaling fleet, and lumber schooners from Oregon, Washington, and the northern California coast. In 1878 the Pacific Mail Line, having established regular sailings to Honolulu, became a medium for supplying the area with raw sugar, pineapples, coffee, and hides from the Hawaiian Islands. From the Orient came ships laden with wood oils, burlap, and tea, and from the South Seas vessels reeking of copra.

The decade of the 'seventies was the last in which the Bay Area was the unrivaled magnet for population migrating to California. Southern California was being discovered by adventurous Europeans, by eastern tourists who drifted south from the Bay Area, and by a few San Francisco and Nevada capitalists. Its most exciting years were just ahead. In the 'eighties the Southern Pacific and the Santa Fe would both complete transcontinental railroads to Los Angeles, thereby precipitating the "land rush" that was southern California's equivalent of the gold rush. The Bay Area, however, was yet to enjoy several decades of dominance in the affairs of California before it would share the privileges and responsibilities of leadership with another great metropolitan area.

CHAPTER FIVE

The Heyday of Enterprise

The 'eighties were years of sober, patient advance, free from the speculative madness, the shattering crashes, and the abject misery of the previous bizarre decade. Men no longer became millionaires overnight or found themselves reduced to poverty by a capricious turn of the wheel of fortune. Adolph Sutro sold out his holdings in Virginia City and invested his millions in San Francisco real estate, even though most of his friends regarded his purchases of acres of sand hills as sheer folly. Time was to prove that there was more money in the sand hills of the bay metropolis than in the tunneled and blasted mountains of Virginia City. The wealth of the 'eighties came only in part from the mines; the greater part of it came from the soils, the new factories, the new inventions designed to increase production, and from the railroad and shipping enterprises that facilitated the development of the state.

The most striking changes in the San Francisco Bay Area took place in the major valleys rather than in the cities. A great shift from the production of grain to the growing of fruit completely transformed the appearance of many rural areas, as a description of the Napa Valley in 1890 indicates: "Where there were wheat fields now are vineyards; where there were pasture fields now are thrifty orchards; where there stood barns for holding the grain and sheds for sheltering the stock now stand imposing wine cellars and fruit houses."[1] A contemporary newspaper account of the agricultural revolution in the valleys of Sonoma County revealed that the vine and the tree "entirely engrossed the attention of the farmers."[2] In almost every area served by adequate railroad transportation the big grain ranches were subdivided into small holdings. Long rows of young fruit trees were set out, and within a few years a rich green canopy shaded the earth that had formerly been mantled in gold. Even the largest nurseries were taxed to supply the demand for budded stock.

Some idea of the upsurge of interest in fruit production can be gained from the historian Bancroft's figures on shipments of fruit from California to eastern states. In 1871, the second year after the completion of the transcontinental railroad, less than 2,000,000 pounds of California fruit was marketed in the East. By 1888 the amount was almost 54,000,000 pounds. In 1872 a mere 182,090 pounds of canned fruit went East, but by 1888 the total shipped beyond the Sierra was more than 39,000,000 pounds. Between 1875 and 1888 the volume of California dried fruit sold in the eastern market increased from a little more than 500,000 to almost 20,000,000 pounds.[3]

In a kind of chicken-and-egg relationship, freight rates lowered as fruit shipments increased, and fruit orchards spread over a vaster acreage as rates fell. In 1889 the rate on canned fruit was ninety-four cents per hundred pounds, whereas a few years earlier it had been $3.51 per hundred pounds. Not that California farmers and canners were satisfied with these freight rates; the cry was for still lower rates. But the railroads at least responded in their grudging fashion to the demands of the new economy that was evolving.

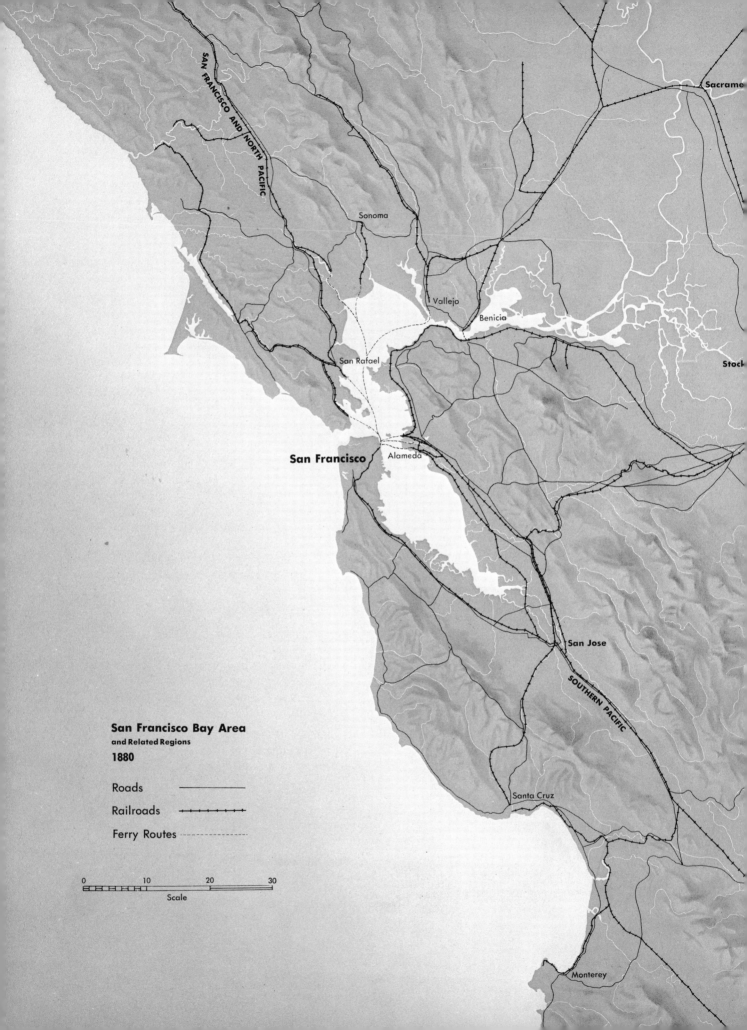

SAN FRANCISCO AND NORTH PACIFIC

Sacrame

Sonoma

Vallejo

Benicia

Stock

San Rafael

San Francisco

Alameda

San Jose

SOUTHERN PACIFIC

Santa Cruz

San Francisco Bay Area
and Related Regions
1880

Roads ————————

Railroads ——+——+——+——

Ferry Routes ——————

0   10   20   30
Scale

Monterey

Sugar, Ships, and Pumps

In San Francisco, where perhaps four-fifths of the manufacturing enterprises of the state were concentrated, the most talked-about establishment in the industrial belt along the southern waterfront was the mammoth sugar refinery erected by Claus Spreckels at the foot of Twenty-third Street in 1883. Freighters from the Hawaiian Islands unloaded raw sugar at the refinery docks, and some five hundred employees converted it into the basic product upon which the operations of a growing number of fruit canneries depended.

Indicative of the transition of Bay Area agriculture from grains to fruit was the entrance of another steamship line into the Hawaiian trade. In the same year that the Spreckels refinery began operating, the Oceanic Steamship Company followed the Pacific Mail in the importation of raw sugar and other products of the Islands. By 1885 the Oceanic had linked San Francisco with Australia and New Zealand, thereby opening new fields for the exportation of manufactured products and providing new sources of raw materials.

Obscure at the time, yet related to the expansion of the Hawaiian sugar trade, to the building of the Spreckels refinery, and to the agricultural revolution, was John Bean's invention and manufacture of an orchard spray pump in the village of Los Gatos in 1883. By providing fruitgrowers with the means of combating insect pests, particularly San Jose scale, the retired inventor contributed to the remarkable increase in production that was one of the economic phenomena of the 'eighties and 'nineties. From his modest plant and several small canning-machinery factories developed the huge Food Machinery and Chemical Corporation, today a gigantic enterprise with headquarters in San Jose and branch plants throughout the United States.

The Grain Trade

In the great Central Valley of California the raising of wheat and other grains was still the chief agricultural activity. The magnitude of production was reflected in grain shipping at Port Costa and other ports along the northern shore of Contra Costa County. Founded by George W. McNear in 1879, just after the railroad was opened through the county, Port Costa quickly became the greatest grain port in the world. Immense warehouses, heaped with sacks of the hard, plump wheat of the San Joaquin Valley, lined the wharves for a mile or more, and it was no uncommon sight by 1884 to see within a single week as many as twenty-five tall-masted ships taking on cargo. By May, 1886, wheat poured into the waiting holds at the rate of one hundred carloads a day, while sometimes as many as five hundred carloads waited on the sidings. Barges and steamers also brought wheat to the docks. At Antioch, too, large numbers of ships loaded wheat, for eastern Contra Costa County was given over almost exclusively to the cultivation of that great staple.

Along the line of the railroad, villages began to develop at the stations of Brentwood and Byron, where warehouses were built to accommodate the rapidly increasing production. Stores sprang up, schools were organized, post offices opened for business.

The golden harvest flowed through Port Costa, Antioch, and even small landings in a veritable torrent throughout the 'eighties. Production hit a peak of 46,200,000 bushels in California in 1884, and land planted to wheat reached the climactic total of three million acres in 1888.[4] Thereafter plantings of wheat began to decline, although the yield remained above 30,000,000 bushels during the 'nineties, except in 1893–94 and 1897–98. The fairly rapid reduction in wheat acreage after 1900 has been attributed to exhaustion of soils in some areas; to the development of irrigation systems and the rise of intensive, diversified farming; and to the competition of new grain areas in the Mississippi Valley, in western Canada, and in Russia. Port Costa, nevertheless, handled an enormous amount of grain, including barley, each year until well after the turn of the century.

Iron and Steel Industry

The grain trade contributed in a curious fashion to the development of California industry. The grain ships arrived with cargoes of coal and coke, which supplied the energy for manufacturing in the days before hydroelectric power and petroleum; they also brought in tons of pig iron, scrap iron, and old steel rails. This raw material, unloaded from ships arriving at Oakland's Long Wharf to take on cargoes of wheat and barley, was indispensable to the growth of the iron and steel industry in the East Bay. The linkage with the major agricultural enterprises of the time was further strengthened by the production, by many of the iron and steel plants, of agricultural machinery, such as threshers, plows, pumps, and windmill equipment.

Most of the early iron and steel plants in Oakland were situated not far from the central business district, on First and Second streets west of Broadway, or on Market and Myrtle streets, just beyond the blocks laid out in 1853 by Kellersberger. An important exception was the Judson Manufacturing Company, which selected a nine-acre site with a frontage of twelve hundred feet on the Central Pacific tracks in what is now the industrial city of Emeryville. Slag and other refuse materials from the company's industrial operations served as fill for acres of near-by tidelands.

Foundries and similar enterprises were not confined to the Alameda County waterfront, however. In the new town of Crockett, founded in November, 1881, and named in honor of State Supreme Court Justice Joseph Bryant Crockett, rose the J. L. Heald Foundry. Until the plant was taken over in the late 'nineties by the California Hawaiian Sugar Refinery, it produced boilers, stationary and movable engines, threshing machines, separators, grape crushers, roller-crushing barley mills, and other agricultural machinery. On the opposite side of Carquinez Strait, at Benicia, the Benicia Agricultural Works likewise turned out a steady flow of agricultural implements that were shipped to many parts of the world, including Australia, New Zealand, South America, China, and Japan.

Industrial Dispersion

The industrial dispersion that has been so much discussed in the San Francisco Bay Area in recent years actually began in the 'eighties when smelting and explosives plants moved from San Francisco to western Contra Costa County. However, the first explosives plant in this area, the Vulcan Powder Works, was originally a Nevada rather than a San Francisco concern. It was established near Stege, in what is now Richmond, in 1878. The Giant Powder Company of San Francisco followed in 1880,

giving the name "Giant" to a site on a peninsula that juts into San Pablo Bay north of Richmond. The next year the California Powder Works, predecessor of the Hercules Powder Company, erected buildings in a series of ravines on a tract on San Pablo Bay, in order to safeguard the surrounding area. In 1882 several smaller plants began to cluster around the Vulcan plant at Stege.

The powder, dynamite, and nitroglycerine produced in these Contra Costa plants blasted away the ore-bearing strata in western mines, leveled hills and mountains that blocked the paths of railroad engineers, cleared boulders from new roads, and did hundreds of earth-moving jobs for companies that were building bridges, tunnels, and embankments throughout the West. The volume of explosives manufactured was, indeed, a fair measure of the physical development taking place in California and in near-by states and territories.

Closely allied to these explosives plants were the smelter and the cartridge factory of the Selby Smelting and Lead Company at Selby, on San Pablo Bay. By 1884 the smelter built at Black Point (Fort Mason) in San Francisco by Thomas Selby in 1865 had so greatly extended operations that Prentiss Selby, who became general manager upon the death of his father, was compelled to purchase a larger site in a more suitable location. He therefore selected a waterfront site in Contra Costa County far enough from any city to escape complaints about air pollution. Operations began at the new smelter

Artist's Drawing of the Refinery of the Pacific Coast Oil Company at Alameda Point, 1898. Photograph courtesy of Standard Oil Company of California.

REFINERY AT ALAMEDA POINT.

in 1885, and production soon reached a volume of $30,000 in gold and thirty thousand ounces of silver a day. The following year the cartridge factory was erected. This factory and the powder manufacturing plants near by coöperated with the Benicia Arsenal in developing newer and more powerful shells, which were tested at a proving ground at the arsenal.

In addition to the iron and steel plants, explosives plants, and the Selby smelter, one other East Bay manufacturing enterprise of the 'eighties was significant. At Woodstock, near Alameda Point, the Pacific Coast Oil Company, organized by San Francisco interests, began operating one of the first oil refineries in California in 1880, manufacturing chiefly kerosene from crude petroleum shipped by rail from Pico Canyon near Los Angeles and by tankers from Ventura. Small amounts of petroleum also were obtained from Moody Gulch, near Los Gatos, and from Sargent, in southern Santa Clara County. When the Standard Oil Company absorbed the Pacific Coast Oil Company in a merger in 1890, about the time that drilling began in the southern San Joaquin Valley oil fields, the eventual construction of a pipe line northward through the Valley to a larger refinery at some point on the eastern shore of the bay perhaps became inevitable. At any rate, the little refinery at Alameda Point may be regarded as a forerunner of the huge Standard Oil Company refinery in Richmond.

The Grip of Monopoly

This thriving Bay Area, resourceful in the organization of manufacturing enterprises related to the needs and opportunities of the times and far ahead of other areas in California in the development of a diversified agriculture, was the focal point of the far-flung railroad empire that the Big Four had begun building in the 'sixties. By the end of 1887 the driving ambition of Stanford, Huntington, and Crocker (Mark Hopkins had died in 1878) had made it possible for a San Franciscan to cross the bay to Oakland and entrain for Portland, Oregon, for Salt Lake City or Chicago, or for New Orleans. The "Sunset Route" to the great cotton port near the mouth of the Mississippi had been opened in February, 1883; and Charles Crocker had driven the "last spike" in the railroad to the Columbia River at Ashland, Oregon, on December 18, 1887. Yet the Southern Pacific system, then consisting of fifty-five hundred miles of track, was still in the formative stages and would eventually be three times as large.

Monopolistic, politically powerful, dedicated to a policy of charging all that the traffic would bear, the Southern Pacific took its toll of Bay Area enterprise and steadily increased the number of its enemies, among whom were civic leaders of great wealth and influence. Their opposition eventually was to crystallize into a scheme for a competitive railroad, but through the 'eighties Huntington and his associates continued to tighten their hold on the Bay Area. They absorbed Senator Fair's South Pacific Coast Railroad in 1887, thereby eliminating another potential rival. Since their purchase included the narrow-gauge railroad's ferryboat service on San Francisco Bay, all transbay interurban service came under single management—or in other words, monopoly control. Toward the end of the decade, the titans also extended their tracks from Napa Junction, on the original California Pacific route, to Santa Rosa by way of the Sonoma and Guilicos valleys. And in 1891 they completed another branch line, the connection that the farmers in the Ygnacio and San Ramon valleys of Contra Costa County had long sought to make with the main line along the shore of Suisun Bay.

Except for the new branch to Santa Rosa, the northwestern part of the Bay Area remained without a railroad operated by the Southern Pacific. In 1889 Peter Donahue built the main line of his San Francisco and North Pacific Railroad northward through the Russian River Valley from Cloverdale to Ukiah, in Mendocino County. Three years later he connected Santa Rosa with the apple country around Sebastopol by a branch road and also extended the Guerneville branch farther down the Russian River to Monte Rio, in the coast-redwood country. Ten years earlier he had pushed the little Sonoma Valley Railroad a few miles farther north of Sonoma to Glen Ellen, thereby providing an outlet for the vineyards and wineries of that historic area.

A railroad was as essential in those days for the exploitation of natural resources as highways and trucks are today—as was demonstrated by the extension of the North Pacific Coast Railroad from the Russian River to Cazadero. Until the rails were thrust six miles farther into the timber country to the lumber town on Austin Creek, logging and milling did not amount to much. They took a sudden spurt when the railroad came.

With the establishment of these additional branches and extensions, the rail network in the Bay Area had reached a stage of development in harmony with the potentialities of the metropolitan region. Practically every part of the area that could supply a railroad with regular freight shipments had been tapped by one. The Southern Pacific monopolized the areas with the greatest resources and the largest concentrations of population. The smaller, local roads served the least accessible and least populated areas and would later be among the first to feel the pinch of competition from trucks and buses.

California Street as Seen from Dupont Street (Now Grant Avenue), San Francisco, 1885.

Transit in San Francisco

The Southern Pacific, known simply as "the railroad," also had a tremendous influence on the growth of the city of San Francisco through its control of the Market Street Railroad. Beginning in 1883, Leland Stanford converted this transit system to a cable system at a cost of $1,750,000, thereby making possible faster travel and encouraging families to live farther from the central business district. The main line on Market Steets from the Ferry terminus to Twenty-eighth and Valencia streets contributed to the development of the outer Mission District, while the Haight Street and McAllister Street branches, particularly, stimulated the growth of the area at the eastern end of Golden Gate Park, two miles from the City Hall.

By the mid-eighties that pleasure ground was exciting great admiration and putting to shame all those early critics who had scoffed at the possibility of transforming sandy wastes into garden spots. Property in the vicinity of Stanyan Street, the eastern boundary of the park, was worth $25 to $50 a front foot in the early 'eighties but by 1891 was "in active demand at $125 to $250 a front foot."[5]

A meandering Hayes Valley branch of the Market Street Railroad and cable lines on Geary, California, and Sacramento streets all contributed to settlement of the Western Addition, particularly after 1885, when the wealthier citizens of San Francisco migrated west of Van Ness Avenue to vantage points from which they could enjoy views of the Golden Gate, the lyric silhouette of Mount Tamalpais, and the islands and inlets in the northern part of the bay.

Little development took place in the sandy open spaces now known as the Richmond and Sunset districts of the city, even though a steam line ran out California Street and around Land's End to the Cliff House after 1887 and another steam line operated to the ocean beach along the southern boundary of Golden Gate Park. The amusement places at the beach seemed a long way off in those days and were frequented chiefly on Sundays and holidays.

The most famous and the most enduring of San Francisco cable lines began operation in 1885. The Powell Street Cable, which then as now ran from Powell and Market streets up over Nob Hill and the eastern slope of Russian Hill to Taylor and Bay streets, made the North Beach district more accessible from the downtown area and aided development of the picturesque quarter later known as "Little Italy."

In 1891 the city hailed the last of the major cable installations, the Hyde Street cross-town line of the California Street Railroad, which traversed Russian Hill.

Connecting the business district and the southern part of the city were several lines of the Omnibus Railroad. One that terminated at Potrero Avenue and Twenty-second Street connected with a horsecar line to South San Francisco. Together the two lines contributed during the 'nineties to the development of that suburb as a meatpacking and manufacturing center.

Congestion in Chinatown

Even though rail lines spanned the entire peninsula, San Francisco in the late 'eighties remained a compact metropolis, confined mainly to the northeast quadrant of the city-county. Business and residential properties were indiscriminately mixed, not only in the heart of the city, but also in the areas surrounding the central core. Congestion had early become characteristic of San Francisco and was nowhere more appalling than in Chinatown, a twelve-block ghetto bounded by Kearny, California, Stockton, and Broadway, with Dupont Street (Grant Avenue) serving as its "Main Street."

A fascinating map of the Chinese quarter in the *Municipal Reports* for 1884–85 shows street-floor occupancy of every building and designates by various hues all the gambling houses, opium resorts, joss houses, Chinese houses of prostitution, and white houses of prostitution. This is probably the most accurate land-use map of a section of San Francisco that has survived from the days before the great conflagration of 1906.

A special committee of the board of supervisors "found that the rule is for two persons to each 'bunk,' and relays of sleepers through the day in many, if not most instances, but women and children seem also to be stowed away in every available nook and corner, without reference to any special accommodation being provided for them. Taking therefore, the total number of 'bunks' and multiplying that total by two, must be at least a safe minimum estimate of the population in these twelve blocks, with every probability favoring the conclusion that an addition of perhaps twenty per cent would not more than cover the real number of Chinese inhabiting that locality."[6] On this basis the committee's "lowest possible estimate" of the population in Chinatown was 30,360—a density of 200 to 300 persons per acre.[7]

The Ferry Building, San Francisco, 1886. Photograph courtesy of Southern Pacific News Bureau and Oakland Tribune.

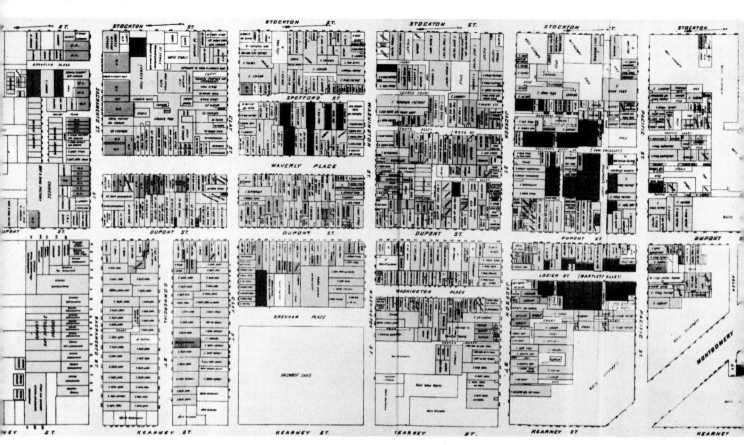

Official Map of Chinatown, San Francisco. The lighter grays show gambling houses, opium resorts, joss houses, and general Chinese occupancy; the darker grays show Chinese houses of prostitution and white houses of prostitution. From the San Francisco Municipal Reports for 1884–1885.

Seeking to fix responsibility for the slum conditions of Chinatown, the committee directed its attention especially to the owner of property in the quarter: "He has had no special reason to regret the occupation of his premises by Chinese in so far as the rate of revenue derived therefrom is concerned, for that revenue, if your Committee are credibly informed, has been materially larger than could have been obtained from any other class of tenants. . . . The property-owner in Chinatown must be made to feel his responsibility in this matter before Chinatown can ever be brought to a level with common public decency."[8]

The committee recommended, among other things, restricting the number of inhabitants in any given block in the city, but did not say how this might be accomplished. It might have learned a thing or two from the New York Tenement House Commission of 1884, the first citizens' commission appointed to investigate housing conditions in that city. On the recommendation of the New York body an act was passed in 1885 regulating the height of dwellings in the eastern city in relation to the width of the street on which they fronted. This was an early step toward restricting the volume of a building and thereby

limiting the number of occupants. From such legislation in time evolved modern zoning ordinances, which regulate population density by controlling the height and bulk of structures and, in some cities, by establishing a fixed ratio between lot area and floor area. In 1885, San Francisco had, however, nothing better than a so-called "Cubic Air Ordinance" to assure a minimum of breathing space to slum dwellers, and this law the Special Committee on the Condition of the Chinese Quarter found "constantly violated."[9]

Beginnings of Control

The incomprehensible and persecuted Chinese were contributors, albeit against their will, to the enlargement of the concept of the police power, the legal basis of all zoning controls. The laundries that the celestials opened in various neighborhoods of the city came to be regarded as public nuisances because the proprietors dumped dirty water into the street, because fires frequently broke out in these establishments, and because groups of Chinese gamblers congregated in them. In the interest of public health, safety, and morals, the board of supervisors in

1885 passed an ordinance excluding laundries from residential areas. Laundry operators Yick Wo and Soon Hing attacked the legality of the ordinance, charging discrimination; but in tests before the California State Supreme Court and the United States Supreme Court the city won noteworthy victories.

"With the decisions in these cases as precedent, other California cities, as well as cities in other states, proceeded to enact ordinances restricting other objectionable businesses," one authority writes. "Within a few years it had become generally recognized that it was within the police power of municipalities to protect residential areas from invasion by such disagreeable businesses as the manufacture of bricks, maintenance of a livery stable, operation of a dairy, stone-crusher, machine shop, or carpet-beating establishment, slaughter of animals, billboards, and a number of other such uses."[10]

Inherent in these early ordinances excluding the most obviously incompatible activities from residential areas was, then, the cardinal principle of zoning—the separation of inharmonious uses of the land and the grouping of establishments carrying on similar activities into special zones or districts. Little by little, as cities struggled with the problem of space for increasing populations and for rapidly growing industries and commercial establishments, they learned to build a new structure of public control over the utilization of land upon the judicial anguage of the Yick Wo and Soon Hing decisions.

First Apartment Houses

San Francisco in the 'eighties and early 'nineties was on the way to becoming one of the most densely populated cities in the United States. Chinatown may have been the most glaring example of overcrowding, but it was not to remain the only thickly settled area. Multiple residences, in the form of flats or apartment houses, made their appearance about 1884, as an article in the San Francisco *Chronicle* in 1887 reveals:

"One architect, who is agent for some foreign property-owners, tried an experiment about three years ago in the erection of a large flat building three stories in height, with four sets of apartments on each floor, so that the building accommodated twelve families under its roof. At the time of its erection the Chronicle fully described the building and commended the idea to capitalists as one which would return a good percentage on the investment. The history of the experiment has fully justified the investment, and the recommendation given to it by this paper. The flats were at once rented to a class of prompt-paying tenants at $16 and $18 a month. Not one of them has ever been vacant more than a day, and the rents have

been advanced to $18 and $20 a month. The building, from the day it was finished to the present time, has given a net income of 12 per cent on the cost. In the Eastern cities the owner who realizes 5 per cent net on real estate considers himself lucky, and the owner of the building spoken of is now having the plans made for three more of the same class. The architect and agent of the owner says that fifty such buildings would be equally profitable, and he is surprised that more of them have not been erected by capitalists seeking a profitable investment."[11]

Perhaps the unsung architect undertook a one-man crusade to open the eyes of moneyed gentlemen to the possibilities of more intensive use of the land. A return of 12 per cent on the investment must surely have been a powerful argument for constructing a dozen dwellings where ordinarily only one or two would be erected. At any rate, by 1890 San Francisco had nearly 900 structures containing accommodations for three or more families. By the end of the 'nineties it had more than 3,300 such buildings, and there had been an actual decrease in the number of single-family residences, from 43,418 in 1890 to 42,255 in 1900.[12] Around the central business district and as far out as Van Ness Avenue, new apartment houses offered families the dubious privilege of living in layers, one above the other.

First Skyscraper

In the downtown area, publisher Michael H. de Young introduced the architectural form now most characteristic of American central business districts from coast to coast —the towering, steel-frame office building, or skyscraper. This structural type, exemplified by the ten-story Chronicle Building at Market and Kearny streets, was an importation from Chicago; and the architects selected by de Young to design the new home of his newspaper were leading members of the "Chicago school," Daniel Hudson Burnham and John Root.

Wiseacres shook their heads over the proposal to erect such a tall building in a city known to suffer serious earthquakes occasionally. De Young, however, had faith in the ability of his architects to design a structure that would defy the most severe temblors—a faith that was rewarded at the time of the upheaval of 1906. Other skyscrapers appeared in the 'nineties, though there was no sudden change in the skyline of San Francisco. Not until the disaster of 1906 demonstrated the resistance of steel-frame construction to violent movements of the earth did the skyscraper become popular in San Francisco.

Nowadays it is ironical that Burnham, the designer of the Chronicle Building, the Mills Building, the Merchant's Exchange, and other early San Francisco skyscrapers, should be remembered hardly at all for structures like these and should be thought of principally as the creator of a "City Beautiful" plan that was almost wholly ignored in the hasty rebuilding of the city after the catastrophe of 1906. Perhaps it is even more ironical that he helped set the pattern for a concentrated commercial center which was the very opposite of the expansive baroque city contemplated in his plan of 1905 for the Association for the Improvement and Adornment of San Francisco. Paris and Washington, D.C., provided the inspiration for that plan, but Burnham through his endeavors of the 'eighties and 'nineties had already assisted in fixing upon American cities a character wholly unlike that of the Paris of Baron Haussmann and the Washington of L'Enfant.

Cosmopolitan Metropolis

At the time the soaring Chronicle Building was a novelty, San Francisco was still addicted to flamboyancy in architecture—in commercial buildings as well as in dwellings. The admiration of a *Chronicle* writer for some detached villas constructed by the firm of Roundtree Brothers at Page and Baker streets, a few blocks from Golden Gate Park, indicates the taste of the times:

"Viewed from the sidewalk, which like the steps and stone coping around the lot, is of artificial stone, it will be noticed at a glance that the style of architecture is a clever admixture of the colonial and the Queen Anne, with more than a suggestion of Eastlake thrown in. There are big gables and rounded bays, fancy shingling and stucco work, small turrets and look-outs, and the combination is pretty without being too pretentious . . ."13

The city in its entirety by then had gained that indefinable, cosmopolitan quality which endears it to travelers and reminds even its own residents of the cities of the whole world. Justin McCarthy, a writer and leader of the Home Rule Party in Britain, epitomized it in his novel *Lady Judith*:

"Convert the hills of Rome into dust heaps and plant them around the harbor of Queenstown; crowd on their sides a city made up indiscriminately of the Strand, Broadway, Wapping, Donnybrook, Hongkong, Denver, Vera Cruz, and Hamburg and you may create in your mind's eye something like an adequate picture of San Francisco.

"It is a city where houses seem indeed to have been literally built on sand; a city climbing up the sides of sandhills, overlooked and girt and crowned by sandhills; a city the color of dust and ashes; a summerless, winterless city, where men and women have no season of change in the substance of garments; where you may wear furs if you like them in July or in December."14

Oakland: "City of Homes"

The transbay city of Oakland presented an extreme contrast to the picturesque melange that was San Francisco. Although there were industrial developments along the Estuary and in West Oakland, the East Bay city impressed a newspaperman in June, 1887, as being "essentially a city of homes." There was, he wrote, "an appearance of comfort and quiet elegance about the residences which reminds one of some of the older cities of New England. Nearly all the houses are built on lots sufficiently large to give room for a garden, and great care is shown in the cultivation of rare and beautiful flowers."15

According to this anonymous scribe, Oakland, or at least that part of it lying between Lake Merritt and the bay, had had for several years "a reputation of being unhealthy on account of the defective sewerage, which caused a great deal of sickness in the shape of diphtheria and low malarial fever." But the San Francisco journalist was happy to report that "all that has been remedied by the construction of a main sewer running from the lake to the bay near Sixteenth Street." Twice a day, at each low tide, floodgates at the head of the sewer were opened and a flood of fresh water from Lake Merritt rushed through, carrying "all the foul, disease-breeding materials which usually find a lodgment in city sewers" into the bay beyond the low-water mark.16 From there the tides presumably swept the raw sewage out through the Golden Gate, though actually, as population and industries increased, the tides proved more and more inefficient as disposal agents. Even in the 'eighties, then, Oakland and other cities around the bay were contributing to the growth of a pollution problem that would someday assume alarming proportions and nauseate everyone who came within smelling distance of the tidal flats.

Lake Merritt was far from being the effective flushing basin that it was represented to be. Engineer George F. Allardt found in 1889 that streams tributary to the lake had deposited 403,000 cubic yards of solid material in it since he first took soundings in 1871. A condition was building up that played into the hands of those who advocated converting the lands bordering the lake into a park. Before long it would be imperative to dredge the lake, and what would be more logical than to fill in the shallows along the shore and reclaim them for public use?

In the early 'eighties, petitions and memorials gave impetus to the park movement, and by 1885 an improvement plan estimated to cost $186,000 was put forth. No money was actually appropriated until 1888, when the city council authorized the expenditure of $20,000 to

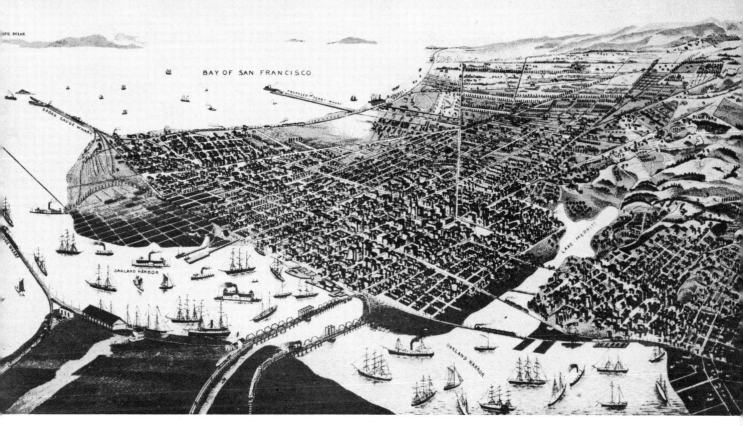

A Bird's Eye View of Oakland, 1893. Photograph courtesy of Oakland Public Library.

begin work on a boulevard on the east side of the lake. As yet, the majority of citizens cared little whether the lake silted up or not, and were apathetic about the agitation for a park.

Those who wanted some beauty in their environment and had the money to buy view lots built houses not within sight of the lake but in north Oakland and in Piedmont, both of which became accessible by cable lines in 1890. Piedmont, especially, attracted well-to-do families who could afford to construct houses costing $15,000 to $25,000—large sums in those days. .

Boom in San Jose

Besides San Francisco, Oakland, and Alameda, the only other city in the whole Bay Area that made appreciable population gains in the 'eighties was San Jose. Toward the end of the decade it benefited unexpectedly from the collapse of the real-estate boom that Los Angeles experienced after the completion of the Santa Fe Railroad. As easterners who were singularly unimpressed by southern California drifted north to investigate the immensely productive Santa Clara Valley, land sales in the San Jose Area hit a peak of $2,000,000 a day in August, 1887. The following year the San Jose Board of Trade became so aggressive as to open an office in Los Angeles, to encourage those who were disheartened by the real-estate fiasco in the southern part of the state to move to the Santa Clara Valley. Civic leaders subscribed funds to build a huge tourist hotel to be called the Vendome; put over bond issues for a new city hall, park improvements, sewers, bridges, and other public works; and even talked about making Alviso a deep-water port. Several new banks and building and loan companies opened for business. By 1891, promoters were attempting to sell lots in a dream city called New Chicago, in the sloughs north of Alviso, and in other developments called New Bethlehem and Hacienda Park. The last-named was a gridiron plat on top of a mountain near the New Almaden Mine.

The San Jose area was too well established to be affected by these swindle schemes, which were as bad as any attempted in Los Angeles County when the Santa Fe and Southern Pacific were carrying on their rate war and were luring Middle Westerners by the thousands to southern California. The enterprising residents of San Jose and the surrounding area went steadily ahead, expanding fruit acreage, organizing new canneries, and building new educational institutions, public buildings, and farm-to-market roads; but the population increase in San Jose itself in the 'nineties was less than 3,500, compared with approximately 5,500 in the previous decade.

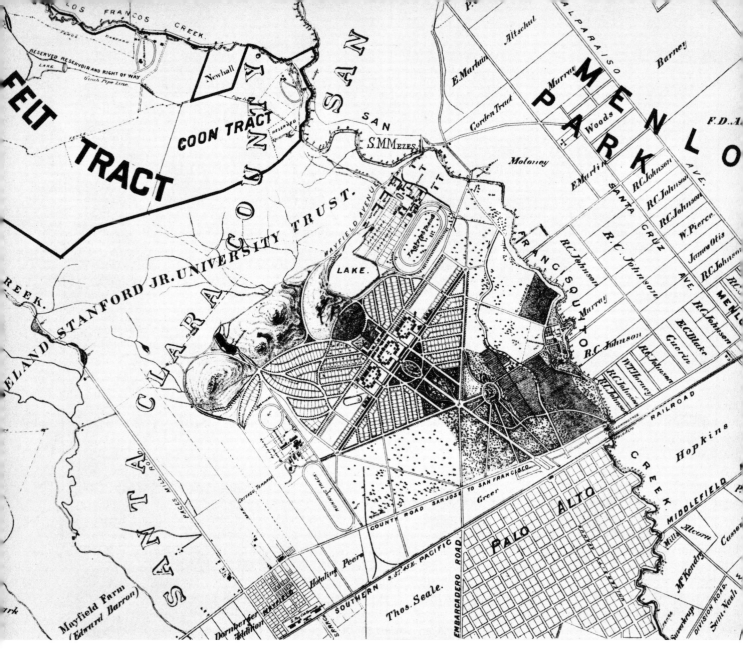

Stanford University, the Town of Palo Alto, and Neighboring Estates in the Late 1890's. From an advertisement for ranch property ordered sold by Mrs. Leland Stanford after her husband's death. Photograph courtesy of Palo Alto Public Library.

Stanford University

While San Jose was exhilarated by an unforseseen boom, a development began to take shape on the San Francisco Peninsula that revealed the aggressive Leland Stanford in a new light. The man who had been a partner in the creation of a railroad empire, who had reorganized transit operations in San Francisco, and who had succeeded in being elected to the United States Senate in 1885, now appeared in the twin roles of bereaved father and co-founder, with his wife, of a great new university. In 1884 his only son, sixteen-year-old Leland Stanford, Jr., had died in Florence, Italy. As a memorial to him, the parents conceived the idea of transforming the Stanford stock farm on San Francisquito Creek in northern Santa Clara County into the campus of a major institution of higher education.

That Stanford's grief for the loss of his heir should be channeled into the building of a university is understandable. Two years before the death of the boy, the father had received an interim appointment as a regent of the University of California and had looked forward to learning at first hand about the administration of a great university. But when a hostile legislature, with a Democratic majority, had indicated that it would not confirm the appointment, Stanford had withdrawn his name. The new university was not only a memorial to a dead son but an opportunity for Stanford to demonstrate his ability to organize an educational enterprise.

Although privately endowed, Stanford University was similar in some respects to the public university in Berkeley. Like the University of California in its early years, it had a "country location." It, too, brought into being a new city—Palo Alto. Timothy Hopkins, the foster son of Mark Hopkins, planned the town, which was at first called University Park but was finally named for the ancient redwood tree that is still its most conspicuous landmark. And Frederick Law Olmsted prepared a plan for the Stanford campus, as he had the plan for the new campus of the College of California, the institution which became the University of California.

Whereas Olmsted's plan for the Berkeley campus was all but abandoned, his plan for the Stanford campus was in most respects followed. Olmsted's first idea for a group of buildings situated on a commanding site in the foothills of the Santa Cruz Mountains was, however, overruled by the Stanfords in favor of the plain at the foot of the hills, because young Stanford had roamed on horseback over that part of the stock farm and because the level site would be less expensive to develop. The buildings, as designed by the Boston firm of Shepley, Rutan, and Collidge in the Richardsonian Romanesque style then fashionable, formed a series of quadrangles connected by arcades. In planning the grounds, Olmsted attempted for the first time to utilize plants especially adapted to the long dry season in California.

Contrary to the opinion of the New York *Mail and Express* that "there is about as much need for a new university in California as for an asylum of decayed sea captains in Switzerland,"[17] Stanford University enrolled 465 students when it was opened in October, 1891. Neighboring Palo Alto, where some of the students and professors lived, grew rapidly and became an incorporated city in 1894, with an estimated population of 1,003.

Slow Growth of the Peninsula

From Palo Alto to San Francisco the Southern Pacific traversed a long, narrow bay plain which, all during the 'nineties and for at least two decades thereafter, was given over almost entirely to large estates and farms. The few towns along the route—Menlo Park, Redwood City, San Mateo, and South San Francisco (laid out in 1891)—remained small, and efforts to promote new communities met with little or no success. Only a few trains a day served the Peninsula, and fares were high in comparison with commutation rates on the transbay ferries. Wellesley Park, a new subdivision in Redwood City distinguished by handsome, curvilinear streets and a small elliptical park, attracted a few buyers, because it was a project of the Bohemian Club of San Francisco. The subdivision of property and sale of lots in the vicinity of San Mateo increased the population enough to bring about incorporation of the community in 1894. But San Carlos, a little north of Redwood City, for many years failed to develop, much to the disappointment of the promoters who planned it—a syndicate of men associated with the Southern Pacific. Likewise, a subdivision opened in 1889 on the Darius O. Mills estate was a business failure until after the San Francisco fire of 1906. Burlingame, too, was little more than a post office and a few houses until 1901, when a business district began to develop. South San Francisco, conceived by G. F. Swift, the founder of Swift and Company, as a new industrial community, also got off to a bad start, because San Francisco butchers opposed the removal of meat-packing plants to the new town. Until the late 'nineties Swift's Western Meat Packing Company was the only establishment of any consequence in the industrial tract west of the old San Bruno Toll Road; then W. P. Fuller and Company built a paint factory there, and after the turn of the century various steel companies erected plants in the town.

Even Marin County, separated from San Francisco by water, grew more rapidly than San Mateo County during the 'nineties and had a larger population in 1900. A good many of the new residents in the North Bay county were former city dwellers who took advantage of the improved commuting service established about 1894. Until then, Marin residents had been unable to reach "the city" before seven o'clock in the morning, or to return home after late performances at the theaters, because the ferryboats ran only during certain daylight hours. Upon the inauguration of more convenient service, Sausalito, Tiburon, Belvedere, the new town of Mill Valley, Ross Valley, and San Rafael all attracted families known as "San Francisco Marin County residents." The census of 1900 reported a population of 15,702 in Marin County, compared with 12,094 in San Mateo County. So many cemeteries were established in the Colma Valley, just beyond the San Francisco city-county boundary line, in the late 'eighties and the 'nineties that the increase in the number of the dead in San Mateo County far exceeded that of the living; the population gain of the county in the entire decade of the 'nineties was only a little more than two thousand.

Electric Railways

The East Bay in the meantime saw the successful introduction of a new form of local transportation that soon began to disperse population from the central cities and to accelerate the growth of peripheral areas and suburbs. The electric railway, antedating the automobile by only a few years, was one of a series of modern technological advances that set in motion the creeping urbanism which is today obliterating the intervening open spaces between communities and robbing municipalities of physical identity. The new agent of dispersal had made a brief, ignominious appearance on a line between San Jose and Santa Clara in 1888. Failure of an underground third rail to function properly had forced the operators to revert quickly to horsecar service. In 1891 the overhead trolleys of the Oakland and Berkeley Rapid Transit Company demonstrated conclusively, however, that the electric railway was a practicable means of locomotion far superior to the most respected form of transit then in use, the cable car. Wisely, the promoters of the new line between the two East Bay cities had taken the precaution of studying at first hand the successful operations of a Seattle electric railway. When they inaugurated service via Grove Street and Center Street, Berkeley, to the west gate of the University of California on May 12, 1891, they expected their venture to prosper. And indeed it did, in a curious fashion at first. The novelty of traveling twelve miles an hour by trolley attracted large numbers of patrons who were not going shopping or to work, but who believed that electricity would in some mysterious way alleviate their rheumatism. Others were curious to see whether their watches would be stopped by the magnetism generated in the motors.

History records no miraculous cures from trolley rides; nor were any watches stopped, so far as is known. Rather, the new form of transit had the effect of accelerating urban life. Because they could travel to work faster than before, many people moved to places somewhat farther from their shops and offices. The electric railway was a much more potent agent of expansion than the horsecar had been in the mid-seventies. The lines dependent upon the muscular energy of the horse had radiated from downtown Oakland to areas generally only three or four miles distant. The electric railway suddenly made accessible territories six to twelve miles away. An elongated urban community that stretched in two directions, to the north and to the southeast, began to take shape along the level lands bordering on the bay. The hilly barrier on the east, of course, forced this trend of development. Laid down along the historic routes of travel, the electric railway systems invaded the areas previously served only by the less convenient steam railroad and steam dummy. And like the promoters of the earlier horse railways, the promoters of the new electric lines were usually interested in profiting from sales of real estate and were willing to operate their transit lines at a loss, provided sales of land were sufficiently remunerative.

The builders of the Oakland, San Leandro, and Haywards Electric Railway, which was incorporated just ten days after the Oakland and Berkeley Transit Company (later the Oakland Consolidated Street Railway Company) began operations, were heavily involved in real-estate and construction activities in the area through which the line ran. Starting in August, 1892, the road rendered service from the southeast limits of Hayward through San Leandro to East Oakland, and soon afterward effected an entrance into downtown Oakland by acquiring the franchise of the Twenty-third Avenue Electric Railway.

"Most of us have large property interests along the line of our road," A. L. Stone, one of the principal stockholders of the Oakland, San Leandro and Haywards Electric Railway, candidly told an Oakland *Daily Evening Tribune* reporter prior to the opening of the road. "Our original purpose in building the road is to improve our property and give it increased value . . ."[18]

In this respect the road succeeded. Entire farms along the route of the new line were subdivided and sold at large profits. The population of San Leandro increased considerably; but the operation of the road itself was "essentially unprofitable."

Conversion of Horsecar Lines

The Oakland Railroad Company, a Southern Pacific affiliate operating a combination horsecar and steam-dummy service to north Oakland along Telegraph Avenue, met so much competition from the parallel electric lines on Grove Street and Shattuck Avenue that it was forced to convert to the newer and faster form of transit in 1893. It thereupon gave great impetus to the settlement of the northern part of Oakland.

In 1893 the transportation companies hastened to transform the antiquated horsecar lines into electric railways. By the beginning of 1894 the East Bay boasted nearly sixty miles of electric and cable railways. Indeed, during this early phase of electric transit, Oakland and near-by communities had one of the most extensive electric railway systems in the entire United States. But the over-all picture was one of irrationality, waste, and exploitation, as one student of this period has pointed out: "Very considerable physical inconvenience resulted from the fact that on Broadway in Oakland there were at one time six sets of tracks for a short distance. Duplicating power plants were built. Service was rendered on tracks of three different gauges. Equipment and personnel were not adapted to permit interchange of service. The fare structures were such that travel was handicapped by that fact alone. All of these conditions definitely limited the quality of service . . ."[19]

San Francisco was served by a transit network as irrational and planless as the one in Oakland, but it included only one electric railway—the so-called Joost line built in 1891 from Steuart and Market streets through the South-of-Market and Mission districts to the site of present-day Daly City, just beyond the San Mateo County boundary. The metropolis clung to the horsecar and the cable car. Only five traction companies remained independent of a consolidation effected by the Southern Pacific in 1893; yet unification of control brought no major realignments of the old zigzag, corkscrew, and parallel routes that had developed in the course of the years.

Grandiose Scheme

The Southern Pacific firmly monopolized transbay ferry services, which connected in the East Bay with the railroad company's "poky" local steam trains serving Alameda, Oakland, and Berkeley. There were, however, two men in Oakland who planned to challenge this monopoly —and so contribute to further growth of communities on the east side of the bay. For several years the unbridled imaginations of Francis Marion Smith, the borax king, and Frank C. Havens, a promoter and land speculator, had been gestating a grandiose scheme for buying up undeveloped East Bay land, consolidating street railways, and extending new lines into vacant tracts. By establishing fast transbay ferry services to connect with the transit lines and by operating picnic grounds, amusement parks, and hotels at the ends of the transit lines, they hoped to assure heavy patronage. In 1893, Smith carried out part of the scheme by gaining control of four East Bay transit lines. The following year he took a further step toward realizing his dream when he got possession of the California and Nevada Railroad, an old narrow-gauge line that ran from Fortieth and San Pablo streets in Oakland to Orinda by way of Berkeley and the canyon worn through the Berkeley Hills by San Pablo Creek. He an-

Francis Marion Smith, Founder of the Key Route Electric Railway. *Photograph courtesy of* Oakland Tribune.

nounced plans to lay broad-gauge double tracks on a section of the line between Oakland and Berkeley, to extend a mole two and a half miles into the bay from the foot of Fortieth Street (or Yerba Buena Avenue), and to run fast electric trains from Berkeley to a ferry terminus at the end of the mole. There passengers would transfer to twin-screw, steel boats for an eleven-minute crossing to San Francisco. Although East Bay residents showed great interest in Smith's proposal to reduce the travel time between Berkeley and San Francisco from fifty-five to twenty-six minutes, the total scheme was too ambitious even for a man reputed to be worth $30,000,000, and nine years elapsed before the Southern Pacific found itself in competition with a superior interurban service.

In the meantime, Smith and Havens formed the celebrated Realty Syndicate and launched a grand-scale speculation in transit, real estate, and utilities. Late in 1897 the company assumed full control of the street railways in which Smith earlier had acquired interests. In 1898 the organization acquired four other companies and consolidated all its transit lines under the name Oakland Transit Company, popularly known as the "Syndicate Railways." By the end of that year the system included approximately ninety-eight miles of street railways, many of which penetrated tracts then being subdivided by the two "empire builders." In fact, the aggressive sales campaigns to sell off properties on the higher levels of ground between Mills College and North Berkeley and in other parts of the East Bay fully exploited the novelty and importance of the growing electric-railway system.

All this subdivision activity and railway building was to have significant political consequences later, as an election on June 24, 1897, demonstrated. On that date several areas between Oakland and Berkeley voted to become part of Oakland. The improved transit service between the two cities had been a major factor in influencing the residents of the unincorporated tracts known as Golden Gate, Temescal, Linda Vista, Peralta, and West Piedmont to favor annexation. Oakland by this election expanded from 11.3 square miles to 16.61 square miles and embraced all the territory within which its initial industrial development had taken place. But the city was to grow much larger through annexation of numerous subdivisions that Smith and Havens were marketing.

"Greater Oakland" Movement

Smith and Havens were also active in the "Greater Oakland" movement that paved the way for civic improvements authorized during the next decade. Initiated about 1896 by several industrial, social, and neighborhood-improvement groups, the movement at first focused attention on the need for a large hotel, an intercepting sewer, the opening of streets to the waterfront, and a major park.

Of all these proposed improvements, the park project appears to have received the most serious consideration. Committees of the City Council, the Board of Trade, the Merchants' Exchange, and the real-estate fraternity inspected proposed park sites near Mills College, in Indian Gulch (northeast of Lake Merritt), on the heights above Piedmont, near Mountain View Cemetery, in Dimond Canyon at the head of Fruitvale Avenue, and in the vicinity of Lake Merritt. In addition, the Realty Syndicate

offered to sell land in any of the areas where it owned property. The prices asked for the various tracts ranged from $100,000 for 476 acres above Piedmont to $360,000 for 280 acres in Indian Gulch.

The choice finally fell upon 62 acres in the Adams Tract on the north shore of Lake Merritt, and a bond issue of $290,000 for acquisition and development of the property was submitted to the electorate in October, 1898. As in an election held in 1892, the park bonds failed to receive the necessary two-thirds approval, though a majority of voters favored the proposition. "In a few years this land, which has been rejected both at $500 per acre and $3,870, will be worth not less than $20,000 per acre, and then the voters who killed the proposition . . . will be looked upon as being almost as blind as those who prevented the city acquiring a park in 1868," the Oakland *Enquirer* commented on October 31, 1898. But the newspaper was mistaken when it concluded that the city had probably "lost its last opportunity to create a park on the shores of the lake." A progressive element in Oakland was showing increased determination to convert the shores of the lake into a park, though this element was destined to receive several more setbacks before overcoming the resistance of a backward minority.

Struggle for the Waterfront

Harbor development during this period of civic frustration consisted mainly of dredging by the federal government, in accordance with an improvement plan approved by Congress in the 'seventies. By 1898 the work contemplated under this scheme was practically completed, at a total expenditure of approximately $2,000,000. Oakland had gained more than a deeper channel, however; the dredging operations had given it a new waterfront, as a State Supreme Court decision of 1897 confirmed.

Unwittingly the Oakland Water-front Company, the Southern Pacific subsidiary that monopolized the frontage on the estuary, prepared the way for a legal revelation. In 1893 it brought suit against a private property holder to quiet title to a parcel of waterfront land between Alice and Webster streets. To the company's surprise, the Superior Court held that the original grant of the waterfront to Horace Carpentier in 1852 was void because it was against public policy.

The startling decision encouraged the city of Oakland to go to court in 1895 to quiet title. Again the verdict of the court was the same: the waterfront grant of 1852 was void because it was not in the public interest.

The Southern Pacific of course appealed the ruling. As successor to the Oakland Water-front Company it brought the matter before the State Supreme Court, only to suffer a still greater defeat. Although Chief Justice Beatty shared the view of the lower court that the original grant was utterly void, he pronounced the so-called compromise of 1868 a valid regranting of the waterfront to the Southern Pacific interests in exchange for a few feet of waterfront property at the foot of Franklin Street. But to the consternation of the railroad, the justice declared that it owned land extending only to the low-tide line of 1852— a line that by 1897 was six hundred to a thousand feet inside the new waterfront line created by dumping detritus from the bottom of the estuary into shallow water near the shore.

The decision foreshadowed the eventual materialization of the Port of Oakland, though Oakland for some years took no steps to develop a port. The city received no applications for privileges of building wharves; the citizens were apathetic toward harbor development; and the Southern Pacific, far from regarding the State Supreme Court decision as the final word, was resolved to employ further legal or political maneuvers to retain its privileges.

A Stifling Combination

Oakland's struggle to free itself from the grip of the powerful railroad had a counterpart in the battle of San Francisco to win some measure of economic independence from the hated monopoly. Even before the unemployed queued up in bread lines at the time of the panic of 1893, San Francisco shippers, merchants, and industrialists were complaining loudly that an economic blight had fallen upon the metropolis. The growth of its trade and its general prosperity were being stifled, they charged, by an unholy conspiracy of the Southern Pacific and the Pacific Mail Steamship Company to throttle competition in transportation and to maintain freight rates at a standard of "all the traffic will bear."[20] In their efforts to deal the combination a crippling blow, the commercial groups not only brought about the entrance of the rival Atchison, Topeka and Santa Fe Railway into the Bay Area; they also gave impetus to the development of the new terminal city of Richmond, in Contra Costa County.

"The rates charged by the Pacific Mail and the railroads on tea from Yokohama to Salt Lake City, Denver, and Missouri River points are 2¾ cents a pound, while from Yokohama to the same points via the Northern Pacific or Union Pacific lines of steamers or sailing vessels the rate is only 1⅛ cents a pound," the San Francisco *Daily Morning Call* pointed out in 1892 in one of a series of articles later reissued under the title "Fettered Commerce." "San Francisco merchants are actually importing tea for customers in Salt Lake City through Portland instead of through their own port."[21]

The newspaper also disclosed that "the rate on (Brazilian) coffee from New York to San Francisco is $1.35 a hundred pounds, while a rate of $1.30 a hundred pounds is charged to the San Francisco shipper of Guatemalan coffee, even though he desires to ship his coffee for no greater distance than that from San Francisco to Denver."[22]

To prevent steamship competition with their transcontinental lines, the Southern Pacific, Central Pacific, and other railroads had paid the Pacific Mail subsidies amounting to $14,550,000 in fourteen years, the *Call* declared, yet the Southern Pacific and Central Pacific were themselves recipients of government subsidies. A bitter cartoon in the newspaper depicted Uncle Sam bestowing a money bag marked "Government Subsidy" upon Collis P. Huntington and remarking, "I give you this money, Collis, to encourage you in extending our trade and advancing the interests of all the people." Huntington's reply is, "Thank you, Uncle, I will do the best I can— (aside) for myself."[23]

Most galling of all were the freight rates charged by the railroads on the movement of goods between San Francisco and San Joaquin Valley points. Rates for some commodities shipped from the port to Bakersfield were actually greater than those charged for goods transported from Liverpool to San Francisco via New Orleans.

San Francisco's indignation against the monopolists expressed itself in the formation of a Traffic Association having as its chief objective the construction of an independent railroad from San Francisco to Bakersfield. First broached in 1891, the project was not seriously recommended to the public until the summer of 1893. Because of the depression in that year, the raising of funds proved impracticable. In 1894, however, the scheme was revived, and the proposed road was named the San Francisco, Stockton, and San Joaquin Railroad. Again the Traffic Association encountered difficulty in inducing San Franciscans to buy shares of the $6,000,000 capital stock.

Birth of a Railroad

In January, 1895, the project suddenly gathered new impetus. Claus Spreckels, the sugar king, subscribed $50,000 at a meeting on January 22 at which speakers vied with one another in denouncing the Southern Pacific. The next day, Spreckels increased his subscription to $500,000. Two of his sons, John D. and Adolph Spreckels, each subscribed $100,000. Almost all the big names in San Francisco quickly responded to the campaign for funds. Nor was the metropolis alone in extending financial aid to the project. Oakland interests contributed $187,350; Stockton put up $125,000 in cash and gave land; and the people of San Jose, which was not even on the route of the proposed railroad, subscribed $65,000. By February 20, $2,248,000 had been raised. Five days later the new line was incorporated as the San Francisco and San Joaquin Valley Railway, popularly known as the Valley Road.

At the state capital friendly legislators introduced a bill to permit the new railroad to lease state property in San Francisco for a terminal. While the measure was running the gantlet of Southern Pacific opposition, the directors of the Valley Road selected a site at China Basin on the San Francisco waterfront and entered into negotiations with the State Board of Harbor Commissioners, pending authorization of a lease by the legislature. On March 26, 1895, the governor signed the bill granting the lease.

In the following month the directors of the new railroad company approved a plan that placed the road in the hands of a trust. According to the document creating the trust, the trustees agreed that the railroad should "not be leased to, nor consolidated with any company which may own, control, manage or operate any of the roads now existing in the San Joaquin Valley";[24] but nothing in the document prohibited the trustees from turning over the independent line to a major railroad not then existing in the valley, namely, the Santa Fe, which was eager to extend its tracks from southern California to the Bay Area. If the trustees had, indeed, secretly agreed to sell out to the Santa Fe when the new road was completed, they kept their intentions to themselves as they proceeded with construction of the line.

The survey for the road began at Stockton on April 18, 1895, and was completed by July 22. The rails reached Merced on Thanksgiving Day of that year but were not completed to Fresno until October 5, 1896. A regular freight and passenger service was then inaugurated between Fresno and San Francisco, with boats making the connection between San Francisco and Stockton. Two years later, Bakersfield became the southern terminus.

Vision of a City

In the meantime, Claus Spreckels and other directors concerned themselves with the problem of bringing the tracks into the Bay Area. Their first plan of routing the rails into Oakland through the Fruitvale hills was abandoned when Augustin S. Macdonald, a real-estate promoter with a vivid imagination, convinced them that Point Richmond, once a part of the vast Rancho San Pablo, was the logical place for a railroad terminal in the East Bay.

Macdonald is credited with being the "discoverer" of Richmond. In his own words, this is what happened when he drove out from Oakland one November morning in 1895 to hunt ducks in the marshes of San Pablo Creek:

"It was a perfectly beautiful morning, sun shining brightly and not a breath of wind, consequently no ducks flying, and after sitting five hours without a chance shot I concluded to quit, walk over the Potrero hill and explore the bay shore. On reaching the summit of the hills a magnificent view greeted my eyes. Mt. Tamalpais looming up at the right, Berkeley to the left and seemingly just across the way San Francisco, without a sign of life to disturb the quiet and peaceful scene. I wondered why such a delightful spot had been neglected, for either pleasure or profit, as not only its beauty, but its commercial possibilities appealed to me at once and I determined to investigate.

"The government map and surveys showed a depth of 65 feet of water, the only point on the east side of the bay shore where land and navigable deep water met. . . ."[25]

". . . I learned a saving of 12 miles could be made by the Southern Pacific company freight ferry from Pt. Richmond, direct to San Francisco. I presented these facts to C. P. Huntington, who thought favorably of the idea and prepared to look over the proposition, but he had . . . to hurriedly leave overnight.

"Not discouraged, however, as soon as the Santa Fe Railway company announced its intention of reaching San Francisco, I submitted my plans to that company. To avoid attracting attention Chief Engineer Storey, the head officials, and I went out on separate routes and carefully examined the waterfront, with the result that it was considered the most feasible, economical and practical site on the bay as a terminal and was adopted. . . .

"As soon as this question was definitely settled I knew that a great city must grow up there and the next thing was to find a proper location. The Potrero was rough and hilly while the immediate land adjacent was low, flat and swampy. Considering the situation, the choice tract was some 500 level acres belonging to Geo. H. Barrett, a pioneer settler.

"This we purchased and named the City of Richmond. The country was uninviting enough at the time, the lone habitation being the Barrett homestead which stood on Tenth Street just north of Macdonald Avenue. . . ."[26]

Actually, the officials whom Macdonald took to see Point Richmond represented the Valley Road, not the Santa Fe, and it was Robert W. Watt, vice-president of the Valley Road, who handed John Nicholl, an owner of property at the Point, a check for $80,000 on February 26, 1897, in payment for 57 acres of high land and some 100 acres of tideland. Claus Spreckels, like stockholders in many earlier railroad ventures in the San Francisco Bay Area, invested money in 250 acres near by, hoping that the rails would contribute to development of a town.

First Sale of Lots in the New City of Richmond, 1902. Photograph courtesy of Richmond Public Library.

Founding of Richmond

Not until 1899 did Macdonald carry out his own scheme for a town of Richmond. By that time negotiations between the financially pressed trustees of the Valley Road and the Santa Fe were under way, and two Santa Fe officials were among the quartet of capitalists who provided the funds with which the Oakland promoter purchased Barrett's 500-acre hay ranch.

Macdonald filed his "Map of the Town of Point Richmond" at the County Recorder's office in Martinez on June 3, 1899. The plat showed a prosaic arrangement of rectangular blocks, divided into five thousand business and residential lots. Boundaries of the tract were Barrett Avenue on the north, Twenty-third Street on the east, Ohio Street on the south, and Garrard Boulevard on the west.

The rails from Stockton did not enter Richmond until almost a year later, because the last section of the road, through northern Contra Costa County, presented difficult engineering problems. Chief Engineer W. B. Storey, who was later president of the Santa Fe, constructed ten miles of earth fill across the tule lands in the northeastern part of the county and built five tunnels through the hills, including one 5,595 feet in length through Franklin Ridge and another just under a thousand feet through the Potrero hills to Ferry Point. Excavations for this last tunnel formed a level area of about three acres at the base of the promontory. From this spot a wharf extended 800 feet into the bay, to a point at which the water was twenty-four feet deep at low tide.

Having secured what amounted to half ownership in the Southern Pacific line between Bakersfield and Mojave, in Kern County, the Santa Fe brought its first through train from Chicago into Ferry Point on July 3, 1900. From there the passengers proceeded to San Francisco on a rebuilt ferryboat called the *Ocean Wave*. The long struggle of the transcontinental line for an outlet to San Francisco Bay was over. The merchants and shippers of San Francisco and the farmers of the San Joaquin Valley had succeeded in their effort to create competition for the Southern Pacific, though there were those who declared that not much had been achieved by transferring an independent line to another big railroad system.

Bay Counties Power Company Crossing of Carquinez Strait, 1901. The single span of the cables was 4,427 ft., with a clearance of 206 ft. above high water to allow for the passage of tall-sparred sailing ships. Photograph courtesy of Pacific Gas and Electric Company.

Horn of Plenty

The Valley railroad project emphasized the increasing interdependence of the regional community developing around the shores of San Francisco Bay and the great valley east of the Coast Range. As the twentieth century began to unfold, the vast interior of the state became the Bay Area's cornucopia, pouring forth oil to supply its refineries and surface its roads, hydroelectric power to light its homes and run the machinery in its factories, and canned and dried fruit for exportation in the vessels that docked at its ports.

In the very first year of the new century, Eugene de Sabla, Jr., and John Martin completed a high-voltage transmission line from the South Yuba River to Oakland, by way of Carquinez Strait. In thus bringing hydroelectric energy to the East Bay from a source 142 miles away, the two partners defeated the hopes of André Poniatowski, a Polish prince and brother-in-law of the San Francisco banker W. H. Crocker, of being the first to deliver power from the Sierra to the Bay Area. Poniatowski encountered

one obstacle after another in building a powerhouse on the Mokelumne River, northeast of Stockton, and was unable to complete a transmission line to San Francisco until 1902. His line, forty miles longer than that of his rivals, entered the Bay Area by way of southern Alameda County and Santa Clara County and served San Jose as well as San Francisco.

Though industry was somewhat slow in making use of hydroelectric power, the Bay Area at last had a readily available form of energy to compensate for its lack of coal resources. As the power field expanded, more and more factories installed machinery operated by electricity.

Farmers in the Santa Clara Valley hailed as a great boon the arrival of hydroelectric power for the operation of irrigation pumps, not foreseeing the effect of uncontrolled pumping on the underground water supply. And before long the artesian wells that had once been a common sight in the area began to disappear. In time the sons of those who had rejoiced at the sight of linesmen stringing wires through the orchard country were to inherit such problems as the depletion of ground water and the settling and flooding of land.

No less important to manufacturing establishments than the "white energy" that flowed through the long transmission lines from the canyons and gorges of the Sierra was the "black gold" that became available in large quantities in the oil fields of Kern County. After western railroads had begun to use crude petroleum in their locomotives as a substitute for soft coal, manufacturers recognized it as a new industrial fuel. Together with hydroelectric energy, it helped to free western industry from dependence on expensive imports of coal and served as the basis for the development of a broader economy in the Bay Area and California.

The state's increasing production of petroleum was of particular significance because it coincided with the advent of the automobile. Oakland residents saw their first "gasoline carriage" in 1897; and people in other Bay Area cities gawked at the new marvel at about the same time. In the edition of the San Francisco *Examiner* heralding the birth of the twentieth century a feature writer named Edward Murphy categorically predicted that the automobile would "disfranchise" the horse and completely invade "all our big cities within a very short time."[27] The construction by the Standard Oil Company of a 283-mile pipe line from oil fields in the Bakersfield Area to its new refinery at Richmond was therefore of major importance. Large quantities of the kind of liquid fuel required by the increasing number of "horseless carriages" were now assured. The Richmond refinery had the distinction of being the second largest in the world when the $13,000,000 pipe line from the southern end of the San Joaquin Valley was completed, early in 1903.

Regional Transportation

The new self-propelled vehicle created a demand for roads that were free from dust in summer and mud in winter. Crude petroleum sprinkled with sand or gravel provided the answer to the problem of devising a relatively smooth, "permanent" surface. Road oiling in the Bay Area began in 1901, when Contra Costa, Napa, and Solano counties, following the example set by Los Angeles County three years earlier, each oiled a few miles of roads. The following year Alameda and Santa Clara counties began oiling roads; and in 1903, Marin, San Mateo, and Sonoma counties made their first experiments with the new surfacing. By the time the State Department of Highways published a bulletin on oiled roads, in 1904, there were more than 470 miles of oiled roads in the Bay Area.

Ironically, the oiled road and the automobile would someday cause the downfall of the interurban electric railway, which at this time was the chief agent of population dispersal in the Bay Area. So many intercity railways were projected or built in the opening years of the twentieth century that the period might well be called the electric railway age, just as the 'sixties and 'seventies of the nineteenth century have been designated the railroad age. But the railroad was to last for many years; the electric railways were doomed almost from the start.

In Marin County the old North Pacific Coast Railroad voluntarily wound up its business in 1901 and reorganized as the North Shore Railroad. The new company laid standard-gauge track from Sausalito to Mill Valley and San Rafael during the winter of 1901–1902 and electrified the lines to these points, in order to provide better commuter service. Steam trains continued to operate on narrow-gauge tracks in other divisions of the system.

About the same time that the Marin County commuter lines were being converted from steam to electricity, Francis M. Smith, the Oakland traction magnate, conceived the idea of building an electric railway from Oakland to San Jose by way of Hayward, with branches to

The Richmond Refinery of the Standard Oil Company, 1902. Photograph courtesy of the Standard Oil Company of California.

The Richmond Refinery of the Standard Oil Company, 1958. Photograph courtesy of the Standard Oil Company of California.

Santa Clara, Saratoga, and Los Gatos. In furtherance of this scheme, his Oakland Transit Company early in 1902 absorbed the Oakland, San Leandro and Haywards Electric Railway, which was the one remaining independent transit company in the East Bay. But Smith found that before he could finance construction of tracks from Hayward to the Santa Clara Valley, he would have to develop a profitable network in the urban areas already heavily populated. He therefore concentrated his efforts on his

earlier plans to link Berkeley, Piedmont, and various districts of Oakland with San Francisco by rapid electric transit and fast ferry service.

On October 26, 1903, Smith opened the Berkeley line, which was an immediate success because his Key Route trains and ferries transported passengers from the university community to San Francisco in only thirty-six minutes, compared with fifty-eight minutes on commuter steam trains and ferries of the Southern Pacific. This gratifying popular venture was followed by unification and improvement of the Oakland electric railway system, construction of the Piedmont line, and plans for a line to Twenty-second and Broadway in Oakland—a program so ambitious that it exhausted Smith's credit for long-term borrowing long before he could carry out his projected line to San Jose.

Valley Network

Meanwhile, down in the Santa Clara Valley two San Jose men, J. W. Rea and F. S. Granger, preëmpted some of the electric-railway empire that Smith dreamed of. After some difficulties with financing, they succeeded in constructing an interurban line from San Jose to Los Gatos via Saratoga, with a branch to the popular Congress Springs resort. Opened in March, 1904, the railway was successful enough to encourage Rea and Granger to begin building a much shorter line from San Jose to Los Gatos via Campbell. But the threat of other companies to invade the Santa Clara Valley caused the St. Louis banking firm that was financing the two local operators to sell its control to the Southern Pacific. That company, after fighting other interests, eventually developed an interurban railway network of sixty-eight miles in the Santa Clara Valley.

One of the objectives of the Southern Pacific appeared to be to block the southward extension of the old Joost line, San Francisco's first electric railway. Extended to San Mateo in January, 1903, this line was thought by many Peninsula and Santa Clara County residents to be the first link in an interurban rapid transit system that would run from San Francisco to San Jose. The future of the line depended not upon decisions made in the Bay Area, however, but upon the policies of the New York banking house of Brown Brothers, which in 1902 had purchased the entire capital stock of the Market Street Railway from Southern Pacific interests and had combined the Sutter Street road and the San Mateo line with the Market Street properties to form the United Railroads Company, later a potential rival of the Southern Pacific in the interurban field. Had the San Mateo line proved as effective as Smith's Key Route lines in the East Bay in stimulating suburban development, the New York investors might have considered building it farther down the Peninsula, but in this respect it was a disappointment.

The Key Route Mole, 1903. The mole extended from the foot of Fortieth Street in Oakland to a pier and ferry slip not far from Yerba Buena Island. The Oakland Army Base now occupies the tideland area to the left of the mole. Photograph courtesy of the Port of Oakland.

No electric railway line was ever to close the gap between San Mateo and Palo Alto, the northern point in the Santa Clara County electric-railway system of the Southern Pacific, just as no line was ever to join San Jose and Hayward on the eastern side of the bay.

Bit by bit an area-wide electric-railway network appeared, nevertheless, to be taking shape in the early years of this century; and barring various quirks of fate, such a network might have materialized. A northern segment of the potential system was the Petaluma and Santa Rosa Railway, which in 1904 inaugurated service on a line running from its own wharf on Petaluma Creek at Petaluma to the county seat and thence to Sebastopol, with branches to Forestville and Two Rock. Success of this line was to inspire a similar venture in the Napa Valley, which by 1911 was to see an electric railway extending from Vallejo to Calistoga by way of Napa and Saint Helena.

Smith and many other electric-railway men of the period had begun to think of the entire area round San Francisco Bay as a territory that could be linked together by fast transportation. They more than vaguely foresaw the possibility of a metropolitan region with many interdependent communities. The East Bay, rapidly developing as a group of interrelated cities served by an expanding electric-railway system, exemplified the kind of urban growth that could be expected in other parts of the Bay Area if time and distance were conquered by fast, convenient transit. Only to a degree, however, was transit to be an integrating influence in the development of the Bay Area. And not just by steady accretion of population along the transit lines were the smaller cities and outlying areas to grow in the years immediately ahead, but by sudden, forced absorption of thousands of families sent fleeing from a stricken metropolis. As the year 1904 began, the dominant city that was to contribute uniquely to the emergence of a recognizable metropolitan regional community could not have been more unaware of the tragic manner in which it was to nurture the growth of its satellites.

CHAPTER SIX

The Burnham Plan for San Francisco

San Francisco was enjoying one of the greatest booms in its history. Not since the bonanza days of the 'seventies had residents of the city seen so many new office buildings, hotels, stores, and palatial residences under construction. Real-estate men, particularly, were inclined to believe that the goddess of prosperity had decided to settle permanently in the metropolis by the Golden Gate. Wherever they looked they beheld evidence of her beneficence. Atop Nob Hill the massive Fairmont Hotel was taking shape. On the west side of Union Square the St. Francis Hotel was nearing completion. Word spread through the city that these hotels would rival the finest in New York, London, and Paris. At the corner of Market and Powell streets workmen were busy on the Flood Building, an office building containing six hundred rooms. Those in the know said that it would establish a new standard of elegance in business structures. Just west of the business district, between Mason and Leavenworth streets, rose dozens of newly completed apartment houses. Others were still under construction. South of Market Street still more apartment houses were being built. So rapid was the increase in population that every structure was filled as soon as it was completed, or even before workmen had finished painting the walls and installing fixtures.

Some real-estate men estimated that the population of the city must be at least four hundred and fifty thousand, although more conservative residents doubted this. Certainly there was an influx from all directions. Ships tying up at the piers along the waterfront brought foreigners by the thousands—Japanese, Italians, Portuguese, Austrians, Greeks, and Russians. From Canada, the Middle West, and from such eastern states as New York and Pennsylvania a Pullman and chair-car invasion was under way, stimulated by the railroads, the California Promotion Committee, and the California Fruit Growers Association. Overland trains also transported large groups of foreigners who had lived for a time in eastern cities or had proceeded immediately to California after landing in New York, Boston, or Baltimore.

A Bright Future

After the low level of economic activities during the 'nineties, the upswing in business was wonderfully stimulating. Building contracts were averaging about $15,000,000 a year, whereas they had totaled only $6,167,000 in 1901. Real-estate sales in both 1902 and 1903 had aggregated more than $47,000,000, compared with $18,500,000 in 1900. By every other index of economic conditions—bank clearings, exports, retail sales—San Francisco was enjoying flush times.

As far into the future as anyone could see, the prospects of the metropolis were excellent. Businessmen spoke of "the certainty of war between Russia and Japan" and predicted that San Francisco would profit by furnishing supplies to both belligerents, although they hastened to add that they did not wish ill to anyone. The entire Orient was awakening: not only was the island empire of Japan seeking new commercial ties; China, with its four hundred

Market Street below Montgomery Street, San Francisco, 1905. Photograph courtesy of Bancroft Library, University of California.

million inhabitants, was also stirring restlessly. Alert exporters could sense a groping of hands across the sea toward the good things that America produced.

In the Western Hemisphere the development on which all eyes were focused was the projected Panama Canal. Although the United States had not yet ratified a treaty with the new Republic of Panama, a United States commission was preparing to begin construction of the "big ditch." Reuben Brooks Hale, a leading San Francisco merchant, was so sure that the canal would be built that he wrote a letter to the directors of the Merchants' Asso-

ciation on January 12, 1904, proposing that the metropolis hold a world's exposition in 1915 to celebrate completion of the gigantic enterprise.[1] San Franciscans fully expected that their city, the major port on the Pacific Coast, would be the chief western beneficiary of the new waterway through the Isthmus of Panama. They smiled when they thought of the attempts of a potential rival, Los Angeles, to create a harbor in the mud flats of Wilmington and San Pedro. The Panama Canal could never mean to that aggressive and noisy community what it would mean to San Francisco, the possessor of a superb natural harbor.

Appeal to the Public-spirited

Allan Pollock, manager of the St. Francis Hotel, was not among those who scoffed at Los Angeles. Many of his fellow citizens, in their smugness, might consider San Francisco unusually prosperous and progressive; but he had seen with his own eyes the constructive things that Los Angeles was doing, and he felt that his townsmen deserved a jolt. "San Francisco has been asleep, while southern California, which offers nothing like the inducements we have within our grasp to lay before visitors, has taken possession of the tourists and the wealthy people from the East who come to California looking for homes," he declared in a newspaper interview. The Bay Area metropolis needed to realize that it had "little really attractive" to offer either tourists or its own residents—no art gallery or museum worthy of the name, no civic auditorium for conventions, no tree-lined boulevards.

Golden Gate Park, the ocean beach, the new hotels, the exhilarating climate, the hospitality of the people—these were merely foundations to build upon. The greater part of the city was ugly, the product of a "bare commercialism" that persisted in erecting wooden buildings "hideous in design and flimsy in finish—architectural shams of lumber and paint." As if he sensed impending tragedy, Pollock asserted that "such disgraceful kind of construction should be discouraged; this can perhaps best be done by extending the 'fire limits' over the entire municipality, and thus prevent the possibility of a general and widespread conflagration." The hotel manager called upon the public-spirited men of San Francisco to organize a committee to work for the welfare of the city, to render the community "beautiful and enticing as a place for tourists and for residence," and "to make San Francisco to Americans what Paris is to Europeans—the great city of pleasure!"[2]

O'Farrell Street, San Francisco, 1905. The tall building at the end of the street is the Call Building. Photograph courtesy of Bancroft Library.

A plea so fervently expressed necessarily aroused instant response. Dissatisfaction with conditions in San Francisco was more widespread than the California Promotion Committee, for instance, would have admitted. The San Francisco *Bulletin* pointed out that "since the Grand Opera House [at Fourth and Mission Streets] was built long ago and the antiquated Mechanics' Pavilion was erected by the Mechanics' Institute, practically nothing has been accomplished on a befitting scale in adding to the attractions of the city." Numerous prominent men joined with Pollock and the *Bulletin* in advocating the construction of a public auditorium and a new opera house. Newton J. Tharp, an architect, proposed lining Van Ness Avenue and other major thoroughfares with trees and incorporating them all into the park system. Andrea Sbarboro, president of the Italian-American Bank, suggested building a great boulevard around the waterfront from the bay to the ocean beach. E. A. Brugiere, identified by the newspapers as a "capitalist," hoped for "a school that shall be to music what our universities—Stanford and California—are to literature and science." Police Commissioner J. R. Howell listed the Golden Gate Park Panhandle extension among public improvements that he wished to see undertaken. M. L. Gerstle and several others who deplored the "jagged, homely street lines that exist throughout the city, even in the most desirable residence districts," urged municipal regulation to preserve uniform street lines and prevent buildings from occupying three or four feet of the public walks. Many citizens called for the elimination of overhead telephone, power, and light wires, the improvement of the streets—"the streets are disgraceful and could not be much worse"—and the establishment of proper grades for sidewalks. Going along lower Market Street, said Julian Sonntag, a real-estate agent, was like walking up hill and down dale. The sidewalks in many places were four feet above the street, in others half a foot below the curb.[3]

Phelan's Proposal for a City Plan

James Duval Phelan, the former mayor, whom *The Wasp* later described as a "clever lawyer and business man, bon vivant, liberal patron of the arts and cultured gentleman,"[4] took a much broader view of the city's needs. First in a general plan of improvement should be the project to secure an abundant supply of water from the Sierra, so that population growth would not be hindered. "Then the city, next in order and before it is too late, should have a plan prepared by a competent person or commission, as has been done recently for the city of Washington, D.C., and for Cleveland, Ohio. This plan would show what old streets should be widened or new

James Duval Phelan. Phelan was president of the Association for the Improvement and Adornment of San Francisco, 1904-1909. Photograph courtesy of the late Noel Sullivan

ones made; where public buildings should be located; where new roads should be laid out, as along the bay shore to the Cliff House, and as to the extension of the panhandle of Golden Gate Park, and once having a plan, we can build with confidence."[5]

In Phelan's opinion, San Francisco was at the turning point of its growth. Either it would be a great and beautiful city, where men and women of taste would desire to live, or a great and ugly and forbidding city, which people would shun. The time had come "to take occasion by the hand to lead the city in the right direction, or to suffer the city to wander aimlessly to an uncertain end."[6]

On January 12, 1904, Phelan and two of his friends, J. W. Byrne, president of the Pacific Union Club, and Willis Davis, president of the San Francisco Art Association, issued an invitation to selected leaders "to meet a committee of about twenty gentlemen" on January 15 at the Merchants' Exchange. "The object of the meeting is to formally discuss a plan for the improvement of San Francisco," the invitation stated. "The plan contemplates making San Francisco a more desirable city in which to live."[7]

The San Francisco *Bulletin* anticipated great results. "Hopes are high," it commented. "The committee seems to mean business, and men who mean business can do wonders in a short while. These men are accustomed to producing results. They have what is called executive ability; that is, the faculty of doing things while others are talking about doing them. It is time for every public-spirited citizen to come forward."[8]

When the *Bulletin* referred to undesignated "others" who merely talked, it meant the current occupant of the mayor's chair, Eugene E. Schmitz, who had been elected Phelan's successor in November, 1901, in the aftermath of the bitter strike of the waterfront unions against the Employers' Association. In that strike Phelan had incurred the enmity of the unions by using police to suppress picket-line violence. His replacement by Schmitz, the candidate of the Union Labor party, left the economically powerful and socially prominent group of which he was a member with almost no influence in city government, yet such was the faith of the group members in their ability to "get things done" that they rose enthusiastically to the challenge of a new civic cause. The Schmitz administration, they reassured one another, could not last long. Its corruption was becoming more apparent every day. A vigorous political campaign at the next election would sweep it from office and restore control to those who had vision and a desire to make San Francisco one of the great cities of America.

An Association to Promote a Plan

At the meeting on January 15 the group formed the Association for the Improvement and Adornment of San Francisco and unanimously elected Phelan its president. Numerous improvements already mentioned in the newspapers were discussed, including a road along the bay shore and also boulevard approaches to Golden Gate Park. Among the new proposals advanced were the extension of Market Street to the ocean and the building of a great outdoor amphitheater. Phelan, however, was convinced that all these separate proposals should be integrated into a single over-all program of development; he had already sounded out the famous Chicago architect Daniel Hudson Burnham concerning his willingness to prepare for San Francisco the kind of plan that he, Frederick Law

Olmsted, and Charles McKim had prepared for Washington, D.C., in 1901. Phelan indicated that Burnham would probably be willing to contribute his services to the association provided the members paid the expenses of assistants and draftsmen.

The first order of business, then, was a program of procedure. To formulate one, Phelan appointed an executive committee composed of W. G. Irwin, Allan Pollock, Herbert E. Law, William Greer Harrison, and a young man named F. W. Dohrmann, who twenty years later was to head the first metropolitan regional planning organization in the San Francisco Bay Area.

The committee decided at the outset that the membership of the association should be broadened to include every citizen who was genuinely interested in improving the city. It drew up an appeal for membership, stating the general and the specific objectives of the organization:

"The main objects of the Association are to promote in every practical way the beautifying of the streets, public buildings, parks, squares, and places of San Francisco; to bring to the attention of the officials and people of the city the best methods for instituting artistic municipal betterments; to stimulate the sentiment of civic pride in the improvement and care of private property; to suggest quasi-public enterprises and, in short, to make San Francisco a more agreeable city in which to live."[9]

A Formal Invitation

By April the Association for the Improvement and Adornment of San Francisco was ready to issue a formal invitation to Burnham to draft a plan for the city. The architect arrived from Chicago and was feted at a dinner in his honor at the St. Francis Hotel on May 4. He spoke eloquently about "the possibilities of enhancing the beauty of the city,"[10] inspiring in his hearers the same kind of excitement that he had aroused among the architects, landscape architects, painters, and sculptors who worked with him when he was chief of construction for the World's Columbian Exposition in Chicago in 1893. At the conclusion of his speech the board of directors of the association adopted a resolution inviting him to prepare a plan.

Two nights later the association held a conference at the Palace Hotel at which more than two hundred representatives of civic groups presented their ideas concerning the general improvement of the city. With great tact the architect spoke as one only slightly familiar with San Francisco, although in the preceding ten years he had made many trips to the city and had designed buildings for clients there.

"Whatever may be my ideas," he said, "I can accomplish little or nothing without the cooperation of the people of San Francisco. I have come here an outsider, and am not in touch with the conditions that exist here. It would require years, perhaps, for me alone to become well enough acquainted with the city to enable me to draft a great general scheme of improvement and adornment that would be a credit to San Francisco if carried into execution. I must have your help. I must be aided by the ideas of the people who have been here for years and who have given this subject their most careful thought and consideration. You know the needs and the possibilities of San Francisco. You must give me your sympathy, for only with it and your appreciation can the highest conception be attained. If San Francisco is to be made more beautiful in the near future, the work to be accomplished must originate from the people of the city. Your suggestions must start the general scheme in operation and must furnish the basis on which I must work."[11]

Probably there has never been a better statement of the importance and the necessity of citizen participation in city planning. Nor have many comprehensive, long-range plans been prepared with a greater fund of citizens' proposals than was available for the Burnham Plan. Spokesmen for the Outdoor Art League, the California Club, the Merchants' Association, numerous neighborhood improvement clubs, the Market Street Club, and other organizations and the magazines *Out West* and *California Municipalities* offered suggestions to Burnham. Most of the projects described had already been proposed by the members of the Association for the Improvement and Adornment of San Francisco, but nothing was lost by their being advocated by others throughout the city.

Not until September 22, 1904, was Burnham able to return to San Francisco to begin work on the plan. In the meantime, President Theodore Roosevelt's Secretary of War, William Howard Taft, had engaged him to prepare plans for Manila and for Baguio, the summer capital of the Philippines. Burnham's schedule included a stay in San Francisco to initiate work on the plan for the association headed by Phelan, then a trip to the Philippines, then further work on the plan for San Francisco upon his return.

Accompanying the architect was his talented young associate Edward H. Bennett, who was to do most of the actual work on the plan for San Francisco. Bennett was, in the words of Burnham, "a poet with his feet on the earth." Burnham, then fifty-seven and independently wealthy, resembled "a railway locomotive under full steam, holding the right of way,"[12] according to one of his contemporaries.

Awaiting the pair and their assistants was a studio

Daniel Hudson Burnham. Photograph courtesy of the Art Institute of Chicago.

bungalow that the association had built, at Burnham's request, on a spur of Twin Peaks, overlooking the entire city, more than one-third of which was then undeveloped. Burnham, the man of broad concepts, always sought some physical eminence from which to view the cities for which he made plans. While working on the plan for the national capital, he had studied the city from the heights of Arlington. Later, when he was preparing a plan for his own city, Chicago, he took up quarters on the top floor of the Railway Exchange. The "shanty" on Twin Peaks, as he designated the bungalow designed by the San Francisco architect Willis Polk, afforded him just the kind of aerie he required while formulating a plan that would be geographically comprehensive, embracing the total area of the City and County of San Francisco.

A Fifty-Year Plan

The Burnham Plan for San Francisco, presented to the board of supervisors on the afternoon of September 27, 1905, was nothing if not grand in conception; but Burnham had no intention that it should frighten citizens and officials by the scope of its proposals. As if anticipating the criticism of those to whom any comprehensive plan is unrealistic, he wrote in the report explaining the plan:

"A scheme of parks, streets and public grounds for a city, in order to be at once comprehensive and practical, should take into account the public purse of today and embrace those things that can be immediately carried into effect, but should in no wise limit itself to these. It should be designed not only for the present, but for all time to come.

"While prudence holds up a warning finger, we must not forget what San Francisco has become in fifty years and what it is still further destined to become. Population and wealth are rapidly increasing, culture is advancing. The city looks toward a sure future wherein it will possess in inhabitants and money many times what it has now. It follows that we must not found the scheme on what the city is, so much as on what it is to be. We must remember that a meager plan will fall short of perfect achievement, while a great one will yield large results, even if it is never fully realized.

"Our purpose, therefore, must be to stop at no line within the limits of practicability. Our scope must embrace the possibilities of development of the next fifty years."[13]

In his view of San Francisco as a young and still-expanding city, in his faith in its potentialities, and in his determination to visualize it as it could be, Burnham was as "modern" as any city planner alive today. One may question his belief that any community could be designed "for all time to come" or even for "the next fifty years," but one cannot disparage the wisdom of attempting to "embrace the possibilities of development." Moreover, since he was aware that many of the proposals embodied in the plan could only be carried out far in the future, if carried out at all, he was careful to point out that the plan was "general" in nature and that "it is not the province of a report of this kind to indicate the exact details very closely."[14] He recognized, therefore, the necessity for some flexibility in the use of the plan, even though he thought of the over-all scheme as having validity "for all time to come."

The Circulation System

No irresponsible dreamer, Burnham set himself the task of making a plan "which shall interfere as little as possible with the rectangular street system of the city."[15] This street system most San Franciscans frankly conceded to be irrational and wholly unsuited to the hilly terrain. But since large-scale alteration of the street pattern appeared to be out of the question, the Chicago architect and his assistants accepted it as a necessary limitation upon their endeavors and contented themselves with planning a system of thoroughfares intended to obviate the major difficulties of circulation within the metropolis. Present-day city planners have taken much the same attitude, although

Bird's-Eye Perspective of the Burnham Plan for San Francisco, 1905

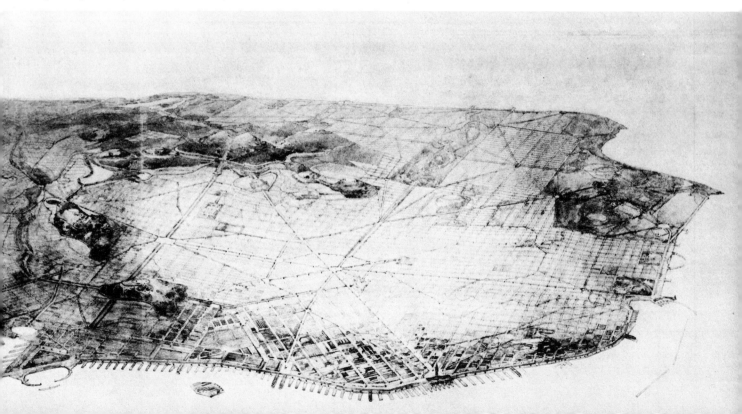

the solutions they have proposed have of course differed greatly from those suggested by Burnham at a time when automobiles were few and the bay bridges were no more than figments of the imaginations of writers in the Sunday supplements.

In principle, at least, Burnham was close to present-day planners in his approach to the design of a circulation system for San Francisco. He recognized that the most efficient pattern of arteries for an urban area is a system resembling a spider web—a series of concentric rings intersected by diagonals radiating from a small central loop or "perimeter of distribution," as in Paris, Berlin, Vienna, Moscow, and London. Such a system permits rapid and easy movement throughout a city and its environs and is regarded by most contemporary city planners as the ideal.

Adaptation of this system to San Francisco obviously required modifications, because the city is surrounded on three sides by water and its topography is highly irregular.

Burnham saw that a small inner circuit or perimeter of distribution could be established at or near the geographical center and that radials could extend from this in all directions, like spokes of a wheel, to an outer or peripheral boulevard traversing, as far as possible, the waterfront. But intermediary circuit boulevards, if carried in a concentric form, would be impracticable because of the numerous hills. He proposed, however, to create an irregular inner chain more or less concentric to the inner circuit.

Civic Center in the Inner Circuit

In his plan this inner circuit enveloped a core area of civic structures—administrative, educational, and cultural —and commercial amusement places and shops of the finer order. The focal point was the intersection of Market Street and Van Ness Avenue, approximately the geographical center of San Francisco in 1905, for the city proper at that time was hemmed in by hills on the west

Plan for a Civic Center in San Francisco, 1899

Burnham's Plan for a Civic Center, Looking from the South Side of Market Street

and south. At this spot Burnham proposed to create a great semicircular *place*, with nine arteries converging upon it from all directions. An extension of the Park Panhandle, for instance, would be carried through the *place* in a direct line to the docks of the Pacific Mail Steamship Company, on the Outer Boulevard near Second and Berry streets, and an extension of Van Ness Avenue would be projected to the south. Eleventh Street would be carried across the *place* toward the northwest. This central open space might be the logical point at which to group major public buildings; but Burnham concluded that the time would come when the civic structures of San Francisco would be too numerous to arrange around this one *place*.

"The Civic Center will, therefore, develop around the center in the form of a number of sub-centers having for location the intersection of the radial arteries with the perimeter of distribution," he explained in his report. "At each of these intersections there should be a public *place*."[16]

The subcenters shown on his plan are the old City Hall, at Larkin and McAllister streets, a union railway station near Eleventh and Bryant streets, and an opera house near Fulton and Gough streets. On the radial arteries within the inner circuit Burnham envisaged schools, museums, academies, theaters, and luxury shops.

These central features of the plan would now be of little more than antiquarian interest had not Burnham's selection of the general area of Market Street and Van Ness Avenue as the location for a civic center tended to fix that area in the public mind as the proper place at which to create one. In the years following the great earthquake and fire of 1906, San Franciscans therefore were willing to accept his recommendation that the principal administrative and cultural structures of the city be grouped in this general vicinity, although the area finally chosen was three blocks north of Market Street and Van Ness Avenue.

Contribution to the Future

Burnham's concept of an inner circuit might appear to have been forgotten during the passage of time, but San Franciscans of today need only consider the new Central Freeway looping round the Civic Center on the west and the central business district on the south. The route corresponds in part to Burnham's inner circuit, although the freeway is more in the nature of a bypass than a distributor thoroughfare.

A glance at a map of present-day San Francisco will reveal that many segments of Burnham's peripheral circuit now actually exist, though not, to be sure, as parts of the thirty-mile-long Outer Boulevard that he designed.

A great, arclike Crosstown Freeway shown in the 1951 Trafficways Plan corresponds roughly to certain connecting drives through a semicircle of parks that Burnham proposed for the southeastern quadrant of San Francisco.[17]

The many diagonal routes suggested by Burnham to facilitate movement in the South of Market area, the financial district, and in the Mission, Bayview, Sunset, and Richmond districts have not reappeared in present-day plans. Even if it were desirable to provide some of these arteries, they could be developed only at enormous cost, because the city is now almost solidly built up. In Burnham's time the Richmond and Sunset districts were, however, almost vacant, as were some parts of the Mission and Bayview districts.

Ahead of His Time

Burnham's recommendations for one-way streets and for subways in the central business district were years in advance of the times, since one-way streets were not adopted in San Francisco, even on a piecemeal basis, until 1942, and since arguments regarding the desirability of subways still continue. Subways had, however, been proposed at the turn of the century.

Traffic engineers currently struggling with the problem of clotted traffic in downtown streets planned in horse-and-buggy days cannot but admire Burnham's prescient recommendation for "a complete system of traffic regulation," including not only the use of one-way streets but also the restriction or even the prohibition of heavy traffic on boulevards designed for fast communication.

In residential areas in the nearly level sections of the city, Burnham saw the possibility of eliminating some of the streets in the monotonous system of blocks and creating a chain of parklike squares "formed in a measure by the unused or misused back-yard areas." These park chains "would become public avenues of beautiful planting, in which one could walk with great comfort, and where children could play, free from danger of traffic," since the main traffic would be routed along the intermediary streets. Such a system, he pointed out, would provide well for children who seldom know any life except that upon the streets of the city and would be the natural approach or connecting link between the larger parks and playgrounds proposed in his plan.[18]

Burnham thus argued for a kind of superblock, employed by many present-day city planners, architects, and site planners in the design of large-scale public and private housing projects as well as in that of single-family residential developments. The generous-dimensioned superblock, permitting the grouping of dwellings round central open space and relegating traffic to the bordering streets, assures maximum amenity, safety, and freedom from noise. It conserves for play space, walks, and gardens, a substantial amount of land that otherwise would be wasted in minor streets.

Many San Franciscans unfamiliar with the Burnham Plan have contemplated the hollow centers of typical San Francisco blocks, with their rows of high board fences dividing the land into twenty-five-foot strips, and have devised similar schemes for pooling individually owned plots and forming socially useful space; but invariably these plans have collapsed under the opposition of those who would rather do as they please on a few square feet of land than share several thousand square feet with their neighbors.

Aside from his recommendations for the formation of superblocks which would be made possible by eliminating some minor streets, and for the provision of small parks and playgrounds distributed throughout the city according to the density of population in various sections, Burnham had little to say about the future development of residential areas. One looks in vain for any mention of a proposed distribution of population, for recommendations concerning the types of residential structures suitable for specific districts, for standards for sites for schools and shopping facilities, or for proposed locations of transit routes—all of great concern to present-day city planners. In that nascent period of city planning most city plans included little besides proposals for boulevards, parks, and a civic center. Though Burnham and his co-workers in San Francisco limited themselves chiefly to these features, they dealt with them imaginatively and in many instances displayed a great deal more foresight than their contemporaries could appreciate.

Plans for New Parks

Burnham was eminently practical in recognizing that San Francisco was deficient in recreation space, even though Golden Gate Park and several squares had been reserved at an earlier period. The Mission and Potrero districts, particularly, lacked parks and were distant from those which did exist. In the city as a whole there were approximately 286 persons for each acre of park, since the Park Board estimated the total park area to be between 1,300 and 1,400 acres and the city population to be perhaps 400,000. The average for "the most important cities of the United States" was, however, 206 persons for each park acre; and Boston had set a standard of 42 persons per park acre.[19] To bring San Francisco into line with other large cities, more parks would be required. And then there were future needs to be considered.

Burnham proposed to add to the park system numerous tracts which possessed a certain natural beauty but which were, in his opinion, ill adapted for private occupancy because of their steepness, their inaccessibility, or difficulties of drainage. The numerous hills then in a pristine state came, of course, within his definition of lands suitable for park development. These hills, indeed, were the unique feature of the site of San Francisco. So concerned was Burnham with their preservation and with the enhancement of their dramatic quality that he allotted an entire section of his report to a discussion of the general treatment of the hills.

"It may be stated in general that the tops of all high hills should be preserved in a state of nature, while their slopes below should be clothed with trees, not presenting a horizontal line where they leave off above, but a line adapted to the varying conditions of each case," Burnham wrote.[20]

He proposed circumscribing the base of each hill with a circuit road, developing contour roads on the slopes, and accenting places of interest with terraces commanding views of the city. Where contour roads ran through residential areas, he recommended reserving fifty to one hundred feet of land on the lower side, in order to retain in some degree the outlook over the city.

In those early years of the century it would have been possible to link numerous unspoiled hills in a great girdle of parks about the entire city; and this Burnham recommended doing. The park chain, as he outlined it, would start at Buena Vista Park near the Golden Gate Park Panhandle, extend across the Twin Peaks group and its continuation to the south, include Bernal Heights, and end at Potrero Heights. Significantly, he remarked: "In case of a great conflagration this system of parks and connecting parkways would form an effective barrier to its spread."[21]

A Great Park West of Twin Peaks

To the west of Twin Peaks Burnham's plan showed a vast park, two or three times the size of Golden Gate Park, extending southwest through Rancho San Miguel to Lake Merced, with an unbroken vista sweeping from an Athenaeum on the crest of the peaks down to the lake and the sea beyond.

The suggested treatment of the hills in the Twin Peaks area reveals the extent to which the planner of the "City Beautiful" era was inspired by the classic world of Greece and Rome. An amphitheater to the north of the peaks "would recall by its location the stadium in the hills at Delphi, which overlooks the Gulf of Corinth, and the theater of Dionysos, at the foot of the Acropolis." An Academy similar to the American Academy at Rome would have a little open-air theater "after the ancient Greek model." The courts, terraces, and colonnaded shelters of the Athenaeum would be arranged "after the manner of the great Poecile of the Villa Hadrian."[22]

In some circles it is the fashion nowadays to ridicule Burnham and the young architects who worked with him, for their deference to the majestic achievements of the ancient world and their admiration for the great designers of the Renaissance. The perspective drawings of Telegraph Hill, the view from the Athenaeum toward the sea, the drill ground from the heights of the Presidio, and the approach to Twin Peaks from Market Street are sneeringly described as "grandiose" rather than grand.

One may indeed criticize Burnham and his associates for following an aesthetic tradition foreign to America, for turning their backs on an emergent native architecture. But one cannot indict them for being genuinely inspired by the noblest architecture and site planning of the past, for grasping the aesthetic quality of the San Francisco hills, and for seeking to translate a passionate response to these natural forms into proposals of great breadth and scope, recapturing something of the spirit of Delphi and something of the more theatrical gardens and public places of Rome. Had some of these imposing projects been carried out, they would have been highly appropriate to San Francisco, a city with a dramatic history.

That the Burnham Plan presented extensive proposals

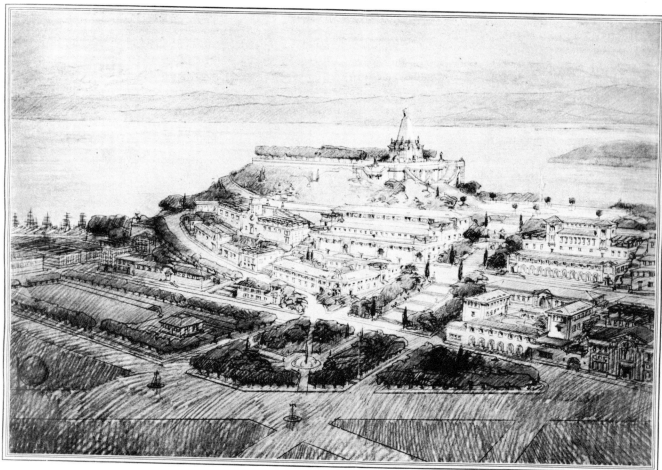

Burnham's "Suggested Architectural Treatment" of Telegraph Hill

for parks, boulevards, and a civic center and dealt only superficially with industrial, commercial, and waterfront areas did not seem strange to the businessmen who invited the Chicago architect to San Francisco. City planning in 1905 had the status of an art, and what was sought from Burnham was primarily a plan for the "adornment" of the city. Only secondarily were the members of the Association for the Improvement and Adornment of San Francisco interested in the plan as an instrument that could be used to facilitate the operations of manufacturers, retailers, shippers, and wholesalers. Today a group of business leaders would require that a long-range plan be based on a thorough analysis of the economic functions of the community and that it anticipate realistically the long-range physical needs of the business community. The brief discussion, in Burnham's report, of relationships within the working city and of the future development of the waterfront is more or less a gratuitous offering, incidental to an explanation of plans for the Outer Boulevard and for yacht harbors and piers for public recreation.

Suggested Controls

Just how his various recommendations for improving the city where to be implemented Burnham did not say. He advocated, "if necessary," an ordinance requiring public and semipublic institutions, such as churches and schools, to be set back from the sidewalk so as not to infringe upon "the rights of neighboring property."[23] But this was practically the only mention in his entire report of the use of local statutes to guide development. In recommending a uniform cornice height for buildings in the business district, he could not have been unaware of a Boston ordinance of 1904 restricting building heights; yet legal means to effect his recommendation were not offered.

Virtually the only concrete proposal for permanently influencing physical aspects of the city was a recommendation that an art commission be provided by charter amendment "to control all matters especially pertaining to civic art."[24] The list of matters that might properly come before the commission reveals, however, that Burnham was not thinking of a public agency that would be zealous in submitting advice on ways to carry out his plan. Rather, he had in mind an innocuous group who would busy themselves with approving or disapproving the designs of street lamps, postboxes, safety stations, electric signs, billboards, and street name plates. There was not at that time in the entire United States a single official city planning agency. The first one was established at Hartford, Connecticut, in 1907. If Burnham had proposed one for San Francisco in 1905, he would indeed have set a precedent.

The Chicago architect undoubtedly assumed that the Association for the Improvement and Adornment of San Francisco would be a continuing organization and that from time to time it would seize the opportunity to advocate a bond issue or an appropriation to carry out some specific proposal in his plan. He suggested that the first projects undertaken should be the extension of the Panhandle and the construction of the Outer Boulevard. "Once these are carried out," he wrote, "the whole civic life will be affected and the development of other parts of the plan will be hastened thereby."[25]

Presentation of the Plan

The banquet at the St. Francis Hotel celebrating the presentation of the plan to the city was outwardly all sweetness and light, but beneath the surface were political enmities that augured ill for the success of the plan. In the absence of James Phelan, who was vacationing in Paris, William Greer Harrison, vice-president of the association, served as toastmaster and spoke of the assembled officials, architects, and real-estate men as "neophytes in the temple of beauty, a temple within whose doors no discord could enter."[26] Mayor Eugene Schmitz, whose picture was just then appearing in the San Francisco *Bulletin* with the word "GRAFT" printed across the forehead, responded enthusiastically to the toast "The New San Francisco," after which the celebrants, all standing, drank to the health of Daniel Burnham. Probably every member of the association present hoped that in the coming municipal election the decorative Mr. Schmitz would be unseated by their fellow member, attorney John S. Partridge; but a clairvoyant might have told them that the mayor was not going to be turned out. And this was a circumstance that was to have peculiar bearing upon the fate of the ambitious plan that they were extolling.

How sincere some of the real-estate men attending the banquet were in their praise of the Burnham Plan is a matter for speculation. In an article written for the *Architectural Record* shortly before the disaster of April 18, 1906, but not published until the following June, a

writer named Herbert Croly observed that at the very moment when the citizens were acclaiming the Burnham report, "that generally ignorant and obnoxious individual, the real estate speculator," was laying out new additions to the south "in the same bad old way."[27]

In order that San Franciscans might study the plan in all its details, the board of supervisors ordered Burnham's report printed as a municipal document. The appropriation for the purpose was $3,000, permitting the production of a volume replete with photographs of the city and with reproductions of the maps, perspective drawings, and plans prepared by Edward Bennett and his corps of artists and draftsmen.

In mid-April, 1906, bound copies of the report were delivered to the City Hall, and from the bungalow on Twin Peaks the handsome originals of the drawings and plans illustrated in the publication were brought for a public display. While the exhibition was being installed in the City Hall, a few copies of the report were released, chiefly to members of the Association for the Improvement and Adornment of San Francisco. The rest were never to be distributed.

Earthquake and Fire

At 5:13 on the morning of April 18 great rock masses along the San Andreas fault slipped, grated against each other, and settled into a new position almost instantaneously. From Upper Mattole in Humboldt County to San Juan in San Benito County, quick, sharp vibrations went out in all directions through the rocks and communicated themselves violently to the soft soils and sands of the valleys, to the made lands in downtown San Francisco, and to the sandy areas thereabouts.

The dome and most of the roof on the south and west wings of the pretentious, poorly constructed San Francisco City Hall spilled into the street. More than fifty miles away, in Santa Rosa, the dome of the Sonoma County Court House toppled onto the roof. At Point Reyes Station, near the head of Tomales Bay in Marin County, a train that was about to depart for San Francisco keeled over. At Agnew, a few miles north of San Jose, the State Insane Asylum collapsed, killing more than a hundred patients and eleven officials. At Stanford University the heavy spire of the chapel dropped through the roof. Some miles to the north, in San Mateo County, the pipe lines that conveyed water to San Francisco from Pilarcitos, Crystal Springs, and San Andreas reservoirs split apart, telescoped, or bent backwards at crazy angles, their precious contents wasting on the ground, while in the distant metropolis little serpents of smoke rose slowly in the still air.

In Oakland, Alameda, and Berkeley some chimneys fell, some walls tumbled, one church lost its tower, a small theater caved in, and some old, ramshackle buildings jostled together. But on the whole, damage was slight. Likewise in Richmond and Vallejo there was little physical evidence of the convulsive movement of the earth. In Petaluma and San Rafael, cities luckily situated on rocky —and therefore less yielding—ground, the destruction was minor. Almost all the towns on the San Francisco Peninsula suffered considerable damage but were able to function.

Toward all these places thousands of terrified residents of San Francisco began fleeing on that catastrophic Wednesday morning. All that day, all the next day, throughout Thursday night, and on into Friday the flames ravaged the city; but on Friday morning the east wind that had fanned the conflagration for almost twenty-four hours ceased and a strong wind from the west sprang up. It turned the fiery scourge toward Russian Hill and North Beach. There, finally, on Saturday morning, April 21, the straggling remnants of the fire sputtered their last as a heavy rain fell.

CHAPTER SEVEN

The New San Francisco

Where some twenty-eight thousand buildings had stood, now stretched a blackened wasteland of more than four square miles—512 blocks. The most historic part of San Francisco was ashes, rubble, contorted scraps of metal, and shattered walls. Above the debris rose only five or six habitable structures, the skeletons of half a dozen unfinished business blocks, and approximately thirty gutted but structurally sound steel-frame buildings, the harbingers of a new city.

The loss of property amounted to at least half a billion dollars. Exactly how great the loss of life was will never be known. Officially the toll was placed at 478; but scores, perhaps hundreds, were never accounted for.

In that part of the city which had escaped the holocaust approximately 175,000 persons congregated, a large proportion of whom looked to bread lines for their daily sustenance. Destitute families were encamped in Golden Gate Park, in the Presidio, in small parks, and on vacant lots. Many a house still standing harbored refugees from the disaster. The task of distributing food, clothing, and medical supplies among the dispossessed proceeded with remarkable smoothness, considering the enormous disruption of services occasioned by the earthquake and fire. As for the refugees themselves, they exhibited heroic courage and cheerfulness, sustained in the knowledge that humanity everywhere would help to relieve their suffering and to rebuild the devastated metropolis.

Refugees in Other Cities

In the cities about the bay thousands of refugees gratefully accepted shelter in private homes or camped in tents hastily erected in the parks by the municipal authorities. The Southern Pacific estimated that between 6 A.M. on the day of the earthquake and Sunday night, April 22, it provided free passage from the stricken city for 225,000 persons, some of whom left California altogether, and

Area Burned in the Great Fire of 1906

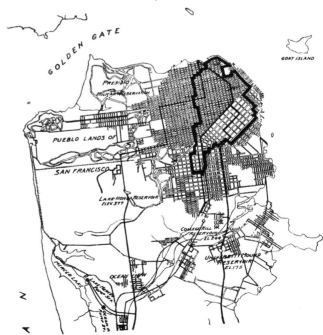

Ruins of the San Francisco City Hall, April 23, 1906. Photograph courtesy of Bancroft Library, University of California.

some of whom migrated to southern California and other parts of the state. Thousands of others fled on foot down the Peninsula or escaped by boat to Alameda County or Marin County.

In Oakland an estimated one hundred thousand refugees crowded into the homes of sympathetic citizens, filled every church in the city, and swelled to overflowing no less than twenty camps established in the city parks. Alameda made provision for ten thousand of the homeless, and Berkeley for fifteen thousand, not counting those who went directly to the homes of friends and relatives. In Richmond, John D. Rockefeller set up a special camp for the victims of the disaster. Vallejo officials estimated that their city cared for thirty thousand men, women, and children in the month following the catastrophe. Here, too, tent cities appeared in the parks, and citizens opened their homes to the refugees.

In Oakland, F. M. Smith and his associates sniffed the smoke of burning San Francisco as if it were the exhalation from an opium pipe—and conjured up "one of the most stupendous undertakings in the history of the advancement of Greater Oakland." They proposed merely to make Oakland "the greatest shipping point on the Pacific Coast." Their plan embraced "the construction of a double pier to the terminus of the Key Route Mole, the construction of a bulkhead from the Long Wharf of the Southern Pacific Company to the Key Route ferry slip, the filling of the five hundred acres lying between the two trestles, and the construction of a slip adjacent to the mole for the docking of the largest vessels that have ever entered San Francisco Bay."[1]

Wickham Havens, an Oakland realtor, bought space in the San Francisco papers to announce his desire to assist the burned-out residents: "To our friends, our clients, and all who may need our services in this hour we offer them freely. We want to help in this vast work of building up. We want to aid in the work of construction of a new metropolis of the Pacific on the East side of the bay."[2] The capitalization of the word "east" no doubt was deliberate.

Beginning of Rebuilding

Most San Franciscans had no thought of abandoning their city. "San Francisco will be rebuilt," the San Francisco *Bulletin* proclaimed while the embers still glowed. "At the supreme crisis in the history of the city her people have risen nobly to a situation which demands all that men and women could possess of courage, fortitude and hope. Plans for the greater, the new San Francisco, are rapidly taking shape, and out of the chaos of shattered buildings and broken fortunes, above the charred fragments of the once-proud metropolis will rise the new city by the western sea, the home of the strongest, bravest, and sturdiest people of their race."[3]

In homelier fashion a business sign on a newly erected stand expressed the spirit of the hour:

> We were at Howard, near 8th St.
> HONEST INJUN
> HERE'S WHAT'S LEFT OF US,
> 1 Shoestring, 1 Collar Button,
> 1 Necktie, 1 Pair Sox, 1 Pair Spex,
> and an INDOMITABLE WILL
> and the greatest of these
> is WILL—THE SPIRIT OF '06.[4]

The ruins of the city were not yet cool when some merchants set up shop on the very sites where they had done business before. They pulled from the debris assorted pieces of corrugated iron, bits of pipe, anything that would serve as building material. Undamaged sections of wall became supports for lean-tos. And in a surprisingly short time stocks of goods appeared in these temporary emporiums.

For the time being, Fillmore Street, in the population-swollen Western Addition, became the principal business street of San Francisco. Already a commercial artery in a small way, it now had the advantage of possessing one of the few undamaged car lines in the city, a service connecting with the Mission district. There was also a good deal of vacant frontage on the street. Every empty lot soon swarmed with workmen hammering together light frame structures to house the leading mercantile establishments of the city. Restaurants, theaters, saloons, and hotels opened alongside the stores, giving the streets the lively, tawdry aspects of the main stem of a frontier boom town. The "sights" of Fillmore Street became, indeed, so magnetic that within three months Oakland papers were complaining of the loss of business to this new gay way.

In Hayes Valley, on the southern edge of the Western Addition, another business district sprang up. Here the streets were well paved, the terrain was flat, and there were two car lines that could be restored to service before long. New homes as well as new stores went up rapidly, including dwellings on the alleys. Lot overcrowding, the curse of this section of the city, had its beginning then.

For the Western Addition as a whole the fire marked the start of a swift decline toward the status of a blighted area. This district was one of the few parts of San Francisco in which urban activities could be carried on with any semblance of normality. The clamor for dwelling space was so great that property owners quickly converted their homes into boardinghouses, even fitting up basements, attics, and storage rooms as bedrooms. Apartment houses, hastily enlarged, became commercial hotels. To meet the demand for commercial space, numerous householders raised their dwellings and built stores underneath them. Stores, restaurants, and workshops opened for business in basements. Industries, too, invaded the area, carrying on noisy and often dangerous operations next door to single-family homes or multifamily structures. Every condition that would make a modern city planner shudder was soon to be found in the Western Addition in exaggerated form: indiscriminate mixture of land uses, excessive density of population, substandard housing, traffic congestion.

Van Ness Avenue, the wide thoroughfare at which the flames had been checked, underwent a brisk transformation into a street of fashionable shops, past which the stylish paraded on Saturday afternoons as they once had on Kearny and Market streets.

In the undestroyed area of the Mission district a fever pitch of activity prevailed. New houses went up; many old ones were remodeled to accommodate more occupants, even though faulty room arrangements and bad lighting and ventilation resulted. The intersection of Mission and Twenty-second streets, a transfer point for the

Twin Peaks and Potrero districts, became the hub of a new retail center. Shopping areas also sprang up at Valencia and Sixteenth streets and at Twenty-ninth and Church streets.

In the outer Mission district, in the Richmond district between the Presidio and Golden Gate Park, and in other sparsely settled areas contractors and builders rushed construction of new houses. Thousands of workers who formerly had lived in the congested area south of Market Street and in the North Beach district rented or bought in the new tracts, and for the first time enjoyed private yards and adequate light and air.

A New Evil—Tenements

But civic leaders who had hoped that reconstruction would bring an improvement in housing were dismayed by the appearance of a new evil—the jerry-built tenement house. Ernest P. Bicknell, General Superintendent of the Chicago Bureau of Charities, warned San Franciscans that "the landlord does not build better unless he is forced to." Said he, "A handful of intelligent, thoroughgoing, enthusiastic people who are not easily discouraged will have to carry the burden if the city is to be saved from the danger of having built here tenements which would be a disgrace and a source of endless disease and trouble, and eventually of tremendous cost to the community in money."[5]

Despite the efforts of social workers, some members of the Commonwealth Club, and other public-spirited people to cope with the situation, the tenement-house problem became acute within six months. Probably at that time no combination of forces could have prevented the building of these rookeries, as Dr. Langley Porter, president of the San Francisco Housing Association, pointed out in 1911 in the first public report of the association: "The people wanted shelter, the workmen needed wages, the contractors in many cases had to rebuild shattered financial standing, and lot owners were anxious for the same reason to get the greatest possible income from their property. It was a time of turmoil and uncertainty. The bravest man was the one with faith enough to risk his money in building. The authorities, glad enough to encourage anyone to build, hardly enforced the mild provisions of the existing building laws. Merely that a building would not fall was all they asked. Thus tenements, not homes, were built."[6]

Unparalleled Opportunity

Hope for a better-planned city also faded as citizens of all classes raised their voices against anything that would delay reconstruction. When the fire was consuming block after block, some people were well-nigh convinced that Providence was at work, effacing the mistakes of the past and providing an unparalleled opportunity for San Francisco to make a fresh start, utilizing the plan prepared by Burnham. But as the weeks passed and the work of rebuilding progressed, it became increasingly apparent that the city was not going to take advantage of the "clean slate" presented by the disaster.

On the very day of the earthquake, Ernest Graham sent a cable to Burnham, who was traveling in France, saying "Come at once!"[7] The architect boarded the liner *Deutschland* at Dover the next night and reached Chicago on May 1. From there he sent a telegram to Mayor Schmitz and the Committee for Reconstruction, announcing that he was on his way to San Francisco.

Before he arrived, city officials and civic leaders held preliminary meetings. At one of these James Phelan exclaimed, "This is a magnificent opportunity for beautifying San Francisco, and I believe that the property owners will gladly coöperate, now that their personal improvements have been swept away. I am sure the city will rise from its ashes greater, better, and more beautiful."[8]

At the same meeting, Benjamin Ide Wheeler, president of the University of California, spoke of "the glorious, gentle sweeps of the hills, offering themselves to contour gradients." Then he added, "I should like to see Nob Hill made into a park and that glorious view preserved for the people."[9]

The San Francisco *Chronicle* immediately sounded a note of caution: "There should be and must be some widening and straightening of streets. But we must not lose our heads. We may allow visions of the beautiful to dance before our eyes, but we must not permit them to control our actions." The newspaper warned, "If we expect to sell bonds we must give evidence of financial wisdom."[10]

The first full meeting of the Committee for Reconstruction or the Committee of Forty, as it was popularly known, began with an admonition from Mayor Schmitz on "the danger of outlining work on an extravagant scale."[11] The city, he said, was less able to reconstruct in accordance with the Burnham Plan than it had been a month before the fire. In his estimation one hundred million dollars would hardly pay the cost of erecting needed public buildings. If the Burnham Plan were adopted, the expense would be "an addition to this sum." He requested that suggestions from committee members be "practical, not theoretical."[12]

Stung by the implication that he, a former mayor, had been impractical in suggesting the extension of the Panhandle and the acquisition of land for boulevards, Phelan was on his feet at once, explaining how the Burnham proposals could be carried out without much cost to the taxpayers. By condemnation proceedings the city could acquire half a block on each side of the Panhandle and other boulevards for their entire length, use as much as necessary for right of way, and then sell the excess land at an advanced valuation based on the new public improvements. The increment would in most instances be sufficient to pay for the cost of the improvements. Lest his hearers consider this suggestion archsocialism, Phelan explained that Paris had employed this method in carrying out some of the plans for boulevards drawn up by Baron Haussmann under Napoleon III. In California, he pointed out, excess condemnation would have to be authorized by a special session of the state legislature.

Many of his hearers doubted that the state lawmakers would look with favor on any such grant of power; some questioned the constitutionality of the proposal. The use of tax funds or monies from the sale of municipal bonds, or both, therefore appeared inescapable. This was the hard reality that the press emphasized to the exclusion of all other considerations.

"Let us have a city beautiful but within our ability to pay," urged the San Francisco *Bulletin* in an editorial which undoubtedly strengthened the popular impression that many of the proposals in the Burnham Plan were purely for "show." "Much may be done without plunging the city in a debt that will impair our credit, or raise the rate of taxation to a point that will cripple business," the newspaper advised. It concluded that San Franciscans "without shrinking from the performance of duty, may leave some things for a future and more opulent generation to do in creating visions of the beautiful."13

Attacks on the plan brought from John Galen Howard, the official architect of the University of California and an advisory member of the Committee of Forty, the statement that the plan was "admirably conceived" and could be carried out, for the very sound reason that it was founded on "basic principles." Howard chose to stress the practical aspects of the plan—"the convenience involved in the arrangement, the provisions for taking care of traffic and for making each part of the city accessible."14

Proposed Improvements

Burnham's arrival fortified Phelan, Howard, Benjamin Ide Wheeler, Willis Polk, Rudolph Spreckels, John McLaren, and others who championed the plan. The Chicago "civic engineer," as some newspapers dubbed him, plunged into a series of daily conferences with various subcommittees, particularly the Subcommittee on Widen-

ing, Extending, and Grading Streets and Restoring Pavements; the Subcommittee on Parks, Reservoirs, and Boulevards; and the Subcommittee on Burnham Plans [sic], headed by Phelan. By May 21 the first-named subcommittee was ready to present to the full Committee of Forty the proposals that it had worked out with the other two subcommittees. Its report, recommending the very minimum of changes that it considered essential in the burned district, revealed how great had been the struggle with the formidable problem of financing the proposed improvements:

"Realizing the necessity for immediate yet conservative action which confronts us, and that in the present financial situation of the city, utility should be a more potent factor than mere beauty in the solving of the problems before us, yet recognizing that both of these important elements may be judiciously and advantageously combined, your committee has concluded to submit its several recommendations in the order of their apparent importance and of the ability of the city to carry them out without imposing too great a burden of taxation on the property owners of the city. To accomplish this end your committee has reached the determination that some of these recommendations should be executed and carried into effect immediately, some may well be deferred for a period of five years and some for longer, say ten years.

"In view of the fact that almost all of the lands through which the projected improvements are to run are now vacant and devoid of improvements, and therefore may be acquired more easily and economically now than at any other time, your committee has devised a plan which seems entirely feasible for securing the required lands at once, even though the projected improvements may not be fully accomplished for some time thereafter. This plan may be carried out without imposing any additional taxation on the property holders of the city by deferring payment until such time as by reason of increase in the amount of taxable property the same rate of taxation will produce the necessary revenue. Briefly, to accomplish this your committee recommends that the Board of Supervisors shall by ordinance declare the city's intention at or before five years from date of issuance. This will enable the city to acquire the lands necessary for the contemplated improvements during the five years without levying any tax therefor, and will at the same time enable the property owner whose land is to be acquired to accept bonds therefor, which bonds he will be able to dispose of at once or may carry as an investment. These bonds will undoubtedly be for a long term and will therefore be very desirable holdings. The improvement is a permanent one, which will enhance real estate values in all parts of the city; the amount of tax levied to meet them will be almost insignificant. The benefits of the added valuation accruing therefrom will increase a thousandfold as compared with the expenses required to produce them."15

Immediate improvements to be financed by bonds that would be repaid by provisions in the general tax levy were seventeen in all. They included proposals for widening to one hundred feet such important thoroughfares as Montgomery Avenue [Columbus Avenue], Golden Gate Avenue, and Pacific, Powell, and Pine streets. New contour streets were to encircle Nob Hill and Russian Hill, since few structures remained on either hill. Other proposals contemplated extending the Panhandle to Market Street and creating a number of diagonal routes, some of which had not appeared in the original Burnham Plan.

Improvements recommended for deferral for five years included the widening of Geary Street, the creation of a Panhandle continuation all the way to the waterfront, extensions of Potrero Avenue, and the widening and opening of Eleventh Street as an approach to the union station proposed by Burnham.

Triumph for Burnham

The unanimous adoption of the subcommittee report by the Committee of Forty was regarded as a triumph for Burnham and the stalwarts of the Association for the

SAN FRANCISCO CHRONICLE, WEDNESDAY, MAY 23, 1906.

NEW PLAN OF CITY ADOPTED BY THE CITIZENS' COMMITTEE

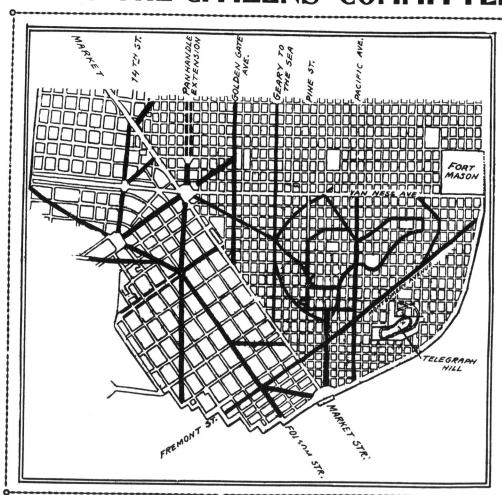

Plan Proposed by the Citizen's Committee for Reconstruction, May 21, 1906. "The heavy black lines show the widened streets, as well as the new diagonal streets which have not yet been named, and the winding streets by means of which easy access may be secured to Nob Hill," the San Francisco Chronicle explained.

Improvement and Adornment of San Francisco. But would the board of supervisors adopt it? Burnham himself attended the meeting at which the board considered the report and explained that the revised plan "had nothing to do with the proposed beautification of the city, but was designed simply to give quick and easy communication and to relieve the congestion of the downtown district." The proposed diagonal streets and the widening of existing streets were, he said, "absolutely necessary." One or two of the supervisors questioned the advisability of slicing blocks into "small triangles" by extending Montgomery Avenue to Market Street, but when the vote on political boss Abe Ruef's resolution for adoption of the plan was taken, all answered "aye."[16]

"The adoption of this plan makes it certain beyond all cavil or doubt that the men of San Francisco are in earnest in their determination to rebuild the city, and to rebuild it on a grander scale than before," Mayor Schmitz declared. "This means business. I am particularly glad that the committee disregarded the ornamental and confined itself to the practical in laying out this plan. Decoration can come later. But the main thing is that we can now get to work. Many prominent men have waited only for the settlement of the new street lines to put up splendid buildings. These will be completed within two years, and the city will stand rehabilitated within five years."[17]

Burnham returned to Chicago elated. The plans, he informed the people of that city, had been adopted "in their entirety." More optimistic than Mayor Schmitz, he prophesied that in a year's time it would not be easy to find a trace of the devastation left by the earthquake and fire. "San Francisco of the future will be the most beautiful city of the continent, with the possible exception of Washington," he rejoiced.[18]

Attack on Proposals

In the metropolis by the Golden Gate there was no premature exultation. The San Francisco *Chronicle* attacked the Committee of Forty for making "a serious blunder in proposing to place the ban of uncertainty for five years upon a large quantity of down-town property." It condemned the plans as being unworthy of consideration because they had not been brought forward "in a business fashion," with estimates of the probable cost of the improvements. "The crying need of San Francisco today is not more parks and boulevards; it is business," the newspaper asserted. "Unless we get back to work and effect a speedy restoration of old conditions, we shall find that we have more parks and wide streets than we can profitably use."[19]

At a meeting of the Down-Town Property Owners Association, M. H. de Young, publisher of the *Chronicle*, who had commissioned Burnham to design the first skyscraper in San Francisco, likened the situation of the California metropolis to that of London after the great fire of 1666, when Sir Christopher Wren evolved his celebrated plan for making over the English capital. The "practical men" of London, de Young told his audience, concluded that if an attempt were made to carry out Wren's project, business would be driven from London. They therefore determined to proceed with the rehabilitation of the city on the old lines, with the result that in five years London was rebuilt and the business of the city was left undisturbed. He urged the "practical men" of San Francisco to follow their example.[20]

The San Francisco *Bulletin*, which had always enthusiastically supported Phelan in his civic work, ran an editorial entitled "Wide Streets Are Wanted, but We Cannot Wait Long."

"Unless the property-owners, or at least the great majority of them, along a street which it is proposed to widen will consent to the improvement and donate to the public use a strip from the frontage of their lots, the project of widening that street may as well be abandoned. Unless the land is given freely it must be purchased, and there is no money available for the purchase. Should the owner be unwilling either to donate the land or sell it, the city must proceed by an action of condemnation, which the defendant landowner can prolong by various methods. There is no time for the slow processes of litigation. Landowners, eager to build, cannot hold back until the line of the street shall be determined by judgment of the Supreme Court. The city needs action, not litigation. Our energy must be spent in building, not in wrangling before juries."[21]

A few days later the same newspaper published another editorial, headed "Dreams and Schemes Must Not Retard Rebuilding," in which it mentioned that some of the proposed street widenings were encountering "violent opposition" from landowners. The *Bulletin* attributed some of the lag in rebuilding to the slowness of insurance companies in paying losses but said that much of the delay was due to "the uncertainty of the proposed widening of divers streets."[22]

On the opposite side of the bay the Oakland *Enquirer* observed, in commenting on Burnham's optimism about the new city-to-be: "It is to be hoped . . . that a year hence one will be able to find some trace of the Burnham plans in San Francisco, if the immediate necessities of the business situation do not mutilate them beyond all recognition."[23]

A New Threat to the Plans

Suddenly the plans were threatened from a new and unexpected quarter. The cunning Abe Ruef, seeing an opportunity to manipulate the street-widening projects to his own advantage, attempted to jam through the state legislature a proposed state constitutional amendment suspending certain provisions of the San Francisco City Charter for two years and conferring almost unrestrained powers upon the supervisors and mayor to acquire, sell, or exchange lands for streets, parks, boulevards, reservoirs, and other public purposes. Adroitly tucked in was a section granting the Ruef-managed supervisors wide authority to alter the terms of franchises for railroads, wires, pipe lines, and conduits. This dangerous measure, to the amazement, chagrin, and indignation of the Committee of Forty, was placed before the legislators as having the endorsement of that public-spirited body.

Without digging beneath the surface of Ruef's barefaced grab for power, the *Chronicle* screamed that "if the committee of forty expects to retain public confidence as to the wisdom of any of its recommendations it must stop giving serious attention to such revolutionary and hysterical proposals as that submitted by the subcommittee of which Mr. Ruef is chairman, and which proposes to proceed by constitutional amendment to rip open the charter of this city and tear out of it [many of] its most salutary restrictions on the power of the Supervisors."[24]

Later, having ferreted out the facts, de Young's newspaper exposed Ruef's methods:

". . . As a matter of fact, there were very few members of the committee of forty who had anything to do with this constitutional amendment. It was drafted by Ruef himself and placed by him for indorsement to a subcommittee in San Francisco, which committee at Century Hall was composed of lawyers alone, and only part of the membership of the sub-committee was present at the meeting when Ruef's amendment was considered. Even had all of the sub-committee been in attendance, it would not have been a body that represented the people of San Francisco. The few lawyers who were present and who gave some attention to the proposition were friendly to Ruef, and while they did not like the scope of the measure, were content to put in it the few limitations which it now carries, and then they 'passed the buck' to the Legislature. The sub-committee report to the committee of forty was a long document, covering many subjects of legislation, and it was given formal approval without discussion when presented. Probably not more than half a dozen members of the committee of forty had read Ruef's measure attentively."[25]

This explanation came too late, however, to save the Committee of Forty from the fire of irate civic organizations. Their spokesmen, hastening to Sacramento to appear in opposition to the proposed amendment, berated Ruef and the Committee of Forty in the same breath. Matt I. Sullivan, representing the Mission Promotion Association, wanted the legislators to remember that "that charter was framed by as eminent a body of citizens as the Committee of Forty" and that its authors had "put in it provisions to protect the people against monopoly." Careful estimates, he asserted, showed that to carry out the committee's scheme of street alterations would subject all taxpayers of San Francisco to a bonded indebtedness of between $30,000,000 and $40,000,000—"solely for the benefit of rich property-owners north of Market Street."[26] Other opponents joined with him in suggesting that there was boodle in the proposition for Ruef and his friends. The crafty boss of the Schmitz Administration stubbornly defended his amendment, but, the *Bulletin* stated, "his talent for the plausible exposition of a sophistical argument was staggered by the job."[27] The legislature emasculated the menacing amendment and sent the spokesmen for the various associations home almost prayerfully grateful that San Francisco had escaped "a worse evil than earthquake and fire."[28]

The Committee of Forty, innocently but negligently entangled in Ruef's web for a brief period, now labored under a double burden. It fought not only the charge that it was impractical, idealistic, theoretical, visionary, and perhaps irresponsible, but also the suspicion, in some bitterly hostile quarters, that its members, or some of them at least, sought personal gain rather than the common good.

An Advisory Commission

Since matters were going from bad to worse, United States Senator Francis Griffith Newlands, of Nevada, one of the owners of the Palace Hotel property, pleaded at a meeting of the California Promotion Committee late in July for property owners to "get together, suggest improvements, compromise conflicting claims and interests and rehabilitate this great city." He suggested the establishment of a commission "with a man like Burnham at the head of it, that can advise the municipal authorities and property owners relative to combining beauty with utility in our new city."[29]

Senator Newlands seems to have recognized the need for something akin to the present-day city planning commission, though it is not clear whether he thought of his proposed commission as a permanent advisory group. At any rate, he deserves credit for having been the first, or at least one of the first, to understand that without a public agency specifically charged with the responsibility of recommending policies for the physical development of a city on the basis of a long-term plan that expresses community goals, there is little hope for substantial civic improvement or orderly growth.

The men who seized upon Newlands' suggestion were the leaders of the Association for the Improvement and Adornment of San Francisco—Phelan, Rudolph Spreckels and Thomas Magee. They joined in urging Mayor Schmitz to invite Burnham to return to San Francisco and supervise the rebuilding of the city in conformity with his plans.[30] But the mayor and his sworn political enemies, Phelan and Spreckels, could no longer maintain the pretense of collaborating in civic affairs. The hour of crisis—of civic prostration and acute human suffering—was over.

The Graft Investigation

A new kind of crisis was approaching, for the mayor and for Phelan and Spreckels. Schmitz perhaps knew that

Eugene Schmitz, Mayor of San Francisco, 1902–1907

Phelan and Spreckels had already agreed to finance an investigation of his administration; he may even have known that their friend Fremont Older, the crusading editor of the *Bulletin*, had obtained a promise from President Theodore Roosevelt that William J. Burns, a detective of the United States Secret Service, and Francis J. Heney, an attorney in charge of prosecuting timberland frauds in the Northwest, would be made available to conduct the investigation. Under the circumstances, it is not surprising that Burnham was not invited to head a new municipal commission, that no further thought was given to such a body, that the rebuilding of the city finally proceeded with hardly a change from the street pattern existing before the fire.

Burns and Heney arrived in San Francisco in October, a new grand jury was summoned in November, and soon thereafter Ruef and Schmitz were indicted for extortion. For the next three years San Francisco was in an uproar as the investigation spread from corrupt city officials to corrupt corporation executives who had paid bribes for privileges. Phelan and Spreckels, deeply involved in masterminding the investigation, had little time to think of anything but the hornet's nest they had stirred up by directing the prosecution toward an exposé of the leaders of San Francisco society and business. Around their heads flew accusations that they were "the despotic tyrants of the city," deciding who should and who should not go to jail and who should and who should not be mayor.[31]

Rapid Reconstruction

Notwithstanding the political storms that buffeted many financiers and large property holders, reconstruction progressed with a speed that astonished the world. The business community apparently did not question the desirability of rebuilding the financial and commercial center in exactly the same place as before. The location that Governor Figueroa and the territorial *Diputación* had selected in 1834 as the site for a commercial town was still the most desirable area in which to carry on the trade of the metropolis. Near by were the shipping facilities and the Ferry Building, which had escaped unharmed in the earthquake and fire. Transit lines, quickly restored to operation, converged upon this core area; to the south and west of it were level blocks in which there was room for commercial facilities to expand; and still standing, even though gutted, were the principal office structures of a big city. From the standpoint of accessibility to other important cities in the Bay Area the central business district of San Francisco was in the best possible location. Since no small part of the patronage of its stores, banks, and professional offices came by ferry from the East Bay,

*Reconstruction in the Central Business District of San Francisco, 1907. Palace
Hotel and Crocker Building, left; Wells Fargo Bank Building and Postal Telegraph
Building, center; Mills Building and Merchants Exchange Building, right. Photo-
graph by Frank Schwabacher, courtesy of Bancroft Library.*

Marin County, Vallejo, and Napa, the hopes of some
property owners that Fillmore Street and Van Ness
Avenue might continue to be leading commercial thoroughfares were never well founded. Within three years
practically every outstanding firm in the city had returned
to San Francisco's highly centralized shopping district.

At first the lack of facilities for removal of debris
handicapped the work of clearing building sites. But
within a few weeks donkey engines were puffing in the
streets, railroad tracks had been extended into the devastated area, and an army of men from the refugee camps
was engaged in clearing bricks and piling them in neat
stacks to be used in rebuilding. From all over California,
work horses were shipped to San Francisco to haul dump
wagons; and it has been estimated that not less than
15,000 were worked to exhaustion and carted off to the

boneyard in the first two years of reconstruction.[32] By
July, 1906, 100 cars of debris were being removed daily,
and by August, 125. Most of the refuse was dumped behind a new section of the sea wall at the foot of King and
Townsend streets, just north of China Basin.

Rehabilitation of the large "fireproof" buildings that
had been gutted but not structurally impaired began almost immediately. Among the major edifices restored
were the Fairmont and St. Francis hotels, the Merchants'
Exchange, the Union Trust Company Building, the Grant,
Monadnock, Shreve, Wells Fargo, and Rialto buildings,
and office buildings bearing the names of San Francisco
millionaires—William Crocker, Claus Spreckels, James
Flood, Darius O. Mills. Within three months, eighteen
of these imposing structures were occupied in part, while
work was progressing on others.

The construction of many substantial new buildings was delayed, however, by arguments over provisions of the proposed new building ordinance and over the proposed fire limits, within which no frame structures would be permitted. Debate in the sessions of the board of supervisors reached a crescendo when the use of reinforced concrete for tall structures was under consideration. Before the fire this type of construction had been prohibited except for floors. In the new building ordinance reinforced concrete was approved for buildings not exceeding 102 feet in height. Only steel-frame structures could be higher than that, and these were limited to a height equal to one and one-half times the width of the street.[33]

West of the main business district the fire limits agreed upon were bounded by Pine Street on the north, Van Ness Avenue on the west, Mission and Howard streets on the south, and the bay on the east. As soon as these were established, property owners on the north side of Pine Street erected large frame structures. On the south side of the street and in the entire area from Powell Street to Van Ness Avenue numerous sites remained vacant until as late as 1912, because of the costlier construction required.

Changes in the New City

Some types of enterprise shifted to new locations after the fire; others remained where they had been before. Wholesale houses, which formerly had been grouped near the waterfront north of Market Street, moved to new sites in the vicinity of Fourth and Townsend streets, in order to be near the railroad yards. This was a logical move, since the bulk of goods to be distributed no longer arrived by ship but by train. Produce merchants, however, elected to continue in business north of Market Street—a decision later regretted, for the area was too small and the location was inconvenient for incoming shipments.

The leaders of the Chinese population decided against transferring their activities to Oakland or to Hunters Point, as some people had hoped they would, and set about rebuilding on a more substantial scale in the blocks known as Chinatown. Unfortunately, some of the worst tenements in the city rose behind the colorful store fronts.

Several banks that previously had occupied buildings in the general area of California and Sansome streets reopened on Market Street, although most financial institutions returned to the time-honored location. Important retail stores deserted Kearny Street and the north side of Market Street for new quarters on Grant Avenue and on Stockton Street between Market and Post.

Few of the new buildings in the central business district provided living accommodations above shops, as had

great numbers before the fire. Socially prominent families who had formerly maintained elegant suites in the commercial area reëstablished themselves in fine houses on Pacific Heights and in the area west of Divisadero Street near the Presidio. Apartment houses and residential hotels made up a high proportion of the new construction in the blocks immediately surrounding the main business center. The southern slope of Nob Hill, especially, was covered with apartment houses. The trend toward this type of urban living had been noticeable before the fire; it now continued at an accelerated rate.

In the fourth month after the fire nearly 1,200 building permits were issued, for buildings to cost a total of $6,330,000, which was almost as much as the value of all construction in the year 1900. The value represented by permits for the year 1906 exceeded $39,000,000 and increased to $50,500,000 in 1907. Within three years 20,500 buildings were constructed, of which 19,000 were new frame structures. The whirlwind pace of building, once the question of payments from insurance companies was settled and the uncertainty about street layout was eliminated, provided employment for 40,000 building-trades workers, compared with less than half that number before the fire.[34]

Need for a City Hall

Conspicuously lacking among the thousands of new buildings was one for which city officials felt an urgent need—a city hall. With the exception of a wing temporarily retained and fitted up for the city treasurer, the auditor, and the registrar of voters, the ornate pile wrecked in 1906 had been razed and cleared away after numerous investigations revealed that rehabilitation would be impracticable and unwarrantedly expensive. Crowded conditions in the near-by Hall of Records, which had been repaired and retained in service, became more intolerable by the day.

Whether a new city hall should be built on the old site or on some other was the question uppermost in the minds of members of the board of supervisors when they decided to act upon the matter in April, 1909. To the satisfaction of Phelan and other members of the Association for the Improvement and Adornment of San Francisco, the supervisors sought the advice of the man whose comprehensive plan had been ignored during the reconstruction—Daniel Hudson Burnham. His presence in the city renewed hope that the plan of 1905 might be utilized in areas not yet entirely rebuilt and in areas still for the most part undeveloped.

At an informal reception of city officials in the mayor's office on April 14, 1909, Burnham seized the opportunity to advocate the creation of a civic center at the intersection of Market Street and Van Ness Avenue, as shown in a revision of his plan. The old triangular site at McAllister and Larkin streets was not only cut off from Market Street and, in his opinion, inconveniently located; it was inadequate to accommodate a group of public buildings and to provide a suitable setting for them. Enough property could now be acquired at a reasonably low cost, he pointed out, to create a large open space at Market Street and Van Ness Avenue and group around it a city hall, a courthouse, a library, a state building, a federal building, an auditorium, and other public edifices as needed. Moreover, the long-desired Park Panhandle extension could be brought down to this new center, and thus a beginning could be made on reorganizing the circulation system in accordance with the plan of 1905.

As to monetary considerations, Burnham contended, as he always had, that the expenditure of public funds for beauty would contribute to the prosperity of every citizen of San Francisco. An attractive city would draw visitors and hold them. Tourists and visitors had spent an estimated $500,000,000 in Paris the previous year, he said,

because Napoleon III had made the French capital so beautiful that no matter where people earned their money, they had to come to Paris to spend it. San Francisco would be false to itself and to its future to do less, the "planner of cities" maintained.[35]

James Phelan, with his customary eloquence, supported Burnham's recommendation for the purchase of a quadrilateral site bounded by Market, Franklin, Hayes, and Polk streets. Here, he urged, was the place to begin planning to make San Francisco an "ideal city."[36]

Civic Center Bond Issue

Five days later the supervisors voted to submit to the people a civic center bond issue of $8,480,000—$4,480,000 for land and $4,000,000 for a city hall. In the newspapers appeared a perspective drawing by Willis Polk, manager of Burnham's San Francisco office, showing a proposed civic center built in the style of the Place de la Concorde in Paris. Facing a semicircular plaza on Market Street between Eleventh and Twelfth streets were a city hall, a courthouse, and a library. Indicated on the south side of the plaza was a site for a union depot.

Willis Polk's Design for a Civic Center in San Francisco, 1909. Photograph courtesy of Bancroft Library.

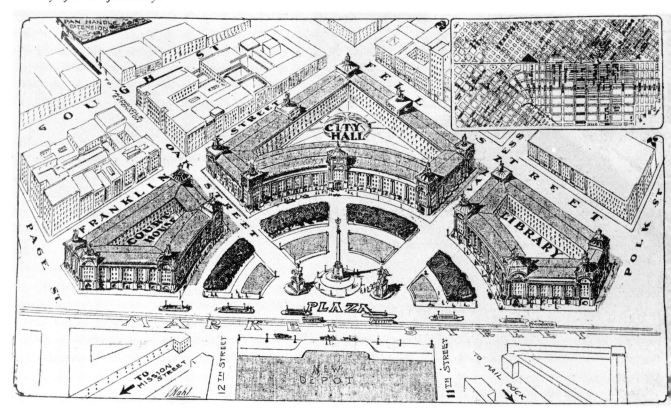

At the demand of residents in various sections of the city, the supervisors also voted to include on the ballot several other bond issues: $600,000 for a polytechnic high school, $160,000 for a detention home, $250,000 for a park on Telegraph Hill, $400,000 for a park in the Potrero district, $500,000 for an aquatic park on the northern waterfront, $25,000 for a park in the Bay View district, $90,000 for Glen Park, and $500,000 for three playgrounds in the southern part of the city. The interesting thing about the park and playground proposals was that every one of them had been included in the Burnham Plan of 1905; yet they were now being placed on the ballot not at Burnham's suggestion but at the insistence of conservative taxpayers.

Burnham was so heartened by the prospect of a civic center that immediately upon his return to Chicago he dispatched a characteristically enthusiastic telegram to Willis Polk:

"Not a day should be lost in beginning the campaign of education for the referendum. A complete and popular argument should be published for distribution. . . . Do everything in your power to help this cause. It is a precedent of great value to San Francisco and the whole country. If this improvement be determined upon it will attract attention to San Francisco from all quarters of the globe. It will stimulate real estate in and around the city. It will be the best thing ever done by an American city to make of itself a magnet attracting from every quarter those men and fortunes which bring lasting prosperity to a great commercial center.

"The San Francisco Report [of 1905] I should think ought to be revised and reprinted. Its wide distribution will be highly beneficial to those who are endeavoring to make a success of the work in San Francisco."[37]

In speeches before various organizations, the members of the Association for the Improvement and Adornment of San Francisco indicated that they, like Burnham, regarded the proposal for the civic center as a test of the possibility of reviving the great plan and carrying it out little by little. If the voters approved the civic center bonds, in time other features of the plan might be translated into reality.

"Too many of us are prone to look at such a plan as a whole, and all we can see is a hundred millions of dollars of cost and a hundred years to carry it out, and at first sight we condemn it," Thomas Magee observed in a talk to the Merchants' Association. "But the difficulty is in regarding it as a whole. All we hope to do in our generation is a small part. Posterity will do 90 per cent of the work. But now that our city is laid waste, and we can choose our location for our City Hall, and the City Hall

must be built somewhere, why not adopt the location recommended by the world's foremost architect in the planning and designing of the modern city beautiful and the modern city useful?"[38]

Editorial Debate

The San Francisco *Bulletin* reminded its readers of all the opportunities lost after the fire to widen streets and acquire parks and playgrounds "for the lowest prices." The opportunity to create a civic center, it said, presented a second chance "to commence the development of the city on the Burnham Plan." To reject the civic center proposal would be "tantamount to throwing the Burnham Plan in the waste basket forever."[39]

M. H. de Young attacked the civic center proposal as relentlessly as he had attacked Burnham's plans for the widening and extension of streets and the recommendations of the Committee of Forty in 1906. From the moment the supervisors contemplated a bond issue for a new city hall on a new site, his newspaper condemned the proposition as an extravagance that would endanger the financial capacity of the city and jeopardize the construction of the proposed Hetch Hetchy water system.

The San Francisco *Call* likewise at first objected to the issuance of bonds for a civic center on the ground that the indebtedness might hamper consummation of the water project, but it soon reached the conclusion that even with the addition of more than $11,000,000 in bonds for a civic center, technical high school, parks, and playgrounds, the city would still have an abundance of available credit reserved for waterworks. The *Call* "unhesitatingly" recommended the bonds to its readers. So did William Randolph Hearst's San Francisco *Examiner*, though not de Young's newspaper. Steadfast in its opposition, the *Chronicle* exhorted its readers at the eleventh hour: "Repair the streets. Rebuild the broken sewers. Provide schools for our children. Conserve the city's credit. VOTE DOWN THE CIVIC CENTRE."[40]

Counting of the ballots revealed the effectiveness of this vehement opposition. The voters authorized only the bonds for the polytechnic high school. The civic center bonds received a majority of votes but failed by 3,215 to receive the necessary two-thirds approval. The park and playground bonds also won the support of substantial majorities but failed of the required two-thirds approval. Most discouraging of all to the members of the Association for the Improvement and Adornment of San Francisco was the small turnout at the polls. Despite the "heat" generated during the campaign, only one-third of the registered voters went to the polls.

No doubt de Young was pleased when other newspapers gave him full credit for defeating the civic center, park, and playground bonds. The *Bulletin* went so far as to feature a letter branding him a "traitor to his city."[41]

James Phelan declared that the public had not been properly informed about the merits of the civic center proposal and announced that the Association for the Improvement and Adornment of San Francisco would raise $15,000 for a new campaign. The Board of Supervisors dampened his ardor by talking of building a new city hall on the old site, then lapsed into a state of prolonged indecision.

The utmost in civic zeal had been demanded of San Franciscans in rebuilding their city. To most of them the accomplishment seemed so prodigious that they were fairly indifferent to the lack of a suitable administrative center. Collective embarrassment over their failure to provide appropriate quarters for their municipal servants would seize them later, when the date for the opening of the Panama-Pacific International Exposition was approaching. Then, in a new burst of local pride, they would finance numerous public improvements. But now they wished to celebrate their labors of the past three years—years in which they had demonstrated that a city is its people, that community character and love of place and faith in the future can transcend the greatest calamity, that the spirit is unquenchable whatever befall the physical manifestations of the spirit—spires, domes, columns, façades, and monuments.

For five full days, from October 19 to 23, 1909, San Franciscans abandoned themselves to revelry. For historic propriety they announced that they were honoring the memory of the discoverer, Don Gaspar de Portolá, but obviously they were congratulating themselves on an amazing comeback. An estimated 480,000 visitors came to rejoice with them, to view parades and outdoor tableaux, to dance in the streets and throw confetti, to listen to school children singing in the public squares, to feast in the cosmopolitan cafés and hotels, to go aboard visiting Italian, Dutch, Japanese, German, British, and American warships in the harbor, and to gaze at the representatives of His Majesty the King of Spain, the Marquis of Villalobar, and at the Minister to the United States from the Netherlands, Jonkheer Dr. J. Loudon. This outpouring of joy, this first Portola Festival, proclaimed to all the world that San Francisco was again, in the words of Will Irwin, "the gayest, lightest hearted, most pleasure-loving city of the western continent"—"the bonny, merry city."[42]

CHAPTER EIGHT

Oakland—
The End of the Village Tradition

In the months just after the fire, Oakland manifested the mingled aggressiveness, pride, elation, insecurity, and nervousness of a bit player unexpectedly thrust into a stellar part. Having given shelter to thousands of refugees who had fled from the burning metropolis across the bay, Oakland quickly realized that much of San Francisco's loss might become her own permanent gain, provided she rose to the occasion. But was she prepared for the greater role to which she had suddenly been elevated? That was the troublesome question.

The formation on April 27, 1906, of the Oakland Clearing House, with eleven member banks, was cause for rejoicing, since the new institution would facilitate transaction of the greater volume of business that the city expected as a result of the establishment of the temporary offices of scores of San Francisco firms in the East Bay. But on the very same day, H. C. Capwell, a leading merchant, warned in a letter to the Oakland *Tribune* that the greed of landlords and property owners was jeopardizing the city's opportunity to become "the metropolis of this state."

"I have met representatives of all the large California and eastern wholesalers," wrote Capwell, "and to my great sorrow they had but one story to tell, viz: that the landlords and property owners had entered upon a policy of cinching them to such a point that they are already thoroughly disgusted with this side of the bay.

"For years we have been trying to lure the people of San Francisco to this side of the bay, and during the past three years we have been to some extent successful. Now is our grand opportunity and we are throwing it away."[1]

Optimism and Problems

Ignoring such warnings, the Oakland Chamber of Commerce several weeks later held a quarterly meeting at which "the fact that Oakland is to be the metropolis of the West was accepted without cavil and the speakers dwelt at length upon the manner in which this consummation was to be most quickly attained." The secretary of the Chamber informed the membership that the staff had "furnished the postoffice department the names and present addresses of over three thousand former San Francisco business houses and professional men now located in Oakland," the Oakland *Times* reported.[2]

If anyone wanted evidence of the great increase in activity in the wholesale and industrial areas of the city, he had only to look at the streets. Heavy teaming was grinding the macadam surfaces to ruin, the *Times* reported on July 27. A million dollars would be required to put the streets in proper shape, the superintendents of streets estimated, adding that he had little hope of being given any such sum to do the job. "It is certain that they will be deplorable when the rains come," the newspaper declared.[3]

The next day the *Enquirer* noted with satisfaction that the city's trading center had moved northward beyond Fourteenth Street, but it feared that a large percentage of the refugee population would drift back to San Francisco unless there were "prompt and concerted effort to make Oakland more metropolitan, especially in the matter of lighting up the streets and supplying that variety of entertainment which is naturally to be found in a large city." The streets, said the *Enquirer*, were filled with "Stygian gloom."[4]

While the newspapers were fretting about the destruction of the surface of the streets and the lack of metropolitan entertainment in Oakland, the city suffered the very kind of blow to its hopes of becoming *the* metropolis of California that Capwell had feared. Early in August no less than two hundred of the refugee San Francisco business enterprises returned to the reviving city on the Peninsula; and the *Enquirer* bitterly accused "certain land owners" of having betrayed the city by raising rents and attempting to sell factory and warehouse sites for exorbitant prices.[5]

The *Enquirer* now expressed serious concern for the welfare of several industrial firms that had moved from San Francisco to a location in Oakland near the western end of the Tidal Canal. In the months just before and after the fire, these plants had selected the Oakland waterfront because it offered the advantage of transcontinental rail facilities of the Southern Pacific and would some day be served by the Western Pacific as well. Discussing the

application of the Southern Pacific for a franchise for a harbor belt line, the newspaper admonished the city council not to grant such a franchise without demanding that it contain a provision to insure interconnection with the trackage of any other railroad that might enter Oakland, specifically, the contemplated line of the Western Pacific. The Southern Pacific, needless to say, had few friends in Oakland, because of its dogged efforts to monopolize the waterfront.

As winter approached, the *Enquirer* also noted that "there will be thousands of additional shoppers in Oakland and it is worthwhile to make a thorough and a systematic effort to put the streets, particularly in the business section of the city, in such condition that shopping in Oakland will be robbed of some of its terrors." What occasioned this suggestion was an unaccountable action of the street department: an order requiring the Oakland Traction Company to put the streets in proper condition along its tracks and to repair sinks and chuckholes in the downtown area before the rainy season. Expressing its surprise in an editorial headed "An Outbreak of Intelligence in the Street Department," the newspaper observed: ". . . Ordinarily it has been the custom of the street department to wait until the streets were miniature quagmires and a congeries of pools, slop, slush and slime

Looking North on Broadway, Oakland, about 1905. Photograph courtesy of Oakland Tribune.

Lower Broadway, Oakland, as Seen from the Top of the Union Savings Bank, about 1905. Photograph courtesy of Oakland Tribune.

so that it was with hazard to her apparel and health that a woman without a diving suit or rubber top boots attempted to navigate the chief thoroughfares of the city."[6]

Another sure sign that Oakland was rising to its new urban responsibilities was the approval by the voters of bond issues for construction of new schools and new outfall sewers.

While the votes on these improvements were gratifying, civic pride really reached new heights in September when the business leaders of the community announced that the building of a "magnificent modern hotel" was assured.[7] This hotel, which would occupy the entire block bounded by Harrison, Thirteenth, Alice, and Fourteenth streets and was to be called Hotel Oakland, had so long been talked about that it had become a symbol of Oakland's commercial aspirations. When finished, the million-and-a-half-dollar edifice was certain to arouse the kind of expansive emotions that San Franciscans of the 'seventies experienced in contemplating Ralston's Palace Hotel. Merely the knowledge that it was going to be built gave Oakland businessmen the feeling that their city had "arrived."

The Robinson Plan

Lest the citizens develop smugness over all these accomplishments, the *Enquirer* reminded them that "one thing remains of vital importance to the future of the city, and that is provision for a comprehensive system of public parks, playgrounds and boulevards." Since the people of San Francisco were not sufficiently farseeing to seize their great opportunity to carry out the Burnham Plan, the newspaper pointed out, Oakland had a "splendid opportunity" to take the lead in city beautification.[8]

"... In grasping for the immediate dollar, they [the men of San Francisco] are likely to sacrifice the future aesthetic beauty and attractiveness of the city. Herein lies Oakland's opportunity. THIS CITY HAS ARRIVED AT A TIME WHEN ITS COMMERCIAL EXPANSION IS ASSURED. NOW THE THING WHICH DEMANDS ATTENTION IS THE CREATION OF THOSE PUBLIC UTILITIES WHICH MAKE LIFE MORE FULL AND ENJOYABLE FOR THE CITIZEN. Charles Mulford Robinson, who has prepared plans for a more beautiful Oakland which ought to be immediately realized, says: 'A city should have a definite plan of development and every step should be made to count in the right direction. With changing conditions, it may be necessary to modify the plans from time to time in some particulars but the chief consideration is a general plan. The old costly, ineffective method of haphazard development is given over.' Oakland has a plan for its development and no time should be lost in proceeding to the creation of a more beautiful Oakland by the layout of boulevards, play grounds and parks."[9]

The Robinson Plan, ordered by the city council in 1905 and submitted to Mayor Frank K. Mott and the Oakland City Council soon after the San Francisco refugees swelled the population of the East Bay city, was by no means so impressive as the Burnham Plan, with its many perspective drawings, elevations, and detailed designs of parks and boulevards, and its large, over-all scheme for the peninsula metropolis. The "plan" conceived by Charles Mulford Robinson for Oakland was a short, printed report appraising existing conditions and recommending "what can be made out of Oakland, not how it might be made over."[10] It contained seventeen recommendations in all, of which eight might be considered of major importance. Of these eight, almost none had the ring of novelty, for the more farsighted Oakland citizens had long dreamed of the possibilities that Robinson described; yet the report had the value of confirming progressive citizens in their good judgment regarding improvements that were desirable.

Robinson found Oakland a city with a superb natural setting and a climate that invited enjoyment of the outdoors. The residents had, however, no access to "their glorious waterfront on one of the most beautiful bays of the world" and no "inalienable right" to free pleasure grounds in the forested hills to the east. The combined acreage of all Oakland parks was only thirty-eight and one-half acres—"a pitiful showing" in comparison with other cities of similar size.[11]

Charles Mulford Robinson, Apostle of the "City Beautiful."
Photograph courtesy of Blake McKelvey, City Historian of Rochester, N.Y.

A Natural Park Site

Viewing the city from the top of one of the few tall buildings in the business district, the Union Savings Bank, Robinson immediately noted the extraordinary possibilities of Lake Merritt and the canyon known as Indian Gulch (later Trestle Glen):

"From the top of the bank building, one overlooks a sea of houses that stretches far except in one direction. This is the northeast, where near at hand is Lake Merritt,

May Day Festival in Indian Gulch (Sometimes Called Sather Park), about 1914. By failing to acquire this natural park site, Oakland lost an opportunity to develop a superb recreation area.

bare bluffs on its eastern side, a little plot of oaks on the northern, while almost to its further end the hills stretch down in all their natural beauty, making a broad gore into the city, a natural park site, marvelously preserved from the builders' hands, and convenient of access."[12]

The city had acquired some land around the lake; it was negotiating for more and had begun construction of a boulevard round the east side of the lake. Robinson conceded that Lake Merritt Park would be "a most attractive and serviceable little park," but he pointed out that it would be altogether insufficient to satisfy the requirements of a rapidly growing community. He urged the people of Oakland to raise their sights and not only develop all the land around the lake but also create a really great park extending through Indian Gulch to and including Dimond Canyon, in the foothills east of the city.[13] From East Oakland, Fourteenth Avenue could be developed as a handsome approach to Dimond Canyon, which was then a popular rendezvous for picnickers and hikers. Thus a loop drive from the heart of the city through canyons and around to East Oakland would be brought into being. Another loop drive, offering superb vistas of the East Bay cities and the bay rather than the closed vistas of the canyon drive, could be created from the head of Indian Gulch along the contours of the hills

to Piedmont Park and thence down Glen Echo Canyon to the north end of Lake Merritt. Oak-bordered Glen Echo Creek would become a park link, or parkway, similar to Boston's famous Fenway Park.

Robinson was well aware that the Sather Tract of some three hundred acres in Indian Gulch at one time had been proposed as a park but had been rejected as being too costly. "I know nothing about the reasonableness or otherwise of the proposed price, but I am sure that in not securing this land in some way or other there was a mistake," he wrote in his report. "It is so nearly a park now, thanks to the taste with which the road was laid out and to the preservation of the scenery's natural charm, that there will be need of very little expenditure beyond that required for the purchase of the land. And it will offer one of the most picturesque and romantic walks and drives that can be found near any large city of my acquaintance in this or other countries. Considering its availability—in convenience of access, in ease of grade, in opportunities for pleasant return by another route, in suitability of extent—I think, in fact, of no park drive of similar nature to which it is clearly second; and as an adequate municipal park system necessarily includes provision for driving and for . . . beautiful walks, I must urge the people of Oakland to obtain this property . . ."[14]

County Park System

Robinson's vision could not be restrained by the territorial limits of Oakland, however. As one acquainted with the great park systems of Europe and with the park systems of metropolitan Boston, Providence, Rhode Island, and Essex County, New Jersey, Robinson considered that he would be remiss in his work if he did not call attention to "the wisdom of cooperation, in the matter of park development at least, between the several communities that make up the greater Oakland."[15]

"Were such coöperation secured there would be no need to change in any respect the great park as I have sketched it. Topographical and social conditions would make it naturally the central feature of a county scheme, the latter mainly concerning itself hereafter with the opening of scenic drives into and along the hills, with the acquisition for the public's enjoyment of striking vantage points here and there, and with the broadening out into local parks for Berkeley and Alameda of the chain of public reservations."[16]

As an example of a development that could be included in a county park system Robinson suggested a parkway from Piedmont Heights to the Tunnel Road and down past the Claremont Hotel into Berkeley.

Certainly no other proposal that Robinson made was so important as his suggestion that a county park system was within the realm of possibility and would be of inestimable advantage to the cities of the East Bay. Unfortunately, there was at that time no leader in Alameda County with vision to match his own. But the idea did not lie buried in his report. Eight years later, Werner Hegemann, the German city planner who prepared a city plan for the municipalities of Oakland and Berkeley and the supervisors of Alameda County, resurrected the Robinson proposal and declared that "coöperation between the cities of the East side of San Francisco Bay can not be emphasized strongly enough."[17] Robinson's suggestion may have contributed to the movement for creation of the East Bay Regional Park District more than two decades later. Undoubtedly his idea was in some measure handed on from civic leader to civic leader for years.

Neighborhood Parks

Because Robinson was as aware as Burnham that one or two large parks or even a system of county parks could not satisfy all the legitimate park needs of a city, he saw the necessity of supplementing the proposed great park with neighborhood parks, some purely ornamental, others to be used for active recreation. Small children, he pointed out, could not "journey frequently at considerable distance" to reach a major park. And since a city ordinance prohibited boys from playing baseball in the streets, the city at least should provide proper play space in residential areas.[18] He urged the acquisition of the de Fremery property on Sixteenth Street, now one of the Oakland playgrounds. He proposed a waterside park near the western entrance to the Tidal Canal, because one Saturday morning he had found seventy-five to a hundred boys and girls playing on vacant land there.

This waterfront area, however, was already in the path of industrial development and was not long to be suitable as a residential section. Had Robinson begun his planning by assigning to the land in each part of the city its most appropriate long-range use, he might have designated the southern waterfront as a logical industrial area; but it would be idle to blame him for not doing something that probably would have been impossible at that early date. Government and business simply did not gather the many kinds of statistical data that now make possible the thorough analyses prepared by urban land economists and city planners. Nor were changes in technology and in ways of doing business so rapid that the study of trends and the projection of trends had become a primary activity of the business world and governmental agencies. Foresight on the part of the early-day city planner was a matter of human sympathies, the desire for improvement, and the wish to take advantage of obvious natural assets. It was not disciplined by the survey form and the punch card. Whatever Robinson's deficiencies, they were not deficiencies of the heart. And so he recognized the immediate need for a playground near the waterfront though he overlooked the long-run conflict between industrial and recreational uses.

His recommendation that the city build a platform, or "recreation pier," above the wharf at the foot of Broadway, so that the public could enjoy watching the shipping in the harbor, was a felicitous one with genuine long-range validity.[19] Any active waterfront evokes the romance of distant lands and attracts fascinated onlookers. The only trouble with Robinson was that he was a "piker" in foreseeing the recreational possibilities of the area that has now become Jack London Square. In his day this section of Oakland was drab but flourishing, but it later fell into decay. Happily it was redeveloped a few years ago, with colorful restaurants. Today patrons in these establishments view an unceasing parade of ships—and perhaps become pleasurably restless to hear the thunder of cataracts plunging into Norwegian fiords or the muffled boom of breakers rolling over coral reefs.

The "desolate and uninviting surroundings" of the Southern Pacific's Sixteenth Street station made so bad an impression upon Robinson that he proposed an imposing entrance parkway from the station to a civic center at Fourteenth Street and San Pablo Avenue. This parkway, three hundred feet wide, would be "comparable to the famously beautiful one from the railroad station at Milan," but Robinson's conception of the civic center toward which it would lead seems to have been restricted by an oppressive awareness of the high cost of land in the heart of Oakland. He suggested no magnificent group of buildings, permitted himself to "point out only the immediately necessary or advisable"—a curving street cut through the triangle formed by San Pablo Avenue, Seventeenth Street, and Telegraph Avenue, so as to link the City Hall with the Post Office.[20]

Municipal Rough Edges

Having formulated his major suggestions for the improvement of Oakland, Robinson offered some minor ones. These are interesting because they present a picture of a municipality with all the rough edges of an unregulated adolescence. Robinson commended the burial of wires on Broadway, "now happily in progress," and urged abolition of telegraph poles, regulation of advertising on and over sidewalks, and installation of handsome street lighting as far north as Seventeenth Street. He suggested substitution, throughout the city, of stone and concrete curbs for wooden curbs installed by the property owners themselves at their own expense. "The wooden curbs must go." To the neighborhood improvement clubs of the city he recommended the purchase and beautification of small triangular plots formed by irregular street platting. On residential streets he saw the need for the establishment of building lines beyond which no structure would be allowed to project, in order that an unobstructed view might be preserved for every householder. He advised the City Council to enact an ordinance banning the "double-decker" billboard and prohibiting the erection of large signs within one hundred feet of parks. He strongly recommended the establishment of two new municipal agencies: a special bureau, under the direction of a competent forester, to undertake uniform planting of street trees, and a park commission to develop and care for city parks. His report closed with a quotation from John Ruskin, that cultural divinity to whom all respectable lovers of beauty genuflected in the days of pyrography and portieres: "You may have thought that beauty was expensive. You are wrong. It is ugliness that costs."[21]

Frank K. Mott, Mayor of Oakland, 1905–1915. Photograph courtesy of Oakland Tribune.

Action on the Plan

Nowhere in the entire report was there any suggestion that a permanent agency was needed to continue the planning process, to advance first one proposal then another, and to revise the over-all scheme from time to time as circumstances demanded. Robinson, the consultant, had been asked for a plan, and a plan he had presented. His duty done, he departed, hoping that the people of the city would follow his advice. In his day the most that any architect, landscape architect, or engineer who practised as an itinerant city planner could hope for was that some of the citizens or officials would endeavor to carry out his plan; but he had no assurance that the plan would not be filed away and forgotten. No official planning group or technical staff remained at the scene of his labors to champion the plan, to remind the citizens that they had spent money for it and ought to make good use of it.

Fortunately for Robinson and for the people of Oakland, Mayor Frank Mott did intend to utilize the plan. He had been ardently in favor of parks before Robinson was engaged as a consultant. At Mott's suggestion the city council ordered the consultant's report published, in

The Northeast Side of Lake Merritt in the 'Nineties. The area to the left later became Lakeside Park. Photograph courtesy of Oakland Park Department.

order that citizens might study it. "Our problem is a very simple one," the mayor told the councilmen, "so simple, in fact, that it is difficult to suggest anything especially new. We all know about what should be done, but he [Robinson] has shown us how do to it."[22]

Mott spent the next several weeks in the East, visiting parks in New York, Boston, Kansas City, Washington, D.C., Cleveland, and Chicago, in order that he might "the more intelligently apply himself to the task of beautifying Oakland along the lines suggested by Charles Mulford Robinson."[23]

Upon his return, the Oakland *Enquirer* stated that Mott was "now more enthusiastic than ever over park improvements and boulevard developments as conducive to the happiness of a city's inhabitants." He signified that he would take steps immediately to further boulevard and park projects, including the extension of the boulevard along the east shore of Lake Merritt, the establishment of a park in West Oakland, the extension of Grand Avenue from the northeastern arm of Lake Merritt toward Piedmont, and the improvement of public squares long owned by the city but never properly developed. As for the lands around the lake, he said, "In my judgment the city should own all lands bordering on Lake Merritt."[24]

Thanks to Mott's vigorous leadership, the city council enacted an ordinance calling for a special election on January 14, 1907, on the question of issuing $992,000 in bonds for the purchase of parks. Of ten properties designated for acquisition, five bordered on Lake Merritt, including the tract now known as Willows Park, on the west side of the lake, some acreage in the area where the Municipal Auditorium later was built, a fine grove of trees on the eastern shore of the lake, and forty-five acres at Adams Point, now known as Lakeside Park. Here was a natural park containing a stand of the handsome old oaks from which the city took its name. The bonds were also to provide for the acquisition of the de Fremery property recommended by Robinson, for the extension of Bushrod Park in the northern section of Oakland, and for the purchase of small parcels in various residential sections of the city.

Robinson's Disappointment

In view of the vast park system that Robinson had urged the city to create, the proposed purchases were modest indeed. In an open letter "to the People of Oakland," the landscape architect, with no effort to conceal his disappointment, wrote from Rochester, New York: "If you vote for the purchase of these tracts, you may be sure that you will not be doing anything very big or very daring. You will be acting with exceeding conservatism, and doing about as little as you decently can do—for a city that does not want to appear, and to be, on the wane."[25]

Whether Robinson was justified in feeling somewhat scornful of the Oakland effort is debatable. For many years the voters had consistently defeated park proposals, or at least a backward minority of more than one-third had done so. Had the city council acceded to Mott's request for a bond issue of approximately one and a half million dollars, organized opposition might again have developed. But the council shrewdly asked the voters to approve a bond issue of just slightly less than a million dollars, and thereby probably mollified some of the regular opponents of bond issues, for Mott was able to an-nounce, four days before the special election, that he was "particularly jubilant" at hearing no "discordant note" in the campaign for "this great civic improvement."[26]

The Village Tradition Broken

On election day, "one of the stormiest and most dis-agreeable days of an unusually stormy and disagreeable winter,"[27] only 15 per cent of the registered voters ven-tured to the polls; but those who did enter the voting booths cast their ballots five to one for the bonds. The vote was 2,702 in favor of the bonds, 566 against. Only in one precinct in North Oakland was an effort made to defeat the proposal.

Citizens who had campaigned for park bonds in pre-vious elections and had known the heartaches of defeat now found belated consolation in the thought that their

Air View of Lake Merritt, 1914. The Civic Auditorium occupies a site at the southern end of the lake. To the right is the area once known as Indian Gulch. Photograph courtesy of Oakland Tribune.

labors probably had contributed to the education of the public. More than anything else, though, the sudden increase in population in Oakland, the sense of greater civic destiny, and the dramatic realization that the town had "to grow up" influenced the results at the polls. There was no denying the categorial imperative of abrupt change: Forward march!

The Oakland *Tribune* proclaimed that the citizens had "at last broken the bonds of conservatism and village tradition."[28] The Oakland *Enquirer* declared, "The new civic spirit of Oakland has asserted itself. At last Oakland has risen to its opportunity."[29]

Within the next two years the city bought the properties for which the voters had authorized bonds. Early in 1909 the city council appropriated $50,000 to dredge Lake Merritt and fill the marsh at the southern end of the lake. And in March of that year the people voted to amend the city charter to create the park commission that Robinson had proposed.

What the "civic adviser" called a "good beginning" had been made, and there was still a possibility that other parts of the great park system that he outlined would be developed. In this beginning the vision of the people of Oakland did not match his own, and it fell far short of that of earlier generations of San Franciscans, who were no more numerous than the people of Oakland when they decided to create Golden Gate Park. But Oakland had never known the gusto and romance and high living of San Francisco. For Oakland the decision to follow even a small part of Robinson's advice was a great step forward and probably was as much as could be expected from a people trying to cast off a "village tradition."

CHAPTER NINE

The Greater San Francisco Movement

For weeks before the census of 1910 was taken, San Francisco newspapers publicized the forthcoming enumeration, insisting that every man, woman, and child in the city must be counted. Editorials declared that the whole world would be waiting to see whether the metropolis stricken by earthquake and fire in 1906 had recouped its population losses and attracted additional thousands. Hopefully, the press predicted that the final count would credit San Francisco with a population of between 450,000 and 480,000. But the note of uncertainty was strong: the very prestige of the city, its hope of inducing businessmen and financiers to make further investments in new factories, office buildings, stores, and houses depended upon an official population figure substantially exceeding the 400,000 that the city was thought to have had at the time of the earthquake.

When the preliminary count of the Bureau of the Census indicated that the final figure would be considerably less than anticipated, San Franciscans felt disappointed but to some extent relieved. The city had at least made gains. The final count showed that the population had increased 22 per cent during the decade and San Francisco was now the home of 416,912 people.

What impressed city officials, civic leaders, and the press most was the growth of areas within a fifteen- or twenty-mile radius of San Francisco. Oakland was now a city of 150,174 residents and had experienced a population gain of 124 per cent. In those parts of the metropolitan district not included in the two principal cities

lived 119,787 people, nearly twice as many as in the same territories ten years earlier. The metropolitan district as defined by the Bureau of the Census embraced not only San Francisco and Oakland but Berkeley, Alameda, Richmond, and San Rafael, as well as some small towns and unincorporated areas.

A Name to be Coveted

The San Francisco press foresaw all parts of this metropolitan district naturally and inevitably gravitating toward the ultimate formation of a single municipality known as Greater San Francisco. Said the San Francisco *Chronicle* in a typical comment: "Probably during the next decade there will be a movement for a Greater San Francisco, one designed to bring in the present metropolitan area and to give the enlarged city a new one. For years the trend has been toward aggregation and away from segregation. Every man takes pride in being in a big town. All Cook County men are now proud of being Chicagoans. The once satisfied Brooklynite or Staten Islander likes to hail from New York. Here with us the name of San Francisco is sure to be coveted by the men across the bay and down the peninsula and by those on the near watershed of Marin County, and by that time the harbor, as well as San Francisco and Oakland, should have its busy subways."[1]

The author of this editorial was hardly unaware that there was already a "Greater San Francisco" movement, initiated quietly by the California Promotion Committee immediately after the disaster of 1906 and taken over in 1907 by a Greater San Francisco Association organized at the call of the San Francisco Chamber of Commerce. The model for Greater San Francisco was, of course, Greater New York, formed by the union of Manhattan, Brooklyn, and adjacent areas in a borough system of government in 1898. Greater San Francisco was to be an amalgamation of San Francisco, Colma, South San Francisco, the East Bay cities from Richmond to San Leandro, and the Marin County cities of Sausalito, Mill Valley, and San Rafael.

That a movement for a supermunicipality would wreck plans for a water system serving cities on both sides of the bay, and that it would antagonize Oakland officials and generate sectional bitterness which would long retard the economic development of the entire Bay Area, apparently did not occur to San Francisco leaders. Or if they did have some misgivings about the eventual success of the Greater San Francisco movement, they optimistically dismissed them. Plans for a great international exposition in 1914 or 1915 celebrating the completion of the Panama Canal aroused so much enthusiasm throughout the Bay Area that it was easy to believe in the possibility of a single municipality embracing populous communities in several counties.

Even the Oakland Chamber of Commerce, which was on guard against the Greater San Francisco movement, pledged its support to San Francisco when business leaders in New Orleans suddenly attempted to convince Congress that their city should be the scene of the official celebration marking the opening of the Panama Canal. In a telegram to Congressman Joseph R. Knowland the Oakland organization declared that it stood "ready to support a million-dollar bond issue by Alameda County, if required, in addition to the amount already subscribed."[2]

Heartened by the coöperation of the East Bay city, San Francisco fought New Orleans with every propaganda and lobbying device known, decisively defeated the southern city, and set to work preparing for the great exposition.

Slow-developing Peninsula

At a superficial glance, renascent San Francisco seemed carried forward on a wave of civic fervor, prosperity, and high hopes. Yet all was not well—or so some city officials and many businessmen thought. While the East Bay communities expanded rapidly and the crowds of commuters on the transbay ferryboats grew larger and larger, only a trickle of population moved into undeveloped areas on the San Francisco Peninsula.

In December, 1907, the Southern Pacific had opened its Bayshore Cutoff, thereby reducing the commuting time from towns on the bay side of San Mateo County. Promoters of the North Fair Oaks subdivision, just south of Redwood City, had advertised: "40 minutes from San Francisco—40 trains daily . . . No tedious and dangerous foggy or stormy ferry trips to make . . . Over 1400 lots sold since opening day. . . ."[3] But in 1910 most of the tract was vacant. South San Francisco and Burlingame, both incorporated in 1908, were still small towns. So was San Mateo, though it had annexed two near-by areas. Lomita Park, San Bruno, and other unincorporated areas within fairly close range of San Francisco had grown moderately; but renewed attempts to promote the town of San Carlos had failed. Hillsborough, hastily incorporated in April, 1910, to avoid becoming part of San Mateo or Burlingame, was a militant stronghold of country-estate owners, intent on maintaining an exclusive, semiurban environment characterized by roads without sidewalks and by very large lots. The entire county had a population of only 26,585, as compared with an only slightly greater total in the East Bay city of Alameda alone.

For the most part, the San Francisco Peninsula was the seat of the wealthy, though there were, to be sure, some middle-income families in the towns. One of the chief reasons why salaried people and families dependent on modest wages hesitated to live in this delightful area was the high cost of transportation. A North Berkeley commuter could reach his home for a 5-cent fare, whereas a commuter living the same time-distance down the Peninsula paid a one-way fare of 13 1/3 cents, in a period when that was the equivalent of 40 or 50 cents today.

Need for Rapid Transit

San Franciscans who wanted to see the Peninsula develop still hoped for an interurban electric line all the way to San Jose, such as the Southern Pacific had planned shortly before the earthquake. In January, 1906, the railroad had incorporated a subsidiary known as the Peninsular Railway and had announced that this company would build 204 miles of electric railways. "Lines are to be built from San Francisco to San Jose through Stanford University, Palo Alto, Redwood City, and San Mateo," advertisements informed the public. "Branches will extend to Los Gatos, Sempervirens Park, Alviso, Oakland, Alameda, Alum Rock Park [near San Jose] and Lick Observatory on Mt. Hamilton. The first lines constructed will be from San Jose to San Francisco and Oakland, one on each side of the bay. The main coast line of the Southern Pacific will be shortened by a cut-off from Mountain View and the trains for Los Angeles will go via Santa Cruz, while San Jose will be served by the new electric lines of the Peninsular Company."[4]

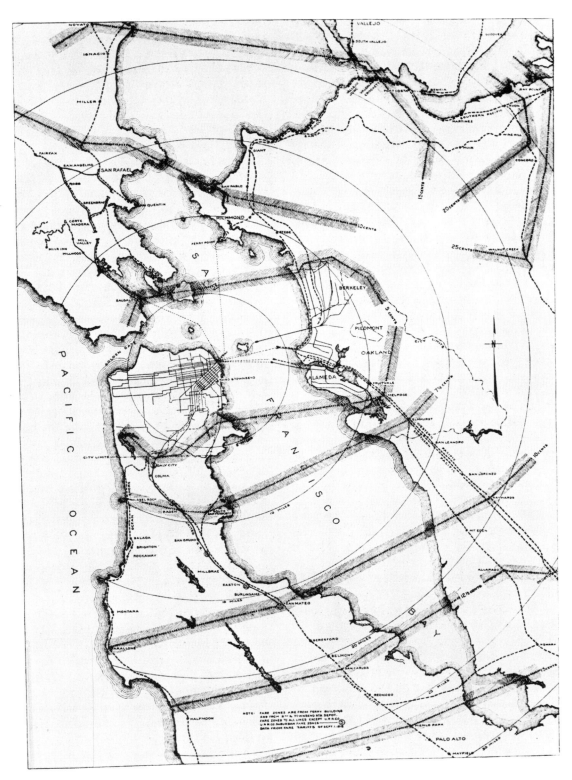

Fare Zone Map of San Francisco and Commuters' Districts, 1910–1912. Novato in Marin County and Menlo Park in San Mateo County mark the beginning of the 15-cent zone. Photograph courtesy of Bancroft Library, University of California.

Unluckily, in the summer of 1905 the Southern Pacific had faced a crisis which foredoomed these extensive plans. The Colorado River burst its banks, flooded the Imperial Valley, and inundated the main line of the railroad between Los Angeles and Yuma, Arizona. The battle with the flood was still going on in the summer of 1906 when the Southern Pacific started construction near Saratoga on a cutoff that was to extend from San Carlos to a point near Los Gatos. Presently the huge stock of rails for the construction of the cutoff had to be rushed to Yuma to build tracks to carry rock trains to crucial points along the rampaging Colorado. Engineers finally returned the river to its old channel in February, 1907, but the rails needed for the cutoff were gone.

In the following months a national depression forced the Southern Pacific to shelve—temporarily, company officials hoped—the plans for an area-wide transit system. The cutoff was completed only to Mayfield, near Palo Alto, and was not used by coast-line trains, which continued to run through San Jose rather than Los Gatos and Santa Cruz.

Gradually the Peninsular Railway became an interurban system with sixty-eight miles of track, linking San Jose with Palo Alto and both these cities with Los Gatos. San Franciscans interested in a low-fare electric line to the Santa Clara Valley wondered whether the Southern Pacific ever would be able to build northward from Palo Alto, or whether the United Railroads, the San Francisco transit organization, would extend its San Mateo line southward—or whether the two systems would come to some kind of agreement and combine forces to link San Francisco with cities south of San Mateo. Until there was fast, inexpensive transportation all the way down the Peninsula, San Franciscans looked for little population movement in that direction.

In San Francisco itself thousands of acres west of Twin Peaks were practically inaccessible, or could be reached only by a roundabout route. In the spring of 1910 the San Francisco *Chronicle* wrote of a Twin Peaks tunnel as "an improvement which should no longer be delayed."[5]

In the face of real-estate men's predictions of an influx of population from Europe as soon as the Panama Canal should be completed, the inability of San Francisco to offer ready access and low-cost fares to near-by residential areas began to assume all the aspects of a major predicament. One Italian pointed out that fares from Italy to San Francisco via the Panama Canal would be only seven dollars more than from Italy to New York and that "hundred of thousands" of immigrants would come to California direct from Europe.[6] Some worried citizens wondered whether San Francisco, bottled up on its peninsula, was going to become as overcrowded as the East Side of New York. Some downtown merchants speculated gloomily on the possibility that a large proportion of middle- and upper-income families would move to the East Bay and Marin County, where there was more room for homes, leaving San Francisco mainly to the poorer classes and immigrants.

Industrial Decline

The San Francisco Chamber of Commerce took as little comfort from the industrial situation as real-estate men did from the undeveloped state of areas beyond Twin Peaks and in San Mateo County. San Francisco in 1904 had been thirteenth among manufacturing cities of the United States, measured by value of product. By 1909 it had dropped to sixteenth place, and six of its fifteen leading industries had shown severe decreases in value of output since the Fire. Production in the men's clothing industry, for instance, had fallen off one-fourth, and in the paint and varnish industry nearly two-thirds. Substantial increases in production in several other industries did not offset the decrease in the actual number of manufacturing establishments, which had dwindled from 2,251 in 1904 to 1,796 in 1909—only a few more than in 1899.

William L. Gerstle, president of the San Francisco Chamber of Commerce in 1910, sought an explanation for the downward trend: "We have the harbor, the climate, transportation facilities, capital, and cheap fuel—in fact, everything requisite to a manufacturing city; but as against this the cost of manufacturing is so high that we cannot compete with neighboring communities. Everything is on a competitive basis excepting labor, and this is due to the fact that we have not had the courage in San Francisco to enforce the open shop principle which prevails in our competitive cities. . . . Unorganized labor has equal rights and the price of labor should be regulated like everything else by supply and demand. . . ."[7]

Others were not so willing to place the blame for the industrial decline of San Francisco on labor unions. The Fire had dealt many manufacturing concerns crippling blows. They had lost plants, markets, employees. Competitors elsewhere had been quick to take advantage of their distress. An even more patent reason for the industrial regression of San Francisco was the rise of the East Bay as a manufacturing area, as a party of chamber of commerce members discovered upon visiting Richmond in June, 1912:

"The visitors saw the great car shops at Pullman, the gigantic Standard Oil refinery, one of the largest in the world; the Enterprise foundry, the plant of the Western Pipe and Steel Company of California, started as a branch of a Los Angeles concern, and by sheer force of superior location now larger than the mother institution; the Pacific Porcelain Works . . . and other industrial concerns that have found cheap fuel, light and power, convenient transportation and other favorable conditions for locating on San Francisco Bay, and whose growth during the past five or six years has astonished their owners.

"From the top of a hill the visitors were shown the inland harbor running up toward the center of the town and the new industrial section that it will bring into use. H. C. Cutting, author of the inland harbor and lord of the lowlands about it, remarked: 'This growth means as much to San Francisco as though it took place within her own city limits, for financially it is all one. We grow together. An immense development is going to take place here, and San Francisco will always be the main office, the money reservoir where these industries will be financed.'"[8]

In effect, Cutting was telling the businessmen of San Francisco that the role of the metropolis in the economy of the Bay Area was changing. Although "the city" no doubt would always continue to carry on considerable manufacturing, in the long run its major functions would be those of an administrative, financial, commercial, and service center in the metropolitan region. This was a thought that the leaders of San Francisco were then somewhat reluctant to accept, though their preoccupation with the Greater San Francisco movement indicated that they already had gone far toward understanding certain social and economic metropolitan regional relationships. What forced them to resign themselves to the evolving status of San Francisco as primarily a commercial, financial, and service center was the aggressive, even chauvinistic, campaign of the Oakland Chamber of Commerce to build up the East Bay as a shipping, transportation, and manufacturing area.

Progress in Oakland

The Chamber of Commerce was not displeased to have a Visalia newspaper characterize Oakland as "the Los Angeles of the Bay section." It was flattered when the Stockton *Mail* declared that it was "not at all improbable that twenty years from now Oakland will be the chief city of the Pacific Coast." Its delight knew no bounds when Henri Halphen, secretary of the board of directors of the Compagnie Générale Trans-Atlantique, the great French steamship company, exclaimed after a tour of inspection on the east side of the bay, "I am convinced that the future of San Francisco lies in Oakland."[9]

If national advertising, drum beating, and exhortations to the citizens to accord their city perfervid loyalty could make a city great, the Oakland Chamber of Commerce

meant to make Oakland a metropolis second to none in the West. In the spring of 1910, when San Francisco was busy raising funds for the Panama-Pacific International Exposition, the Oakland Chamber was engaged in a costly publicity campaign. Double-page spreads appeared in the *Saturday Evening Post*. Display advertisements extolling Oakland as the most desirable location for West Coast manufacturing and distributing plants ran each week in daily papers in the South, Middle West, East, and Canada. Trade papers, house organs, and other media carried the Oakland story. At intervals of two weeks, letters of a sequential series went to five thousand selected manufacturers and others throughout the United States, describing Oakland as a potential supplier of goods to the Orient, Oakland as a transfer point for transcontinental freight destined for Pacific ports, Oakland as a strategically situated port with twenty-seven miles of waterfront where ship and railroad car meet, Oakland as a market for the great producing areas of the Pacific Slope, and Oakland as the gateway to the fertile interior valleys of California.

The city had made phenomenal gains as a manufacturing city between 1904 and 1909, data of the Bureau of the Census disclosed. Within that time the value of its manufactured products had risen almost 150 per cent, or more than $13,000,000, thanks in large part to the growth of the brewery, lumber, foundry and machineshop, bakery, printing and publishing, and canning and preserving industries. Value of the output of the canning and preserving industry alone had increased more than fifteenfold. The city boasted approximately 450 factories and was proud to point out that there were more than 130 in near-by Berkeley and Alameda. The Oakland Chamber of Commerce even wrote of new plants in Richmond as if they somehow were a credit to the initiative of Oakland enterprisers and officials.

The monthly *Bulletin* of the Chamber greeted each new development in the East Bay as heralding the growth of a tremendous new industry. For instance, in an account of the launching of the oil tanker *Coalinga*, the first steel ship to slide down the ways in an Oakland yard, the publication noted that the estuary was "as wide as the Clyde at the point at which the 'Mauretania' was launched,"[10] thus implying that Oakland sooner or later might become a rival of Glasgow as a shipbuilding center.

The announcement in the summer of 1910 that New York capitalists would spend $1,000,000 in the construction of electric lines in the San Joaquin Valley and that these lines would connect at Antioch with the Oakland and Antioch Railway, an interurban on which construction had begun at Bay Point (now Port Chicago) in February, 1909, immediately inspired the conclusion, in

Cover of Promotional Booklet of the Oakland Chamber of Commerce, 1910.
Photograph courtesy of Bancroft Library.

capital letters: "This means that Oakland is to be the electric terminal city, the point from which will radiate roads to the great interior valleys of central California." The Chamber of Commerce thereupon began promoting plans for a central traction depot in the heart of Oakland, and it carried on agitation for such a depot for several years, though with less and less hope for actual consummation of the project.

The Western Pacific

The event which, above all others, sent Chamber of Commerce members, and Oakland residents generally, into ecstacies of rejoicing was the arrival of the first passenger train of the Western Pacific, on August 22, 1910. For this momentous occasion the Chamber organized a parade four miles long, the public schools declared a holiday, and business houses closed their doors. In the words of one newspaper reporter, the train came to a stop at the Third and Washington streets station amid "an acclaim riotous, unrestrained, and unrestrainable."[12]

The new line between Oakland and Salt Lake City, a distance of 923 miles, connected with the Denver and Rio Grande Railroad, giving the Bay Area a third transcontinental outlet. Like the early railroad of the same name, the twentieth-century Western Pacific entered the Bay Area via the Livermore Valley and Niles Canyon. Between Oakland and San Francisco it established its own ferry service, operating from a new Western Pacific Mole on the West Oakland waterfront.

The opening of this road merely whetted Oakland's appetite for additional railroad connections and for projects of all sorts that would extend its influence to surrounding areas. In the coastal counties of Mendocino and Humboldt the Southern Pacific and the Santa Fe jointly were building a railroad to link the Bay Area with Eureka, the largest city on the northern California coast. The new road, consolidating the North Shore Railroad of Marin County, the San Francisco and North Pacific, and three other short lines, started as the California Northwestern but was eventually to be known as the Northwestern Pacific. Watching progress on construction of this road through the Eel River Canyon in the northern forest country, the Oakland Chamber of Commerce decided in April, 1911, "it is time to start an active campaign for an upper bay cutoff from the Marin bay shore near Point San Pedro to Point San Pablo, linking Marin County shores with that of Alameda County, and giving the California Northwestern direct communication with Oakland."[13]

The Chamber also advocated ferry service across Carquinez Strait between Vallejo and Crockett because the service "would make the immense country to the north tributary to the east bay shore cities and afford a direct route for automobile travel which would attract thousands of visitors." The organization supported a proposal for extension of the Foothill Boulevard to Alum Rock Park, near San Jose. It urged direct service on the Santa Fe Railroad between Oakland and Antioch. And it supported a movement for a tunnel under the estuary between Oakland and Alameda.[14]

Of this project, which was not to be constructed until 1925-1927, the Oakland *Tribune* wrote:

"It is the next great improvement which Alameda County and the two cities most directly concerned ... will have to tackle, to relieve the estuary of the obstructions to its navigation and its commerce centered in the two drawbridges crossing it at the foot of Webster and Harrison streets. These drawbridges are now maintained solely by the sufferance of the War Department and the intimation has been given by the United States engineer in charge (which is equivalent to a notice to quit) that the future improvement of the channel of Oakland harbor by the United States government for the benefit of commerce is largely dependent upon the removal of these obstructions to free use of the waterway. . . ."[15]

Showdown on the Waterfront

The maritime ambitions of Oakland came into focus with the advent of the Western Pacific, for the entrance of this railroad into the city brought to a head the long struggle between the city and the Southern Pacific over control of the waterfront. The last chapter of this historic fight began to unfold in 1906. When the City of Oakland, in that year, granted the Western Pacific a franchise and wharfing-out rights over an area a little more than a mile long and from six hundred to a thousand feet wide along the north jetty of the estuary, the Southern Pacific quickly sought an injunction in the United States District Court to restrain its new competitor from using the waterfront property, asserting that the City of Oakland had no right to grant wharfing-out franchises.

To the dismay and surprise of Oakland city officials and attorneys for the Western Pacific, the District Court in San Francisco pronounced in favor of the Southern Pacific, notwithstanding the State Supreme Court decision of 1897, holding that land just inside the new waterfront line created by the federal government's dredging operations belonged to the City of Oakland. The Western Pacific, however, was unwilling to accept the judgment of the District Court. Carrying the case to the United States Circuit Court on appeal, the railroad won a reversal of the District Court decision.

The sympathetic attitude of Oakland officials and citizens toward the new transcontinental railroad turned to wrath when the Western Pacific yielded to the desperate urgings of the Southern Pacific—still bent on controlling the waterfront—and coöperated with it in attempting to induce the state legislature to enact a bill creating a state harbor commission to administer the waterfront. Long used to having its way in state politics, even though it was then facing loss of political influence, the Southern Pacific assumed that control of the waterfront by a state agency would be preferable to control by city officials, whose memories of the railroad's defiant actions were all too vivid.

The new turn of events, far from saving the day for the Southern Pacific, served only to consolidate civic feeling and to send Oakland representatives hurrying to Sacramento to kill in the Assembly the Harbor Commission bill that had already passed the state senate.

The City of Oakland then faced a crucial choice: it could let the railroad company appeal the waterfront case to the United States Supreme Court, a procedure that might involve years of further litigation; or it could reach a settlement with the railroad. Mayor Frank Mott chose the latter alternative, met with Vice-President E. E. Calvin of the Southern Pacific, and arrived at a tentative agreement under which the railroad would accept the Appellate Court decision as final, would relinquish all claim to the waterfront, and would receive in return a fifty-year franchise on the property it was then using. The agreement also provided for removal of the railroad's Long Wharf by 1918, so that the city might have free access to the waterfront north of the Southern Pacific Mole.

While the negotiations between Mott and Calvin were under way, Oakland took still another step toward achieving its goal of becoming a major port. The annexation election of March, 1909, added 36.68 square miles to the city, including the once reluctant suburbs Fruitvale, Elmhurst, Melrose, Fitchburg, and Claremont and that part of the bay between the shore and the San Francisco boundary line. This tideland area included the Southern Pacific Mole, the Western Pacific Mole, and the Key Route Pier.

Later in the year the proposed settlement, or "compromise," with the Southern Pacific became the central issue of Mayor Mott's campaign for reëlection. In spite of charges by his opponents that the tentative agreement was a "sellout," the voters returned Mott to office with a substantial majority. On July 6, 1910, they ratified the settlement by passing a charter amendment reaffirming the city's right to control the waterfront; but it was not until November 8 of that year that the city council voted to grant the franchise upon which the agreement between

Mott and Calvin was based. A week after the granting of the franchise, Oakland citizens launched a municipal harbor-improvement program by voting $2,503,000 in bonds for a quay wall on the Estuary, a wharf in East Oakland, and a sea wall in the Key Route Basin and the "White Meat" district, between the Southern Pacific and Western Pacific piers.

Only one other matter required action before municipal control of the waterfront would be absolute. This was the transfer of title to the tidelands, vested in the state, to the city. The state legislature made the transfer in 1911, with the proviso that none of the waterfront should thereafter pass into private ownership.

Oakland, after fifty-eight years of controversy, finally was in possession of nearly two-thirds of its waterfront. The rest remained in the hands of private interests, from whom the city, as its needs required, purchased certain parcels.

The federal government, which had appropriated $1,000,000 in 1905 for dredging the inner harbor to a uniform depth of twenty feet, promised further coöperation in the improvement of the harbor soon after the citizens approved the charter amendment reaffirming municipal control over the waterfront. On July 25, 1910, the Secretary of War adopted a plan providing for a channel five hundred feet wide and thirty feet deep from the bay to the Tidal Basin, three hundred feet wide and twenty-five feet deep along the shore of the Tidal Basin, and eighteen feet deep in the center of the Tidal Basin. The estimated cost of the new program was $1,110,000.

The waterfront issue assumed overwhelming importance not only because of the basic dispute with the Southern Pacific but also because Oakland hoped to benefit, proportionately, as much as San Francisco from the opening of the Panama Canal. Even with the limited harbor facilities that Oakland had in 1910, its port handled approximately 30 per cent of the estimated total freight tonnage passing through the Golden Gate and nearly 20 per cent of the estimated total ship tonnage.[16] Civic leaders confidently believed that with the development of adequate docks, wharves, and warehouses, Oakland could attract an ever-increasing volume of shipping.

Bonds for Public Works

The driving force which enabled the city to triumph in the struggle over the waterfront, to look forward with San Francisco toward a solution of its water supply problem, and to lend support to a wide variety of private and semipublic endeavors to increase commerce and manufacturing found its best expression in efforts to improve the city for the people who lived in it. The old resistance to bond issues had crumbled in the 1907 election at which the voters approved $992,000 in bonds for parks. In the 1909 election the people not only voted $2,503,000 for harbor improvements but also voted $1,150,000 for a new City Hall, to be erected in the triangle at Fourteenth Street, San Pablo Avenue, and Broadway. A year and a half later, on May 16, 1911, they again authorized the expenditure of public funds for needed public buildings—$1,775,000 for elementary schools, $738,000 for high schools, and $500,000 for a civic auditorium to be erected at the south end of Lake Merritt.

President William Howard Taft laid the cornerstone of the Oakland City Hall on October 13, 1911, then departed for San Francisco to break ground for the Panama-Pacific International Exposition the same day. The City Hall was to be something new in civic architecture—a skyscraper, designed by the New York architectural firm of Palmer and Hornbostel. The limited site perhaps suggested the form of the building, though there was something peculiarly fitting about the selection of the skyscraper type for a city with the mercantile ambitions of Oakland.

The Hotel Oakland, already well advanced in construction as the City Hall began to rise, was in some ways an even more significant expression of community desires than the civic building. Financed by Oakland bankers and intended to be the East Bay equivalent of the Palace Hotel in San Francisco, the block-square Hotel Oakland was another indication that the city founded by Moon, Adams, and Carpentier had "thrown off the swaddling clothes of suburbanism and become distinctly urban," as a Santa Fe Railroad booklet observed in describing the growth of the city.[17] The Chamber of Commerce suggested that the city would soon have an opportunity to advertise: "Come to the Panama-Pacific International Exposition, and stop in Oakland."[18]

Rivalry and a Water Plan

In view of the heightened sense of community individualism evident in Oakland, San Francisco politicians and civic leaders might well have been cautious about spurring too vigorously their Greater San Francisco movement. East Bay spokesmen in the state legislature stubbornly fought approval of a proposed constitutional amendment providing for consolidation, and the Oakland Chamber of Commerce actively opposed the measure from the time it was first introduced, in 1910. Yet the San Francisco Chamber of Commerce, the Greater San Francisco Association, and other groups, not to mention the San Francisco press, fondly believed that cities within the metropolitan district could be induced to unite. The serious

interest of East Bay cities in joining with San Francisco in building an aqueduct from the headwaters of the Tuolumne River undoubtedly persuaded San Francisco groups that both sides of the bay had more in common than not, and that in time consolidation could be brought about.

Certainly, city officials in Oakland, Berkeley, and Alameda read every line of a long-awaited report on the metropolitan water supply that San Francisco hoped might be developed through a special district formed under the Metropolitan Water District Act of 1909. Soon after passage of this enabling legislation (which all the large cities of the Bay Area had urged the state legislature to enact), Secretary of the Interior Richard A. Ballinger had cited San Francisco to show cause why he should not revoke part of a permit issued by his predecessor in 1907 giving the city certain rights to the headwaters of the Tuolumne River. Ballinger was inclined to believe that San Francisco would never need to tap the waters of Hetch Hetchy Valley in Yosemite National Park and should be content with its primary rights to the comparatively small amount of water available from Lake Eleanor and Cherry Valley sources; but since city officials feared that revocation of secondary rights to sources in the Hetch Hetchy Valley would preclude the development of a water supply adequate for a metropolitan district, they had engaged John R. Freeman, an internationally known hydraulic engineer, to prepare a report demonstrating the need for all the water sources mentioned in the Garfield Permit of 1907. The City of Berkeley had assigned an engineer to assist Freeman, and the city council of Oakland had adopted a resolution in June, 1911, stating that the voters of Oakland would join with other Bay Area cities in providing for the joint use of the Hetch Hetchy water supply through formation of a metropolitan water district or through "any other practical method which may hereafter be agreed upon."[19]

Published in July, 1912, Freeman's report rejected a proposal made in 1901 for developing a supply of 60,000,000 gallons daily for San Francisco alone and boldly suggested a plan for supplying an entire metropolitan water district with 240,000,000 gallons daily from the Hetch Hetchy Valley through a first aqueduct, and eventually with 400,000,000 gallons daily by adding a second pipe line. The primary rights assigned in the Garfield Permit, Freeman stated, were "insufficient for present needs and for future conservation."[20]

In an introductory statement, the hydraulic engineer wrote: "For simplicity, in all of the following descriptions the word San Francisco has been used to indicate the group of cities of which that city is the commercial center,

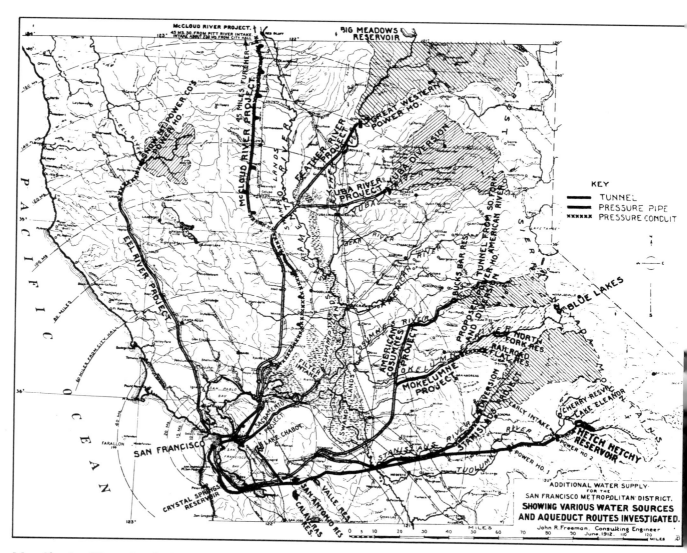

Map Showing Water Supply Sources Investigated by John R. Freeman, 1912.
Photograph courtesy of Bancroft Library.

comprising substantially all of the cities and smaller communities bordering upon the bay, from San Francisco around southerly, easterly, and northerly to Oakland, Berkeley and Richmond, some twenty-six municipalities, comprising thirty-seven separate communities in all. As will appear later, the matter of uniting more or less of these communities in closer municipal relations, possibly into a metropolitan water district, in some respects similar to that which supplies the Boston metropolitan district, is now being actively promoted, with practical certainty of ultimate success."[21]

A Population Forecast

Freeman predicted that the population of the district contemplated would "surely" be 2,000,000 within forty to fifty years, and that at some time near the end of the present century the population of "Greater San Francisco" would reach 3,000,000. He conceded, however, that there was a possibility that a population of 3,000,000 might be reached within half a century, depending upon "the wisdom and vigor with which San Franciscans seize their opportunity."[22] Time has shown that his more conservative prediction of a population of 2,000,000 within forty or fifty years was a reasonably good forecast, for San Francisco, San Mateo, Santa Clara, Alameda, and Contra Costa counties together had a population of more than 2,300,000 in 1950. A two-aqueduct system supplying 400,000,000 million gallons daily would be required when the urban population of the proposed water district reached 3,000,000, Freeman estimated.

The engineer based his prediction of rapid and continuous growth in the Bay Area on broader interchange of goods with the Orient and on increased trade with Europe and the eastern United States through the Panama Canal. He viewed the development of intensive farming in the Central Valley as contributing to this more extensive trade. Apparently by no means all civic leaders in the Bay Area shared the enthusiasm of chambers of commerce for industrial expansion, for Freeman remarked, "While thoughtful men have doubts about it being advantageous to the civic welfare to multiply a factory population here, the attractions of climate, food, and the high prevailing rate of wages and the zeal of steamship agents may bring it faster than desired." He himself was inclined to forecast only "some moderate increase in manufacturing." Significantly, he did not undervalue as a stimulus to growth "an awakening in civic pride and an apprecia-

tion of their remarkable opportunities throughout the communities of Greater San Francisco."[23]

Freeman proposed distribution of Hetch Hetchy water to Bay Area cities from an aqueduct terminal on the hills above Irvington, in southern Alameda County. From this point branch lines would extend southward to San Jose, westward across Dumbarton Strait to the Peninsula and San Francisco, and northward along the east side of the bay to a greatly enlarged Lake Chabot, near San Leandro, from whence water would be distributed to East Bay communities. An alternative route for the branch supplying San Francisco would be northward to Alameda and across the bay from Alameda Point to the Potrero district in San Francisco.[24]

The engineer recommended building the Hetch Hetchy Aqueduct full size in the beginning, for two main reasons. By actual diversion of the full appropriation, the water

Kolana Rock, Hetch Hetchy Valley, Before Construction of O'Shaughnessy Dam.
Photograph by Joseph N. LeConte, courtesy of Helen LeConte and Ansel Adams.

district would be making its water rights secure and placing them beyond all possibility of future adverse claims. Equally important, since tunnels through solid rock in rough, mountainous country could not be enlarged later, it would be necessary to construct them full size at the start. Los Angeles and New York, Freeman pointed out, were building their great aqueducts to full capacity, and Boston fifteen years earlier had designed its Wachusett Aqueduct to carry an augmented flow at some later time.

Errors of Judgment

The tremendous cost involved in the Hetch Hetchy project was, of course, one of the reasons why San Francisco was anxious for the participation of other communities in the undertaking. True, in 1910 the people of the city had voted $45,000,000 in bonds for construction of a complete water system; but that was before Freeman developed his plan for a system supplying a much greater quantity of water. In the appendix to his report was a letter from Leslie E. Burks, secretary of the Greater San Francisco Association, to Percy V. Long, City Attorney of San Francisco, stating that one of the objectives of the association was "the desire of procuring an adequate and inexhaustible supply of water for the communities about the bay, which San Francisco alone is not able to procure."[25]

That neighboring cities were genuinely interested in sharing the costs and benefits of the proposed system was indicated by resolutions included in the appendix. The city councils of San Jose, Palo Alto, Daly City, Oakland, and Berkeley had all officially gone on record as favoring the Hetch Hetchy Valley as a common source of water supply for the communities surrounding the bay. Four members of the Board of Trustees of Redwood City also had written to the city engineer of San Francisco expressing their personal belief that "ultimately a water supply at all adequate to meet the demands of the municipalities in and around San Francisco Bay, especially San Francisco, as well as our own city, will have to be obtained from the Sierra Nevada Mountains, and especially from Hetch Hetchy, which is the only source not now under adverse control."[26]

The numerous references throughout the Freeman report to "Greater San Francisco" and the inclusion of the letter of the secretary of the Greater San Francisco Association in the appendix to the report perhaps represented errors of judgment on the part of the author and San Francisco officials, since the movement for a metropolitan water district thus became identified with the political consolidation movement that was distasteful to the powerful Oakland Chamber of Commerce. San Francisco groups, having met defeat in the state legislature in their attempts to obtain approval of a state constitutional amendment providing for consolidation, had resorted to circulation of an initiative petition to place the proposed amendment on the ballot at the general election in November, 1912. The amendment, as finally submitted, embodied changes suggested by an attorney representing the Oakland Chamber of Commerce; nevertheless, that organization viewed the measure as a bare-faced attempt to reduce Oakland to the status of a borough of imperialistic San Francisco. From the point of view of the Oakland Chamber, Burks' letter contained paragraphs that were offensive in the extreme:

"The sentiment for the consolidation is very strong in every locality, not excepting Oakland, which, because of the hostility of the political ring that has dominated Alameda County and Oakland for many years, appears to be hostile.

"The requisite number of signatures to the petition, which will place the constitutional amendment on the ballot, has been obtained without difficulty.

"As indicating the sentiment, I may instance the fact that less than two years ago the City of Alameda at a general city election adopted a proposition favoring consolidation with San Francisco by a majority of four hundred and forty-four out of a total vote of twenty-five hundred. Shortly afterwards, upon a proposal to annex Berkeley to Oakland, the voters of Berkeley, by a vote of six to one, defeated the proposal for the well-understood reason that they favored consolidation with San Francisco, but not with Oakland.

"The benefits expected to be derived from a consolidation will be a substantial reduction of taxes and the improvement of municipal affairs by giving those whose interests and business are in San Francisco, but who reside out of the limits of the city, participation in its affairs."[27]

Burks' belief that only a "political ring" in Oakland opposed consolidation, and his interpretation of the results of the election in which Oakland sought to effect an *Anschluss* with Berkeley, indicated the extent to which San Franciscans deceived themselves concerning East Bay sentiment about the Greater San Francisco movement. His letter, however, throws light on a technological development that was beginning to focus attention on the need for physical integration of the Bay Area through bridges and improved highways—the increasing use of the automobile. He stated that among the results expected to be obtained through consolidation were not only area-wide solution of the water supply problem but also "improved transportation facilities, which involve the construction of a bridge across the bay."[28] Motor-vehicle registration in California in 1912 was about ninety thousand, and already transbay ferries were having difficulty in handling automobile traffic at peak hours and on week ends. Moreover, the San Francisco Board of Supervisors had before it by this time an application of Allen C. Rush, of Los Angeles, for a franchise to construct a double-decked suspension bridge from Telegraph Hill to Yerba Buena Island and thence to Emeryville. Rush described the proposed bridge as being capable of carrying railroads, streetcars, automobiles, and horse-drawn vehicles.

However logical or worthy of consideration, arguments in favor of the proposed state constitutional amendment might be, in the East Bay they fell for the most part on deaf ears, especially after the Oakland Chamber of Commerce, the Alameda County League, the Oakland press, and the administration of Mayor Frank Mott joined forces to defeat it. The San Francisco Chamber of Commerce and the Greater San Francisco Association vainly sought to explain that under provisions of the amendment no community could be consolidated with any other unless a majority of each so voted, and that no county could be divided except with the consent of a majority of the voters of the entire county. Oakland opponents flatly branded the measure an annexation scheme and appealed to voters throughout the state to help them bury it under an avalanche of "No" votes.

Opposition to Unification

San Francisco discovered that though all parts of the state wished her success with the exposition, few areas looked favorably upon her efforts at metropolitan unification. The Pasadena *Star* sympathized with Oakland for resisting an effort "to drag it into the mire of San Francisco politics and despoil it of its individuality." The Sacramento *Union* observed that "San Francisco has pursued for many years a policy of belittling Oakland, yet wonders now why the big city across the bay should object to the submergence of its identity by consolidation." The Stockton *Independent* pointed out that "the political history of San Francisco will lend no strength to the campaign to make all the bay people members of one great municipal family."[29] The Burbank *Review* reflected the popular suspicion of bigness stemming from the trust-busting activities of Theodore Roosevelt and from the then current agitation for a federal income tax on huge incomes:

"We earnestly advise all our readers to vote against the annexation amendment. The tendency of the times for all large business bodies to absorb the smaller, thus creating trusts and big interests, is against the interests of the

masses of the people, in fact is taking their life blood. . . . The attempt of big cities to absorb contiguous smaller cities and towns will also prove greatly detrimental to the advancement of the business interests of the outside communities and to all of their resident people."[30]

The Oakland Chamber of Commerce, only two years earlier the champion of a movement to annex Berkeley, saw nothing ironical in its own use of this last quotation as propaganda against the consolidation amendment.

Citing the Burks letter in the appendix of the Freeman report, the Oakland *Tribune* charged that the Greater San Francisco Association was organized as early as 1907 "for the express purpose of consolidating all of the bay cities and forming a single city and county government thereof to secure a water supply for San Francisco from Hetch-Hetchy and impose a share of the burden on the territory annexed."[31]

The newspaper said, further: "It has been later disclosed, since the filing of the initiative amendment, that Spring Valley [Water Company] is and has been also an active agent in promoting the plot, so as to saddle on the proposed new consolidated city and county its own system as an appendage to the Hetch-Hetchy scheme at a cost of $38,500,000, and that there are a multitude of other costly enterprises in which San Francisco alone is concerned but cannot provide . . . [except] through consolidation by appropriating the bonding resources of the populous communities annexed. . . ."[32]

Although it was true that eventually the Spring Valley properties would have to be purchased, by the City of San Francisco or by a metropolitan water district, it was equally true that a Greater San Francisco or a metropolitan water district also might have to purchase, at a cost of many millions, the extensive properties of the People's Water Company, the utility then serving fifteen communities in the East Bay. Moreover, the Oakland City Council had already appointed a municipal water commission to investigate the possibility of condemning the Oakland division of the People's Water Company.

The Oakland campaign against the consolidation amendment, however, had reached the point where emotion rather than cool analysis of the facts prevailed. The Oakland Chamber of Commerce had some "facts" of its own that it wished San Franciscans to consider. It resented the assertion that Oakland had been "built up by San Francisco's misfortune" and the charge that the majority of Oakland residents "lived off" San Francisco. The East Bay city had begun to grow rapidly before the earthquake and fire of 1906, the Chamber insisted, but its "real substantial and permanent development" dated from the successful outcome of the litigation over control of the waterfront. As for the irritating portrayal of Oakland as a bedroom of the metropolis, the Chamber offered these findings:

"Carefully compiled statistics show that no more than 18,000 people, living on the east or continental side of the bay, earn their living in San Francisco. 282,000 people living on the east side of the bay not only live here, but earn their living on this side or derive their income from sources outside of San Francisco."[33]

The real issue, so far as Oakland bankers, merchants, and businessmen were concerned, was the preservation of Oakland's identity. They feared that the opportunity for them to assert proprietary rights to the community prestige they were building would be jeopardized. In a front-page "Appeal to Voters" on the eve of the election, Mayor Frank K. Mott expressed exactly the sentiments of the men who financed the state-wide campaign against the "annexation scheme":

"The adoption of this amendment means: That the way will be opened for the disintegration of Oakland as an important municipality. It means that the way will be opened for the absorption of our city, the destruction of its splendid credit, the cessation of its independent activities, the stopping of every big project of public development, the wasting of years of thoughtful effort by its public-spirited citizens and, finally, its obliteration as an independent factor in the social, commercial, industrial and political upbuilding of its superb natural advantages.

"This amendment as proposed is to be the first step toward the wiping out of Oakland as a city. Its adoption will be followed by recurrent elections, producing a chaotic condition which can, in the very nature of things, result in nothing but stagnation of public and private development. Investors will keep aloof from the city so long as the confused conditions shall exist that will, beyond any question, follow in the train of the constant turmoil and agitation that annexation elections will cause. . . .

". . . Let us make this vote so overwhelming that it shall stand as a rebuke to this or any future attempt to take from us that which a fine civic patriotism has upbuilt."[34]

Defeat of the Amendment

So effective was the work of the Oakland groups fighting consolidation that on election day a majority of voters in every county except three cast ballots against the proposed constitutional amendment. Besides San Francisco itself, only San Mateo County and Marin County approved the measure. Marin County favored it two to one, San Mateo County two-and-a-half to one. Alameda County voters

snowed it under: 16,919 votes for, 40,190 against. The state majority against the measure was some 60,000, out of 383,000 votes cast.

Former State Senator Frank W. Leavitt, secretary of the Alameda County League, an organization that had delivered some of the most telling blows against the initiative measure, pointed out that the votes of counties south of the Tehachapi Mountains made up only one-half the majority against the proposed amendment. "In other words," he gloated, "the vote in Northern California, outside of San Francisco, was sufficient to more than offset the 47,000 majority which San Francisco gave to the measure. That shows just how much influence in Northern California San Francisco wields when Oakland is opposing her on a platform of justice."[35]

A. A. Denison, secretary of the Oakland Chamber of Commerce, who had been particularly galled by the statement that Oakland and the East Bay cities "lived off" San Francisco, urged, "Now let us go to work and remove all grounds for this taunt in the future by demonstrating that Oakland is not an economic or political dependency, by making this a self-sufficient and self-sustaining city in every respect. Let us develop our wholesale and jobbing business, and our industrial life, so that we will be absolutely independent."[36]

In the metropolis across the bay there was much editorial licking of wounds. The San Francisco *Chronicle* found that "it was not in accord with justice that the people of the State have refused to so amend the Constitution as to permit the municipalities comprising the one city around San Francisco Bay to politically unite themselves for the management of common interests." The newspaper contended that the voters had gone to the polls without proper understanding of the proposed amendment. It concluded: "The greater city is here and it makes not the slightest difference except for advertising and sentimental purposes whether it be called San Francisco, Oakland, Berkeley, Alameda, Richmond, or San Mateo. It is one city and it has common purposes which cannot be properly dealt with except by a single political organization for these purposes."[37]

Rapid growth had indeed brought into being a vast urban community transcending city and county boundary lines and the dividing waters of the bay; and this extensive community undeniably did have certain problems that should become the concern of an area-wide government. But that this government should be a supermunicipality and nothing else was an indefensible argument. The *Chronicle* discounted the value of strong identification with a local environment and its human associations, including the ties between local politicians and their constituents. A vigorous democracy depends as much upon the participation of citizens in "home town" affairs as it does upon general concern over national issues. The newspaper dismissed the attachment to local institutions as mere "sentiment," but it did not address itself to the problem of building loyalty to the metropolitan region. It suggested no alternative to the supercity that the voters had emphatically rejected.[38]

Six years earlier, one perspicacious editorial writer had foreseen that political consolidation of the cities in the Bay Area would be distasteful and that a considerable degree of local autonomy would have to be preserved even if municipalities did unite for action on matters affecting all of them. The Oakland *Enquirer* had suggested formation of "a confederation of bay cities" to plan "a comprehensive scheme of development" and carry out projects of area-wide importance, among which would be a metropolitan water system.[39] But the proposal had aroused little interest and had been almost forgotten, though the idea of confederation was to receive renewed consideration from time to time as area-wide problems increased in intensity.

Proposed Unified Railway System and Distribution of Population, San Francisco, 1912. Photograph courtesy of Bancroft Library.

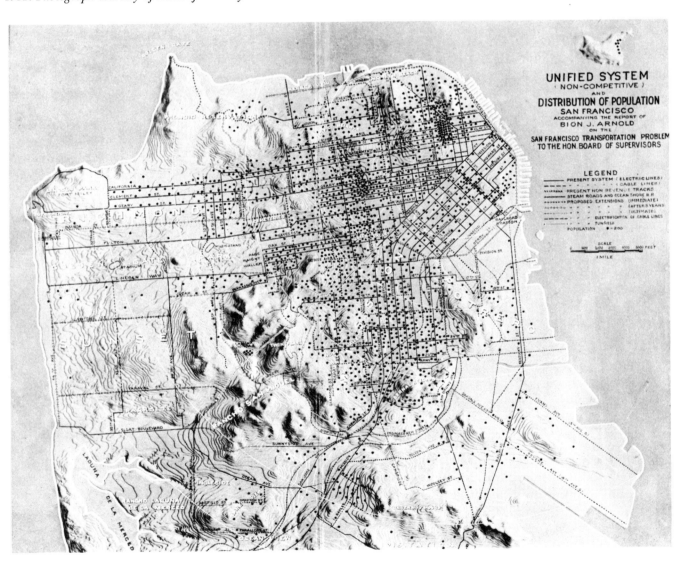

Bion Arnold's Proposal

In the heat of battle over the consolidation amendment hardly anyone noted a farsighted suggestion made by Bion Joseph Arnold, a Chicago consulting engineer and transit expert employed by the San Francisco Board of Supervisors to study the transportation facilities of the metropolis. In a report submitted just two months before the election, Arnold—without referring to the Greater San Francisco movement—urged San Francisco to "attempt to evolve, in conjunction with adjacent cities, some form of Metropolitan District Control by means of which the normal and adequate development of utilities and other enterprises vital to its life may be effected."[40] He specifically mentioned industries as being among the "other enterprises" that would come within the purview of a metropolitan district plan of control. Apparently he foresaw the need for long-range planning that would carefully relate manufacturing areas, transit, water and power lines, highways, and rail and shipping facilities throughout the metropolitan region, though he did not amplify his suggestion and it is difficult to know whether he thought a multiple-function special district or a metropolitan authority should do the planning—or whether cities should coöperate voluntarily in carrying out a plan prepared by some metropolitan regional planning agency.

When Arnold submitted his report there was not a single city planning commission in the San Francisco Bay Area; hence the idea of controlling development throughout the metropolitan area—an idea implicit in the conception of Greater San Francisco — was decidedly advanced. Arnold recommended that San Francisco create a city planning commission; and at a special election on December 10, 1912, the voters approved, among other ballot measures, a city charter amendment providing that the board of supervisors might by ordinance establish such a commission. But the close vote on the measure showed that public understanding of the need for even local planning was inadequate: the number of votes cast for the charter amendment was 33,819, the number against, 33,296. Since San Franciscans were almost evenly divided on the question of local planning, there was no great likelihood that Arnold's metropolitan-district plan of control would excite much comment, still

less provoke serious investigation of its possibilities. Six years had passed since Senator Newlands had proposed an advisory planning commission "headed by a man like Burnham," and San Franciscans were just accepting, by the narrowest of margins, the idea of forming a commission. Many more years were to pass before they and the residents of neighboring cities would know about city planning from actual experience and would be prepared to consider extending the planning function from the local community to the whole Bay Area.

To the metropolis that was chagrined by the blow to its hopes of organizing a complex of municipalities into a borough system, Arnold offered sage advice which, though it was given before the election, was especially pertinent after the ballots had been counted: "San Francisco . . . will always continue to be the business and social center [of the metropolitan district]; and instead of attempting to curtail trans-bay development, it should turn to the development of the immense acreage within its own borders and down the Peninsula. This will undoubtedly come through improved transportation and as a reflex of the Panama Canal, if the opportunities are taken advantage of."[41]

Arnold emphasized that "transportation must precede settlement of any territory." Any policy which attempted to reverse this process, he cautioned, would certainly lead to "utter failure to develop the resources of the city to the fullest extent."[42]

San Francisco had, indeed, a planning and development job to do within its own city-county boundaries, and to this work it now turned. But San Francisco was not a city without prestige and influence, set back on its heels by neighboring communities. Whether or not these communities recognized the fact, San Francisco had made a significant contribution to the growth and development of the Bay Area by advancing the important idea that major problems of the metropolitan region, such as water supply, transportation, and harbor development, should be solved on an area-wide basis. San Francisco advocated the unpopular method of political consolidation, but the rejection of this method by other communities did not kill the idea that there should be concerted action on problems common to the entire area. Today this idea has more champions than at any time since 1912.

CHAPTER TEN

The Panama Canal—
Stimulus to Planning

The fierce controversy over the consolidation amendment had engendered so much ill feeling that communities on both sides of the bay soon became conscious of the danger to the whole Bay Area of allowing rancorous division to continue. All expected to benefit economically from the opening of the Panama Canal; all foresaw the same need to plan for population growth and industrial expansion; and all had pledged themselves to make a success of the Panama-Pacific International Exposition. Repentant for the harsh things they had said about one another, the business leaders of the area began the year 1913 by exchanging olive branches.

The Oakland Chamber of Commerce invited William T. Sesnon, president of the San Francisco Chamber of Commerce, to speak at its housewarming banquet at the new Hotel Oakland on January 22. With peace pipe in hand, the honored guest might gave glossed over the recent unpleasantness with gracious platitudes; but he decided that the occasion demanded frankness and spoke accordingly: ". . . There is no good reason why two great cities like Oakland and San Francisco should not co-operate and work in harmony, situated as we are on the shores of the greatest harbor in the world, possessing unequalled shipping and manufacturing possibilities. But

the truth remains that we do not work in harmony. More or less jealousy seems to possess us; unkind things are said, with the result that both of us suffer and fail to get the full measure of benefit that is justly due us.

"It is all very well for us to sit here, to attend banquet after banquet, and tell each other what nice fellows we are. Unless we are willing to give and take, meet each other half way, our banquets and meetings count for naught. And what I say of San Francisco and Oakland applies to every section of the state. . . .

"Let tonight be the beginning of a new era. If you do this, I'll start the ball a-rolling by pledging the hearty support and cooperation of the San Francisco Chamber."[1]

Next morning the Oakland *Tribune* observed that the welcome given Sesnon "was an assurance that San Francisco has no enemies in Oakland and that she can count on the cooperation of the cities on this side of the bay in her efforts to make the Panama-Pacific Exposition the greatest thing of the kind the world has yet seen."[2]

The San Francisco Chamber of Commerce, making good on Sesnon's promises, invited delegates from other Bay Area cities to a conference called for the express purpose of doing away with petty jealousies and developing the type of metropolitan regional patriotism that would bring all the bay cities to consider themselves part of one great community. With the opening of the "Big Ditch" uppermost in their minds, prominent speakers discussed selective immigration and colonization, the establishment of a state immigration commission, the location of factories and industries, and proposals for attracting tourists. Mayor Frank Mott of Oakland "raised everyone to a high pitch of enthusiasm and local pride" with his speech on industrial expansion; and impromptu remarks of guests after the formal talks gave evidence of a pervasive one-for-all-and-all-for-one sentiment. An area-wide committee "to make plans and execute measures for the common good" was appointed.3

"If any bay community has ever had any small hatchet, even a toy one, out for any other bay community, it was decently and effectively buried," the San Francisco Chamber of Commerce *Journal* commented. "Everybody recognized the spirit of mutual helpfulness and the principle of co-operation. The following localities were represented: Alameda, Antioch, Benicia, Berkeley, Hayward, Martinez, Newark, Niles, Oakland, Palo Alto, Redwood City, Richmond, San Francisco, South San Francisco, San Jose, San Leandro, San Mateo, San Rafael, Santa Clara, Sausalito, Vallejo."4

Harbor Development

Having reëstablished amicable relations, the various communities about the bay proceeded, each in its own way, to prepare for the opening of the Panama Canal. None showed any interest in the formulation of a plan for over-all development and management of harbor facilities or in the organization of a harbor district including the metropolitan area around the bay, as proposed by Professor C. T. Wright of the University of California.5 The prophecy of the Board of State Harbor Commissioners, who controlled the Port of San Francisco, that "the time will come, and it is not far off, when one State Harbor Commission shall have control and management of the entire Bay of San Francisco and perhaps of many of its tributary waters"6 seemed to be no more than wishful thinking. Disregarding the board's warning that local control of bay ports inevitably meant "foolish cutting of rates, a practice leading surely to economic waste and chaotic conditions,"7 San Jose, Vallejo, Richmond, Oakland, and other cities pursued completely independent harbor-development programs.

Aping Los Angeles, which had annexed a narrow strip of territory sixteen miles long in order to gain access to its harbor at San Pedro and Wilmington, San Jose annexed a strip of land two hundred feet wide and eleven miles long, from the northern city limits to the site of a proposed port near Alviso. The Port San Jose Committee of the San Jose Chamber of Commerce entertained visions of a municipal boulevard extending the full length of this strip, with a privately operated electric railway in the center connecting with docks, warehouses, and terminals at the port, but this ambitious scheme was never to come to fruition, although many attempts were made to revive it.

At the opposite end of the long bay the civic leaders of Vallejo discussed a proposal for reclaiming waterfront lands for industrial sites. The War Department planned to deepen the channel between that city and the Mare Island Navy Yard. If the city should construct a bulkhead, the mud pumped from the channel could be used to fill the tidelands, but first all private claims to the tidelands would have to give way to settlements in favor of the city. To this legal business City Attorney W. T. O'Donnell addressed himself while civic leaders made preparations for a campaign for a bond issue to finance the reclamation project.

The East Bay cities of Oakland, Berkeley, Emeryville, Albany, and Richmond had before them a grand scheme of waterfront development proposed by Lieutenant Colonel Thomas R. Rees, Division Officer of the Corps of Army Engineers. Primarily it was designed to overcome the major obstacle to use of the East Bay waterfront for shipping—the wide shoals or tidal flats that extended several miles from the shore. Rees suggested creating a large inner basin at Richmond just inside Point Potrero and Brooks Island, with an entrance channel six hundred feet wide extending inward past Point Richmond and Point Potrero to this dredged harbor. From the inner basin at Richmond a great channel would extend along the waterfronts of Albany, Berkeley, and Emeryville to the Southern Pacific Mole at Oakland. Three thousand acres of tidelands between the bulkhead lines and the shoreline would be reclaimed with dredged material, and a dike on the western side of the channel would also be constructed from it. Between Berkeley and Oakland the eastern side of the channel would be lined with piers.

Rees realized that the requirements of commerce and navigation at that time did not demand the extensive development he outlined. Consideration of his plan was justified, he believed, only by the probable requirements of the more distant future and by the existing demand for additional land, adjacent to deep water and suitable for industrial and warehouse sites and for railroad yards and terminals. He deemed that it would be "most unwise" for any one of the East Bay cities to undertake harbor improvements that did not conform to a comprehensive plan for the ultimate development of the entire bay

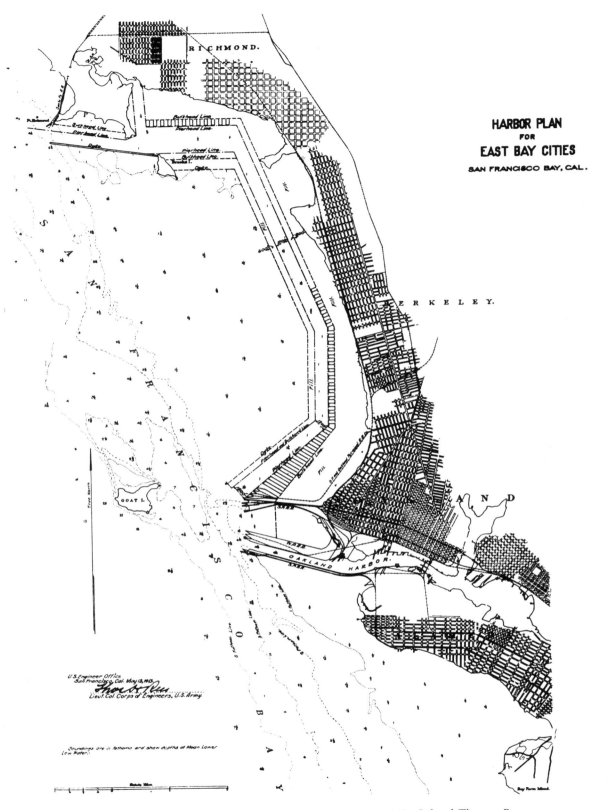

Plan for Unified Harbor Development in the East Bay, 1913. Colonel Thomas R. Rees proposed creation of "one continuous and unobstructed deep water frontage extending along the reclaimed shores from deep water at Oakland Estuary to deep water at Point Richmond."

frontage, because detached and nonrelated improvements would result and would involve greatly increased costs and diminished benefits to all. Coördinated projects, on the other hand, would give the East Bay cities "the finest harbor and the best harbor facilities in the world," he maintained.[8]

Dredging and construction of dikes and breakwaters would of course be undertaken by the federal government if Congress approved the plan and made the necessary appropriations. Projects carried out by the individual cities shoreward of the pierhead lines established by the government would complement the federal improvements.

Richmond Harbor

Richmond alone of the East Bay cities undertook harbor improvements related to the Rees Plan. P. A. Haviland, the San Francisco engineer whom the Richmond City Council had engaged in 1912 to formulate a long-range program of municipal harbor improvements, fully shared Rees' vision of the southern waterfront of the city as a major shipping and industrial area. Here, where Henry Cutting was dredging the canal now known as the Santa Fe Channel, were mud flats and sloughs that presented no more serious a challenge to engineers than the marshlands Los Angeles was then transforming into navigable ship channels, turning basins, and sites for warehouses and factories.

In his report on a program for harbor development Haviland proposed the construction of eleven deep-water piers along the entrance channel from Point Richmond to Point Potrero, a continuous bulkhead wharf round the projected northern arm of the inner basin, and twenty-one piers along the northern edge of this basin, where Liberty ships built by the Kaiser shipyards were to slide down the

The Richmond Waterfront as It Was During World War I. Looking toward the area in which the Santa Fe Channel, sites for industries, and the Inner Harbor were later developed. Photograph courtesy of Richmond Chamber of Commerce.

ways during World War II. To provide access to the piers along the entrance channel, he recommended construction of a tunnel and roadway through the Potrero hills, near the tunnel of the Santa Fe Railroad. The entire southern waterfront, Haviland said, should be served by a belt-line railroad and by a highway 150 feet wide. Further, the engineer urged the city to insure municipal control of land on the waterfront by acquiring the submerged areas that would be reclaimed by harbor dredging.

Even for a city many times the size of Richmond (the population was then approximately 10,000), the cost of the entire Haviland program—$18,500,000, or about $55,000,000 in present-day dollars—would have been burdensome. The Richmond City Council therefore took Haviland's advice and in 1913 began to develop the harbor in stages, starting with the tunnel through the Potrero hills and some limited wharf facilities near Point Richmond. Not until 1917 did Congress adopt a modified version of the Rees Plan for Richmond Harbor and appropriate the first funds for developing the entrance channel, the turning basin at Point Potrero, and a channel to Ellis Slough. Work on the large inner harbor was deferred until some date far in the future.

Oakland appeared to have dismissed the greater part of the Rees Plan without giving it proper study, for Oakland was drifting along without any discernible plan for the development of harbor facilities. Instead of concentrating on some well-conceived project that might benefit groups with various interests, it was expending the funds provided by its 1909 bond issue at various locations along the Estuary and in the Key Route Basin, now known as the Outer Harbor. In disregard of the Rees proposals, which contemplated eventual removal of the Key Route Pier and the creation of the southern entrance to the great Rees Channel directly through the Key Route Basin, the city had granted the Key Route a fifty-year franchise for its piers; and now the company was extending a solid fill into the fairway of the projected channel.

San Francisco interests, who might at the height of the Greater San Francisco movement have applauded any plea for area-wide harbor control and development, seem to have retreated from advocacy of single control and development and to have adopted a philosophical attitude which assumed that any development anywhere in the Bay Area would benefit the metropolis. An editorial in the San Francisco *Chronicle* of June 19, 1913, indicated the new mood of the leading city:

"The improvement of the tidelands which is projected at Vallejo, following the much greater enterprise contemplated between Richmond and Alameda, should serve to renew and increase our confidence in the future of the littoral of San Francisco bay. . . .

"But so long as the region about San Francisco bay prospers the financial center of the district will get its full share of prosperity. And the office buildings and the wholesale establishments and the multitude of minor industries which serve them will make business for the retailers. . . .

"When the man of affairs from the Eastern cities, or from Europe or Asia pays us a visit he does not think so much of San Francisco or Oakland or any other of the bay cities as he does of our magnificent bay. And if he thinks of founding an establishment here, he will look for the spot where he can get what he needs for the least money and will not care a rap in what political subdivision it lies. And that is a good way for all of us to think of it."

The Hetch Hetchy Grant

Although the Bay Area might grow and develop without political unification and without over-all harbor control, San Francisco officials—and East Bay officials as well—knew that the major urban areas could not grow beyond a certain point without an abundant, dependable water supply. The metropolis on the Peninsula had not given up hope of persuading other communities to join with it in creating a metropolitan water system. In 1913 it won the technical and legislative victories that put it in a position to offer them the prospect of an unceasing flow of water from the High Sierra to meet their increasing domestic and industrial needs.

On February 19, 1913, the Board of Army Engineers appointed to review evidence of San Francisco's need of Hetch Hetchy water reported to Secretary of the Interior Walter L. Fisher that this source of supply was not only the most readily available but also the cheapest and most economical. Heartened by the pronouncement of the board, the city decided to ask Congress for an outright grant of the use of public lands in Yosemite National Park, the Stanislaus National Forest, and other Sierra reserves rather than for a permit which might be subject to the whims of successive administrations in Washington. But to obtain the grant, the city had to overcome the opposition of irrigation and private utility interests and of the Sierra Club, an organization which feared the establishment of a dangerous precedent for encroaching on national parks quite as much as it dreaded the destruction of a valley almost as grand as Yosemite. Victory for the city came on December 19, 1913, when President Woodrow Wilson signed the Raker Act, granting San Francisco rights of way and the use of public lands for the construction of reservoirs, dams, conduits, and other structures necessary or incident to the development and use of water and power.

Congress recognized the interests of other Bay Area cities in Hetch Hetchy water by extending the provisions of the act to the "City and County of San Francisco and such other municipalities or . . . water districts as may, with the consent of the City and County of San Francisco or in accordance with the laws of the State of California, hereinafter participate in or succeed to the beneficial rights and privileges granted by this Act."

San Francisco ratified the Raker Act in the spring of 1914 and prepared to start construction on the Hetch Hetchy system immediately, as the act required. That San Francisco would be alone in the gigantic undertaking now began to appear almost certain. Dr. George C. Pardee, a former governor of California, had become president of a Municipal Water District League in the East Bay and was campaigning for a separate water district serving the cities of Oakland, Berkeley, Alameda, Albany, Emeryville, Piedmont, and San Leandro.

Troubles beset the East Bay leader, however. As the day drew near for an election on the proposed municipal water district, opponents harped on the suggestion that the appointive directors of the district might buy out the "mortgage-logged and piecemeal constructed distributing system" of the People's Water Company at a fancy price without a referendum by the people.[9] In vain Dr. Pardee pointed out that funds for purchase of the company's properties would have to be raised by bonds approved by two-thirds of the voters of the district and that under the enabling legislation the State Railroad Commission would have to fix the valuation of the properties. His cause was damaged when he was forced to admit that the law under which the district would be formed was "not a perfect law" and might encourage litigation.[10] Other proponents also acknowledged that the law was defective, but proposed to have it amended at the next session of the state legislature. The voters, consequently, were not enthusiastic about the proposed water district. On June 2, 1914, they cast 13,581 votes against it to 10,989 in its favor. For the most part, though, the East Bay electorate was indifferent. Of more than 84,000 registered voters, only 24,328 took the trouble to go to the polls.

San Francisco officials and those East Bay citizens who still favored a metropolitan water district again took hope, but they failed to understand the persistence of Dr. Pardee. Although he had suffered a defeat, he and his co-workers had not abandoned the goal of a separate publicly owned water system for the East Bay. Other in-

fluential men in Oakland and Berkeley would continue to appeal to their fellow citizens to unite with San Francisco on the Hetch Hetchy development, but by the summer of 1914 there was only the most remote possibility that the East Bay would ever accept the suggestion.

Exposition and Civic Center

Political differences and a growing belief that the East Bay must avoid "entangling alliances" with San Francisco did not, however, diminish the interest of East Bay residents in the Panama-Pacific International Exposition and in the civic activity in San Francisco stimulated by it. The vitality displayed by this city which only a few years before had been shattered by earthquakes and gutted by fire evoked admiration even from Oakland and Alameda politicians who most feared its influence. Its citizens had an amazing capacity for rising to great occasions and throwing themselves wholeheartedly into undertakings which symbolized their faith in its future.

In 1911 the community leaders of San Francisco began to think of the exposition and a proposed civic center almost as twin enterprises. Even those who had formerly opposed the building of a new city hall and related public buildings agreed that it would be unthinkable for San Francisco to play host to the world without having suitable buildings in which to welcome visiting dignitaries and to use for other public functions. For a time during the summer of 1911 the directors of the exposition company contemplated planning a dispersed exposition that would build up the city generally and add the greatest possible number of permanent improvements. A special committee on selection of a site, advised by Willis Polk and other architects, recommended developing a yacht harbor, park, and aquarium at Harbor View (now the Marina), constructing a boulevard along the northern and western waterfronts from Telegraph Hill to the western end of Golden Gate Park, building an art gallery and various other structures at the eastern end of Golden Gate Park, and erecting a combination opera house and convention hall "at a civic center somewhere in the location of Van Ness Avenue and Market Street."[11] One of the arguments for this proposal was that it would give the city another opportunity to carry out some of the features of the neglected Burnham Plan, such as the Yacht Harbor, Outer Drive, and the Civic Center. But upon further consideration the exposition directors concluded that a concentration of buildings at Harbor View would assure exhibitors the mass attendance they desired. The directors did agree, however, that the exposition company should erect an auditorium in the civic center on a site provided

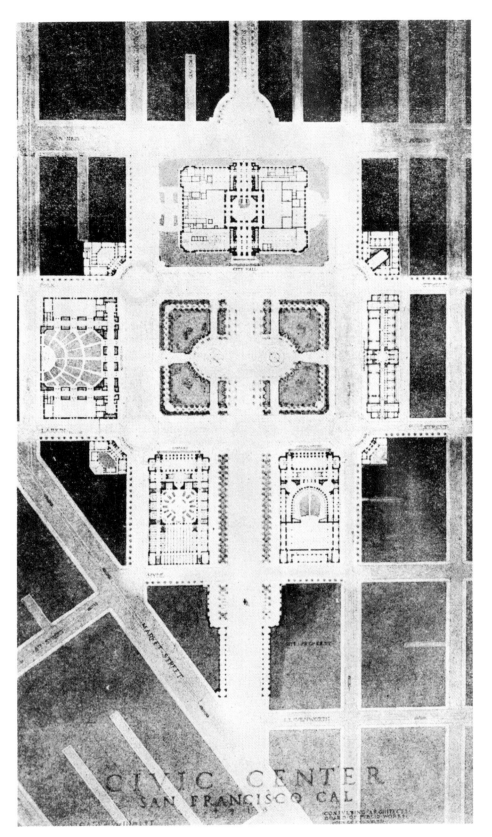

Plan for the San Francisco Civic Center, 1913. The City Hall, Civic Auditorium, and State Building are situated as shown in this scheme by architects John Galen Howard, Fred H. Meyer, and John Reid, Jr. The Public Library occupies the site suggested for an opera house. A twin structure proposed for the site on the opposite side of the mall has never been built. Photograph courtesy of Bancroft Library, University of California.

by the city. The prospect of a permanent building as a gift to the city served as a powerful incentive to city officials to come to a decision regarding the development of a civic center.

In planning this focal point of governmental activity the San Francisco Board of Supervisors sought the advice of a committee of distinguished architects, among whom were Edward H. Bennett, Willis Polk, and John Galen Howard, the official architect of the University of California. These three had always been equally ardent in championing the Burnham Plan; yet when the time came for them to submit a report to the public buildings committee of the board, they were at odds. Howard, W. B. Faville, Clarence R. Ward, and H. D. Connick recommended that the new city hall be built on the old site at Larkin and McAllister streets and that the other buildings of the civic center be grouped around it. Considerations of convenience, economy, and aesthetic possibilities supported the choice of this location, they asserted. Bennett and Polk, on the other hand, cited almost identical reasons in favor of their minority recommendation that the civic center be developed around the intersection of Market Street and Van Ness Avenue, which Burnham had approved in 1909.

Plans and suggestions submitted by more than fifty other architects to the public buildings committee of the board of supervisors tended to reinforce the choice of Howard and his majority group. The committee of the board therefore recommended on January 15, 1912, that lands for a civic center be purchased within the area bounded by Van Ness Avenue, Hayes Street, Market Street, and Golden Gate Avenue and that the new city hall be erected on the old site.

Aesthetic reasons for favoring the old site appeared to loom as large in the committee's thinking as practical ones, such as nearness to major commercial areas and avoidance of the necessity of rearranging streets. The old site offered "exceptional opportunities for vistas" of the city hall along Eighth Street and Fulton Street; it lent itself to "loftier and more monumental elevations"; and it offered a connection with the "best topographical route for an extension of the Park Panhandle to the Civic Center."[12] Mention of this perennially popular project indicated that the Burnham influence was still at work.

Because of the overwhelming sentiment in favor of the old site, the board of supervisors proceeded with plans for a civic center in the eighteen-block area recommended. It sought definite assurances from the exposition company that that organization would spend $1,000,000 to erect "a monumental auditorium" if the people voted to acquire a site in the civic center; it appointed John Galen Howard,

Fred H. Meyer, and John Reid, Jr., as consulting architects to advise on the procedure to be adopted to secure plans and specifications for the proposed city hall and civic center; and it scheduled a special election to authorize the issuance of bonds to acquire lands for the civic center and for construction of a city hall.

Approval of the $8,800,000 bond issue by a vote of ten to one on March 28, 1912, was followed the next day by a formal invitation to San Francisco architects to file their credentials by April 5 for a competition to be held to select an architectural firm to design the city hall. Competitions were then the favorite means of choosing architects for important public buildings. For this one the first prize was $25,000. Architects whose designs placed among the twenty "next best" were each to receive $1,000. The keen interest of the architectural profession in this contest was evidenced by requests from 110 individuals and firms for copies of the rules governing the competition.

On June 20, 1912, a jury composed of the mayor, one member of the board of public works, one member of the public buildings committee of the board of supervisors, the three consulting architects, and an architect selected by the competitors announced that plans submitted by the firm of John Bakewell and Arthur Brown, Jr., had been awarded the first prize.

From Plan to Reality

Commissioned on June 24, Bakewell and Brown set about designing a $3,500,000 edifice to be erected not on the old site at Larkin and McAllister streets but on a new site in the blocks bounded by Van Ness Avenue, and McAllister, Polk, and Grove streets. While the competition had been under way, the consulting architects had prepared two schemes for a civic center, one with the city hall on the old site, the other with the city hall on the Van Ness Avenue site and an opera house and public library on the site of the old city hall. Study of these two schemes by numerous civic organizations and by the local chapter of the American Institute of Architects had resulted in unanimous support of scheme "B," which would place the city hall on Van Ness Avenue. To make sure that opinions were carefully formed, the consulting architects had asked the civic groups and architects to consider specific points, such as the approach to the civic center, architectural effect, convenience of location, the position of a central plaza around which buildings would be grouped, the prevailing direction of the winds, and the relation of the buildings to the streetcar system. Fortified by the verdict of the civic organizations, the board of supervisors had voted fourteen to four to approve the scheme relocating the city hall.

Elevation Drawing of the San Francisco City Hall, Arthur Brown, Jr., and John Bakewell, Architects. Photograph courtesy of Bancroft Library.

Under this plan a new, broad avenue on the axis of Fulton Street was opened from Market Street to a five-acre central plaza with formal gardens. The City Hall and other major structures were built facing this open space. Leavenworth and Hyde streets were extended to Market Street through the site of the old city hall.

Of the first buildings erected in the Civic Center, only the Civic Auditorium was ready for use at the time the exposition opened, on February 20, 1915. The great convention hall, which the city's consulting architects had designed at the request of the exposition company, was the scene of a magnificent masked ball on the evening of January 9, 1915, when it was officially dedicated. The City Hall was not dedicated until the exposition was about to close, and not until March 1, 1916, did city employees actually move in. Construction of the Public Library did not begin until March, 1915, a month after the exposition opened. And the opera house that the San Francisco Musical Association was prepared to finance was not built—at least it was not built at that time and was never to be on the proposed site at Larkin and Grove streets.

Mayor James Rolph, Jr., and the wealthy men who had subscribed to the opera house fund reached an impasse when they asked for the privilege of bidding at public auction for permanent ownership of the boxes. The mayor denounced the request as "vicious and undemocratic" and vetoed the ordinance setting aside land for the opera house. Not until 1918 was another attempt made to raise funds for an opera house, and after a year that campaign was abandoned, far short of the goal of $2,000,000.

The Civic Center that came into being in accordance with the site plan prepared by Howard, Meyer, and Reid was in the tradition of L'Enfant, Baron Haussmann, and the World's Columbian Exposition at Chicago in 1893. It was in every respect the product of the "City Beautiful" movement and could be regarded as a partial fulfillment of the city plan prepared in 1905 by Burnham and Bennett, even though the arrangement of the buildings differed radically from that of the original plan. The City Hall, surmounted by a dome reminiscent of the one Michelangelo designed for St. Peter's, and the Civic Auditorium, with its low octagonal dome and classic façade, were truly monumental, as city officials, citizens, and the architects of the time wished them to be. So, too, was the Public Library designed by George W. Kelham. Italian Renaissance in style and adorned with heroic figures representing Art, Literature, Philosophy, Science, and Law, it was as frankly derivative as the other structures facing the huge plaza. These were buildings intended to glorify the city in much the same way that Renaissance cathedrals were intended to glorify the institution of the Church and baroque palaces the institution of monarchy. In a democracy holding the belief that government is the servant of the people there was something essentially false about them. As a group they overpower the citizen and reduce him to insignificance, whereas less pretentious structures arranged round a square bearing a closer relation to the architectural elements might communicate to the taxpayer and voter a sense of identification with local government. It is not the grand tradition that is out of place in San Francisco; rather it is the misconception of what the grand tradition is that seems alien. And yet there are

those who pay high tribute to this Civic Center and honor the San Francisco of 1911–1916 for setting an example of large-scale, axial planning for other cities of the United States to follow in developing administrative centers. Christopher Tunnard, for instance, says that this group of monumental buildings may be regarded "as one of the very best civic complexes in the United States."[13] Certainly it is one of the most imposing.

Pleasure Domes

While this structure, of Ecole des Beaux-Arts inspiration, was taking shape, its impermanent sibling, the exposition, was born, lived briefly, and died, except for one superb architectural fantasy that San Franciscans cherished more than all the gray grandeur in the Civic Center—Bernard Maybeck's Palace of Fine Arts. This beautifully realized expression of a timeless melancholy won a popular reprieve from destruction at the close of the exposition and entered upon a perilous survival. Among older residents of the city it now evokes memories of a civic adventure

Palace of Fine Arts, Panama-Pacific International Exposition, 1915. As Architect Bernard R. Maybeck intended, this building gives the impression of "sadness modified by the feeling that beauty has a soothing influence."

that was one of the high points in the history of San Francisco.

To provide a site for the exposition, engineers completely transformed the waterfront area lying between Fort Mason and the Presidio. In 1911, when the exposition company decided that this section, then known as Harbor View, was most appropriate as a site for a world's fair with a maritime theme, a shallow cove indented the shoreline and a brackish lagoon extended into the Presidio between Baker and Lyon streets. Scattered about the adjacent bottom lands were more than four hundred structures, large and small, including a fifty-room apartment house, a gas reservoir, and the Fulton Engineering and Shipbuilding Works. All these buildings, the cove, and the lagoon disappeared as engineers prepared the 635-acre site for building operations. More than a hundred acres of submerged land curving along the shore within the Presidio reservation also were filled with dredged material. By February, 1913, land extending two and a half miles along the northern waterfront was ready for building operations. Included in the site were 18 acres of Fort Mason, 330 acres (eighty-one blocks) of Harbor View, and 287 acres of the Presidio.

Here, facing inward upon a series of connecting courts, rose eleven main palaces, constituting a related and particularly harmonious group of buildings. Their arrangement, based on a site plan developed by Edward Bennett, suggested a compact, walled city, somewhat oriental in character. The atmosphere of the East was further conveyed by low Byzantine domes, red tile roofs, and mellow, muted colors selected by Jules Guerin for the domes, portals, columns, walls, and architectural ornament. Except for the dominant Tower of Jewels, an architectural wedding cake shimmering with gems of purest glass, the architecture of the exposition eschewed the festive and frivolous and was of a generally high quality, though eclectic. Not only did such well-known San Francisco architects as George W. Kelham, Louis C. Mullgardt, Arthur Brown, Jr., Clarence R. Ward, Willis Polk, and William B. Faville participate in designing the various structures; Thomas Hastings, Henry Bacon, and the firm of McKim, Mead and White, all of New York, also received commissions from the exposition company. Polk was to have designed the Palace of Fine Arts but generously withdrew in favor of Maybeck when the latter, after conversations with Polk, was inspired to produce some sketches in charcoal and subdued colors depicting a loggia and dome rising from a lake, against a colonnade partly encircling it. These sketches, the exposition architects agreed, promised a building of surpassing beauty. Their expectations were more than fulfilled.

"The Palace of Fine Arts is so sublime, so majestic, and is the product of such imagination that it would have graced the age of Pericles," declared Dr. Van Noppen, Professor of Dutch Literature and Art at Columbia University. "For the first time have I seen color and form blended into perfection. It is not only the glory of San Francisco, but it ought to be the pride of all America. Nothing in any eastern city is at all comparable with it."[14]

Judgments equally rapturous emanated from art critics and humble laymen alike. Maybeck had, in his own words, sought to produce an effect of "sadness modified by the feeling that beauty has a soothing influence."[15] How well he succeeded! His palace touched the emotions of all who beheld it. It was the most talked about, the most photographed building of the entire exposition. In a world then engulfed in the flames of war the note of sadness perhaps was doubly meaningful, but this building was also eloquent of human values that endure. It had its place in an exposition dedicated to the future—an exposition bravely completed and opened on schedule even though many European countries had been forced to cancel plans to erect buildings in the area reserved for the states of the Union and for foreign governments.

"The spirit that made San Francisco dare to invite the world to an institution of international rejoicing in this year of international chaos is merely the expansion of the spirit in which San Francisco met her own calamity," Chester H. Rowell wrote in the *California Outlook* of April 24, 1915. "It is the finest spirit in the world. And the surest pledge that the human race is going to survive unscathed this year of catastrophe is the example which, on a small scale but before a world audience, San Francisco is now giving of the unwearying resilience of human nature. The world is only San Francisco's calamity writ large. As there are more to suffer it; so there are more to face it. What San Francisco is doing, the world can and will do."

The City Beneficial

World War I not only restricted the participation of foreign governments in the exposition; it limited the commercial use of the Panama Canal and reduced maritime trade, so that the West Coast did not benefit appreciably from the opening of the new intercoastal route until the early 'twenties. Before the outbreak of the war, however, Pacific Coast port cities, especially those in the Bay Area, were so sure of a new era of prosperity and population growth that they became seriously interested in city planning. So great, indeed, was the impetus given the city planning movement in California during 1913 and 1914 that it gathered momentum all during the war years and achieved the enactment of enabling legislation under which numerous cities established city planning commissions and adopted zoning ordinances intended to insure more orderly use of land.

In San Francisco the traditions of the "City Beautiful" movement remained strong, because the press and many prominent architects and public figures remembered the Burnham Plan and looked to it as an ideal; but in the East Bay the apostles of city planning accented a new note—the "City Beneficial" or the "City Practical." In a series of articles written for the Oakland *Tribune* in October, 1913, at the time the famous German city planner Werner Hegemann was invited to come to Oakland, Charles Henry Cheney, a California architect, pointed out that "modern city planning places small emphasis on the aesthetic and the beautiful, except that they may be productive of economical results, and lays particular stress upon practical and constructive ideas." Not that Cheney failed to recognize that Oakland needed "a proper civic center about which to group its buildings, a park system, a landscape study of the lay-out of a complete boulevard system, and particularly a study of the important matter of proper placing for future buildings of every kind that are at all monumental." But he wanted all this "as a part of a complete city planning study, which embraces also traffic and traffic arteries and the study of housing conditions and sanitation. . . ."[16]

Duncan McDuffie, a Berkeley developer who was one of the leaders of a state-wide movement to beautify cities by planting street trees, discovered that Hegemann, when invited "to tell Berkeley she ought to beautify herself," was a good deal less interested in looking at treeless residential streets than in "going down to the waterfront, walking the length of the municipal wharf, examining our outfall sewers, talking with manufacturers about shipping facilities, and with West Berkeley residents regarding rents and housing conditions." The German visitor, McDuffie soon saw, was "a planner, not only of cities good to look at, but of cities good to live in."[17] He represented a new conception of city planning, which the cities of the East Bay, at least, were then eager to embrace.

In 1912 Hegemann had been brought to the United States by the People's Institute of New York. Though a comparatively young man, he was already internationally renowned as secretary of the Committee for the Architectural Development of Greater Berlin and as general secretary of the City Planning Exhibitions of Berlin and Düsseldorf. As he traveled through the eastern states giving lectures and preparing city planning reports on New York, Philadelphia, Baltimore, Syracuse, and Rochester, his fame spread to the Middle West and the Far West. His advice was sought by Cleveland, by cities in the Mississippi Valley, by Denver, and then by Sacramento. From there he was invited to Oakland by the City Council. Soon after his arrival in Oakland, early in October, 1913, the Berkeley City Council, at the urging of Cheney and Professor Thomas H. Reed, of the Political Science Department of the University of California, engaged him "to inspect and report on conditions . . . and make recommendations."[18]

The Economic Basis

Hegemann, unlike the "City Beautiful" planners, approached the future circumspectly, asking himself some fundamental questions: What is a city? What are the reasons for its existence? On what does its future depend? Having posed these questions, he could not begin with plans for civic centers, parks, and boulevards. His starting point was the city economic, because he understood that a city is, above all, a place in which men pool their material resources, skills, and talents to make a living. It is a focus of production and distribution, and its opportunities for cultural advancement and civic achievement depend on the health of its economy. "The development of the wide area of a modern great city necessarily rests on the economic basis of commerce and industry," he began the first chapter of his *Report on a City Plan for the Municipalities of Oakland & Berkeley*. But he came swiftly to a conclusion that present-day economists would question: "The most efficient instrument of commerce and industry is a large harbor. The harbor binds together railroad and water transportation and produces at the place of exchange between land and water the ideal industrial site with the possibility of cheaply transforming, combining and distributing the transient goods. All large cities necessarily must have large harbors." And so he was convinced that "the future of the cities on the Bay and especially on the east side of San Francisco Bay, will depend on the development of a harbor."[19]

If subsequent economic developments have shown ports to be relatively less important in the economy of the Bay Area than they appeared to be at the time of the completion of the Panama Canal, Hegemann can hardly be blamed for failure to foresee conditions twenty, thirty, or forty years later. What he did see was that the East Bay cities had given "little forethought" to the development of one of the finest harbors on the Pacific Coast and that the opportunities for growth based on port development were great indeed. In his enthusiasm for harbor development he reflected the intense interest of Bay Area residents in building a new maritime trade with the Atlantic seaboard and Europe. That such trade, coupled with the

Pacific trade, would be the key to future prosperity of the West Coast, few people in the Bay Area then doubted. More significant than Hegemann's overemphasis on the importance of shipping in the future economy of the Bay Area was his appreciation of the city as an economic complex and his realization that city planning could contribute to the efficient functioning of the city. His was not the narrow, utilitarian approach that belittles the value of neighborhood amenities, stately public buildings, and effects that please the eye and uplift the spirit; he was aware that if city planning was to gain the popular support it deserved, it would have to stress those things which make the city more productive, more healthful, more convenient. "If civic art is the sublime flower that finally can be hoped for," he wrote, "the necessary roots, stems, and leaves must be found in the economic, social, hygienic and recreational life of the communities."20

As a first-class harbor seemed to him essential for the future growth and development of Oakland, he endorsed the Rees Plan for comprehensive development of the East Bay waterfront from Richmond to Oakland. On the west shore, rather than in the confined Inner Harbor formed by the estuary, Oakland would find the greatest possibilities for port expansion, he pointed out. But he deplored the city's having granted the Key Route a franchise that permitted it literally to "throw stones" across the entrance to the proposed deep-water channel along the East Bay waterfront. This franchise, he insisted, must somehow be revoked; and Oakland, Berkeley, and Richmond must unite in support of the Rees Plan. "Only a harbor that is large and that is growing larger each day can in the long run attract trade and wealth, and be the powerful instrument of civilization that attracts national activities," he contended.21

The Bay as the Harbor

Hegemann did not limit his study of harbor problems to the East Bay. He viewed separate and uncoördinated development of port facilities at various points around the bay as a mistake as great as that of the haphazard and disconnected method of providing harbor facilities in Oakland. "This regime [of administration of harbor facilities by different local bodies] has made comprehensive development impossible; it invites inefficient rivalry; it is a serious menace for the future and is against the fundamental rule of harbor organization," he wrote. "Somehow, and the sooner the better, the recommendable 'Hands Around the Harbor' movement must for the sake of higher efficiency lead to a uniform management of the Bay as a whole, a management of course, in which the East Bay interests are represented in a manner that cor-

responds to the superior strategic value of the East Bay section as a harbor to be."22

Had the distinguished German planner been alive in 1951 to read a report of the state senate's Fact-Finding Committee on San Francisco Bay Ports, he would have been interested in statements attributing some of the noticeable loss in the Pacific coastwise and intercoastal trades to lack of promotion of San Francisco Bay as a single harbor. "Much is being done by individual port and political units to make themselves competitive [with harbors elsewhere in the United States]. Very little is being done to make the *harbor* competitive. As some witnesses indicated, it is not necessarily the fault of the communities, ports, or terminals that this situation prevails; it is the result largely of the geographical aspects of the harbor area. The water of the harbor physically divides the units, whereas, from the point of view of the users of the harbor facilities, the water should unify every unit that borders on the Bay."23 Although the committee recommended voluntary coöperation to make the harbor more competitive, rather than uniform management under a Bay Area port authority, its findings indicated that Hegemann was farseeing in warning of the dangers of failure to view San Francisco Bay as *the* harbor. Time may yet prove that he was wise to propose unified management of the harbor.

A Variety of Proposals

As was to be expected of a man who viewed city planning as a broad function capable of contributing to both the economic well-being and the livability of the community, Hegemann offered suggestions on everything from railroads and transit to parks and civic centers. He pointed out the desirability of consolidating the railroad traffic of the East Bay on two wide, grade-separated "railroad highways"—one to the north along the bay shore, the other to the east along the Oakland Inner Harbor. He noted that the suburban transit services of the East Bay had been planned mainly to provide connections with San Francisco and that transit from Oakland to other East Bay cities was intolerably slow and poorly routed. For proper growth of the East Bay he recommended extending rapid transit to all parts of the area and providing special transit highways, perhaps on elevated structures, between Oakland and Berkeley. To relieve the congestion caused by the convergence of radial streets in the heart of Oakland, he proposed creating a "delivery loop" capable of detouring as much traffic as possible around the center —a proposal so thoroughly sound that every planner who followed him within the next thirty-five years suggested something similar. Unusually appreciative of the vast social importance of decent, low-cost housing for workingmen and their families, Hegemann pinned his hopes for better housing less on municipal regulations advocated by the housing reformers of the time than on eventual rationalization of the building process, large-scale planning and construction, and lower interest rates on loans for the purchase of homes. Like the elder Olmsted and Charles Mulford Robinson, he recognized the possibilities of developing parks and scenic parkways along the creeks and canyons in the Berkeley Hills, including the beautiful Indian Gulch, or Sather Tract, northeast of Lake Merritt in Oakland. In addition to these, he proposed a Midway Plaisance or chain of parks and playgrounds through central Berkeley and an Island Park on the fill that would form the west side of the projected Rees Channel. Opportunity to develop the Midway Plaisance was lost within a few years by rapid building in the area designated, but something similar to the Island Park might be achieved in the future if Berkeley ever fills the thousands of acres of tidelands that belong to it. In his final chapter Hegemann suggested, among other things, a group of public buildings in the general area in which Oakland is slowly building an administrative and cultural center, near the southwestern end of Lake Merritt.

Campus Development

At the time Hegemann was in the East Bay, John Galen Howard published a revision of his plan of 1908 for the campus of the University of California. The revised scheme, relating numerous detached buildings to a broad, formal, east-west axis parallel to the axis proposed by the elder Olmsted in 1866, impressed the German planner as being a design for a development that would surpass any civic center in the state and even the capitol grounds in Sacramento. He had, however, grave doubts that the plan could be adhered to as the needs of the university changed, and he questioned whether, "in view of the menacing lack of space," it would be possible—and artistically desirable—"to try the difficult experiment of basing the final formal effect upon grouping of detached buildings." He was inclined to believe that a scheme which made provision for physically connecting buildings as additions were needed would produce a more satisfying campus in the long run, although he conceded that "the idea of having the buildings all detached is more worthy of California, where the climate makes every walk from one building to another a real delight."[24]

Howard's revised plan of 1914 was adopted by the Regents of the University as a basis for guiding the future building program and was, with occasional modifications, followed until the 'forties. In the period 1902–1914

Howard had arranged the Hearst Memorial Mining Building, the Charles Franklin Doe Library, Agriculture Hall, and other buildings for which he prepared plans, in relation to the axis shown in his 1908 and 1914 plans. Upon the passage, in November, 1914, of a state bond issue of $1,800,000 for new construction at the university, three new buildings—Wheeler Hall, Gilman Hall, and Hilgard Hall—were immediately begun, all placed in accordance with the revised plan. Thus the scheme of detached buildings related to an axis centering on the Golden Gate was well along toward realization soon after Hegemann wrote his report.

Planning Commissions

The German planner closed his report with a recommendation that the city councils of Oakland and Berkeley adopt ordinances providing for the appointment of city planning commissions at once. Indeed, he saw the need for planning bodies in all the East Bay cities, for frequent convocations of all the commissions, and for exchange of information among the "permanent secretaries" of the commissions. He did not, however, mention the need for metropolitan regional planning, or what Bion Arnold called "metropolitan district control," although a plea for such planning might have been expected from one who regarded San Francisco Bay as a single harbor. Hegemann tended, in the short time that he was in the Bay Area, to become a partisan of the East Bay. Nevertheless, he influenced the whole Bay Area by advocating the creation of planning commissions with "sufficient funds at their disposal not only to employ permanent secretaries but also outside expert advice on important issues in the solution of each of their particular problems." And he stated clearly what the individual communities needed: "a city-plan, very flexible in detail but firm in all matters of principle," which once having been worked out could be "safeguarded and made efficient by legislative acts, ordinances, funds, and daily practice."[25] In other words, the plan was not an end in itself but a guide for developing a better city. The process of carrying it out was as important as the plan itself.

Hegemann's report, though completed in 1914, was not published until 1915. By that time it was but one of many documents emphasizing the need for local planning bodies. San Francisco and Berkeley had already taken steps toward establishing official city planning commissions—the former by passing an ordinance authorizing the appointment of a city planning commission, the latter by creating a semiofficial body called the City Planning Committee. A permanent, official commission would have been established in Berkeley, however, if the city charter

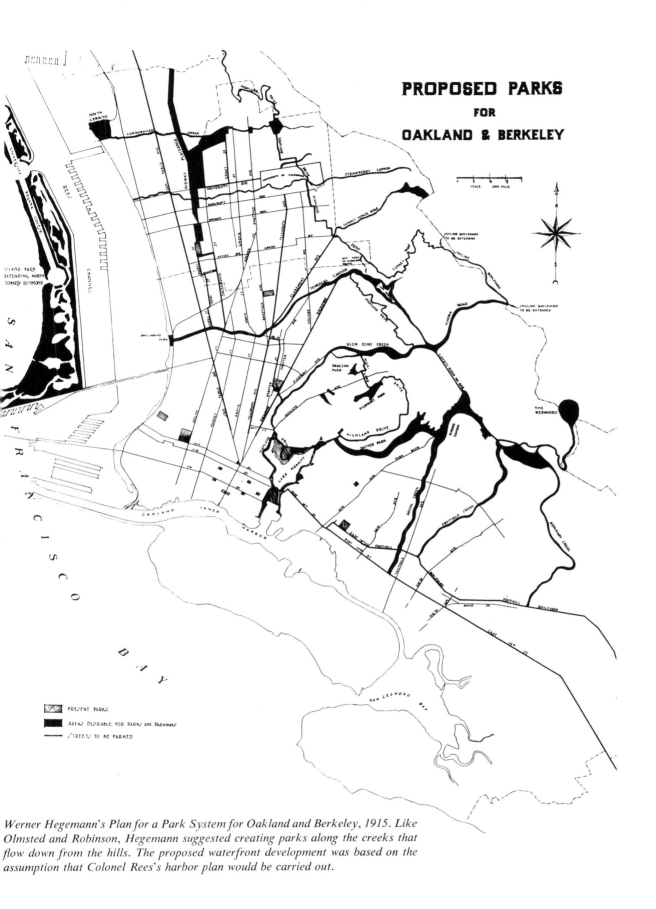

PROPOSED PARKS
FOR
OAKLAND & BERKELEY

Werner Hegemann's Plan for a Park System for Oakland and Berkeley, 1915. Like Olmsted and Robinson, Hegemann suggested creating parks along the creeks that flow down from the hills. The proposed waterfront development was based on the assumption that Colonel Rees's harbor plan would be carried out.

had not provided for setting up a city planning organization to be called the Civic Art Commission. Since the term "civic art" was then in disrepute, the city council was unwilling to risk passing an ordinance establishing an official body with the title mentioned in the charter.

A Crusader for Planning

The major credit for new planning developments in the Bay Area belongs not so much to Hegemann as to Charles Henry Cheney, who seems almost to have used the German planner as an instrument for fulfilling his own burning desire to have city planning accepted as a new and permanent function of local government. Cheney was one of those able propagandists who appear in the vanguard of every important movement. After he was graduated in architecture from the University of California in 1905, he studied at the Ecole des Beaux-Arts in Paris, traveled extensively on the continent and in England, and lived in New York, learning everything he could about "the best city planning thought and development in this country."[26] When he returned to California in 1912, he was fired with zeal for the cause of city planning. He wrote articles on planning for newspapers, advocated the employment of Hegemann by Oakland and Berkeley, was prominently instrumental in bringing to Oakland and San Francisco a huge city planning exhibit prepared by the American City Bureau of New York, and was a prime mover in the organization of the city planning section of the Commonwealth Club.

Through the Commonwealth Club the young architect met Percy V. Long, San Francisco City Attorney, who became his steadfast partner in the crusade for city planning. Long at first thought that city planning was primarily a matter of aesthetics; but once Cheney convinced him that it was a "sensible and practical" means of effecting municipal economies and saving the taxpayers money, he plunged into the work of drafting enabling legislation for local planning and helped Cheney arrange a state-wide conference on city planning, to be held in Monterey, October 12–14, 1914.

Long enlisted the talents of the San Francisco Bay Area City Attorneys' Club in formulating the desired planning act. Cheney sent invitations to the conference to the city councilmen of every city in California, city engineers and city architects, chambers of commerce and other promotional organizations, city clubs and municipal leagues, improvement clubs, real-estate associations, societies of engineers and architects, the Commonwealth Club, and park, harbor, housing, industrial, and other commissions. In southern California he had active support for his and Long's organizing efforts from a number

Charles Henry Cheney, Crusader for City Planning. Photograph courtesy of Warren Cheney.

of men who had attended the national planning conferences held annually in the East ever since 1909.

The first California Conference on City Planning was neatly calculated to impress the state legislature with the widespread support for proposed planning legislation. It was held simultaneously with the seventeenth annual meeting of the League of California Municipalities, so that city officials attending sessions of the League might also participate in conference deliberations. Long, Cheney, and Gordon Whitnall, who was among the stalwarts of the planning movement in southern California, made many converts to their cause, and by the close of the conference had won overwhelming endorsement of the proposed planning law drafted by the city attorneys of the Bay Area.

The Local Planning Act

As passed by the legislature on May 21, 1915, the first city planning enabling act of the State of California differed only in minor details from the measure discussed at Monterey. It made physical planning permissive for cities rather than mandatory, because a mandatory provision would not have been in accord with the local home-rule provisions incorporated in the State Constitution. It authorized the legislative body of each municipality to create a nonpaid citizens' commission which, as an advisory body, would make recommendations to various officials, the legislative body, and even to private corporations and individuals concerning the future growth, development, and beautification of the municipality. To provide a basis for its recommendations, the commission was authorized "to prepare maps or plans" for the physical development of the city, including not only plans for streets, parks, public and private buildings, works, and grounds, but plans for sanitation, utilities, harbor, shipping, and transportation facilities. Thus this pioneer legislation extended the scope of city planning far beyond what it had been in the "City Beautiful" days. Further, the new law provided that the city council should refer plans of proposed subdivisions to the planning commission for report and recommendation before taking final action. The act also authorized the council to zone the city on the advice of the city planning commission, designating appropriate areas for residence, commerce, and industry.

Like all legislation in a new field, the act contained phraseology that was broad, vague, and ambiguous. It was, moreover, almost an open invitation to cities to undertake piecemeal planning, because it failed to indicate the interrelatedness and interdependence of the various plans mentioned. But its explicit authorization of physical planning ended permanently all controversies over whether cities could legally carry on city planning as a continuing, official function under the broad grants of power given them in the State Constitution.

Commissions in Action

San Bruno, in San Mateo County, is generally credited with being the first charterless California city to establish a city planning commission under the 1915 planning enabling act. Other cities in the Bay Area which promptly availed themselves of the authorization to create planning commissions were San Rafael and Martinez. Palo Alto and San Jose followed their example in 1916, Alameda in 1917, Richmond in 1918, and San Mateo in 1920.

After passage of the 1915 act the Berkeley City Council mustered sufficient courage to enact an ordinance establishing a city planning commission with the unpopular name Civic Art Commission, as the charter required. Duncan McDuffie, its president, undertook to allay the suspicion that this aesthetic designation aroused. In talks to citizens he sought to emphasize the broad approach of the commission to the planning function: "The commission must know all there is to know about Berkeley . . . before it can plan wisely."[27]

From his remarks a citizen might have gathered that the new commission intended to prepare a comprehensive plan showing what Berkeley could become if it made the most of its economic and cultural opportunities. But the Civic Art Commission actually had no funds for the preparation of such a plan. Moreover, though the members of the commission talked about broad-scale planning, their primary interest proved to be zoning, then being adopted as a practical means of safeguarding cities from the obvious chaos created by the invasion of apartment houses, stores, and even factories into single-family residential districts. The preparation of a zoning or districting ordinance was the first undertaking of the Civic Art Commission.

The measure it recommended to the Berkeley City Council in 1916 set up eight classifications of zones that could be established for particular areas upon petition of the owners of at least 25 per cent of the street frontage. Since more than 90 per cent of all the buildings in Berkeley were single-family residences, the primary purpose of the ordinance was to substitute municipal regulation for the deed restrictions imposed by private developers. These restrictions were expiring in some residential areas and had only a few years to run in other areas. Property owners, therefore, feared that the value of their homes would be destroyed by unwelcome flats and apartments or, worse still, by stores and small factories. The ordinance did provide, however, for two classifications of districts in which industry would be protected from the intrusion of residences—a most unusual feature at a time when residential areas were being accorded much protection and industrial districts were offered little or none.

Under this experimental legislation, which the city council adopted on March 28, 1916, Berkeley embarked upon a program of piecemeal zoning that preserved existing conditions. The whole practice of zoning was so novel that the planning commissioners and Cheney, their consultant, were of the opinion that an apartment house which happened to be in a single-family residential area would have to be zoned in a separate classification, instead of being included as a nonconforming use.

The Demand for Zoning

Four months after Berkeley adopted its ordinance providing for zoning by petition, New York City adopted the first comprehensive zoning ordinance in the United States, under which every block in the five boroughs of the city was placed in one of three classes of use districts: residential, commercial, and unrestricted (chiefly industrial). The ordinance also created five classes of districts limiting the height of buildings and five limiting the percentage of the lot that might be built upon. The example thus set by the largest municipality in the nation tended to focus the attention of cities throughout the country on problems of haphazard and unregulated development—overcrowding of the land, lack of air space and light between buildings, excessive density of population in tenement areas, and dangerous and unhealthful mixtures of machine shops, laundries, smoke-producing factories, and residential structures. Uncritical enthusiasts failed to note that the "model" New York ordinance was a fantastically unrealistic enactment which permitted enough building to house 77,000,000 people. To these new champions of zoning, this form of regulation was principally a device for preventing property losses. City assessors, particularly, viewed zoning as a type of fiscal salvation. "Improper development" in residential areas, they informed worried citizens, would considerably reduce assessed valuations and thereby cause the city to lose large sums of taxes, whereas zoning would assure the maintenance of the tax base. Zoning was a "must." To be without it was to invite individual and collective ruin.

In the spring of 1917 the city planning section of the Commonwealth Club sent a questionnaire to more than three hundred and fifty bankers, real-estate owners, and the city assessors of San Francisco and neighboring cities asking them to list examples of the intrusion of garages, stables, laundries, planing mills, undertaking parlors, and apartment houses in residential districts. On the basis of replies received, the section concluded that "many concrete instances clearly show the enormous cost of lack of regulation" and that "in San Francisco proper over one-half the total property, assessed for over three hundred million dollars, is . . . adversely affected for lack of a zone ordinance, such as Los Angeles, New York, Minneapolis and every other progressive city already has put into effect."[28]

Concern over zoning had now become so great throughout California that people interested in city planning gave little thought to anything else. Indeed, zoning *was* city planning to many city officials, real-estate men, and property owners. But there was much doubt whether the police power granted to cities by the State Constitution of 1879 was sufficient to permit them to enact valid zoning ordinances, and whether unchartered cities governed under the Municipal Corporations Act of 1883 legally could adopt zoning ordinances. The city planning enabling legislation of 1915 mentioned zoning as one of

the functions of city planning commissions but did not make clear the purpose or scope of zoning. Hence the California Conference on City Planning, the League of California Municipalities, the Commonwealth Club, and other organizations united in sponsoring enabling legislation authorizing cities to enact zoning regulations. The state legislature approved the proposed legislation in 1917.

The Zoning Enabling Act

The statute gave cities the explicit power to regulate private property by establishing zones or districts within which the use of property, the height of buildings, and the amount of open space could be controlled. In enacting zoning ordinances, city councils were to give reasonable consideration, among other things, to the direction of building development in accord with a "well considered plan"; but just what constituted "a well considered plan" the 1917 act did not state. Indeed, the act encouraged zoning with no reference to long-range planning by permitting cities which had no city planning commission to adopt zoning ordinances. Consequently, within the next two decades many cities adopted zoning regulations framed by city attorneys, city engineers, and others with little or no knowledge of the relationships between city planning and zoning. Instead of being used as a means of bringing about more appropriate and efficient uses of land, zoning often was an instrument for freezing existing uses, however undesirable these might be in some instances.

In San Francisco, which was still without a city planning commission even after the zoning enabling act went into effect on July 26, 1917, Mayor James Rolph, Jr., suddenly found himself under tremendous pressure to appoint planning commissioners. First, however, he demanded that the ordinance providing for the commission be revised. He notified the city planning section of the Commonwealth Club that he would name a committee of citizens to redraft the ordinance, and that if the revision met his approval, he would name the commissioners. Among the members of the committee he selected to revise the ordinance was Charles Cheney, the tireless and omnipresent Mr. City Planning.

By this time the agitation for a planning commission in San Francisco had shifted from arguments based on planning considerations to arguments based on the maintenance of property values through zoning. In 1915, when the Panama-Pacific International Exposition was in full swing, the San Francisco *Call*, the Downtown Association, the Home Industry League, the Rotary Club, and various architects, including Willis Polk, had all urged the appointment of a planning commission, so that the city might take steps to preserve as permanent improvements the Marina, the Palace of Fine Arts, the California Building, and certain other outstanding features of the exposition. Those interested in saving as much as possible of the exposition hoped that the formulation of detailed plans for the Marina and its vicinity would lead to preparation of a general plan that would show proposed improvements for all parts of the city. But a year or more after the exposition closed, the hue and cry for zoning drowned out pleas for a comprehensive plan. The Chamber of Commerce, the Real Estate Board, and other influential organizations wanted a city planning commission that would first of all prepare a zoning plan and a zoning ordinance.

And that is exactly what the commission appointed by Mayor Rolph on December 28, 1917, set about doing. It became almost exclusively concerned with a survey of the utilization of land in the city as a basis for determining various classes of zones rather than as the basis for preparing a flexible, over-all plan of the kind Hegemann would have recommended.

The Engineer as Planner

In the meantime, Michael M. O'Shaughnessy, the broad-gauge city engineer of San Francisco, continued to serve the community as a sort of city planner ex officio, as he had almost from the time he first became head of the engineering department. In the period 1912–1934 his name is associated with numerous public improvements that greatly influenced the course of physical development in the metropolis. Many of the projects carried out under his direction were, moreover, projects that had been suggested by Burnham, Bennett, Bion Arnold, and others who had a large vision of what San Francisco might become if its public officials, as representatives of the electorate, made certain farsighted policy decisions. O'Shaughnessy, although he was at times arrogant and inclined to impose his will upon others, understood that city development requires not only official action but also public participation, especially in the approval of bond issues, and the coöperation of private interests, particularly subdividers. He was tireless in his work with civic groups, with other city officials, with citizens and officials in neighboring cities and counties, and with state and federal agencies. His influence consequently extended beyond the sphere of his own department and made itself felt in matters affecting the entire Bay Area.

As one of the projectors of the Municipal Railway, O'Shaughnessy helped to develop areas of San Francisco which had long remained inaccessible—areas in which thousands of workers who lived in the East Bay might have made their homes had transportation been available.

These were the districts west of Twin Peaks, the Richmond and Marina districts, the remoter sections of North Beach, and the Mission district. Like Bion Arnold, O'Shaughnessy saw that new railway lines should be extended to these districts even though the lines might operate "in the red" for years. The primary purpose of a municipal public utility is to give service, he was fond of pointing out to critics who opposed the policy of using the "Muni" as a means of "developing the city's growth in well-ordered and predetermined directions."[29] With him as its ardent champion, this policy was consistently followed year in and year out, until the Municipal Railway was expanded from the initial, relatively short, Geary Street line in 1912 to sixty-three miles of single track in 1919. New houses sprang up by the hundreds in all the areas penetrated by the publicly owned transit facilities— the visible vindication of the policy of constructing extensions in advance of actual necessity.

Two important tunnel projects were involved in the program of railway expansion—the Stockton Street Tunnel, completed in December, 1914, and the Twin Peaks Tunnel, through which the Twin Peaks Tunnel Railway began operating on February 3, 1918. This latter bore was 11,750 feet long, fully a mile shorter than the tunnel proposed by one of the engineers employed by Bion Arnold. Since the project had to be financed by an assessment district, O'Shaughnessy had shortened the route of the tunnel, in order to reduce the cost from $7,000,000 to $4,000,000.

New Residential Tracts

The Twin Peaks Tunnel was vital to the development of residential tracts west of the hilly barrier in the geographical center of the city. Among these tracts were Westwood Park, Forest Hill, and St. Francis Wood, all on land once included in the San Miguel Rancho and later owned by Adolph Sutro. The developers, who purchased the raw land from the Sutro heirs in 1911 and put the tracts on the market in 1912, had difficulty attracting buyers at first, because of the inadequate transportation. Once the tunnel was completed, properties sold more readily, for the tracts were among the best planned in San Francisco.

Another project which aided the development of the area west of Twin Peaks was Portola Drive, a scenic route extending from St. Francis Circle to an extension of Market Street. In planning this highway through the pass between the peaks and Mount Davidson, O'Shaughnessy followed the general line of the old San Miguel Ocean House and Beach macadamized road, built in the 'sixties as a toll road to the popular Ocean House, an early-day equivalent of the modern roadhouse.

O'Shaughnessy was particularly interested in all the newer subdivisions opened in San Francisco before and during the exposition. At the annual convention of the League of California Municipalities in 1915 he quoted what Frederick C. Howe, an eastern city planner, had said about the city:

"I know of no city in America more keenly alive to its natural advantages than San Francisco. I spent several hours with the city engineer looking over St. Francis Wood, Ingleside Terraces, Forest Hill, West Clay Park, Seacliff, and other newly finished residence parks. I have seen nothing in America to equal these parks from the standpoint of brilliant suburban development."[30]

Howe was also impressed with the boulevard system which took shape rapidly between 1916 and 1920. Besides the Marina Boulevard, it included another unit that could be traced to Burnham's proposal for an Outer Drive, the road known as El Camino Del Mar, linking the Presidio with the Great Highway and the Esplanade along the Ocean Beach. Drives constructed by the federal government through the Presidio provided the necessary connections between the Marina and the Camino, on which some work had been done before the exposition opened. O'Shaughnessy also planned Sloat Boulevard, the southern boundary of the Sunset district, as a wide thoroughfare from the Great Highway to St. Francis Circle, the western terminus of Portola Drive. By the end of the decade, San Franciscans would take out-of-town visitors for a scenic automobile drive along the Marina and through the Presidio to Lobos Creek, thence through Lincoln Park to the Cliff House, down the Great Highway to the vicinity of Fort Funston and Lake Merced, eastward along Sloat Boulevard to St. Francis Circle, and then over Twin Peaks by way of Portola Drive, and down Market Street to the Civic Center.

The Metropolitan View

The city engineer would have been a backward San Francisco official if he had not taken as much interest in outlets to the Peninsula as he did in city thoroughfares. At the time the Twin Peaks Tunnel was bored, O'Shaughnessy observed that its construction would "also facilitate providing adequate means of transportation to the towns down the Peninsula, when adjacent communities see fit to become components of Greater San Francisco."[31] He recognized, though, that there was little public agitation for an interurban line from the tunnel to San Mateo County via Junipero Serra Boulevard, while there was some agitation for a Skyline Boulevard from San Fran-

cisco to Santa Cruz County and for a Bayshore Boulevard following the general route of the old San Bruno Road to a connection with El Camino Real near San Bruno. He was busy with plans for these two roads about the time the United States entered World War I.

To a man like O'Shaughnessy the eventual unification of San Francisco and San Mateo counties seemed logical and desirable. Though he recognized that the East Bay rejected consolidation with San Francisco, he still hoped, as late as 1918, that all the cities within the metropolitan area would unite in solving such common problems as water supply and transportation. Why not, he asked, form a single great public-utility district that would provide water, operate transit facilities, and perhaps perform other functions as well? Bion Arnold had seen the need for planning and developing essential utilities on a metropolitan basis. The city engineer liked the efficiency and the economy of the idea.

Looking across the bay, O'Shaughnessy saw the cities of Alameda County hard hit by a water crisis that he himself had predicted in 1916. In that year he had warned that the occurrence of two dry years in succession would cause a serious crisis in transbay urban areas. Now, in the summer of 1918, the East Bay cities were forced to prohibit the use of water for lawns and gardens. The East Bay Water Company, which had succeeded the People's Water Company as supplier of water to cities from Richmond to San Leandro, met the crisis by developing plans for a dam and reservoir on San Pablo Creek, behind the Berkeley Hills in Contra Costa County. Before this dam was completed in 1920, however, Oakland and Berkeley lost several important industries to the Los Angeles area, including a branch plant of the Goodyear Tire and Rubber Company, which could not be guaranteed a daily water supply sufficient for its needs. Nor did the new reservoir increase the supply enough to assure proper conditions for industrial growth.

Had San Francisco made great progress on the Hetch Hetchy project, the East Bay might by this time have been more interested in joining with it in forming a metropolitan water district; but disturbed financial conditions brought about by World War I had prevented the sale of some of the bonds authorized in 1910, and construction had proceeded at a snail's pace. Not until after the war was the city able to market approximately $7,000,000 in bonds and speed work on the Hetch Hetchy Dam. In the meantime, sentiment had been crystallizing in the East Bay for the formation of the type of municipal utility district advocated by Dr. George Pardee.

CHAPTER ELEVEN

Seeds of Metropolitan Regionalism

Although the Bay Area was politically unfederated, opposed to the idea of unified harbor development and management, and divided on the issue of a metropolitan water system, after 1912 it began to achieve, through the construction of state and county highways and the inauguration of additional ferry services, that greater measure of physical, economic, and social cohesion which interurban transit companies at one time gave promise of bringing about. These companies, reaching their peak of expansion about 1915, failed to provide the missing links that would have made it possible to journey from Santa Rosa to Sausalito, from San Francisco or Oakland to San Jose, from Oakland to Martinez, or from Benicia to Calistoga—or by electric railway and ferry through all the counties in the Bay Area. Yet certain vital gaps came near being filled; and the Oakland, Antioch and Eastern did link Oakland with Sacramento and other points in the great Central Valley in September, 1913.

Perhaps the greatest disappointment was expressed over the failure of the Southern Pacific to join San Francisco and San Jose by trolley and over the inability of F. M. ("Borax") Smith to extend the Key Route south of Hayward to the county seat of Santa Clara County. In 1913, in a final effort to carry out its projected line from San Francisco to San Jose, the Southern Pacific offered to include the trackage of the United Railroads between San Mateo and San Bruno in its San Francisco–San Jose route, leasing trackage rights. To this proposal the San Francisco traction company was by then agreeable, and eight new cars were ordered for the Southern Pacific's

subsidiary, the Peninsular Railway. Then came the outbreak of war, which meant the end of the through line. A scarcity of steel rails again prevented the building of the missing link between San Mateo and Los Altos, on the San Jose–Palo Alto line.

The bitter warfare between the Southern Pacific and the Key Route, which caused the former between 1908 and 1912 to build parallel lines within a few blocks of several Key Route lines, effectively checked F. M. Smith's last attempt to reach San Jose. In 1912, when he appeared to be ready to try for the third time to join Oakland and San Jose by electric railway, the Southern Pacific made plans to extend the Peninsular Railway to Oakland over the Dumbarton railroad bridge and the old South Pacific Coast Railroad route. Track was laid from Palo Alto to the bridge, while in Oakland a line was built from the downtown area to the Southern Pacific's Sixteenth Street depot. The upshot of these competitive maneuvers was a truce between the Southern Pacific and Smith whereby both agreed to refrain from connecting Oakland and San Jose by interurban. Actually, Smith's credit for large-scale, long-term borrowing was practically exhausted, and it is doubtful whether he could have completed the extension to San Jose if he had begun it.

First State Highways

Although private transit companies failed to bind together the metropolitan region with steel rails, the state and various counties succeeded in doing so with concrete roads, in response to the ever-increasing use of the private

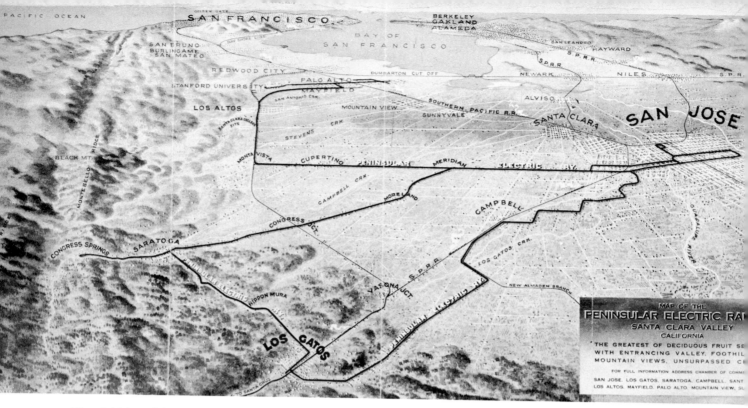

Pictorial Map of the Peninsular Electric Railway System, about 1915. Photograph courtesy of Palo Alto Public Library.

automobile, motorcycle, and truck. The state took the lead, inaugurating construction of a highway system corresponding in general with the plan formulated by the old Bureau of Highways in 1896. This system, for which the people of the state authorized $18,000,000 in bonds in 1910, was to include, in its final form, 3,052 miles of road. Its main features were two great highways, one running north and south through the Sacramento and San Joaquin valleys, the other traversing the western slope of the Coast Range from the Oregon border to Mexico. Both highways were planned to connect as many county seats as possible and to pass through the principal centers of population. Branch roads to county seats lying east and west of the two trunk highways were an integral part of the scheme. Sections of the system within the Bay Area nearly everywhere followed the historic lines of communication established during the Spanish-Mexican era.

Ground-breaking ceremonies for this far-flung system took place at South San Francisco, in San Mateo County, on August 7, 1912, and marked the beginning of the transformation of El Camino Real from a dusty county road to a two-lane state highway twenty-four feet wide, with an asphalt-on-concrete surface. By the end of 1915 El Camino Real had been paved from San Francisco to Gilroy, at the southern end of the Santa Clara Valley, and

an East Bay highway had been completed from Oakland to San Jose except for a stretch of a few miles between Niles and the Santa Clara County line. In other parts of the Bay Area there were small sections of concrete roadway: from Richmond to Pinole, from Benicia to Vacaville, from Livermore to the eastern boundary of Alameda County, and from the Marin County line to Willow Brook in Sonoma County.

The $18,000,000 voted for highway construction in the previous decade had by this time all been expended. Few, indeed, had thought that the funds would be sufficient to build even the modest state system projected in the State Highways Act of 1909, and Governor Hiram Johnson had commiserated the State Highway Commission for being expected to build for this amount a system that the best engineers in the county had estimated would cost from $35,000,000 to $50,000,000. The voters, however, were ready by 1916 to approve a second highway bond issue, providing $12,000,000 for completion of the original system and an additional $3,000,000 to be used in coöperation with counties for certain lateral roads, which, under the terms of the second bond act, were added to the state highway system. In the 1916 election, moreover, not a single county cast a plurality of votes against the bonds. The vote was four to one for good roads, whereas six years earlier the first bond issue had passed by a bare majority, fourteen counties being opposed to the state highway program.

Toward the close of the decade those parts of the state system that served the Bay Area constituted the framework of a metropolitan regional highway system. From Gilroy a motorist could travel north on the state system to San Jose, Oakland, and Martinez, cross Carquinez Strait by ferry to Benicia, and continue by way of Vacaville to Sacramento. Or he could travel from San Jose to San Francisco, cross by ferry to Sausalito, and enjoy the luxury of a paved surface all the way to Healdsburg, in northern Sonoma County, except for one small section south of Santa Rosa. A branch of the system extended eastward through Alameda County to the San Joaquin Valley, entirely paved except through Niles Canyon. In the North Bay an east-west lateral connected Petaluma, Napa, and Fairfield.

Bonds for County Roads

Counties in the Bay Area, as well as elsewhere, by this time were supplementing the state highway system with well-paved county roads. San Mateo County was the first in the Bay Area to meet the demand of its residents for improved highways by issuing county road bonds. Voters trooped to the polls on April 8, 1913, to approve $1,250,000 in bonds by a vote of four to one. With the funds provided by the bonds the county constructed an alternate route to El Camino Real, already a congested highway. The alternate road ran from San Bruno north along the shore of the bay through South San Francisco to the county line, following the route of the old San Bruno Road and, to a degree, the route of the modern Bayshore Freeway. Only slightly less important to the county than this road was the highway built along the coast from Colma to Pescadero and the Santa Cruz County line, paralleling

The Five O'Clock Rush in Richmond, 1916. Photograph courtesy of Richmond Public Library.

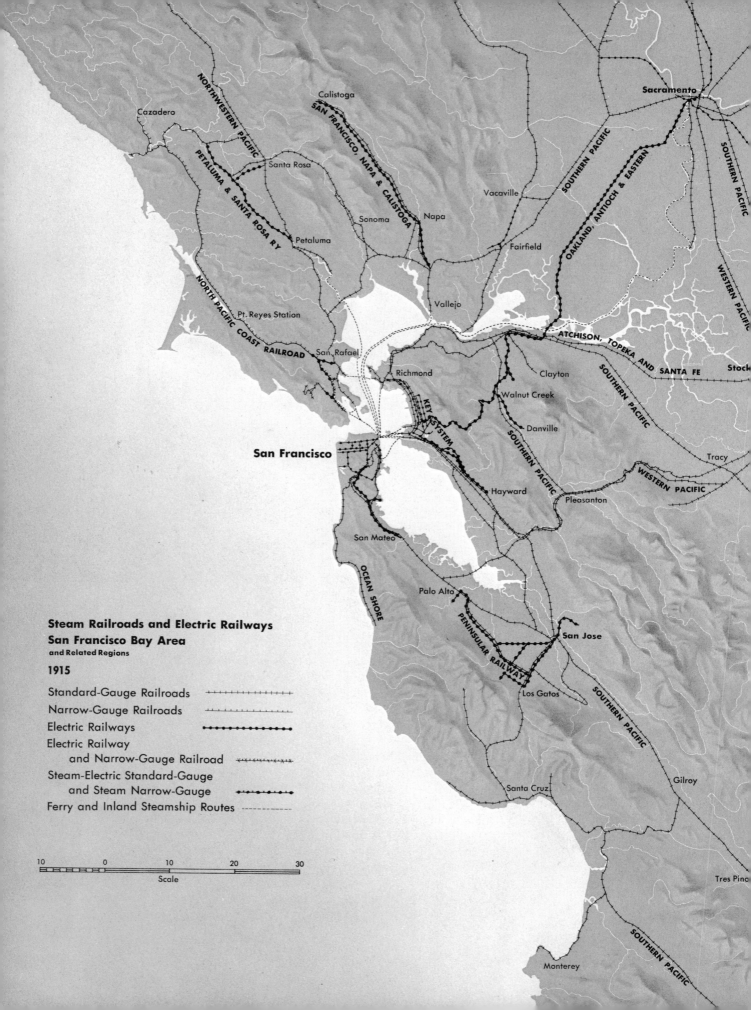

Cazadero

NORTHWESTERN PACIFIC

Calistoga

SAN FRANCISCO, NAPA & CALISTOGA

PETALUMA & SANTA ROSA RY

Santa Rosa

Sonoma

Napa

Vacaville

Sacramento

SOUTHERN PACIFIC

OAKLAND, ANTIOCH & EASTERN

SOUTHERN PACIFIC

WESTERN PACIFIC

Petaluma

NORTH PACIFIC COAST RAILROAD

Pt. Reyes Station

Fairfield

Vallejo

San Rafael

Richmond

ATCHISON, TOPEKA AND SANTA FE

Stock

SOUTHERN PACIFIC

Clayton

Walnut Creek

KEY SYSTEM

Danville

SOUTHERN PACIFIC

Tracy

San Francisco

Hayward

Pleasanton

WESTERN PACIFIC

San Mateo

OCEAN SHORE

Palo Alto

PENINSULAR RAILWAY

San Jose

SOUTHERN PACIFIC

Los Gatos

Steam Railroads and Electric Railways
San Francisco Bay Area
and Related Regions

1915

Standard-Gauge Railroads +++++++++

Narrow-Gauge Railroads ++++++++++

Electric Railways ●●●●●●●●●●

Electric Railway
    and Narrow-Gauge Railroad ×+×+×+×+×+×

Steam-Electric Standard-Gauge
    and Steam Narrow-Gauge ●+●+●+●+●

Ferry and Inland Steamship Routes ----------

Santa Cruz

Gilroy

10   0   10   20   30
Scale

Tres Pinc

Monterey

SOUTHERN PACIFIC

U.S. 40 near Vacaville in the Days of the First Paved Highways. Photograph courtesy of State Division of Highways.

the tracks of the Ocean Shore Railroad, which by 1920 was meeting so much truck, bus, and private automobile competition that it was obliged to appeal to the State Public Utilities Commission for permission to discontinue operations. From the coast highway to the bay side of the county ran two scenic lateral roads, one from Half Moon Bay to Belmont, the other from San Gregorio to Redwood City by way of La Honda, the heart of the old redwood logging area.

Though there were now better highways on the peninsula, San Mateo County did not attract many newcomers during this early period of highway construction. In the decade 1910–1920 its population increased only a little more than 10,000 and totaled 36,781 in 1920. On week ends San Franciscans invaded the county in their cars, but few families moved there. One explanation may be that new residential areas were opened for settlement within the metropolis itself. Interurban transit still was comparatively expensive, and automobile commuting, always costly, had not yet become the vogue. Furthermore, most towns in San Mateo County offered little opportunity for employment, and commercial and industrial activity during the war tended to be concentrated in major urban centers.

Other counties, finding that road building by direct tax was slow, attempted to follow the example of San Mateo County, but were not always successful. Sonoma County failed to approve road bonds in 1914. A Santa Clara

County citizens' committee worked hard for a $1,500,000 bond issue in the spring of 1917, only to see the electorate reject the measure by a vote of two to one.

In 1919, Sonoma County tried again and succeeded in putting over a $1,600,000 bond issue. In that same year, Napa County also voted $500,000 in road bonds and Contra Costa County $2,600,000. Sonoma County provided paved roads first in highly developed agricultural areas, then surfaced the roads to Russian River resorts, the favorite summer recreation spots of San Franciscans. With its bond funds Napa County built a highway twenty-seven miles long through the fertile Napa Valley. Contra Costa County, which had built only forty-eight miles of paved roads in five years by direct tax financing, planned a comprehensive county road system to connect at Martinez with the state highway. A first link in this county system was a highway originating at Stockton, in the San Joaquin Valley, and passing through Antioch, Pittsburg, and other points along Suisun Bay.

Coöperative Projects

A coöperative project financed and carried out by Marin, Sonoma, and Napa counties as a scenic route supplementing the state highways in the Bay Area was the road now known as the Black Point Cutoff, running from Napa across the marshes of southern Sonoma County to Ignacio, in Marin County. The three participating counties had hoped to have this road ready for the Panama-Pacific International Exposition, so that tourists might encircle the entire bay on paved roads; but difficulties in raising county funds postponed its completion until 1920.

Another coöperative project undertaken at the end of World War I was the Skyline Boulevard, from San Francisco along the crest of the Buri Buri Ridge in San Mateo County and on southward into Santa Clara and Santa Cruz counties. Under a law passed by the state legislature in 1917 to permit counties to associate themselves in a joint highway district, the four counties along the route of the boulevard formed Joint Highway District Number One and purchased rights of way for the scenic drive. Automobile clubs had carried on a publicity campaign for this mountain road for several years before it was included in 1919 among the highways to be financed by a third state highway bond issue, which, incidentally, was approved by a vote of seven to one and provided $40,000,000 for highway construction in California.

New Ferry Services

As the population of the Bay Area became more mobile, the water barriers which retarded communication—Sui-

The Automobile Ferry City of Richmond, *1915. Ferryboats plied between Castro Point and Point San Quentin until the opening of the Richmond–San Rafael Bridge in 1956. Photograph courtesy of Richmond Chamber of Commerce.*

sun Bay, Carquinez Strait, San Pablo Strait, the Golden Gate, and the great southern arm of the bay—presented increasingly serious problems. At one time or another, engineers, railroad tycoons, editorial writers, and plain citizens had proposed the building of bridges across every one of these bodies of water. The first wave of proposals came with the building of railroads. A second group accompanied the construction of electric railways. A third series of proposals very naturally burgeoned as motor vehicles multiplied on the highways in the counties around the bay. But additional ferries rather than costly bridges met the needs of the times.

As early as 1909 the communities of Martinez and Benicia, which had been out of direct communication by ferry ever since the late 'seventies, cited the increase in automobile travel as one reason for reëstablishing ferry service. Finally, on July 19, 1913, the long-sought service was inaugurated with the former Puget Sound steamer *City of Seattle*.

At the western end of Carquinez Strait another ferry service began operating about 1915 under the name Carquinez Ferry Company. The successor of this concern, the Rodeo-Vallejo Ferry Company, organized in 1918, later formed the American Toll Bridge Company, which obtained a franchise in 1922 to build a span across the strait. The wharf properties purchased by the Carquinez Ferry Company and taken over by the successor company were in time to become the bridgeheads of the first Carquinez Bridge.

In May, 1915, the Richmond–San Rafael Transportation Company started running automobile ferries between Point San Quention in Marin County and Castro Point in Contra Costa County. Within two years the company was serving more than 265,000 passengers annually; yet financiers were not sufficiently impressed with the volume of traffic to finance a toll bridge designed by John G. Little, a San Francisco engineer. Moreover, the entrance of the United States into World War I halted projects requiring large amounts of steel. Little's proposal did, however, foreshadow the building of the span that was completed by the state in 1956.

A Board of United States Army Engineers held hearings on several plans for a crossing between San Francisco and Oakland in August, 1916, but rejected all of them as possibly interfering with military use of the harbor. The board recommended that consideration be given to a scheme that would combine a tunnel under the main part of the bay with a bridge over the eastern side. Soon after the Army engineers released their report, however, the declaration of war sidetracked further planning for a central crossing, and not until five years later did the War Department schedule another hearing on the matter.

Although most people joked about proposals to span the Golden Gate, City Engineer O'Shaughnessy of San Francisco was among the few who believed that a bridge across the mile-wide entrance to the bay was within the realm of possibility. In due time he interested Joseph B. Strauss, the famous Chicago engineer, in developing plans for a bridge to cost "twenty-five to thirty million dollars at the most."[1] In 1919 Strauss presented what he considered feasible plans roughly within the cost limitation laid down by O'Shaughnessy and other San Francisco officials. And then the word battle over the bridge began, continuing almost until the time great piers began to rise above the surging tide, in the early 'thirties. Some engineers declared that the bridge would cost more than $100,000,000 to build; others said that it could not be built at all. To convince the skeptics, Strauss saw that he would have to undertake further studies.

Autos and Regional Parks

New concrete highways, automobile ferries, bus lines and bus depots, plans for bridges—these were only a few of the many evidences of a new period in history: the automobile age. On every hand there were others: corner service stations, garages, repair shops, automobile sales rooms, automobile supply stores, used-car lots, parking lots, huge new oil refineries and tank farms in Contra Costa County, additional oil pipe lines from the San Joaquin Valley to these refineries, docks for new fleets of oil tankers, resorts in previously inaccessible areas, new subdivisions beyond the limits of electric railway transportation, roadside commercial slums, and garish billboards in rural landscapes. The motor vehicle, truly, was not an unmixed blessing.

Its increasingly widespread use not only materially affected the physical environment and expanded the economy by stimulating new enterprises and creating new employment; it began to change patterns of living and forms of recreation. For many families the Sunday automobile trip gradually began to replace the Sunday afternoon promenade in the urban park or the visit to the amusement park. City dwellers took new interest in exploring the scenic areas that were either too distant or too difficult to reach before the private touring car came into use, and as this interest in the natural beauties of the Bay Area developed, there was a dawning realization that unless steps were taken to preserve outstanding wilderness areas, they might be destroyed if private owners were careless or commercial exploitation was misguided.

With the exception of Golden Gate Park in San Francisco, which had always attracted people from all parts of

First Chevrolets Manufactured in Oakland, 1916. The increasing popularity of the automobile contributed to agitation for construction of bridges across San Francisco Bay and the Golden Gate. Photograph courtesy of Oakland Tribune.

the Bay Area, there were only two publicly owned areas of metropolitan regional significance in the counties around the bay. Muir Woods, at the foot of Mount Tamalpais in Marin County, was a 425-acre national monument, presented to the federal government in 1908 by Congressman William Kent, who purchased the magnificent stand of coast redwoods (*Sequoia sempervirens*) to save it from destruction by a lumber company. The other public reserve of regional importance was Alum Rock Park, in Penitencia Canyon six miles east of San Jose. Once part of the pueblo lands originally belonging to the city of San Jose, it had become a municipal park in 1872 by authorization of the state legislature, which at that time exercised considerable control over presumably self-governing cities.

Both of these large scenic reserves might properly be incorporated in a metropolitan regional park system. Indeed, Stephen Child, a landscape architect employed by the city of San Jose in 1916 to prepare plans for the expansion and further development of Alum Rock Park, pointed out that this park was, "in fact, a 'Metropolitan Reservation' rather than an urban park and in its development should be treated as such."[2] He observed that the

state had begun building a comprehensive system of state highways and that parts of the system serving the Bay Area would make Alum Rock Park accessible to the residents of at least five counties. In the future it would be used not alone by the people of San Jose but "in increasing numbers" by the people of the metropolitan community surrounding the bay. Child believed, therefore, that the city of San Jose "would be entirely justified in urging upon your representatives at Sacramento the propriety of State aid,"[3] perhaps through establishment of a metropolitan district in which taxes for park purposes would be levied on the residents of many cities. "There is a precedent for this in the famous Metropolitan Park System of Boston," he pointed out.

The Metropolitan Park District of Boston, a state agency unfortunately removed from direct control of the people for whose benefit it was created by the Massachusetts State Legislature in 1893, was often cited as an example of the kind of special district that might be established in the Bay Area. In 1914 Professor Thomas H. Reed of the University of California had mentioned it in a lecture in which he urged the formation of three unified park systems in the Bay Area—one in the East

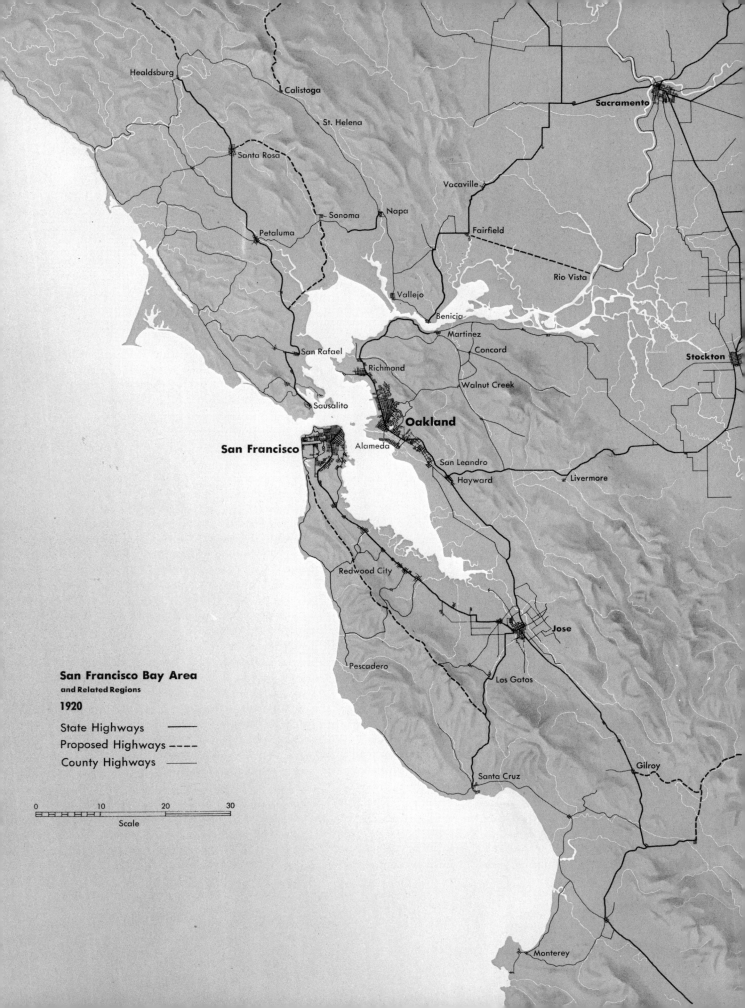

San Francisco Bay Area
and Related Regions

1920

State Highways ——————
Proposed Highways ------
County Highways ——————

0   10   20   30
Scale

Healdsburg
Calistoga
St. Helena
Santa Rosa
Sonoma
Napa
Petaluma
Vallejo
Benicia
San Rafael
Martinez
Concord
Richmond
Walnut Creek
Sausalito
Oakland
San Francisco
Alameda
San Leandro
Hayward
Livermore
Redwood City
Jose
Pescadero
Los Gatos
Santa Cruz
Gilroy
Monterey
Sacramento
Vacaville
Fairfield
Rio Vista
Stockton

Bay, one on the San Francisco Peninsula, and one in Marin County—all three of which might some day be combined to form a single area-wide system. But suggestions for a metropolitan regional park system aroused little response in the days of World War I. Automobile ownership was increasing rapidly but was not so widespread as to make every family potentially the supporters of a regional park movement. Nor were cities spreading at a rate that made the disappearance of open areas alarming.

What might be called "metropolitan thinking" did not become a force in the Bay Area until the 'twenties, when a new influx of population, a phenomenal increase in the number of automobiles, and the growing complexity of the problems of circulation, water supply, and bay development focused attention on the need for coöperative action.

Controversy over transbay transportation, for instance, tended to emphasize the interrelatedness of area-wide problems. How would a bridge, or bridges, across San Francisco Bay affect navigation and the expansion of harbor facilities? Should not there be a crossing between the East Bay and the North Bay at San Pablo Strait, and might it not be a barrier to the salt water that was making incursions into Suisun Bay? Might not the creation of a fresh-water lake in San Pablo Bay solve the water supply problems of the East Bay? These and a hundred other questions challenged the people of the whole Bay Area.

Problem of a Bay Crossing

By the fall of 1921, engineers had advanced thirteen different proposals for a bay crossing between the San Francisco Peninsula and Alameda County, including one proposal for a crossing near San Mateo and another for a crossing at Dumbarton Strait, thirty miles south of San Francisco. Great public interest attached to the plans of General George W. Goethals for a tube from the foot of Market Street to the Oakland Mole. Provided with two decks, the tube would accommodate vehicular traffic on the upper deck and trains on the lower. John G. Little, who had presented a tunnel plan at the 1916 hearing held by a Board of United States Army Engineers, suggested a combination tube and trestle, the tube section to be on the San Francisco side of the bay, where an unobstructed ship channel was imperative. J. Vipond Davies and Ralph Modjeski, employed by the San Francisco Bay Bridge Committee, likewise recommended a combination tunnel and bridge, extending from some point between Mission Rock and Potrero Point in San Francisco to a place on the Alameda County shore satisfactory to the naval authorities. Rear Admiral Joseph L. Jayne, commandant

of the Twelfth Naval District, made the familiar proposals that the Key Route trestle be extended to Yerba Buena Island, that a union ferry terminal be built on the island, and that a ferry be operated between the island and San Francisco until a tunnel could be constructed to replace the ferryboats. There were also two proposals for a high-level cantilever bridge, with 2,000-foot spans, from Telegraph Hill to Yerba Buena Island, and proposals for concrete viaducts from various locations south of Hunters Point to Alameda, Bay Farm Island, or the vicinity of San Leandro.

Present-day residents of the Bay Area will note that every location later suggested for a second mid-bay crossing was included among proposals for the first. John G. Little, moreover, based his plan on the assumption that many bridges would be required to accommodate future traffic.

Again the War Department felt compelled to schedule a public hearing on the problem of a bay crossing. The hearing was conducted on October 7, 1921, and on December 1, 1921, the Chief of Engineers of the United States Army announced the conditions that would govern the building of a bridge or tunnel or a combination of the two. No bridge of any kind north of Hunters Point would be approved, the Chief of Engineers stated, and no low bridge north of San Mateo. A tunnel crossing in any location, provided it was at least 50 feet below mean low water, would be approved. A combined bridge and tunnel at a location south of the proposed Alameda naval base site would be approved provided the tunnel was so placed as to leave the channel along the San Francisco side unobstructed to a depth of 50 feet at mean low water for a width of 3,000 feet. Finally, the War Department stated that not more than once crossing in any location north of San Mateo would be approved at that time.

Alternative Projects

The War Department's announcement met with varied responses. Some groups believed that through public pressure the Department could be induced to abandon its stand against a bridge north of Hunters Point. Others were inclined to accept the conditions stated by the Chief of Engineers and to concentrate on plans for a southern crossing. The Harbor Control Section of the Commonwealth Club thought that a bridge "somewhere south of San Mateo" would be "justified by the very considerable relief it would afford to traffic between San Francisco and other peninsular points and the east side of the bay and even to the East Bay cities themselves in emergencies." As for a crossing north of Hunters Point, the section concluded that "neither the present traffic nor the prospective traffic for the next twenty years, at least, justifies the cost of building such a structure as would be absolutely essential to avoid interference with the prospective and necessary expansion of the harbor."[4]

A. J. Dickie, editor of the *Pacific Marine Review*, assured the club that "the east shore terminal at Yerba Buena Island [as suggested by Rear Admiral Jayne] is the logical next step in the development of that ferry system which is now the finest in the world, but is yet not quite good enough for San Francisco Bay."[5] The ferries, he pointed out, had transported more than 49,000,000 passengers, nearly 800,000 automobiles, and approximately 2,000,000 tons of freight in 1921. By running a ten-minute schedule regularly from the foot of Market Street to Yerba Buena Island, it would be possible immediately to double the total capacity for San Francisco–Oakland traffic in passengers and more than double that for automobiles, Dickie contended.

C. E. Grunsky, former City Engineer of San Francisco, not only favored a mid-bay transit and ferry terminal; like the Big Four in the 1870's, he envisaged shipping operations at this point, and, like members of harbor improvement associations, he suggested leveling Yerba Buena Island and creating a man-made island on the shoals north of it, with deep-water harbor facilities alongside. Mainland freight trains could be routed over a viaduct from the end of the Key Route Mole to warehouses and piers on this artificial island, the visionary counterpart of present-day Treasure Island.

Proposed Salt-Water Barrier

Grunsky did not limit his interest in Bay Area transportation problems to the movement of people and goods between San Francisco and Oakland, however. He foresaw the need for the improvement of traffic between the East Bay and Marin County, as did John G. Little and many others. Grunsky pointed out that a crossing between Richmond and San Rafael might take the form of a vehicular roadway and a railroad right of way on top of a dam built to act as a barrier to salt water in Suisun Bay, as suggested by Captain C. S. Jarvis, of the Corps of Engineers of the United States Army, in a paper presented before the American Society of Civil Engineers in 1921.[6]

The possibility of constructing a dam to prevent salt-water encroachment into the upper bay and the delta region at the confluence of the Sacramento and San Joaquin rivers had been discussed periodically ever since the great drought of the mid-sixties, when the reduced flow of the rivers invited salt-water incursion. As Assistant State Engineer under William Hammond Hall, Grunsky had carried out an investigation in 1879–1880 to determine

whether such a barrier at Carquinez Strait were needed but had reported adversely on the idea. In the years following that study many industries requiring large amounts of fresh water had been established on Carquinez Strait and Suisun Bay, and had at first taken their supply from these waters, then, as salinity increased, from wells. The California and Hawaii Sugar Refinery at Crockett for ten years employed barges to bring fresh water from many miles upstream on the Sacramento River. In 1920 it began obtaining water from a more convenient source, the Marin Municipal Water District, which delivered water to the barges at Point San Quentin. The plight of other industries became serious in 1918 and in 1920, two dry years during which reduced stream flow and overdraughts for irrigation in the Central Valley permitted the salt water of the bay to work its way far up into the delta region and to contaminate the underground basins in Contra Costa County that were a principal source of water supply for farmers, industries, and municipalities. These conditions, which occasioned a prolonged law suit (the Antioch suit) involving water users of the upper Sacramento Valley, the delta region, and Contra Costa County industrialists, prompted Captain Jarvis to revive the idea of converting San Pablo and Suisun bays into fresh-water lakes by building a dam across the narrows below San Pablo Bay.

Present-day residents of the Bay Area will recognize in the Jarvis proposal the genesis of one element of the controversial Reber Plan for converting the northern and southern arms of San Francisco Bay into fresh-water lakes. Because other drought years and renewed struggles between Central Valley agriculturists and Contra Costa County industrialists were to follow in the middle and late 'twenties, the subject of a salt-water barrier was to assume increasing importance in all discussions of harbor development, bay crossings, tideland reclamation, and industrial growth. Moreover, the barrier issue served to reëmphasize the close relation between the economic development of the Bay Area and that of the Central Valley. At the heart of the problem facing the farmers in the delta region and the manufacturing plants and municipalities in northern Contra Costa County lay the larger problem of the future use of the water resources of the vast territory drained by the Sacramento and San Joaquin rivers and their numerous tributaries. Indeed, the solution of this problem concerned the whole Bay Area just as much as it did the people of Contra Costa County.

Threat of Water Shortages

The water problem in another form troubled the East Bay communities of Oakland, Berkeley, Alameda, and Richmond. As population growth continued, it became increasingly certain that there would be water shortages unless action were taken to augment the supply available from local watersheds and wells. The Jarvis proposal for transforming San Pablo Bay into a fresh-water lake that could supply water for industrial use attracted considerable interest but hardly seemed a solution to the problem of impending water deficiency which the East Bay cities were trying to solve.

By 1922 these cities were at least equipped with legislation under which they could form a utility district. After a committee of officials from the principal East Bay cities had dissolved in 1920 because of disagreement on a plan for solving the common water supply problem, the mayor of Berkeley had appointed a committee to draft a bill to be presented at the next session of the state legislature. The result was the Municipal Utility District Act of 1921, providing for the creation of a utility district that would embrace parts of more than one county, and for the inclusion of unincorporated as well as incorporated territory. The way thus being paved for joint action by the East Bay communities, sentiment was rapidly crystallizing for formation of a district embracing most of the territory then served by the East Bay Water Company.

San Francisco nevertheless still hoped that the East Bay would participate in the construction of the Hetch Hetchy system and would share the costs and the benefits. Lake Eleanor Dam had been completed in 1918; one powerhouse of the gigantic development was in operation and work on another had begun; and construction of O'Shaughnessy Dam in the Hetch Hetchy Valley had been under way for more than two years. As Robert M. Searls, special counsel for the city, pointed out to prominent East Bay men attending a Commonwealth Club discussion, San Francisco was going to complete the Hetch Hetchy project with or without the aid of the communities on the opposite side of the bay, but "a water supply for the bay cities is something in which we should all share both the credit and the expense, and all develop in harmony."[7]

Warren Olney, ever the East Bay champion of area-wide coöperation, agreed. "There is but one thing for the East Bay communities to do," he said, "and that is to get together through some proper governmental organization, such as a water district, and unite with the city of San Francisco and go ahead with the development, so that all may be served from the common source."[8]

Edwin O. Edgerton, president of the East Bay Water Company, likewise conceded that it would be "vastly better" if a single water supply could be considered for San Francisco, the Peninsula, and the East Bay. Separate systems for the two sides of the bay would involve "undoubtedly a duplication of investment." But he saw no possibility of reaching accord on a single system. "The situation today," he said, "is that the communities are not together on this question, so that at the moment the East Bay Region must consider for itself what source of supply it will use."[9]

Further delay on the part of the East Bay communities in reaching agreement on a plan of action would be disastrous, Edgerton warned. "Our bay communities have become very ambitious to expand and grow, to attract industry, to persuade people to settle and build homes, to become large manufacturing and business communities, to emulate Los Angeles, if you please, and even to outdistance Los Angeles. I want to say to you that if the East Bay Region had the opportunity tomorrow to become as large as the city of Los Angeles, to have the industries that are now in the city of Los Angeles, and that are coming there at the rate of one industry a day, it could not be done. Why? Lack of an adequate future water supply. And yet every effort is made to expand and grow and attract industries, with no serious attention to the fundamental basis of the possibility of growth, which is water."

He summed up the situation bluntly: "The present supply of water in the East Bay Region is not sufficient for a period longer than ten years. Well before the end of that ten years there must be under way the construction of works to bring in a very substantial additional water supply."[10]

Formation of a Utility District

The warning, voiced by many leaders besides Edgerton, finally was heeded. On May 8, 1923, the voters of Oakland, Berkeley, Alameda, San Leandro, Emeryville, El Cerrito, Piedmont, and Richmond went to the polls to cast their ballots for or against the formation of the East Bay Municipal Utility District. In all the cities except Piedmont and Richmond the vote was favorable, but within a short time these two cities also joined the district.

The organization of the district did not preclude obtaining water from San Francisco's Hetch Hetchy system. When engineers of the East Bay Municipal Utility District began field surveys in July, 1924, to determine what source of water could best be drawn upon, they included the Hetch Hetchy project among sources to be investigated. Others were the Eel River, the Sacramento River, the American River, the McCloud River, and the Mokelumne River. In the end, though, a board of eminent engineers, composed of Chief Engineer Arthur P. Davis, William Mulholland, builder of the Los Angeles Aqueduct, and General George W. Goethals, recommended the Mokelumne River as the most promising and economic source of supply. The last hope that San Francisco and the East Bay would find a common solution to the water supply problem died in November, 1924, when the electorate of the East Bay Municipal Utility District approved a $39,000,000 bond issue for construction of an aqueduct from the Mokelumne River.

Ironically, this project was to be completed some years before the Hetch Hetchy system was in operation. Indeed, there was to be an emergency in San Francisco in 1930 during which the East Bay Municipal Utility District would supply the city across the bay with millions of gallons of water a day, in effect demonstrating the value of one big system.

Had San Francisco and the East Bay been able to reach agreement on a single water system, the coöperation between the two large urban areas in planning for the best use of water might have led, or at least could have led, to planning for a better distribution of population and industrial establishments, as had been suggested by Bion Arnold in 1912. Since water and transportation are essential for any form of urban development, they might well be used to influence and direct growth, though they have seldom been so used, because until recently communities have not prepared general plans that could be implemented through the construction of basic utilities. The projection of street-railway lines into the sparsely populated areas west of Twin Peaks in San Francisco is an example of official policy directed toward the settlement of territory that is "ripe" for development, though good physical planning in this instance did not precede the planning and construction of transit facilities. Today a municipality that is guided in its growth by a long-range, general plan can, if it owns and controls its water supply and its transit system, bring about the most desirable type of development in outlying areas. The failure of San Francisco and the East Bay to unite on a plan for providing the major concentrations of population in the Bay Area with a common water supply was a setback for coördinated metropolitan development. If these communities had formed a metropolitan water district with a board composed of representatives of the city councils of the various cities, they could have exercised a strong control over the whole pattern of urbanization in the Bay Area and could have regulated the "where and when" of subdivision activity and perhaps prevented the haphazard and wasteful expansion characteristic of the past decade. But this grand opportunity for guiding the growth of the Bay Area was lost when the East Bay formed a separate utility district with a board unrepresentative of the governing

bodies of the municipalities which it serves. The utility district provided for in the act of 1921 is so divorced from other functions of government in the East Bay that it offers no more opportunity for planning and programing the development of outlying areas than would a private utility. It is an outstanding example of the independent special district that enormously complicates the problem of achieving coördination in the planning and development of a great metropolitan region.

Proposals for Rapid Transit

San Francisco in the early 'twenties really expected little coöperation from the East Bay on the water supply problem. Of greater importance to both sides of the bay was eventual accord on the matter of a bay crossing, but rapid solution of this problem did not appear possible. In the meantime, San Francisco needed outlets to the only land area to which she could gain ready access, the Peninsula.

The City Planning Section of the Commonwealth Club, reorganized in November, 1922, after several months of inactivity, scheduled several talks that reflected the interest of the metropolis in establishing closer relations with San Mateo County. Architect Willis Polk addressed the section on the subject "The San Francisco–San Mateo Regional Plan," and C. J. Rhodin, a consulting engineer, discussed rapid transit with particular reference to express service down the Peninsula.

"What a wonderful thing it would be for San Francisco," Rhodin exclaimed, "if there were a rapid transit system following, let us say, Howard Street, where you could take an express train that would run, without grade crossings, to San Mateo and other points south!"[11] But he estimated that a double-tracked system from San Francisco to San Jose would cost $30,000,000; and he doubted that it could operate profitably under the traffic densities then existing. Perhaps, he suggested, the Southern Pacific facilities could be adapted to rapid transit service.

San Francisco City Engineer O'Shaughnessy, speaking in the fall of 1923, pinned his hopes for rapid transit to the Peninsula on extension of the municipal railway system. "At the last election a charter amendment was carried, by which the city has the right to buy the railway lines in San Mateo County, connected with the Market Street Railway system, whenever we make up our minds to buy that system. . . . We have a road through the Twin Peaks Tunnel, 12,000 feet long, on a 3 per cent grade, double-tracked. It ends now in St. Francis Circle. We are building an extension from there about two miles long down to Ocean View. The right-of-way has been obtained, and that line will be finished inside of a year. From there down to San Mateo County is only half a mile, and the

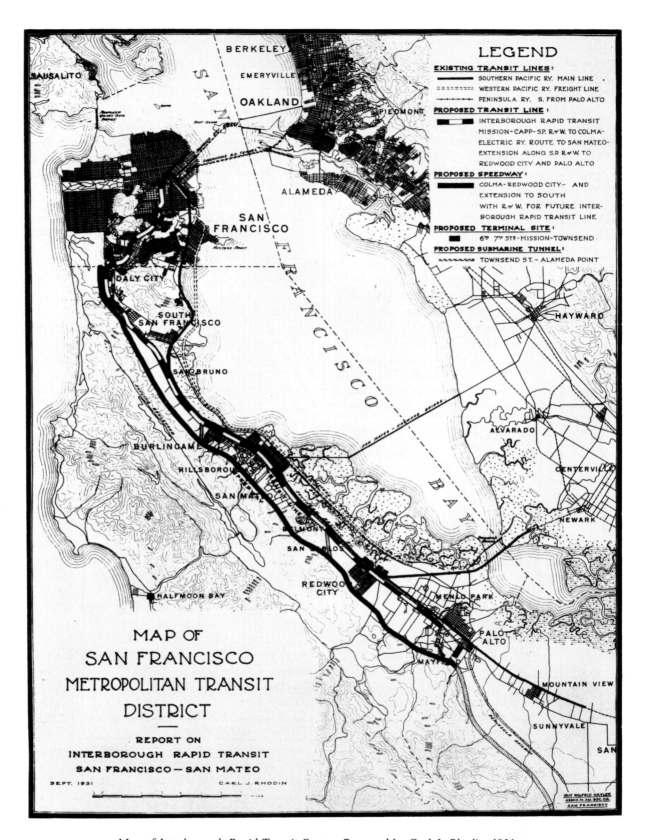

Map of Interborough Rapid Transit System Proposed by Carl J. Rhodin, 1931

natural gradient for a rapid transit line at a relatively moderate cost, not any thirty million or fifty million dollars, but four million or five million dollars. . . ."[12]

Not even that much money was available for a rapid transit system. To stimulate development west of Twin Peaks, the city had spent millions for tunnels and railway lines; but the new transit operations were not profitable, however essential they were for city growth. Under the circumstances, it was little wonder that the city did not embark on a program of interurban rapid transit.

New highways were to provide San Francisco with the outlets it needed. O'Shaughnessy told the City Planning Section of the near-completion of the Skyline Boulevard and of plans for the construction of the Bayshore Highway. The latter, to be built under state supervision with funds supplied by the City and County of San Francisco, was to run through Visitacion Valley to South San Francisco and thence along the marshy shore of the bay, bypassing the string of cities through which congested El Camino Real ran.

"We have hopes," O'Shaughnessy said, "that San Mateo, which has not been jealous of San Francisco, which has never broken a pledge they have made us for any coöperation, will join with us and form a Greater San Francisco, so that we can solve . . . the transportation problem, the water problem, and other problems."[13]

The Consolidation Movement

So far as the city engineer and a good many other San Franciscans were concerned, the Greater San Francisco movement was not dead; it had, of necessity, merely shriveled. It now aimed at amalgamating only San Mateo County, or at least the northern part of the county, with San Francisco.

In San Mateo County the Three Cities Chamber of Commerce, representing San Mateo, Burlingame, and Hillsborough, was the chief proponent of consolidation with the metropolis. This organization advanced a number of reasons for fostering union with the larger neighbor. Local limitations prevented most Peninsula cities from developing intensively or thoroughly, it contended. Further, the Peninsula was suffering from a lack of industrial development. Consolidation with San Francisco would open thousands of acres along the bay shore for factory sites. The Three Cities Chamber insisted, however, that San Francisco meet three major conditions if consolidation should be effected. It should establish and maintain the borough form of government for the consolidated territories; it should extend the municipal railway south to the town of Belmont; and it should establish and maintain an open port at San Mateo.[14]

San Mateo County opponents of consolidation saw in the movement another attempt of San Francisco to swallow all or part of their county. They doubted that the three basic conditions specified by the Three Cities Chamber of Commerce would be honored by San Francisco once consolidation was consummated. And they believed that San Francisco was advocating consolidation to achieve its own ends of acquiring a greater bonding capacity and more room for expansion.

From 1923 until 1932 the residents of both San Mateo County and San Francisco studied and debated every aspect of the proposed consolidation. Citizen groups, chambers of commerce, newspapers, the San Francisco Bureau of Governmental Research, the San Francisco Board of Supervisors, and the state legislature all became involved in the movement, which by 1928 had become a burning issue. "Consolidation, it can be concluded, failed of achievement in the 1928–1932 period largely because the opposition worked effectively, even with inferior tools, in concentrated areas where a single unfavorable election could defeat the whole effort," John Bollens has written.[15] Intermittent attempts to revive the movement were made between 1935 and 1957, but no later effort reached the intensity of that made in the late 'twenties.

Some elements who opposed consolidation suggested alternatives that would preserve the political identity of San Mateo County yet bring about improvements in governmental operations. Intercounty special districts, such as that formed to build the Skyline Boulevard, might be set up; a state agency of the sort commonly called a metropolitan district commission might be organized to perform specified functions, as in the Boston metropolitan area; or metropolitan regional planning might be initiated to facilitate coördination of the decisions of local governmental bodies with respect to physical developments affecting more than one of the political units of the Bay Area. All three suggestions were more advanced than any proposals made after the clash between Oakland and San Francisco over consolidation before World War I, because all three aimed at avoiding the bitterness generated by attempts at political unification.

Of the three alternatives, the suggestion that metropolitan regional planning be undertaken had perhaps the greatest appeal for public-spirited Bay Area residents at that time, because regional planning then had the attraction of novelty and seemed to meet the needs of large urban areas that were having difficulty in solving area-wide problems. In addition to New York, the cities of Chicago, Boston, Philadelphia, Baltimore, Cleveland, Buffalo, and Detroit all had private, unofficial regional planning organizations.

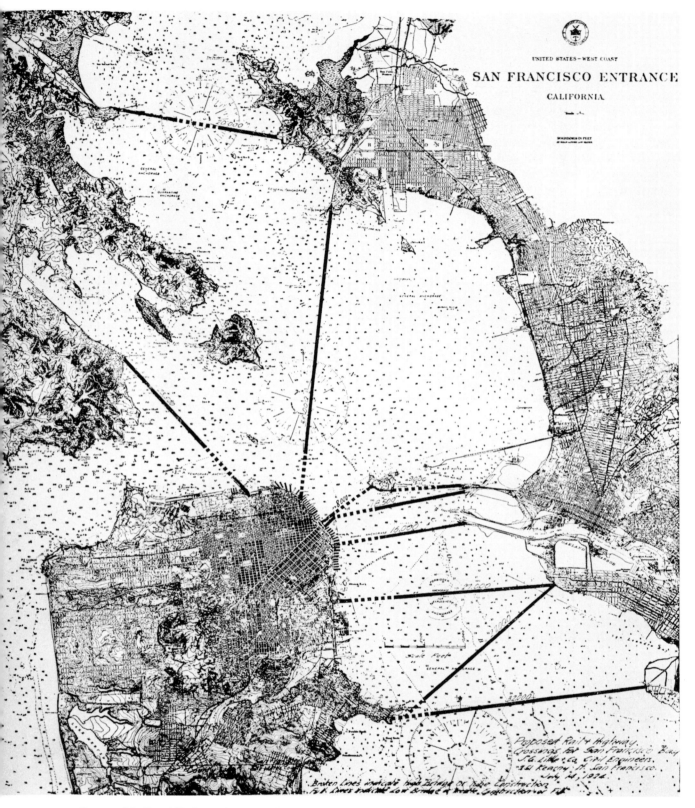

Proposed Rail and Highway Crossings for San Francisco Bay, 1924. The map shows bridge routes studied by J. G. Little and Co., Civil Engineers.

The Conjunction of Events

In the San Francisco Bay Area the members of the City Planning Section of the Commonwealth Club spearheaded the movement for a regional planning organization. And it is perhaps significant that their first important meeting on the subject of regional planning was held in September, 1923, about the time that the physical knitting together of the Bay Area began. The key figures in the San Francisco City Hall and leaders in the North Bay had recently revived the agitation for construction of a bridge across the Golden Gate, and the state legislature had just enacted permissive legislation under which a federation of counties, by forming a bridge and highway district, could construct the proposed mile-long span. In the spring of that year the American Toll Bridge Company had started construction of a high-level span across Carquinez Strait, thereby heralding the day when there would be uninterrupted automobile travel between the East Bay and the North Bay. In May the voters of Alameda County had approved a bond issue of $4,496,000 for the construction of a tube under the estuary between Alameda and Oak-

Proposed Bay Bridge from San Francisco to Alameda, 1925

land. A private company was preparing plans for an automobile toll bridge across Dumbarton Strait in the South Bay; and there was also talk of a toll bridge at San Mateo. Meanwhile, discussion of the need for a bridge or tube between San Francisco and the East Bay had prompted engineers to devise new schemes for a central crossing.

For information on metropolitan regional planning the Commonwealth Club turned to men who knew of the work initiated in the Greater New York area in 1921 by the Russell Sage Foundation. San Francisco City Engineer O'Shaughnessy explained that Mrs. Sage upon her death had left a large sum of money to be used for some unspecified metropolitan benefit. After careful deliberation, the board of trustees of the foundation had concluded that one of the most effective ways to use the funds would be to finance the preparation of a comprehensive plan for the future development of the metropolitan region of which New York City is the center. A Committee on a Regional Plan of New York and Its Environs was appointed; and under the chairmanship of Charles D. Norton, who had been the first chairman of the group which sponsored the Burnham Plan of Chicago, this committee selected a corps of outstanding city planners to undertake a complete physical, economic, and social survey of the metropolitan region as a basis for preparation of the comprehensive plan.

Los Angeles an Inspiration

Another metropolitan planning program that interested the Commonwealth Club was the then newly initiated program of the Los Angeles County Planning Commission, the first county planning agency in the United States. Fortunately, Los Angeles County had its own home-rule charter and could, without waiting for the enactment of state enabling legislation, establish a county planning agency to study problems that were of serious concern to municipalities throughout an extensive urban area. The county board of supervisors established the commission by ordinance in December, 1922; the members of the commission were appointed in January, 1923; and in June of that year the commission opened an office with a technical staff. Gordon Whitnall, who described the Los Angeles County agency to the Commonwealth Club in September, 1923, told how the Los Angeles City Planning Commission, of which he was then the head, had found a large part of its own program stalemated by municipal boundaries until the county commission was brought into being "to seek to interest the various municipalities and political subdivisions of the county in a joint effort to understand and solve the common problems of development confronting them and the county."[16] Among these

common problems, as enumerated in the ordinance establishing the county agency, the principal ones were flood control, unregulated residential development in unincorporated territory, the need for large park reservations and beaches for the use of people throughout the county, and the need for highways serving the entire county. Another problem, not specifically mentioned in the ordinance, was pollution of the underground water supply of cities at lower elevations by cities near the mountains, Whitnall pointed out.

All five of the county-wide conferences that led to the creation of the Los Angeles County Planning Commission were heralded as regional planning conferences; hence, although the county agency had no authority to plan for parts of the metropolitan region lying outside Los Angeles County, it came to be known popularly as a regional planning commission. It was, nevertheless, essentially a county planning agency and could not possibly serve as the model for an agency to facilitate coördination of planning in the San Francisco Bay Area, which was a much larger and vastly more complex area, physically, politically, and in every other respect. The Los Angeles County Planning Commission was, at best, an example of what was needed in each of the Bay Area counties before area-wide planning could be effective. Still, it was a source of inspiration to those who wanted metropolitan regional planning in the Bay Area.

A Proposed Organization

Not long after the meeting at which O'Shaughnessy and Whitnall spoke, the Commonwealth Club appointed a Subcommittee on a Regional Plan for the San Francisco Bay District, with Russell Van Nest Black as chairman. Under his leadership the subcommittee drew up a report proposing a semiofficial, permanent organization that would concern itself with "problems of water and food supply, sewerage, transportation, highways and bridges, port development, zoning, parks, and the conservation and development of natural resources" in a metropolitan region which would include all of Sonoma, Napa, Solano, Marin, Contra Costa, Alameda, San Francisco, and San Mateo counties and the northerly half of Santa Clara County.[17]

Black outlined a general program of procedure for the proposed organization which contemplated first of all a preliminary survey constituting "a general scanning of the district from a planning point of view." A report on this survey, he suggested, could be widely distributed to present the case for a regional plan and to gain financial support for "a much more exhaustive survey" on which to base the plan. "The plan itself . . . would determine the most economical use of the various portions of the entire district and then lay down a general system of highways, transportation, park and recreation facilities, regional zoning et cetera, taking into special consideration the regional phases of such problems as those of port and harbor development, water supply and sanitation."[18] Matters of "purely local concern" would be omitted from the plan.

To finance the preliminary survey and organizational effort, Black proposed that an initial fund of $5,000 to $8,000 be raised, and after that, enough additional funds to bring the total to $250,000, although he acknowledged that "much could be accomplished" with $100,000 or $150,000.[19]

The desirability of continuing the regional planning effort on a semiofficial basis was something about which Black evidently had doubts, as this statement testifies: "Much can be done with the plan through moral suasion coupled with a broad program of education and publicity and by providing mediating machinery for the cooperation of political units in solving common problems, but to be fully effective it may be found to be ultimately necessary to have the plan officially recognized. After the preliminary plans . . . have been completed and well published, it is possible that the work can be better handled through a special regional or metropolitan district, to be created by act of the legislature and directly administered by an official regional plan commission acting in conjunction with and elected within the membership of the preceding General Citizens Committee or Regional Plan Association."[20]

Choice of a Leader

To launch the regional planning movement, the City Planning Section of the Commonwealth Club arranged a one-day conference on regional planning on April 11, 1924. This was attended by approximately one hundred delegates from communities throughout the Bay Area. After hearing such noted city planners as George B. Ford, Edward M. Bassett, John Nolen, Flavel Shurtleff, and Harland Bartholomew, the delegates adopted a resolution favoring the creation of a regional planning association and authorizing Carl J. Rhodin, chairman of the City Planning Section, to appoint an organizing committee to devise a plan of procedure to be submitted to the conference at a later date.

The committee appointed by Rhodin held two meetings, then decided to enlarge its membership to include a number of particularly influential citizens of the Bay Area, among whom was Senator James Duval Phelan, who had served as the first chairman of the City Planning Section of the Commonwealth Club ten years earlier. Phelan became head of a small committee on organization and ways and means at a meeting on November 20, 1924. Other members of this group, besides Rhodin and Black, were Frank D. Stringham, Mayor of Berkeley, Marshal Hale, a San Francisco merchant, Fred E. Reed, an Oakland realtor, and George Roos.

The choice of Phelan as chairman of the ways and means committee was especially significant, because it was he who suggested that the problem of organizing the proposed regional planning association be placed in the hands of his old friend Frederick W. Dohrmann, Jr., who had been one of the original members of the earlier Association for the Improvement and Adornment of San Francisco. Thus the new regional planning movement was linked, in a very personal fashion, with the "City Beautiful" movement that had flourished in an earlier day.

Dohrmann belonged to that circle of wealthy, influential men with whom Senator Phelan had always associated. From his father, a pioneer merchant in San Francisco, Dohrmann had inherited interests in half a dozen enterprises in which the family name appeared and was a director in several other companies. Brought up in the tradition of service to the community, he had served continuously as a committeeman of the Community Chest from its inception, had been for several years a director of the San Francisco Chamber of Commerce, and was also a director of the Recreation Council. He was particularly proud of his membership on the San Francisco Board of Education and was reluctant, because of that civic responsibility, to undertake another which might interfere with it. But he had very early acquired an interest in the form and appearance of cities through the study of architecture in Europe for three years after his graduation from St. Ignatius College. The idea of developing a comprehensive plan for the entire San Francisco Bay Area so strongly appealed to the artist and the idealist in him that he could not refuse the invitation to undertake to organize the much-desired regional planning association. When he accepted this task in January, 1925, he probably did not realize that he had entered upon his greatest public service.

CHAPTER TWELVE

Fred Dohrmann and the
Regional Plan Association

Fred Dohrmann undertook the stupendous job of attempting to arouse a whole metropolitan region to the desirability of planning for orderly growth and development. Even in 1925, when the population of all nine counties surrounding the bay was less than a million and a half, the task of reaching public officials and civic leaders in more than fifty cities distributed throughout an area almost as large as the states of Connecticut and Delaware together must have seemed staggering. At first Dohrmann agreed to serve the cause of regional planning for only three months, during the organization period. But to himself he must have admitted that he would serve indefinitely, for scarcely three months had slipped by when he wrote Phelan a letter saying that he had "resolved to devote myself to this movement as much as it may require in the way of time and energy for anything up to the next eight or ten years."[1] He had enthusiasm and zeal, and so had Russell Black, whom the new Regional Plan Association of San Francisco Bay Counties employed for a few months as "planning engineer," and so had Mayor Stringham of Berkeley, and Carl Rhodin, and Percy V. Long, the attorney, and many others who undertook, in the early months of 1925, to present the challenge of regional planning to service clubs and chambers of commerce from Santa Rosa and Petaluma to San Jose and Los Gatos.

The Regional Plan Association "aimed not only to educate, but actually to devise in a technical sense solutions to the interrealted civic problems" of the Bay Area,

Dohrmann told the Public Spirit Club of Berkeley in one of the first talks that he made after assuming the presidency of the new organization.[2] He listed six problems which he said were regional in scope and could not be met except through the coöperation of two or more or perhaps all the cities and counties in the Bay Area. At the head of the list was "a unified plan for port and harbor development on all sides of San Francisco Bay, similar to that which has been made for New York Harbor." Next in order came "a coördinated system of highways and scenic boulevards and bridges," and related to it were "rapid transit connections between all parts of the bay district, with special attention to commuting facilities." A fourth objective of the association was to be public "acquisition and development of recreational areas and large park reservations while they are obtainable at a reasonable cost and in a fair state of preservation." A fifth was the removal of the growing menace of pollution of the bay by sewage and waste. Lastly, Dohrmann cited the need for "regional zoning for the determination of the areas best suited to home-building, to industry, and to agriculture, and to insure a convenient and proper relation between home areas and industrial sites." In other words, the Regional Plan Association contemplated a study that would produce, in essence, a long-range, comprehensive land-use plan for the Bay Area, showing how every part of the area might be appropriately developed.

Dohrmann explained that the association would strive to unify the various plans being prepared by the several

Fred Dohrmann, Jr., President of Regional Plan Association, 1925–1928. Photograph courtesy of Mrs. Dohrmann.

communities of the Bay Area and to become a clearing house for future plans and developments. And it would attempt to inform the public about planning, by issuing bulletins and press releases and holding frequent public meetings.

Mayor Stringham of Berkeley, who followed Dohrmann on the program, invited the audience to consider the long-term future: "Fifty years ago the bay region had a population of one hundred thousand. Today the same area has probably more than a million and a half. In fifty years it will likely exceed ten million. So we must think in large terms and face the human as well as the physical problems."[3] Even if his population prediction was something less than scientific, at least it had the merit of startling his hearers.

Way to a Civic Renaissance

In speeches before other groups, Dohrmann earnestly pleaded for "a real sense of cooperation" among communities of the Bay Area. "If a great ideal such as a better city and region is the promise of tomorrow," he told the Vallejo Rotary Club, "there is no reason why cooperation cannot be secured in lighting the way to a great civic renaissance. City planning has something more to it than the technical outlining of improvement schemes. In its essence it is a forward movement for better citizenship and for elevating the conditions of life which surround all who are making our civilization. Places are like people and must be surrounded by love in order to lift them to a level at which the citizens will do more than merely live and make a living. If nations can demand and secure the allegiance and self-sacrifice of countless multitudes to uphold their ideals, why should not cities, which are the birthplaces and homes of whole families, be equally honored and strengthened. Our regional planning movement first proposes to inform the peoples of the conditions that surround them, to educate them to the necessities, and to agitate for a solution of public problems. It can do this only by cooperation among those who think alike and who may be relied upon to educate the communities to think alike. Once this is accomplished, not only will the San Francisco Bay Area have entered upon a program of orderly development, but the whole standing and influence of the region will be enhanced."[4]

This speech, perhaps more than any other Dohrmann ever made, revealed his vision, his crusading idealism, his confidence—or rather, overconfidence—in the appeal of the idea of regional planning. The gains to be made through area-wide coöperation appeared so manifestly desirable that he could not doubt that once reasonable and intelligent men became familiar with the pertinent facts about regional problems, they would feel compelled to solve the problems through united effort. "You know, as I know," he once told the Commonwealth Club, "that when the public knows what the fact is, if that fact presupposes and demands . . . the accomplishment of something, *the public usually gets what it wants when it knows what it wants.*"[5] And so he thought of the Regional Plan Association as an organization that would tell the public "what we think would be the answers to their problems, and then help them to understand the answers, and then help them to get results." He had an abiding faith in the willingness of the public to act decisively when confronted with accurate information on any problem. "The public is not stupid," he was fond of saying; "it is only ignorant of the facts."[6]

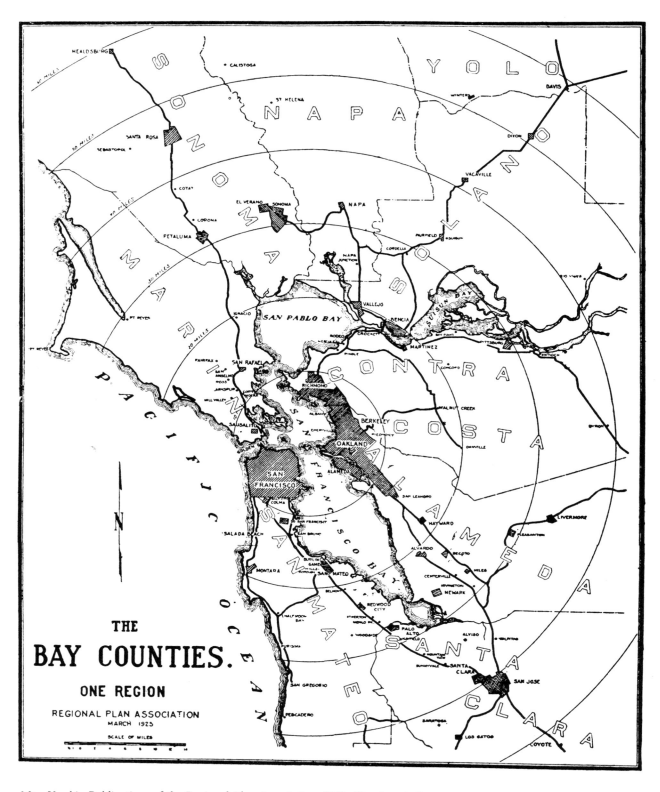

*Map Used in Publications of the Regional Plan Association, 1925. The Association
predicted that the San Francisco Bay Area would have 3,175,000 residents in 1950.
The Bureau of the Census reported in 1950 that 2,681,322 persons were living in
the nine counties of the area in April of that year.*

In those early days of the new planning movement Dohrmann and his associates apparently brushed aside any misgivings that assailed them and refused to ask themselves: "Is this too great an undertaking? Can we possibly succeed in raising sufficient funds, in collecting sufficient data, in achieving sufficient publicity for our purposes?" Patience, perseverance, and performance would enable them to triumph over the ignorance, indifference, suspicion, and timidity of less inspired men, they evidently believed.

Building an Organization

Dohrmann spoke often before community organizations while the employees of the association gathered data on Bay Area problems and compiled lists of prospective members. Black concentrated mainly on obtaining information from city planning commissions, city engineers, county surveyors, chambers of commerce, and real-estate boards. Their replies indicated that Bay Area communities then were chiefly concerned about bridging the bay, improving streets and highways, and developing port facilities. City engineers almost invariably reported that local sewer systems discharged directly into the bay, and none of these officials appeared to question the desirability of this method of sewage disposal. Generally, the information supplied to the association was so sketchy as to be of little value, but its very inadequacy showed there was need of systematically collecting and analyzing data on physical, social, and economic conditions in the Bay Area.

A field representative named John F. Kennedy, who had previously been employed by the San Francisco Chamber of Commerce, called on prominent businessmen and industrialists to solicit memberships in the association. His efforts, though supplemented by telephone calls and personal letters from Dohrmann, unfortunately failed to yield the results anticipated. There was no rush to join the Regional Plan Association.

Dohrmann himself found that most of the men on whom he had counted for financial support—the kind of men described by journalists as "captains of industry" and "powers in the community"—were indifferent to his newly espoused cause. Of a dozen or more prominent manufacturers, financiers, real-estate men, and merchants to whom he addressed his first appeal for funds, only Marshal Hale and Phelan responded, each with $500. These two contributions merely equalled the amount Dohrmann had lent the association by way of "starting the ball a-rolling," as he said. Since the office rent, salaries, and operating expenses amounted to almost $1,000 a month, Dohrmann was soon subsidizing the association

heavily from his own pocket; yet he showed no inclination to abandon his civic enterprise.

He concluded that in order to enlist active interest in the program of the Regional Plan Association, he should proceed at once to have the preliminary planning survey originally recommended by Black prepared by a well-known planning consultant. A report on the survey would give prospective members a clearer idea of the nature of regional planning and of the problems with which a general plan for the Bay Area would deal. He engaged as consultant Harland Bartholomew, of St. Louis, who had been one of the principal speakers at the Commonwealth Club conference on regional planning in April, 1924.

The Bartholomew Report

Bartholomew found that "the outstanding deficiency in the Bay Region" was "lack of unity in physical improvements and comprehensive planning."[7] Not mincing words, he singled out "psychological obstacles of local pride and prejudice" as the most serious difficulties to be faced. Lest communities mistake regional planning as a threat to their identities, however, he hastened to point out that this type of planning "need not deprive existing municipalities of local autonomy."[8] Such powers as a regional planning agency might exercise would necessarily be "distinctively regional in character" and would relate to problems which no local government could successfully cope with individually.

Bartholomew agreed that bay crossings by bridge or tube were of immediate necessity, but he observed: "The spectacular nature of the features of engineering design appear to have totally obscured the equally and perhaps more important questions of types of traffic accommodation and their influence upon present conditions and future growth. Will they result in accentuation of present congestion or effectually relieve it? The ultimate needs of the region in railroad connections, in rapid transit, in motor truck and passenger car traffic should be planned with care in advance of any hasty decision upon the location and type of bay crossings."[9]

If these statements had been written yesterday or last month, they could not be more pertinent to present-day discussions of additional bay crossings and problems of over-all development. Their logic is as sound today as it was more than thirty years ago.

Even in 1925 Bartholomew could point out that "the Bay Region requires rapid transit more than any other metropolitan community, because of the physical characteristics of the region."[10] Transportation planners have recognized, in the years since then, that no system of highways and freeways, however extensive, alone can solve the problem of moving masses of people swiftly, safely, and economically. Both a rapid transit system and a comprehensive trafficway system are needed.

The lack of united effort in the development of port facilities prompted the consultant to recommend "a general plan for development of the entire bay and waterfront." "It is not to be expected that any such plan would ever be carried out in its entirety, but if well done would give direction to growth and serve to effect economy and to prevent wasteful and needless local competitive undertakings."[11]

The poverty of the Bay Area in waterfront recreation areas was matched, Bartholomew found, by its poverty in other types of public reservations. "The Bay Region," he wrote, "is notably lacking in volume and distribution of recreational areas. The history of all great cities has been that unless generous provision of recreational space has been made early in the history of the city, the most suitable recreational areas either become absorbed or so increased in value that their acquisition becomes prohibitive. To serve the future population of this region there should be an enlargement of present public recreational spaces of several hundred per cent, and this will scarcely equal the average of other regions, such as Boston, New York and Chicago."[12]

He particularly recommended watershed areas as regional parks—a recommendation that had been made by Charles Keeler, Managing Director of the Berkeley Chamber of Commerce, in 1923 with the thought that the watershed lands of the East Bay Water Company in the Berkeley Hills would be suitable.

On the subject of water supply Bartholomew was brief, merely noting that the Marin Municipal Water District, the East Bay Municipal Utility District, and the Spring Valley Water Company together could serve but a small percentage of the total Bay Area and that "a regional plan must concern itself with the water needs of the ultimate population,"[13] which presumably would be spread over a vast territory.

The means Bartholomew suggested for improving the physical conditions obtaining in the Bay Area and for coördinating the planning activities of a multiplicity of governmental units was a vaguely described regional planning commission that would "make plans for the future development of the region" and "possibly" administer subdivision and zoning regulations in unincorporated territory throughout the nine-county area.[14] Bartholomew apparently was feeling his way in this proposal and intended that the Regional Plan Association should make a thorough study of the whole subject of enabling legislation, effective organization for planning, and the knotty problem of financing area-wide planning.

Dohrmann and his associates, however, showed only mild interest in enabling legislation of any kind; whereas the League of California Municipalities, the California Real Estate Association, and various city planning commissions were then struggling for the enactment of legislation authorizing the establishment of planning agencies in counties not operating under freeholder charters. Without county planning, regional planning would be impossible, these organizations understood, but they faced at least two more years of campaigning for an act authorizing county planning, because Governor C. C. Young had failed to sign a county planning bill approved by the legislature at its 1925 session. Correspondence between Dohrmann and the groups interested in legislation that would broaden the scope of planning in California reveals that he and other members of the Regional Plan Association were aware of the struggle for an enabling statute, but they assumed an almost detached attitude toward the entire undertaking, mainly because of Dohrmann's own feeling that there was no urgency about establishing additional planning agencies. He said on more than one occasion that the governments of the cities and counties in the Bay Area would support regional planning only after a private organization had demonstrated its value— and he expected that the demonstration would take several years.

Struggle for Support

The Bartholomew Report, presented to the members of the Regional Plan Association at a dinner given by Dohrmann at the St. Francis Hotel on September 16, 1925, provided the association with the kind of "ammunition" its president believed was necessary for a successful membership campaign. With this document on hand, Dohrmann resolved to place the organization on a firm foundation by filing papers of incorporation, broadening the financial support, and enlarging the membership. Some months previously he had sought to enhance the prestige of the association by inducing Dr. Ray Lyman Wilbur, president of Stanford University, and Dr. David P. Barrows, a former president of the University of California, to serve with several others on the board of trustees of the organization. In selecting officers, he turned to those who had been advising him on legal and financial matters: Percy V. Long (vice-president), Mrs. Parker Maddux, a prominent clubwoman (vice-president), Randolph V. Whiting, an attorney (secretary), and Matthew A. Harris, a businessman (treasurer). But Dohrmann still needed the participation of the business leaders of San Francisco. Unless he could elicit more than vague expressions of good will and meaningless praise for the "wonderful work" he was doing, the association might be doomed.

He invited the financiers and outstanding executives of the city, eight or ten at a time, to meet with him at the offices of the Regional Plan Association, so that he could "show them . . . just what this association means to individuals in San Francisco and thereby sell to them the idea that each one of them should contribute $100.00 toward this cause."[15] Within three weeks, forty of the men who accepted his invitation contributed $100 each to the association; but it is doubtful whether many of them were deeply impressed with the desirability of regional planning, even though they assured him that they were. Probably for business and social reasons they could not refuse his personal appeal for funds; very likely, too, they had the feeling that their donations relieved them of further concern about a matter that seemed remote from their day-to-day affairs. Certainly, few of them thereafter participated in the activities of the association.

Dohrmann ardently believed, nevertheless, that he was building a genuine area-wide movement. "San Franciscans must realize," he wrote one prospective contributor, "that what is good for any of the counties and the places around the bay is also good for us here in San Francisco and vice versa; and that any legitimate and unselfish movement like this will surely rebound to the individual as well as the collective benefit of all residents."[16]

Resolutions and Questionnaires

Having replenished the exchequer of the Regional Plan Association somewhat, Dohrmann and his associates and staff began preparing for a membership solicitation throughout the nine counties of the Bay Area by requesting organizations that were familiar with the program of the association to adopt resolutions approving its purpose, scope, and activities. Organizations which endorsed the efforts of the association were chiefly the chambers of commerce before which its leaders had appeared in 1925 and the first six months of 1926. In some organizations all members voted on a resolution, in others only the board of directors. Just how valuable this type of support was would be difficult to judge. Much of it, surely, meant little more than the perfunctory praise offered Dohrmann by men who had no intention of joining him in his civic labors. Most organizations easily accept and quickly forget resolutions approving worthy causes.

The Regional Plan Association was a good deal less successful in inducing chambers of commerce and other associations to respond to a questionnaire seeking information on local industries, public utilities, housing,

traffic, transportation, and community facilities. "The information asked for in your questionnaire is so voluminous and technical in nature as to make it impracticable for us to attempt to fill it out," the secretary-manager of the Oakland Chamber of Commerce complained in a rather typical reaction to the lengthy form distributed by the association. To answer all the questions in detail would require considerable research that the Oakland Chamber of Commerce was not prepared to undertake, he said; and then he added: "It seems to me that such a survey would have to be made by those who are promoting the Regional Plan Association, in which the Oakland Chamber of Commerce is not participating."[17]

The letter must have depressed Dohrmann, who had attempted more than a year earlier to persuade Joseph R. Knowland, publisher of the Oakland *Tribune*, to serve as vice-president of the Regional Plan Association and had been turned down. The organization simply had no effective support in Oakland. The leaders in that city were so preoccupied with its downtown congestion that area-wide problems, other than a transbay crossing, seemed beyond the realm of immediate concern. Oakland merchants, bankers, and terminal operators who formed the Major Highway and Traffic Committee of One Hundred did respect Dohrmann enough, however, to accept his recommendation that they employ Harland Bartholomew to prepare a major street plan for their city.

The Regional Plan Association never was able to form local advisory committees on various problems in every one of the Bay Area counties, although it endeavored all during 1926 and a good part of 1927 to perfect this type of organization. A board of twenty-seven regional representatives, including members from all nine counties, was the nearest it came to presenting even the appearance of area-wide participation. Outside San Francisco the most active members of the association came mainly from San Mateo, Marin, and Santa Clara counties, with a sprinkling of members from Napa, Contra Costa, and Alameda counties. Guy Wilfrid Hayler, who became planning engineer for the association in 1926, said that "it took a long time to get people on a selected list, because they were afraid of the domination of San Francisco."[18] In short, the very auspices under which the association came into being probably handicapped it from the beginning. It was suspect in many areas because most of its leaders were identified with the metropolis.

Regional Studies

In spite of the ever-present financial problem (which Dohrmann continued to meet by contributions from his own resources) and the difficulties of persuading promi-

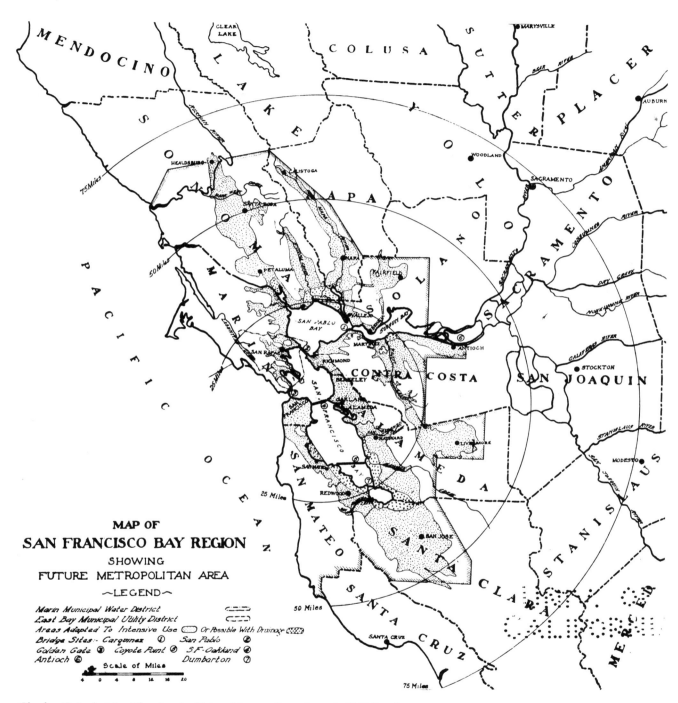

MAP OF
SAN FRANCISCO BAY REGION
SHOWING
FUTURE METROPOLITAN AREA
~LEGEND~

Marin Municipal Water District
East Bay Municipal Utility District
Areas Adapted To Intensive Use ⬭ Or Possible With Drainage ▨
Bridge Sites - Carquinez ①   San Pablo ②
Golden Gate ③   Coyote Point ④   SF-Oakland ⑤
Antioch ⑥   Dumbarton ⑦

Scale of Miles

Charles H. Lee's Map Showing the Future Metropolitan Area. In 1926 Lee forecast an "ultimate" population of 5,000,000 to 6,000,000 in the areas "adapted to intensive use" (shaded on the map). Photograph courtesy of Seismological Society of America.

nent men and women in various Bay Area communities to become members, the association did manage in 1926-1927 to make some progress on its announced program of developing a regional plan. Hayler prepared a series of maps depicting various types of existing regional development, such as highways, sanitation facilities, airfields, bridges, transportation, recreation, water supply, and zoning. On some of these maps, which technical divisions of the association used, Hayler indicated suggested regional improvements.

At no time, however, did the Regional Plan Association attempt the kind of projections made in a study published by Charles H. Lee, a San Francisco consulting engineer, in the *Bulletin* of the Seismological Society of America in June, 1926. Lee sought to determine the extent of the ultimate urban development in the Bay Area, not as a basis for the kind of city and metropolitan regional planning Dohrmann was promoting, but in order to outline "what might be done to reduce future hazards to life and property from earthquake and earthquake fires."[19] In particular, Lee was interested in the ultimate water supply requirements of this metropolitan region and in the kind of interconnected storage and water distribution facilities that would be effective in the event of a great distaster, such as occurred in 1906. His studies should have suggested much to the members of the Regional Plan Association, but they did not.

From a study of detailed topographic sheets of the United States Geological Survey and from personal knowledge and inspection of terrain, Lee roughly determined the uses to which the land in the entire territory surrounding San Francisco Bay might be put in the future. This would mean classification of areas according to their suitability for agriculture, industry, commerce, and urban and suburban residential development. Thus Lee arrived at a calculation of the amount of land useful for intensive occupation—876,000 acres, plus perhaps some 100,000 additional acres that might be reclaimed from marshes and tidelands. Of the 876,000 acres classified as "useful for intensive occupation," he designated 564,400 acres, or approximately 882 square miles, as useful for urban and suburban development.[20]

On the assumption that the ultimate population density would not exceed twice that in the San Francisco–Oakland metropolitan district in 1920, which averaged 3.2 persons per acre, Lee predicted a population in the metropolitan area of five to six millions, out of a state population of approximately seventeen millions.[21] From their knowledge of available water supplies, present-day analysts assume that California will have a population of sixty millions and the Bay Area several millions more than Lee

prognosticated; but in 1926 the forecast of an ultimate population of seventeen millions in the state must have seemed fantastic. The population of California in 1920 was only 3,426,861.

Population predictions aside, Lee made the kind of land use studies that are essential for any genuine regional planning. No one before him had attempted to show graphically the possible size and shape of the future urban complex in the Bay Area. Had the Regional Plan Association taken its cue from this engineer's studies, it might have made some progress toward the development of a regional plan. But for any single organization to carry out the kind of planning program Lee's approach suggested would have required a large staff, at least the $250,000 originally proposed by Russell Van Nest Black, and many years of patient labor. The Regional Plan Association had a skeleton staff, limited funds, and an unknown life expectancy. Inevitably, it pursued a piecemeal rather than a comprehensive approach to regional planning.

Detailed Studies

One of the detailed studies decided upon was an analysis of the difficulties of delivering produce from San Mateo and Santa Clara counties to the wholesale district in the general area of Clay and Davis streets in San Francisco, which thirty years later was to be declared a blighted area subject to redevelopment. Heavy traffic on El Camino Real and on city streets leading to the district delayed trucks coming from agricultural areas, thereby complicating the operations of commission houses and retarding the distribution of produce to markets throughout the city. Mapping of the routes used by produce trucks led to comprehensive mapping of highways in the entire Bay Area, then to study of the need for widening certain heavily traveled routes and for constructing additional routes. The Regional Plan Association hoped later to propose a system of circumferential roads, such as Bartholomew had suggested in his preliminary survey.

The study of wholesale produce delivery related to a problem that even in the 'twenties seemed serious and is now alarming to many Californians—the loss, through urban sprawl and "scatteration," of tens of thousands of acres of first-class agricultural land. "At the present time," Hayler wrote, "the wholesale produce delivered into San Francisco is coming more and more from remote points in San Mateo and Santa Clara counties, owing to land going out of cultivation in localities closer in. The East Bay situation may be said to be similar. This same condition has been found to exist in many other large cities in America where the situation has been investigated, and in every case it has played a great part in forcing up the cost of living in these particular cities."[22]

Although the Regional Plan Association pleaded for "earnest consideration" of the desirability of preserving land near cities for a variety of agricultural uses—truck gardening, fruit growing, poultry farming, and dairying, not even farmers at that time passed resolutions on the subject. Only within the past five or six years have agricultural associations attempted to save some areas from urbanization and to ponder the implications of withdrawal from cultivation of one fertile valley after another.

As settlement along the level lands bordering the bay increased, another problem grew worse: pollution of the waters of the bay. The Regional Plan Association studied the information it had gathered from cities and sanitary districts and found that there were more than fifty outfall sewers draining into the shallow waters along the eastern side of the bay between Richmond and San Leandro. "Much the same state of affairs exists from San Francisco southward on the peninsular side," Hayler pointed out.[23] Nevertheless, as new subdivisions opened and cities expanded, the number of outfall sewers polluting the bay increased. By 1927 the total was no les than 175.

To stimulate action on the pollution problem before it became truly menacing, the Regional Plan Association arranged a meeting in San Francisco in October, 1926, to which it invited representatives from municipalities and sanitary districts throughout the Bay Area. Sixty-five persons attended the meeting and heard officials of the United States Public Health Service, the State Board of Health, and local health departments recommend a survey of the problem. But when a special committee later estimated that a survey would cost $30,000 or more, interest in the pollution problem subsided. More than twenty years were to pass before Bay Area cities would make serious efforts to deal with the problem.

Dohrmann's personal interest in aviation as a new and important commercial activity caused the association to give a great deal of time and effort in 1926 and the early months of 1927 to a campaign for enabling legislation that would authorize the State Board of Harbor Commissioners to construct and operate a landing platform for commercial aviation over the waterfront piers in San Francisco. Although Governor C. C. Young signed the act drawn by the association, Dohrmann's dream of a landing platform a million feet square rising a hundred and fifty or two hundred feet above high-water mark never materialized. More commodious airports developed by San Francisco and Oakland in San Mateo County and on Bay Farm Island, respectively, answered the needs of the growing aviation industry.

A Conference in Oakland

In 1927, the last full year in which the Regional Plan Association was active, many city officials and all the city planners then employed in California joined forces to push through the state legislature an improved version of the local planning enabling legislation that had been pocket vetoed by the governor in 1925. That interest in this movement was widespread was indicated by the large attendance at a two-day conference on city planning arranged by Fred E. Reed, chairman of the City Plan Division of the California Real Estate Association and head of the City Planning Committee of the Oakland Real Estate Board. More than a thousand representatives of municipalities, county governments, the state legislature, chambers of commerce, women's clubs, and business organizations came to hear such prominent planners as John Nolen, Harland Bartholomew, Gordon Whitnall, Carol Aronovici, Hugh Pomeroy, Charles Cheney, and Stephen Child. Besides these speakers, heads of citizen groups, public health officers, managers of chambers of commerce, attorneys, real-estate men, and officials of the League of California Municipalities also spoke.

Asked to appear on the program, Dohrmann seized the occasion to make another plea for East Bay support and to explain the purpose of his organization. "I prefer to think of the waters of San Francisco Bay as uniting the various communities rather than dividing them, and on that account I consider that their common problems demand a common solution," he said. "The idea of planning the San Francisco Bay Area on a broad, comprehensive scale is one which should appeal to every community and to none more particularly than to Oakland and its sister communities." He assured his listeners that the Regional Plan Association had "no political aims or interests to serve for any one particular city or area" and that it would benefit each community in proportion to the coöperation given. Citing various features of the East Bay that might serve as inspiration for "a wide system of regional planning," he pointed out that "the one thing wanting is the striking of the popular imagination to what might be accomplished if the cities can only see with one eye."[24]

By way of "striking the popular imagination," Dohrmann pictured the Bay Area as "the home of an enormous population" in the future, but he warned that "we must not be led away by thinking that a great increase in population is the only thing necessary for progress." The great cities of the East, with their congested living conditions, their inadequate trading facilities, and their ever-increasing municipal costs, were paying the penalty for mistakenly equating population gains with "progress." In

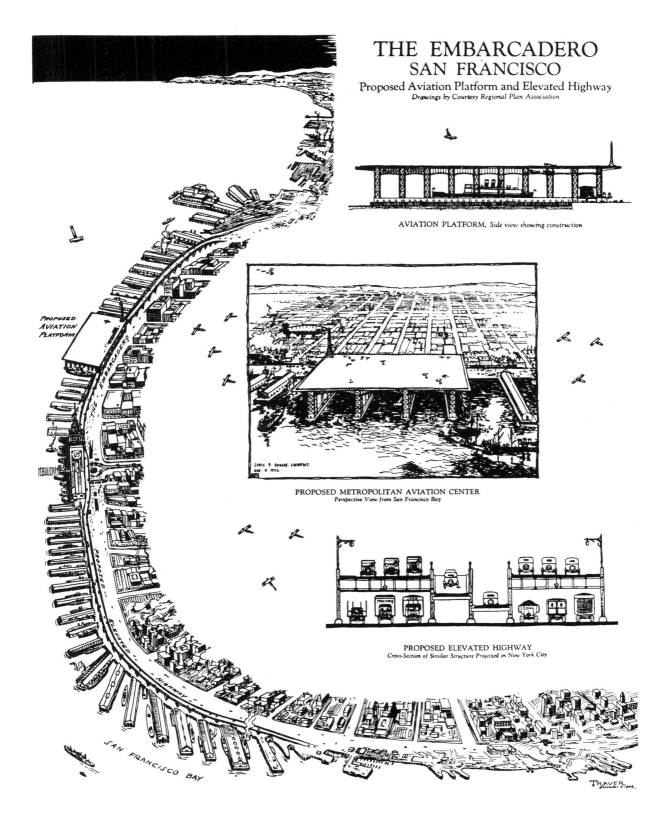

THE EMBARCADERO
SAN FRANCISCO
Proposed Aviation Platform and Elevated Highway
Drawings by Courtesy Regional Plan Association

AVIATION PLATFORM, *Side view showing construction*

PROPOSED METROPOLITAN AVIATION CENTER
Perspective View from San Francisco Bay

PROPOSED ELEVATED HIGHWAY
Cross-Section of Similar Structure Projected in New York City

*Aviation Platform Proposed by the Regional Plan Association, 1927. The elevated
highway shown in the drawings would have followed a route similar to that of the
Embarcadero Freeway. Drawings by Louis P. Hobart, Architect.*

the newer West "the grotesque menace of an ill-planned region" could be avoided by "concerted action" to utilize growth and development to the best advantage.[25]

Stephen Child, who spoke later in the session addressed by Dohrmann, was no less concerned than his friend with area-wide coöperation, but he was willing, as Dohrmann never was, to look beyond the preparation of a regional plan to the still more difficult process of making use of the plan. He chose to discuss the political problems involved in carrying out a comprehensive scheme for the future development of the Bay Area. In somewhat fanciful vein the landscape architect and consultant on city planning described a dream in which he awakened, like Rip Van Winkle, from a long sleep and discovered on the summit of Yerba Buena Island a temple-like structure that was the assembly hall of the Federation of the Boroughs of San Francisco Bay. Over the entrance was this inscription: "Dedicated to Unity of Purpose for the San Francisco Bay Region."[26]

Years before, he was informed by a knowing mentor who found him gazing at the beautiful white marble building, "a great deal of suspicion and narrow provincial municipalism" had produced so many "petty quarrels and jealousies" that the wiser and more farseeing men in the Bay Area began to realize that dissension was hurting everyone. They were in a mood to listen to a visitor from a far country who prophesied that the twentieth century would be the "century of the Pacific" and that millions of people would live in the Bay Area. Taking his words to heart, they saw that it behooved them to prepare for growth. Accordingly, after many months of discussion, they evolved a regional federation, since "it was evident that no real merger of all these communities into one single great city was either possible or needed."[27]

Each borough in the regional federation included "those communities whose important civic problems, such as drainage, sewage disposal, water supply, conservation, and the like, could best be solved by communal action." On the San Francisco Peninsula there were the boroughs of San Francisco, San Mateo, and Palo Alto; in the northern part of the Santa Clara Valley, the borough of Santa Clara, which included San Jose, Santa Clara, Saratoga, and several other communities; in the East Bay, the borough of Oakland, and so on. Each had a council, a borough manager, and all the officials required by a modern, efficient city government. In return for "a very considerable degree of liberty in regard to its own affairs," each borough recognized that it was the job of the federation "to undertake to solve those problems that no one borough could solve alone."[28]

This remarkable system of boroughs had all come about, according to the mentor, after Dohrmann's Regional Plan Association had prepared a preliminary regional plan and had "sold regional planning to the Bay District." "It was when it came to undertaking to put this plan into effect, however, that it was found necessary to establish this Federation of the Boroughs of San Francisco Bay . . ."[29] There was needed some over-all government that could authorize, finance, and construct projects of benefit to the entire metropolitan region or to subregions.

Still quoting his imaginary mentor, Child pictured the regional federation as having solved the area-wide water supply problem, as well as the problem of developing area-wide harbor facilities and a plan for utilizing every foot of bay shoreline, including sections for recreational use. Partly completed or under construction was "a splendidly effective system of main highways," following a well-considered scheme of the regional planners. The trackage of competing railroads had been consolidated wherever possible, a belt line had been built along the waterfront to serve industrial areas, and many grade crossings had been eliminated. The federation had also solved the problem of bridging the bay, "for this again was a problem far too big and too comprehensive for any one community."[30] Through the influence of the federation a metropolitan park commission had been appointed, which had included beautiful mountain canyons, watershed areas and their storage reservoirs, and scenic hilltops in a regional recreation system connected by a series of pleasure-ways in which there was a link named for each of the presidents of the United States from Washington to Coolidge.[31] In outlining this metropolitan park system, Child was expressing ideas he had cherished for more than ten years.

At the close of his talk, the main idea of which had been inspired by a federation organized in the Ruhr Valley a few years previously, Child asked his hearers, "Was it not something more substantial than a dream that I had, and is it not for us to bring it to earth, establish it upon firm foundation . . . , so that it may achieve its aims—unity of purpose for the San Francisco Bay Region?"[32]

Child was, of course, ahead of his time. Unfortunately, too, he was an elderly man, very deaf, and anything but a forceful speaker, though he did have a certain charm. His speech "fell flat," one delegate to the conference recalls.[33] The political realists of the day pinned their hopes for improvement of the Bay Area not on regional federation or some other form of metropolitan government but on a new local planning enabling act based on a model planning act prepared by the Advisory Committee on City Planning and Zoning of the United States Department of Commerce and on the planning act passed by the state of New York in 1926.

The Planning Act of 1927

The draft of the proposed California act not only provided for repeal of the city planning law of 1915 but also authorized for the first time county and regional planning in California. No proposed legislation providing for any form of metropolitan government to carry out area-wide plans accompanied it. The proponents of the legislation—the League of California Municipalities, the California Conference on City Planning, the California Real Estate Board, and the Commonwealth Club of California—had not faced that issue.

Besides providing for the organization of city, county, and regional planning commissions, the planning enabling act of 1927 authorized the preparation of a master plan for the area in which the city, county, or regional commission had jurisdiction, whereas the 1915 legislation had not embodied the concept of a single comprehensive plan. The new act stated: "The plan shall be made with the general purpose of guiding and accomplishing a coordinated, adjusted, and harmonious development of the municipality, or county, and its environs, which will, in accordance with present and future needs, best promote the amenities of life, health, safety, morals, order, convenience, prosperity and general welfare, as well as efficiency and economy in the process of development . . ."[34]

Seemingly the new legislation granted planning commissions powers broad enough to enable them to function effectively as advisory agencies to city and county governing bodies; yet many persons, including Governor Young, entertained doubts about this statute. It was expected to raise many new problems of city and county procedure and many new legal questions. As a condition of his approval the governor exacted a promise from the California Conference on City Planning that it would appoint a committee of representative citizens, versed in planning matters and in real-estate problems, to watch its operations and prepare any needed amendments in advance of the 1929 session of the state legislature.

The language of the act was vague concerning what constituted a region for planning purposes, and this vagueness tended to encourage small divisions within larger physiographic areas to form so-called regional planning commissions. The Palo Alto Chamber of Commerce, for instance, appointed a committee to make a field survey for a proposed "regional plan" for Palo Alto and its vicinity, but this movement progressed no further than the discussion stage. There was another misguided effort toward "regional planning" in southern San Mateo

County, under the leadership of a group in Redwood City. Like the Palo Alto movement, this also died after a few committee meetings.

East Bay Association

So far as the Regional Plan Association of San Francisco Bay Counties was concerned, the most serious threat to genuine regional planning was the East Bay Regional Plan Association formed by Fred E. Reed, an Oakland realtor, in the spring of 1927. This organization, composed of citizens of Alameda and Contra Costa counties, petitioned the governor to designate the two East Bay counties a region for planning purposes, and although Governor Young did not act upon the petition, the East Bay organization succeeded in vitiating the efforts of Dohrmann's association to establish the concept of the nine counties bordering on the bay as a single geographical, economic, and social unit.

The East Bay Regional Plan Association busied itself at first chiefly with publicizing the streets and highways plan prepared by Harland Bartholomew for the Major Highway and Traffic Committee of One Hundred. This plan proposed the creation of a distributor loop around the central business district of Oakland, a superhighway along the East Bay waterfront from San Leandro to Richmond (similar to the route of the present freeway), parallel routes to relieve congestion on East Twelfth and East Fourteenth streets, several cross-town routes above Lake Merritt, and the widening and extension of the Skyline Boulevard in the Berkeley Hills.

Reed, who was named chairman of the newly formed Oakland City Planning Commission soon after presentation of the Bartholomew Plan, had written cordial letters to Dohrmann for many months preceding the formation of the East Bay Regional Plan Association; and the two continued to correspond politely even after the East Bay association was established. But the gentlemanly exchange of views did not alter the fact that for Dohrmann the attempt to keep alive his own Regional Plan Association had become a heartbreaking endeavor. In 1925 he had personally contributed $13,250 to the organization, in 1926 more than $10,000, and in 1927 nearly $14,000, not to mention hours and hours of time, his most earnest thought, and the very essence of his hopes and aspirations as a citizen of a metropolitan community not yet fully aware of the material and spiritual interdependence of its parts. Desperately resorting to his social position as a member of the merchant aristocracy of San Francisco, he had arranged a series of dinners at his own home, in 1927, to which he had invited the cream of San Francisco business executives, and, as before, he had wangled con-

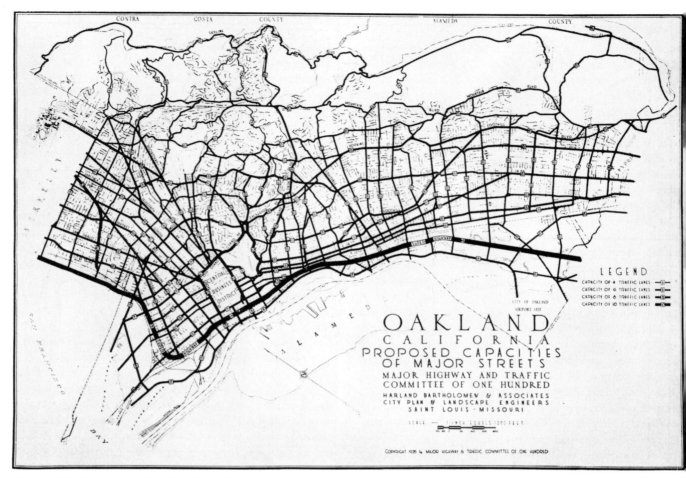

Harland Bartholomew's Plan for Major Streets in Oakland, 1927. The proposed superhighway along the waterfront foreshadowed the Eastshore Freeway built after World War II.

tributions from them that brought donations from other sources to $8,000. Yet he had not built an area-wide organization with a large and enthusiastic membership. In a letter to a political candidate who asked to appear before the Regional Plan Association, he disclosed that "the active members probably do not comprise more than ten."[35] This was all that the association amounted to after three years of steady effort, reams of publicity in newspapers and magazines, hundreds of speeches before other organizations, publication of several significant reports and a stream of factual bulletins, convocation of large groups to consider special problems of the Bay Area, and literally hundreds of letters from Dohrmann, Hayler, Black, Kennedy, Long, and others to prospective members, public officials, and inquiring citizens.

End of the Association

After futile efforts to raise money through the San Francisco Chamber of Commerce and through the Community Chest, Dohrmann and his fellow officers of the Regional Plan Association in April, 1928, discharged the staff, closed the office in the Phelan Building, and moved the records of the association to a vacant room adjoining the offices of an attorney member in the Foxcroft Building. In a memorandum headed "The Past, Present, and Future of the Regional Plan Association," Dohrmann avowed that the organization was "not going to die a full death," but was "going to try and hibernate for about a year."[36] He provided $125 a month for eight months to "enable the organization to keep itself before the eyes of the public," but after this fitful hibernation the Regional Plan Association slept the sleep of oblivion—or rather it became for Dohrmann a ghost that might some day return to life and achieve all that he had labored in vain to accomplish.

The president of the Regional Plan Association of San Francisco Bay Counties was one of those unsung civic heroes whose full contribution to the advancement of the metropolitan community can never be known. Somewhat aloof and humorless as a speaker, unexceptional as a thinker, and lacking the masterfulness that proclaims the genuine leader, he nevertheless made thousands of people aware that city planning and metropolitan regional planning are means of creating a better physical environment. He shared the typical businessman's distrust of politics and government and perhaps devoted too much effort to missionary work among his fellow businessmen when he should have been spending at least part of his time cultivating politicians and their cronies. He for the most part ignored the important job of helping to draft planning enabling legislation, and he regarded any consideration of political amalgamations or metropolitan federation as "controversial" and therefore taboo. But with all his limitations, he was far above the average in vision, in appreciation of the aesthetic qualities of his surroundings, and in devotion to the truly great ideal of metropolitan regional unity. He never regretted having spent thousands of dollars sustaining the Regional Plan Association; nor did he ever look upon his expenditure of time and effort as a fruitless sacrifice. He retained until his death in January, 1936, faith in the belief that at some time in the future other groups would prepare and carry out the regional plan of which he dreamed.

There is one indispensable ally that any new movement must have, and that is time. Time was not Dohrmann's companion in arms. Though he fought valiantly to establish the concept of the nine counties and nearly three score cities of the Bay Area as one community, he led a crusade for which the vast majority of people were unprepared. There were comparatively few city planning commissions and no county planning commissions in the Bay Area in the mid-twenties. The only county planning body appointed under the planning enabling legislation enacted in 1927 was in Santa Barbara County. The number of people in the Bay Area who had direct knowledge of the planning function through the operations of a local planning agency was relatively insignificant. Dohrmann publicized the role of planning and stimulated interest in forming local planning bodies, but he himself lacked the moral support that a substantial number of planning commissions might have given him. The absence of such support, together with other handicaps under which the Regional Plan Association labored, proved to be a fatal drag on the struggling regional planning movement.

Despite its brief and almost consumptive existence, the Regional Plan Association did provide a valuable legacy for later groups inspired by the ideal of area-wide cooperation. It succeeded in identifying almost all the major problems that affect the metropolitan region in its entirety, with the exception, of course, of the problem of air pollution, which is new since World War II. It emphasized that these problems are interrelated and should be attacked through a comprehensive, area-wide planning program, even though the association itself was unable to develop such a program. Through its very failure, the organization demonstrated that area-wide participation is essential to the success of a regional planning program and that local governments, especially, must support the program. It correctly conceived the functions of a regional planning agency to include conducting research, analyzing the data collected, serving as a clearing house for data on the area as a whole that would be needed by numerous local governmental agencies and private organizations, preparing an area-wide general plan in coöperation with local governments, and facilitating the coördination of local plans with the regional general plan. The greatest legacy of the association was, however, intangible: the inspiration it has afforded citizens and planning officials who desire development of the metropolitan region in accordance with a comprehensive, guiding plan.

CHAPTER THIRTEEN

Prosperity and Projects

In the 'twenties San Francisco enjoyed another of those periods of heady prosperity that have recurred at irregular intervals ever since it became a metropolis in the days of the gold rush. So congested were piers along the Embarcadero that many vessels seeking to discharge or take on cargo were diverted to Oakland or Richmond, which thus had the benefit of maritime commerce they had not expected. Within the decade the tonnage handled at the port of San Francisco doubled, and the value of the cargoes moving across its wharves soared in the year 1929 to the unprecedented figure of $1,613,100,000—twice that of cargoes handled at all the other ports in the Bay Area. San Francisco, the chief distribution center in the West, could boast in 1929 of almost half the wholesale trade of California, though southern California, growing more rapidly than the central and northern sections of the state, was soon to invade trade areas long monopolized by San Francisco. In retail trade, too, the city that was once "the miserable village of Yerba Buena" held an enviable position. In 1929 its stores rang up on their cash registers sales amounting to almost half of all those made in the nine counties bordering on the bay, although only two-fifths of the population of the Bay Area lived in San Francisco. And year after year that most sensitive barometer of economic conditions, the annual total of building permits, remained between fifty and sixty million dollars.

Structural steel workers precariously balanced on beams high above the streets reared a new skyline for the metropolis—a skyline that was to continue almost un-

changed until after World War II. In 1926 and 1927 they fashioned the huge skeleton of the Russ Building, still the tallest and largest office building in San Francisco. Two blocks to the south on Montgomery Street rose the Hunter-Dulin Building, twenty-three stories high, with hundreds of offices for corporation executives and professional men. Near by, other massive structures, fifteen to twenty-two stories high, rose from piles driven into the sand and mud that once marked the edge of Yerba Buena Cove. And then there was the impressive edifice of the Pacific Telephone and Telegraph Company, twenty-six stories high, aloof on New Montgomery Street.

Suburban Growth

In this concentrated metropolis, "decentralization" only occasionally roused mild forebodings, yet growth in areas far beyond San Francisco's corporate limits had begun to accelerate. The challenge of the outlying shopping center, with its acres of parking space, was of course more than two decades in the future, but the kind of growth that was to give rise to the suburban shopping center was already evident in San Mateo County.

"The Peninsula has suddenly come into its own," the *California Real Estate Magazine* observed in June, 1927. "Where two years ago there were perhaps less than ten subdivision developments, there are now nearly one hundred in progress. Big profits have been made on lot resales and the developers of new lands are finding a ready market for their offerings."

Some of the large, old estates that had become islands of undeveloped acreage in the midst of small-lot developments finally were sold. One such was the 375-acre estate purchased by John Parrott in 1860 and named Baywood. Situated in the heart of the city of San Mateo, it had blocked development of the city to the west of El Camino Real ever since the time of the great earthquake and fire in San Francisco. The developers, who purchased it with the intention of dividing it into fifty-foot lots, reportedly paid a million dollars for it.

Real-estate groups would have been willing to pay similar sums for other large estates had the owners been willing to part with them, but the tradition of manor-house living died slowly in San Mateo County. For another two decades many big land holdings were to continue intact in the midst of subdivision plattings, thereby causing a peculiarly spotty pattern of urbanization unlike that of almost all other areas within a thirty-mile radius of San Francisco.

The growth of the Peninsula in the late 'twenties reflected the extensive adoption of the private automobile as a means of traveling to and from work and the desire of city dwellers for more space and more of the amenities of living. By 1930 the population of San Mateo County was twice as large as in 1920, and most of its 77,000 residents lived in towns and unincorporated areas on the bay side.

San Francisco itself added almost 128,000 new residents in the 1920's; but on the opposite side of the bay, in Alameda County, the same kind of low-density development that was occurring in San Mateo County absorbed an increase of more than 130,000. Growth of the small cities of Marin County that were within commuting range of San Francisco also reflected the search for more living space. San Jose, in the Santa Clara Valley, likewise continued to spread out in an uncrowded pattern. Agriculture in the surrounding area flourished, and the number of food-processing plants increased, providing many new jobs. Only the cities in the northern counties of Sonoma, Napa, and Solano failed to make noticeable population gains and to get used to the sight of surveyors laying out new blocks in fields and orchards beyond the existing residential districts.

Insecure Metropolis

The growth of San Francisco actually made it an insecure city, with a very real cause for worry. In the late 'twenties, when its population was approximately 600,000, it was still dependent upon the local water sources controlled by the Spring Valley Water Company, and it was using these almost to the maximum, with little or no margin of safety

in the event of a critical drought. True, work on the Hetch Hetchy project was progressing in the distant Sierra Nevada, but no one could say for certain how many years would pass before the melted snows of Yosemite would reach the Peninsula and the metropolis. Deep in the mud at the bottom of the southern arm of the bay lay a riveted steel pipe, five feet in diameter, that would form a section of the Hetch Hetchy Aqueduct and convey water under the navigable channel between Alameda County and the Peninsula; but still to be completed were a pipe line across the San Joaquin Valley and a twenty-five-mile tunnel through the Coast Range.

On May 1, 1928, the voters of San Francisco made reasonably sure, however, that when the waters from Hetch Hetchy Reservoir should come coursing through the long aqueduct, they would flow into storage reservoirs and a distributing system wholly owned by the City and County of San Francisco. On that date they approved by a vote of four to one a $41,000,000 bond issue for purchase of the properties of the Spring Valley Water Company. On four previous occasions, the last as recently as June 14, 1927, they had defeated bonds for acquisition of the private system. This time only one newspaper, the *Bulletin*, opposed the bonds.

After some difficulty in marketing the bond issue, the city took possession on March 3, 1930, of a private water system that had been developing for more than seventy years. It included 62,612 acres of reservoir and watershed lands in San Francisco, San Mateo, Santa Clara, and Alameda counties; four impounding reservoirs with a total capacity of sixty billion gallons; the Pleasanton well system at the lower end of Livermore Valley; the Sunol gravel beds in Alameda County, from which percolating water is drawn; main aqueducts totaling 111 miles; and a distributing system consisting of twenty reservoirs and tanks, 750 miles of pipes, and numerous pumping stations. The large landholdings acquired from the private utility now form valuable public open spaces in a more and more intensively developed metropolitan region.

Soon after San Francisco purchased the Spring Valley Water Company properties, the city faced the kind of severe water shortage that City Engineer O'Shaughnessy and others had long feared. The latest in a series of unusually dry seasons had reduced local water supplies throughout the Bay Area to a minimum. But fortunately for San Francisco, the East Bay Municipal Utility District was able to come to the rescue. In a six-month period in 1930 the city purchased twenty to thirty million gallons of water daily from the district, taking the supplementary supply from Lake Chabot and Upper San Leandro Reservoir in Alameda County and conveying it to the Peninsula

Pardee Dam and Reservoir, Chief Source of Water Supply for the East Bay.
Photograph courtesy of East Bay Municipal Utility District.

through pipes laid in the bed of Dumbarton Strait.

Mokelumne River Aqueduct

The East Bay, too, would have been in a desperate plight had not the East Bay Municipal Utility District completed the Pardee Dam on the Mokelumne River and built its ninety-eight-mile-long aqueduct in record time. The first contracts for construction of the aqueduct were awarded in September, 1925. In the summer of 1927 the construction of Pardee Dam was started. Two years later, on June 23, 1929, water from Lake Pardee flowed into San Pablo Reservoir, which supplied about one-third of the water used in the East Bay, and which at that time con-

tained only a few days' supply. Two other reservoirs, which also provided one-third of the supply, held only water enough to last a few weeks; and most of the wells in the East Bay had been pumped to capacity and were becoming saline. Large quantities of Mokelumne River water immediately were released to all the local storage basins, ending the menace of a shortage that had been threatening the East Bay for years.

Less than a year later, on May 4, 1930, Dr. George C. Pardee, president of the East Bay Municipal Utility District, looked out over the waters of the great mountain reservoir named in his honor, saw that it was filled for the first time, and said: "While other cities in California and on the Pacific Coast are concerned as to where their domestic water is coming from during the next few months we are sitting on top of the world with nearly five years' supply of the best water than can be secured. There has hardly been a time during the past ten years when there was not a possibility of a water shortage which would have crippled, if not ruined, these communities. We have seen the end of that. Our water problems are over."[1]

The threatened water shortages to which Dr. Pardee referred had frightened away many an eastern industrialist who had been looking for a site for a branch plant in the East Bay. Now that vexing problem had been conquered, but the price of victory was great. Not only had the East Bay Municipal Utility District contracted an enormous indebtedness in order to build Pardee Dam and the Mokelumne Aqueduct; it also had purchased, as a distributing system, the entire properties of the East Bay Water Company at a price of $33,752,000. This transaction brought the district's total investment to more than $72,000,000.

Water Problems in the Upper Bay

The northern part of Contra Costa County was in no such fortunate situation as the East Bay communities. Along the shores of San Pablo Bay, Carquinez Strait, and Suisun Bay stood large industrial plants that pumped water directly from the bay and had no other sources of supply sufficient for their needs. By 1929, a drought year, the amount of salt-water encroachment in Suisun Bay had become so alarming that these industries feared extensive damage to pipes and machinery. Teredo damage to pilings in company wharves already had cost millions to repair. Through the Industrial Water Users Association the major plants joined with the Salt Water Barrier Association in renewing the clamor for a barrier to protect the upper bay against salt-water intrusion and to conserve the fresh water brought down by the rivers.

Men who took a broad view of state water problems pointed out that a barrier unrelated to other water projects in central and northern California would not solve the industrial water supply problem of Contra Costa County. "The great expanding uses of water in the Sacramento and San Joaquin Valleys, unless they should be stopped, will, in a few years, increase the amount and frequency of deficiencies in summer flow in the river, such as occurred in 1924, so that there will be less and less water for the barrier to conserve as time goes on unless mountain storage is constructed," said Paul Bailey, an engineer who addressed the Commonwealth Club on November 21, 1929.[2]

The water problem of northern Contra Costa County was actually only a small part of a water problem of enormous scope, affecting the entire Central Valley of California. To solve this larger problem of providing more water for thousands of acres under irrigation in the great interior valleys, not only mountain storage was needed but also a gigantic revision of nature's arrangements. With no logic at all, nature supplies the Sacramento Valley, which has only one-third of the arable land of the five-hundred-mile-long Central Valley, with two-thirds of the rain and snow of northern California, while the San Joaquin Valley, with twice as much arable land as the upper valley, receives only half as much rain. Since 1921 the state legislature had been attempting to act on a bold scheme for correcting this imbalance—a scheme which,

Dr. George Pardee, Father of the East Bay Municipal Utility District. Photograph courtesy of Oakland Tribune.

as finally carried out, was incidentally to provide fresh water for agriculturists, industries, and municipalities from Antioch to Martinez. The daring plan, proposed in 1919 by Colonel Robert Bradford Marshall, chief hydrographer of the United States Geological Survey, envisaged, among other things, great storage reservoirs on the Sacramento River system and two large canals on each side of the Central Valley for transferring water from the Sacramento Valley to the San Joaquin Valley. In 1929 this grand design was in a fluid state, undergoing constant changes in the light of extensive research into all phases of the water problems of the state. Eventually it was to crystallize into the Central Valley Project, one part of which would be a canal to divert water from the delta at the confluence of the Sacramento and San Joaquin rivers to northern Contra Costa County. In the fall of 1929, however, the people of the county were pinning their hopes for fresh water on a salt-water barrier and were little concerned with the vast, long-range project evolving in the minds of certain state and federal officials.

Arguments presented by representatives of the Salt Water Barrier Association to the War Department's Board of Engineers for Rivers and Harbors concerning the necessity for federal contributions to the barrier scheme no doubt served to impress government officials with the importance of greater federal participation in solving California's water problems. Indirectly the Association thus helped to deepen federal interest in the grand plan that was to emerge as the Central Valley Project. Eleven years were to pass before the Contra Costa Canal, as one element of the project, provided water for industries along the shores of Suisun Bay.

New Supplies of Energy

Although people in the major urban communities and satellite industrial areas of the bay counties, when faced with possible shortages of water, concluded that they should resort to public ownership of water supply systems, they were content to leave in private hands the operation of utilities that were not in short supply. Long-established gas and electric companies expanded their facilities as population and industrial growth necessitated and continued to supply almost all the light, power, and heat required in the Bay Area.

The Pacific Gas and Electric Company became one of the largest private utilities in the nation and developed more and more extensive facilities for providing electric energy and natural gas to Bay Area communities, among hundreds served in central and northern California. In 1927 it took over the properties of the Sierra and San Francisco Power Company, the Western States Gas and Electric Company, and the Coast Valleys Gas and Electric Company. Then in 1930 it made the Great Western Power Company and two large San Joaquin Valley light and power corporations part of its system through stock purchase. These consolidations effected by the company gave the Bay Area the advantages of service from a vast, interconnected system transmitting and distributing energy from dozens of hydroelectric and steam plants.

Natural gas from Buttonwillow, in the San Joaquin Valley near Bakersfield, and from the Kettleman Hills, fifty miles north of Buttonwillow, first reached the Bay Area over a Pacific Gas and Electric Company transmission line in the summer of 1929. From the northern terminus of this main line at Milpitas, in northeastern Santa Clara County, two branch lines were constructed northward on the Peninsula to San Francisco and a third was laid along the eastern side of the bay to Oakland. The following year a second transmission line, owned jointly by the Standard Oil Company of California and the Pacific Gas and Electric Company, was laid through the San Joaquin Valley to San Pablo, just north of Richmond.

With these supplies of natural gas and electric power, supplemented by heavy fuel oils, coal from Utah, and minor fuels, the Bay Area by 1930 had energy more than sufficient to meet its needs. Actually, energy supply had not been a problem since about 1910, when industries were assured of adequate supplies of both electric energy and heavy fuel oils.

Regional Park Movement

In the process of buying out private water companies and placing the function of providing an adequate water supply in the hands of public agencies, the people of the larger urban communities of the Bay Area moved toward solution of still another metropolitan regional problem—the need for extensive natural areas that could be developed for picnicking, hiking, riding, overnight camping, nature study, and other leisure-time activities. Public acquisition of thousands of acres of watershed lands formerly owned by the Spring Valley Water Company and by the East Bay Water Company presented opportunities for the creation of regional parks and scenic drives only a short distance from centers of population. (The San Francisco Water Department, however, has never favored opening peninsular watershed areas for public recreation, because it fears that the water supply would thereby be polluted.)

The purchase of the holdings of the private water companies took place at a time when people throughout the state had become intensely interested in developing wilderness areas for public use. For several years a state park movement had been gathering momentum, stimulated to a considerable degree by a campaign to save the giant redwoods in the northern coastal counties. And California was not alone in its realization of the importance and value of recreation resources; since the early 'twenties many states had been acquiring state parks. In 1925 the California State Legislature had passed a state park bill, only to have it pocket vetoed by the governor. At the 1927 session the lawmakers tried again and this time succeeded in winning the governor's approval of three measures that initiated a state park system. One of the three acts created the Division of Parks in the Department of Natural Resources and established a State Park Commission to administer, protect, and develop a state park system. Another appropriated $15,000 for a state-wide survey to determine which lands were suitable and desirable for the ultimate development of a comprehensive and well-balanced state park system. And the third act provided that a proposal for a state park bond issue of $6,000,000 be submitted to the electorate at the general election in November, 1928.

The same session of the legislature also enacted a statute providing for the formation and management of local park, recreation, and parkway districts and a special bill providing for the creation and management of Mount Tamalpais State Park in Marin County. California at that time already had five state parks, although it had no state park system as such. The bill pertaining to Mount Tamalpais was an emergency measure, introduced at the urgent request of the Tamalpais Conservation Club soon after private real-estate interests announced that they intended to sell 550 acres on the south slope of the mountain. The legislation provided for a condemnation suit to fix the value of the land and appropriated $20,000 as the state's contribution toward its acquisition. The Tamalpais Conservation Club was aided in its fund raising by the Sierra Club, the California Camera Club, various hiking clubs, and several wealthy men. Together with the state's contribution, the $32,000 raised privately was sufficient to purchase 520 acres of the property. To this acreage Congressman William Kent added, only a few hours before his death, an area of 204 acres known as Steep Ravine. These parcels and other lands combined to produce a recreation preserve of 892 acres north and west of Muir Woods National Monument. Since the establishment of the park in 1930, additions have increased its size to more than 1,335 acres.

The state park survey conducted in 1928 by the distinguished landscape architect and city planner Frederick Law Olmsted, son of the great American whose name was practically synonymous with parks, served to make communities from one end of California to the other aware of natural assets that had potential recreational value. More than 330 park projects were suggested to Olmsted and his staff as they progressed through the twelve survey districts into which they had divided the state. From this number, 171 projects were eliminated for various reasons, chief of which was that many of the areas proposed were unsuitable for state parks or were more of local than of state-wide value. Included in the 150 or more projects designated as desirable for state acquisition were several in the Bay Area: the coastal area from Bodega Bay to the mouth of the Russian River, 612 acres of redwood forests and open grazing land on the headwaters of Harrington Creek in San Mateo County, 5,000 to 6,000 acres on Mount Diablo in Contra Costa County, approximately 4,500 acres on Mount St. Helena in Napa County, additional lands at Fort Ross in Sonoma County, the M. G. Vallejo home at Sonoma, and the Petrified Forest in northeastern Sonoma County, five and a half miles from Calistoga. Not included among the proposed state parks were extensive undeveloped hill and woodland areas within easy reach of the major cities of the Bay Area, although advisory groups assisting the survey staff had come to appreciate the recreational possibilities of these areas, particularly the holdings of the private water companies.

The Olmsted report on the state park survey was not completed until after the general election of 1928 and was not available as a campaign document in the fight for the state park bonds. The electorate nevertheless approved the state park bonds by a vote of three to one, thereby indicating that many months of discussion about the survey and countless newspaper stories about hearings on proposed state parks had been good publicity for the bonds.

East Bay Park Organizations

Apparently the talk about state parks had also helped to create sentiment in the Bay Area for metropolitan regional parks; for the East Bay Municipal Utility District had no sooner reached agreement with the East Bay Water Company for purchase of its holdings, including some forty thousand acres in the Berkeley Hills, than park enthusiasts organized citizen groups to determine which parts of the surplus water district lands would be suitable for use as parks and to apprise the public of the opportunities for recreational use of the hills and canyons. Only a few weeks after the utility district and the water company came to terms in September, 1928, the East Bay Metropolitan Park Association, the Oakland Park League, and several other citizens' associations presented resolutions to the utility district which in effect asked that lands not needed by the district in the future be withheld from sale until public sentiment with respect to the development of parks could be ascertained.

The East Bay Metropolitan Park Association, with the assistance of Ansel Hall, of the National Park Service, then made a preliminary survey that showed the surplus lands to be admirably suited for recreation purposes. This initial investigation revealed, however, that a more detailed study was needed.

The Bureau of Public Administration of the University of California assumed responsibility for the comprehensive survey, using funds given for the purpose by the Kahn Foundation, established by Irving Kahn, an Oakland merchant. The bureau, headed by Dr. Samuel C. May, one of the leaders in the East Bay Metropolitan Park Association, engaged Ansel Hall and Olmsted to conduct the survey.

The report of the two consultants, dated December 1, 1930, disclosed that additional parks were indeed greatly needed in the East Bay. The urban area from San Leandro to Richmond, embracing 150 square miles and inhabited by 450,000 people, included only 900 acres in parks—less than 1 per cent of the total area, whereas recreation authorities agreed that 5 to 10 per cent of an urban community should be in recreational and open use. The obvious deficiency in parks and playgrounds could be overcome in part, the report showed, by developing 10,000 to 11,000 acres of the surplus watershed lands of the utility district as a chain of regional parks. The proposed park system would extend for nearly 22 miles through the hills from Richmond to San Leandro and would be easily accessible to all nine cities included in the utility district.

Need for a Park System

Olmsted and Hall were too well aware of the recreational needs of the entire Bay Area, however, to limit their study to consideration of the needs of the East Bay alone. The two consultants suggested that the proposed chain of parks in the Berkeley Hills might form an important link in a Bay Area park and parkway system that would extend from Richmond through the proposed East Bay parks to Hayward on the south, thence across the San Mateo Bridge (completed in 1929) to the Skyline Boulevard, thence northward through the watershed lands formerly owned by the Spring Valley Water Company, along the Great Highway to Golden Gate Park, thence to the Presidio and across the proposed Golden Gate Bridge to Sausalito and Muir Woods, Mount Tamalpais, and the watershed lands of the Marin Municipal Water District, thence to San Anselmo and San Rafael, and from there over a proposed bridge across San Pablo Strait to Richmond. The metropolitan park system and the existing and proposed bridges would make possible a scenic circuit drive of 130 miles.

Here was vision of the kind needed to give the subregional plans for the East Bay truly metropolitan significance. Like Thomas Reed, Harland Bartholomew, and Stephen Child, the consulting team of Olmsted and Hall foresaw the time when a metropolitan regional system of parklike drives and public reservations would be invaluable in a highly urbanized environment. Though parks and playgrounds undeniably were needed, state parks alone or city parks and playgrounds in themselves could not serve the same ends as a metropolitan chain of large, unspoiled natural areas relatively close to the homes of the majority of city dwellers. If quick and easy escape to wooded canyons and scenic ridges was desirable for the urbanites of the East Bay in the year 1930, how much more desirable not to say imperative, it would be for all the people of the Bay Area when the population was two or three times as great as it was in 1930 and the pressures of highly organized living were proportionately intensified! The leaders of the East Bay obviously intended to see that regional parks were established in their area, either under the East Bay Municipal Utility District or some special district. But who would take the initiative in acting upon the suggestion that a metropolitan park chain should be created?

Like all proposals of scope and imagination, this one would take a long time to carry out. The larger goal of developing an area-wide park system would be lost sight of again and again as individual cities and counties or special districts took piecemeal action to acquire available sites. There would be numerous unrelated acquisitions similar to those made by the Santa Clara County Board of Supervisors when it purchased the 400-acre Stevens Creek Park in 1924 and the 2,933-acre Mount Madonna Park in 1927. The board simply seized the opportunity to buy attractive holdings for presumably reasonable prices. Other governing bodies could be expected to act in much the same fashion until county planning and metropolitan regional planning became well established in the Bay Area and citizens agreed that a metropolitan park system should be created as part of a general scheme of development. Separate, piecemeal acquisitions of natural parks would not necessarily contribute toward the achievement of the most desirable type of regional park system, yet for many decades this seemed to be the way in which an ultimate area-wide system would take shape.

Hills of the Bay Area, Inspiration for the Creation of a Regional Park System.
Photograph courtesy of David Arbegast and Robert Tetlow.

The Connecting Links

As Olmsted indicated, a metropolitan park system in an area with as marked physical divisions as the San Francisco Bay Area would require several bridges as connecting links in a circuit drive uniting all the major regional parks. In 1930, when he outlined a system embracing five of the nine bay counties, only one of the bridges essential to the system had been built—the San Mateo Bridge, spanning the southern arm of the bay between the city of San Mateo and the Mount Eden–Hayward area. The Golden Gate Bridge was only in the preliminary engineering stage; and a proposal of the American Toll Bridge Company to build a $15,000,000 bridge from Richmond to San Rafael had been abandoned because estimated traffic volume was not great enough to interest investment

houses in lending funds for construction. The Bay Area had, however, entered a period of major achievement in overcoming the divisive influence of the great body of water that was its chief physical feature.

The first of the automobile crossings thrown across the continuous water barrier from Stockton to Alviso was the Antioch Bridge, five miles above the mouth of the San Joaquin River. This crossing had been in use since January 1, 1926. Built by the American Toll Bridge Company at a cost of $2,000,000, this comparatively narrow drawbridge—with a roadway of twenty-one feet—joined the Contra Costa shore with Sherman Island in the delta country of Sacramento County and shortened the distance between Oakland and Sacramento by many miles.

The first automobile bridge across the bay itself was the mile-long span built at Dumbarton Strait, in the

The Antioch Bridge, Connecting Contra Costa County with Sherma Island. Drawing from The Golden Link, publication of the Antioc Ledger, June, 1924.

southern part of the bay, by the Dumbarton Bridge Company, a group composed principally of San Francisco capitalists. This toll bridge, opened to traffic on January 15, 1927, saved a fifteen-mile journey round the lower end of the bay for motorists traveling between San Mateo County and southern Alameda County. It also provided for speedier communication between the Bay Area and the San Joaquin Valley. Glenn D. Willaman, secretary of the California Real Estate Association, hailed it as "the advance agent for the bridges that will connect the shores of the Golden Gate and bridge the gulf between the Oakland mainland and the San Francisco shore."[3]

A more appropriate candidate for the role of advance agent for the Golden Gate Bridge and the San Francisco–Oakland Bay Bridge was the Carquinez Bridge, which, completed four months after the Dumbarton Bridge, was jubilantly dedicated as "the world's highest bridge."[4] Although some engineers had doubted that piers for a bridge could be constructed in the deep, swift waters of Carquinez Strait, the span carried a 30-foot roadway four-fifths of a mile across the swirling currents at a height of 314 feet. One hundred and thirty-five feet below mean low water level its piers rested firmly on the sandstone and blue clay that lay beneath 40 feet of silt. An engineering marvel of its day, the bridge evoked enormous pride in the thousands who attended the dedicatory ceremonies. The occasion wore the aspects of a national celebration: the Stars and Stripes were loosed over the

highest point of the steel towers by a telegraphic impuls transmitted by President Coolidge from the yacht *May flower* on the Potomac.

The year 1928 might have seen the dedication of a new drawbridge across the Oakland Estuary had not shipping interests waged a campaign to free this waterway of obstructions. The War Department agreed that a draw bridge would cause delays and be a hazard to navigation A subway with a clearance of 40 feet below mean low water was therefore built from Harrison Street in Oakland to Webster Street in Alameda to replace the old Webster Street Bridge. The main part of this nearly mile-long subway is a tube 2,400 feet long and 32 feet in diameter with two roadways for automobiles. Newspaper account of it made much of the fact that it was the first underwater vehicular tunnel in the world constructed entirely of reinforced concrete. Travelers between Oakland and Alameda were more inclined to appreciate the fact that the Pose Tube (named for its designer, George A. Posey) eliminated delays formerly caused by shipping movements.

A fourth toll bridge constructed in the Bay Area by private initiative was the seven-mile-long San Mateo Bridge, which, like the Dumbarton Bridge, was a low-level crossing with a vertical lift span above the main channe of navigation, to give passage for vessels bound for Alviso and other landings in the lower part of the bay. It, too made possible an uninterrupted journey between the San Francisco Peninsula and the San Joaquin Valley.

Had the proposed Richmond–San Rafael Bridge been built by the American Toll Bridge Company, it would probably have been the last crossing undertaken by private enterprise in the Bay Area. By November, 1927, a majority of San Francisco voters had reached the conclusion, in a vote of policy, that a central crossing between Oakland and San Francisco should be publicly owned and operated. Sentiment in other communities also appeared to be veering toward public ownership of important bridges.

Central-Crossing Proposals

In 1926 the San Francisco Board of Supervisors had been besieged with applications by various private syndicates for franchises to build a central crossing. In an effort to arrive at some complete proposal that might be put before the War Department, which was still opposed to any bridge north of Hunters Point, the board held hearings from August 3 to October 26, 1926, on seventeen applications for franchises. Still later in the year four more proposals were advanced. So many different types of structures and so many promising locations for a bridge were suggested that the board could come to agreement on none. The harassed members finally asked four Bay Area educators—the presidents of California, Stanford, and Santa Clara universities and St. Mary's College—to

prepare a list of qualified and disinterested bridge engineers from whom the Board of Public Works could choose three to collaborate with it in selecting a site and preparing preliminary plans.

The appointment of Robert Ridgway, Chief Engineer of the Board of Transportation of New York, Arthur N. Talbot, Professor of Engineering, retired, of the University of Illinois, and John D. Galloway, a consulting engineer of San Francisco, as a board to work with City Engineer M. M. O'Shaughnessy, marked a great forward step in the solution of the problem of a central crossing. Between the time of their appointment on March 23, 1927, and the completion of their report early in May, these experts studied not only bridge sites but traffic conditions, harbor developments, terminals, transit services on both sides of the bay, and the physical aspects of the bay. They selected a preferred location for the bridge, as well as two alternate sites. The preferred location was from Rincon Hill to the Alameda Mole; an alternate location was from Telegraph Hill to Yerba Buena Island and thence to San Pablo Avenue in Oakland by way of the Key Route Mole. Since the location actually chosen at a later time was a combination of these two, this board materially advanced the bridge project. It outlined three steps for the city to take: first, obtain permission from the War Department to build a bridge at the Rincon Hill–Alameda Mole site;

Carquinez Bridge, Dedicated in 1927 as "the World's Highest Bridge." Photograph courtesy of State Division of Highways.

second, explore this location by borings to determine foundation conditions; and third, prepare a proper design, make cost estimates, and carry out an economic study of the entire project.

Oakland was as much in favor of the Rincon Hill–Alameda Mole location as San Francisco was, because a bridge in that position would in no way interfere with long-range harbor projects planned by Oakland.

San Francisco sent a delegation to Washington to re-request a modification of the conditions laid down by the War Department in 1921 for the bridge, but in the meantime it attempted to anticipate another refusal of the department by seeking enactment of a bill in Congress that would authorize a bridge in the desired location. Senator Hiram Johnson won approval of the measure in the Senate. Congressman Richard Welch, meeting opposition in the House of Representatives, failed to secure passage of the bill.

Seemingly the bridge project was at an impasse. The year 1928 was, however, a presidential election year, and a California resident named Herbert Clark Hoover was talked about as a presidential possibility. The idea occurred to George T. Cameron, publisher of the San Francisco *Chronicle*, as he was en route to Kansas City as a delegate to the Republican National Convention, that if Hoover were nominated and elected, he might be willing, in coöperation with Governor C. C. Young of California, to name a commission to study and report on the feasibility of building the bridge. With a definitive report on the project in hand, the California representatives in Congress then would probably be able, with the support of the President, to overcome the opposition of the War Department and obtain Congressional approval of a bill authorizing a centrally located span.

As Cameron had hoped, Hoover won the Republican nomination and was elected President the following November. State and county officials were optimistic about the prospects of solving the bridge problem, but before approaching the new President they took steps to settle some important matters of public policy. Because the bridge project was by then of state-wide interest, a meeting of state and county officials was called to discuss future state policy with regard to construction, financing, and operation of toll bridges.

Creation of Toll Bridge Authority

As a result of this meeting the state legislature on May 7, 1929, passed a measure designating the governor, the lieutenant-governor, the director of the State Department of Public Works, the director of the State Department of Finance, and the chairman of the California Highway Commission as the California Toll Bridge Authority. The Authority was empowered to direct the State Department of Public Works to build and construct toll bridges and toll highway crossings and to arrange for financing through the sale of revenue bonds. The act declared that it was the policy of the state to acquire all toll bridges eventually; and it amended the existing law so as to vest in the State Department of Public Works the power to grant franchises for private toll bridges. Specifically, the act authorized the California Toll Bridge Authority to "lay out, acquire, and construct a highway crossing from the City of San Francisco to the County of Alameda." The legislation thus formally recognized as a state problem a matter that until then had been thought of mainly as a Bay Area problem.

Since the interest of the national government in the bridge project had been acknowledged from the time the first plans were presented, the central crossing, in reality, had been of more than local or state importance for more than twenty years. The great bay, one of the major harbors on the West Coast, was a national asset, and anything vitally affecting it as a harbor was automatically of national importance, from the standpoint of national defense and from the standpoint of peacetime trade.

The increasing emphasis on state and national interest in a central crossing may have indicated to the people of the Bay Area that as their problems became more difficult and more costly to solve, they would tend to rely more and more upon state and federal assistance—and perhaps would discover that sometimes their own legitimate interests were rudely subordinated to those of the state or national government. In the size of its population and in the scope of the problems that confronted it, the Bay Area had arrived at that stage of its development when it could no longer act independently in many matters. Its own cities and counties were increasingly interdependent, and all were becoming involved with state and federal agencies in solving problems of water supply, transportation, communication, sanitation, harbor development, recreation, and physical planning.

The appointment on September 25, 1929, by President Hoover and Governor Young of the Hoover-Young San Francisco Bay Bridge Commission marked the beginning of a new phase of greater federal participation in Bay Area affairs, well before the days of Franklin D. Roosevelt's New Deal. Thoroughly familiar with the bridge controversy and well aware of the urgency of expediting planning and construction of a central crossing, Hoover chose his close friend Mark L. Requa, a famous engineer, to head the group that was to investigate the engineering and financial feasibility of the bridge.

The commission reviewed all available data on the proposed bridge, visited suggested locations, and found, as had the Ridgway-Talbot-Galloway board, that before it could come to any final conclusions, it required preliminary borings, designs, and cost estimates, as well as estimates of traffic and potential toll revenues. The commission therefore requested the State Department of Public Works to provide the necessary information.

A Route for the Bridge

The borings revealed the existence of a ridge of submerged rock from Yerba Buena Island to Rincon Hill in San Francisco. On each side of this ridge, rock foundations lay at far greater depths. Obviously, a bridge at any other location than the submerged ridge would present more difficult engineering problems and would be more costly. In fact, it was estimated that a bridge could be built from Rincon Hill to Yerba Buena Island to Oakland for $23,000,000 less than the cheapest bridge from Rincon Hill to the Alameda Mole. Chairman Requa remarked as the commission opened public hearings on the proposed bridge that "the Almighty apparently has laid out this route for the bridge."[5]

Studies of transbay passenger and automobile traffic and forecasts of future travel also supported the selection of the Rincon Hill–Yerba Buena Island–Oakland location. Besides carrying interurban trains, the proposed double-decked bridge would divert four-fifths of the vehicular ferry traffic, investigations by the State Department of Public Works showed. The department foresaw a traffic volume of at least sixteen million cars a year; and it estimated that a structure costing approximately $72,000,000 could be paid for in less than twenty years.

A familiar question remained unanswered: Would the Army and Navy approve a bridge at this location?

At a private session of the commission on July 31, 1930, Rear Admiral W. H. Standley, Assistant Chief of Naval Operations, indicated that the military were softening. "No bridge north of Hunters Point is free from naval objections," he declared. ". . . Rincon Hill–Goat Island [Yerba Buena Island] is, however, the least objectionable. . . . It would not be a vital menace to naval operations."[6]

A few days later, Rear Admiral Luther E. Gregory, retired, one of the federal representatives on the commission, removed all doubt about the attitude of military authorities when he moved that the commission recommend a high-level bridge of four spans from Rincon Hill to Yerba Buena Island to the Oakland shore.

The commission had not been requested to consider the possibility of additional crossings in the future, but it

foresaw a time when the San Francisco–Oakland crossing would be used to capacity. In its final report it remarked in passing that "location 5 [from the Hunters Point–Candlestick Point Area to Alameda] be considered for future bridge expansion when a crossing centrally located has become congested."[7] This was advice that was to be quoted frequently in the period 1947–1953, during controversy over a second crossing between San Francisco and Alameda County.

The struggle for the long-desired bay bridge was not over, but victory was in sight. In accordance with one of the recommendations of the Hoover-Young Commission, the California Toll Bridge Authority on November 6, 1930, authorized the construction of the bridge and the preparation of the necessary plans, specifications, and estimates of construction costs. No major difficulties in obtaining Congressional approval and War Department approval of the location and the construction plans were expected. The state legislature appeared ready to provide loans for additional surveys and engineering studies. Financing was still to be worked out, however; engineering problems of almost baffling complexity were yet to be surmounted; and the hazards of actual construction lay ahead. It appeared that the 'thirties would be well advanced before anyone traveled across the bay on a completed bridge.

Controversy over Golden Gate Bridge

Substantial progress had been made meanwhile toward construction of a bridge across the Golden Gate. Only brief consideration was ever given to the possibility that the bridge might be privately financed and constructed. By the spring of 1924, before any formal organization had been worked out to undertake the project, the City and County of San Francisco and Marin County jointly had applied to the War Department for authority to build the bridge in accordance with plans prepared by engineer Joseph B. Strauss. Surprisingly, military authorities raised no objection to a span across the entrance to San Francisco Bay. The War Department held a hearing on the application in San Francisco on May 16, 1924, and on December 20, 1924, Secretary of War John W. Weeks tentatively approved the project. Thereafter the organization of a bridge and highway district to finance and build the span was blocked for four years by litigation initiated by various local interests opposed to the project.

Besides ferry, railroad, and timber interests, the Golden Gate Bridge was opposed by those who feared that it would spoil the scenic beauty of the entrance to the bay, and by some engineers and geologists who doubted that it could be built at all. Some of the litigation which blocked the project was carried on by citizens who sincerely believed that the burden of financing the bridge should rest on all taxpayers of the state rather than on those within a special district composed of the counties that supposedly would benefit most from the project—San Francisco and the North Bay and northern coast counties. Those who favored utilizing the district form of organization as a means of constructing and operating the bridge contended, however, that a district could proceed more expeditiously than the state and that district bonds would bring a higher market price than those issued by the state. Lawsuits filed to block formation of a district under the Bridge and Highway District Act of 1923 prevented incorporation of the proposed district until December, 1928, when the counties of San Francisco, Marin, Sonoma, Napa, and Del Norte, and a part of Mendocino County finally succeeded in establishing the Golden Gate Bridge and Highway District. In the course of the protracted litigation, Humboldt County had joined the district, then later had withdrawn, as had a part of Mendocino County.

The formation of this superregional agency, with a board of directors appointed by the boards of supervisors of the member counties, took place only a few months before the state legislature enacted the California Toll Bridge Authority Act, which included a declaration that the state eventually should acquire all toll bridges. The adoption of that statute foreshadowed the eventual taking over by the state of the bridge then being planned by San Francisco and the group of northern counties. Logic could hardly support the proposition that the Golden Gate Bridge was less a bridge of state-wide importance than the San Francisco–Oakland Bay Bridge. No one attempted, even in the 'twenties, to argue that the Golden Gate Bridge was of interest only to residents of the Bay Area.

Preliminary Steps

The board of directors of the newly incorporated bridge and highway district immediately turned its attention to the selection of engineers for the proposed span. Joseph B. Strauss, as many had expected, was appointed chief engineer in August, 1929.

To provide funds for engineering expenses and preliminary organization, the board levied two taxes on the counties in the district, the first, of three cents per hundred dollars of assessed valuation, on July 24, 1929, and the second, of two cents, in July, 1930. These levies raised $467,367.75. No other taxes have ever been imposed upon the Golden Gate Bridge and Highway District.

The announcement of an election in November, 1930, to authorize a bond issue of $35,000,000 for the construction of the bridge precipitated a battle on a grand scale between those who wanted the bridge and those who still hoped to kill the project. Some opponents charged that a bridge of the required length would collapse of its own weight. Others advanced the idea that the foundations would lie over an earthquake fault and that heavy tremors would destroy the span. Andrew C. Lawson, professor of geology in the University of California, demolished this notion after conducting an exhaustive investigation of test borings covering all foundation areas. Still other opponents contended that the great costs of constructing the bridge would cause many taxpayers to lose their homes. Whispering campaigns were directed against the engineers and the financial operations of the district. Proponents accused the "ferry trust" of inciting the Pacific American Steamship Association and the Shipowners' Association of the Pacific Coast to issue propaganda against the bonds.

Notwithstanding the variety and intensity of the attacks, the bonds carried by a vote of more than three to one—145,057 in favor, 46,954 against.

The election was not the final showdown, as subsequent events would prove. Further litigation initiated by some of the opponents was to postpone the start of construction until January, 1933. But there was no longer any doubt that the people of the Golden Gate Bridge and Highway District meant to build a bridge across the entrance to the bay. Every delay had merely deepened their conviction that the bridge was necessary and that it could be built.

End of Ferries

When at last the mighty steel cables swung from pylon to pylon across the Golden Gate and across the waters separating San Francisco from Oakland, the ferryboats would soon disappear. But in 1930 forty-three of these boats, the largest number ever to operate in the bay, transported a total of forty-seven million passengers and more than six million vehicles from shore to shore. Each day, fifty to sixty thousand people crossed the bay between San Francisco and Alameda County; 25 per cent of them rode in automobiles, whereas five years earlier the overwhelming majority had used the Key System and the East Bay transit lines of the Southern Pacific. In a five-year period the number of transit passengers had declined more than five million—a portent of further losses in patronage on the interurban railways once the bay bridge was completed.

The year 1930 did not pass without demonstrating what

bridges would do to transbay ferries. Two of the most famous of all Bay Area ferryboats went out of service toward the end of the year. These were the Southern Pacific's huge car-transfer ferry steamers, the *Solano* and the *Contra Costa*, which for many years had carried freight cars and entire passenger trains across Carquinez Strait between Port Costa and Benicia. The construction of the 5,603-foot Martinez-Benicia railroad bridge, the longest and heaviest railroad bridge west of the Mississippi at that time, forced the retirement of the ferries from service. The $10,000,000 structure was begun in May, 1929, and opened to rail traffic on October 15, 1930. It was the second railroad bridge across the waters of the bay (the Dumbarton railroad bridge, completed in 1910, was the first) and the sixth span across the water barrier extending from Stockton to Alviso.

The Bayshore Highway

In the 'twenties the cities and counties sought other means besides bridges and tubes to improve travel and communication. In November, 1924, just before work on the toll bridge across Dumbarton Strait was started, Supervisor (later Congressman) Richard J. Welch of San Francisco pointed out that once this bridge was in use, congestion on El Camino Real, the only major highway on the Peninsula, would become intolerable unless the Bayshore Highway was built, as planned, all the way from San Francisco to San Jose.

At that time, work was in progress on a first section of five miles between South San Francisco and Burlingame, financed by a contribution of $500,000 from San Francisco. By 1928 this section had been surfaced and a large underpass had been built under the Southern Pacific main tracks at South San Francisco. Meanwhile the State Division of Highways had pushed the highway three miles farther south to San Mateo; but the road was of little use to city-bound motorists because a three-mile section within the city limits of San Francisco and a three-and-a-half-mile section between the city boundary and South San Francisco remained unfinished. The closing of the gap in February, 1929, gave San Francisco traffic a second major outlet, at least part of the way down the Peninsula. Immediate construction of the road as far south as Palo Alto and the Dumbarton crossing was scheduled. But public officials and civic groups in San Jose had hoped that the Division of Highways would complete the new highway all the way to their city in the 1929–1931 biennium, and when they found out that the state had budgeted funds only for extension of the highway to the Embarcadero Road in Palo Alto, they joined forces with San Francisco, San Mateo County, and Alameda County

groups to agitate for immediate construction of the fourteen-mile section between Palo Alto and San Jose. At a meeting in the San Francisco City Hall, representatives of four counties put "the heat" on State Highway Commissioner F. S. Moody, who politely but firmly told them that the Bayshore Highway "could not possibly be built as far as San Jose before the next biennium."[8]

In its day the Bayshore Highway set a new standard for highway construction. The right of way within the city of San Francisco was 125 feet and the paved roadway was 100 feet wide, providing for three lanes of traffic in both directions. Except in steep cuts and on fills, the roadway in San Mateo County also was 100 feet wide, but highway engineers had not yet come to the conclusion that on high-speed, heavy-traffic roads a center dividing strip is necessary to prevent head-on collisions. Lack of such a safety feature later earned for this once model highway the appellation "bloody Bayshore."

Barriers to East Bay Expansion

San Francisco prior to the opening of the Dumbarton and San Mateo bridges and the Bayshore Highway undoubtedly was one of the most bottled-up cities in the nation. But it was not the only community in the Bay Area that complained of physical barriers. When the East Bay Regional Planning Association held a meeting at the Hotel Oakland on March 1, 1928, to discuss the need for the construction of tunnels through the Berkeley Hills to suburban areas in Contra Costa County, more than a thousand persons, representing every district and community of Alameda and Contra Costa counties, attended. Three tunnels were proposed: the Broadway Low-Level Tunnel, a tunnel near Shepherd Canyon, and a tunnel piercing the hills at the end of Thirty-fifth Avenue in Oakland. The prospects of building all three projects were slight. Chief attention centered on a new tunnel at a considerably lower level than that of the old Broadway Tunnel, which had been opened in 1904.

Alameda and Contra Costa counties had already asked the State Highway Commission to build a low-level bore on the Broadway route, but their petition had been rejected. The mass meeting at the Hotel Oakland gave impetus to the formation by the two counties of a joint highway district, for the purpose of constructing the tunnel and widening the highway to Walnut Creek. Financial complications then developed that were to delay the beginning of construction until the spring of 1933. The Broadway Low-Level Tunnel was one more addition to a substantial list of major public works conceived in the booming 'twenties and hailed as a worthy means of providing employment during the Depression of the 'thirties.

A Modern Port for Oakland

The prosperous conditions and population increases that made people throughout the Bay Area impatient to overcome natural obstacles to movement also made the people of the East Bay eager to take advantage, from an economic standpoint, of the landlocked waters that hindered free circulation in the area. By the mid-twenties the residents of Oakland and Richmond were dissatisfied with the lagging pace of harbor development and were casting about for programs to accelerate the improvement of harbor facilities.

Until the late 'twenties, most of the harbor developments in the Oakland-Alameda area were undertaken by private operators, except for the further dredging of the estuary, which was done by the federal government. Fred D. Parr, a steamship executive, opened the Parr Terminal in 1920 on land leased from the City of Oakland at the Key Route Basin. He equipped the terminal with the most modern mechanical loading and unloading apparatus and induced the Southern Pacific to construct a new spur track to shipside. Vessels of several steamship lines began to make regular calls at the terminal; and Parr planned to expand the facilities. Then he became involved in a dispute with the city over terms of his lease. To force the city to reimburse him for improvements he had made at the waterfront, he filed a lawsuit. This he won, but his enthusiasm for expanding his operations at Oakland was dulled. When better opportunities presented themselves in Richmond, he was quick to grasp them. The harbor expansion undertaken at that city from 1927 onward can be credited in large measure to Parr, although studies by the engineering firm of Leeds and Nicholson had prepared the municipality for a program of port development. Oakland finally took over the Parr Terminal at the Key Route Basin and expanded it under a program formulated by a port commission created in 1926.

Another development in the Oakland outer harbor in the early 'twenties was the huge warehouse constructed by the Albers Brothers Milling Company. The wharf alongside this great storage facility became a Bay Area center for grain shipping.

Early in the decade, John L. Howard expanded the small terminal that he operated at the foot of Market Street on the estuary by adding a new wharf and new warehouses. The upswing in business prompted the construction of additional warehouses after 1925 for the storage of case goods, dried fruit, and manufactured articles. Like the Parr Terminal, the Howard Terminal attracted ocean-going vessels in increasing numbers. Copra, sulphur, lumber, coal, and other bulk commodities were unloaded there, and California canned and dried fruits were conspicuous among exports.

Under the management of the Lawrence Warehouse Company the municipally owned dock and warehouse at the foot of Grove Street in Oakland became a regular place of call for ships of several West Coast shipping lines.

In February, 1925, the Encinal Terminal opened in Alameda, not far from the basin in which the Alaska Packers berthed their picturesque fleet of sailing ships. The first unit of the new terminal, seven hundred feet long and two hundred feet wide, cost more than $1,000,000. Three other units, equally large, were added in quick succession, until the terminal had half a mile of berthing space.

Board of Port Commissioners

In spite of these gains in shipping facilities in both the outer and inner harbors, the majority of Oakland citizens believed that the port was greatly underdeveloped. In 1925 the presentation of a report by three nationally famous engineers recommending improvements in the outer and inner harbors was followed some months later by a special election at which the voters approved $9,600,000 in harbor bonds by a vote of more than eight to one. A year later, in 1926, the charter was amended to provide for a permanent Board of Port Commissioners, with control over the entire port area owned by the city. The real development of this East Bay port dates from the time the new board took office in February, 1927.

Between 1927 and 1930 the board added more than a mile of berthing space at the outer harbor, constructed new transit sheds that were equipped with devices for moving any kind of cargo, and dredged a channel to connect with the mile-long entrance channel dredged by the federal government. In the inner harbor the new agency completed the Grove Street Terminal and enlarged the Ninth Avenue docks. In all, the new transit sheds constructed at the various wharves provided more than fifteen acres of floor space. Oakland citizens began to feel that the potentialities of their port were at last being realized.

Economic and administrative developments likewise aided the growth of the Port of Oakland. In 1929 the railroads, under orders of the Railroad Commission, finally offered the same rates for the port area as for certain districts in San Francisco, thereby ending a discriminatory situation that had prevailed until then. That same year the Treasury Department greatly enhanced the prestige of the Port of Oakland by making it a full port of entry and establishing local customs service. Formerly shippers had complained of the inconvenience of dealing with the Custom House in San Francisco.

Perhaps the greatest boost to the port was the decision of Rosenberg Brothers, the largest dried-fruit packing concern in California, to ship at least fifty thousand tons of prunes and other dried fruit from Oakland annually. The company leased a site at the outer harbor on which the city erected a $400,000 warehouse. This soon became inadequate to accommodate the sorting, grading, processing, and packing operations carried on, and additional space was added. From the beginning, the company exported far more than the minimum specified in the contract with the city. The extensive Rosenberg operations at Oakland attracted other major food-exporting concerns to the port and led to the establishment of regular shipping schedules, which in turn brought still more business to the port.

Port Development at Richmond

In the meantime, the city of Richmond, like Oakland, was engaged in a program of harbor improvements, spurred on by an engineering report pointing out that the city had failed to take advantage of the opportunities which federal appropriations for harbor projects offered for industrial and shipping developments. Because the report recommended private rather than public operation of port facilities, the Richmond Chamber of Commerce invited Fred Parr to consider the possibility of assuming responsibility for control and management of the port. Having experienced difficulties in Oakland, Parr was in a receptive mood when approached by the Richmond organization in 1925. He outlined a program calling for dredging of harbor channels to a depth of thirty feet, filling of waterfront lands to create new industrial sites, provision of spur tracks and car storage yards by the Southern Pacific and Santa Fe railroads, the attraction of some nationally known industry to give impetus to industrial development, and the submission of a bond issue to the voters for the purpose of financing municipal improvements at the port. He himself proposed to acquire one hundred acres of waterfront land, establish the Parr-Richmond Terminal Corporation, and build a modern terminal facility jointly with the city.

This carefully detailed program kindled immediate enthusiasm for private management of port facilities and for municipal coöperation in developing the port. In 1926 the city leased its Terminal 1, in the outer harbor, to Parr, and at the same time it began building Terminal 2 in the inner harbor, wit̶ ̶ ̶ ̶ ̶ention of leasing this also to him. ̶ ̶ ̶ ̶ters overwhelmingly approved ̶ ̶ ̶ ̶or harbor improvements. With ̶ ̶ ̶ ̶the bonds, the local government ̶ ̶ ̶ ̶filled waterfront areas, installed

streets and sewers, and matched Parr's expenditures for the construction of Terminal 3, at the inner harbor. Put into operation in 1929, this major facility included a wharf with berthing frontage of 1,280 feet, a terminal building with nearly three acres of storage space, and an adjacent open storage area. To provide necessary rail service, the Santa Fe and Southern Pacific railroads extended trackage to the new terminal.

More than two years before the terminal was opened, Parr had carried out his design to attract a major industry to the inner harbor at Richmond. He vanquished South San Francisco in a contest for a branch assembly plant of the Ford Motor Company, even though that city could offer the company a site with hard-rock foundations and a waterfront location, while the site Parr suggested was then merely tidelands, into which thousands of piles would have to be driven. The Ford Company leased seventy acres from Parr and made plans to erect a $2,000,000 factory. This plant was not opened until 1931.

Other industries attracted to the Richmond waterfront by Parr soon after he became a power in the city were the Pacific Molasses Company, the Filice and Perrelli Cannery, and tank storage units of the Richfield Oil Corporation.

The vigor and determination with which this promoter, the Richmond Chamber of Commerce, terminal operators in Oakland and Alameda, the Board of Port Commissioners in Oakland, and various shippers combined to build up the East Bay ports did not escape San Francisco businessmen. The developments across the bay meant but one thing: that the Port of San Francisco, state operated, would have strong competition in the future. The East Bay was the terminus of transcontinental railroads, it had large waterfront sites to offer industries, it had by 1930 an adequate water supply, it was closer than San Francisco to the great agricultural areas of the state, and now it had up-to-date port facilities. Many San Franciscans feared that the ports on the *contra costa* would grow at the expense of the Port of San Francisco. And they were right, as a State Senate committee study revealed in 1951:

"In considering traffic at the Ports of Oakland and San Francisco, a steady increase in oceangoing tonnage from 1928 to the present was noted for Oakland, and, if military cargoes are included, a spectacular increase. No such tendency was noted for San Francisco. In fact, when the trade level of 1928–30 is taken for a basis of comparison, the trend of oceangoing tonnage handled at San Francisco appears to be downward."[9]

The port of San Francisco, nevertheless, is still the dominant port in the Bay Area if shipments of petroleum and its products are omitted from consideration.

Study for a Municipal Airport near China Basin, San Francisco, 1927. This proposed airport would have included 320 acres, of which 120 acres would have been land reclaimed from the bay. Drawing by C. H. Baldwin and M. Chappey.

Search for an Airport Site

Another kind of rivalry between San Francisco and the East Bay began to attract attention in the late 'twenties. This was in the comparatively new field of airport development. The unobstructed air space above the great bay soon appeared to be a commercial asset that had not previously been fully appreciated. The tidelands and certain level islands close to the shoreline took on new significance as potential airports. Not only municipalities and commercial airlines but also the Army and Navy initiated investigations to determine the best sites for landing fields.

Early in 1926 a decision of the United States Post Office Department to let its airmail contracts to private individuals started San Francisco on a search for an airport site. "The Board of Supervisors had better get busy and provide a place for the airmail to land," Colonel James E. Power, Postmaster of San Francisco, told Supervisor Milo Kent. "The government will not let the private companies land at the army base in Crissey Field [at the Presidio] and the alternate field at Concord [in Contra Costa County] is too far away."[10]

Supervisor Kent thereupon introduced a resolution calling for the appointment of a committee to obtain for San Francisco a site suitable for a "landing field." The resolution was adopted and Kent was named chairman of the committee.

After the members had satisfied themselves that there was no site in San Francisco itself suitable for an airport, they turned to a report prepared by the city engineer's office listing six possible sites in San Mateo County. These included property near the industrial area of South San Francisco, a part of the Mills Estate at San Bruno, small commercial airports at San Mateo and Millbrae, some property adjoining the Mills Estate, and a completely submerged site near San Mateo Point.

In the midst of discussion of these sites an attorney for persons who had recently purchased Bay Farm Island, just southeast of Alameda, offered to sell an eight-hundred acre site on the so-called island for $1,200,000. Numerous expert flyers testified that they favored Bay Farm Island because it was freer from obstacles and had less fog and better visibility than any other site offered.

Much impressed, the supervisors were giving serious consideration to the East Bay location when the San

Francisco Chamber of Commerce and Mayor James Rolph, Jr., emphatically declared that they believed an airport for San Francisco should be situated on the Peninsula. "It is at once apparent that the conveniences in transportation by motor over the new Bayshore Highway to the peninsula sites will enable the transport of the airport traffic at a minimum of handling risk and maximum of convenience," Louis E. Haas, assistant manager of the chamber, told the supervisors.[11] The mayor was certain that the Peninsula "will some day be part of San Francisco" and said that it would be a mistake "to give any thought to the putting of San Francisco's money in any other place than bears the name of San Francisco."[12] The

San Francisco governing body promptly cooled toward Bay Farm Island.

The Aerial Affairs Committee of the Chamber of Commerce then recommended that a temporary site be selected on the Peninsula, and that while it was in use, weather surveys be made at all possible sites to find the best location for a permanent airport. Guided by advice from the city engineer's office, the board decided in March, 1927, that the site known as Mills Field was the best place on which to conduct the experiment of operating a municipal airport. Ogden Mills, executor of the estate of his late father, was appealed to as a public-spirited citizen to permit San Francisco to lease a part of the family

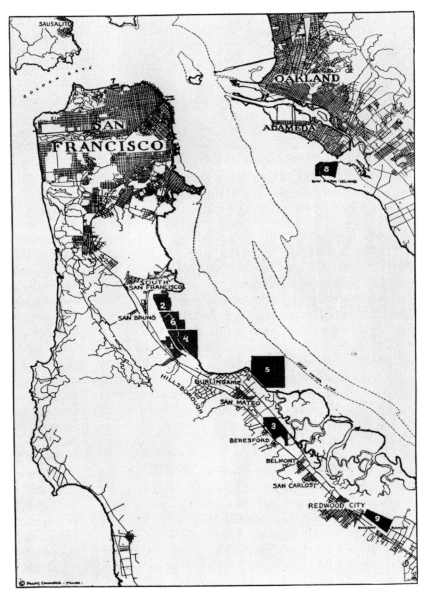

Sites Considered for a Municipal Airport for San Francisco, 1927. (1) Millbrae Airport; (2) South San Francisco Airport; (3) San Mateo Airport; (4) Millbrae Waterfront Airport; (5) San Mateo Point Airport; (6) San Bruno Airport; (7) The Marina; (8) Bay Farm Island; (9) Tweedy Ranch.

holdings at San Bruno for use as a temporary airport. This site, the city engineer's office had reported, was not near a high-powered transmission line, such as made hazardous a number of the other sites, and it was probably the northernmost site on the bayshore free from certain climatic drawbacks that made sites nearer San Francisco objectionable. In the meantime, the board proposed to conduct a series of observations, extending over a year, to get meteorological data on the entire Peninsula.

Mayor Rolph dedicated Mills Field, until then a pasture, as a municipal airport on May 7, 1927, shortly before a lanky youth named Charles A. Lindbergh made his epochal solo flight across the Atlantic and converted almost the entire nation into aviation enthusiasts.

Shoreline Airport for Oakland

Bay Farm Island, scorned by San Francisco, did not go begging as an airport site. No sooner had San Francisco turned it down than the Board of Port Commissioners of Oakland entered into negotiations to purchase 680 acres as a municipal airport for Oakland. By July a long runway was ready for use, and the Oakland Airport was selected as the take-off point for an air race to the Hawaiian Islands. The sponsor of the competition, James Dole, the pineapple king, offered a cash prize of $35,000 to the winner. Of thirty-five entrants in the long hop over the ocean, only two reached the Islands.

The public outcry over this tragic event was soon forgotten in the rush of fifty thousand people to greet "Lindy" upon his arrival at the Oakland Airport on September 17, 1927, in his monoplane, *The Spirit of St. Louis.*

Under the policies established by the Board of Port Commissioners, the Oakland Airport rapidly achieved a reputation as one of the best airports in the nation. By May, 1930, it had developed an operations area of 260 acres, 161,000 square feet of hangar space, a small hotel, and a restaurant. Five transport companies operated planes from it on regular schedules. Speedboats transported airline passengers between San Francisco and the airport. During the fiscal year 1929–30 the airport served 4,000 air transport passengers and 47,000 passengers on nonscheduled planes.

Controversy over Mills Field

Mills Field, unlike the Oakland Airport, seemed to be plagued by bad luck, even though Lindbergh had declared at the time of his visit that the field had the possibilities for becoming one of the world's most renowned air terminals. Boeing Air Transport, holder of an airmail contract, selected the field for its San Francisco base in October, 1927. On the day set for the official take-off of

the line's first airmail plane, the field was covered with fog. Boeing pilots became so strongly prejudiced against the field that the company left the airport a month later. In May, 1928, Western Air Express and Maddux Air Lines, operating up and down the Pacific Coast, both chose Mills Field for their Bay Area base of operations; but without explanation they moved to Oakland a short time later. Political bickering added to the unfavorable impression that many people seemed to have of the field.

Controversy over the field increased, even though the United States Weather Bureau recommended, on the basis of a meteorological survey conducted from July 1, 1927, to July 1, 1928, that the field be selected as the permanent location for the terminal airport for San Francisco. It had been found to be the closest to the metropolitan center in point of time and distance, and the freest from physical barriers, of any available site at which the topography was suitable and aerological conditions were safe, the bureau said. Nevertheless, enough voters remained skeptical about the field to defeat a $1,700,000 bond issue in November, 1928, for improvement and development of the facilities.

The following year a mishap suffered by Colonel Lindbergh caused Mills Field again to be held up to ridicule and contempt. As the flyer was taking off in the *Patrician*, the largest airplane (capacity: 32 passengers) that had ever been built up to that time, another plane appeared at the far end of the runway, ready to land. Wishing to afford the incoming plane all the room it needed, Lindbergh turned; his wide undercarriage, with its sharp tires, swept off the runway, cut through the one unfilled spot beside the runway, and sank into the blue mud. The accident was so minor that the plane, extricated by tractor, was air-borne five minutes later; but the damage to the reputation of the field was immense. Thousands of people concluded that Mills Field was a place where flyers ran the risk of getting stuck in the mud.

Officials operating the field waged an uphill fight to change public opinion. The publication of records showing that there were fewer hours of poor flying conditions at Mills Field than at any field or airdrome around the bay helped to dissipate the critical attitude. Maneuvers of hundreds of Army planes under the command of General William E. Gilmore, of the Air Corps, also aided in building optimism about the terminal.

The airport was still a political hot potato in 1930, however, when the three-year lease on the property expired and the San Francisco Board of Supervisors decided to open negotiations with Ogden Mills for purchase of the site. Mills was reluctant to sell, because he believed that the land had large potential value as a site for industrial development. It was August before the conferences begun in February terminated in an agreement under which San Francisco was to acquire 1,112.5 acres—the entire holdings of the Mills Estate between San Bruno and the deep water of the bay—for a total price of $1,050,000 through a ten-year purchase plan. Although 550 acres of the property lay west of the Bayshore Highway and could not be used for airport purposes, the supervisors gladly accepted Mills' terms, hoping eventually to sell this acreage as sites for aircraft industries.

In order to develop the airport properly and acquire adjoining subwater land that was needed, the board of supervisors decided to submit another bond issue to the voters. In spite of a carefully planned campaign in which almost all civic organizations and newspapers coöperated, the $4,000,000 bond issue failed, as had that of 1928, by only a few thousand votes.

Still, San Francisco at last had a municipal airport that it could call its own, and the majority of voters did favor development of this new public facility. Its future as a major air terminal seemed assured as more and more experts pronounced it the best available site in the Bay Area for a San Francisco airport. It was theoretically only twenty-two minutes from the heart of the city via the Bayshore Highway; there were no limitations to expansion as longer runways were required; and the southward movement of population on the Peninsula indicated that in the future the site would be convenient for an ever-increasing number of people.

"Nerve Center" of Defense

Some years before San Francisco and Oakland became interested in developing municipal airports, the Army and Navy had decided that there were three strategic areas, or "nerve centers," on the Pacific Coast in which additional military facilities should be concentrated—the region around Puget Sound, the San Francisco Bay Area, and the Los Angeles–San Diego area. Among the new installations to be built were, of course, air bases, including a base for dirigibles, though exact locations had not been determined for any of the bases.

In the fall of 1928 aviation enthusiasts in the San Francisco Junior Chamber of Commerce initiated a campaign to induce the Navy to decide on Sunnyvale, at the southern end of the bay, as the site for one of the bases. Nearly three years later, however, word reached the members that a Navy Airship Base Investigating Committee had recommended Camp Kearny, near San Diego, as the site for the West Coast dirigible base. Rather than see San Diego get a base without a fight, the San Francisco Chamber of Commerce joined the junior organization in

a move to force reconsideration of the entire question of possible Pacific Coast sites, no matter how many telegrams and letters had to be sent to northern and central California members of the House of Representatives requesting that they insist upon further investigations.

The investigating committee made a new survey of sites, inspecting ninety-seven in all, of which twenty-three were in the San Francisco Bay Area. In the end the choice was between Camp Kearny and Sunnyvale. Four members of the committee voted for Sunnyvale, one for Camp Kearny.

To make sure that there would be no reversal of this decision, the San Francisco Chamber of Commerce pledged itself to raise half a million dollars, purchase a thousand-acre site, and give it to the Navy. Fund raising was not easy in the year 1931; but by making the campaign a Bay Area affair, the chamber was able to fulfill its pledge within three months.

"We appealed to our neighbors—to San Jose, Oakland, Alameda, Berkeley, Palo Alto, San Mateo County cities, Marin County—all bay communities, corporations, and individuals," Leland Cutler, president of the San Francisco organization, told Admiral W. C. Cole, Commandant of the Twelfth Naval District, as he handed him the deed of gift of the Sunnyvale site on August 3, 1931. "Nobody failed us."[13]

No small part of the satisfaction of Bay Area leaders in this achievement was, some acknowledged, the defeat handed southern California. But the chief interest of businessmen in the new military establishment, aside from its importance for national defense, was in the sizable annual payroll that would be added to the Bay Area economy, and in the initial expenditures for construction of hangars, air strips, housing, and equipment. In the lean years of the early 'thirties nothing looked so substantial and desirable as a federal installation supported by all the taxpayers of the United States. Moreover, no one doubted that the whole Bay Area would benefit by the new base. The campaign for purchase of the Sunnyvale site was therefore a stimulating example of the way in which the business community of the Bay Area could reach agreement on a specific project for economic development. The success of the endeavor suggested that united action might be possible on other projects—and straightway the opportunity for a new demonstration of Bay Area coöperation presented itself.

A Gift to the Army

Having seen how effective the offer of a free site was in inducing the Navy to decide on Sunnyvale, the Marin County Board of Supervisors determined to make the

U.S.S. Macon *at Moffett Field, Sunnyvale, in the Early 1930's. Official photograph, U.S. Navy.*

United States Army a gift of the Marin Meadows acreage that Assistant Secretary of War F. Trubee Davison had inspected in 1929 as the possible site for a bombing base. The only trouble was that the board's generosity exceeded the financial resources of the county. Although the supervisors had the enthusiastic support of Marin County taxpayers, they could afford to appropriate no more than $122,000 toward acquisition of the site, now known as Hamilton Field. This amount would make possible the purchase of 764 acres, whereas the Army needed an additional 163 acres. Public subscription of $53,000 appeared to be the answer to the problem. The board therefore agreed to spend tax monies only on condition that other Bay Area counties, civic organizations, and interested persons would contribute funds for the additional acreage.

Again the spirit of area-wide coöperation manifested itself. At a meeting called by the Downtown Association of San Francisco, the San Francisco Chamber of Commerce pledged itself to raise $12,500 and the Downtown Association and other civic organizations volunteered to contribute $14,000. The Oakland Chamber of Commerce made a pledge of $12,500. Citizens of Marin gave a guarantee of $14,000, but an appropriation by the Sonoma County Board of Supervisors of $5,000 toward purchase of the site reduced to $9,000 the amount that had to be raised among individual contributors in Marin County. In a little more than two months all the money required for the additional acreage was on hand.

"Amid cheers of a crowd that packed the Supervisors' chambers in San Rafael yesterday, the checks to purchase the land were handed over and the deed was transferred to the United States," the San Francisco *Chronicle* reported on March 18, 1932.

An initial Congressional appropriation of $1,412,117.87 in June of that year for development of the 927-acre site, followed in September, 1933, by a second appropriation of $3,462,184.41, brought the national investment in the new military establishment to almost $5,000,000.

In the meantime, the possibility that Alameda might be selected as the site for a second Navy air base in the Bay Area inspired still another demonstration of area-wide unity. Through the San Francisco Bay Industrial Committee, representing chambers of commerce in the area, cities in the nine counties agreed to support Alameda in its efforts to interest a Congressional subcommittee in the possibility of developing an aviation field at the western end of the city, where shoal areas could be filled and added to approximately one thousand acres of available land. A third time the one-for-all-and-all-for-one spirit proved its value. The subcommittee was favorably disposed toward the Alameda site. A more intensive survey by another committee in 1935 and an inspection by a Naval Board of Survey about the same time finally led to a decision to establish a naval air base in Alameda.

Underlying Unity

The addition of three new bases in an area which already had military establishments on both sides of the Golden Gate and at Mare Island and Benicia dramatized the fact that the federal government considered the whole Bay Area, in effect, one big base. But there were other ways in which the underlying unity of the area became increasingly evident. As bridges spanned the northern and southern arms of the bay and as public interest centered on the importance of constructing a bridge across the Golden Gate and a crossing from San Francisco to Oakland, it became clear that a long-deferred union of the several parts of the Bay Area was taking place. The growth of cities was shrinking the great bay, for the bridges were but highways across water from city to city, bringing the shores closer together. The cities themselves were reaching out beyond their corporate boundaries for access to areas of potential urban development, for regional parks, and for airports, as they had reached out earlier for all the near-by sources of water. This new penetration of the outlying areas was far different, however, from that older appropriation of what the cities needed; it was a profound demonstration that the cities functioned economically and socially as parts of a metropolitan complex and therefore could not be limited by mere lines of political jurisdiction. To meet the challenge of living in a metropolitan region, the residents of cities were prepared to resort to such governmental devices as special districts and state authorities. Yet they refused even to take seriously the advocates of metropolitan regional planning—and prophets of metropolitan government were scarcely to be heard. Expediently, project by project, the city councilmen and county supervisors and the voters who elected them were revising the physical environment they had inherited, making it in one sense smaller, by shortening its distances, and in another larger, by expanding its living space, and in every way more certainly a unit, by creating conditions that would eventually compel the cities to act together on matters of area-wide concern.

CHAPTER FOURTEEN

Progress in Troubled Times

The depression that created bread lines throughout the United States in the early 'thirties dealt especially harshly with the San Francisco Bay Area. "The slow recovery of major industries after 1932 was unexampled elsewhere in the state," the California State Planning Board observed in a report published in 1941.[1] Indeed, in 1939 the value added by manufacturing in the factories of the Bay Area was more than one hundred million dollars less than it had been in 1929. Wholesale and retail trade, too, suffered serious monetary declines, although employment in trade did expand slightly, toward the end of the decade.

A unique casualty of this period of human misery and economic regression was an industrial promotion program jointly sponsored by the San Francisco Chamber of Commerce and the Oakland Chamber of Commerce in 1931. Perhaps as a kind of defensive reaction to the intense competition from other Pacific Coast metropolitan areas, the two organizations issued a book with the cover title *San Francisco–Oakland Metropolitan Area: An Industrial Study*. The text and the charts in the book offered comparisons of the Seattle, Portland, San Francisco–Oakland, and Los Angeles areas as manufacturing and distribution centers, with emphasis on the special advantages of the Bay Area. The "apparently uninterruptible" tendency of the population of the United States to gravitate westward was cited as a chief reason for eastern manufacturers to "manufacture in the West for the western market."[2]

"It is not intended that there be any less individual effort to exploit the various sections around the bay than in the past but the new presentation of basic facts will unite all districts in a wholesome spirit of Bay Region unity," *San Francisco Business*, an official publication of the San Francisco Chamber of Commerce, declared hopefully. "This is how the outside investor is most favorably impressed."[3]

Without mentioning Los Angeles by name, the journal pointed out that "the most serious competitor . . . long ago learned the important lesson of the value of unified efforts."[4] The publication referred to the nine San Francisco Bay counties as "one economic unit" of 6,979 square miles and mentioned that the "progressive movement" for industrial promotion in the area actually had been conceived two years previously, in 1929.[5]

Unfortunately, this well-intentioned "selling campaign" was foredoomed. Each month the indices of economic activity in the nation fell lower and lower, and as they continued their downward course, other chambers of commerce in the Bay Area tightened their purse strings and declined to support the campaign with cash. By the fall of 1932 not even the most sanguine eastern industrialist was entertaining the notion of building a branch plant in the Bay Area. East of the Sierra it was no secret that some plants in the bay counties had shut down, that many others were operating with skeleton forces, and that any plant which had not to some degree trimmed the payroll was an exception.

Ill-starred though it was, this movement for area-wide industrial development did indicate that under favorable conditions some metropolitan regional coöperation might be achieved. Like many promotional efforts, it was not selective in its appeal to eastern manufacturers and it aimed to attract any industry, regardless of its labor relations record, its wage scales, or its operational efficiency, that might be thinking of expanding in the West. Entirely lacking were studies showing where certain types of industries might be established in the Bay Area to the greatest advantage of the industries themselves as well as to the greatest advantage of the area. In fact, little if any thought had been given to the relation between economic development and metropolitan physical development, but at least the ideal of coöperation among bay cities had been enunciated. In years to come this pioneer attempt at united effort would be remembered and cited as a precedent for further essays at advancing the economic fortunes of the entire area through a representative organization.

Progress Despite Depression

Regardless of economic strain, in the early 'thirties the people of the Bay Area did succeed in bringing to completion—or at least in materially advancing—some of the undertakings they had conceived and started in the prosperous 'twenties. On the night of October 15, 1932, for instance, an audience that was as fashionable as any that had assembled in 1926 or 1927 filled the sumptuous new War Memorial Opera House in the San Francisco Civic Center for the first performance in that now historic edifice, the birthplace, in 1945, of the United Nations. Begun in the late 'twenties, the gray granite structure at the time of its opening was the only municipal opera house in the entire United States. As the handsome gold curtain rose on the first act of Puccini's *La Tosca*, a burst of applause greeted the first words sung from the stage— *Ah! finalmente!* Finally, after more than a quarter of a century of being without an opera house, San Francisco had one; but it belonged not alone to San Francisco—it was a cultural institution claimed from the very beginning by the whole Bay Area. The audience that listened to Claudia Muzio, Alfredo Gandolfi, and Dion Borgioli sing the leading roles was composed of men and women from cities throughout the nine counties bordering on the bay, and from communities beyond the Bay Area, too.

At the time the acoustically superb opera house was being christened with song, San Franciscans showed that they could display just as much Old World fervor about the city's historic past, its scenic hills, and matters of urban aesthetics as they could about opera. With part of the money left to the city by the late Lillie Hitchcock Coit, who had been an honorary member of an early-day volunteer fire company known as Knickerbocker No. 5, the

San Francisco Park Commission proposed to erect a tower on Telegraph Hill to the memory of the volunteer fire fighters of the 'fifties and 'sixties. But many San Franciscans wanted no tower at all on Telegraph Hill, and just as many others particularly did not want the tower designed by Arthur Brown, Jr., the architect who had designed the War Memorial Opera House. Even at that date, the Palace of Fine Arts, sole remnant of the Panama-Pacific International Exposition of 1915, was beginning to crumble, and there were groups who urged that the Coit bequest be used to restore it rather than to build a tower. Several art groups protested that the massive shaft would "ruin" Telegraph Hill and spoil its silhouette.[6] A member of the San Francisco Board of Supervisors delighted the Federation of Artists when he declared that the proposed structure would look "like a chimney on a new incinerator."[7] Nevertheless, after all the protests had been heard, the Park Commission, with the approval of a bare majority of the Art Commission, built the tower as Brown had designed it. One hundred and seventy feet high and thirty feet in diameter at its base, it has become, since its dedication in October, 1933, an accepted landmark on the famous hill overlooking the Embarcadero. Only occasionally does some critic refer to it as "a Gargantuan milk bottle." If it were less conspicuous, if its design had not provoked a memorable controversy, if it were not associated with the name of an almost legendary character, it might go unmentioned in a volume dealing with the entire Bay Area; but the Coit Tower is symbolic of the kind of civic uproar that San Franciscans can create when their sense of beauty and their deeper feelings regarding the historic past are involved.

East Bay Regional Parks

On the opposite side of the bay a controversy just as bitter had broken out between the directors of the East Bay Municipal Utility District and citizens who in the late 'twenties had initiated the movement for development of regional parks in surplus watershed lands of the district. The East Bay Regional Park Association sought the coöperation of the directors of the utility district in persuading the state legislature to amend the Municipal Utility District Act of 1921 to enlarge the powers of the district to include park functions. But the chairman of the board of directors of the utility district unalterably opposed broadening the activities of the district, although this would have been the simplest way to provide for regional parks and would also have made easier the protection of the water system of the utility district. According to some reports, nothing more than a clash of personalities between the board chairman and certain advocates of regional parks was involved. It appears more likely, however, that the board chairman had a deep conviction that the utility district was, in effect, a business and should be managed as such, whereas a park division within the district would be, in his view, a "governmental agency" and would therefore be "sloppily run" and would cost more than it was worth.[8] The primary obligation of the utility district, he declared, was to reduce the bonded indebtedness of the district as fast as possible, not to increase its operating expenses. So strong was his opposition that he threatened to resign if the charter of the utility district were amended. His colleagues therefore adopted his inflexible attitude, despite the most cogent counterarguments that could be advanced by a Mayors' Provisional Regional Park Board appointed by the mayors of nine East Bay cities.

The only course left to the proponents of regional parks was to appeal to the state legislature to enact special enabling legislation authorizing the East Bay cities to create a park district. This the legislature did in 1933 with but one dissenting vote. The Regional Park District Act provided that two or more cities with contiguous territory, whether in one or more counties, might form a park district within the boundaries of an existing utility district. The Alameda County Board of Supervisors permitted seven cities—Alameda, Albany, Berkeley, Emeryville, Oakland, Piedmont, and San Leandro—to vote on a proposal to create the East Bay Regional Park District; but the supervisors of Contra Costa County refused to permit El Cerrito and Richmond to vote on the measure. The voters of the Alameda County cities approved the formation of the new district by a vote of 93,405 to 37,397 on November 6, 1934. Residents of the nonparticipating cities of El Cerrito and Richmond were thus assured the use of regional parks for which they would pay no taxes!

The park district made its first purchases of land in 1936, acquiring more than 2,200 acres in the Berkeley Hills, mostly on the eastern or Contra Costa County side. Sixty acres purchased from a private seller formed the nucleus of Redwood Regional Park, in the hills east of Oakland, where in early days the pioneers had cut timber to build houses in San Francisco, Oakland, and other Bay Area towns. Four parcels acquired from the East Bay Municipal Utility District provided Roundtop Regional Park, Lake Temescal Regional Park, and the greater part of Charles Lee Tilden Regional Park. Lake Temescal, above the Claremont district of Berkeley, which had been the first source of water for Oakland, was no longer needed for water supply.

Later in the decade, the park district expanded its holdings to some 4,250 acres, adding substantially to Tilden Park and to Redwood Park. All but 249 acres of these later acquisitions were from the East Bay Municipal Utility District, which continued to own thousands of acres of watershed lands described by Olmsted and Hall as suitable for park development.

If the surplus watershed lands available for parks had all been in Alameda County, that county might have assumed the responsibility for park development, as some other Bay Area counties have done; but since the areas desirable for recreational use lay almost wholly in the neighboring county of Contra Costa, the people of the East Bay cities were obliged to entrust the park function to a district, although it need not have been an entirely new district. The creation of a separate East Bay Regional Park District unnecessarily complicated the governmental structure of the Bay Area and certainly effected no economies from an over-all standpoint. In the long run, the multiplication of special districts in a metropolitan region increases the difficulty of finding solutions to area-wide problems and carrying out metropolitan development projects.

State Parks

The State Park Commission created in 1927 also was active in the Bay Area during the 'thirties in providing publicly owned recreation areas, chiefly of the type that would be classified as regional—ocean beaches, mountain areas, and botanically important reservations. Thus the commission added to the recreation facilities of the metropolitan region several new areas similar to those owned by counties, the East Bay Regional Park District, the federal government (Muir Woods National Monument), and the state itself (Mount Tamalpais State Park). Outstanding among the areas developed for public use by the state were Mount Diablo State Park in Contra Costa County and the Sonoma Coast State Park, extending from the northern end of Bodega Bay to the mouth of the Russian River. Mount Diablo had been a scenic attraction ever since 1874, when a private toll road was built to the summit. After the two-thousand-acre park was dedicated on April 26, 1931, approximately fifty-five thousand people visited it in the next ten months. The Sonoma Coast State Park, eleven miles in length, includes sandy beaches and rocky cliffs entirely west of the coast road. Most of this park was acquired between 1931 and 1935, through various purchases.

Not well known to most Bay Area residents is another state park established in the 'thirties, the Kruse Rhododendron Reserve, on the northwest coast of Sonoma County, ten miles north of Fort Ross. The gift in 1933 of Edward Kruse, of San Francisco, the area is noteworthy for its beautiful growth of rhododendrons and its spectacular ocean frontage.

A transaction of special interest was the transfer of ownership, from Sonoma County to the State Park Commission, of the Armstrong Grove of redwoods, a stand of magnificent trees about two and a half miles north of the Russian River town of Guerneville. Colonel James B. Armstrong had wished to deed the grove to the state some years before his death in 1900, but since there was at that time no state agency to administer the property as a public recreation area, he was unable to make the gift. In 1917 his heirs aided in the purchase of the four hundred acres of *Sequoia sempervirens* by Sonoma County, which held the property as a county park until 1934, when the State Park Commission purchased it and began constructing trails, a water system for the convenience of campers, and an outdoor theater. This transfer of a county park to the state set a precedent for the acquisition by the state of other county parks, although the transaction involving the Armstrong Grove was unique, in that it would have become a state park decades earlier had the law permitted.

In addition to all these large acreages, the State Park Commission took title to an important historical monument in the Bay Area, the house built by General Mariano Guadalupe Vallejo at Sonoma soon after California entered the Union. The acquisition of the Victorian structure was in accordance with the policy of the State Park Commission of preserving significant historical buildings.

At no period prior to the 'thirties had the Bay Area gained so much public recreation space of regional importance as it did during that decade—more than seventy-seven hundred acres, excluding the Armstrong Grove, which was already in public ownership. Much of this acreage, such as the Sonoma Coast State Park and the Mount Diablo State Park, had, however, been used by the public while it was still in private hands. The acquisitions by the state, by the East Bay Regional Park District, and by a political subdivision not previously outstanding in recreation, San Mateo County, guaranteed that the people of the Bay Area would be able to enjoy large tracts of natural landscape permanently.

The San Mateo County park program was made possible by a new charter, adopted in 1932. A provision of the charter authorized the county supervisors to make annual appropriations to a Land Acquisition Fund, which was to be used to purchase sites designated on a master recreation plan. Under this pay-as-you-go procedure the county acquired several miles of coastal beaches between 1935 and 1940. Later it suggested that the State Park Commission also purchase some of the beaches included in the county-wide plan.

In 1937 a movement to "save the beaches" gained impetus in Marin County but did not become effective until after World War II.

Although much progress was made through state and local agencies in the 'thirties, regional recreation areas in the Bay Area were not well distributed. In Napa and Solano counties there were no large tracts set aside for permanent public use. Contra Costa County itself had done nothing to provide regional parks. Santa Clara County had no long-range park program, and the supervisors of Alameda County were content to let the East Bay Regional Park District meet the need for large-scale recreation areas. Yet the vast expansion of regional park acreage in the metropolitan area during the decade did make the public generally more aware of the opportunities for the creation of additional recreation reserves. Numerous sites then appraised by public-spirited citizens as being potential county or state parks have since passed into public ownership.

Water Problems

As in the field of regional recreation, the Bay Area made progress in the solution of its water supply problems through various subregional projects, one of which, the Contra Costa Canal, was part of the vast Central Valley Project begun in the 'thirties. The city-around-the-bay that was gradually developing was still so unconnected that most residents of the Bay Area identified themselves with this or that part of it and rarely considered the needs of the whole area. The annexation of new territories to the East Bay Municipal Utility District, the completion of the Hetch Hetchy Aqueduct by San Francisco, and the construction of the Contra Costa Canal all emphasized the growing dependence of the Bay Area upon a distant source of supply—the Sierra watershed. In the Santa Clara Valley the struggle to conserve local water supplies met with some success; but a major question remained unanswered: What would the valley do if population and industry greatly increased? Would not this section, like others in the Bay Area, have to import water?

Though the times were hard, San Francisco voters did not hesitate to vote additional bond issues to finance completion of the initial stages of the Hetch Hetchy project and to provide local distribution facilities. In May, 1932, they approved a $6,500,000 bond issue to complete construction of the tunnels through the Coast Range, one of which was twenty-five miles long and the other three and a half miles long. In June, 1933, the voters went to the polls again and authorized issuance of $12,095,000 of general obligation bonds to pay for a second pipe line across the bay and for other water system extensions. And five months later they voted still another bond issue of $3,500,000 to raise O'Shaughnessy Dam from its original height of 344.5 feet to 430 feet above bedrock, so that the storage capacity of Hetch Hetchy Reservoir might be increased from 67,000,000,000 gallons to 117,000,000,000 gallons.

Long before the dam was enlarged, however, the San Joaquin Pipe Line, the Coast Range tunnels, and new distribution system reservoirs and mains in San Francisco were completed. On October 24, 1934, the first Hetch Hetchy water flowed into the Crystal Springs Reservoir, thirteen miles south of San Francisco in San Mateo County, and thence through the distributing system to the metropolis. Twenty years had passed since construction of the Hetch Hetchy project was begun, and thirty-three years had gone by since Mayor James D. Phelan filed applications for permission to tap the headwaters of the Tuolumne River in Yosemite National Park. In that third of a century the people of San Francisco had approved a total of $89,600,000 in bonds for the project, to say nothing of more than $53,000,000 in bonds for new distribution facilities and for purchase of the properties of the Spring Valley Water Company. These huge investments assured them of an ample water supply for many years to come; but the future would require other large expenditures for a dam in the Cherry Valley, for a second pipe line across the San Joaquin Valley, and for additional tunnels through the Coast Range paralleling those already bored. The Hetch Hetchy water system in 1934 had been developed to produce less than half of its potential yield of 400,000,000 gallons daily; and although this partial development was then more than adequate to meet the needs of San Francisco and the Modesto and Turlock Irrigation districts (which had prior rights to the "natural flow" of the Tuolumne River), the time would come when it might not be sufficient, in a period of unusual drought, to avoid water shortages in a metropolis and in near-by cities that would become much more populous. San Francisco faced the job of eventually building the water system to the full capacity proposed by John R. Freeman in 1912.

The East Bay Municipal Utility District in the meantime extended its services to an ever-widening territory as one small water district after another sought a better water supply through annexation to the utility district. In 1931 the Lafayette, San Pablo, and Kensington areas in Contra Costa County and the Castro Valley in Alameda County became parts of the utility district. In 1932 and 1933 the Saranap and Fairview areas in Contra Costa County were annexed, and in 1933 and 1934 the Eden and Chabot districts in Alameda County. The inclusion of other areas followed, until by 1938 the utility district was

serving a territory of 179 square miles and a population estimated at more than half a million.

Had a large city, such as Oakland, owned and controlled the Mokelumne River water supply, the jealous control of that supply might have stimulated a succession of urban consolidations and territorial annexations similar to those which preceded and followed the completion of the Owens River Aqueduct by the city of Los Angeles. But since no one city in the East Bay had undertaken to reach out to the Sierra without the help of its neighbors, and since a utility district had appeared to be the most satisfactory solution for all concerned, community identities were preserved and no supercity came into being.

The Contra Costa Canal

Industries situated between Martinez and Antioch on Suisun Bay had to wait until the summer of 1940 to get ample supplies of good water, because the solution of their water problems depended upon a grand plan of the state for impounding and redistributing the waters of the Sacramento and San Joaquin rivers—the Central Valley Project. The state legislature authorized the great development in 1933, but private utilities attacked the hydroelectric power provisions and forced the project to a state referendum on December 19, 1933. The voters upheld the project by a winning margin of 33,603 votes out of a total of 885,821 votes cast. State officials, who from the beginning had hoped for some federal contributions toward the project, made no particular effort to sell the $170,000,000 of revenue bonds authorized in the Central Valley Project Act and bent all their efforts toward getting the federal government to finance the project. To their very great satisfaction, President Franklin D. Roosevelt approved the project as a reclamation development on December 2, 1935. An initial allocation of $4,200,000 to the Bureau of Reclamation for field studies was followed by further appropriations in 1936, and by 1937 construction of various major features of the project (which in the meantime had been revised by the bureau) began. Among the first structures undertaken were Shasta Dam spanning the Sacramento River at the northernmost tip of the Sacramento Valley; the Friant Dam, astride the San Joaquin River twenty miles northeast of Fresno; and the Contra Costa Canal, designed to bring fresh water from Rock Slough, a tributary of the San Joaquin River in the delta region in the eastern part of Contra Costa County, to the farms, cities, and industries in the northern area of the county.

Before the Contra Costa Canal could obtain federal financing and be included in the Central Valley Project, it was necessary for the people of northern Contra Costa

The Contra Costa Canal, with Mount Diablo in the Distance. Photograph courtesy of the United States Bureau of Reclamation.

County to organize their own water district. The election for the purpose of forming the Contra Costa County Water District was held on May 26, 1936. Active in campaigning for the district were many members of the Salt Water Barrier Association of the 'twenties, whose proposal for erecting a barrier to prevent salt-water incursion into Suisun Bay and the delta area had been abandoned when plans for the Central Valley Project cystallized.

Governor Frank F. Merriam participated in the ground-breaking ceremonies for the canal near Oakley on Sunday, November 7, 1937. Thirty-two months later, on July 10, 1940, the first water surged into a tidewater section of the canal and, raised by four pumping plants to an elevation of 135.6 feet, started on its forty-six-mile journey by gravity flow to a terminal reservoir near Martinez. In the following month the city of Pittsburg became the first city to use water from the Contra Costa Canal. The

Columbia Steel Company, at Pittsburg, was the first industry in the new water district to sign a contract for water from the $4,000,000 conduit. Twenty-two thousand acres of farmland in northern Contra Costa County before long also received water from the Canal for irrigation. The water problems that had plagued an important part of the county for two decades or more at last were solved.

Water-Conservation Plan

In another Bay Area county, Santa Clara, the years during which the people of Contra Costa County struggled to find a dependable source of fresh water were marked by a continuing effort to educate voters on the necessity for the flood storage dams, conduits, and percolation works first proposed by engineer Fred H. Tibbetts in 1921. In the eighteen years between 1915 and 1933 the ground-water level in the Santa Clara Valley had dropped 95 feet because of heavy pumping from more than two thousand wells, even in years of normal or above-normal rainfall. Pumping draft had risen by 1933 to an annual average of 134,000 acre-feet, but replenishment of the underground reservoir through infiltration was estimated to average only 70,000 acre-feet per year. Depletion therefore should have been some 64,000 acre-feet per year; it actually was about 40,000 acre-feet, according to engineering estimates. What had happened to account for the discrepancy of 24,000 acre-feet was that the formerly saturated dense blue clays underlying large parts of the north valley had been squeezed like a sponge when pumping lowered the water table and caused the heavy upper soils to press down upon them, compacting them and bringing about a settling of the entire central area of the valley.

This sinking of approximately two hundred square miles in the northern part of the Santa Clara Valley first came to light in 1920 when a survey by the United States Coast and Geodetic Survey revealed a slight change in the elevation of San Jose from the original 1912 survey. A new survey in 1932 disclosed that the central business district of the city was more than four feet lower than it had been in 1912—all because of the steady overdraft on the underground reservoir, the lessening of hydrostatic pressure on the blue clay subsoil, and the consequent compression of the clay. The storage capacity of the underground reservoir had been permanently reduced by about 500,000 acre-feet.

The lowering of the water table and the sinking of a large part of the valley created a whole complex of problems for the people of the valley, not all of which were immediately apparent. One thing agriculturists did know was that their costs for power to pump water from deeper levels increased, as well as their capital outlays for deepening wells and installing larger pumping equipment. Few of them realized, however, that the dewatering of the blue clay caused a reduction in the moisture content of the topsoil and required even more irrigation than before. Thus unwittingly they found themselves trapped by nature in a game that they were not likely to win, even by adopting a conservation program. The lowering of the water table, furthermore, invited salt-water intrusion into low-lying areas near San Francisco Bay. And the sinking of the land set the stage for a drama of floods and destruction in some season of unusual rainfall. Not that the low-lying plains of the Santa Clara Valley had escaped periodic inundation, but the area now subject to potential flooding had been greatly increased by the ground subsidence. Incalculable damage already had been caused to well casings, sewers, water mains, and other subsurface installations.

The first step toward carrying out a remedial program was taken in 1934, when the voters of the Santa Clara Valley Conservation District voted seven to one for bonds for a "well replenishment project," thereby reversing their seven-to-one rejection of a conservation plan submitted to them in 1931. The 1934 plan was based on the same principles as the Tibbetts plans of 1921 and 1931 but was more modest in cost. Instead of an estimated $6,000,000, it cost $2,683,000; but this sum proved to be $400,000 short of enough to complete the Coyote Dam, one of the most important projects in the plan. The voters authorized the extra funds in May, 1936.

"The dominant feature of this entire project and of the Coyote Reservoir, as well as of the other reservoirs, is the detention of flood water which would otherwise run to waste, and the gradual release of such flood water into natural streams at a rate so reduced that it will be entirely absorbed in the natural streambeds as released and passed into underground storage," Tibbetts explained.[9]

Measurements taken in 1931–1932 had shown that out of 155,000 acre-feet of runoff from the north valley watershed, only 45,000 acre-feet went into underground storage and 110,000 acre-feet went to waste in San Francisco Bay: 29 per cent was saved, 71 per cent was wasted.

The six retention reservoirs completed by the end of 1936 provided for storage of 49,000 acre-feet of runoff. Through gradual release of water into percolating canals and water-spreading beds, about 43,000 acre-feet was annually filtered to the underground reservoir. In March, 1938, Tibbetts was able to report that "from an all-time low in 1934 to January 1, 1938, the water table has risen more than 100 feet in places near the stream percolation works. In the main or central portion of the valley the average annual rise has been rather uniform. The total has been more than thirty feet, of which nearly one-half occurred during 1937. This was practically a normal year and the first year in which all the district's works were in use."[10]

Between 1937 and 1940 there was a cycle of wet winters, which enabled the retention reservoirs to make maximum contributions toward replenishing the subsurface water. But the people of the conservation district enjoyed only the illusion that they had improved conditions. Within the next ten years the water table was to recede even lower than in 1934. War, the growth of cities, shifts in agricultural production, and industrialization were all to intensify the problems created when early settlers began to upset nature's primal arrangements. The Santa Clara Valley sooner or later would be looking for external water supplies with which to augment its own local supplies.

From an over-all standpoint the San Francisco Bay

Area undoubtedly was more adequately supplied with water by the end of the 'thirties than it had been at any other time. But piecemeal solution of the area-wide problem of insufficient supply represented a long retreat from the unified approach of 1910, when for a time the city councils of San Jose, the East Bay cities, and some Peninsula communities were willing to consider joining with San Francisco in the Hetch Hetchy project. The various separate programs for obtaining water tended to perpetuate the habit of thinking narrowly about sectional problems and needs and to counteract the psychological good that may have come to the Bay Area from the San Francisco–Oakland industrial promotion program and the coöperative efforts on military air bases. Social and economic forces, however, in this geographically divided area, have always been acting to strengthen intercommunity ties; and action on one front no sooner fails than the struggle for area-wide coöperation opens anew on some other front. In the long run the idea of metropolitan regional unity perhaps makes some gains. Thus the diverse efforts to establish regional parks without relation to an over-all plan, to build subregional water systems and conservation works, and to attract industries to this or that locality were offset, to a degree, by a second attempt to promote metropolitan regional planning and by public works of importance to the entire Bay Area, such as the San Francisco–Oakland Bay Bridge and the Golden Gate Bridge.

Area-wide Planning—Second Try

The regional planning movement of the mid-thirties was peculiarly an outgrowth of the troubled times. In Washington, D.C., Franklin Delano Roosevelt's vigorous administration, supported by an anxious and coöperative Congress, was disbursing millions, nay billions, to feed the unemployed, put men to work, aid state and local governments, and stimulate the reopening of idle factories. The national capital and the regional offices of the federal relief and public works agencies became centers in which state and local officials and civic groups with job-creating projects to propose vied for favor. After the Works Progress Administration was started on May 6, 1935, every community that wanted a new highway, a new recreation building, a survey of its historical records, or a study of the adequacy of its school buildings turned to the WPA for assistance. The very possibility of getting WPA workers to staff a project suggested all manner of worthwhile activities that might not otherwise be undertaken.

To Hugh Pomeroy, who was consultant to several county planning commissions in the Bay Area, the new

work program looked like the means of getting some of the spade work of metropolitan regional planning done. Although thirty cities and five counties—Alameda, Contra Costa, San Francisco, Santa Clara, and San Mateo—had official planning commissions by 1935, not to mention an unofficial commission in Marin County, the value of city and county planning had barely been demonstrated in the Bay Area, because severe limitations of budget and personnel prevented commissions from doing any substantial amount of the data gathering that is a necessary first step in planning. Pomeroy, as a member of a WPA advisory committee for the coördination of professional and technical projects, believed that if some kind of regional planning organization were formed, the WPA might assign workers to it for field surveys and research projects.

At his suggestion the San Mateo County Planning Commission invited the other county planning commissions in the Bay Area, as well as the unofficial commission in Marin County and the Santa Cruz County Planning Commission, to join it in forming a so-called regional planning commission, which actually would be a voluntary association of planning commissions rather than the kind of elected commission required for a regional planning district organized under the planning enabling legislation approved by the state legislature in 1929. Santa Cruz County, of course, had not been included in the Bay Area as defined by the Regional Plan Association of the previous decade; nor has it in recent years been considered a part of the Bay Area. San Mateo County found the coöperation of Santa Cruz County necessary, however, on certain highway and recreation problems, and therefore sought its participation in the new regional planning effort. No doubt there also was something to be gained by bringing together as many citizen commissioners as possible in a period when planning commissions and professional planners were still struggling for recognition.

The letters of invitation to the seven-county conference held in August, 1935, stated that there were several problems of area-wide concern—old and familiar problems to anyone who had ever given any thought to regional development: "The highways in the counties surrounding San Francisco Bay should be developed as a coordinated network, in which adequately planned county highway systems will satisfactorily fit into the State Highway System. Roadside zoning is of similar inter-county interest, in that the traveler on a highway is not concerned with the location of county boundary lines but desires a safe and pleasant thoroughfare upon which to travel. The construction of the San Francisco–Oakland Bay Bridge and of the Golden Gate Bridge will more closely knit together the counties of the San Francisco Bay regional area and is requiring coordination of their transit and transportation plans. The major recreation facilities and potentialities of the region must be considered parts of a regional recreation system, not for the service of the individual counties within which the respective recreation areas may lie but for the use of the people of the entire region. Pollution by sewage of the waters of San Francisco Bay and the streams tributary to it constitutes a regional problem of interest to all the communities adjacent to the bay . . ."[11]

At the conference Pomeroy pointed out that in addition to coördination of their planning programs, the counties needed research on problems of regional concern, such as the distribution and densities of population, trends in the use of land, transportation requirements, and any number of other matters. A regional planning commission, he said, would be able to supervise several research projects.

The delegates signified their intention of forming such an organization, gave their blessing to an effort by Pomeroy to interest the WPA in providing research workers, and agreed to invite the counties of Sonoma, Napa, and Solano to participate in the proposed regional planning commission whenever those counties established their own planning commissions.

The California Works Progress Administration indicated that it would recognize the proposed regional planning commission as soon as it became a reality. L. Deming Tilton, director of the new California State Planning Board created as a division of the State Department of Finance, told Pomeroy that the state board would welcome suggestions from the commission-to-be and would sponsor projects it proposed.

Thus encouraged, the county planning commissions in the Bay Area organized the San Francisco Metropolitan Area Planning Commission in September, 1935, elected C. A. Buck, the chairman of the San Mateo County Planning Commission, to the presidency, and named Pomeroy secretary. But because this was only a voluntary association of planning commissioners and was without official status as an organization representing county governments in the Bay Area, negotiations for WPA assistance came to naught. Sadly the commissioners concluded that an effort would have to be made to strengthen planning in the various counties of the area before they could hope to succeed with regional planning.

A curious aspect of this short-lived regional planning venture was that cities other than San Francisco were given no opportunity to participate in it. San Francisco,

of course, is legally both a city and a county, and on this occasion was represented as one of the bay counties. No regional planning organization could well omit the largest city of the Bay Area, regardless of the fact that it enjoyed the dual status of city and county combined. But Oakland, always sensitive about being accorded due recognition in the metropolitan scheme of things, was without representation except through the Alameda County Planning Commission, although this commission has no statutory authorization to carry on the planning function within the corporate boundaries of cities. Likewise, Berkeley, Richmond, San Jose, and many other cities were only indirectly represented.

Certainly, no organization that disregarded the cities, which collectively contained the preponderance of the regional population, could justifiably call itself a metropolitan regional planning commission. If the county commissioners had been able to keep the new regional organization functioning and had not sooner or later asked the cities to participate, there would eventually have been trouble. Because they failed to extend invitations to city planning commissions at the outset, they may have overlooked a source of strength that just possibly might have sustained the whole endeavor, even though the city planning commissions in the Bay Area in 1935 were, with a few exceptions, pitifully weak. This second attempt to establish a regional planning agency was a good example of how not to organize such an agency in an area embracing scores of municipalities.

Imminence of Change

In the mid-thirties many city councils in the San Francisco Bay Area were perhaps more aware of regional relationships than some of the county boards of supervisors. The rapid construction of the San Francisco–Oakland Bay Bridge and the Golden Gate Bridge brought ever closer the time when old patterns of trade and transportation in the area would be superseded by new ones. The crews of workmen who had been engaged since 1933 in fashioning the miracles of steel that were to link city with city were building change itself. Public works departments on both sides of the bay were constructing approaches to the bridges, and draftsmen were already at work on plans for a new transit terminal in San Francisco. As surely as the currents of traffic and the routes of transit lines shifted, the economic and social relationships of many communities would alter.

But how extensive and of what sort would the expected changes be? Who would be hurt by them and who benefited? San Franciscans knew that the Golden Gate Bridge would make possible ready access to the redwood can-ons, scenic mountains, and beautiful beaches of Marin County; but would it cause their city to lose some population to the North Bay counties? Would it bring more shoppers from San Rafael and Petaluma and Santa Rosa to downtown San Francisco, or would trade follow migrating population? Some East Bay residents hoped that their side of the bay would attract San Francisco families who otherwise might move to San Mateo County, but the thought of bridge tolls raised doubts. Uncertainty marked the future—uncertainty that might have been dispelled somewhat if there had been a regional planning agency to investigate all the possible changes that might be effected by the two bridges and to present a general forecast of the new relationships that were likely to emerge.

Because there was no such agency, various specialists independently surveyed the future and made prognostications. None of the studies undertaken was based on a comprehensive analysis of all the factors that should have been taken into consideration; consequently, none was noteworthy for accuracy.

One of the earliest investigations was prompted by diverse opinions among Oakland businessmen concerning the effect the Bay Bridge would have on the economy of Oakland. Some were sure that upon the opening of the bridge, San Francisco would enjoy an increase in retail trade at the expense of Oakland; others were convinced that the East Bay would attract both population and trade from the larger city. The Residential Development Committee of the Oakland Chamber of Commerce therefore sponsored a study, by an advertising agency, of the effect the San Francisco–Oakland Bay Bridge would have on the population and on the retail trade of Oakland.

The report of the agency, issued in February, 1934, pointed out that similar bridges built in four eastern cities, Pittsburgh, Washington, D.C., Philadelphia, and New York, had all stimulated settlement in desirable outlying residential areas that became more accessible from the metropolitan center, regardless of the amount charged for bridge toll. For Oakland the agency predicted a minimum increase of approximately ninety thousand people in the decade, instead of "normal growth" of seventy thousand people, which it said might be expected if there were no bridge.[12]

This study was unusual in urging Oakland to prepare for a larger population by reserving sites for new schools, by extending transportation to suburban areas that would probably be developed, by improving zoning, and by taking steps to avoid speculation in land.

San Franciscans took comfort from the findings of a sample survey conducted by the San Francisco *Examiner* among housewives in fifty-one northern California com-

munities that would be within "four hours automobile driving time" of the city after the opening of the two big bridges. For retail stores and for hotels, restaurants, and garages the newspaper forecast a 50 to 60 per cent increase in patrons.[13] The survey, which was thought to be representative of the opinions of four hundred thousand families in the coastal area from Ukiah to Monterey, and in the Central Valley from Red Bluff to Fresno, presumably showed that approximately three-fourths of the families in communities outside the Bay Area believed San Francisco stores had advantages over those in their home communities, and that three-fifths of Bay Area families considered San Francisco stores generally superior to local establishments, particularly in the wide assortment of merchandise available.

The forecast included a veiled warning to San Francisco businessmen by predicting a 54 per cent increase in the use of automobiles by women shoppers. It indicated that there should be advance planning to provide more parking space for cars, but it placed no special emphasis on this point.

In answer to the puzzling question of how much population San Francisco might lose when the two great spans were completed, the forecast estimated that "about 6 per cent" of families in the city would depart.[14] On the basis of average family size in San Francisco in 1930, that would have meant a loss of more than thirty-four thousand people—the equivalent of the entire population of some of the state assembly districts in San Francisco in 1930. Had this happened, San Francisco would indeed have received some setbacks; but whatever outward movement of population the bridges did actually bring about was offset by in-migration; the 1940 census showed that population in San Francisco at least remained constant. The survey analysts were as wide of the mark as the advertising agency that predicted a decennial gain of ninety thousand for Oakland—the actual increase in that city was only eighteen thousand.

Stimulus of Fear

Fear that the population would decrease was, however, a powerful stimulus to action in official circles in San Francisco. As early as 1931, City Engineer M. M. O'Shaughnessy had written a report urging the development of a rapid transit system in San Francisco as one means of counteracting the attractions of reduced commuting time between the East Bay and San Francisco after the opening of the Bay Bridge. By 1934 the San Francisco Public Utilities Commission had begun work on the selection of a location for a terminal for transbay electric trains and had become fully aware of the danger to the metropolis of faster service to the East Bay. In its annual report for 1934–35 the commission stated:

"Studies of this problem [of selecting a location for the terminal] indicated the necessity for constructing rapid transit lines in San Francisco to offset the decrease in running time between San Francisco and the East Bay cities. The operation of suburban trains into San Francisco will cut the travel time by twelve minutes, and by bringing the terminal closer to the point of origin and destination of a larger number of commuters, the western part of San Francisco would be placed at a great disadvantage as it will require less time to cross the Bay via the Bridge than it will to reach a number of the desirable residence sections of the City by the present street car system. Also traffic congestion on Market Street has reached a point where street car operation during rush hours is so slow as to be detrimental to the best interests of the City."[15]

With an appropriation of $25,000 provided by the San Francisco Board of Supervisors in December, 1934, the Public Utilities Commission engaged Robert Ridgway, formerly Chief Engineer of the Board of Transportation in New York City, and Alfred Brahdy, Designing Engineer of the same agency, to review rapid transit studies already prepared by the commission and to make recommendations and estimate the cost of an initial rapid transit system. The two engineers, who had been responsible for most of the design and construction of New York subways costing $750,000,000, submitted a proposal on July 9, 1935, for a system of subways in which cars of connecting surface lines would operate until such time as the growth of population and the extension of the subway transportation system made it necessary to provide multiple-unit trains. Conditions in San Francisco, they said, did not yet warrant such extensive and costly subway systems as had been built in London, Paris, New York, and Philadelphia, in which multiple-unit trains operated entirely separated from surface lines.

The proposed system included three routes, all intended to provide faster service to the more distant residential areas of the city: a principal subway under the most heavily traveled portion of Market Street, with surface connections west of Van Ness Avenue to the Twin Peaks and Sunset tunnels; a branch from this main subway to the Mission district that might in time become a rapid transit route to the Peninsula; and a subway under Geary Street to Hamilton Square in the Western Addition. Cars of all three routes were to connect with the projected bridge terminal near Howard and Fremont streets.

Although this subway plan was spoken of as the Ridgway-Brahdy proposal, it was in reality the plan of the Public Utilities Commission, the two experts from New York merely having approved the plan after examining it in detail. The system recommended had evolved since 1931 from a proposal for a single subway under Market Street, with minor extensions into McAllister and O'Farrell streets.

Two features of the plan immediately aroused opposition: the estimated cost of $52,700,000 and the restriction of the subways to use by Municipal Railway lines only. Alarmed at the high cost, the members of the board of supervisors delayed approval of the plan. The failure of the plan to make any provision for the operation of the cars of the privately owned Market Street Railway in the subways brought protests from the company, from its organized employees, from some other unions, and from civic associations friendly to the company and its employees. Staunch proponents of municipal ownership of public utilities suggested that the first step toward improvement of transit in San Francisco should be the consolidation of transit services and the reorganization of routes and schedules.

Completion of the Bay Bridge

While debate on the proposed subway system raged, the San Francisco–Oakland Bay Bridge was completed and was opened to traffic, on November 12, 1936, six months ahead of the scheduled date of completion. For forty months the people of the Bay Area had been watching the great span take shape. During those months the nation had been making heroic efforts toward economic recovery. For the people of the Bay Area the finished bridge was something more than an aerial highway between two shores; it was a singular example of accomplishment in a period of hard struggle. The sight of the bridge towers standing against the cool sky, and of the long cables swinging in serene arcs between them, evoked emotions more intense than those that might have been felt if this gigantic structure had been completed in the prosperous 'twenties, when people tended to accept even sensational feats of engineering as foreordained achievements in the pattern of progress. When, on the day of the dedication ceremonies, Governor Frank F. Merriam with an acetylene torch burned asunder the heavy chain barrier across the bridge, he seemed to burn away the curtain of gloom that had hung over the Bay Area for years. "Cannons roared, bombs burst in air, sirens and whistles shrieked, and massed thousands of enthusiastic citizens at the east and west approaches of the great structure blasted the welkin with their cheers."[16] Fifteen squadrons of navy planes zoomed overhead, a marine parade of gaily decorated yachts and motor boats streamed under the bridge, and

The San Francisco–Oakland Bay Bridge as Seen from Yerba Buena Island. The
Southern Pacific ferryboats shown in this view were the last to ply the bay.
Photograph courtesy of State Division of Highways.

the United States battle fleet, anchored just south of the span, volleyed forth salutes.

"That this is the greatest bridge yet constructed in the world requires no repetition by me," former President Herbert Hoover declared. "Its construction also spans the whole advance in industrial civilization—our discoveries in science, our inventions, our increasing skill. It is the product of hundreds of years of cumulative knowledge."[17]

Earl Lee Kelley, Director of the State Department of Public Works, expressed what the bridge meant to the residents of the Bay Area. "The opening of this bridge is the first step in eliminating the isolation of San Francisco . . . It will bring the cities of the bay district into closer union . . ."[18]

As if to give immediate fulfillment to Kelley's prediction, approximately a million people traveled across the bridge in two hundred and fifty thousand automobiles, buses, and trucks in the first 108 hours of its operation as a state highway. Thousands of East Bay residents employed in San Francisco tried the novelty of driving to work, even though the toll was sixty-five cents during the

One of Joseph B. Strauss's Preliminary Designs for the Golden Gate Bridge. Perspective drawing published in Western City in March, 1930.

first three months after the bridge was completed. Then at 5 P.M. they dashed from their offices to garages and parking lots, raced home, and announced triumphantly, "I made it in twenty-two minutes tonight."

The majority of commuters, however, continued to make the daily journey back and forth across the bay by ferry, because the lower deck of the bridge was not yet equipped for interurban trains. Plans for the Bay Bridge Terminal had been completed early in 1936; but financing of the bridge railway, the terminal building, and the viaducts proved to be long and involved. Not until the summer of 1937 did construction on the $15,000,000 project get under way.

In the meantime more and more commuters formed car pools and stopped using the transbay services of the Key System and the Southern Pacific. Between 1936 and 1937 the number of transbay passengers carried by the Southern Pacific declined from 13,687,209 to 11,965,052.

The Key System experienced a similar decline in transbay passengers—from 12,334,743 to 10,749,307. For the two systems the total decrease in passenger trips was 3,307,593 during the first year the bridge was in operation, whereas both companies had enjoyed a slight increase in patronage between 1935 and 1936. The sharp drop in 1937 raised grave doubts whether the Bay Bridge Terminal would ever serve the large crowds for which it was designed.

Golden Gate Bridge

Six and a half months after the Bay Bridge was dedicated, the Golden Gate Bridge was completed. It had taken four years, four months, and twenty-two days to construct. As it was the largest and highest single-span suspension bridge built up to that time, it inspired millions of words of description in the newspapers of the world. Writers called it a "steel harp," "the bridge that sings," "the span of gold."[19] Its red towers, designed with four portal struts rather than conventional cross bracing, were more than three hundred feet higher than the Russ Building in the heart of the financial district of San Francisco. Its wire cables, each thirty-six and a half inches in diameter, were then the largest in the history of suspension-bridge construction; yet the concrete anchorage blocks to which they are attached are so huge that they could withstand twice the pull that the cables exert. But this "bridge that couldn't be built" is more than a feat of engineering; in an age in which architecture tends to become engineering, this span has the majesty and magic associated with the greatest architecture of all time. The two hundred thou-

sand pedestrians who swarmed across the bridge on May 27, 1937, the first day it was opened, responded not only to its colossal dimensions but also to its lyric beauty. By midafternoon they were walking across it at the rate of thirty thousand an hour. Automobile traffic was prohibited and they were free to gaze in awe at the soaring towers and the great sweep of the cables.

On the Marin County side of the Golden Gate the State Division of Highways had built an approach to the bridge that was one of the most costly stretches of highway in the Bay Area. Known as the Waldo Approach, this three-and-a-half-mile highway, with its thousand-foot

Air View of the Golden Gate Bridge, Looking Toward San Francisco. Photograph courtesy of State Division of Highways.

tunnel and heavy grading, cost more than $2,000,000. District Engineer John H. Skeggs pointed out that in the days when California was building highways with its first highway bond issue of $18,000,000, the money spent on the Waldo Approach would have built sixty miles of paved highway—the equivalent of the complete original Redwood Highway from Sausalito to Healdsburg. He probably would have been utterly incredulous if a prophet had then told him that within another sixteen years the state would schedule for construction a parallel duplicate of the Waldo Approach, tunnel and all, in order to provide for the heavy volume of traffic over this hazardous route.

The Waldo Approach bypassed the town of Sausalito, which immediately felt the effects of the opening of the bridge. As an increasing number of Marin County residents who were employed in San Francisco began driving to work, the daily ebb and flow of commuters through the Sausalito ferry terminal of the Northwestern Pacific Railroad steadily declined, until by 1939 the railroad was applying to the State Railroad Commission for permission to abandon its interurban service. The desired authorization was withheld, however, until motor coach service could be substituted. In the meantime, business fell off in the town, and the population decreased slightly. By 1940 Sausalito had 127 fewer residents than it had had in 1930, when its population was 3,667. Its historic importance as a land-water transfer point was lost altogether on February 28, 1941, when the interurban electric trains and ferry boats of the Northwestern Pacific made their last runs; but within another year the population rapidly increased as large numbers came to work in the wartime shipyard opened near Waldo Point on Richardson Bay. The renewed growth of Sausalito as a suburban residential outpost of San Francisco was to be a postwar development.

Other towns in Marin County within commuting distance of San Francisco made small population gains during the late 'thirties, thanks partly to the increased accessibility of the area. These communities included Mill Valley, Corte Madera, Larkspur, Kentfield, Ross, San Anselmo, and San Rafael, all on the warm bay side of the Marin Peninsula. In general, old residents of the county were not eager to have San Franciscans move into their domain. The proprietary lovers of "Marvelous Marin" winced at seeing the oaks and madrones cut down to make way for streets in new subdivisions. The farmers and timber operators farther north found the bridge a great convenience, but many an old family in Mill Valley and Ross and San Rafael regarded it as decidedly a mixed blessing for southern Marin County.

Greater Congestion in "the City"

In San Francisco an obvious result of the opening of the two huge bridges was greater traffic congestion, especially in the central business district. "In the past year Market Street congestion has increased very rapidly," the report of the Public Utilities Commission for the fiscal year 1936–37 observed. "This increase is in no small way due to additional automobile traffic which has been brought into San Francisco by the completion of the San Francisco–Oakland and Golden Gate Bridges."[20]

A report on a city-wide traffic survey conducted by WPA workers under the direction of Miller McClintock, a nationally known traffic consultant, pointed out that between 1914 and 1937 the number of registered motor vehicles in San Francisco had risen from only 12,000 to more than 160,000 and that completion of the San Francisco–Oakland Bay Bridge had brought into close communication with the metropolis a highly urbanized area in which there were approximately as many vehicles registered as there were in San Francisco itself.

McClintock discovered that "certain substantial volumes of traffic which are now forced through the central congested area are seeking destinations beyond this area."[21] The city therefore needed, in his opinion, routes bypassing the central area.

His recommendations for alleviating the many traffic problems of the city included a "basic cure" known as a "Limited Way Plan." Drawings in McClintock's report showed some of the proposed limited ways as elevated structures similar to the Westside Highway in New York City, others as semidepressed or fully depressed routes, and still others as trafficways at grade or on elevated earth fills with landscaped banks. In all, there were to be sixty-five miles of these divided, free-flow routes throughout the city, including an elevated limited way along the Embarcadero. All were designed for "an over-all operating average speed of 40 miles per hour, which is more than a 100 per cent increase over existing average experience."[22]

The cost of this early form of city-wide freeway system was set at $26,120,800, half the estimated cost of the subway plan proposed by the Public Utilities Commission. Like the subway plan, the Limited Way Plan was put forth as insurance against competition from the territories made accessible to San Franciscans by the new bridges. McClintock did not suggest means of financing the scheme but indicated that some of the burden might properly fall on the state, because the plan was "not only city-wide in its benefits but regional and state-wide as well."[23] It would assure swift passage through the city for

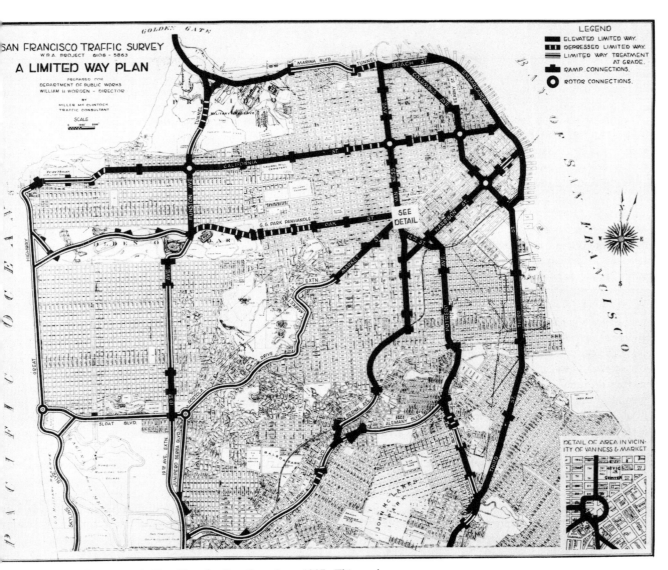

*Miller McClintock's Limited Way Plan for San Francisco, 1937. This early pro-
posal for a system of elevated, depressed, and surface freeways invites comparison
with the system now being developed by the State Division of Highways.*

motorists going from one part of the metropolitan region
—or one part of the state—to another; it would provide
easy access to the central business district; and it would
reduce traffic congestion in that area.

The plan is of historic significance because it foreshadowed many of the freeways built after World War II.
At the time it was proposed, however, it impressed local
officials as being much too ambitious, especially since San
Francisco was then facing an election on the subway plan
recommended by the Public Utilities Commission in 1936.

Although the original cost of the subway plan had been
shaved to $49,000,000, determined opposition of the pri-
vately owned Market Street Railway and of self-appointed

transportation experts who had schemes of their own to
champion brought defeat to the proposal. In November,
1937, only 68,834 voters cast ballots in favor of the plan;
95,246 voted against it. San Francisco was to make no
real effort to improve transportation and traffic until
after World War II.

Transbay Train Service

The transbay rail service that San Franciscans had both
anticipated and worried about did not become available
until January 15, 1939, the day after the Bay Bridge
Terminal was dedicated, although motor coaches of the
Key System had since 1937 been using the lower deck of

the Bay bridge in transporting passengers from Richmond, East Oakland, and Hayward to the metropolis. When the interurban trains finally did begin rolling into the new terminal on Mission Street between First and Fremont streets, the day of the Ferry Building as the great reception center of San Francisco was over, even though some ferries continued to nose into its slips. Hordes of commuters no longer crowded lower Market Street, and retail business in the blocks below Fremont Street shrank to a fraction of what it had been.

The shift from ferry to bridge travel had other economic repercussions. Both the Key System and the Southern Pacific–Interurban Electric Railway incurred heavy expenses in adapting their trains to the grades on the bridge and to the new signal system, but neither company would convert its lines to the voltage of the other. Consequently, the California Toll Bridge Authority, after some delay, installed a dual voltage system on the bridge. In the meantime, so many thousands of commuters had taken to using their own automobiles that by the time transbay rail service could be inaugurated, the Southern Pacific–Interurban Electric Railway was doomed. It had been operating at a deficit for some years. In the first year of railway service over the bridge the number of passengers carried fell one-half million below the total transported in 1938. By 1940 the deficit had become so great that the railway filed an appeal to the State Railroad Commission to abandon all transbay rail service, and in the spring of 1941 the "big red cars" ceased to run.

The Key System, which had enjoyed an increase in patronage in 1939 and then had suffered a decline in 1940, now had the entire East Bay transit field to itself. It offered motor coach service on many of the routes formerly served by the Interurban and extended some rail lines. It also united all transit service, local and interurban, under single management and instituted the universal transfer system—an added convenience for the traveling public.

Notwithstanding all improvements in service, the number of transbay transit passengers declined. In four years the increased use of the automobile on the Bay Bridge had so far altered riding habits that less than two-fifths of all transbay trips were made by train; whereas before the bridge was opened, more than two-thirds of all transbay journeys had been by interurban service. The reduction in bridge tolls from fifty cents to thirty-five cents to twenty-five cents of course contributed greatly to the increasing popularity of commuting by automobile. And toll reductions also put out of business the Golden Gate Ferry between Berkeley and San Francisco, thereby diverting additional hundreds of vehicles a day to the

bridge. The traveling public had, however, become mo and more conscious of speed and time and more and mo impatient with transit schedules, the walk to and from th train, and the wait at the station. Even though traffic jan and parking problems often negated the convenience the private motor vehicle, people cherished the illusic that personal transportation had many advantages ov public transit—and an illusion could be the undoing transit companies that were unable or unwilling to adju to the demand for faster, more comfortable, more co venient service.

On the eve of American participation in World War the San Francisco Bay Area was even farther from achie ing a metropolitan regional transit system than it ha been at the time of World War I, when, with the constru tion of three or four missing links, at least five of the nin counties in the area might have been united by interurba railways. In Santa Clara County the once extensive Pe insular Railway had abandoned all its lines and ha legally disincorporated in 1935. In Sonoma County th Southern Pacific had discontinued all passenger servi on the Petaluma and Santa Rosa Electric Railway. Th Golden Gate Bridge had doomed the rail-ferry service the Northwestern Pacific in Marin County. The bu steam train, and electric-railway services that did provi transportation were not coördinated. It was impossib to proceed in an unbroken journey from cities on th Peninsula to cities in the East Bay or Marin County, ar it was equally impossible to go from Marin County Oakland or Berkeley without interrupting the journey San Francisco. New highways, the Golden Gate Bridg and the San Francisco–Oakland Bay Bridge had broug about a physical unification of the Bay Area that had n been accompanied by any attempt to unify transit servic An opportunity had been neglected—but it was not pe manently lost.

Disappearance of River Boats

New highways and the new bridges were fatal not only two rail-transit systems and several automobile and pa senger ferries but also to scores of barges and river boat One by one they disappeared from the bay and its trib taries. Local shipping tonnage, trending steadily dow ward since 1925, dropped appreciably in 1937 as truc began transporting agricultural and other bulk commo ties formerly shipped from the interior of the state metropolitan centers by inland waterways.

Several improvements in routes from the San Joaqu Valley to the East Bay and the San Francisco–Oaklan Bay Bridge stimulated this increase in trucking. Near three years before the bridge was opened, the State D ision of Highways widened to four lanes the Dublin Canyon route through the hills east of Hayward. In 1938 the division further improved this highway from Stockton and Tracy to Oakland by relocating the roadway through the Altamont Pass, east of the Livermore Valley, and making it a wide, divided highway. Transport from the interior by way of Contra Costa County increased in speed and convenience upon the opening of the Broadway Low-Level Tunnel through the Berkeley Hills in December, 1937. The tunnel and its highway connections were constructed as links in an eventual route from Stockton to Oakland that would be ten miles shorter than the route through Dublin Canyon. Almost two years later an eight-mile section of the Arnold Industrial Highway across the Diablo Valley (Franklin Canyon to Willow Pass) brought Richmond and the fertile Central Valley into closer communication.

Like the Waldo Tunnel on the Marin County approach to the Golden Gate Bridge, the Broadway Tunnel was to prove inadequate within fifteen years, but the decade of the 'thirties was a period when population experts foresaw a leveling off of population in the United States about 1970; and even optimistic Californians were not expecting such rapid population increases as had characterized the past growth of the state. Highway engineers doubtless thought that the tunnel would be able to handle traffic between the East Bay and the interior for at least two decades. Even if they had had some misgivings about their forecasts, however, they would hardly have dared to propose building a larger tunnel, for fear of being accused of extravagance. California highways were among the best in the nation, yet funds were entirely insufficient to meet needs. In 1938 John H. Skeggs, district engineer of the state highway division that included eight of the Bay Area counties (Solano County excluded) and Santa Cruz County, estimated that $67,409,200 would be required to bring the roads, bridges, and other structures of his district up to the standards of the time; yet the state legislature appropriated only $28,000,000 for the entire state highway program for the 1939–41 biennium.

This budget included no funds for freeways proposed in the late 'thirties. State highway engineers advocated construction of a Bayshore Freeway on the San Francisco Peninsula and a similar freeway on the east side of the bay between Oakland and San Jose, both routes to connect with the San Francisco–Oakland Bay Bridge. Neither freeway was undertaken until after World War II.

Bay Pollution Problem

Perhaps the most unexpected result of the opening of the Bay Bridge was a movement to stop pollution of the Oakland-Emeryville-Berkeley waterfront. Until the bridge was built, the western waterfront of Oakland was little more than the "back door" of the city. Passengers on Key System trains got a malodorous whiff from the tidal flats as they traveled along the Key System Mole to the ferry terminal near Yerba Buena Island. But aside from the momentary exposure to obnoxious gases, they had little personal acquaintance with the foul conditions created by the discharge of untreated sewage into the shoal waters on the east side of the bay. Only dock workers and employees of industrial plants near the harbor had to live with the evil smells emanating from offshore deposits of putrefying sewage sludge. When the Bay Bridge was completed and the western waterfront became, in effect, the "front door" of the East Bay, the stench from the mud flats quickly became a civic scandal—an affront to community pride and common decency. The press, chambers of commerce, and citizen groups began demanding action on conditions that had been troubling some city engineers for several years.

In the year after the opening of the bridge, noisy sessions in the council chambers of East Bay cities convinced councilmen that they were confronted with a problem that could not be solved satisfactorily through piecemeal programs initiated by individual municipalities. Along a twenty-mile shoreline between San Leandro Bay and the Standard Oil Refinery at Richmond approximately sixty outfall sewers were dumping raw sewage into the bay. In the vicinity of certain sewer outlets along the Oakland Inner Harbor great quantities of solid waste floated on the surface during the canning season and were transported by the current into the tidal canal connecting the harbor with San Leandro Bay. Faced with the necessity for coöperative action, the governing bodies of Alameda, Albany, El Cerrito, Emeryville, Piedmont, Richmond, and San Leandro responded with alacrity to an invitation from Mayor W. J. McCracken of Oakland to send representatives to a meeting in the Oakland Council Chamber to discuss plans for dealing with the common problem.

The outcome of this conference on November 3, 1937, was the formation of an East Bay Municipal Executives Association and the appointment of a committee of city engineers to prepare a preliminary report on sewage disposal. Submitted eight months later, the report recommended that the cities appropriate funds for a comprehensive survey of the sewage disposal problem by a board of consulting engineers.

As often happens, preparing the report seemed to make everyone feel that something had been accomplished. A year passed with almost no action on the chief recommendation of the report, and in the meantime San Leandro grew impatient with the dilatory tactics of other communities and began the construction of trunk sewers and sewage treatment works. Various groups began to fear that the opportunity for joint action by the cities would be lost. Again prodded by the public, city officials of seven cities—Alameda, Albany, Berkeley, Emeryville, Oakland, Piedmont, and Richmond—created an executive committee on June 21, 1940, to supervise the East Bay Cities Sewage Disposal Survey. Collectively the cities appropriated $57,000 for the survey and engaged Charles Gilman Hyde, Harold Farnsworth Gray, and A. M. Rawn as consulting engineers to conduct the investigation.

The consulting engineers reported that "foul conditions...have rendered the shores and shore waters hardly utilizable for recreational uses (boating, fishing, and the like); completely unsuitable for bathing; and a handicap to industrial development and shipping."[24] They perhaps minimized the seriousness of the problem by concluding that it was "one of aesthetics, primarily, rather than one definitely concerned with the public health, except perhaps indirectly."[25] But they made an important contribution toward eventual solution of the problem when they recommended that the construction and operation of sewage treatment plants and facilities for disposal of sewage be entrusted to the East Bay Municipal Utility District "for the reason that its administrative and engineering organization, with few additions to its technical staff, is exceedingly capable and well equipped to execute these functions."[26] This special district was indeed to become responsible for creating the facilities needed, but not until many years later.

Hyde and his associates completed their report only a few months before the Japanese attack on Pearl Harbor and the entrance of the United States into World War II. For some time thereafter the public gave no thought to the problem of bay pollution; then the wartime influx of population so aggravated the problem that it again came to the fore, though nothing could be done about it until hostilities ceased.

A New Island

The two great bridges that brought so many changes to the Bay Area were hardly begun before there was a movement for a celebration that would mark their completion. Gathering impetus, it quickly developed into a movement for an exposition on an international scale. A Bridge Celebration Founding Committee appointed by Mayor Angelo Rossi of San Francisco in October, 1933, was soon considering a problem familiar to every organization that has ever planned an exposition: the selection of a suitable site.

Of six possibilities—Golden Gate Park, the Presidio, China Basin, filled lands south of Hunters Point, the Lake Merced area, and the shoals north of Yerba Buena Island—the committee finally chose the shoal area because it was accessible from all parts of the Bay Area and it afforded an opportunity for an exposition of unique beauty. There was an even more compelling reason for the choice: the island created on the shoals could later become an airport for San Francisco.

Early in 1931 the San Francisco Junior Chamber of Commerce had become concerned about the need for additional runways to handle the growing volume of air traffic in the metropolitan region. Prodded by this organization, San Francisco officials persuaded the state legislature and the governor to approve a bill transferring title of the Yerba Buena shoals from the state to the City and County of San Francisco for development and use as an airport. Years might have passed before the shoals actually were filled, however, had not the Junior Chamber happily concluded that the way to speed reclamation of the shallow waters was to urge the use of the airport-to-be as an exposition site.

No sooner had an advisory planning committee appointed by the Bridge Celebration Founding Committee expressed the opinion that the mid-bay location would "guarantee freedom from sectional disputes and community jealousies" than the San Francisco Junior Chamber of Commerce discovered that "certain narrow interests" in San Francisco were fearful lest an exposition on the Yerba Buena shoals "bring a profit to Oakland at the expense of San Francisco." Again the specter of intercommunity rivalry! The leaders of the Junior Chamber steamed. "We believe that the time has come for San Francisco to throw off the yoke of provincialism and smug satisfaction and work in harmony with her sister cities in an effort to achieve her destined greatness, now threatened by the tremendous growth and enterprise of the cities of southern California," the young men advised those who would disrupt plans for the exposition.[27]

The "narrow interests" who muttered about Oakland were talked down, and the directors of the San Francisco Bay Exposition proceeded to make arrangements with the WPA and the United States Corps of Army Engineers for the creation of "Treasure Island." Barges dumped tons of rock into the bay to form the outline of a rectangle a mile and a quarter long and two-thirds of a mile wide; then dredges scooped thirty million cubic yards of sand and mud from near-by areas of the bay to fill the four hundred acres enclosed by the rock walls. Finally, engineers created a causeway connecting this man-made island with Yerba Buena Island.

Dignitaries and civic organizations participated in the dedication of the exposition site on November 21, 1937. Fourteen months later the Golden Gate International Exposition, a $50,000,000 wonderland dominated by a slim, octagonal Tower of the Sun, sparkled in the center of the bay. In the courts formed by the principal buildings were gardens, fountains, sculpture, and murals created by most of the well-known artists of the Bay Area. The architecture ranged from the romantically eclectic to the creatively modern, best exemplified in the Federal Building by the late Timothy Pflueger and the Yerba Buena Clubhouse by William Wurster. Several of the buildings were of permanent construction, designed for use as maintenance and operation buildings of an air terminal. The advisory planning committee appointed by the Bridge Celebration Founding Committee, however, had observed that "the shoals also lend themselves to development for Naval purposes,"[28] and it was to naval purposes that the man-created site was converted after the fountain ceased to play in the Enchanted Garden and the lights went out on the Towers of the East.

At first, occupancy by the Navy was considered temporary; but later this branch of the service took permanent possession of Treasure Island, thereby putting an end to the idea of a mid-bay air terminal.

Bridges and "Decentralization"

In 1940, when the exposition was in its second year, many San Franciscans began to wonder whether they really had any reason for celebrating the completion of the two mighty bridges. The decennial census returns tended to confirm some early predictions that the bridges would drain population from the metropolis, or at least arrest the development of the city. In the 1930's the city had gained only 142 residents, whereas every other county in the Bay Area had made gains in the thousands. The plight of San Francisco could not be attributed entirely to the bridges, of course, because improved highways on the Peninsula and in the East Bay, the establishment of additional industries in the East Bay, and many other developments had contributed to the growth of other areas; but the bridges had certainly played some part in denying the city the gains that various experts had predicted. At the beginning of the decade, the chairman of the City Planning Section of the Commonwealth Club had forecast a population of 760,000 in 1940;[29] and as late as 1937 Miller McClintock had "conservatively" estimated that the population would be 725,000 at the end of the decade.[30] Instead, the Bureau of the Census credited San Francisco with 634,536 residents, to the consternation of the local press and the Chamber of Commerce, who were sure that the federal agency must be wrong. What they did not recognize was that without

in-migration, the total population of San Francisco would have been approximately 8,000 less than in 1930, because deaths in the city had exceeded births during the decade, according to records of the California State Department of Health.

"Decentralization," a word with terrible connotations to numerous San Franciscans, was the term most often used to explain what had happened to San Francisco, but it was inaccurate and misleading. In the 'thirties, as in the 'twenties, much of the growth in the satellite fringe of the Bay Area was new, rather than a shift of population from central cities to the suburbs. What actual decentralization there was had a twofold character. Some families who had long lived in central areas moved to outlying cities and towns. Some other families who had come to the metropolis from other parts of California or from other states in the 'thirties had remained in San Francisco only a few years and then had joined the outward march to suburbia. San Francisco had thus served as a "reception center" in the Bay Area, and despite its poor showing in the 1940 census had continued to function as a magnet for new population in the metropolitan region.

Oakland, too, had experienced similar inward and outward flow of population, though it had more than held its own. An increase of 18,100 gave it a total population of 302,163.

The significant thing about the census returns for the East Bay was that they revealed greater relative gains in cities such as Albany, El Cerrito, Hayward, and San Leandro—all on the periphery of the built-up area in the East Bay—than in Oakland and Berkeley. As on the San Francisco Peninsula, population was shifting to small cities from established centers, and newcomers to the Bay Area were being attracted to them.

For the nine bay counties as a metropolitan unit the rate of growth during the 'thirties was the lowest since the American occupation—a mere 9.9 per cent, representing an increase of only 156,229 persons. By comparison, Los Angeles County gained 568,719 new residents and in 1940 had a total population exceeding that of the nine bay counties by more than 1,000,000. The figure for the Bay Area was 1,734,308, one-fourth of the population of the state of California, whereas Los Angeles County alone had more than two-fifths. In the latter area the discovery of a new oil field at Wilmington, the development of radio broadcasting in Hollywood, the rise of the aircraft industry, and the expansion of manufacturing plants utilizing new low-cost power from Hoover Dam all provided more employment and induced further in-migration. Since the Bay Area had nothing comparable to these varied developments, it did not attract large numbers of newcomers until World War II. And then they came in hordes, doubling and tripling the population of some cities.

CHAPTER FIFTEEN

Crisis in an Arsenal of Democracy

More than a year before the Japanese attack on Pearl Harbor brought the United States openly and precipitately into World War II, the San Francisco Bay Area had begun to shift from peacetime activities to "defense" production. The shipbuilding industry, which for the most part had been idle for twenty years, sprang to life as the United States Maritime Commission awarded huge contracts for cargo carriers and the Navy Department placed contracts for light cruisers, destroyers, and auxiliary craft. Skilled workers laid new keels in old shipways, rehabilitated long unused drydocks, made motors whine and sparks fly in machine shops that had been almost deserted for years. And in scores of related industries men worked round the clock to produce special materials and parts for ships. But the defense boom was not limited to shipbuilding. Plants throughout the Bay Area filled orders from the War and Navy departments for large quantities of denim working trousers, oilskin slickers, feather pillows, mattresses, flavorings, paraffin wax, trunk lockers, canned fruits and vegetables, laundry soap—a bewildering assortment of goods seldom thought of as "sinews of war." By the time the Japanese struck at Pearl Harbor a large proportion of Bay Area industry was operating on a wartime basis, expanding plant facilities, recruiting and training new workers, employing "expediters" to obtain critical materials, and curtailing production of many kinds of consumer goods.

For many years the shadow of war had been gathering over the Bay Area—if the development of military facilities could be taken as a sign of impending conflict. The selection of the western end of Alameda as the site for a naval air base in November, 1935, may have seemed at the time to be only remotely related to the Japanese fortification of distant islands of the Pacific. The negotiations of Navy Department officials with the Board of Port Commissioners of Oakland in the spring and summer of 1936 for 390 acres of tidelands in the Oakland Middle Harbor as a site for a supply depot certainly prompted no civilians to study the map of New Guinea or Guadalcanal. But when the Alameda Naval Air Station was commissioned, on November 1, 1940, a considerable segment of the local population realized that military men associated this and other Bay Area military installations with future campaigns in a Pacific Theater of War.

"Arsenal of Democracy"

The Bay Area had become by the summer of 1941 a major "arsenal of democracy." From Moffett Field at the lower end of San Francisco Bay to the Benicia Arsenal overlooking the waters of Suisun Bay, it was an enormous complex of military establishments, some dating from the early days of California statehood, some brand new. Army establishments included the Presidio, Letterman Hospital, and Forts Mason, Funston, Scott, and Miley in San Francisco; Fort McDowell on Angel Island; Hamilton Field and Forts Barry, Baker, and Cronkhite in Marin County; a new supply depot at the Oakland Outer Harbor; and the Benicia Arsenal. Even in the spring of 1941 approximately twenty thousand troops and a large complement of civilian employees were on duty in these

*The Kaiser Shipyards at Richmond During World War II. Photograph courtesy of
Kaiser Industries Corporation.*

various facilities. The Navy likewise had large numbers of enlisted men and civilians at its establishments, which included the new base on Treasure Island, the Hunters Point and Mare Island navy yards, a naval radio station in Marin County, Moffett Field, the new supply depot in Oakland, the Alameda air base, and a naval station at Tiburon, in Marin County. The labor force at Mare Island alone was scheduled to number twenty-eight thousand by the end of 1941.

So important to the defense effort and the lend-lease program of aid to Great Britain were the private shipyards that they were virtually in the category of military installations. Among the first to be revitalized by the armament program were the General Engineering and Drydrock Corporation in San Francisco, the Bethlehem and the Western Pipe and Steel Company yards in South San Francisco, the Moore Drydock Company in Oakland, and the Bethlehem Steel Company Shipbuilding Division in Alameda. In January, 1941, the Todd-California Shipbuilding Company, of which Henry J. Kaiser was president, began constructing one of the largest yards of all, on the southern waterfront of Richmond, where there were acres of unoccupied land alongside deep water. The company's first order was for thirty freighters for Great

Britain, to be built at a cost of $48,000,000—a mere starter in a program that was to keep expanding until four mammoth yards were in operation, one hundred thousand workers were employed, and ships by the hundreds were sliding down the ways, sometimes at the rate of one a day.

As the defense build-up accelerated and more manufacturing plants were drawn into it, the pattern of activities in the nine counties surrounding the bay gave striking evidence that despite city and county boundary lines and overlapping special districts, and despite the geographical division created by the bay itself, the thousands of square miles from Gilroy to Cloverdale and from the Pacific Ocean to the confluence of the Sacramento and San Joaquin rivers constituted in reality a single metropolitan region, marshaling its manpower, its machines, and its fertile farmlands for a single purpose. Some of the workers in the Mare Island Navy Yard lived as far away as San Mateo and Calistoga. Headquarters offices in San Francisco procured materials for plants in Pittsburg and Richmond. Troops from the Presidio in San Francisco maneuvered in Marin County. San Francisco contractors built demountable housing in Vallejo. Alameda shipyards obtained parts from plants in Richmond, Sunnyvale, and South San Francisco. Canneries in Santa Rosa, Santa Clara, and Oakland supplied fruits and vegetables for army and navy bases throughout the area. Every part of the nine-county area was dependent in various ways upon every other. Every part had something to contribute toward the war effort.

But this interdependent area was not organized to function with maximum efficiency, either under ordinary circumstances or during an emergency. In few of its widely distributed manufacturing districts did the factories form related industrial groups, in which certain plants supplied parts and materials needed by other units. Its highways were unduly taxed with the movements of trucks conveying semifabricated materials from plants in East Oakland or South San Francisco to Richmond, or from Pittsburg to Emeryville, because no organization representing the economic interests of the metropolitan community had ever studied the problem of industrial linkages and attempted to develop clusters of "homogeneous" industries. And since housing in the vicinity of the various shipyards was inadequate to meet the sudden demand, a new and heavy load of crosshaul traffic was thrown onto the already overburdened main routes. Even less well supplied with mass transit facilities than before the Golden Gate Bridge and the San Francisco–Oakland Bay Bridge were completed, the area was more dependent than ever upon private transportation—and would be in

great difficulty should rationing of gasoline and tires become necessary. None of its cities had completed even preliminary long-range, general plans to which they could turn for guidance in locating new housing projects, military installations, and factories; nor was there for the metropolitan community any kind of over-all plan that might help in solving emergency problems. In the development of new streets and highways, sewer lines and water mains, schools, and commercial areas, the cities and counties were certain to compound new mistakes with old ones, just as they had done in the years of depression, when an unemployment crisis forced them to act quickly in constructing public works.

Need for Area-wide Planning

"Defense activities concentrated in this area will require concerted thinking and action of us all," a speaker representing the State Council of Defense declared at a hearing called by the California State Planning Board on March 28, 1941, to consider establishment of a San Francisco Bay regional planning district. "Some regional agency to effectuate and assist such collaboration is imperative, to expedite defense undertakings, to help solve local problems arising from defense, and to assure the maximum ultimate benefit when a transition from warlike to peacetime pursuits is possible."[1]

Other speakers representing the press, the State Railroad Commission, the United States Public Roads Administration, the Pacific Gas and Electric Company, the State Bureau of Sanitary Engineering, the Home Builders' Institute, the United States Housing Authority, the Berkeley regional office of the National Resources Planning Board, and the old Regional Plan Association of the 'twenties all agreed that the numerous cities and nine counties surrounding the bay were in effect one metropolitan community and that they would benefit by regional planning, especially in a time of crisis. More than a hundred city and county officials and civic leaders of the Bay Area generally likewise accepted the idea that regional planning would be desirable. But the state law under which a planning region would be established proved to be a stumbling block to coöperation.

As amended in 1937, the Planning Act of California placed upon the State Planning Board the duty of dividing the state into regions for planning purposes. Since no areas of the state—except Los Angeles County, which had asked to have its planning body designated a regional planning commission ex officio—had made any clear-cut demand for the establishment of regional planning districts, the state board had taken no steps to carry out the mandate of the law. In 1941, however, certain members

f the state legislature signified their interest in having it
o so. Since the counties which touched upon San Fran-
isco Bay seemed to have "enough problems in common
o justify the establishment of a planning region," the
tate board decided to begin its districting of the state in
he Bay Area.[2]

Attached to letters of invitation to the hearing in San
Francisco were excerpts from the planning law pertaining
o the duties of the board, to the appointment of regional
lanning commissions, and to the relationship of city and
ounty planning commissions to a regional commission.
These sections of the law contained certain phrases which
he well-meaning members of the State Planning Board
robably had not thought of as "dynamite"—phrases
vhich were intended to provide for coördination among
tate, regional, county, and city planning bodies, but
vhich aroused the suspicions of some city and county
lanning commissioners. One section of the act, for in-
tance, stated that the State Planning Board "shall im-
lant" upon the master plan of a region "those things
vhich it considers pertinent," such as public improvements
lanned by state departments and by agencies of the
ederal government. Another section provided that city
nd county planning commissions "shall accept and em-
ody in the respective master plans under their control
he features and findings of the respective regional planing commissions in matters pertaining to the regional
nd state welfare." Did these provisions constitute a
ormula for state interference in local affairs? Did they
nean that the state could "dictate" to cities and counties
hrough a regional planning commission?

Opposition to a District

Representatives of Contra Costa County were particularly
ubious about the proposed regional planning district.
Under this act you people [the State Planning Board] . . .
ave the right to implant your ideas on our own master
lans [*sic*] for Contra Costa County," the district attorney
f the county declared. "I think Contra Costa County
eels, as do all bay counties, that one cohesive system of
lanning for the entire Bay Area would be a splendid
hing. We are a little bit surprised, however, to be per-
ectly frank with you, to find that you have these powers. . . .

"We'd like to see you act as a group and make sugges-
ions to us, but we don't like to feel that if we take a part
n this thing, we have to take your suggestions."[3]

Somewhat in vain did officials of the state board at-
empt to explain that the intent of the authors of the
lanning act was simply to make sure that city and county
lanning commissions did not prepare plans in ignorance
f state and federal plans. A member of the Contra Costa

County Board of Supervisors still objected to the "rather
broad sentence" about implanting state plans on regional,
county, and city plans.[4]

A member of the Santa Clara County Planning Commission expressed fear that the establishment of a regional
planning district might be a step toward consolidation of
counties. Not that he was necessarily opposed to county
consolidation, but he disliked having it "forced by pressure from the state."[5]

A member of the San Jose City Planning Commission
observed that the state law provided only for representation of counties on a regional planning commission and
that cities were "left out in the cold."[6] Like other city
planning commissioners present, he was well aware that
the overwhelming majority of people in the Bay Area
lived in municipalities, and he was not converted to the
idea of regional planning by a county-dominated body
when a member of the state legislature assured him that
cities would have "indirect representation" through the
counties.

Although many participants in the discussion endorsed
the idea of regional planning and praised the State Planning Board for its desire to encourage over-all planning in
the Bay Area, a good many of the city and county officials
attending the hearing remained lukewarm about state
designation of a regional planning district. L. Deming
Tilton, administrative officer of the board, was frankly
irked by what he termed "an effort . . . to develop and
emphasize all the negative aspects of the planning act of
California";[7] but what he and some members of the
board interpreted as undue suspicion of the motives of
the state body was to a degree a manifestation of the vigor
of local democratic self-government. Again and again the
local communities of the Bay Area have demonstrated
their desire to maintain their identity, to make policies for
themselves, and to be free from standardized and sometimes arbitrary programs imposed by the state and federal
governments. In this desire to be as self-reliant as possible,
local communities have, to be sure, occasionally displayed
gross misunderstanding of beneficial policies formed by
higher levels of government. To members of the State
Planning Board the spokesman for some of the bay cities
and counties appeared to be unreasonably skeptical of the
proposal to create a regional planning district; but distrust of government-from-a-distance runs deep in the
American mind, and impatience with this attitude rarely
accomplishes anything. There were three good reasons
why the response to the State Planning Board's proposal
was somewhat negative. The cities and counties themselves had not initiated the move for a planning district;
they had not had sufficient experience with planning to be

sure of their own rights and responsbilities; and the state act did exclude cities from direct participation in regional planning. The members of the State Planning Board and its professional employees could not ignore these obvious facts. As soon as they faced them, they were able to formulate another approach to the problem of organizing the Bay Area for coöperative planning.

A "Voluntary" Organization

On December 8, 1941, the day after the surprise Japanese attack on Pearl Harbor, the State Planning Board suggested the formation of a temporary, advisory Regional Development Council "to investigate and report upon the resources and needs of the region and the benefits to be gained by a broader type of cooperative public planning."[8] Not only would the counties of the Bay Area be represented on this body by a member from each county board of supervisors and a member of each county planning commission; each city would also be represented either by its mayor or a member of its city council and by a member of its city planning commission. The State Planning Board stressed that participation in the proposed council would be "voluntary."

The board announced that it would seek nominations for the Regional Development Council and would call the members together for organization and election of officers. "The approval of a work program and subsequent management of its affairs will be the responsibility of the officers and members of the Council," the board stated, but it then went on to outline what it expected the new organization to do. It proposed the formation of three subregional councils, North Bay, East Bay, and Peninsula, to study major problems created by the war, as well as problems associated with postwar readjustment. It hoped that at the end of a trial period of one year the subregional councils would submit reports to the Regional Development Council, so that the council might evaluate the experience and accomplishments of the unofficial planning effort and prepare a final report for the State Planning Board. In this summary report the board expected to receive recommendations concerning "(1) the desirability of proceeding with a permanent, official San Francisco Bay Regional Planning District as provided by law, (2) boundaries of such district, if one be approved, and (3) changes in the Planning Act deemed necessary or desirable to facilitate regional planning."[9]

Without wishing to appear to be motivating a regional planning movement, the board still was in the awkward position of trying to provide the directional force for such a movement. Its new proposal showed, however, that it was endeavoring to apply the lessons learned from two

discouraging earlier hearings on the establishment of a regional planning district. In recognition of the important role of the cities in area-wide planning, the board now was anxious to accord each city, even the smallest, representation in the Regional Development Council. But the unincorporated area of a county was to have no more representation than, say, a city of five thousand population; and if even a fourth of the cities in the Bay Area participated in the new organization, they would completely dominate it, perhaps to the dissatisfaction of the members representing the counties. Truly, the issue of proper representation in a regional body was a thorny one.

When, on April 11, 1942, Charles O. Busick, Jr., vice-chairman of the California State Planning Board, called to order those who had assembled at the Claremont Hotel in Berkeley to organize the San Francisco Bay Regional Development Council, it was clear that metropolitan regional planning had little support. Only twenty-eight persons representing the cities and counties of the Bay Area attended, and few of these were city councilmen and county supervisors. The meeting was in the main a convocation of the "faithful"—the planning commissioners and staff members who could usually be counted on to assist in any effort toward area-wide planning. Such a beginning augured ill for the success of the council, for that body could accomplish nothing significant without the help of city councils and county boards of supervisors.

More Ships, More Guns!

The hopeful few who believed that ways could be found to overcome community rivalries, to exorcise suspicion of the State Planning Board, to revise the local planning enabling act, and to demonstrate the practicability of intercommunity coöperation in planning were like men carrying torches in a night of raging winds. As World War II spread ever wider, the cry for more tanks, more planes, more ships, more fighting men rose to a pitch of desperation. Get more labor, build more housing, blast away the bottlenecks, keep the machines running and the trains moving, never mind the future, plan for today— or there won't be any future for free peoples!

From the Ozarks, from the plantations of Louisiana, from the farmlands and small towns of Iowa, Minnesota, and Missouri, from all parts of the United States war workers poured into the Bay Area. Nearly half of them were young people between the ages of fifteen and thirty-four. Of those from the South, a large proportion were Negroes. Men who had never operated a rivet gun and women who had never handled an acetylene burner came in such numbers that by May, 1942, the population of the Bay Area was estimated to be one hundred and thirty thousand more than in April, 1940; but the newcomers were only the vanguard of an influx that was to swell the civilian population of the area at least half a million before the war ended.

Between June, 1941, and June, 1942, the number of wage earners employed in Bay Area industrial plants rose from 101,000 to 174,000. Six months later, in January, 1943, more than a quarter of a million production workers were employed in manufacturing establishments of the "San Francisco Bay industrial area," which included only five of the Bay Area counties—San Francisco, San Mateo, Alameda, Contra Costa, and Marin. By April, 1943, the number had risen to 269,700, of which 221,600 were in industries producing durable goods, chiefly the shipbuilding industry and allied industries.[10]

The Bay Area was now so overcrowded, its peacetime patterns of economic activities and daily living were so thoroughly disrupted, and its local governmental services were so strained—overwhelmed by the demands of populations which, in some localities, were three, four, or five times as great as in 1940—that it presented a picture of the greatest confusion. The situation was somewhat comparable to the sudden dispersion of population at the time of the great Fire in San Francisco in 1906, when communities in Marin County, San Mateo County, and in the East Bay from Hayward to Vallejo overnight found themselves responsible for the care of thousands of homeless refugees, many of whom never returned to San Francisco to live. San Francisco during World War II was not a city hit by disaster, and it did absorb new population almost to the saturation point; but because most of the plants engaged in war production were distributed over a wide area outside the metropolis, many of them also outside the Oakland-Alameda-Emeryville industrial complex, the war had the effect of sending waves of newcomers into outlying areas. This was largely a matter of geography—of the role nature had destined the Bay Area to play in a global war in which tanks, men, and supplies had to be transported across vast oceans. Shipyards had to be at deep water or on dredged channels providing ready access to deep water. Of the most advantageous locations for shipbuilding, four were on the fringes of the main urban areas: at Vallejo, Richmond, Sausalito, and South San Francisco, all small communities wholly unprepared at the beginning of the war for the hordes of war workers who descended upon them. Even in peacetime it would have been difficult to provide quickly thousands of new housing units in these less well developed territories, to expand transit services to serve them, to organize and accommodate new commercial, educational, recreational, and health services, to install sewers and build sewage

treatment plants, and to recruit additional policemen, firemen, sanitarians, and garbage collectors. In wartime, with private building curtailed, with new transit equipment unavailable and existing equipment breaking down from overuse, with municipal employees being drafted or being lured to war industries by higher wages, conditions in the new population centers were practically chaotic. But the chaos in these war-swollen communities reflected the disorganization and lack of coördination in the entire metropolitan region. By the spring of 1943 the congestion and disorder had become so great as to threaten to delay proper prosecution of the war.

Congressional Investigation

In mid-April a subcommittee of the House Committee on Naval Affairs opened hearings in San Francisco for the purpose of learning just how bad the situation was and discovering, if possible, what Congress might do to improve matters. Startling testimony came from officials of the cities which had been more severely dislocated by the war effort than any others in the Bay Area—Vallejo and Richmond. Mayor John Stewart of Vallejo estimated that the population of Greater Vallejo was "close to" 100,000, two-thirds of whom lived outside the city limits. Three years earlier the population of Vallejo itself had been 20,027, and that of Vallejo Township outside the city limits had been 9,991, or a total of 30,018. At that time the Mare Island Navy Yard had employed less than 5,000 workers; now it employed 40,000, and would hire more workers if housing could be provided for them. Not only was practically every older dwelling, empty store, and dilapidated shack occupied; 25,000 people were living in new dormitories and temporary housing projects erected by the federal government. One project, Chabot Terrace, four miles north of Vallejo, consisted of three thousand units and was a city in itself; yet it had no public schools, even though applications for needed school buildings had been made at the time the project was first promoted. More than 4,000 people were living in private trailers, under conditions that were a constant source of worry to health authorities.

Far more serious than any complaints city and county officials made about inadequate finances and the difficulty of providing community facilities were the complaints of Navy Yard officials about the high rate of absenteeism, especially among workers who traveled excessive distances to and from work. Fourteen thousand of the men and women employed at Mare Island traveled three, four, or five hours a day to and from work. Navy buses, operated by the Pacific Greyhound Lines, brought them from points as far away as Healdsburg (sixty miles), Calistoga

Aerial View of Chabot Terrace, Housing Project for War Workers, Vallejo.
Photograph by Gardner, courtesy of Vallejo Chamber of Commerce.

(forty-one miles), Hayward (forty-one miles), Woodland (fifty-five miles), and South San Francisco (forty-four miles). Thousands of others rode to and from work in private automobiles, some of them traveling distances as great as those covered by the Navy buses. Twelve or thirteen hours of their day being consumed by work and travel, workers had little time for proper rest, family life, recreation, shopping, and community life—and rather than break under the strain, they took time off whenever they felt they had to. This costly but understandable absenteeism, together with the unceasing induction of skilled workers, taxed the administrative ability of Navy Yard officials to continue production on schedule.

Richmond, a War Casualty

Richmond, a city of 23,642 in 1940, had a population in April, 1943, variously estimated at 100,000 to 110,000. Exclusive of the four government-owned, Kaiser-operated

shipyards, the city boasted fifty-five major war industries, producing gasoline, jeeps, tanks, troop cars, munitions, and dozens of other essentials of war. Employment in the city had risen from less than 15,000 persons in January, 1941, to more than 130,000. Congressman E. V. M. Izac, Chairman of the investigating subcommittee, observed that if all the people working in Richmond were brought there with their families, the population of the city would be half a million.[11]

To provide housing for the newcomers, private contractors had built 4,557 houses, the Richmond Chamber of Commerce and local real-estate organizations had persuaded home owners to rent a total of 4,800 rooms, and the Richmond Housing Authority and the Maritime Commission had built 21,000 units. Dormitory accommodations for four thousand single men were planned. But in spite of all efforts to solve the housing problem, workers were sleeping in shifts in "hot beds," and in unncorporated areas outside the city limits they were living, s former sheriff John A. Miller said, "in trailers, tents, in houses, cardboard shacks, glass houses, barns, garages, 1 automobiles, in theaters, or just in fenced off corners vith the stars for a roof."12

Community facilities were totally inadequate. The chief f the fire department testified that there was no fire tation within approximately a mile of any of the four hipyards; yet within that area were thousands of the vooden temporary housing units.13 Schools designed to ccommodate gradually expanding enrollments during he next ten years were operating double or even triple essions, with sixty children to a classroom at every session. In local hospitals the patients were sleeping on floors nd in hallways. Roads expected to last scores of years vere disintegrating under the impact of heavy trucking. A city jail built to accommodate eight prisoners was inolerably overcrowded with thirty-five, and at times with s many as sixty. People stood in line to get into stores, ecause commercial facilities hadn't kept pace with the opulation increase. As at Vallejo, overloaded outfall ewers discharged raw sewage onto tidal flats close inhore, creating a potential health menace.

The transportation problem of Richmond workers was nly a little less critical than that of workers in the allejo-Benicia area. Since shipyards and many other war industries were operating twenty-four hours a day, jammed buses, trains, and automobiles arrived and departed three times daily. The Maritime Commission had pressed into service large double-ended ferryboats, which operated from San Francisco direct to the shipyards, and harassed transportation officers of the Twelfth Naval District recommended that much more extensive use be made of water transportation. Basically the problem was a shortage of transportation equipment, both rail and bus, and the lack of a unified transit system serving the entire metropolitan region. The importation of old elevated-railway cars from New York and the inauguration of the Richmond Shipyard Railway along San Pablo Avenue from Fortieth Street in Oakland to Richmond some months after the subcommittee held its hearings afforded only partial relief of the transportation problem. Trains and buses were still overloaded, and many workers had to allow more than a reasonable length of time to get to work, because train after train, crammed from front to rear, might pass them by before they could get aboard one.

So spectacular was the impact of the war upon Richmond that many tended to overlook the fact that other communities in Contra Costa County also were struggling with manpower, housing, and transportation problems—and managing to set production records in spite of bottlenecks. The population of the county as a whole had risen

Temporary Housing for Shipyard Workers, Richmond. These structures, intended nly for wartime use, were occupied for several years after the war and were finally cated and torn down in 1956. Photograph courtesy of Housing Authority of the ity of Richmond.

The Shipyard Railway, Oakland to Richmond, During World War II. This tempo-rary line used old elevated-railway cars from New York City. Photograph courtesy of Richmond Public Library.

from one hundred thousand in 1940 to more than three hundred thousand by April, 1943. Industries of the county were producing 3.5 per cent of all the war products being manufactured in the nation. Three-fourths of all the powder manufactured on the Pacific Coast was being produced in Contra Costa County explosives plants; and seven-tenths of the chemicals being refined in the eleven western states were being processed in this one county. Industrial establishments in Antioch, Pittsburg, Crockett, Selby, Oleum, Rodeo, Hercules, Giant, Nitro, and other points along the county's sixty-eight-mile waterfront were operating like the shipyards on a three-shifts-per-day basis. At Port Chicago, the old lumber importing center founded in 1907 as Bay Point, a new Naval Ammunition Terminal was the shipping point for vast quantities of munitions manufactured in the county. Here, some months after the subcommittee held its hearings, occurred one of the worst home-front disasters of the war when two Liberty ships exploded, killing hundreds.

Marinship and Marin City

Suburban Marin County, which had never attracted a single major industry in its entire history, acquired one in a hurry in the spring of 1942. Near Waldo Point, on Richardson Bay—a location mentioned years earlier as the possible site for a naval base, the W. A. Bechtel Company, a Kaiser subsidiary, laid the first keel in its Marinship yard three months after construction of the yard began. By April, 1943, the working force was close to twenty thousand and the yard had one of the fastest moving ship assembly lines in the country. In front of the ways, waiting to be lifted into position, were piled dozens of prefabricated sections of ships—bulkheads, ship sides, splinter shields for guns, and even afterpeaks, or stern sections.

Near by, to the west of the state highway, rose a brand new community for six thousand shipyard workers—Marin City. Although Marin County residents, who have enerally been exceptionally appreciative of the scenic eauties of their environment, deplored the selection of ne of their most beautiful meadows and the surrounding ills as the site for this war housing project, they conceded hat it was outstanding among war born developments, oth in site planning and in community facilities. It included seven hundred apartments in single-story, eightamily buildings and eight hundred units in demountable uplexes and single houses, all of redwood and all so arefully related to the contours of the irregular site as to reate an aesthetically satisfying whole. In a horseshoehaped valley one mile north of the main development tood eleven dormitory buildings, accommodating twelve undred men without families. In addition to its housing nits and dormitories, the project had a nursery school for mall children of working mothers, an elementary school, n auditorium designed to be used as a church on Sunays, playgrounds, a cafeteria and coffee shop, a library naintained by the county, and a post office. But it was ome months before adequate shopping facilities were vailable. When completed, these included a meat maret, grocery store, delicatessen, drugstore, shoe-repair hop, a laundry and dry cleaning establishment, a small ariety store, a beauty parlor, a barber shop, and a andy store.

Congressman George J. Bates, of Massachusetts, a member of the subcommittee of the House Naval Affairs Committee, confirmed local opinion that this project was nusual when he said: "We have visited hundreds of war ousing projects in the United States and we have seen one that so ideally meets the requirements of a comunity of war workers as does Marin City. Marin City nd Dormitories have all the essentials that go into the nakeup of a well rounded war housing project. Marin City furnishes sound housing at low cost and it builds up n active community life. It is the best administered and est organized war housing project that I have seen in ur tour of the country."14

Dormitory Metropolis

ince South San Francisco shipyards were relatively close o San Francisco and the larger Peninsula communities, he problem of housing war workers did not assume the ramatic proportions that it did in Vallejo and Richmond, or instance. Several small temporary housing projects vere built in the northern part of San Mateo County, but nost war workers in South San Francisco shipyards and nanufacturing plants utilized existing housing in near-by ommunities.

San Francisco became something of a dormitory meropolis in the war years, providing housing for thousands of workers employed in Oakland, Alameda, Richmond, Sausalito, and South San Francisco shipyards, as well as for military personnel stationed in the Bay Area temporarily or for the duration. The city was also a distraught host to thousands of war visitors—people who came to see someone in the armed services, to bid farewell to men leaving for combat overseas, or to welcome battle-weary soldiers and sailors returning from the Far Pacific. By the time the subcommittee under Congressman Izac arrived in the Bay Area, the population of the city had increased by more than ninety thousand people, and thousands more were expected to arrive every month.

Because of the acute shortage of critical building materials, the Housing Authority of the City and County of San Francisco had been obliged to defer construction of six permanent housing projects. As agent for the federal government, it was building temporary war housing, which required only about 20 per cent as much critical material per dwelling unit as did permanent housing. On the barren hills above Hunters Point and on the slopes around Candlestick Cove, near the San Mateo County boundary, building-trades workers were constructing fifteen hundred dormitory units and four thousand temporary family dwellings—an entirely new community to house some thirty-five thousand people, among whom would be the welders, shipfitters, and mechanics needed at the San Francisco Naval Shipyard at Hunters Point. The yard was then employing two thousand men, and officials expected to increase the working force to ten thousand within a year, and to twenty thousand within two years. Like the temporary housing at Richmond, Vallejo, and elsewhere in the Bay Area, all the units at Hunters Point presumably would be demolished at the end of the war, in accordance with the terms of the "Lanham Act," under which it was being constructed; but most of this housing—frankly substandard—was still in use many years after World War II because of housing shortages and the outbreak of war in Korea.

In San Francisco, as in other overcrowded cities, the National Housing Agency, under which thirteen federal housing agencies had been united in February, 1942, launched, with considerable fanfare, a conversion program intended to ease the critical housing shortage. The NHA estimated that five to ten thousand properties—houses, vacant stores, even warehouses—could be remodeled to increase the dwelling supply in San Francisco; but comparatively few property owners were willing to participate in the program. Housing experts such as Catherine Bauer warned that "the long-term ill effects of conversion may well over-balance the very small addition to the emergency housing supply."15

Problems in a Blighted Area

Some of the worst overcrowding in San Francisco occurred in the already deteriorated Western Addition. "Particularly is this true of the old Japanese district . . . into which the majority of our increased colored population has moved," Dr. J. C. Geiger, then Director of the San Francisco Department of Public Health, told the subcommittee of the House Naval Affairs Committee. "These people have occupied stores, rear porches, in fact practically any space available in this area. Occupancy consists of everything from single persons to married couples with four and five children. Some of the premises so occupied are lacking in proper light, ventilation, plumbing, and cubic area. Many of these units were previously considered substandard, and the individuals now occupying them have certainly not added to the desirability of the dwellings. Careless housekeeping and generally insanitary conditions prevail. The majority of the individuals housed in this section seem perfectly content with the accommodations and apparently are not interested in obtaining more desirable quarters. They do not seem to have any particular idea as to proper housing facilities nor do they seem interested in the dangers to health through improper ventilation of stoves, gas appliances, and other such household commodities. Careful survey of this area has been undertaken and a definite drive to relieve the congestion and improve housing conditions is well under way."[16]

In all fairness, the health officer might have pointed out that many of the families of whom he was speaking were from particularly poor rural sections of the South, had never lived in cities, were unfamiliar with gas stoves and heating appliances, had had little opportunity for education, and most of them were the products of a social system that resolutely kept them "in their place." Their escape from their former environment was in itself evidence that they desired more of life. In San Francisco they were like immigrants from another continent, squeezed together in an enclave which afforded them, if not decent housing, protection from a world that was really "foreign" to them.

By mid-November, 1943, seven months after the subcommittee hearings, the San Francisco Chamber of Commerce and twenty-nine other groups who were concerned with the housing crisis were determined to discourage any further in-migration. Through new construction, conversions, and the use of every available hotel room the shelter capacity of the city had been increased sufficiently to accommodate approximately 775,000 people, but there were thought to be 800,000 in the city. Many families were "doubling up" with other families. Two months earlier the War Housing Center had turned away 6,000 people who sought housing. For the first time in the history of the city numerous civic groups suggested holding no more conventions, sales promotion meetings, or other events which would attract mass attendance; visitors and sightseers definitely were not wanted.

East Bay Congestion

The city managers of Oakland, Alameda, and Berkeley all told the Congressional subcommittee of acute housing shortages in their cities. Charles R. Schwanenberg, City Manager of Oakland, estimated that his city needed nine thousand additional housing units, the lack of which was causing in-migrant war workers to leave the city.[17] City Manager Don McMillan of Alameda said that the twenty-five hundred units then being completed, the two thousand units scheduled to be built, and an additional two thousand about to be authorized would use almost all the available land in the city, but that the seven shipyards in the city would still be drawing the greater part of their labor force from other areas—men and women who would have to travel to work through the two-lane Posey Tube or across the three narrow bridges spanning the estuary.[18] An additional tube and improved transportation were the most pressing needs of Alameda, he pointed out. City Manager Chester C. Fisk of Berkeley reported that the wartime population influx had eliminated a 5.4 per cent vacancy ratio and had increased the population of the city by approximately twenty-two thousand. Fisk declared that he thought Berkeley should have more allocations and priorities necessary for building FHA housing, but that he was opposed to "a lot of barracks."[19]

All three city managers indicated by their testimony that they realized that some of the conditions with which they were attempting to deal in their particular cities were complicated by area-wide problems. Although thousands of units of temporary war housing were constructed in almost every city except Berkeley, the majority of workers could not find living quarters near their jobs. Consequently, interurban transit lines were so overloaded that McMillan, for one, feared "a complete disintegration of transportation facilities" unless drastic measures were taken to solve the problem of transportation.[20] Wartime conditions, in effect, were emphasizing the value to a metropolitan region of having a comprehensive transit system, just as they were emphasizing the desirability of housing workers, in peacetime as well as in wartime, close to their places of employment, so as to reduce movement and minimize the necessity for an excessive amount of costly rolling stock.

"The lack of adequate and properly coordinated transportation facilities in the San Francisco Bay area is undoubtedly the primary factor in the failure to obtain the highest degree of efficiency from the available labor supply," the subcommittee investigating the progress of the war effort in the Bay Area concluded in its report to Carl Vinson, Chairman of the House Naval Affairs Committee. "This same lack is unquestionably having an adverse effect upon the procurement of the additional migrant labor that is so badly needed. Because of traffic congestion and delays, thousands of workers are forced to put in 12 or 13 hours a day in order to work 8 hours. The peculiar geographical situation in the bay area probably makes the transportation problem more acute than in any other section of the country."[21]

Related Problems

The problems of transportation, housing, and manpower go hand in hand to a large degree, the subcommittee pointed out. Like many city planners, it wished that wasteful crosshauls could be eliminated by "finding the worker employment in the vicinity of his residence";[22] but it made no proposal for reshuffling workers so as to match men and jobs in the same community. Had it suggested anything of the kind, it probably would have been accused of advocating totalitarian methods on the home front. The subcommittee contented itself with stating that "the Office of Defense Transportation should be given full authority and responsibility for handling all phases of transportation, thereby avoiding the confusion and delays which result from divided authority."[23] In this recommendation the investigating group recognized an important principle of metropolitan transit operations—centralized control.

Only one area-wide need had been adequately met, the subcommittee found. "It is indeed fortunate that the available water supply is plentiful to meet the needs of the vastly increased population in the bay area," its report stated.[24] Within some communities and in some outlying areas the extension of water mains was needed, but otherwise the metropolitan region was not faced with an emergency situation. The related problem of sewage disposal had, however, grown worse. "Some expansions have taken place in the trunk sewers and laterals, but the added population has resulted in increased sewerage, and this has brought about a great problem in the pollution of the inland waters of the area," the subcommittee noted.[25]

In view of the marked shortage of essential facilities for the augmented population of the Bay Area and the alarming lack of necessary manpower, the Congressmen recommended that no further war industries be brought into the area.[26] They had found a bewildering number of federal agencies—the Federal Works Agency, the National Housing Agency, the War Manpower Commission, the War Labor Board, the War Production Board, the War Shipping Administration, the Maritime Commission, the Office of Price Administration, the Food Distribution Administration, the Office of Defense Transportation, the Office of Civilian Defense, the Army, the Navy—all working more or less independently and all experiencing frustrating delays in Washington. To complicate the already aggravated situation in the Bay Area by attempting to expand industrial operations "would be not only foolish but disastrous," the subcommittee members believed.[27] What was clearly needed at once was coördination and an end to red tape, locally and in the national capital. The legislators recommended that the Committee for Congested Production Areas, established by executive order just a few days before they opened hearings in San Francisco, immediately appoint an area representative to bring about teamwork among the federal agencies and promote solutions to the problems brought out at the hearings.

Acting on this recommendation, the Committee for Congested Production Areas did designate a coördinator for the Bay Area and conditions did improve somewhat, although the reports of the area representative continued, month after month, to speak of the urgency of further allocations of critical materials for housing, schools, recreation centers, and other community facilities, and of the need for additional Congressional appropriations. By February, 1944, new schools were completed in Richmond, San Pablo, and Vallejo, and in Napa, Sonoma, and Santa Clara counties. Additional child care centers were opened in South San Francisco, Oakland, Pittsburg, Richmond, and San Pablo. A desperately needed general hospital with 250 beds and a 100-bed nurses' home was nearing completion in Vallejo. A sanitary sewage system was finally in operation at the Chabot Terrace housing project in Vallejo, and there was a new sewer for an area of San Pablo inhabited by approximately six thousand people. In two communities in which the rate of juvenile delinquency had skyrocketed, adolescents themselves were managing new teen-age centers, under adult supervision. In short, some of the physical and social needs that regional offices of many of the federal agencies had struggled almost in vain to get Washington to recognize were at long last being met—but only to a small degree. There was no possibility that the cities and towns most drastically affected by the war migration would be able to provide adequate services while the war lasted. What their situation would be after the war they had no idea—

and this was as great a cause for worry as the shortages of housing and classrooms and nurses and doctors.

Victory in Sight

Up to 1944 the Bay Area had received more than four billion dollars in war supply contracts and was first in the United States in contracts for ships. The civilian population of the area had increased an estimated four hundred and fifty thousand since April, 1940, to say nothing of thousands of military personnel stationed permanently or temporarily in the area. Within the same period more than one hundred thousand housing units, public and private, had been constructed, and half as many more were either under construction or programed. And all this extraordinary expansion, greater than anything the area had ever known in a similarly brief period, had been brought about by a war that was well on the way to being won.

At Teheran in late November and early December, 1943, President Roosevelt and Prime Minster Churchill

The Change of Shift at Kaiser Shipyard No. 2, Richmond. Photograph courtesy of the City of Richmond.

d discussed with Premier Stalin their plans for the ening of a second front in western Europe and had set e date for invasion at the end of May or early June, 44. In the meantime, Royal Air Force and American mbers were pulverizing German industrial centers; the ussians, having raised the siege of Leningrad in the rth, in the south were driving the Nazis from Kiev ward the Polish border; while in the Pacific the Amer- n forces, seizing the offensive, were invading the outer fenses of the Japanese Empire in the Gilbert and arshall Islands. In the Bay Area the peak employment war industries had been passed in September, 1943; d though production continued at an unprecedented e, toward the end of 1944 there was already talk of a

shift from construction of "Liberty" ships to construction of "Victory" ships. The time had arrived to talk in earnest of postwar planning.

What would become of all the thousands of war workers who had pulled up stakes and come to the Bay Area to build ships? How many of them would go home after the war? Could the peacetime economy of the area possibly provide jobs for those who remained and for returning veterans of the war? What kinds of jobs? Would a tre- mendous postwar WPA be necessary? Or could private enterprise create most of the new jobs that would be needed?

No one had any glib answers to questions such as these. And everyone remembered the Depression before the war.

CHAPTER SIXTEEN

Postwar Planning

The danger of becoming so completely absorbed in winning the war as to neglect preparations for readjustment to a peacetime economy had been foreseen by President Roosevelt as early as November, 1940, well over a year before the attack on Pearl Harbor. At that time the Chief Executive had requested the National Resources Planning Board to undertake a study of what was then called post-defense planning. This advisory agency, accordingly, had concentrated almost its entire energies on "correlating plans and programs under consideration in many Federal, State, and private organizations for post-war full employment, security, and building America."[1] In particular, it urged state and local governments to plan to assist private industry in the conversion of war plants and the development of new postwar industries; to prepare carefully planned programs, engineering plans, and specifications for needed postwar public works; to enact legislation under which urban redevelopment could be undertaken; and to build up fiscal reserves for postwar work through increased taxation and debt liquidation during the war period.

In the San Francisco Bay Area the national planning agency made its influence felt through the Pacific Southwest regional office in Berkeley, which not only supplied consultants to assist war production centers, such as Richmond and Vallejo, in solving their housing problems but also published detailed analyses of the effect of the war on California and its major metropolitan areas. In a report issued in May, 1943, entitled *After the War—New Jobs in the Pacific Southwest*, the regional office warned of potential postwar employment crises and pointed o[ut] that "neither complete economic planning with regime[n-] tation of all productive enterprise, nor complete absen[ce] of advance planning by both private industry and gover[n-] mental agencies can be relied upon to bring about rea[d-] justments satisfactory to the American people."[2] If, how[-] ever, both industry and government should accept t[he] necessity for gradual relaxation of wartime controls a[nd] should develop plans and programs in their respecti[ve] fields to expedite immediate postwar reëmployment a[nd] to help distribute and sustain employment, then t[he] Pacific Southwest Region (California, Arizona, Nevad[a,] Utah) could create a new peacetime economy in whi[ch] human and natural resources would be used to grea[ter] advantage than ever before.

"The ever widening flow of employment opportuniti[es] stemming from technological progress has enabled t[he] Pacific Southwest to absorb huge population increas[es] decade after decade," the report stated. "By continui[ng] to take advantage of new inventions, new methods [of] production, new types of industrial organization, and n[ew] opportunities for trade and services, the Region can sh[ift] its expanded labor force from full employment for war [to] full employment for peace. After victory a new fronti[er] will be awaiting exploitation—an economic fronti[er] opened by technology."[3]

While the regional office foresaw opportunities for po[st-] war expansion of manufacturing, especially among ind[us-] tries producing consumer goods for the greatly increas[ed] populations of western metropolitan areas, it stressed t[he] possibilities for new jobs in wholesale and retail businesses and in a wide variety of service enterprises. "Even though the post-war volume of manufactured goods may be greatly in excess of pre-war output, continual streamlining of production should eventually reduce the proportion of workers needed in factories," the regional office observed.[4] It therefore predicted a continuation of a long-term trend toward higher percentages of workers in distribution and service activities; and it discussed at length the number of jobs that could be created through development of better medical care, increased recreation facilities, broader educational opportunities, and more adequate social security.

Public Works Planning

Since the National Resources Planning Board expected no small part of the new service employment to stem from the activities of city and county governments, and since it was interested in having these smaller units of government develop a backlog of public works to provide jobs in the event of a postwar unemployment crisis, it made available a staff member from the Berkeley regional office to assist cities and counties with the programing of public health clinics, branch libraries, parks, roads, and other public facilities to be built after the war. The experience of the depression years, during which state and local governments were faced with the necessity of putting men to work on public improvements but lacked plans for worthwhile projects, had not been forgotten; hence the board's suggestion that cities and counties prepare a list of capital expenditures for public works proposed for construction within the six years immediately after the war met with generally favorable response.

San Mateo County was one of the first counties to request the assistance of a public works analyst from the NRPB regional office. A report entitled *A Planned Program for Public Works*, published in June, 1942, served as a model for other governments in the Bay Area in long-range planning of needed facilities. All county departments were requested to submit projects for necessary capital improvements and to indicate the desirable order of their construction. After analyzing social and economic resources of the county, trends of population growth, and past and prospective revenue and disbursements, a joint committee of the San Mateo County Board of Supervisors and the County Planning Commission assembled the projects submitted into a comprehensive program showing which public works would be undertaken each year for a six-year period. The program did not anticipate a commitment of funds beyond the first year's budget, but it did indicate future requirements for public works and

the probable availability of the funds that would be needed. County officials contemplated that the program would be revised each year in the light of changing conditions and needs, and that, after proper approval, the budget of the first year of the revised program would become the capital budget for the next fiscal year. Thus the county hoped to established a continuing, orderly procedure for construction made necessary by population increases and the wearing out of existing facilities.

Perhaps the greatest advantage of capital improvement programing to the county was that it gave the planning commission an opportunity to consider whether proposed projects were in conformity with long-range plans and to recommend appropriations only for those that would contribute to the planned development of the county. At the same time, the entire procedure imposed upon the planning commission a heavy obligation to prepare a sound general plan for the physical development of the county, which could be used to evaluate the actual need for various proposed projects. In thus encouraging legislative bodies to consider long-term growth and to set up a definite means of translating plans into reality, the National Resources Planning Board contributed materially to the improvement of government. Many cities and counties began preparing reports similar to the one issued by San Mateo County, and ever since then they have been scheduling their public works in an orderly fashion that tends to stabilize tax rates.

Accent on Economic Planning

A Congress which believed that the national planning agency had gone too far in advocating a program of national social security similar to the cradle-to-the-grave Beveridge Plan of England abolished the agency in June, 1943, before it was able to demonstrate ways in which it might be helpful to private enterprise in preparing for the postwar transition. The NRPB, nevertheless, had performed a valuable service for both government and private enterprise by emphasizing the importance of planning for full employment after victory. It served as the inspiration for countless postwar planning committees in individual industries and in manufacturing and trade associations, chambers of commerce, and state and local governmental agencies directly concerned with harbors, airports, and similar facilities vital to commerce. Groups of leading citizens appointed by city and county governments to serve as advisory postwar planning committees studied NRPB reports and pamphlets. Almost all these organizations considered their function to be the creation of postwar employment, either directly or indirectly. Economic planning therefore overshadowed physical plan-

$1 MILLION $2 MILLION

	1939			
PAST	1940			
•	1941			
WAR	1942			
•	1943			
PROGRAM	1944			
	1			
	2			
	3			
	4			
	5			
	6			

EACH SYMBOL REPRESENTS $100,000

Postwar Program of Public Works for San Mateo County, 1941. Above: Financial basis for the program. Below: Improvements included in the program.

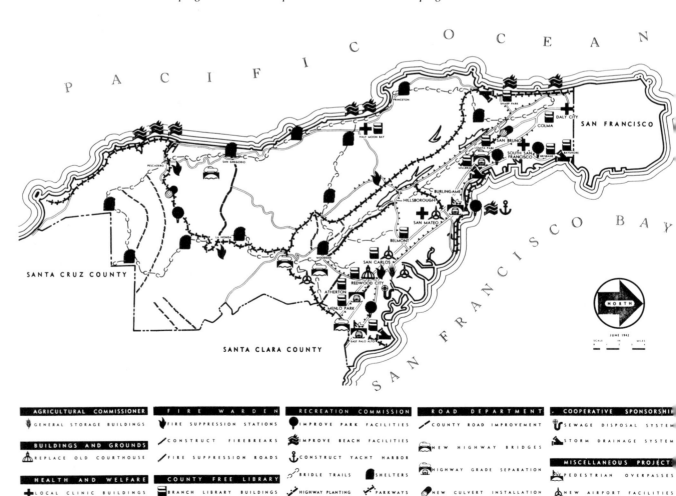

P A C I F I C   O C E A N

SAN FRANCISCO

SANTA CRUZ COUNTY

SAN FRANCISCO BAY

SANTA CLARA COUNTY

NORTH

JUNE 1942

SCALE IN MILES

AGRICULTURAL COMMISSIONER	FIRE WARDEN	RECREATION COMMISSION	ROAD DEPARTMENT	COOPERATIVE SPONSORSHIP
GENERAL STORAGE BUILDINGS	FIRE SUPPRESSION STATIONS	IMPROVE PARK FACILITIES	COUNTY ROAD IMPROVEMENT	SEWAGE DISPOSAL SYSTEM
BUILDINGS AND GROUNDS	CONSTRUCT FIREBREAKS	IMPROVE BEACH FACILITIES	NEW HIGHWAY BRIDGES	STORM DRAINAGE SYSTEM
REPLACE OLD COURTHOUSE	FIRE SUPPRESSION ROADS	CONSTRUCT YACHT HARBOR	HIGHWAY GRADE SEPARATION	MISCELLANEOUS PROJECT
HEALTH AND WELFARE	COUNTY FREE LIBRARY	BRIDLE TRAILS SHELTERS	NEW CULVERT INSTALLATION	PEDESTRIAN OVERPASSES
LOCAL CLINIC BUILDINGS	BRANCH LIBRARY BUILDINGS	HIGHWAY PLANTING PARKWAYS		NEW AIRPORT FACILITIES

ing, and the job-creating potentialities of any proposed project tended to be the measure of its social value. Much that passed for planning was simply industrial promotion unrelated to any considered program for broadening and integrating the state and metropolitan regional economies; and at the lowest level of "planning," chambers of commerce prepared "work pile" plans by gathering information from industries and businesses on how much they would spend for remodeling, repairs, construction, and equipment in the first six months after victory—ignoring the fact that the availability of materials, government controls, and many other factors actually would determine how much remodeling and reëquipping business could undertake.

One consequence of the emphasis on postwar full employment was that the state legislature, never too friendly to the California State Planning Board, abolished it at the same time that Congress did away with the National Resources Planning Board. Even though the state board had operated in the field of economic planning to the extent of collaborating with the Berkeley regional office of the NRPB on economic and industrial surveys of the Los Angeles Area and the San Francisco Bay Area, and even though it had obtained some twenty-eight hundred prospectuses for postwar construction projects from various state agencies that had been asked to study their construction needs for the coming decade, it was accused of being impractical, visionary, and ineffective—the usual charges brought against agencies that must take the long view. A hostile legislature replaced it with a Reconstruction and Reemployment Commission with broad powers "to prevent unemployment, conserve and develop the natural, social and economic resources of the State, promote development of new industries, create new markets, promote the reemployment of discharged service men and readjustment of displaced war workers, and the conversion of industry and commerce from war to peace standards, to provide for postwar readjustment and reconstruction, and to encourage economic and social improvement of the general public."[5]

The New Agency in Action

Under its legislative mandate the new commission could do anything that the State Planning Board had done, but it was obvious that the legislature intended it to stress industrial expansion and the planning of public works. The appointment of a San Francisco businessman, Alexander R. Heron, as director of the agency tended to confirm the impression that it would focus its efforts on stimulating postwar planning by private enterprise and only incidentally would attempt to strengthen physical planning as a function of city and county governments.

The commission sought metropolitan regional coöperation, but of the sort that chambers of commerce and other business groups had sought from time to time in the past fifteen years. This became clear when the state agency held a public hearing on postwar problems of the San Francisco Bay Area in the chamber of the Oakland City Council on August 23 and 24, 1944. Of forty spokesmen who testified before the commission, only a few were public officials, and of these public officials, only three or four were city and county planners. The majority who offered their views on the future of the Bay Area were merchants, industrialists, bankers, executives of utility companies, real-estate developers, and officers of shipping companies, airlines, chambers of commerce, and unions.

The hearing began with a talk by Assemblyman Gardiner Johnson, vice-chairman of the State Assembly Committee on Postwar Rehabilitation, on the distorted labor pattern created by the war and on the threat of postwar unemployment that might "dwarf the last depression."[6] A speaker who followed him presented a survey indicating that three-fourths of the wartime newcomers to the Bay Area hoped to remain after the war. Then came suggestions from various prominent persons for meeting the need for new jobs. They ranged from proposals for old-fashioned industrial ballyhoo, such as Santa Clara County was then indulging in, to proposals for a wide variety of public works, including a new bridge parallel to the San Francisco–Oakland Bay Bridge. State Senator Arthur H. Breed, Jr., vice-chairman of the Senate Postwar Reconstruction Committee, expressed the general sentiment at the hearing when he remarked, "Industry can do the job—but government must step into the gaps."[7] The "gaps," however, appeared to be larger than some might have supposed. They were, indeed, of metropolitan regional dimensions, for the testimony of various speakers brought out the need for solution of the area-wide sewage disposal problem, redevelopment of blighted neighborhoods and areas filled with temporary war housing, development of additional regional parks, provision of schools for all the new residential tracts envisioned after the war, establishment of many new airports, improvement of ports and terminals, reclamation of tidelands, construction of new highways and freeways, and development of an area-wide mass transit system. Clearly, without the action of city and county governments, or of the state and federal governments, on almost every phase of regional physical development, private enterprise could not create a healthy postwar economy in the Bay Area. Area-wide planning of the kind desired by city and county planners was needed, but how was it to be achieved? The hearing in Oakland provided no definite answer to this question. In fact, no one even raised the question.

As Heron and the Reconstruction and Reemployment Commission had hoped, the outcome of the hearing was the appointment of a committee to organize a "San Francisco Bay Region Council," which would stress united effort among Bay Area communities and business firms. Frank N. Belgrano, Jr., president of the Central Bank of Oakland, was named chairman of the committee and R. E. Fisher, vice-president of the Pacific Gas and Electric Company, was selected as vice-chairman. Members of the staff of the state agency were assigned to assist in completing the organization.

A Bay Area Council

The hearing in Oakland had indicated that the Reconstruction and Reemployment Commission was interested primarily in promoting economic development and that it conceived this to be a job for private enterprise, with such public assistance as might be necessary. The group which met in the State Building in San Francisco on December 8, 1944, to form the San Francisco Bay Area Council (then called the Bay Region Council) was therefore composed mainly of businessmen. Mayors of cities and chairmen of county boards of supervisors were decidedly in the minority. No professional planners were present. The organization approved by the gathering was a private organization presumably interested in advancing the well-being of the entire nine-county Bay Area. Heron assured the sixty persons participating in the proceedings that the facilities and staff services of the Reconstruction and Reemployment Commission would be available to the new council "at any time."[8] Funds for the operation of the organization were, however, to be provided by private enterprise.

Bay Area unity was the theme of the organization meeting. R. E. Fisher stressed the importance of avoiding the "mistakes of the past" by enlisting the support of every business, civic, and governmental organization, by "telling a common story to the world," and by giving voice to every community on the bay.[9] Other speakers echoed these sentiments, especially Mayor Roger D. Lapham of San Francisco, who declared that he believed the Bay Area—all nine counties—should be kept in mind at all times, since "it is the Bay Area as a whole that counts."[10] The mayor said that it did not matter whether industry settled on the San Francisco side of the bay or elsewhere in the area, so long as each industry found the most economical place for its own operations. Mayor John F. Slavich of Oakland made a plea for submerging local selfish interests.[11]

Had a new era dawned? Could this new organization serve as the catalytic agent that would change urban jealousies and suspicions into concerted endeavor? Would its membership become sufficiently broad and representative to establish the concept of the multiplicity of cities and counties around the bay as a single great community? Would it work toward some form of metropolitan regional government, particularly to deal with problems clearly of a regional nature? Or would its leaders be satisfied merely with stimulating greater commercial and industrial development?

Until the council had had an opportunity to explore the possibilities for serving the Bay Area, such questions could not be answered. As yet it had only vague objectives and no concrete program. Some of those who took the floor at the initial meeting were anything but vague, however, about certain needs of the area. Significantly, these needs, when considered together, amounted virtually to a program for the physical organization of the nine-county community. R. E. Fisher, for instance, listed seven "major common problems" which he thought deserved the attention of the council.[12] Two of these—the promotion of foreign trade and the correlation of research, information, and advertising—related directly to economic development of the Bay Area; but the other five—increased aviation facilities, transportation in all forms, bridge and highway development, sewage disposal, and public works —had to do with the physical development of the Bay Area. C. D. Lafferty, industrial agent of the Southern Pacific, discussed three main points, two of which— regional highways and the removal of temporary war housing from properties previously available for industrial purposes—were within the sphere of physical planning. E. J. Farina, president of the Contra Costa Development Association, dwelt on the seriousness of intercommunity transportation problems, but without once observing that this was a matter to which city and county planners in the Bay Area already had given considerable study. Mayor Roger D. Lapham, of San Francisco, speaking on public works programs of regional significance, came closer than anyone to advocating area-wide physical planning when he called for regional parks, shoreline improvement in the nine counties, sewage disposal works to end pollution of the bay, a nine-county mass transit system, and unified port development, perhaps under an area-wide authority. Had any professional planners been at the meeting, they might have concluded that the battle for metropolitan regional planning was already half won, because both businessmen and public officials seemed to realize that improving the area physically would aid its economic development. But although e various speakers were talking about elements of a etropolitan regional planning program, not one of them ppeared to be aware of that fact. At least, none specif- lly suggested the need for studying all related physical oblems simultaneously and comprehensively, with the jective of producing a general plan for the entire Bay ea. Had any of them done so, many questions might ve arisen concerning the advisability of having a private ganization develop a plan that could be effectuated ly through actions of the governments of the area. Yet e recognition of numerous physical problems of the Bay ea by the participants in the first meeting of the new uncil showed that there was a good basis for creating derstanding of the need for area-wide planning. The lure of the organizing group to invite a single profes- nal planner to the meeting was evidence, however, that e lines of communication between planners and busi- ss groups were practically nonexistent.

falls and Issues

e San Francisco Bay Area Council deserved careful rutiny as an organization attempting to serve as a uni- ng force in the nine-county area. Before it lay countless portunities to make the people of the area aware of the errelatedness and interdependence of the bay cities and unties. Historically it has been the function of citizen oups to undertake this kind of activity in American etropolitan communities, but the efforts of citizen oups have ever been beset by difficulties. There is always danger that their aims will be either too narrow, cen- ing on the interests of an oligarchic controlling group, so broad and nebulous as to result in a futile dissipa- n of energies. There is the further danger that basic and ghly controversial issues will be side-stepped in the erests of maintaining harmony, and that the organiza- n will consequently become ineffective and lose the pect of numerous influential groups. The problem of ances is inescapable and is twofold: the organization st be sustained over a long period, and contributions st be made by a sufficiently representative number of nors to prevent a few large supporters from acquiring ested interest in it and using it as an instrument for vancing their own policies and programs.

The San Francisco Bay Area Council appeared to have ntified two major tasks that demanded consistent, in- sive effort, aside from the basic task of furthering eptance of the nine-county concept. These were the omotion of economic development and, almost as a ollary, the promotion of area-wide physical planning. first the leaders only vaguely sensed the extent of this ond major responsibility and did not seem to realize

that some day they would have to make an important de- cision: either to initiate an unofficial regional planning program of their own or to seek a wholly public solution of the regional planning problem—a problem which poses questions of public policy. Whichever course they chose, they would be grappling with a fundamental question, by no means theirs alone to answer: How should the San Francisco Bay metropolitan community be organized— both physically *and* politically—so as to satisfy the ma- jority of people who live in it?

Preparations for Peace

Nearly five months after the initial meeting of the Bay Area Council the leading diplomats of the nations fighting Germany and Japan gathered at the War Memorial Opera House in San Francisco to draw up the charter of the United Nations.

Many of the delegates attending sessions at the Opera House in San Francisco valued as a souvenir a handsome publication issued by the San Francisco Bay Area Coun- cil. Written by Oscar Lewis, *Within the Golden Gate* introduced the distinguished visitors to "a large, varied, and uniquely cosmopolitan community," the seven thou- sand-square-mile area surrounding the bay.[13] This book- let was the first effort of the new organization to publicize the concept of unity among the nine counties and sixty-six municipalities then comprising the metropolitan region. It came off the press in as hopeful an atmosphere as pervaded the meetings of the diplomats at the Civic Center; but the problem of welding the numerous com- munities of the Bay Area into something like a metro- politan union promised to be no less formidable than building a world organization from a multiplicity of nations.

The end of the war, now foreseen, did produce unique conditions for growth of the idea of metropolitan coöp- eration. Nearly every city and county in the Bay Area had an official postwar planning committee at work preparing a report on public improvements to be undertaken after victory. Besides the official groups there were numerous postwar committees active in chambers of commerce and civic organizations. Perhaps at no other time in the history of the Bay Area—not even in the days preceding the opening of the Panama Canal—had so much systematic stocktaking been attempted. Not only were purely local problems identified and projects for solving them sug- gested; the various groups assessing community needs became aware of the importance to their own city or county of area-wide highway programs, joint sewage dis- posal projects, and regional parks. Such a scheme as John Reber's San Francisco Bay project, for instance, served

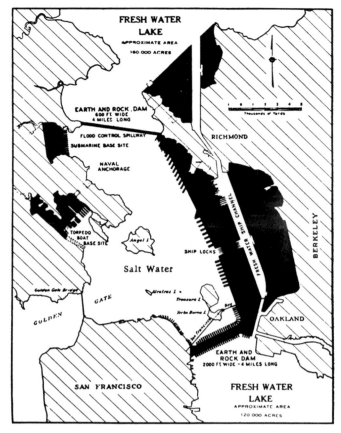

The Reber Plan for Creating Fresh-Water Lakes in San Francisco Bay. Photograph courtesy of John Reber.

to stimulate thinking about future development of the entire bay, even among people who dismissed Reber's proposals as "fantastic" and condemned the Senate of the California Legislature and the San Francisco Board of Supervisors for adopting resolutions recommending governmental study and investigation of the project. Reber's proposal that the south arm of San Francisco Bay and the smaller bays north of Point San Quentin be transformed into fresh-water lakes by construction of earth and rock-fill dikes and that large areas of tidelands be filled for industrial sites, airports, and naval base sites was bold and inclusive enough to provoke responses from communities throughout the Bay Area. Whatever its merits might be, it raised important questions about water supply, national defense, navigation, industrial development, aviation, and regional circulation—questions that were of concern to all the counties and most of the cities. So far as it definitely proposed an area-wide solution of major problems it increased interest in coöperative long-range planning. The Citizens' Postwar Planning Committee appointed by Mayor Lapham of San Francisco

acknowledged that the plan challenged the imaginatior but the members refrained from making any recommer dation concerning it, because it involved other munic palities as well as the state and federal governments. Th very existence of a plan for the entire bay was tonic, fc it promised to evoke other plans and it turned the spo light on the future. The Bay Area found the business c preparing for the postwar period absorbing and in mar ways exhilarating.

A City "Down at the Heels"

The Postwar Planning Committee in San Francisco toc a critical view of the city and reached the conclusion tha San Francisco had "become careless and allowed itse to 'run down at the heels.' " The committee believed tha the situation was "far from hopeless," but could becom "very serious in a surprisingly short time" if the city d not "correct its deficiencies and take advantage of tl opportunities now knocking at its door."[14] Investmen recently made by such nationally known firms as R. I Macy of New York, F. W. Woolworth, Sears Roebuc Western Crown Cork and Seal, Bullock-Magnin, ar Apparel City Corporation (a clothing manufacturing o ganization promoted by the Reconstruction and R employment Commission) impressed the citizen leade as evidence that business had faith in San Francisco, b they recognized that the city needed to demonstrate mo faith in itself. They hoped it would meet the challenge the future by spending a total of $177,454,000 for publ improvements within the next six years and by preparir and following a master plan for the physical developme of the city.

Appointed on April 5, 1945, shortly before the Unit Nations Conference on International Organization, t committee began its work by reviewing a six-year pr gram for planning, land acquisition, and constructi issued by the San Francisco City Planning Commissic This program had been formulated by the commissi from more than 550 projects submitted by all departmer of the city government and by the planning body itself, much the same way that the San Mateo County "shel of postwar public works had been developed in 1942. T official San Francisco program included 277 proje totaling $131,847,294. But the Citizens' Committee p its stamp of approval on many more projects than t planning commission was willing to endorse, and it dicated that they could all be financed through annt budgets, revenue bonds, general bond issues, and fur derived from other sources. In the course of fifteen pub hearings the committee had heard from seventy-one c zens, who had spoken either as representatives of orga zations or as individuals, and it was convinced that San Franciscans were willing to invest large sums to modernize and augment public facilities.

The committee report submitted to Mayor Lapham on August 20, 1945, six days after the Japanese accepted the demand of the Allies for unconditional surrender, reflected the awareness of civic leaders that San Francisco would have to gird itself for increased competition from other metropolitan centers and from other cities within the Bay Area. Because competition among American cities for the aviation industry already was "becoming very, very keen," the committee recommended an investment of $20,000,000 in the San Francisco Airport.[15] In recognition of the fact that San Francisco had traffic and transit problems of the first magnitude, it approved the expenditure of more than $23,000,000 for street railway rehabilitation, $3,000,000 for a study and plans to relieve "the Market Street problem," $17,544,000 for streets and highways, $3,000,000 for off-street parking facilities, $3,200,000 for a tunnel under Russian Hill, and other large sums for viaducts, freeways, and grade separations.

"Unless means are found to move people freely in and out of the City and within the City limits and to provide adequate off-street parking facilities, our community cannot reach its full development, business cannot expand and there is the danger that business normally done in the City will be forced away," the committee warned.[16] It assigned high priorities to recreation, park, and urban redevelopment projects, indicating that the members perhaps had studied carefully a recent report in which the City Planning Commission had urged "generous provision for local parks, school sites, and playgrounds"[17] as one means of offsetting the movement to suburban areas—a major cause for alarm in the metropolis before the war.

Highly significant was a statement about city planning: "From the outset the Committee recognized the necessity of a Master Plan to guide the future development of the City, and of weighing the many plans for postwar construction in their relation to such a plan. It rejected the idea of approving individual projects as such and instead considered their relative importance to the over-all needs

The Broadway Tunnel Through Russian Hill, San Francisco, 1953. One of the projects included in the postwar planning program formulated with the help of a citizens' advisory committee. Photograph courtesy of San Francisco Department of Public Works.

With all available land in urban use, the proportion of dwellings of each type and the densities of
population in each type of dwelling are influenced by the increasing requirements of non-residence uses

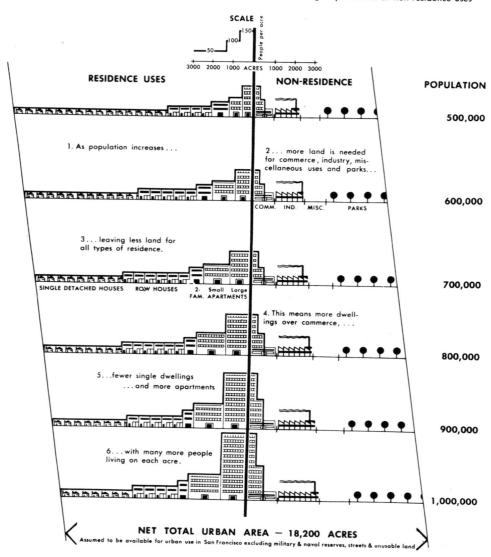

Chart Showing How Increases
in Population Affect the Use of
Land in San Francisco. From a
report of the San Francisco City
Planning Commission, 1945.

of the City. It believes that the programs of all City Departments should be better interrelated than has been the practice in the past, and that they should be coordinated with the Master Plan. All programs and plans should be subject to constant reexamination and expansion as the needs of a growing city dictate."[18]

Future Uses of the Land

As yet San Francisco really had no master plan, although the planning commission was making progress toward one. In November, 1944, it had issued a report entitled *Present and Future Uses of the Land*, analyzing the distribution of population in the city and the amounts of land used for every public and private purpose. This report, containing data needed for the preparation of a master plan, presented a fundamental issue for the people of San Francisco to decide:

"The real problem is to find out how many people the city can comfortably house, without so reducing living space as to drive out those whose work requires daily movement to the centers of business or industry. With such a maximum established, the emphasis could be upon constructive measures to increase the attractiveness and stability of neighborhoods, the elimination of substandard development, and the improvement of interurban transportation facilities. Improvements in regional transportation would make the city's cultural, business and industrial facilities more accessible to the population of the surrounding area.

"In this way, the selected maximum would be almost sure to be reached, and would tend to contain a larger proportion of permanent residents, actively identified with the city's true functions. Good homes, good schools and playgrounds, with safe and easy access to places of employment will attract the type of family which is an economic asset. But the pursuit of numbers alone may lead to serious problems of unemployment and relief.

"The decision to be made, therefore, is whether to aim at a somewhat greater population than we now have, with full understanding of the effect upon the average density on residence land, or to aim at a lower average density without loss of population by encouraging the full use of areas now undeveloped. In either case, emphasis will be upon securing better arrangement of land uses, and a more even distribution of population through the establishment of more careful building and zoning regulations, including provisions for control of density in terms of rooms per acre and percentage of site covered.

"At the same time the most congested areas would need to be redeveloped in accordance with modern methods of design. By the use of the latter, densities of population in certain close-in areas might be even higher than at present, but with far better living conditions because of improvements in the plans and in the relationship between building bulk and open spaces."[19]

The idea that a city can establish a population limit and institute policies to attain and not exceed that limit is inherent in all planning and zoning. But seldom have American cities faced the issue of controlling population growth and striving for desirable population densities and a physical environment of generally high quality. Rather, they have accepted a continuing increase in population as inevitable, however unpleasant the attendant crowding might become. Even the suggestion that a ceiling might be set on population growth is generally regarded as contrary to the laws of nature and economics, as basically un-American, or at the very least as totally impractical and unworkable. Yet any city that is serious about making life healthful, safe, convenient, and comfortable for its citizens through city planning must determine limits of population density in various areas and must maintain these limits. That means that unless the city can annex more land for expansion, it must consciously reject growth beyond a certain maximum.

San Francisco, a city with a fixed area, may have doubted in 1940 that it needed to take the trouble to establish a population maximum, for the census returns seemed to suggest that it was standing still. The growth of the city during the war encouraged the belief, however, that it would retain much of the population it had gained during the war and would perhaps slowly make additional gains as the Bay Area attracted more people. In order to determine the maximum population that would be desirable for the city, it would be necessary to analyze its economic prospects realistically and to envision what functions it could continue to perform in its central position among Bay Area communities, because its population prospects would be directly related to the economic activities that it could successfully maintain. The staff of the City Planning Commission, members of the Citizens' Postwar Planning Committee, and many others realized that San Francisco would be affected by the growth of population, industry, and trade in outlying areas and that it would be obliged to rely heavily upon certain administrative, service, cultural, and other functions in which it could excel other cities. What these functions were was not then entirely clear. Without a doubt, though, no other city in the nine counties around the bay would henceforth be so sensitive to regional influences as this one. Its planning problems really could be solved only in relation to those of all the cities and counties in the area. The Postwar Planning Committee failed to say this when it supported the preparation of a master plan; and one of the greatest dangers to the city was that other civic groups also might not recongize that for San Francisco, area-wide planning was practically a matter of economic survival. The metropolis felt that it must assert leadership in a new movement for metropolitan regional planning even though it risked the accusation, heard many times before, that it was seeking to dominate other cities.

A Program for Oakland

Across the bay in Oakland a postwar planning committee appointed by Mayor Slavich on March 2, 1943, submitted "a sound and conservative plan" for the future to the city council in September, 1945. Of sixteen recommendations included in the report, the last, "that the City Planning Commission, in cooperation with the Alameda County Planning Commission, should be the agency to coordinate and develop this entire program," was the most arresting.[20] It was evidence that, over the years, responsible citizens had come to value city planning as the most effective means of insuring a well-organized city, even though Oakland did not yet have a general plan to guide its future growth and development. The Postwar Planning Committee expected a "period of exceptional construction activity" in the years ahead and recommended "that the Oakland City Planning Commission be

urged to develop a 'master plan' for residential development throughout the Oakland Area, giving study to ALL
factors important to a sound program including future
residential developments, industrial areas, downtown
business center, retail trade areas, schools, utilities, sewage disposal, storm water disposal, transportation, etc.'[21]
From the committee's description of "a 'master plan' for
residential development" it was apparent that the members actually meant a long-range, comprehensive, general
plan for Oakland and its environs. Other suggestions
made by the committee were that the Oakland Real Estate
Board, the Chamber of Commerce, the Oakland Housing
Authority, the Board of Port Commissioners, and the
Pacific Gas and Electric Company coöperate in a survey
of the housing requirements of the Oakland Area. In all
these recommendations the committee recognized the
leadership the planning commission could exercise in
seeking a high quality of development.

Like other governments in the Bay Area, the Oakland
city government had made an inventory of its future
needs and had compiled a long list of projects. Since the
capital outlay for the 464 improvements submitted by
various departments would be $181,219,111, the city con-
templated construction over a period of six years or more.
The voters already had approved some of the most urgently needed projects, however, at a special bond election
on May 8, 1945, and were looking forward to street improvements costing $4,590,000; long-overdue storm and
sanitary sewers, $5,311,000; swimming pools and play-
grounds, $1,023,000; a hall of justice, $2,707,000; and a
new main library and four branches, $1,763,000. Other
expenditures foreseen would be for public schools, further
port development, expansion of the Oakland Airport,
additional parks and playgrounds, streets, and police and
fire stations.

The Public Voice in Berkeley

In neighboring Berkeley the postwar report submitted by
City Manager Gerrit Vander Ende to the city council
in September, 1945, was unusual in that it included recommendations of the Public Administration Service, a
Citizens' Postwar Advisory Committee, the Junior Chamber of Commerce, the Berkeley Art Association, and
improvement clubs. Already before the council were a
long-range recreation plan and a street and highway survey by Ronald Campbell, a planning consultant. From
the numerous suggestions received, the city manager
selected and recommended to the city council an immediate program totaling $2,690,595—a modest total which
reflected the interest of the Citizens' Postwar Advisory
Committee in a program that could be "financed by the

city" and would not require its officials to "wait with
outstretched and suppliant palms for either the federal or
state government to dole out subsidies or financial
grants."[22] Laudable as might be the committee's desire
for civic self-reliance, it had taken an extremely narrow
view of community needs and had said nothing about
long-range civic development, as suggested in the city
council's resolution creating it.

A month later the Berkeley Chamber of Commerce
through its Civic Development Committee, sounded the
progressive note that might have been expected from the
official committee. Referring to Berkeley as "a patchwork
community," the Chamber of Commerce committee
called for a comprehensive planning program and asserted
that "no major development in a city should be made
without study of the relationship of this development to
the whole city."[23] It proposed that a committee of citizens
be formed to "visualize the Berkeley of 1975" and chart
the course for the future in coöperation with the city
government and all other agencies. The report indicated
that Berkeley, too, was ready for a genuine planning program, as were Oakland, San Francisco, and some other
Bay Area cities.

Not by Bread Alone

The postwar problems faced by most cities in the area
were as nothing compared with those confronting smaller
communities which had suddenly become centers of war
production in 1941 and 1942. City officials of Richmond,
one of the most drastically affected by the global struggle,
estimated that just to provide for the kind of services required by any normal peacetime city with a minimum
population of fifty thousand, they would have to spend
$7,000,000 for municipal improvements and $2,000,000
for schools. But Richmond was a city of approximately
one hundred thousand people, and what if half of them
did not depart, now that the war was over and the shipyards were closing down? The bill for new schools,
sewers, streets, highways, recreation centers, and other
needed public facilities might run as high as $18,000,000
if Richmond continued to hold the new population that
it had attracted—and already the tax rate was twice as
high as the rate in many cities. How could Richmond raise
the money to meet the huge backlog of community
needs? And what should it build first?

Other Bay Area cities were frankly surprised by Richmond's answer to these questions. On November 20,
1945, the voters of Richmond approved four to one a
$3,850,000 bond issue for construction of a Memorial
Civic Center to honor Richmond citizens who had fought
and died for their country. Why should a city desperately

ı need of additional classrooms, places for children to ·lay, sanitary sewers, and new paving on its streets first f all construct a new city hall, main library, hall of ıstice, and a civic auditorium?

There were two main reasons for the decision to erect group of public buildings before undertaking other ›rojects. The old city hall was totally inadequate and the ·arious departments of city government were widely cattered in rented quarters, making efficient operation ›f the municipality almost impossible. But aside from the lifficulties experienced daily by city officials and em-›loyees, there seemed to be an urgent need to provide ·ome tangible evidence that the motley assortment of ›eople brought together in Richmond under wartime ·onditions intended to create a new civic life for them-

selves. Civic leaders as well as city officials believed that a well-designed civic center, with adequate space for expansion of departments as the city grew, would serve as a rallying point for civic pride and would convince industrialists, investors, and other communities that Richmond proposed to move steadily forward in the postwar years rather than lose ground and suffer loss of morale. The investment in the new civic center was the city's way of signifying anew that man does not live by bread alone. After the overwhelming vote in favor of the civic center bonds, Richmond citizens felt confident of their ability to solve many of the other problems that pressed upon them. The election was a turning point in the history of the city, just as the vote for park bonds had been in Oakland in 1907.

'he Eastshore Freeway Through the Industrial District of East Oakland. Alameda ınd Bay Farm Island in the distance. Photograph courtesy of State Division of lighways.

Emergence of a New Problem

The many bond issues approved by voters in Bay Area cities, the extensive lists of public projects to be built in years to come, the plans announced by industrial firms for the conversion and expansion of plants and by commercial establishments for repairs and modernizations all indicated the beginning of a period of intense construction activity and widespread growth in the new and hopeful era of peace. The State Division of Highways was prepared to build, stage by stage, the Bayshore and East Shore freeways planned before the war, giving the nine-county area the first major units of an ultimate super-highway network. Progress in the solution of the problem of bay pollution was foreshadowed by work on plans and specifications for new sewers and sewage treatment plants in San Francisco (for which the voters of that city had approved a $12,000,000 bond issue in November, 1944) and by reports and investigations of sewage disposal under way in Special District No. 1 of the East Bay Municipal Utility District, created by the six East Bay cities of Alameda, Albany, Berkeley, Emeryville, Oakland, and Piedmont about the time the voters of San Francisco took action on their sanitation problem. On the statute books of California was a new Community Redevelopment Act, passed by the state legislature to enable cities to establish redevelopment agencies and make plans for clearing, replanning, and rebuilding the blighted areas produced by decades of inadequately controlled growth and development. So much activity by private enterprise and by local, county, state, and federal governments seemed assured that the fear of postwar depression began to recede. Not unemployment but the pace of postwar development promised to be the major problem of the Bay Area.

Once wartime restrictions on building materials were relaxed, once construction machinery and skilled labor again were available for building, and once industrialists could start new plants and developers new suburban tracts, would it be possible to fashion the kind of well-ordered cities and towns envisioned in all the postwar planning committee reports that endorsed city planning? None of the cities had general plans; nor did the counties. There was no legal apparatus in the entire Bay Area for coördinating the planning of a multiplicity of cities, counties, special districts, and the state and federal governments. Metropolitan government was totally lacking. The San Francisco Bay Area, at the start of the most gigantic building boom in its history, seemed pathetically ill-equipped to meet the new peacetime conditions. It did have, however, a new awareness of the importance of planning. From the many poor decisions that citizens and public officials alike seemed sure to make, in time would come an appreciation of the value of shaping local policy for physical development in accordance with broad policies suggested by a continuing, long-range planning program for the entire metropolitan region—and perhaps to be carried out, in the main, by some form of metropolitan government.

CHAPTER SEVENTEEN

The Regional Metropolis

Anyone who flew over the San Francisco Bay Area soon after the end of World War II saw large open spaces between the cities on the San Francisco Peninsula, vast prune orchards and truck gardens in the northern Santa Clara Valley, a few small, sleepy towns amid the farms on the eastern side of the bay south of San Leandro, valleys and plains in eastern Contra Costa County still green with apricot orchards and walnut groves, and in the northern counties mile after mile of dairy lands, vineyards, and field crops surrounding historic towns and villages that had grown very slowly for decades.

The Bay Area had increased in population by perhaps half a million between 1940 and the summer of 1945; yet relatively little land on the peripheries of cities had been utilized to accommodate the new population. The war had left its deposits of temporary housing and hastily built private dwellings mostly in or near urban areas adjacent to deep water, where the shipyards and related industrial establishments were. Elsewhere there had been lack of growth, a weathering of the houses, and neglect in the maintenance of city halls, schools, parks, and street surfaces.

By V-J Day there was an enormous pent-up demand for new homes, new industrial plants, schools, and community centers that was like a flood about to break over the levees. Soon the forces of expansion burst in all directions. The cities started spilling over into the fields and orchards on their outskirts. Even if no more people had moved into the Bay Area in the immediate postwar years, tract houses and shopping centers would have spread over thousands of acres. But newcomers poured into the area from every state in the Union, and a new wave of births also swelled the population. The increase in residents between the end of the war and April, 1950, when the census was taken, was almost as great as it had been during the war. And this unpredicted new growth, which brought the increase in population during the decade to 947,014, still further extended the tide of development that had begun to engulf the open spaces.

Industrial Dispersion

For two or three years after the Japanese surrender the dispersion of industry was a subject of even more newspaper editorials than was residential building, since industrial construction was possible, whereas building materials for houses were for a time in short supply. At the end of 1947 the San Francisco Bay Area Council reported that approximately one-third of a billion dollars had been spent on new industrial plants and expansions in the nine-county metropolitan region since January 1, 1945. Many of the new factories were in the smaller cities, such as San Leandro and Hayward in Alameda County and San Jose and Santa Clara in the Santa Clara Valley. The 1947 Census of Manufactures showed that San Francisco had 182 fewer manufacturing establishments than in 1939, whereas Alameda County during the same period had gained more than 200 establishments and Santa Clara County more than 100. Even San Mateo County, a largely residential area that had a reputation for being "cool" to industry, increased the number of its manufacturing firms from 97 to 228, although only 19 of the concerns employed a hundred workers or more. To describe all this industrial development in outlying areas as "decentralization" would be misleading, because many of the new plants were branches of eastern companies that were appearing on the Bay Area scene for the first time. The industrial boom represented expansion of the Bay Area economy even more than it represented some movement of plants from older centers such as San Francisco and Oakland.

The most spectacular of the new plants constructed in Alameda County were the huge, one-story automobile assembly plants and truck and bus body manufacturing

establishments in and about San Leandro. Near major highways and railroads, these industrial facilities covered many acres, provided spacious parking areas for the automobiles of employees, and presented attractive administrative offices and landscaped grounds to the view of passing motorists. The land the establishments occupied had been planted to truck crops as recently as the war years.

By the spring of 1949 the San Jose Chamber of Commerce listed eighty new industries acquired since 1944. Although many of them were in the food-processing category, a rather large number represented a new trend in the county toward industrial diversification. Branch plants of such industrial giants as General Electric Company, International Minerals and Chemical Company,

Industrial Dispersion: Factories and Wholesale Distribution Warehouses near San Leandro. Photograph courtesy of State Division of Highways.

nternational Business Machines Corporation, Owens-Illinois Glass Company, Owens-Corning Fiberglas Corporation, Pittsburgh–Des Moines Steel Company, and Westinghouse Electric Corporation rose on sites formerly given over to tomatoes or peas or to prunes and apricots.

The conservative agricultural element in Santa Clara County was anything but happy about this industrial invasion. In a foreword to an industrial survey of the county, the San Jose Chamber of Commerce, organizer of the national promotional campaign that had influenced many of these companies to establish western branches, acknowledged that "there were some sincere and intelligent people who looked askance at this industrial development. They had genuine fears that smokestacks would encircle the city'; that 'blighted areas' would spring up in industrial sections; that orchards would be torn up 'by the hundreds'; and that by past standards, this accelerated trend in the establishment of new industry might result in an unbalanced, top-heavy economy destined to collapse at some undetermined time in the future."[1]

The fears that orchards would be torn up by the hundreds were indeed well founded; and smokestacks, though they by no means encircled the city, did undeniably contribute to the development of a new problem. The Chamber sought to assure the skeptical that industrial growth was not incompatible with desirable living conditions. Yet it was not long before the Santa Clara County Board of Supervisors found it necessary to designate the entire county an air pollution control district; the skies over the Santa Clara Valley were becoming a dirty gray. In March, 1950, the county health officer, who also served as county air pollution control officer, declared that "smog," the murky atmospheric condition familiar to Los Angeles, was not only a Santa Clara County problem but also a "Bay Area problem."[2] The new factories in San Jose and Santa Clara were producing air pollutants, and, in addition, industrial smoke and fumes from the San Francisco–Oakland area were being wafted into the county. Sooner or later there would have to be area-wide control of the new menace to the human respiratory tract, the health officer asserted.

Acres of Tract Houses

Air photographs of the San Jose–Santa Clara area and air views of Alameda County published in the promotional literature of the Oakland Chamber of Commerce revealed that the march of industry into agricultural areas had been accompanied every step of the way by mass-produced tract houses. San Lorenzo Village, begun by the David D. Bohannon Organization in 1944 in the area south of San Leandro, was a forerunner of the scores of new "planned communities" of almost identical houses. A whole new town in itself, it housed approximately five thousand people and had its own shopping center, schools, and recreation facilities. In its planning it was, however, superior to many later ventures in large-scale construction of low-cost houses, because the street system at least included service roads paralleling a main highway (which unfortunately sliced through the development) and the interior streets were designed to assure as much safety and convenience as possible.

In many of the other speculative developments built in the immediate postwar years, when returning veterans were taking full advantage of the home-purchasing provisions of legislation enacted during the war, the street layouts were not so carefully planned, and no sites were set aside for needed schools and playgrounds. Some houses faced traffic arteries, and some living-room windows looked toward supermarkets, the handy distribution centers through which the developers assured themselves of long-term returns on the daily expenditures of families in rows and rows of small stucco houses.

In 1949, when columns of the financial pages of newspapers mentioned a "difficult period of change-over from a sellers' to a buyers' market" and a "return to hard-headed competition," the number of building permits issued for family dwelling units in the San Francisco Bay counties exceeded twenty-five thousand. The construction industry seemed immune to the strains being experienced in other segments of the economy. Officials issued permits for nearly fifty-nine hundred units in San Mateo County, for five thousand in Alameda County, for almost as many in Santa Clara County, for thirty-seven hundred in Contra Costa County, for more than a thousand in Marin County, and for more than four thousand in San Francisco, which was fast using up its limited resources of vacant land.

The startling fact about this great volume of building was that a high proportion of it was in unincorporated areas under the jurisdiction of county boards of supervisors, who were suddenly asked to deal with a variety of new problems essentially urban in complexity—problems of police and fire protection, neighborhood and community recreation, library service, sanitation, street lighting, and storm drainage. Most of these were matters that county governments were scarcely equipped to handle. In Alameda County more than two-fifths of the new homes were in unincorporated territory; in Santa Clara County more than one-half were outside the boundaries of municipalities, in Marin County almost two-thirds, and in Contra Costa County more than two-thirds.

In 1950, when the volume of permits issued for family

Tract Houses near the Eastshore Freeway, Sa Lorenzo. Photograph courtesy of State Division o Highways.

dwellings in the Bay Area rose to more than forty thousand, even larger proportions of new units were constructed in the fringe areas of some counties. In Alameda County, for instance, almost one-half were in unincorporated territory; in Contra Costa County, three-fourths.

"Dingbats" and Future Slums

In one of its publications the United States Bureau of Labor Statistics described the typical house built in the San Francisco–Oakland Metropolitan Area in the summer of 1949. It was a one-story, detached structure, had five rooms and approximately a thousand square feet of floor space, and was of frame construction with wood or stucco exterior. It had one bathroom, a one-car garage, and a fireplace in the living room. Usually it was in a large tract developed by an operative builder.

Only about 15 per cent of all houses had more than eleven hundred square feet of floor space, and very few had more than six rooms. Many were what the building fraternity called "dingbats," indifferently designed, put together with the cheapest of materials, and intended for quick sale on the installment plan, with low down payments. The public often referred to them as "the slums of tomorrow."

In certain unincorporated areas in Alameda and Santa Clara counties, and even in some cities in San Mateo County, the builders of these low-cost houses snapped up

acreage which by any reasonable criterion for the appro priate use of land would have been better adapted t industrial use, since it was near railroads and major high ways. Lack of zoning, inappropriate zoning, or change in zoning ordinances made under pressure from deve opers and landowners accounted for these ill-advised an detrimental uses of the land. A consulting engineer ad dressing a committee for the development of light industr in San Mateo County in 1951, after many areas mor suitable for industry than for residences had already bee covered with tract houses, scored city and county govern ments "for permitting encroachment of residential devel opment on industrial fringe areas";[3] but by that time hi complaints were hardly effective.

The situation in San Mateo County, as in other rapidl developing counties, posed a troublesome long-rang problem for planning commissions and civic organiza tions interested in the economic future of the Bay Area How could land that would be needed for industr twenty, thirty, or forty years later be maintained as re serve open space? Zoning alone was not the answer obviously, because city councils and county boards o supervisors sometimes yielded to the pressure for re zoning; and public opinion often supported the land owner who could make more money by selling potentia industrial land for residential development.

There was also, for all cities and counties, the stil

arger problem, seldom acknowledged, of bringing about suitable distribution of industrial areas throughout the metropolitan region. How much dispersion or concentration of industry should be encouraged? And to what kind of metropolitan regional distribution of population and economic activities should any pattern of industrial areas relate? In the early 1950's most people concerned with industrial development scarcely asked such questions, and perhaps they are not asking them even today.

Changing Relationships

The census taken in April, 1950, disclosed how much the dispersion of industry and the rapid construction of peas-in-a-pod housing developments in outlying cities and unincorporated areas had altered the prewar distribution of population in the Bay Area. Although San Francisco gained more than 140,000 people and Oakland more than 2,000 in the 1940's, these two central cities together had only 43 per cent of the population of the nine-county metropolitan region in 1950, whereas ten years earlier they had included 54 per cent of the regional total. The proportions of the Bay Area population living in the relatively unindustrialized counties of Marin, Napa, and Sonoma remained approximately the same; but Contra Costa, San Mateo, Santa Clara, and Solano counties all had larger proportions of the regional population than before. Contra Costa County, the fastest growing county in the Bay Area, had had less than 6 per cent of the regional population in 1940, whereas in 1950 it had more than 11 per cent. Its population had increased from a little more than 100,000 to almost 300,000. The populations of both San Mateo and Solano counties had more than doubled—a gain of 123,877 in the former, and of 5,715 in the latter. In Santa Clara County 115,598 new residents represented a two-thirds increase in population.

All nine counties of the Bay Area together included 681,322 residents, or almost 55 per cent more than in 1940. More than a third of them had arrived on the scene during the decade.

From time to time in 1950 and 1951, as the Bureau of the Census released statistics on the growth of individual cities and counties, newspapers of the Bay Area showed ingenuous pride in whopping percentage gains. The figures confounded the experts. As recently as November, 1947, the Federal Reserve Bank of San Francisco had ventured an admittedly "hazardous" prediction that "the extraordinary expansion of population experienced in the Twelfth District [seven far western states] between 1940 and 1947 has perhaps come to an end and . . . a much more moderate rate of growth is to be expected in the immediate future."[4] All such judgments were proved er-

roneous, and although there was general rejoicing over the continuing influx of newcomers and the tidal wave of births, occasionally some writer sounded a sober note. Said the San Francisco *Chronicle* editorially:

"Growth of this sort means nothing less than social upheaval, and it is the responsibility of broad-visioned planning to mitigate the disruptive effects and to capitalize on the beneficial effects of the California trend. It is obvious that we've got to concern ourselves first and incessantly with the problem of increasing our water and power supply. This is the basic anxiety, not alone in Southern California, dependent as it is on the out-of-State resources of the Colorado River, but also of our own community around the Bay Area, and of the Central Valley.

"With water needs go others—the sound location of industries and control of attending atmospheric pollution; the expansion of highway communications; the building of schools to keep pace with the children; the development of . . . community planning.

"These challenges will be met intelligently or unintelligently, depending upon the awareness of them that Californians display. The plain fact is that we're pioneering again, a hundred years after the gold rush, and we've got to invent new patterns for a State that on some future day will be second to none."[5]

New Aqueducts

The Bay Area, like any boom community, was so busy trying to catch up with itself that efforts to anticipate new long-term needs tended to be thwarted by the demands of the immediate present; yet in meeting the needs of the present and of the "middle future," some public agencies and private companies necessarily provided for the demands of the distant future. Among such organizations were utility districts, municipal water departments, and companies supplying the Bay Area with natural gas and electricity.

Long before the end of World War II the cities on the San Francisco Peninsula and in the East Bay had foreseen that they would have to reach out for more water from the distant sources from which they were already drawing the greater proportion of their supplies. Voters in the East Bay Municipal Utility District approved a $12,000,000 bond issue in November, 1946, to finance the construction of a Second Mokelumne Aqueduct; and a year later the voters of San Francisco authorized a $25,000,000 bond issue for expansion of the San Francisco water system, which also supplies water to most of the municipalities on the Peninsula.

The twin aqueduct placed in service in August, 1949,

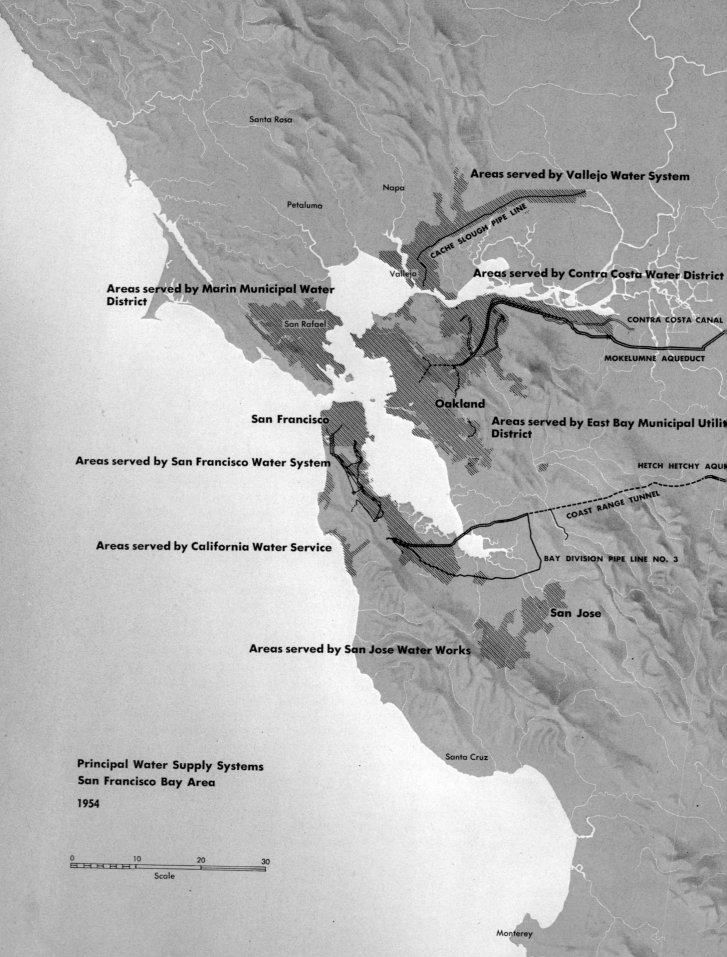

Santa Rosa

Napa

Petaluma

Areas served by Vallejo Water System

CACHE SLOUGH PIPE LINE

Vallejo

Areas served by Contra Costa Water District

Areas served by Marin Municipal Water District

San Rafael

CONTRA COSTA CANAL

MOKELUMNE AQUEDUCT

Oakland

San Francisco

Areas served by East Bay Municipal Utility District

HETCH HETCHY AQU

Areas served by San Francisco Water System

COAST RANGE TUNNEL

Areas served by California Water Service

BAY DIVISION PIPE LINE NO. 3

San Jose

Areas served by San Jose Water Works

**Principal Water Supply Systems
San Francisco Bay Area**

1954

Santa Cruz

0   10   20   30
Scale

Monterey

y the East Bay Municipal Utility District assured the
ast Bay of a daily supply of one hundred million gallons
y gravity flow. By operating pumping plants, the district
ould increase this daily flow through its parallel aque-
ucts to 210,000,000 gallons, or enough to serve approx-
mately twice the number of people then living in the
ities and unincorporated areas within the district.

Although San Francisco had water rights to 400,000,000
allons daily from the Tuolumne River, it had imported
hrough a single pipe line across the San Joaquin Valley
nly 60,000,000 gallons daily during the war and had
tilized local water supplies in San Mateo, Santa Clara,
nd Alameda counties for the rest of its requirements of
pproximately 100,000,000 gallons daily. By 1947 the San
rancisco Public Utilities Commission saw the need for
uilding a second pipe line of equal capacity across the
alley and for constructing a third Bay Division pipe line,
hirty-four miles long, round the southern end of the bay.
A further reason for routing the new Bay Division line in
n arc round the bay was to avoid the possibility that a
ubmarine disturbance might cut off the total supply
rom east of the bay. The bond issue of 1947 provided the
unds for these and other expansions of the San Francisco
ystem.

Laid in 1949 and 1950, the new Bay Division line had a
apacity of 76,000,000 gallons and brought the total
apacity for delivery of water from the mountain and
Alameda systems to the Peninsula reservoirs up to approx-
mately 190,000,000 gallons daily—more than ample for
San Francisco and Peninsula needs for several decades.

In the meantime, in 1948 a drought in California had
aused curtailments in the use of power and had threat-
ned San Francisco with a water shortage. In order to
ulfill its obligations to the Modesto and Turlock Irriga-
ion districts, the city had had to reduce the water stored
n the O'Shaughnessy Reservoir in the Hetch Hetchy
Valley to a dangerously low level. The city saw that it no
onger enjoyed a safe margin of water and power supply.
n fact, engineers had been in the field making surveys and
nvestigations for a dam in the Cherry Valley, some miles
orthwest of O'Shaugnessy Dam, ever since 1940. In
November, 1949, San Francisco voters approved a bond
ssue of $4,000,000 for constructing the new dam; the
ederal government, because of flood control aspects of
he project, was willing to contribute $9,000,000 toward
ts costs. From the reservoir formed by the Cherry Valley
Dam the city would be able to meet the needs of the two
rrigation districts, the water rights of which are protected
nder the Raker Act, and to save for its own use the
waters of O'Shaughnessy Reservoir.

Thus, San Francisco, steadily pursuing the "build-as-

needed" policy (by which it avoided paying interest on
the staggering bond issues that would have been required
to finance a water system built to full capacity in the beginning) moved several steps nearer completion of the
multifeatured Hetch Hetchy system.

More Water for More People

Population growth in other parts of the Bay Area created
the same kind of uneasiness about water supplies as that
felt in the central and more populous areas. In Marin,
Solano, and Santa Clara counties millions of dollars went
into the development of additional sources of supply,
although none of the projects undertaken promised permanent solution of the water problem if population continued to increase in accordance with long-term forecasts.

The Marin Municipal Water District, serving the commuter zone of Marin County from three reservoirs developed between 1887 and 1918, built the Bon Tempe Dam
in 1948 and immediately started planning another dam
on Lagunitas Creek that would impound more water than
all the other reservoirs in the district together. This fifth
reservoir, created in 1954 upon completion of the James
S. Peters Dam, stored the runoff from a watershed of
approximately ten square miles. Other local watersheds
remained to be utilized, but by 1957 a state legislature
mindful of the rapid growth of California would be ap-
propriating money to plan an aqueduct to bring water
from the delta of the Sacramento River to Marin and
other North Bay counties.

In Solano County the cities of Vallejo, Benicia, and
Fairfield-Suisun had made arrangements during the war
to supplement their own inadequate local sources of water
supply (mostly ground water) with seven million gallons
daily supplied by the East Bay Municipal Utility District
through a temporary pipe line across the Carquinez
Bridge. Since this arrangement was scheduled to terminate
in 1952, the Solano County cities had to find additional
water elsewhere. One possibility was to press for immediate construction of the proposed Monticello Dam on
Putah Creek by the Bureau of Reclamation; the other
was to act quickly and build a pipe line to the delta of the
Sacramento–San Joaquin rivers. When controversy over
the dam threatened to become prolonged and Navy
officials at Mare Island grew alarmed over the risk of
being without safe margins of water supply, Vallejo decided to construct a thirty-mile pipe line to Maine Prairie
Slough, a tributary of Cache Slough, in the delta. The
new line, completed in 1952, can supply 20,000,000 gallons
daily and is considered adequate to meet local needs
until about 1970.

In Santa Clara County the San Jose Water Works

annually gained so many new customers in its one-hundred-square-mile service area in the northern part of the county that it could no longer depend upon the wells and reservoirs already in use. In 1951 it built the Austrian Dam, a large, earth-fill dam, on Los Gatos Creek in the Santa Cruz Mountains. Upon completion of the new reservoir, the company announced that its sources of supply had a production capacity somewhat greater than the capacity of the first Hetch Hetchy Aqueduct built by San Francisco.

People in the Santa Clara Valley nevertheless engaged in endless discussion about how long the valley could depend exclusively on local supplies of water both for domestic use and for irrigation. Even though the Santa Clara Valley Water Conservation District had built five dams in the late 'thirties to spread stream runoff in percolating beds, so that the badly depleted underground water would be replenished, the recurrence of a dry cycle and heavy pumping during the war had by 1948 reduced the water table below the previous all-time low of 1934. In 1951 the construction of two additional dams, the Leroy Anderson Dam on Coyote Creek two miles east of Morgan Hill and the Lexington Dam on Los Gatos Creek just above the city of Los Gatos, promised to improve the situation temporarily but not to eliminate the long-term prospect of water shortages.

Ironically, the unusually rainy winter of 1951–52, like nothing seen in the past sixty years, suddenly turned Santa Clara County from an area with too little water to one with terrifying surpluses. The Guadalupe, Coyote, Saratoga, Los Gatos, and other creeks draining into San Francisco Bay became furious torrents, overflowing their banks and spreading havoc through new subdivisions and across croplands. Bridges and roads were washed away; silt covered the floors of new tract houses; the buildings of Agnews State Hospital stood feet deep in muddy water; all the residents of the town of Alviso had to be evacuated.

The possibility of all this destruction had been foreseen for many years by the county planning commission, which had warned in 1944 that the county urgently needed a comprehensive plan for disposal of storm water, but no valley-wide drainage study had been authorized. Local districts, self-governing municipalities, county departments, federal agencies, and individuals had all attempted piecemeal, uncoördinated solutions to a highly complex problem that had been getting steadily worse for many years. Land subsidence caused by overdrafts on the underground water storage reservoirs had enlarged the level plain in which storm waters collected during periods of heavy rainfall; the compacting of soils for roadbeds had formed inverted dams that restricted subsurface drainage;

the diking of large areas near the bay to prevent tidal flooding had limited the points at which storm runoff could discharge into the bay; and the building of thousands of impervious roofs, walks, and paved streets in new subdivisions had greatly reduced the land surface capable of absorbing storm runoff.

The county planning commission observed in a report issued after the flood that "the county is little better off today than twenty years ago, excepting for the flood checking features of the conservation dams and the drainage structures in the Alum Rock–Evergreen area." The county needed a comprehensive plan for the utilization and control of local runoff, but no amount of conservation could solve the long-term problem of an adequate water supply. The commission stated plainly what everyone knew: "An outside source will be needed." Indeed officials of the Santa Clara Valley Water Conservation District already had applications on file with the State Water Resources Board for water from several outside sources, including the Central Valley Project.

New Sources of Energy

The increasing dependence of the Bay Area on distant sources of water had a parallel in its dependence on sources of energy that were, in some instances, even more remote from the area than the watersheds of the Sierra Nevada. The largest private utility company in the Bay Area, the Pacific Gas and Electric Company, which served most of northern and central California, reached all the way to the Permian Basin of west Texas and southwestern New Mexico and to the San Juan Basin in the "four corners" area of New Mexico, Colorado, Utah, and Arizona for natural gas to operate its new steam plants and to supply domestic and industrial customers. It also built many new hydroelectric plants, from the McCloud and Pit rivers in the far northern part of the state to the Kings River in the southern canyons of the Sierra Nevada.

More than a little skeptical about predictions of a postwar slump and a population recession in California, the company announced before the end of World War II that it would embark on a ten-year construction program requiring expenditures totaling $1,500,000,000. The program contemplated additional hydroelectric plants in the Sierra, expansion of high-voltage electric transmission lines and distribution lines, steam-generating plants using fuel oil and natural gas, and natural-gas pipe lines hundreds of miles long.

Between 1948 and 1953 the utility company completed seven large hydroelectric plants in the Sierra; yet the entire generating capacity of these new plants did not equal that of either of two huge steam plants constructed in

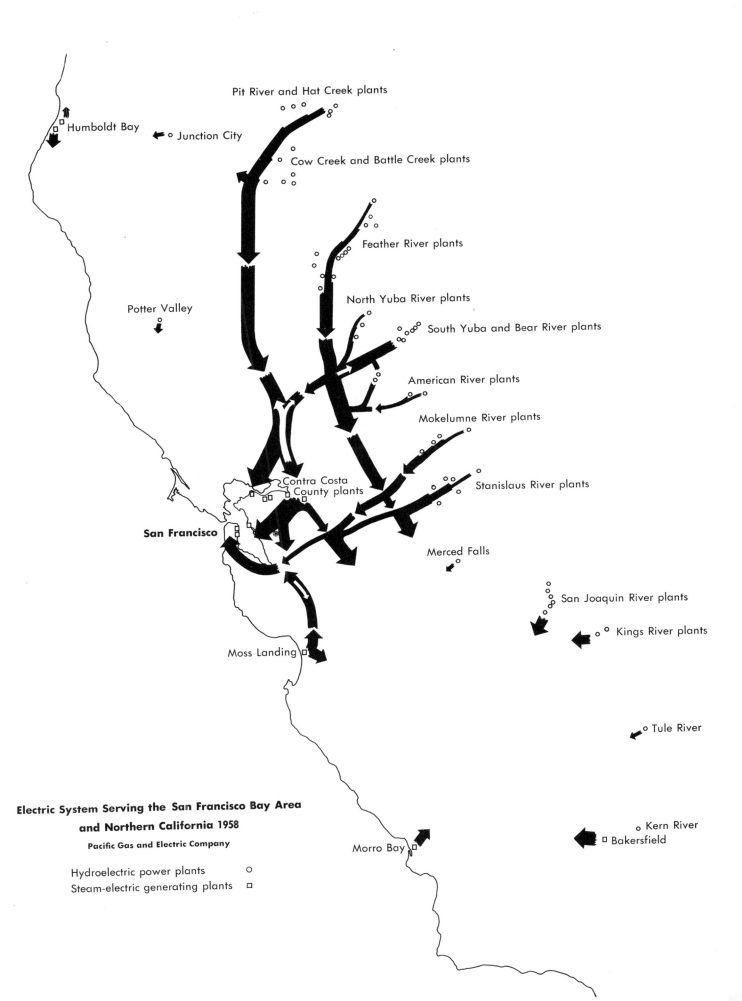

Pit River and Hat Creek plants

Humboldt Bay

← Junction City

Cow Creek and Battle Creek plants

Potter Valley

Feather River plants

North Yuba River plants

South Yuba and Bear River plants

American River plants

Mokelumne River plants

Contra Costa
County plants

Stanislaus River plants

San Francisco

Merced Falls

San Joaquin River plants

Kings River plants

Moss Landing

Tule River

**Electric System Serving the San Francisco Bay Area
and Northern California 1958**

Pacific Gas and Electric Company

Kern River

Bakersfield

Morro Bay

Hydroelectric power plants   o
Steam-electric generating plants □

Contra Costa County near Pittsburg. One of these has a generating capacity of 575,000 kilowatts, or almost enough to supply two cities the size of San Francisco; the other has a capacity even larger—600,000 kilowatts. A third enormous plant at Moss Landing in Monterey County also supplies some parts of the Bay Area with power. In addition, the company increased the generating capacity of a plant in San Francisco and set to work on other steam plants in Kern, San Luis Obispo, and Humboldt counties.

The importation of natural gas from sources in other states was necessitated by the fact that even before the end of World War II no discoveries of new natural-gas fields of substantial capacity were being made in California. In 1944 the Pacific Gas and Electric Company joined two southern California companies in investigating the possibility of building pipe lines to tap the reserves of the Permian Basin and the San Juan Basin. The southern companies were the first to arrange for the El Paso Natural Gas Company to build a pipe line to make deliveries to them at the California border. In 1948 the Pacific Gas and Electric Company made similar arrangements to take deliveries from the Texas company at Topock on the Arizona-California border. By 1950 the P. G. and E. had constructed its "Super Inch" high-pressure gas transmission line (34 inches in diameter) from Milpitas in Santa Clara County to the junction at Topock with the pipe line of the El Paso Natural Gas Company, a distance of 502 miles.

The initial capacity of the "Super Inch" was 150,000,000 cubic feet daily. As the demand for gas rose sharply, the company again and again enlarged the capacity of the line by installing compressor stations, building "looping" or parallel sections, and enlarging compressor stations, until by 1954 the line was delivering 700,000,000 cubic feet of gas daily—enough to serve the needs of eleven cities the size of Oakland (population approximately 400,000). The greater part of this imported gas was consumed in the San Francisco Bay Area.

Looking ahead, company officials acknowledged that within a few years they would have to parallel the entire line, in order to raise the daily capacity 700,000,000 cubic feet above the 1954 figure.

Flood Tides of Growth

The population growth that compelled these extensive expansions in utilities was especially great during the Korean War; it slowed down during the recession of 1953 and 1954, and from about the summer of 1955 until the summer of 1957 again accelerated while California and the nation surged forward on another wave of prosperity

and inflation. As it had all during its history, the Bay Area attracted hordes of newcomers in good years but seemed much less the promised land during economic downturns. The State Department of Finance estimated that the population of the nine bay counties increased more than 140,000 during the fiscal year 1951–52, whereas the estimated increase for the fiscal year 1954–55 was just one-half as much. By 1956–57 the numerical increase was again more than 100,000, of which almost one-half accrued to Santa Clara County, where bulldozers uprooted orchards by the hundreds to make way for tract houses, new industrial plants, and shopping centers surrounded by acres of parking space.

During all these years of economic peaks and setbacks the flood tides of suburban development kept rolling across the once rural landscape on the outskirts of the urban areas. From time to time, restrictions on building materials or "tight money" policies that limited borrowing for home construction retarded their progress, but nothing actually stopped their steady elimination of open spaces. One urban wave swept southward along the bay side of the San Francisco Peninsula into northern Santa Clara County, creating an almost unbroken pattern of low-density development. Other waves surged outward in all directions from the San Jose area. Or perhaps it would be more accurate to say that something like an explosion littered the countryside with subdivisions; for the pattern of urbanization was disorderly and irrational, a testimonial to the failure of city and county governments to say when and where agricultural land could be subdivided for residential use. On the eastern side of the bay another flood of development advanced southward past Hayward into the green acres of Washington Township. And in the San Ramon and Ygnacio valleys of Contra Costa County, east of the Berkeley Hills, still other waves of development displaced walnut groves, apricot orchards, and vineyards. The northern counties experienced to a lesser extent the same kind of "runaway" suburbanization.

The regional metropolis that some people prophesied in the 'twenties and 'thirties took shape with startling rapidity—without benefit of metropolitan regional planning. In 1951 the officials of building departments in cities and counties of the Bay Area issued permits for nearly thirty thousand dwellings, in 1952 for more than thirty-one thousand, in 1953 for almost thirty thousand, in 1954 for approximately forty-one thousand, and in 1955 for more than forty-five thousand. In approximately the same four-year period the California Division of Real Estate approved subdivisions that used up almost eighty square miles of agricultural land; of course a great deal of land had been converted from fields to homesites be-ore then, and a vast amount has been taken over by the ubiquitous "ranch house" since then. If all this land were in one place, say on some coastal plain or in the Central Valley, it would provide space for three or four cities with the area of San Francisco (44.3 square miles). But the regional metropolis that the developers have hastened into being in recent years is strung in relatively narrow strips round the northern and southern arms of the bay, is loosely scattered over some two hundred square miles in the northern Santa Clara Valley, and is strewn haphazardly over eastern Contra Costa County. It is at least eighty miles long from north to south and at its widest point spreads east and west more than forty miles. It has somewhat the form of a thick rubber band, with the bay in the center. Future development will probably extend the metropolis northward and southward.

Desire for Space

The pattern now generally imposed upon the once rural acres reveals the extent to which the dream of home ownership and the desire for space of one's own, even if it be no more than six thousand square feet of land in a "look alike" development, have captured the popular imagination. Many of those who could afford no more than the tract house on its small lot have held the illusion that they were moving from a too-congested urban environment to "the country." With deep nostalgia and romantic notions of success, they have read the tract developer's Sunday advertisements and have overlooked the guile in his query: "Have you ever lived as a country gentleman?" Sometimes the country, with its tree-shaded knolls and its fields of spring wild flowers, has indeed been close by when a family has come into the new "planned community"; but all too often, within a few years the country has receded and the dreamers have awakened fretfully to the reality of an environment that is neither rural nor urban—a vast suburbia of houses constructed from jig-built framing panels and other prefabricated parts. When schools have been overcrowded and recreation centers lacking, when municipal services have been inadequate and taxes high, when monthly payments on the house and on the TV, the car, and the hi-fi set have strained the family budget to the limit, disenchantment has often deepened to despair. But if there is ever a revolt against suburbia, it may take the form of a movement to remodel the suburban scene and way of life rather than a mass migration back to the central city, no matter how handsomely the once blighted city areas may have been redeveloped. Present-day dwellers in the San Francisco Bay Area, as in other large metropolitan regions, are usually only one or two generations removed from the farm and the small town or small city; and the "big city"—the concentrated city of the late nineteenth century and early twentieth century, with its densely built blocks—has never been a place in which they or their parents have felt really at home. The tract development, with all its deficiencies, physical and social, is perhaps a closer approximation of what they want than the older city ever was. Moreover, the urban sprawl, some might say, was almost inevitable, given the automobile and the mass-production techniques of the mid-twentieth century American economy.

This economy, from the time of the Civil War or before, has been generating an awesome capacity to produce. Its corporate enterprise has tended toward giantism and its products toward standardization. Small wonder that urban areas, too, should reflect this bigness and this standardization! For the past four decades they have been shaped by one of the most conspicuous products of this mass-production and mass-distribution economy: the automobile. All suburbia, in the San Francisco Bay Area as elsewhere, depends upon it and could not exist without it. Even if the Bay Area should some day finance and build a mass rapid transit system, large parts of the area would still be dependent upon the automobile.

The freeways that now stretch through the urban belts surrounding the bay and through the valleys filled with tract houses are the expensive progeny of this mechanical invention. In recent years they have been powerful agents of metropolitan growth and dispersion. To be sure, a good deal of tract development preceded the completion of freeways; but every new section of these divided, limited-access superhighways that has been opened to traffic has encouraged further subdivision of farmlands and has, in effect, poured the city out upon the fields.

Since scores of new tracts have been linked to older centers only by freeways, many of these channels of movement have become intolerably congested at morning and evening rush hours. Indeed, some freeways have carried capacity volumes of traffic almost from the day they were completed. Consequently, state highway engineers now emphasize that "it is not realistic to consider that freeways alone will be the answer" to problems of metropolitan transportation. Their plans for additional freeways are predicated on the assumption that rapid transit lines as well as freeways will serve the Bay Area in the future.

In the spring of 1957, state highway engineers reported that they had completed two hundred miles of freeways in the San Francisco Bay Area since World War II. They had plans at the end of 1957 for an additional one hundred miles of freeways and were spending $75,000,000 a year on the construction program in the nine bay coun-

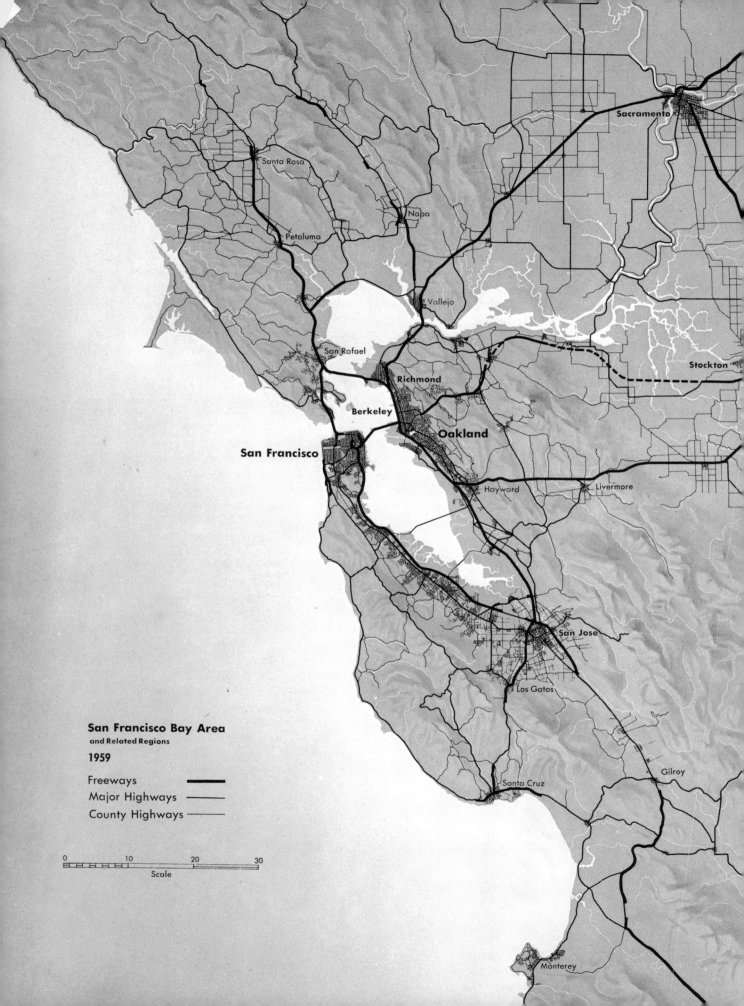

San Rosa

Napa

Petaluma

Vallejo

Sacramento

Stockton

San Rafael

Richmond

Berkeley

Oakland

San Francisco

Hayward

Livermore

San Jose

Los Gatos

Gilroy

Santa Cruz

Monterey

San Francisco Bay Area
and Related Regions

1959

Freeways ▬▬▬▬

Major Highways ――――

County Highways ――――

0   10   20   30
Scale

ies, with every expectation that the annual expenditure would increase.

Shopping Centers

A new type of landmark in the outlying areas served by the sweeping freeways is the "regional," or district, shopping center, with its landscaped mall, its department store, specialty shops, and branch bank. The rise of this now-popular retail mecca was foretold by the development of branch stores of San Francisco and Oakland establishments in some of the smaller cities, such as San Mateo, Palo Alto, and San Rafael, even before 1950. The more discerning merchants in the central cities realized at the very beginning of the big suburban expansion that there would be new opportunities to do business in the

midst of the tract developments. But the significant change in retail merchandizing in the outlying areas has occurred in the past seven or eight years and has been characterized by the large, planned shopping center.

Like the freeway, the mammoth shopping center is another product of the automobile age; the space allotted to parking is three, four, or five times as great as the floor area of the buildings. Too, the shopping center is peculiarly the symbol of the vast, spread-out tracts, for it consists mostly of one-story structures and reflects, surely much too self-consciously, the "leisurely living" associated with the suburban patio.

One of the first of the new shopping centers, Stonestown, was built not in a typical suburban community but in the Lake Merced Area of San Francisco, near one of

Stonestown Shopping Center, San Francisco. Right: Stonestown Apartments. Upper right: San Francisco State College, with the Park Merced housing project of the Metropolitan Life Insurance Company. Photograph courtesy of State Division of Highways.

the main routes from San Mateo County to the Golden Gate Bridge and Marin County. The developers hoped that it would attract customers not only from near-by neighborhoods but also from residential areas in San Mateo and Marin counties. Opened in 1952, it includes a branch of The Emporium, the largest department store in downtown San Francisco, and branch stores of many other downtown establishments.

Shopping centers similar to Stonestown have since sprung up in Hillsdale near San Mateo, on the extensive grounds of Stanford University near Palo Alto and Menlo Park, on the Stevens Creek Road near the city limits of San Jose and Santa Clara, and at San Leandro, Hayward, El Cerrito, and Walnut Creek. Those at Stanford, El Cerrito, and Walnut Creek have branches of the Emporium-Capwell Company, those at Hillsdale and San Leandro, branches of Macy's. Commercial rivalry, more intense than sound, has given the San Jose–Santa Clara area branch stores of both these retail establishments, in huge shopping centers just across the street from each other.

Besides these several large centers, some of which have sites of fifty or sixty acres and provide parking space for as many as four thousand automobiles, there are many small ones, such as the Boardwalk Shopping Center in Tiburon and the Pala Shopping Center in East San Jose.

Because these new asphalt islands of commerce do solve the retail parking problem, eliminate the conflict between street traffic and pedestrian traffic, bring together at one location a well-selected variety of stores, and offer some of the holiday atmosphere of a fair, they hasten the obsolescence of the older suburban shopping district, with its limited parking facilities and general lack of "glamour." The business districts of Palo Alto and San Jose, for example, have been hurt by the new centers. But these developments have not always been the money-makers that their promoters expected. In time the increase in suburban population may boost the sales of some of those shopping centers that have not yet warranted the faith of investors; but in the meantime, plans for certain additional centers may have been shelved because of the belated realization that a large-scale shopping center must have little or no competition within a trading area inhabited by a hundred thousand to a quarter of a million people. Some of the new centers are simply too close together to be profitable today.

Administrative Offices

The expansion of retail trade in standardized goods in the outlying areas has been accompanied in some places by an increase in professional offices and even by the estab-lishment of administrative offices such as one used to find principally in San Francisco and Oakland. San Mateo, for instance, has attracted a regional office of the General Petroleum Corporation, the West Coast headquarters of the Holly Sugar Corporation, and the headquarters of the Olson steamship company, formerly in San Francisco. A special "professional" zone in Menlo Park includes the editorial offices of Sunset Magazine, which previously were in San Francisco, the offices of several insurance companies, and a Pacific Coast office of the United States Geological Survey. The success of the Menlo Park and San Mateo "executive" and professional zones has been so well publicized, in fact, that it has inspired several other cities to create similar zones in the hope of attracting firms looking for suburban locations.

The site planning and architecture of the establishments in the Menlo Park professional zone explain at a glance why a carefully restricted area in a suburban environment appeals to some companies. Each structure is on a site large enough to provide space for parking the cars of employees, for a variety of game courts, and for terraces and gardens where employees can eat their lunches or take a "breather" in the sunshine. The one- and two-story buildings have a slightly domestic quality and are surrounded by broad lawns, trees, and flowering shrubs. The "decentralized" location has certain kinds of amenities that no metropolitan center can offer.

"Professional and administrative offices may very well become the basic industry of Menlo Park in the future, replacing the harried commuter (who is rapidly becoming less of a predominant figure in Menlo Park)," planning consultants Harold F. Wise and Simon Eisner speculated in their *Master Plan for Menlo Park*, prepared in 1952. "When this day comes, the social, economic, and cultural life of the city and the region will be healthier for it. Living five minutes or less from work will simply mean more time for recreational, educational, and cultural activities; more time to spend with the family; a healthier and more alert citizenry. This certainly should be the aim and end of the economic and social organization of our cities. In the case of Menlo Park, it looks as if an increasingly large number of people will be able to live and work in an environment which will permit the enjoyment of this type of living."[6]

Wise and Eisner had discovered, by means of a sample survey of the residents of Menlo Park made in the summer of 1951, that only 28 per cent of the employed people in the city actually worked in San Francisco. All the others were employed on the Peninsula, and of this group one-half were employed locally, in Menlo Park, Palo Alto, or Redwood City. The survey startled those who had not realized that communities somewhat removed from San Francisco were becoming much less dependent upon it for employment than upon areas close to it.

But the big exodus of top administrative and professional offices from the central cities of the Bay Area that was predicted several years ago has not occurred. A study conducted in 1953 showed that approximately 65 per cent of all firms employing one hundred or more persons and maintaining a single, main administrative office in the Bay Area still had quarters in the central sections of the metropolitan region—central San Francisco, central and northwestern Oakland, Berkeley, and Emeryville.[7] Forty-nine per cent were concentrated in central San Francisco alone, and approximately 17 per cent were clustered within the small "core" known as the financial district. Most of the firms that have shifted their administrative functions from San Francisco to suburban locations have housed them in offices attached to manufacturing plants, warehouses, or transportation terminals. The number of headquarters offices transferred from "the city" to suburban quarters not connected with such facilities is negligible.

The same study did indicate, however, that large firms are selecting suburban locations for certain operations while maintaining their main offices in central areas. Some have established research or accounting offices in the suburbs; others have opened district sales or administrative offices in suburban communities. Only a few have left the sales office in San Francisco or Oakland and moved the regional administrative office to an outlying location.

How many smaller firms have shifted their headquarters from the central cities to suburbia no one knows, for no studies have been made of administrative offices employing fewer than one hundred persons. Whatever the number, these smaller enterprises probably account for a relatively small proportion of the jobs in the territories fifteen to fifty miles from San Francisco and Oakland. The great amount of new employment in these areas is simply the result of metropolitan regional and western growth. Since World War II the school districts in these outlying areas have built hundreds of new schools; private organizations and hospital districts have constructed many new hospitals, and groups of physicians have opened well-equipped clinics; the small cities have expanded their municipal offices and have built new community centers, playgrounds, libraries, and fire stations; and commercial and service enterprises of all sorts have come into being to serve the families in the new tracts and fringe areas. Together with the new manufacturing and wholesale firms in the outlying areas, all these governmental and private establishments employ hundreds of thousands of workers, many of whom live within a few miles of their places of employment.

Problems of Small Cities

Some of the smaller cities struggle desperately to become "balanced" communities, with sufficient industrial and commercial enterprises to provide a high proportion of the jobs needed by their residents. Hayward is an example. In 1952 a high school student who won an annual "Hayward's Future" contest declared that "the men who have moved here with their families and who are still employed in Oakland, Alameda, or even San Francisco do not intend to be commuters forever."[8] But six years later Hayward still was largely a "bedroom" community, 65 per cent of its working people being employed in other cities. Between December, 1952, and May, 1956, its land area had increased, through fifty-nine annexations, from approximately thirty-one hundred acres to more than fifty-seven hundred acres; but almost all the territory annexed had been developed with single-family residences or was committed to such development. Endeavoring to correct the "imbalance" in the growth of the city, the city council in 1957 succeeded in bringing into the city through further annexations sixteen hundred gross acres of potential industrial property, as well as nine square miles of tideland property belonging to the Leslie Salt Company. The newly annexed areas included several manufacturing plants, and various companies had plans for building factories within the new industrial zones. Hayward thus has hopes of expanding local job opportunities and of shortening, for a greater number of its residents, the long journey to work; but its fiscal situation remains especially trying.

The average new house in the Hayward Area is assessed at $2,500 and returns (if the owner is not a veteran) about $225 a year in taxes for all services provided by the city, the county, the schools, and various special districts; but the cost of educating one elementary school child is in excess of $200 a year. If the schools did not receive substantial amounts of state aid, the governmental units in the Hayward Area would be under even greater financial strain than they are at present.

Cities in many other parts of the Bay Area, especially in San Mateo County, have the same problems as Hayward. Hard pressed to find the tax revenues to build schools and other community facilities and to employ teachers, school nurses, recreation directors, librarians, sanitarians, and engineers, they compete for industries, warehouses, research laboratories, publishing houses, and other establishments that would swell their lean tax rolls.

Although these widespread efforts to cope with skyrocketing local tax rates have contributed to a more general distribution of employment in the Bay Area, they have not necessarily given every community a well-selected group of industries or resulted in the most desirable distribution of industries throughout the metropolitan region. Some municipalities that might have been happier without any industries at all have sought industries; others that had sites and installed utilities to accommodate many new plants perhaps have not enjoyed the industrial development that they should have had.

New Municipalities

Even though many municipalities with few enterprises of high assessed valuation have faced financial difficulties, since World War II several unincorporated residential areas in the bay counties have voted to incorporate. Among them are Campbell, Saratoga, Monte Sereno, Los Altos, Los Altos Hills, and Milpitas in Santa Clara County, Fremont and Union City in Alameda County, and Pacifica and Woodside in San Mateo County. Of these new cities, the three on the eastern side of the bay—Milpitas, Fremont, and Union City, appear to have the best possibilities for balanced development, since all three have large amounts of potential industrial land near freeways and railroads. Union City includes Decoto, Alvarado, and neighboring areas.

Monte Sereno, Los Altos Hills, and Woodside, a socially exclusive community that wished to avoid being annexed to Redwood City or Atherton, seem to be less concerned with the quality of local governmental services than with maintaining a certain detachment. Community identity is a value highly prized by some of the other communities also, but they are concerned with being cities in the true sense of the word rather than municipalized bits of the semiurban fringe area. When the residents of five small but growing towns in Washington Township in Alameda County—Mission San Jose, Niles, Irvington, Centerville, and Warm Springs—considered banding together to form the city of Fremont, they hoped eventually to assure themselves of better services than they could obtain from county government or from overlapping special districts. But the opportunity to transform seventeen thousand acres of farmland and five small towns into a well-planned city, with adequate schools, recreation areas, libraries, police and fire services, and sanitary facilities, was an even greater incentive to incorporation. And the citizens of Fremont soon demonstrated that their goal was a genuine city. Asked by their planning consultant whether they wanted a city that would be mainly a further development of five separate communities or a city that would express its unity through the development of an

important center of governmental, commercial, and cultural activities at approximately the geographic center of the newly incorporated territory, they said they preferred the latter.

The same desire to control development and to pool financial and civic resources for the common good seems to have motivated the formation of Pacifica, on the coastal side of San Mateo County. The communities of Linda Mar, Sharp Park, Edgemar, Westview, Pacific Manor, Rockaway Beach, Fairway Park, Vallemar, and Pedro Point were merely so many subdivisions and towns until they merged in 1957 as a single municipality. Now the twenty thousand people who live within the twelve square miles embraced by Pacifica have the opportunity to create a city that will be more than the sum of many parts, difficult as that will be without the industries and some of the larger service enterprises needed to provide tax revenue.

Like Fremont and Pacifica, most of the other new municipalities are an expression of faith in an urban way of life. Their residents are determined to provide, in areas that are still under development, all those facilities and services associated with urban living. As the cities mature, all parts of the Bay Area suitable for intensive development will offer a reasonably high quality of city-type services; and there will be few areas in which local democratic self-government does not provide the means for improving the immediate physical environment. But the governmental mechanism for guiding the growth and development of the entire Bay Area is still lacking.

A full-circle examination of the San Francisco Bay Area reveals that the former highly centralized metropolitan region developed in the heyday of the steam train and the electric railway has been drastically revised by the state highway engineers who design and build freeways, manufacturers in search of large sites, tract house developers supported by federal mortgage insurance policies, financiers with money to invest in shopping centers, and county assessors who have assessed farmland as potential subdivision acreage and have thereby forced the farmer to sell his holdings. The regional metropolis that now almost encircles the bay still has strong centers in San Francisco and Oakland and older subcenters such as Santa Rosa and San Jose, but elsewhere it is no more than loosely polarized. Even in suburban communities some dispersion of trade and service establishments is taking place in accordance with the trend in the entire Bay Area toward a broader distribution of economic activities. The creation of planned industrial parks and planned shopping centers has not everywhere prevented the scatteration of industries and stores. The strip commercial develop-

The Central Business District of San Francisco. James Lick Skyway in the foreground. Photograph courtesy of State Division of Highways.

ment still flourishes, and industrial zones are perhaps more widespread than might be desirable. In short, the Bay Area is in a transitional stage; its ultimate form is unpredictable until its residents make some important decisions, one of which is whether they wish to depend in the future entirely upon freeways for transportation or are willing to finance and build a regional transit system that might induce the development of fairly concentrated commercial and cultural centers at a limited number of station stops.

The Central Cities

In the meantime, the cities in the geographical center of the Bay Area struggle with problems inherited from the past and with new problems thrust upon them by the enormous growth of the outlying areas. Both San Francisco and Oakland have large blighted areas in which the houses are old and in disrepair and the school sites and recreation areas inadequate by present-day standards. Both cities have central business districts in which the streets are congested and the off-street parking facilities are as yet insufficient to meet peak demands. Reasonably efficient in an earlier period when traffic consisted of horse-drawn vehicles and streetcars in which almost all workers and shoppers rode, these streets at rush hours become clotted with the automobiles pouring out from garages and parking lots. Although San Francisco has sought by various means to improve its municipally owned transit system, private use of the automobile has increased and patronage of the "Muni" has steadily declined. Oakland and its neighbor Berkeley have had their troubles with an ailing privately owned transit system that has been shunned by greater and greater numbers of passengers until its ability to render service has been severely impaired. Freeways built by the state engineers through San Francisco and Oakland have relieved certain streets of much of the traffic that previously used them, but freeways have removed huge amounts of private property from municipal tax rolls and have displaced many businesses and homeowners. More accessible to outlying areas because of these costly arteries, the central cities are better able to serve the entire Bay Area, but not in the same ways that they once did. Their retail and wholesale trade in standardized goods is relatively less important, their trade in specialized goods even more important than heretofore. Their roles as cultural and amusement centers and as centers of finance and administration have been enhanced; but they cannot capitalize fully on the advantages of central location until they clear away blight, modernize their central business districts, improve parking facilities and transit (including regional transit), and offer the beauty and splendor expected in the heart of a regional metropolis as famous as New York and Paris.

San Francisco is burdened with approximately nine square miles of residences that are blighted or threatened with blight—at least one-half the area occupied by residences. Besides these run-down residential sections, the city has several blighted industrial and commercial areas such as the old wholesale produce district just east of the financial district and certain parts of the area south of Market Street. All represent a continual drain upon the local treasury in the excessive amount of municipal services they require. All present formidable economic problems, and those of the blighted residential areas that have become ghettos of racial minorities present social problems that affect the entire Bay Area. As long as the outer sections of the metropolitan region erect discriminatory barriers against Negroes and other nonwhite families, the difficulties of relocating the tenants of areas slated for redevelopment will increase and the struggle of the city to free itself from blight will be prolonged. The more protracted the efforts of the city to renew itself, the longer it will be in developing the new business and cultural facilities and services needed to serve the whole Bay Area.

Shock—and Action

San Francisco was one of the first cities in California to advocate passage of the Community Redevelopment Law enacted by the state legislature in 1945. Its leading citizens had been profoundly shocked by the revelation that the city had made no population gains in the 'thirties, while the suburbs had grown markedly. These citizens had accepted the thesis that if the city was to survive, it would have to clear and rebuild the old, decayed areas and make them even more alluring than the suburbs. Through its department of city planning the city therefore mapped its blighted areas and made a pilot study of the possibilities of redeveloping the Western Addition—two years before Congress passed the Housing Act of 1949, providing for loans and grants to assist cities in clearing blighted areas and preparing such areas for resale or lease to private enterprise.

In 1948 the San Francisco Board of Supervisors officially designated the Western Addition (280 blocks) a blighted area and "activated" a redevelopment agency to undertake a project in the district. The members of the agency realized that redevelopment would be a lengthy process, but they nevertheless entertained some illusory hopes that they would make more rapid progress than they actually did. Evidence of this is their reaction to the acute housing shortage of the postwar period. They viewed it as one of the chief obstacles to their plans for redeveloping the Western Addition, since the law required that before deteriorated buildings could be cleared, the

milies living in them would have to be relocated. The
most urgent course therefore seemed to be to develop
new housing elsewhere in the city to house at least some
of the families who would be displaced; however, the
housing shortage that then appeared so large a hindrance
to redevelopment was to lessen before the agency could
begin demolishing substandard buildings. Since the members of the agency did not foresee this, they turned their
attention to a nearly vacant section of the city known as
Diamond Heights, situated almost in the geographical
center of the city but long arrested in its development by
a pattern of streets wholly inappropriate to the hilly
terrain. Indeed, some streets existed only on city maps
and had never actually been laid out, because the grades
would have been excessive. The staff of the agency and
consultant architects began preparing a plan for this
blighted area, meanwhile continuing work on plans for
redeveloping a number of blocks along Geary Street in
the Western Addition.

Plan for Diamond Heights

The plan for the arrested Diamond Heights area envisions
a unique new neighborhood housing twenty-three hundred

families. The streets in the area are to be properly related
to the contours of the land; the residential sections are to
include a wide variety of dwelling types: single-family detached houses, step-down apartments on the steeper
slopes, tall apartment houses with balconies for each
family on the scenic eminences in the area. Ample sites
will be provided for schools, playgrounds, shopping centers, and churches.

The tentative plan for Diamond Heights was issued in
the fall of 1951 and was revised in March, 1952. In that
same month the redevelopment agency published its preliminary plan for the Geary area in the Western Addition.
But subsequent events proved that the preparation of
plans is the least difficult part of the redevelopment process. "The law's delay" became the bane of the redevelopment program. A test case involving the constitutionality
of the California Redevelopment Law moved slowly
through the courts and was not adjudicated by the United
States Supreme Court until December, 1954, when the
high tribunal upheld the California statute by refusing to
review a decision in which the Supreme Court of California had approved the law.

Not until January, 1956, did the Housing and Home

Proposed Redevelopment of Diamond Heights, San Francisco. Perspective drawing
by Vernon De Mars, A.I.A., for the San Francisco Redevelopment Agency.

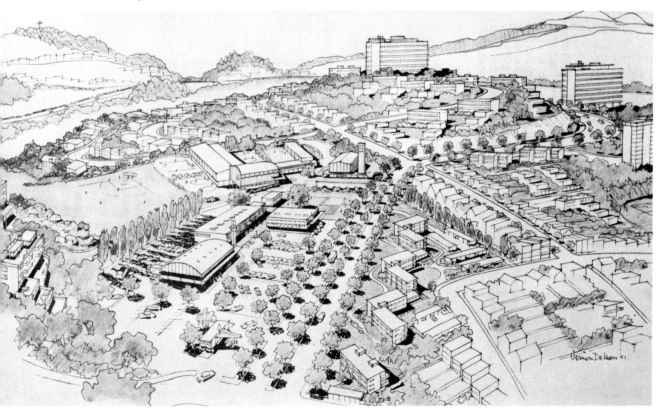

Finance Agency of the federal government approve a loan and a capital grant to assist the San Francisco Redevelopment Agency in redeveloping the 325 acres of Diamond Heights. And not until May, 1956, did the San Francisco Board of Supervisors accept the final plan for redeveloping twenty-eight blocks in the Western Addition, thereby clearing the way for federal financial assistance to the project. At that time the redevelopment agency estimated, perhaps optimistically, that it would take five years to acquire properties in the area, to clear deteriorated structures, and to prepare the land for re-use by private enterprise. Two years later the agency still had not obtained possession of all 604 properties required for the Diamond Heights project, because of condemnation suits. The San Francisco Redevelopment Agency now estimates that it will not be able to sell the land in Diamond Heights to builders until 1961 or to dispose of some of the cleared land in the Geary area until 1960.

The Golden Gateway

Controversy, financial troubles, and delays have marked the progress of another redevelopment project in San Francisco—the Golden Gateway development that would replace the unsanitary wholesale produce market area. In this project many of the issues that beset a central city endeavoring to adjust to metropolitan change have come into focus. Because the Golden Gateway lies directly east of the financial district and will be penetrated by an off-ramp of the Embarcadero Freeway, it is strategically situated to demonstrate ways in which a central city can serve the metropolitan region, and even more than the metropolitan region—the whole West and even lands overseas. Here could be housed an impressive array of administrative offices, financial institutions, export and import companies, and public relations and advertising agencies. Here, too, could be developed elevator apartments for executives and for some of the office workers who now commute long distances to their jobs in downtown San Francisco. Near by, in the vicinity of the Ferry Building, parks and a waterfront recreation area could be created that would be attractive to tourists and visitors, despite the aesthetic blight inflicted on the area by a ponderous elevated freeway. All this the plans prepared by architectural consultants propose; but governmental red tape, lack of coördination among government agencies, and disagreements among public officials, produce firms, and civic groups have plagued the redevelopment scheme. Further, officials of the redevelopment agency discovered, after plans for a twenty-six-block area had been prepared, that eight blocks would have to be eliminated from the first phase of the project so that tow apartments would cover more than half of the total are of the project, in accordance with the federal requireme that slightly more than half of an area not previosuly residential use be allocated for such use in the future. the meantime, private capital that might have been use to rebuild the decaying blocks in the produce area h gone into huge new office buildings all around them, the great alarm of public officials, who fear that the ne structures will provide so much additional office spa that there will be only a limited market for space in tl redevelopment project.

The apprehension of proponents of the Golden Gat way may not be justified, for San Francisco lies at tl heart of a metropolitan region that may have eight millic or more residents by the end of the century. With fa sighted leadership, the city could become even more in portant than it is today as a financial, cultural, and touri center; but that kind of leadership has been lacking, witness various failures attending the effort to redevelc the produce market area.

In 1955 a plan for simultaneously removing the co mission merchants to South Basin and redeveloping t old produce district fell through, chiefly for financi reasons. The redevelopment agency had never asked t city to vote a bond issue to create a redevelopment r volving fund that might have provided the money to b the South Basin area and to purchase the properties the market operators, who insisted on being assured fa value for their old quarters before they would comm themselves to move.

In something of a revival of the spirit exhibited in 19 and 1905 when James D. Phelan and other wealthy m financed the Burnham Plan, a committee headed by J. Zellerbach and Charles R. Blyth rescued the Gold Gateway project in 1956 by providing funds to the budge starved city planning department for the development site plans. Yet after the plans prepared by the archite tural firm of Skidmore, Owings and Merrill had be released in 1957, downtown groups in San Francisco to a stand that threatened to cut off federal financial aid the project. Real-estate and business associations balk at proposals of the city planning department to limit flo space in downtown office buildings, so that the redevelc ment project would be protected from future congesti and from undue competition of high buildings in the su rounding blocks. Only when the federal government sisted upon density controls did they grudgingly acce regulations that were more liberal than those origina proposed by the planning department.

...ack of Leadership

...pologists for the San Francisco redevelopment program
...te various reasons for its halting pace: the many plans,
...ublic hearings, and approvals required by the California
...w, bureaucratic deliberateness in Washington, D.C., in
...e early stages of the program, resistance of property
...wners, rising costs that have necessitated revisions in
...ans, and political friction stemming from the fact that
...e redevelopment agency is a creature of the state rather
...an a department of the municipal government.

...Hindrances imposed by state legislation, cumbersome
...deral procedures, and inflationary costs are, however,
...roblems which cities throughout the United States also
...ave had to deal with; and in spite of such problems,

several cities that were slower than San Francisco in initiating redevelopment programs have already completed
some projects. A visiting city planner from Philadelphia
pointed out in March, 1959, that San Francisco could
have proceeded more rapidly if its elected officials had
displayed less "hostility and skepticism toward city planning," if its redevelopment agency had organized a
"crash" program, and if more citizens had supported the
effort to rid the city of blight.[9]

San Francisco wishes to remain an influential center in
a great metropolitan region; yet most of its public
officials and many of its business executives display no
genuine civic leadership. The office-building boom in the
lower Market Street area is evidence of the economic
vitality of the city. The construction of new hotels and

*...odel of Proposed Golden Gateway, Redevelopment Area E, San Francisco. Ferry
...ilding and Embarcadero Freeway in the foreground. Photograph courtesy of
...idmore, Owings and Merrill, Architects, and Kurt Bank, photographer.*

Model of the Crown Zellerbach Corporation Headquarters Office Building, San Francisco. Hertzka & Knowles and Skidmore, Owings & Merrill, Architects. Copyright photograph by Morley Baer.

otels and a host of proposals for better convention
cilities, more tourist attractions, and additional parks
e evidence that there is an awareness of the increasing
nportance of San Francisco as a recreation center. But
e famed beauty of the city is eroding in some places,
id some parts of the central business district are growing
eap and shabby. Market Street west of Powell is a
nfusion of neon signs and sleazy displays. Oversize bill-
oards blot out the view of the downtown skyline from
e James Lick Skyway. South of Market Street new
otels wedged in among the warehouses and factories
ok as out of place as gentlemen in morning coats among
orkers in overalls. Opportunities to create shopping and
otel-entertainment areas with inviting pedestrian malls,
casional green spaces, and perhaps outdoor sculpture
id fountains, such as one sees in some of the suburban
opping centers, go unheeded while inept politicians
ntinue the boast that San Francisco is "the city that
ows how." That was what President Taft said more
an forty years ago, but it is no longer true. The city
ounders in smugness and indecision, ignores the need
r a bold, imaginative program to prepare it for a new
le in a Bay Area that will have twice the present popu-
tion in thirty or forty years. San Francisco should scrap
e rickety charter that was patched together in 1932 and
ould provide itself with a form of government adapted
 the demands of a new age. Its board of supervisors
ould increase the budget of the city planning depart-
ent, to enable it to complete and publish a general plan
at the city can follow in reorganizing the uses of land
thin its boundaries and in conserving its natural and
an-made beauties. But little will be gained by complet-
g the plan that has been many years in preparation
less political leaders will utilize it to the full and will
ek the advice of the city planners who developed it. San
ancisco needs, above all, policy makers who can inspire
 citizens to determine their civic goals, to draw up a
ogram for achieving them, and to pursue that program
nsistently until San Francisco again has stature and a
served reputation among the cities of America.

enewal in Oakland

uch slower than San Francisco in attacking the problem
 blight, Oakland did not begin to develop any kind of
ban renewal program until 1955. A few years earlier
e apartment-house interests in the city had taken the
id in defeating a proposal for the construction of ad-
tional public housing projects and had created a political
mate in which even redevelopment proposals were re-
rded with suspicion. A Citizens Committee for Urban
enewal appointed in 1954 necessarily proceeded cau-

tiously in its efforts to awaken the community to the need
for action. Many residents were unwilling to believe that
their own neighborhoods were threatened with blight and
to concede that more than one-tenth of the residential
area of the city was so seriously deteriorated as to require
replanning and a large amount of clearance and rebuilding. The committee went no further at first than to
recommend the appointment of an urban renewal coördinator to investigate the possibilities of a rehabilitation
program in the Clinton Park area on the east side of Lake
Merritt, an old but only partly blighted section.

The investigations of the coördinator, Fred H. Squires,
Jr., gradually revealed that if the city wished to undertake
a full-scale program of urban renewal it would need both
a redevelopment agency to clear slums and a department
of urban renewal to enforce housing laws and induce
property owners in neighborhoods threatened with blight
to improve, repair, and modernize their houses and apartments. The Oakland City Council appointed the members
of the redevelopment agency in the fall of 1956, and in
February, 1957, established an Urban Renewal Department. Squires became the executive director of both new
agencies.

As expected, the city launched its first rehabilitation
program in the Clinton Park area. City departments and
the board of education spent approximately five hundred
thousand dollars in the area on public works and received
almost twice as much as that from the federal government, under the liberal provisions of the Housing Act of
1954, for the expansion of an elementary school site and
other needed public improvements. Real-estate and financial groups assisted the rehabilitation program by establishing the Oakland Renewal Foundation, Inc., to provide
advice and services to property owners that the city was
not legally empowered to offer.

In the fall of 1957 the city council further strengthened
the renewal effort by enacting a housing code with provisions somewhat more detailed and exacting than those
of the State Housing Act previously enforced in Oakland.
To administer the new code, the council created a unified
department of building and safety.

The decision to undertake a succession of projects that
would transform the two hundred and fifty blocks of
West Oakland into new industrial zones and attractive
residential areas within a decade was perhaps the high
point in the municipal effort to lift Oakland from the
deadly mediocrity that has characterized it in recent
decades. In 1957 the Housing and Home Finance Agency
of the federal government allocated $64,000 to the city
for planning studies in West Oakland, and at the same
time the agency earmarked $1,800,000 as a federal con-

tribution toward the cost of clearing and preparing a first project area of twenty-five blocks for redevelopment by private enterprise.

Oakland faces many controversies as it strives to renew blighted West Oakland. The area is inhabited mainly by low-income Negro families, whom it will be difficult to relocate unless additional public housing projects are developed; yet many interests in Oakland at present oppose any expansion of public housing. The federal government will not approve redevelopment of the area exclusively for Negro occupancy; hence other neighborhoods in Oakland will have to be opened to Negro families who are displaced by other groups. Certain business interests will undoubtedly advocate high land coverage and high population densities in the area, whereas other groups will contend that the city must provide recreation areas and a good deal of open space in the redeveloped neighborhoods and must limit population densities to an average of not more than one hundred persons to the acre in the greater part of the district, as the city planning commission recommends.

Goals for Oakland

The preliminary general plan prepared by Oakland's city planning commission in 1957 and officially adopted by the city council in 1959 suggests public improvements and changes in the physical organization of the city that would enable it to achieve an importance, commercially, industrially, and culturally, far greater than if it sought to serve largely its own residents. The plan seeks to enhance the position of Oakland as part of the regional center by assuring fast, safe, efficient movement between the city and other parts of the Bay Area, by concentrating and intensifying activities within its central business district, by increasing its industrial space by nearly three thousand acres, and by developing city-wide parks, museums, and other cultural facilities that would attract people from many parts of the Bay Area. Significantly, the plan suggests that one of the goals of Oakland should be "to achieve a high standard of beauty in all future development"—a forthright advocacy of quality in civic enterprises that has been almost entirely lacking in city planning reports for several decades.

Oakland city planners foresee an increase in the population of the city from approximately four hundred thousand at present to half a million by 1980. To provide for the social needs of a population of that size, Oakland will need sixty-five neighborhood centers and twenty-two community centers that combine schools, parks, and playgrounds, the general plan states. Each neighborhood center would serve five to six thousand people, each community center twenty to twenty-five thousand people. Eventually more than seven hundred acres will have to be added to the five hundred now occupied by schools in Oakland if the standards proposed for the neighborhood and community centers are to be met.

In suggesting a strengthening of the central business district of Oakland, the planning commission expects no expansion of the area of this East Bay hub, since much of it is not intensively developed. Rather, the commission believes that "concentration will result in efficiency and convenience and can also increase the glamour and excitement characteristic of the downtown areas of big cities."[10] But the professional staff of the commission recognizes that streets in the downtown area must be free from congestion. The general plan realistically proposes a ring of major streets surrounding the central business district which will funnel traffic from freeways and major streets into well-situated parking garages and parking lots. Also, the plan recognizes that without a regional rapid transit system, downtown Oakland can no more hope to function effectively as part of a regional center than can downtown San Francisco. Essential features of the system proposed by the San Francisco Bay Area Rapid Transit Commission in 1956 have been incorporated into the city plan, with slight modifications.

Soon after this carefully prepared plan was issued, the staff of the city planning commission initiated studies of the central business district, to determine what could be done to transform this far from "glamorous" area into the kind of center described in the comprehensive plan. The planners were encouraged in their task by the fact that several tall buildings had risen in downtown Oakland in the past few years, including the First Western Building, a slim structure of blue enameled steel panels. Moreover, just as they began their labors, Henry J. Kaiser signed the final contracts for construction of the twenty-eight-story building on the western shore of Lake Merritt that will be headquarters for his industrial empire. Between the lake and the buildings concentrated near the city hall, the planners envisioned still more skyscrapers, and near the lake some tower apartments to house executives and professional people.

Whether Oakland in time becomes the well-planned and beautiful city that its city planners think it is capable of becoming will depend on the kind of leadership it develops. In the period 1905–1915 Oakland had great civic spirit and accomplished much. Since then it has grown industrially and commercially and has become an important port, but it has achieved little distinction. Except for Lake Merritt and a few sections in the hills, it is an uninspiring city. But it has great potentialities, as the

...aiser Center, Overlooking Lake Merritt, Oakland. Left: The Central Business ...istrict of Oakland. Photograph courtesy of Kaiser Industries Corporation.

...eliminary general plan suggests. Moreover, certain de-...lopments of recent years indicate the opportunities for ...vic achievement. The decaying warehouses and com-...ercial buildings that formerly crowded around the foot ... Broadway have been replaced by the colorful restau-...nts of Jack London Square, a waterfront mecca perpet-...ating the name of a writer who first learned about sailing ...ips and the romance of distant lands as a roustabout on ...e docks along the Estuary. An outstanding park depart-...ent has imaginatively redesigned many of the parks in ...e city and has brought Oakland fame throughout the ...tion. If the residents of the city enlarge their perspective ... view it as one part of a central complex in a regional

metropolis, and if they adopt broad, courageous programs for improving its residential, commercial, and industrial areas, Oakland a quarter of a century hence, or even ten years from now, can enjoy prestige that it has never known.

Regional Problems

Overshadowing the problems faced by individual cities and counties are the still larger problems confronting the entire Bay Area: pollution of the bay and of the skies above the area; decline of transit services throughout the nine bay counties; limited sources of water supply in many of the outer sections where further development should take place; disagreement on methods of reserving land for industrial use; the lack of plans for unified development of the bay; the threatened loss of open spaces that would be suitable for inclusion in a system of metropolitan regional parks or for uses now unforeseen; the possibility of further destruction of the scenic beauties of the area through ill-considered development; the difficulty of coördinating the physical planning being done by cities, counties, special districts, the state and federal governments, and by private enterprise; and the lack of some form of metropolitan government to establish policy on matters affecting the entire area and to carry out physical improvements in accordance with policy decisions.

With the exception of the problem of atmospheric pollution and possibly the problem of reserving open space, these are not new problems. The Regional Plan Association of the 1920's was aware of most of them. The rapid growth and development of the past twenty years has, however, intensified the problems. And at the same time the residents of the Bay Area have begun to realize as they never did before that the problems are interrelated, because life in the present-day metropolitan region is inevitably all of a piece. The same factory that pollutes the bay may also pollute the atmosphere. The wastes that foul the waters of the bay imperil fish, and when fish die sportsmen curse and cannery operators see their livelihood endangered. A subdivision on watershed lands that might have been used for a regional park not only robs a large urban population of needed recreation space, it also creates fiscal problems for the municipality that annexes it if that municipality is already lacking in commercial and industrial establishments of high assessed valuation. The freeway that slices through wooded hills to speed commuters and shoppers on their way funnels problems of congestion into the very heart of the central city. The dump truck that deposits fill on a tideland marsh to create sites for factories deprives cranes and herons of a refuge—and city children of an opportunity to become acquainted with some of nature's creatures. Indeed, the quality of life in any one city or county depends, in ways that are often difficult to comprehend, upon the quality of life in all the other Bay Area communities.

Since World War II, the Bay Area has given greatest attention to the problems of air and water pollution, to the need for safeguarding suitable lands for industry, and to problems of regional circulation, as witness the controversies over the routes of freeways and the arguments over a proposed rapid transit system. Although the approach to each of these problems has been separate, as if each one in no way impinged on the others, a more and more audible chorus just offstage has been asserting that the problems are all aspects of the one big problem of

making the area livable for the millions now here and for the millions expected in the future. Recently some leading businessmen have even emerged from the wings to speak of the need for metropolitan government to deal with all these area-wide problems, whereas only ten years ago some of these gentlemen would have considered all talk of metropolitan government utopian.

Pollution in the Bay

At the end of World War II almost all the cities and sanitary districts in the territory immediately surrounding the bay were defiling its waters. The bay was, in fact, a vast sinkhole, so contaminated along the San Francisco waterfront that Aquatic Park was closed to swimmers, so saturated with polluting materials along the East Bay shore that the tidal mud flats stank, and so poisoned with cannery wastes and human excreta below Dumbarton Strait that ducks inhabiting the tidal marshes could no longer serve as food. But the Bay Area was not unique among California urban regions in having a pollution problem. Every other area that had felt the impact of wartime migration worried about polluted beaches or rivers or underground water. When the State Board of Public Health decided to revoke, as of January 1, 1947, all permits for disposal of raw, untreated sewage into any of the waters of the state, the Bay Area faced the same necessity for action that all other populous areas in California faced.

The central cities in the Bay Area had long been conscious of the problem and had been making plans to construct trunk sewers and large sewage treatment plants. They were the first to act. San Francisco enlarged its Richmond-Sunset Sewage Treatment Plant, which handled about one-third of the sewage of the city, built a huge plant at North Point to serve almost the entire eastern part of the city, and constructed still another plant in the vicinity of Islais Creek to serve the southeastern section of the city. Special District No. 1 of the East Bay Municipal Utility District (serving Alameda, Albany, Berkeley, Emeryville, Oakland, and Piedmont) constructed a single large sewage treatment plant near the eastern end of the San Francisco–Oakland Bay Bridge, with an outfall for the discharge of effluent into the deep waters of the bay.

While these huge treatment plants and trunk line sewers connecting with them were still under construction, the state legislature in 1949 made comprehensive changes in the state laws controlling water pollution. The new legislation authorized nine regional pollution control boards, including one in the Bay Area, and a state board with power to correct conditions should the regional boards fail to do their duty.

In November, 1949, the governor appointed the members of the regional board for the Bay Area. Ten years later the executive officer for this board reported that in the period 1950–1959, cities, sanitary districts, the state and federal governments, and private industries had completed, put into construction, or financed facilities for the treatment of sewage and industrial waste, in the San Francisco Bay Area, costing more than $130,000,000. Only a few small communities had taken no steps to provide adequate treatment of their wastes. Every large community had responded to the proddings of the board, though some had just begun to build the necessary facilities.

But not all residents of the Bay Area were satisfied with the progress report of the regional water pollution control board. Sportsmen, commercial fisheries, and conservationists, especially, accused it of being "soft" on some of the larger industries that discharge noxious waste products into the bay. An official of the State Department of Public Health asserted that the board did not have "enough authority" under the 1949 act to prevent certain types of pollution;[12] and the executive director of the board complained that he was handicapped by the lack of a research program.[13] Critics of the regional board have suggested that its budget and staff be augmented and its powers strengthened.

Air Pollution Control

The vigor with which residents of the more populous sections of the Bay Area have attacked the problem of air pollution contrasts with their apathy toward the problem of reducing pollution of the bay. Rather than allow atmospheric pollution to become as serious as it is in the Los Angeles Area, political and civic leaders in the more heavily industrialized cities and counties of the Bay Area sought authority from the state legislature to establish an air pollution control district embracing the entire metropolitan region. The act introduced by Assemblyman (later Senator) Richard J. Dolwig of San Mateo County at the 1955 session of the legislature permits all nine counties of the Bay Area to join the district, although initially only the six central and southern counties banded together to form a district. Napa, Sonoma, and Solano counties still remain outside the district but may be included later at their own request.

The district opened the first phase of a long-term campaign to control air pollution when its administrator, Benjamin Linsky, announced on October 1, 1956, that in about three months open rubbish fires would be banned throughout the six counties. The chief targets of this prohibition were the city dumps at various points along the shoreline of the bay, all of which sent skyward thick black columns of smoke. Immediately there were protests from many municipalities. Loudest of all were those from the East Bay cities, some of whose mayors and city managers talked as if they had never observed the layers of filthy air that settled over the bay on warm, windless days. Reasonable but firm, the district extended the time during which the cities and operators of private dumps were to make other arrangements for disposing of refuse and garbage. It set October 1, 1957, as the deadline for compliance with its ban; but in the meantime, to show that it intended to use its authority, it appointed a three-man administrative "court" to hear charges against violators.

Most of the municipalities resorted to the fill-and-cover method of getting rid of refuse before the deadline. Forty-six wrecking firms and dump operators in San Francisco resisted through various legal maneuvers, then finally capitulated under threats of prosecution by the district attorney or were forced by court injunctions to cease open-burning operations. On February 4, 1959, when the Superior Court of San Francisco issued a preliminary injunction against one of the most stubborn contenders for the privilege of polluting the air, Control Officer Linsky was able to tell his board of directors, "As far as we know, the last dump fire is out!"[14]

The problem of ending open burning on agricultural land is, however, still under study. Scientists of the University of California are coöperating with the district in an attempt to solve the problem of disposing of fungus-diseased fruit-wood clippings and other farm rubbish otherwise than by burning.

Throughout the early months of 1959 the staff of the district was at work on a second regulation, designed to control emissions from industrial processes, incinerators (other than those used by occupants of one- and two-family dwellings), and heating and power plants. The district also plans to regulate automotive exhausts as soon as automobile manufacturers develop a practicable and satisfactory device for consuming emissions from motor vehicles, now among the chief producers of smog. And by 1963 or 1964 the district hopes to prohibit the use of small incinerators and the burning of rubbish in back yards.

Leaders interested in the eventual establishment of some form of metropolitan government in the Bay Area find the governing board of the air pollution control district an especially provocative example of an area-wide policy-making body. Each of the six counties included in the district is represented by two members: a county supervisor, who serves mainly as a spokesman for unincorporated areas, and a member of one of the city coun-

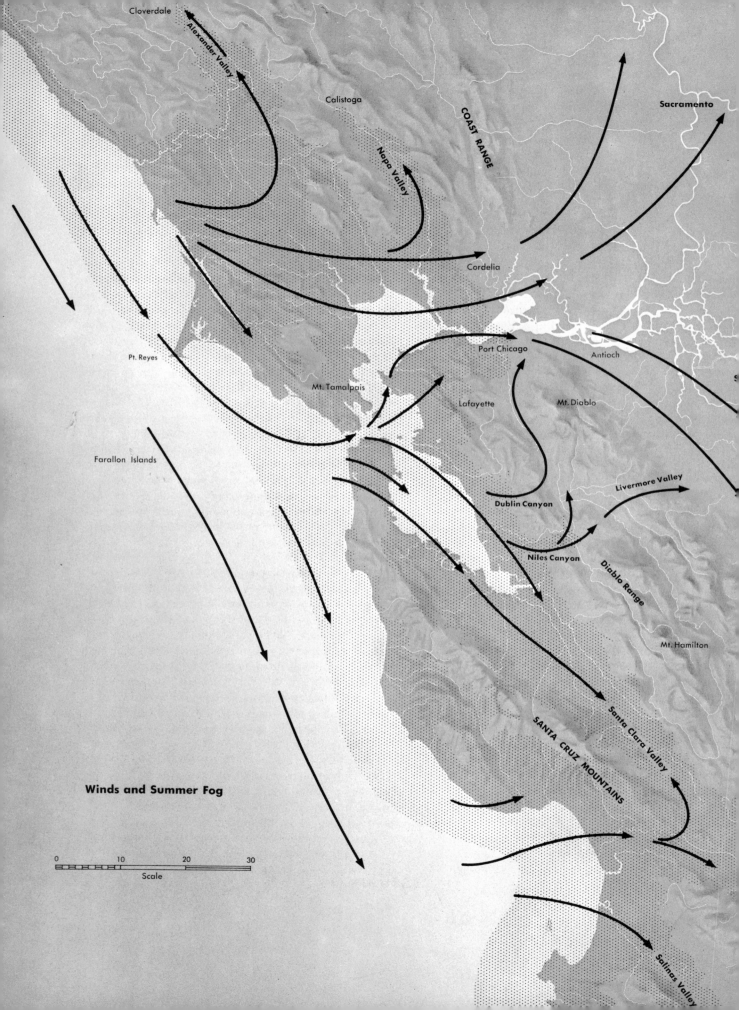

Cloverdale

Alexander Valley

Calistoga

COAST RANGE

Sacramento

Napa Valley

Cordelia

Pt. Reyes

Port Chicago

Antioch

Mt. Tamalpais

Lafayette

Mt. Diablo

Farallon Islands

Livermore Valley

Dublin Canyon

Niles Canyon

Diablo Range

Mt. Hamilton

Winds and Summer Fog

SANTA CRUZ MOUNTAINS

Santa Clara Valley

0   10   20   30
Scale

Salinas Valley

ls in the county, who presumably expresses the urban
view on matters of policy. The composition of this board,
the proponents of metropolitan government point out,
suggests one way of representing cities and counties in
any federation that might be created to handle several
matters of area-wide concern.

eservation of Land

Unlike the problems of controlling air pollution and
water pollution, which have become the responsibilities
of regional boards, the problem of reserving land for
various purposes, including land that will be needed for
future industrial expansion, remains the concern of city
and county governments, with a few significant exceptions. The East Bay Regional Park District is a subregional governmental unit interested in adding to the
land reserves available for recreation in the East Bay. The
state government, through its Division of Beaches and
Parks, likewise has responsibilities for safeguarding shoreline, mountain, and riverbank lands in the Bay Area that
would be valuable for recreational use of all Californians.
But there is as yet no agency empowered to provide a
metropolitan regional recreation system for the entire
Bay Area; nor is there any board or district authorized to
reserve open space as a necessary regional resource—
open space to be used permanently for agriculture, or for
future atomic installations, or for industry, or for developments now altogether unforeseen. The swift obliteration of fields and orchards has, however, prompted some
city planners and political scientists to suggest that if
metropolitan government should be established in the
Bay Area, one of the powers that it should have would be
that of reserving open space in accordance with a plan
for long-term development of the area.

Some of the recent conflicts over the use of land have
dramatized the value of long-range, comprehensive planning and the need for effective measures to hold undeveloped land for appropriate uses. A few years ago in
Alameda County, for example, industrial realtors and
industrial promotion groups became so alarmed over the
loss of potential factory sites to tract builders that they
demanded that the county government prepare a master
or general plan showing the most desirable use of all
lands in the county, and especially the open lands subject
to intensive development. Specifically, the realtors wanted
some "ground rules" established so that there would be
no further disputes over the type of development that
would be allowed in areas eminently suitable for industry.
And they wanted lands designated on the general plan as
industrial areas to be zoned accordingly and held for new
manufacturing plants and other industrial establishments.

In Santa Clara County, where population is estimated
to have increased from 352,000 in 1953 to 620,000 in 1959,
agriculturists who were once lukewarm about legal restrictions on the use of land have turned to planning and
zoning as means of halting the transformation of farmlands into subdivisions and industrial sites. Beginning in
1953, Santa Clara County pioneered in the establishment
of exclusive agricultural zones to protect some of its
richest farmlands. By 1958 the county had set aside more
than thirty thousand acres in well-defined blocks of land,
almost always at the request of agriculturists themselves.
As far as possible, this zoning has been based on planning
studies showing areas judged to be suitable for long-term
preservation as farmland, though undoubtedly much of
the effort to save agricultural land in Santa Clara County
has been merely expedient—a matter of saving what could
be saved after many opportunities for a more orderly
pattern of urban and agricultural lands had been lost.
Growth has been so rapid and municipal annexations of
undeveloped lands have been so numerous and so oppor-
tunistic that the county government cannot be said to
have established an ideal scheme of greenbelts. It has
postponed urbanization in some areas, and it has perhaps
salvaged some lands that may make good parks for the
city dwellers of the future. If, indeed, some of the acreage
now zoned in greenbelts does in time become publicly
owned recreation space, later generations will owe a debt
of gratitude to the agriculturists, county planners, and
county supervisors who protected it from intensive development.

One of the great weaknesses of city and county planning
in the San Francisco Bay Area today is that in attempting
to satisfy local groups, planning agencies sometimes overlook the long-term needs of the whole metropolitan region. The quality of planning in the Bay Area is in
general high, and probably a greater amount of local
planning is being done in this metropolitan region than
in any other in the United States. Unfortunately, none of
the city and county plans made in the past ten years have
been based on a detailed and inclusive analysis of regional
economic and social trends. Even those plans which are
genuinely comprehensive at least for individual political
jurisdictions are not necessarily based on the same regional assumptions and population forecasts; they do not
recognize the same broad regional goals and do not apply
the same general principles and standards. This is because
the Bay Area still lacks a metropolitan regional planning
agency that could do research on the whole area, make
studies of important area-wide problems, stimulate debate
on goals for the area, and gradually win acceptance for a
set of goals that would represent the desires of a majority

of residents, or at least those residents who are vocal and politically active.

The above statement must be modified, however, by pointing out that since 1955 all the city and county planning agencies in the Bay Area/ have had the benefit of regional studies made by consultants to the San Francisco Bay Area Rapid Transit Commission. In the course of preparing a rapid transit plan for the area, the firm of Parsons, Brinckerhoff, Hall and Macdonald did a vast amount of research on the area and developed an outline regional plan as a basis for proposing routes for a transit system. Data collected by the staff engaged in the transit study have been used by many local planning offices, and some of the city and county plans prepared within the past two or three years have incorporated many of the suggestions in the outline regional plan. But the consultants to the transit commission would themselves be the first to acknowledge that their outline plan is no substitute for the kind of guide for regional development that could be prepared by planners with ample time to determine upon area-wide goals and to investigate the full range of economic and social data that should be studied in developing a comprehensive plan. Moreover, the transit plan, which cannot be considered apart from the outline regional plan on which it is based, will not be submitted to a vote of the people of the Bay Area until November, 1960, and therefore does not yet serve as a general guide reflecting the formally expressed desires of the metropolitan regional community. It is, nevertheless, a milestone in the history of the Bay Area, because it suggests, as nothing else ever has, the importance of reaching agreement on goals for the entire region; and it also stands as a reminder that local plans prepared without reference to some widely approved scheme for regional development are at best piecemeal plans.

Regional Transit

The transit plan proposes far more than a system of transit lines and "feeder" routes served by buses. It proposes a functional and spatial organization of the metropolitan region that might actually be brought about by construction of the system, since the influence of transportation facilities on the "structure" of an urban area probably exceeds that of every other element. Instead of the loosely nucleated regional metropolis that we see today, there might be by 1975 or 1980 a regional metropolis with a hierarchy of well-defined centers: a great center including San Francisco, Oakland, and Berkeley; important subcenters at San Jose and at Concord, in central Contra Costa County; and several district centers, each of which ultimately would serve a population ranging

from one hundred and fifty thousand to three hundred thousand. These district centers, situated approximately twelve miles apart, would be cities in which retail outlets for standardized goods, large business and professional offices offering standardized services, and social and cultural facilities at present appear to be concentrating: Santa Rosa, Petaluma, and Napa in the North Bay; San Rafael and San Mateo in the West Bay; Richmond, Berkeley (in the dual role of district center and part of the metropolitan regional center), and Hayward in the East Bay; Palo Alto and Fremont in the South Bay; and Vallejo and Walnut Creek in a territory designated on the plan as the East Inland Area.

The conception of the metropolitan nerve center as a tri-city complex is an especially striking feature of the plan. Ordinarily, people think of the heart of the Bay Area as downtown San Francisco or as a combination of downtown San Francisco and downtown Oakland, whereas the transit planners would make San Francisco, Oakland, and Berkeley virtually one great hub of activity, unified by swift transit, so that the central business districts of San Francisco and Oakland would be only a few minutes apart by an underwater tube, and the University of California and central Berkeley would be readily accessible from both larger cities.

The plan accepts a dispersion of nighttime or residential population in low-density residential communities, somewhat as at present. It proposes a concentration of employed population during the daytime in large, medium, and small centers, because our economy is characterized by ever-increasing specialization of individuals and firms —and specialization demands that those who serve one another be readily accessible to one another. High-density centers of employment would recognize the interdependence of specialists but would be free from the congestion created by an excessive number of automobiles, since the regional transit system would transport thousands of workers to their jobs swiftly, safely, and economically. The transit system would, in fact, "maximize" opportunities for employment. A worker could change jobs without having to change his residence to avoid an unduly time-consuming or fatiguing journey to work. No matter where he lived, he would have rapid access to any one of a score of centers of employment.

In the largest of these, the tri-city regional center, would be concentrated the major headquarters offices, the top professional offices, the most highly specialized business services, regional wholesaling outlets, the most important educational and cultural institutions, and the specialized retailing activities that serve the entire metropolitan region. Establishments in the subregional and district cen-

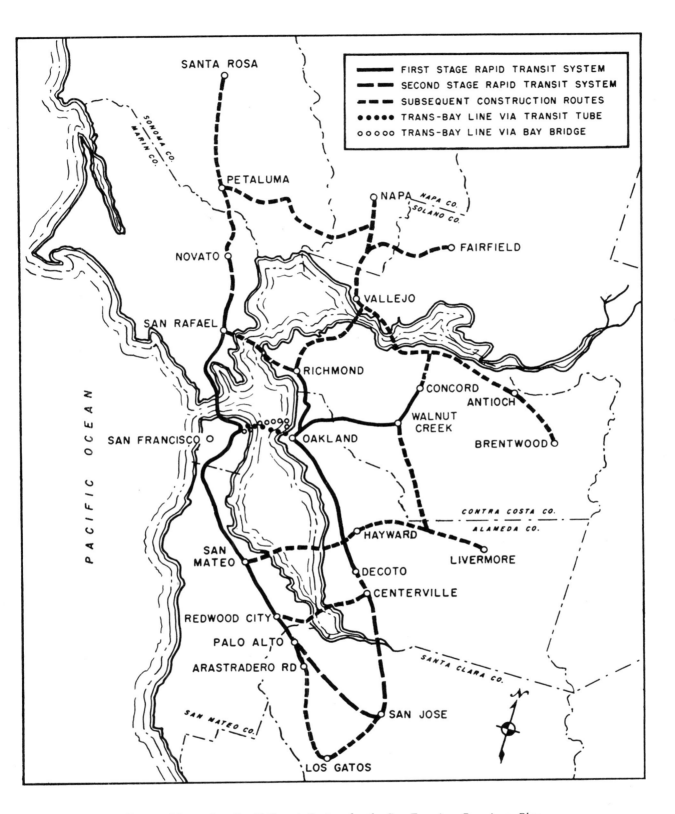

Proposed Interurban Rapid Transit System for the San Francisco Bay Area. Plan prepared by Parsons, Brinckerhoff, Hall and Macdonald, Engineers, New York, for the San Francisco Bay Area Rapid Transit Commission.

ters would provide standardized goods and services and would serve their respective market areas.

The transit planners point out that by linking large and small centers, the projected transit system would serve the greater proportion of workers in the Bay Area, for most of the employment in the area is distributive and service employment, and it tends even now to be concentrated in comparatively small areas. Only approximately one-fifth of the employed persons in the metropolitan region are employed in manufacturing industries, and of these a significant, but unmeasured, number work in San Francisco and Oakland headquarters offices of manufacturing corporations. Furthermore, manufacturing establishments producing light goods and employing large numbers of persons tend to seek locations close to urban centers. Such establishments, then, could also be served by the transit system. The freeways, relieved of much of the traffic that now overloads them, would be adequate in the future to serve the factory districts that form belts along harbors and rail lines, because employment in these areas is relatively low per acre and will undoubtedly continue to fall as automation increases.

In sum, the transit plan envisions a solution of the circulation problems of the Bay Area through the centering of places of employment. The transit system itself would be the chief instrument for bringing about this centering.

Since much of the recent commercial and service development in outlying areas has been predicated upon continuing widespread use of the private automobile and has therefore been somewhat diffuse, would a transit system halt the trend toward loose nucleation and encourage dense clustering of offices, stores, light industries, and similar establishments? Population forecasts leave no doubt that an enormous amount of new development could be directed toward definite centers within the next thirty or forty years; but is this the kind of physical organization of the regional metropolis that the people of the Bay Area want? Do residents of the area understand that they have before them not just a plan for a transit system but a plan for the arrangement of their whole environment?

It is doubtful that more than a very small percentage of Bay Area residents appreciate that they are being asked to make decisions that will in large measure determine how the regional metropolis develops in the future. Discussion of the transit plan has revolved around two questions: Would workers leave their automobiles at home and use a transit system if one were built? What would be the best way to finance construction of the system? Few public officials even mention the influence that the transit system would have on the spatial pattern of economic activities.

Rapid Transit District

Because the rapid transit district formed in the fall of 195 has preceded a metropolitan regional planning agenc and some form of metropolitan government, it perhap has some of the obligations that either such an agency o such a government would have for explaining and drama tizing the issues inseparable from future Bay Area develop ment. But, unfortunately, the district includes only fiv of the nine bay counties—San Francisco, Alameda, Con tra Costa, Marin, and San Mateo. It cannot reach all th people who must deal with the problems facing th regional metropolis, though it can reach most of them If it places the problem of transit in the larger perspectiv in which the consultants to the earlier transit commissio viewed it, then the district might well stimulate interes in the establishment of a regional planning agency an its necessary accompaniment, metropolitan regional gov ernment, such as Toronto, Canada, has enjoyed sinc 1953.

Logically, of course, both area-wide planning and met ropolitan government should be instituted before so im portant a determinant of future development as a rapi transit system is financed and constructed. Planners an political scientists would approve such a sequence o events, but history seldom follows the neat patterns con ceived by rationalists. Regional planning, talked abou in the Bay Area for several decades, is still abstract t most residents. Overloaded freeways, crowded interurba buses, and congested downtown streets are vivid realities so easily comprehended that anyone who has experience them has some basis for judging the merits of a propose rapid transit system estimated to cost $500,000,000 o more in its initial stages and approximately $1,000,000,00 when completed. So again the political leaders and th prominent citizens, with the tacit support of a large num ber of residents, have taken steps to solve a tangible problem, while the few who realize the need for area-wide planning and metropolitan government still struggle to make these needs equally well understood. One more special district has been added to the multiplicity of governmental units serving the Bay Area, and one more agency that might logically function as an operating branch of metropolitan government has been set up independently. At least, another effort has been made to solve a regional problem on a regional basis. The proponents of metropolitan government can some day ask with insistence: Why not merge all area-wide functions—control of water pollution, control of air pollution, management of regional parks, reservation of open space, operation of regional rapid transit, airports, heliports,

nd shipping facilities, and perhaps other functions—
nder one policy-making council or assembly representing
l the cities and counties in the Bay Area?

If the board of the rapid transit district, in pursuing its
ampaign for approval of the proposed system, should
irectly or indirectly renew interest in the establishment
f a metropolitan regional planning agency, it would be
erforming an invaluable service to the Bay Area. After
lore than a century the area is still in the early stages of
s growth and may double its population well before the
ear 2000 and quadruple it by the year 2050. The decis-
ons to be made on matters affecting the entire regional
letropolis will be countless. Those made in the next
venty years will be especially important, for they will
etermine for a very long time many of the physical ar-
angements in the territories surrounding the bay.

egional Planning

a recent years, planning commissioners and professional
ty and county planners in the Bay Area have devoted a
eat deal of time to study of the need for a regional
lanning agency. In 1952 one hundred and eighty com-
issioners representing forty-seven local planning bodies
commended the appointment of a study committee "to
efine and clarify the nature and scope of regional plan-
ng in the Bay Area and to recommend the type of
gency which could most effectively perform the function
f regional planning in the Bay Area . . ."15 Two years
ter, the study committee formed at the suggestion of the
ommissioners issued, through the San Francisco Bay
rea Council, the first of two reports on regional planning,
egional Planning Needs of the San Francisco Bay Area.
he report described familiar problems of the area and
ointed out that without a comprehensive, long-term plan
r all nine counties, "local planning agencies cannot
dequately appraise the probable effects of their plans on
eir own and other communities and on the area as a
hole."16 The second of the two reports, issued in 1956,
resented a proposed statute creating a San Francisco
ay Area regional planning district specifically designed
• fit the complex governmental pattern of the area. This
port recognized that earlier attempts to form a regional
anning commission under the regional planning law of
937 had failed and that if the Bay Area were to succeed
establishing a regional planning agency, a "fresh start"
ould be necessary.

The authors of the proposed statute, consultant William
. Doebele, Jr., and a subcommittee composed of Profes-
•r T. J. Kent, Jr., and the planning directors of the cities
* San Francisco and Oakland and the counties of Ala-
eda and San Mateo favored creation by the state legis-

lature of a regional planning district embracing the entire
metropolitan region. To give the governing bodies of
cities and counties representation on the board of directors of the district, they provided for a board that would
include eighteen city councilmen and county supervisors
and eight citizens-at-large. This board, as an advisory
body only, "would prepare, adopt, and maintain a regional plan for the physical development of the Bay Area
based upon the master plans of the city and county governments of the area and upon studies of region-wide
needs," the report on the proposed statute explained.17
The regional plan, of course, would "serve as a guide for
local plans and planning programs and for state and
federal agencies and special districts."18 Like regional
planning boards in Detroit, Atlanta, Chicago, Toronto,
and other metropolitan communities, the board of the
Bay Area planning district would require a professional
staff to make regional population, economic, traffic, and
land use studies for its own purposes and for the purpose
of assisting and strengthening city and county planning
programs. The authors of the proposed statute believed,
however, that the members of the board would themselves
bear a large measure of the responsibility for promoting
and encouraging coöperation among city, county, regional, state, and federal agencies and private groups in
evolving effective procedures for dealing with regional
development problems that concern everyone in the Bay
Area.

The proposed statute was introduced in the state legislature in 1957 before planning commissioners and professional planners had had sufficient opportunity to
explain it to residents of their localities. In the absence of
informed support for the bill, many legislators perhaps
failed to appreciate the need for creating a planning district including all the cities and counties in the Bay Area.
And they perhaps also did not understand that the Bay
Area has governmental, physical, economic, and social
problems that are very different from those of other metropolitan regions in California. The bill emerged from the
legislative mill as a statute applicable to any metropolitan
community in the state, and it provided that any two
counties could form a district. Thus Alameda and Contra
Costa counties, for example, though constituting only a
subregion of the Bay Area, could become a planning district under the legislation approved by the legislature and
signed by the governor. The establishment of such a
district, however, would contribute little to the solution
of area-wide problems. The Bay Area would be as greatly
in need as ever of a planning agency capable of dealing
with the kinds of regional problems outlined in the first
report of the Planning Commissioners' Study Committee.

Planning commissioners and professional planners in the Bay Area realize that an effort of several years may be required to secure enactment of legislation creating a regional planning district embracing the entire metropolitan region. They face no easy task, though, because there is as yet no ground swell in favor of metropolitan regional planning, despite occasional editorials in the daily press pointing out that a regional planning program would facilitate decisions on the location of additional bay crossings, on the development of the bay for shipping and recreation, and on innumerable other matters that have little relation to city and county boundary lines. The augury of eventual success of a regional planning movement is perhaps the increasing frequency with which regional problems come to the attention of local legislative bodies and private groups. Again and again the solution for some local problem appears to depend on solution of a regional problem; and since local political leaders have come to depend more and more on the advice of their planning staffs, the time is probably approaching when they will believe what the professional planners tell them: that decisions on local matters affected by regional considerations can be farsighted only if made with reference to a plan for regional development.

Obstacles to Success

Assuming that a metropolitan regional planning agency could be established in the San Francisco Bay Area in the next five to ten years, there might be one and possibly two great obstacles to its success: (1) the lack of a metro politan regional council or assembly with responsibilit for area-wide functions and (2) the lack of a state plan ning agency responsible for preparing a general plan fo the state that urban regions could use as a guide i matters of population distribution, allocation of stat water resources, conservation of agricultural areas, an interregional circulation. Both metropolitan governmer and state planning are virtually indispensable to sati factory performance by a metropolitan regional plannin agency.

Unless the Bay Area someday establishes a politica entity empowered to deal with related area-wide gover mental functions, any metropolitan regional plannin body it creates probably will be little more effective tha a private planning organization. To be sure, some priva planning organizations, such as the Regional Plan Asso ciation of New York, have made significant contribution to the development of the areas they serve; but no priva planning organization, however capably staffed an amply financed, can ever accomplish as much as a publi regional planning agency which would submit its recon mendations directly to a metropolitan decision-makin body capable of carrying them out. The implementatio of an area-wide general plan cannot well be left to th voluntary coöperation of cities, counties, and a mult plicity of special districts. Each city or county legislativ body would accept or reject proposals of the region; agency according to the way the local political winds wer

The Need for Area-Wide Unity as Seen by the San Francisco Chronicle. Courtesy of San Francisco Chronicle.

Progress Demands That the Bay Area Be De-Balkanize

lowing at the moment. Spotty implementation of a regional plan would leave so much to be desired that the results would be little more than failure. Transfer of certain local legislative prerogatives to a metropolitan policy-making body is the only long-term answer to the problem of coördinated development in the nine-county Bay Area. Regional planning recommendations presented to such a body could be carried out with little more difficulty than now attends the approval and financing of a local public works program by a city council in any well-governed municipality today.

But to advocate metropolitan regional government as a necessary corollary of metropolitan regional planning is not to ignore some thorny problems. Local political interests must be convinced that a regional government could deal satisfactorily with numerous matters on which they are now unable to take effective action. The division of responsibility between metropolitan and local governments in the many fields that would require action by both must be clarified. Equitable representation on a metropolitan council must be agreed upon, and the operations of various departments and agencies of metropolitan government must be adequately financed.

The record of attempted coöperation among the cities and counties of the Bay Area raises almost as much doubt as it does hope concerning the possibility of metropolitan government. Did not San Francisco and the East Bay cities fail in their efforts to develop a common water supply? Was not the idea of a great municipality embracing both sides of the bay violently opposed by the East Bay? Has not every proposal for a unified harbor district been rejected? And has not voluntary coöperation among ports of the Bay Area deteriorated in the past year or two? Have not Oakland and San Francisco pursued opposing policies on a southern crossing and on alterations to the Bay Bridge? Yet six of the nine bay counties are included in an air-pollution control district, and five have formed a rapid transit district. The counties that have joined neither district probably will seek to be included as they experience the pressures of additional population growth and industrial expansion. Many of the planning commissions in the Bay Area desire regional planning; and now that leading businessmen are becoming interested in metropolitan government, it is only a matter of time until the politicians who oppose it will find themselves in an untenable position.

We cannot assume that the jealousies, rivalries, and shortsightedness that have plagued this metropolitan region during most of its history will persist forever. Only in the past quarter century has there been much recognition of metropolitan problems, and only since World War II has there been much study of them. As the gaps in our present knowledge of conditions and problems are narrowed through more intensive research, and as information on the findings of authorities in various fields is more widely disseminated and more vigorously discussed, public understanding of the opportunities for coöperative solution of problems will inevitably increase. Universities and colleges in the Bay Area are graduating more and more students who have studied the problems under eminent authorities; and these graduates are taking their places in local governments and in regional offices of the state and federal governments, as well as in private business organizations. State senators and assemblymen, many of whom studied metropolitan problems in the university classroom, are becoming intensely interested in devising political machinery that will effectively meet area-wide needs, as witness the quantity of bills on metropolitan problems introduced at recent sessions of the state legislature. Interest in metropolitanism as a cardinal fact of modern state and national life is cumulative. Rapid population growth and inadequately controlled urban expansion cannot but produce additional crises that will focus attention on the political problems of the metropolitan community. Out of these crises will come, in time, the solutions to problems, perhaps not in the way that political scientists would approve, perhaps not in logical sequence, and almost surely not with the thoroughness that would be desirable. In accordance with the political realities of the moment, there will be compromises that factions of almost equal strength will be obliged to make in the interest of resolving bitter conflicts, and there will be concessions that certain influential citizens or dominant political figures will demand. But the problems sooner or later will be solved, apparently through the creation of various area-wide special districts and boards, and possibly through one or more multipurpose metropolitan authorities, until in the long run, let us hope, there will be a consolidation of area-wide functions under one democratically elected council.

Although the establishment of metropolitan government may be many years in the future, there is good reason to believe that the state legislature may authorize creation of a genuine state planning agency within the next few years. The prospect of an ultimate state population of sixty million or more is frightening and sobering to many state legislators. They are beginning to realize that the future distribution of population in California and the growth of new cities should not result from piecemeal and uncoördinated development of dams, aqueducts, highways, and other large-scale state projects, but rather should come about through planning which carefully examines the consequences of every proposed program of public works and relates the projects of all departments of state government to a state plan for the accommodation of a greatly increased population under desirable conditions. Such a plan is needed not only to guide the activities of state agencies but also to assist local governments and to aid the state in dealing with federal agencies. The activities of the Defense Department, especially, are having a great effect—often a disruptive effect—on the development of many communities in California; yet localities and state agencies usually feel handicapped in dealing with the military because they themselves cannot argue in support of well-conceived plans of their own. The state would be in a better position to come to the assistance of local governments in their dealings with the federal government if it had a comprehensive plan indicating the development that would be appropriate in each important subregion; and the very fact that the state had such a plan might spur localities to work out their own plans with greater thoroughness. Rather than let the state make some of the major decisions about their development for them, the metropolitan regions might decide to organize for effective bargaining with the state, through metropolitan governments properly served by regional planning agencies. Indeed, the state legislature probably could do more to promote metropolitan government and regional planning by establishing a strong state planning agency than by any other action it could take.

The Way to a Goal

In view of the desirability of establishing metropolitan government and instituting state planning prior to creating a metropolitan regional planning agency, should citizens in the Bay Area who are anxious to bring about coördination of the activities of city and county planning agencies in the area therefore refrain from attempting to promote a regional agency and instead concentrate their efforts on educating the public to the need for metropolitan government and state planning? Ideally, perhaps they should, but the first-things-first approach to governmental problems sometimes produces slim results. The roundabout way to a goal often proves to be the shortest way, since human beings are not strictly rational creatures and are restrained by habits, traditions, emotional ties, and vague fears of the new and unknown from being logical. It is much more likely that the people of the Bay Area would be willing to experiment with metropolitan regional planning *without* metropolitan government and state planning than with either or both of these ultimately necessary developments in government. An official metropolitan regional planning agency could be established

without altering the structure of local government in the Bay Area in any way. Most city hall politicians and county courthouse "gangs" doubtless would find in the situation a persuasive argument for such an agency. Political realists with more knowledge of course would use it as the principal argument against undertaking any metropolitan regional planning at all, since a regional agency unattached to a metropolitan governmental organization would be a kind of parentless body—a waif among official agencies, integrated with neither local government nor state government. But at least such an agency might perform an educational service. Even its failures to induce local governments to coöperate in carrying out area-wide plans would be illuminating. Each debacle on the metropolitan planning front—indeed, there would surely be some—would emphasize the need for devising new governmental machinery for solving area-wide problems. In the more optimistic view, however, a metropolitan regional planning agency might actually accomplish a good deal by defining problems, setting goals, providing reliable population projections and economic analyses, and developing a general plan based on reasonable assumptions concerning future economic, social, and political conditions. If public-spirited citizens and officials throughout the Bay Area would fully support the agency, its influence might far outweigh its ambiguous status among governmental organizations. The agency could be no more effective, though, than the people of the metropolitan community wanted it to be. It might be a dismal failure—and it might be a great success.

Now the question is: Are the residents of the Bay Area ready to take the chance? Although most professional planners and many of the planning commissioners in the Bay Area recognize the need for metropolitan regional planning, most citizens appear to be intent on solving local problems and cannot always see that a local highway location problem is part of an area-wide circulation problem, or that the struggle to increase the local tax base by attracting new industries is related to the whole problem of a unified approach to taxation in the close-knit metropolitan community. Never before in the history of the Bay Area have there been so many citizens' leagues, neighborhood improvements associations, parent-teacher associations, taxpayers associations, and local planning groups attempting to find solutions to problems of rapid and poorly regulated growth, insufficient taxes to support schools and other community services, and inadequate government in unincorporated areas. Few of these suburban organizations seem to realize, however, that the matters with which they are concerned have metropolitan implications and can be properly understood only in re-ion to a scheme of development for the entire Bay Area.

Is it surprising, though, that many local groups fail to appreciate the metropolitan aspects of local zoning, subdivision regulation, and public improvement programs? In community after community one-fourth, one-third, or even half of the people are newcomers, not only to the locality but also to the Bay Area and to California. They have not lived long enough in this metropolitan region to know its history, to identify their immediate environment with the larger urban complex, or to have gained much insight into the future of the nine-county Bay Area. In the schools the children learn something about their home community and the State of California, but rarely are they introduced to the concept of the metropolitan community, because the teachers themselves usually have not become acquainted with the broader view of the urban area. To counteract the rootlessness, the mobility, and the

limited perspective of residents in suburban communities, especially, Bay Area leaders should undertake a long-term program to develop a new type of citizen—one who is metropolitan in outlook. Civic participation at the local level should be encouraged, but the endeavor to improve the immediate environment must somehow be given a new orientation, so that local effort may contribute to area-wide progress.

A Council of Civic Groups

The many civic groups that have recently sprung up in Bay Area cities and unincorporated areas should first of all be allied in a metropolitan council of civic groups, through which they could become aware, by the exchange of information on their local problems, of the area-wide implications of local struggles. The wider knowledge thus gained could be translated, in time, into material for use

The Encroachment of the City on the Hills: Step One. Photograph courtesy of David Arbegast and Robert Tetlow.

in the public schools throughout the Bay Area. The schools are now presenting a wealth of material on municipal government and urban problems at various grade levels, but they are not emphasizing the metropolitan region as the significant community of our time. Until the metropolitan community is seen as the larger environment in which the family lives and works and plays, there is not too much hope of planning that environment well or governing it properly. The forces of formal and of informal education should be mobilized to advance the welfare of each local community in the Bay Area principally by seeking solutions to problems that are area-wide, because perhaps most so-called local problems are not local at all but metropolitan.

Does the Bay Area have the kind of leadership that can educate citizens to the larger responsibilities of membership in a metropolitan regional community? Before there can be large numbers of citizens with a metropolitan point of view, there first must be an active corps of men and women dedicated to the proposition that urban life in our age requires a new allegiance—to the entire urban area rather than to some part of it. Residents of Maine and Alabama and Wisconsin and Arizona manage to think of themselves first of all as Americans and secondly as residents of a particular commonwealth. It should be possible some day for residents of San Francisco and Oakland and San Jose and Santa Rosa to sublimate pride in a locality to pride in a metropolitan union of cities. But imaginative leaders will have to show the way by rising above home-town sentiments whenever matters of metropolitan regional concern are involved. To date the leaders who can comprehend more than the economic aspects of metropolitan regional development and more than the possibilities of creating an integrated circulation system have been few. These few must now add to their numbers and with their new colleagues must undertake to fashion a true metropolitan society.

Their first task is the twofold one of organizing a metropolitan council of citizen associations and planning a systematic program of educating the public, intended to reach the schools and every responsible civic group in the Bay Area. From the foundation laid by the educational program—which should be a program making use of every available means of communication—in time should come the popular determination to organize the metropolitan region politically, economically, and physically in a manner clearly in accord with the demands of our mass production, mass consumption, and mass leisure society. That society, making use of more and more technological wonders, has shrunk physical distance and has telescoped time until every part of the metropolitan region is potentially just around the corner from all other parts. The concept of the self-contained city is obsolete. The regional metropolis requires physical integration, economic development coördinated with the physical pattern, and the kind of over-all government that will enable its economic enterprises and social institutions to function efficiently in a vast area, unimpeded by conflicting local ordinances

The Future Metropolis

Today we see in the Bay Area only the beginnings of the regional metropolis. By the end of the century it will be one continuous urban development around the bay, with extensions into the valleys to the north, south, and east. It will be a world metropolis in every sense of the word, composed of people from all nations, linked by transportation and communication to other world centers, nurtured in its daily life by raw materials, manufactured goods, and cultural exchanges from every corner of the globe. Much that is today old and blighted or new and shoddily built will have disappeared and will have been replaced by better-planned developments. Large areas of the bay will have been reclaimed for waterfront parks, manufacturing sites, residential communities, and additional airports. An area-wide freeway system and an area-wide transit system, perhaps including some aerial services, should by that time have been in operation for two or three decades.

But the danger is that much of the unique charm of the Bay Area may be sacrificed in the development of this world metropolis, by removing scenic hills to reclaim marshlands and tidelands, by bulldozing and blasting huge cuts in wooded slopes in order to construct freeways, and by recklessy permitting residential building in hillcrest and mountainous areas that would be ideal for regional parks. Great and rapid growth, such as this area is now experiencing and probably will experience for decades, imposes herculean responsibilities upon a community. Because the San Francisco Bay Area has been more generously endowed with natural beauty than most of the large urban areas of the world, its residents have an especially weighty stewardship to discharge. Not for ourselves and our own posterity but for the global community should we strive to safeguard the beauties of this magnificent combination of bays and islands, mountains and valleys—and to enhance the heritage received from nature by skillfully wedding the structures and roadways of the evolving regional metropolis to the physical environment. To achieve so lofty a goal we must do no less than perceive new obligations of the individual to society, fashion new laws for controlling individual action in the interest of the entire community, devise a workable system of metropolitan government, and weld into a new creative force the talents of all those concerned with metropolitan regional development—elected officials, businessmen, industrialists, and their employees, members of the professions, and workers in the many governments of the San Francisco Bay Area, Are we equal to the challenge?

The Magnificent Natural Setting of the San Francisco Bay Area, a Heritage to be Safeguarded. Photograph courtesy of Max Yavno.

Notes

NOTES TO CHAPTER 1 (PAGES 1–22)

Heritage

[1] Fr. Francisco Palóu, *Relación histórica de la vida . . . Junípero Serra*, pp. 88–89, translated and quoted by Fr. Zephyrin Engelhardt in *Missions and Missionaries of California*, II, 55.

[2] H. E. Bolton, *Fray Juan Crespi, Missionary Explorer on the Pacific Coast, 1769–1774*, p. 229.

[3] Letter of José Francisco de Ortega to Fr. Francisco Palóu, Feb. , 1770, quoted by George Davidson, in "The Discovery of San Francisco Bay," *Transactions and Proceedings of the Geographical Society of the Pacific*, IV, Ser. II, p. 76.

[4] Quoted by C. E. Chapman in *A History of California, The Spanish Period*, pp. 229–230.

[5] Quoted by Neal Harlow in *The Maps of San Francisco Bay*, p. 7.

[6] Quoted by H. E. Bolton in *Font's Complete Diary*, p. 341.

[7] Quoted *ibid.*, p. 346.

[8] George Vancouver, *A Voyage of Discovery to the North Pacific Ocean, and Round the World*, III, 32.

[9] *Ibid.*, p. 34.

[10] *Ibid.*, p. 40.

[11] Quoted by William Halley in *The Centennial Year Book of Alameda County, California*, p. 73.

[12] Nicholas "Cheyenne" Dawson, *Overland to California in '41 and '49, and Texas in '51*, p. 33.

[13] *Ibid.*, pp. 29–30.

[14] *Ibid.*, p. 33.

NOTES TO CHAPTER 2 (PAGES 23–38)

Mother of Cities

[1] San Francisco *California Star*, Jan. 23, 1847, p. 3.

[2] W. T. Sherman, *Memoirs of General William T. Sherman*, I, 33.

[3] Quoted by J. W. Caughey in *Gold is the Cornerstone*, p. 42.

[4] H. H. Bancroft, *History of California*, VI, 159.

[5] Frank Soulé and others, *The Annals of San Francisco*, p. 243.

[6] Quoted by C. G. Murphy in *The People of the Pueblo: The Story of Sonoma*, p. 152.

[7] Quoted *ibid.*, p. 151.

[8] Sherman, *op. cit.*, I, 74.

[9] California, *Journal of the Legislature, 1850*, pp. 498–502.

[10] Munro-Fraser, *History of Alameda County, California*, p. 65.

[11] *Golden Era* (San Francisco), July 31, 1853, p. 2.

[12] Soulé and others, *op. cit.*, p. 482.

[13] *Golden Era*, July 17, 1853, p. 2.

[14] *Ibid.*, July 3, 1853, p. 4.

[15] Bancroft, *op. cit.*, VI, 778.

[16] Soulé and others, *op. cit.*, pp. 489–490.

NOTES TO CHAPTER 3 (PAGES 39–56)

The Plow, the Iron Horse, and New Towns

[1] Quoted by Marguerite Hunt and Harry Lawrence Gunn in *History of Solano County . . . and Napa County, California*, p. 240.

[2] William Halley, *The Centennial Year Book of Alameda County, California*, p. 125.

[3] J. P. Young, *San Francisco: A History of the Pacific Coast Metropolis*, I, 311.

[4] This line later was used exclusively for local service.

[5] *Map of Holly Oak Park, Part of Suscol Rancho, Napa County*, 1869.

[6] F. M. Stanger, *History of San Mateo County, California*, p. 158.

[7] Oakland *Daily News*, Feb. 8, 1869.

[8] J. Ross Browne, *Letter from the Hon. J. Ross Browne . . . in Relation to the Proposed Town Site of Lower Berkeley and the Value of Property and Growth of Population in and Around Oakland*, p. 19.

[9] F. L. Olmsted, *Preliminary Report in Regard to a Plan of Public Pleasure Grounds for the City of San Francisco*, p. 11.

[10] "Opinion of Mr. Justice Field . . .," U. S. Circuit Court, *Opinions . . . City of San Francisco vs. The United States*, p. 9.

[11] *Ibid.*, p. 10.

[12] Letter, Frederick Law Olmsted (San Francisco) to Calvert Vaux (New York), Sept. 28, 1865. MS, Library of Congress.

[13] Olmsted, *Preliminary Report*, p. 12.

[14] *Ibid.*, p. 8.

[15] *Ibid.*, p. 30.

[16] San Francisco Board of Park Commissioners, *The Development of Golden Gate Park*, p. 8.

[17] F. L. Olmsted, *Berkeley Neighborhood: Report upon a Projected Improvement of the Estate of the College of California at Berkeley, near Oakland*, p. 23.

[18] S. H. Willey, *A History of the College of California*, p. 2.

[19] *Ibid.*

[20] *Ibid.*, p. 3.

[21] *California Constitution* (1849), Art. IX, sec. 4.

[22] Willey, *op. cit.*, p. 36.

[23] Olmsted, *Berkeley Neighborhood*, p. 23.

[24] *Ibid.*, p. 24.

NOTES TO CHAPTER 4 (PAGES 57–70)
Urban Rivalries

[1] Quoted by J. S. Hitteel in *The Prospects of Vallejo*, p. 42.

[2] Quoted *ibid.*, pp. 60–61.

[3] Quoted by J. Ross Browne in *Letter . . . in Relation to . . . the Growth of Population in and Around Oakland*, p. 36.

[4] San Francisco *Daily Morning Call*, Oct. 6, 1871, as quoted by Hittell, *op. cit.*, p. 54.

[5] Oakland Daily Transcript, *Information Concerning the Terminus of the Railroad System of the Pacific Coast*, p. 31.

[6] Quoted by William Halley in *The Centennial Year Book of Alameda County, California*, p. 348.

[7] All estimates cited are by H. H. Bancroft, *History of California*, VII, 696–697.

[8] A. C. Loosley, "Foreign-born Population of California, 1848–1920," p. 23.

[9] B. J. Arnold, *Report on . . . Transportation Facilities in San Francisco*, p. 422.

[10] Oakland *News*, June 12, 1873.

NOTES TO CHAPTER 5 (PAGES 71–94)
The Heyday of Enterprise

[1] San Francisco *Chronicle*, Jan. 1, 1891, p. 13.

[2] *Ibid.*, p. 15.

[3] H. H. Bancroft, *History of California*, VII, 743.

[4] California Crop and Livestock Reporting Service, *California Field Crops Statistics 1866–1946*, p. 14.

[5] San Francisco *Morning Call*, Jan. 5, 1891.

[6] *Municipal Reports for the Fiscal Year 1884–85* (San Francisco, 1885), p. 168.

[7] *Ibid.*

[8] *Ibid.*, p. 207.

[9] *Ibid.*, p. 178.

[10] R. A. Walker, *The Planning Function in Urban Government*, pp. 55–56.

[11] San Francisco *Chronicle*, June 25, 1887, p. 6.

[12] L. G. Hughes, "Housing in San Francisco, 1835–1938," p. 95.

[13] San Francisco *Chronicle*, Jan. 1, 1891, p. 29.

[14] Quoted *ibid.*, p. 26.

[15] San Francisco *Chronicle*, June 26, 1887, p. 8.

[16] *Ibid.*

[17] Quoted by D. E. Wood in *History of Palo Alto*, p. 43.

[18] Oakland *Daily Evening Tribune*, Jan. 2, 1891, p. 8.

[19] D. W. Smythe, "An Economic History of Local and Interurban Transportation in the East Bay Cities," p. 86.

[20] San Francisco Morning Call, *Fettered Commerce—How the Pacific Mail and the Railroads Have Bled San Francisco* (1892), p. 5

[21] *Ibid.*, pp. 6–7.

[22] *Ibid.*, p. 7.

[23] *Ibid.*, p. 12.

[24] Quoted by J. P. Young in *San Francisco: A History of the Pacific Coast Metropolis*, II, 657.

[25] A. S. Macdonald, "The Beginnings of Richmond," *Bank News* October, 1916, p. 3.

[26] Richmond *Independent*, Dec. 20, 1939.

[27] San Francisco *Examiner*, Sunday Magazine, Dec. 30, 1900, p. 4

NOTES TO CHAPTER 6 (PAGES 95–108)
The Burnham Plan for San Francisco

[1] F. M. Todd, *The Story of the Exposition*, I, 35–37.

[2] San Francisco *Bulletin*, Jan. 4, 1904, p. 1.

[3] *Ibid.*

[4] *The Wasp* (San Francisco), June 3, 1904.

[5] San Francisco *Bulletin*, Jan. 7, 1904.

[6] *Ibid.*

[7] San Francisco *Call*, Jan. 13, 1904.

[8] San Francisco *Bulletin*, Jan. 14, 1904.

[9] Untitled brochure of the Association for the Improvement and Adornment of San Francisco, 1904.

[10] San Francisco *Bulletin*, May 5, 1904.

[11] San Francisco *Chronicle*, May 7, 1904.

[12] Charles Moore, *Daniel H. Burnham, Architect, Planner of Cities*, II, 57, 173.

[13] D. H. Burnham and E. H. Bennett, *Report on a Plan for San Francisco*, p. 35. Hereafter cited as Burnham *Plan*.

[14] *Ibid.*

[15] *Ibid.*

[16] *Ibid.*, p. 39.

[17] San Francisco City Planning Commission, *Transportation Section of the Master Plan of the City and County of San Francisco*, par 37.

[18] Burnham *Plan*, p. 44.

[19] *Ibid.*, p. 144.

[20] *Ibid.*, p. 114.

[21] *Ibid.*, p. 145.

[22] *Ibid.*, pp. 158, 167.

[23] *Ibid.*, p. 180.

[24] *Ibid.*, p. 179.

[25] San Francisco *Chronicle*, Sept. 28, 1905, p. 9.

[26] *Ibid.*, p. 9.

[27] Herbert Croly, "The Promised City of San Francisco," *Architectural Record*, June, 1906, as quoted in Oakland *Enquirer*, June 13 1906, p. 4.

NOTES TO CHAPTER 7 (PAGES 109–122)
The New San Francisco

[1] San Francisco *Bulletin*, April 25, 1906, p. 4.

[2] *Ibid.*, April 23, 1906, p. 2.

[3] *Ibid.*, April 21, 1906, p. 1.

4 Quoted by F. W. Aitken and Edward Hilton in *A History of the Earthquake and Fire in San Francisco*, p. 179.

5 "The Tenement House Question in California," *Transactions of the Commonwealth Club of California*, October, 1906, pp. 85–86, as quoted by Lillian G. Hughes in "Housing in San Francisco 1835–1938," p. 110.

6 Langley Porter, "Report of the President," in San Francisco Housing Association, *First Report*, p. 6.

7 Charles Moore, *Daniel H. Burnham, Architect, Planner of Cities*, 141.

8 San Francisco *Chronicle*, April 29, 1906, p. 3.

9 *Ibid.*

10 *Ibid.*, p. 6.

11 San Francisco *Bulletin*, May 3, 1906, p. 3.

12 San Francisco *Chronicle*, May 4, 1906, p. 5.

13 San Francisco *Bulletin*, May 5, 1906, p. 4.

14 *Ibid.*, p. 4.

15 San Francisco *Chronicle*, May 22, 1906, p. 3.

16 *Ibid.*

17 San Francisco *Bulletin*, May 22, 1906, p. 4.

18 *Ibid.*, May 26, 1906, p. 4.

19 San Francisco *Chronicle*, May 23, 1906, p. 6.

20 *Ibid.*, June 6, 1906, p. 14.

21 San Francisco *Bulletin*, May 24, 1906, p. 4.

22 *Ibid.*, May 29, 1906, p. 6.

23 Oakland *Enquirer*, June 6, 1906, p. 4.

24 San Francisco *Chronicle*, May 27, 1906, p. 18.

25 *Ibid.*, June 6, 1906, p. 1.

26 *Ibid.*, June 7, 1906, p. 1.

27 San Francisco *Bulletin*, June 14, 1906.

28 *Ibid.*

29 Oakland *Enquirer*, July 25, 1906, p. 4.

30 *Ibid.*, Sept. 5, 1906, p. 4.

31 *The Nation*, June 3, 1909, as quoted by Robert Glass Cleland in *California in Our Time* (*1900–1940*), p. 23.

32 Rufus Steele, *The City That Is*, p. 37.

33 Aitken and Hilton, *op. cit.*, p. 260.

34 Steele, *op. cit.*, p. 46.

35 San Francisco *Bulletin*, April 14, 1909.

36 *Ibid.*

37 Telegram, D. H. Burnham to Willis Polk, from Chicago, April 22, 1909, in Phelan Scrapbook, "Adornment Association 1908 to 1911," Bancroft Library, University of California.

38 "Address of Thomas Magee before the Merchants' Association, May 27, 1909," MS in Phelan Scrapbook.

39 San Francisco *Bulletin*, June 1, 1909.

40 San Francisco *Chronicle*, June 22, 1909.

41 San Francisco *Bulletin*, June 28, 1909.

42 W. H. Irwin, *The City That Was*, pp. 7 and 47.

NOTES TO CHAPTER 8 (PAGES 123–132)

Oakland: The End of the Village Tradition

1 Oakland *Tribune*, April 27, 1906, p. 9.

2 Oakland *Times*, July 18, 1906, p. 1.

3 *Ibid.*, July 27, 1906, p. 2.

4 Oakland *Enquirer*, July 28, 1906, p. 4.

5 *Ibid.*, Aug. 4, 1906, p. 4.

6 *Ibid.*, Sept. 14, 1906, p. 4.

7 *Ibid.*, Sept. 21, 1906, p. 4.

8 *Ibid.*, Sept. 25, 1906, p. 4.

9 *Ibid.*

10 C. M. Robinson, *A Plan of Civic Improvement for the City of Oakland, California*, p. 3.

11 *Ibid.*, pp. 4 and 8.

12 *Ibid.*, p. 5.

13 *Ibid.*, pp. 6–7.

14 *Ibid.*, p. 6.

15 *Ibid.*, p. 9.

16 *Ibid.*

17 Werner Hegemann, *Report on a City Plan for the Municipalities of Oakland and Berkeley*, p. 132.

18 Robinson, *op. cit.*, p. 12.

19 *Ibid.*, p. 14.

20 *Ibid.*, pp. 14–17.

21 *Ibid.*, pp. 17–20.

22 Oakland *Enquirer*, June 12, 1906, p. 9.

23 *Ibid.*, June 9, 1906, p. 3.

24 *Ibid.*, Aug. 10, 1906, p. 6.

25 *Ibid.*, Jan. 10, 1907, p. 6.

26 *Ibid.*

27 Oakland *Tribune*, Jan. 15, 1907, p. 6.

28 *Ibid.*

29 Oakland *Enquirer*, Jan. 15, 1907, p. 4.

NOTES TO CHAPTER 9 (PAGES 133–148)

The Greater San Francisco Movement

1 San Francisco *Chronicle*, April 30, 1910, p. 6.

2 F. M. Todd, *The Story of the Exposition*, I, 97–98.

3 *Souvenir of Golden Gate Park—Rehabilitation Edition of the Golden Gate Park News*, p. 7.

4 Quoted in *Wheel Clicks*, Peninsular issue, Vol. V, No. 1 (July, 1944), p. 4.

5 San Francisco *Chronicle*, April 19, 1910, p. 6.

6 *Ibid.*, June 11, 1910, p. 11.

7 William L. Gerstle, "President's Annual Report," *Sixty-first Annual Report of the Chamber of Commerce of San Francisco*, pp. 17–18.

8 San Francisco Chamber of Commerce *Journal*, Vol. I, No. 9 (July, 1912), p. 11.

9 Oakland Chamber of Commerce *Bulletin*, Vol. I, No. 10 (October, 1910), p. 2; Vol. II, No. 10 (October, 1911), p. 3; Vol. II, No. 12 (December, 1911), p. 1.

10 *Ibid.*, Vol. I, No. 5 (May, 1910), p. 4.

11 *Ibid.*, Vol. I, No. 6 (June, 1910), p. 3.

12 Quoted in Oakland *Tribune*, Centennial Edition, May 1, 1952, p. 4-X.

13 Oakland Chamber of Commerce *Bulletin*, Vol. II, No. 4 (April, 1911), p. 5.

14 *Ibid.*, Vol. II, No. 9 (September, 1911), p. 3; Vol. V, No. 4 (April, 1914), p. 3.

15 Oakland *Tribune*, Aug. 18, 1910, p. 6.

16 *Report on Richmond Harbor Project*, p. 35.

17 Quoted in Oakland Chamber of Commerce *Bulletin*, Vol. I, No. 9 (September, 1910), p. 2.

18 Oakland Chamber of Commerce *Bulletin*, Vol. II, No. 8 (August, 1911), p. 1.

19 John R. Freeman, *On the Proposed Use of . . . Hetch Hetchy, Eleanor and Cherry Valleys . . . as Reservoirs . . . for the Water Supply of San Francisco, California, and Neighboring Cities*, p. 162.

20 *Ibid.*, p. 144.

21 *Ibid.*, p. 9.

22 *Ibid.*, p. 77.

23 *Ibid.*

24 *Ibid.*, pp. 112–127.

25 *Ibid.*, p. 165.

26 *Ibid.*, p. 163.

27 *Ibid.*, p. 166.

28 *Ibid.*

29 The quotations from the three newspapers were printed in Oakland Chamber of Commerce *Bulletin*, Vol. III, No. 8 (August, 1912), p. 1.

30 Quoted *ibid.*

31 Oakland *Tribune*, Nov. 1, 1912, p. 8.

32 *Ibid.*

33 Oakland Chamber of Commerce *Bulletin*, Vol. III, No. 10 (October, 1912), p. 1.

34 Oakland *Tribune*, Nov. 1, 1912, p. 1.

35 *Ibid.*, Nov. 9, 1912, p. 1.

36 *Ibid.*, Nov. 7, 1912, p. 1.

37 San Francisco *Chronicle*, Nov. 7, 1912, p. 6.

38 *Ibid.*

39 Oakland *Enquirer*, June 27, 1906, p. 4.

40 B. J. Arnold, *Report on the Improvement and Development of the Transportation Facilities of San Francisco*, p. 4.

41 *Ibid.*, pp. 5–6.

42 *Ibid.*

NOTES TO CHAPTER 10 (PAGES 149–168)

The Panama Canal: Stimulus to Planning

1 Oakland *Tribune*, Jan. 23, 1913, p. 12.

2 *Ibid.*, p. 8.

3 San Francisco Chamber of Commerce *Journal*, February, 1913, p. 8.

4 *Ibid.*

5 *Transactions of the Commonwealth Club of California*, VII (December, 1912), 539–540.

6 *Biennial Report of the Board of State Harbor Commissioners for the Fiscal Years Commencing July 1, 1910 and Ending June 30, 1912*, as quoted by Werner Hegemann in *Report on a City Plan for the Municipalities of Oakland & Berkeley*, p. 22.

7 *Ibid.*

8 Letter, Col. T. H. Rees to Werner Hegemann, *ibid.*, p. 35.

9 W. W. Ferrier, *Berkeley, California*, p. 315.

10 Oakland *Tribune*, May 6, 1914, p. 2.

11 San Francisco *Call*, July 29, 1911.

12 *San Francisco Municipal Reports for the Fiscal Years 1915–16*, p. 979.

13 Christopher Tunnard, *The City of Man*, p. 326.

14 F. M. Todd, *The Story of the Exposition*, II, 315.

15 B. R. Maybeck, *Palace of Fine Arts and Lagoon, Panama-Pacific International Exposition, 1915*, p. 9.

16 Oakland *Tribune*, Oct. 13, 1913, pp. 11–12.

17 Duncan McDuffie, "City Planning in Berkeley," *Berkeley Civic Bulletin*, March 15, 1916, p. 108.

18 Berkeley *Gazette*, Oct. 14, 1913, p. 1.

19 Hegemann, *op. cit.*, p. 19.

20 *Ibid.*, p. 16.

21 *Ibid.*, p. 36.

22 *Ibid.*, p. 22.

23 California Senate Fact-finding Committee, *Ports of the Sa Francisco Bay Area*, pp. 381–382.

24 Hegemann, *op. cit.*, p. 155.

25 *Ibid.*, p. 156.

26 C. H. Cheney, "How California Communities Can Profit b Active City Planning," *Pacific Municipalities*, XXVIII (Januar 1914), 31.

27 Duncan McDuffie, *op. cit.*, p. 113.

28 *Transactions of the Commonwealth Club*, XI (January, 1917 638.

29 M. M. O'Shaughnessy, "The Hetch Hetchy Water and Pow Project, the Municipal Railway, and Other Notable Civic Improve ments of San Francisco," p. 18.

30 "Recent Municipal Activities in San Francisco," *Pacific Munic palities*, XXIX (October, 1915), 439.

31 *San Francisco Municipal Reports for the Fiscal Year 1916–1* p. 822.

NOTES TO CHAPTER 11 (PAGES 169–187)

Seeds of Metropolitan Regionalism

1 E. L. Finley, ed., *History of Sonoma County, California*, p. 42

2 Stephen Child, *A Plan for the Development of Alum Rock Pa (Reservation) at San Jose, California*, p. 13.

3 *Ibid.*, p. 17.

4 *Transactions of the Commonwealth Club*, XVII (1922), 162.

5 *Ibid.*, XVII, 171.

6 *Ibid.*, XVII, 173–175.

7 *Ibid.*, XVII, 127.

8 *Ibid.*, XVII, 141.

9 *Ibid.*, XVII, 132.

10 *Ibid.*, XVII, 134.

11 *Ibid.*, XVIII (1923), 270–271.

12 *Ibid.*, XVIII, 277.

13 *Ibid.*, XVIII, 277–278.

14 J. C. Bollens, *The Problem of Government in the San Francis Bay Region*, p. 73.

15 *Ibid.*, p. 92.

16 Los Angeles County ordinance, quoted by J. C. Stephens "The Development of County Planning in California," p. 18.

17 R. V. N. Black "A Report in Recommendation of a Region Plan for the San Francisco Bay District by the Regional Plan Su Committee of the Commonwealth Club of California" (Feb. 2 1924), MS in the possession of Mr. Black, p. 2.

18 *Ibid.*, pp. 4–5.

19 *Ibid.*, p. 4.

20 *Ibid.*, p. 5.

NOTES TO CHAPTER 12 (PAGES 188–201)

Fred Dohrmann and the Regional Plan Association

1 Letter, Fred Dohrmann to James D. Phelan, San Francisc May 13, 1925, copy in files of Regional Plan Association, Bancro Library, University of California. Hereafter cited as files of Region Plan Association.

2 MS in files of Regional Plan Association.

3 Berkeley *Daily Gazette*, March 13, 1925.

4 F. R. Dohrmann, "Cooperation for Regional Planning," M in files of Regional Plan Association.

5 *Transactions of the Commonwealth Club*, XX (1925), 436.

6 Letter, Fred Dohrmann to Homer R. Spence, San Francisco, n. 30, 1926, copy in files of Regional Plan Association.

7 Harland Bartholomew, *The San Francisco Bay Region*, p. 10.

8 *Ibid.*, p. 30.

9 *Ibid.*, p. 11.

10 *Ibid.*, p. 12.

11 *Ibid.*, p. 11.

12 *Ibid.*, p. 12.

13 *Ibid.*, p. 18.

14 *Ibid.*, p. 30.

15 Letter, Fred Dohrmann to Marshal Hale, Nov. 20, 1925, copy files of Regional Plan Association.

16 Letter, Fred Dohrmann to Robert I. Bentley, Dec. 12, 1925, py in files of Regional Plan Association.

17 Letter in files of Regional Plan Association.

18 Statement made to the author by Guy Wilfrid Hayler.

19 C. H. Lee, "The Future Development of the Metropolitan Area urrounding San Francisco Bay," *Bulletin of the Seismological ociety of America*, XVI (June, 1926), 81.

20 *Ibid.*, p. 103.

21 *Ibid.*, pp. 104–105.

22 G. W. Hayler, *The San Francisco Bay Region of the Future*, p. 8.

23 *Ibid.*, p. 7.

24 Fred Dohrmann, "Regional Planning of the San Francisco Bay ounties," MS in files of Regional Plan Association.

25 *Ibid.*

26 Stephen Child, "A Planning Federation for the Bay Region," S in files of Regional Plan Association, p. 14.

27 *Ibid.*, pp. 2–3.

28 *Ibid.*, p. 6.

29 *Ibid.*, p. 9.

30 *Ibid.*, p. 12.

31 *Ibid.*, p. 12.

32 *Ibid.*, p. 14.

33 Statement made to the author by G. W. Hayler.

34 *California Statutes*, 1927, chap. 874, sec. 5.

35 Letter, Fred Dohrmann to Russell Wolden, 1928, copy in files f Regional Plan Association.

36 Memorandum in files of Regional Plan Association.

NOTES TO CHAPTER 13 (PAGES 202–223)

Prosperity and Projects

1 W. W. Ferrier, *Berkeley, California*, p. 331.

2 *Transactions of the Commonwealth Club*, XXIV (1929), 469.

3 *California Real Estate Magazine*, VII (February, 1927), 50.

4 F. C. Merritt, *History of Alameda County, California*, II, 583.

5 Quoted by Hale Champion in "How Nine Men Finally Got Bay ridge Started," San Francisco *Chronicle*, March 23, 1953, p. 1.

6 Quoted *ibid.*

7 Quoted *ibid.*

8 San Jose *Mercury-Herald*, Dec. 4, 1929, p. 1.

9 California Senate Fact-finding Committee, *Ports of the San rancisco Bay Area*, p. 253.

10 San Francisco Board of Supervisors Airport Committee, *San rancisco Airport: A Report* (1931), p. 9.

11 *Ibid.*, p. 13.

12 *Ibid.*, pp. 16–17.

13 *San Francisco Business*, Aug. 5, 1931.

NOTES TO CHAPTER 14 (PAGES 224–243)

Progress in Troubled Times

1 California State Planning Board, *An Economic and Industrial Survey of the San Francisco Bay Area*, p. xxxi.

2 San Francisco Bay Area Chambers of Commerce, *Serving Pacific Markets*, p. 5.

3 *San Francisco Business*, June 3, 1931.

4 *Ibid.*

5 *Ibid.*

6 San Francisco *Chronicle*, May 26, 1932, p. 24.

7 *Ibid.*, Aug. 19, 1932, p. 12.

8 Albert Raeburn, "The East Bay Regional Park District," p. 9.

9 Quoted by R. G. Martin in "Water Conservation in the Santa Clara Valley," pp. 58-59.

10 Quoted *ibid.*, p. 65.

11 *California Public Record*, XVII, Sept. 9, 1935, p. 1.

12 Tomaschke-Elliott, Inc., *The Effect of Bridge Construction on Population Movement*, p. 34.

13 San Francisco Examiner, *How Will the Bridges Affect San Francisco Business? A Forecast . . .*, p. 3.

14 *Ibid.*

15 *Report of the San Francisco Public Utilities Commission, Fiscal Year 1935–1936*, p. 143.

16 *California Highways and Public Works*, November, 1936, p. 1.

17 *Ibid.*, p. 5.

18 *Ibid.*, p. 2.

19 San Francisco *Chronicle*, May 28, 1937, p. 1.

20 *Report of the San Francisco Public Utilities Commission, Year 1936–1937*, pp. 151–152.

21 Miller McClintock, *Report on San Francisco City-wide Traffic Survey*, p. 110.

22 *Ibid.*, p. 251.

23 *Ibid.*, p. 254.

24 East Bay Cities Sewage Disposal Survey, *Report upon the Collection, Treatment and Disposal of Sewage and Industrial Wastes of the East Bay Cities*, p. 8.

25 *Ibid.*, p. 9.

26 *Ibid.*, p. 6.

27 Yerba Buena Exposition Association, *A Site for the 1938 Exposition*, p. 6.

28 Advisory Planning Committee to Bridge Celebration Founding Committee, *Report to J. W. Mailliard, Jr., Chairman, Bridge Celebration Founding Committee*.

29 *Transactions of the Commonwealth Club*, XXVI, 355.

30 Miller McClintock, *op. cit.*, 30.

NOTES TO CHAPTER 15 (PAGES 244–257)

Crisis in an Arsenal of Democracy

1 O. W. Campbell, "Regional Defense Problems," in California State Planning Board, *San Francisco Bay Regional Planning District —Proceedings of Hearing, March 28, 1941*, p. 34.

2 Letter, Samuel C. May, Chairman of California State Planning Board, to city and county officials of the San Francisco Bay Area, Feb. 18, 1941.

3 California State Planning Board, *op. cit.*, pp. 54–55.

4 Remarks of James N. Long, *ibid.*, p. 57.

5 Remarks of Will Weston, *ibid.*, p. 51.

6 Remarks of P. Victor Peterson, *ibid.*, pp. 63–64.

7 Remarks of L. Deming Tilton, *ibid.*, p. 56.

8 California State Planning Board, *A Proposal for the Formation of a Temporary Regional Planning Organization for the San Francisco Bay Area*, p. 1.

9 *Ibid.*, p. 5.

10 *Investigation of Congested Areas*, Part 3, Hearings, House Subcommittee on Naval Affairs, 78th Cong., 1st sess. (Washington, 1943), p. 899.

11 *Ibid.*, p. 858.

12 *Ibid.*, p. 867.

13 Testimony of W. P. Cooper, *ibid.*, p. 890.

14 Housing Authority of the County of Marin, *Fighters on the Home Front: First Annual Report*.

15 Catherine Bauer, "Outline of War Housing," *Task* (no date), p. 6.

16 *Investigation of Congested Areas*, p. 661.

17 *Ibid.*, p. 765.

18 *Ibid.*, p. 804.

19 *Ibid.*, p. 1006.

20 *Ibid.*, p. 804.

21 *Report on the San Francisco Bay Area*, House Subcommittee of the Naval Affairs Committee Appointed to Investigate Congestion in Critical War Production Areas, p. 810.

22 *Ibid.*

23 *Ibid.*, p. 811.

24 *Ibid.*, p. 809.

25 *Ibid.*

26 *Ibid.*, p. 818.

27 *Ibid.*

NOTES TO CHAPTER 16 (PAGES 258–270)

Postwar Planning

1 National Resources Planning Board, *Post-War Plan and Program*, p. 1.

2 National Resources Planning Board, Pacific Southwest Regional Office, *After the War—New Jobs in the Pacific Southwest*, p. 18.

3 *Ibid.*, pp. 3–4.

4 *Ibid.*, p. 37.

5 California statute as quoted by California Housing and Planning Association in "New Commission Aids Postwar Readjustment," *Agenda*, II (October, 1943), 10.

6 California State Reconstruction and Reemployment Commission, *The Bay Region Takes Stock*, p. 2.

7 *Ibid.*, p. 16.

8 *Ibid.*, p. 20.

9 San Francisco Bay Region Council, Minutes of the first meeting, p. 7.

10 *Ibid.*, p. 4.

11 *Ibid.*, p. 6.

12 *Ibid.*, p. 2.

13 Oscar Lewis, *Within the Golden Gate*, p. 2.

14 Citizens' Postwar Planning Committee, *Report . . . to Mayor Roger D. Lapham*, p. 4.

15 *Ibid.*, p. 23.

16 *Ibid.*, pp. 6–7.

17 San Francisco City Planning Commission, *Present and Future Uses of the Land*, p. 53.

18 Citizens' Postwar Planning Committee, *op. cit.*, p. 3.

19 San Francisco City Planning Commission, *op. cit.*, pp. 53–54.

20 Oakland Postwar Planning Committee, *Oakland's Formula for the Future*, p. 48.

21 *Ibid.*, p. 46.

22 *Recommendations of the Citizens' Postwar Advisory Committee* (Berkeley), p. 1.

23 Berkeley Chamber of Commerce, *A Report to Berkeleyans*, p. 2.

NOTES TO CHAPTER 17 (PAGES 271–309)

The Regional Metropolis

1 Industrial Survey Associates, *Santa Clara County: Its Prospects of Prosperity*, p. 4.

2 Palo Alto *Times*, March 3, 1950, p. 13.

3 *Ibid.*, May 9, 1951.

4 "Outlook for Future Growth," *Monthly Review of the Federal Reserve Bank of San Francisco*, November, 1947, as quoted in San Francisco Bay Area Council, *San Francisco Bay Area: Its People, Prospects, and Problems*, advance review edition, pp. f–g.

5 San Francisco *Chronicle*, July 25, 1950, p. 16.

6 H. F. Wise and Simon Eisner, *Master Plan for Menlo Park*, p. 27.

7 D. F. Foley, *The Suburbanization of Administrative Offices in the San Francisco Bay Area*, p. 4.

8 Quoted in Hayward City Planning Commission, *Hayward Prepares a Master Plan for Future Development*, p. 16.

9 Aaron Levine, *The Urban Renewal of San Francisco*, San Francisco Planning and Housing Association and the Blyth-Zellerbach Committee, March, 1959.

10 Oakland City Planning Commission, *Preliminary General Plan* (Oakland, 1958).

11 San Francisco *Chronicle*, Jan. 12, 1958, p. 2.

12 *Ibid.*, Jan. 13, 1958, p. 2.

13 *Ibid.*, Nov. 6, 1957, and Jan. 12, 1958.

14 Bay Area Air Pollution Control District *Air Currents*, Vol. 1, No. 1 (April, 1959), p. 4.

15 San Francisco Bay Area Council, Planning Directors' Committee, *A Regional Planning Agency for the San Francisco Bay Area*, p. ii.

16 V. B. Stanbery, *Regional Planning Needs of the San Francisco Bay Area*, p. 29.

17 San Francisco Bay Area Council, *A Regional Planning Agency*, p. v.

18 *Ibid.*

Bibliography

MANUSCRIPTS

Bowman, Jacob N. "The O'Farrell Swing." MS in author's possession.
———— "The Roads of Provincial California." MS, Bancroft Library, University of California, 1946.
Bowman, Jacob N., and George Whiting Hendry. "The Spanish and Mexican Adobe and Other Buildings in the Nine San Francisco Bay Counties, 1776 to about 1850." 7 vols. MS, Bancroft Library, University of California, 1945.
Burgess, Sherwood Denn. "Early History of the Oakland Water Supply, 1850–1876." Unpublished M.A. thesis, University of California, 1948.
Burns, Thomas P. "Centennial of the City of San Francisco, 1835–1935." MS, Bancroft Library, University of California, 1935.
Houston, Mary Ruth. "The Early History of Berkeley, California." Unpublished M.A. thesis, University of California, 1925.
Hughes, Lillian Gobar. "Housing in San Francisco, 1835–1938." Unpublished M.A. thesis, University of California, 1940.
Kesseli, Thelma Dorothy. "The Railroad as an Agency of Settlement in California, 1870–1890." Unpublished M.A. thesis, University of California, 1948.
Key, Leon Goodwin. "The History of the Policies in Disposing of the Public Lands in California, 1769–1900." Unpublished M.A. thesis, University of California, 1930.
King, Margaret Goddard. "The Growth of San Francisco, Illustrated by Shifts in the Density of Population." Unpublished M.A. thesis, University of California, 1928.
Klein, Julius. "The Development of Manufacturing Industry in California up to 1870." Unpublished M.A. thesis, University of California, 1908.
Loosley, Allyn Campbell. "Foreign-born Population of California, 1848–1920." Unpublished M.A. thesis, University of California, 1927.
Martin, Richard G. "Water Conservation in the Santa Clara Valley." Unpublished M.A. thesis, University of California, 1950.

Maverick, Lewis Adams. "Activity in Real Estate in Alameda County, California, 1853 to 1930." Unpublished Ph.D. dissertation, University of California, 1931.
Miller, Louis Richard. "The History of the San Francisco and San Jose Railroad." Unpublished M.A. thesis, University of California, 1948.
Nickell, Sadie F. "Economic History of California, 1850–1870." Unpublished M.A. thesis, University of California, 1926.
Phelan, James Duval. Scrapbook. Bancroft Library, University of California.
Raeburn, Albert. "The East Bay Regional Park District." Unpublished M.A. thesis, University of California, 1943.
Rinne, Rose Marie Shiely. "The San Francisco–Oakland Bay Bridge: Its History and Economic Development." Unpublished M.A. thesis, University of California, 1936.
Smythe, Dallas Walker. "An Economic History of Local and Inter-Urban Transportation in the East Bay Cities, with Particular Reference to the Properties Developed by F. M. Smith." Unpublished Ph.D. dissertation, University of California, 1937.
Solovsky, Ruth Mary McGinty. "Spanish and Mexican Ranchos in the San Francisco Bay Region: San Antonio, San Pablo, and San Leandro." Unpublished M.A. thesis, University of California, 1921.
Stephens, James Charles. "The Development of County Planning in California." Unpublished M.A. thesis, University of California, 1938.
Teese, Edith. "Waterfront Developments in the San Pablo and Richmond, California, Region to 1917." Unpublished M.A. thesis, University of California, 1947.
Voget, Margarette Lamberta. "The Waterfront of San Francisco, 1863–1930: A History of Its Administration by the State of California." Unpublished Ph.D. dissertation, University of California, 1943.
Williams, R. L. "Eighty Years of Subdivision Design: An Historical Evaluation of Land Planning in San Mateo County, California." Unpublished M.C.P. thesis, University of California, 1951.

Woodruff, Jacqueline McCart. "History of Benicia, 1846–1880." Unpublished M.A. thesis, University of California, 1943.

In addition to the foregoing manuscripts, letters from the following persons to the author have been used in the preparation of this book: Glenn A. Harris, City Engineer of Vallejo, August 12, 1954. William R. Seeger, Assistant General Manager, Marin Municipal Water District, January 8 and 26, 1954. Robert R. Gros, Manager, Advertising and Publicity Department, Pacific Gas and Electric Company, November 3, 1954.

PUBLIC AND SEMIPUBLIC DOCUMENTS

Bartholomew, Harland. *The San Francisco Bay Region: A Statement Concerning the Nature and Importance of a Plan for Future Growth.* [San Francisco, 1925?] Cover title: Preliminary Report on Regional Plan Problems of San Francisco Bay Counties. (Submitted to the Regional Plan Association of the San Francisco Bay Counties, September, 1925.)

Bay Area Real Estate Report. San Francisco, 1949–1957. (Published by the Bay Area Real Estate Research Committee, an affiliate of the San Francisco Bay Area Council.)

Berkeley. Chamber of Commerce. *A Report to Berkeleyans: Major Post War Problems That Face the City of Berkeley, as Viewed by Berkeley Business Men.* Berkeley, 1945.

——— Citizens' Postwar Advisory Committee. *Recommendations.* Berkeley, 1946.

California. Department of Finance. Division of Budgets and Accounts, Financial Research Section. *Estimated Population of California, 1950–1954, with Projections to 1955.* Sacramento, 1954.

——— Department of Health. *Status of Sewage Disposal in the San Francisco Bay Area.* Berkeley, 1948. (Mimeographed.)

——— Department of Industrial Relations. *Monthly Estimates of Employment in California.* San Francisco, February and May, 1943.

——— Department of Natural Resources, Division of Mines. *Geologic Guidebook of the San Francisco Bay Counties . . .* Prepared under the Direction of Olaf P. Jenkins. San Francisco, 1951. (Bulletin 154.)

——— Highway Advisory Committee. *Report of a Study of the State Highway System of California.* Sacramento, 1925.

——— Railroad Commission. *Report . . . July 1, 1917, to June 30, 1918.* Sacramento, 1918.

——— ——— *Report . . , July 1, 1921, to June 30, 1922.* Sacramento, 1923.

——— San Francisco Bay Area Rapid Transit Commission. *Preliminary Report.* [Sacramento, 1953.]

——— Secretary of State. *California Blue Book, 1950.* Sacramento, 1950.

——— Senate, Fact-finding Committee on San Francisco Bay Ports. *Ports of the San Francisco Bay Area—Their Commerce, Facilities, Problems, and Progress.* Sacramento, 1951.

——— ——— Interim Committee on San Francisco Bay Area Metropolitan Rapid Transit Problems. *Mass Rapid Transit, Answer to Traffic Congestion in the San Francisco Bay Area.* [San Francisco.] 1953.

——— ——— Interim Committee on State and Local Taxation. *Report.* Sacramento, 1953.

——— State Park Commission. *Report of State Park Survey of California.* Prepared by Frederick Law Olmsted (the younger). Sacramento, 1929.

——— State Planning Board. *An Economic and Industrial Survey of the San Francisco Bay Area.* By Robert D. Calkins and Walter E. Hoadley, Jr. Sacramento, 1941.

——— ——— *A Proposal for the Formation of a Temporary Regional Planning Organization for the San Francisco Bay Area.* Sacramento, December 8, 1941. (Mimeographed.)

——— ——— *San Francisco Bay Regional Planning District—Proceedings of Hearing, March 28, 1941.* Sacramento, 1941.

——— State Reconstruction and Reemployment Commission. *The Bay Region Takes Stock: An Account of the Public Hearing on Postwar Problems of the San Francisco Bay Region, August 2 and 24, 1944.* [San Francisco, 1944.] (Pamphlet No. 3.)

——— ——— *Richmond, California; A City Earns the Purple Heart.* Sacramento, 1944. (Pamphlet No. 2.)

——— State and Regional Water Pollution Control Boards. *Water Pollution Control: Progress Report for 1950 Through 1952.* Sacramento, 1952.

——— *Statutes,* 1849, 1927, 1937.

California Conference on City Planning. *Procedure for Zoning or Districting of Cities.* By Charles Henry Cheney. Bulletin No. 2. San Francisco, 1917.

California Crop and Livestock Reporting Service. *California Field Crops Statistics 1866–1946.* Prepared by Lowell M. Clarke and George A. Scott. Sacramento [1947].

East Bay Cities Sewage Disposal Survey. *Report upon the Collection, Treatment and Distribution of Sewage and Industrial Wastes of the East Bay Cities of California.* To the Mayor and Council representing the City of Berkeley as the sponsoring agent for the seven cooperating cities . . . by the Board of Consulting Engineers: Charles Gilman Hyde, Harold Farnsworth Gray, A. M. Rawn. [Berkeley], 1941.

East Bay Municipal Utility District. *Engineering Board of Review Report on Sewage Disposal for the District* [Special District No. 1]. By Samuel A. Greeley, Clyde C. Kennedy, and N. T. Veatch. Oakland, 1946.

——— "Future Water Requirements of the San Francisco Bay Region." Oakland, 1947. (Unpublished technical report.)

——— *The Story of Water . . .* Oakland, [1931?].

——— *Water: Where It Comes From . . . How It Reaches Your Faucet.* Oakland, n.d.

Hayward. Planning Commission. *Hayward Prepares a Master Plan for Future Development.* Hayward, 1953.

Industrial Survey Associates. *Santa Clara County: Its Prospects of Prosperity.* Digest of a Report for the Santa Clara County Industrial Survey Advisory Council and the San Jose Chamber of Commerce. San Francisco, 1948.

Joint Subaqueous Tunnel Commission. *Report on a Proposed Additional Tube.* Oakland, 1940.

Marin County. Housing Authority. *Fighters on the Home Front: First Annual Report.* San Rafael, 1943.

McClintock, Miller. *Report on San Francisco Citywide Traffic Survey.* Prepared for the Department of Public Works. San Francisco: [Pisani Printing and Publishing Co.] 1937. (W.P.A. Project 6108–5863.)

Menlo Park. *Master Plan for Menlo Park, California.* By Harold F. Wise and Simon Eisner. Menlo Park, 1952.

Oakland. Chamber of Commerce. *How to Win the Markets of the New West.* Oakland, 1948.

——— City Planning Commission. *Annual Report for the Fiscal Year Ending June 30, 1944.* Oakland, 1944.

———— ———— *Shoreline Development: A Part of the Master Plan.* Oakland, 1951.

———— Park Commission. *The Park System of Oakland, California.* [Oakland, 1910.]

———— Postwar Planning Committee. *Oakland's Formula for the Future.* Oakland, 1945.

Olmsted Brothers and Ansel F. Hall. *Report on Proposed Park Reservations for East Bay Cities* (California). *Prepared for the Bureau of Public Administration, University of California, in Consultation with the East Bay Regional Park Association.* [Berkeley], 1930.

Richmond. City Council. *Postwar Richmond, California . . . 1945–1949.* [Richmond], 1949.

———— ———— *Report to the City Council of Richmond on the Port of Richmond.* By Main and Company. San Francisco, 1950.

———— ———— *Report on Richmond Harbor Project, with Supplementary Report on Tunnel and Roadway. To the Council of the City of Richmond.* San Francisco: Haviland & Tibbets, 1912.

San Francisco. Board of Park Commissioners. *The Development of Golden Gate Park . . .* San Francisco, 1886. (Report of William Hammond Hall, Consulting Engineer, is on pp. 7–20.)

———— Board of Supervisors. *General Ordinances . . .* San Francisco, 1907. Ordinance No. 31 (New Series).

———— ———— *Municipal Reports for the Fiscal Years 1884–85, 1905–1906, 1906–1907, 1915–16.*

———— ———— Airport Committee. *San Francisco Airport: A Report.* San Francisco, 1931.

———— Chamber of Commerce. *San Francisco Tackles Its Housing Problem.* San Francisco, 1943.

———— ———— *Sixty-first Annual Report.* San Francisco, 1911. ("President's Annual Report," by William L. Gerstle, is on pp. 17–18.)

———— Citizens' Postwar Planning Committee. *Report to Mayor Roger D. Lapham.* San Francisco, 1945.

———— City Planning Commission. *The Case for the Southern Crossing.* San Francisco, 1949.

———— ———— *History of Public Transit in San Francisco, 1850–1948.* San Francisco, 1948.

———— ———— *Present and Future Uses of the Land.* San Francisco, 1944.

———— ———— *Transportation Section of the Master Plan of the City and County of San Francisco.* San Francisco, 1951.

———— ———— *Western Addition District Redevelopment Study.* San Francisco, 1947.

———— Department of City Planning. *The Population of San Francisco, 1900–1950: A Half Century of Change.* San Francisco, 1954.

———— Housing Authority. *Fifth Annual Report.* San Francisco, 1943.

———— Mayor. *Annual Message to the Board of Supervisors of the City and County of San Francisco.* By Roger D. Lapham. San Francisco, 1946.

San Francisco. Public Utilities Commission. *Report, Fiscal Year 1935–1936.* Also: *Report, Fiscal Year 1936–1937.*

———— ———— *San Francisco Water and Power.* San Francisco, 1949.

San Francisco Bay Area Chambers of Commerce. *Serving Pacific Markets from the Center: A Study of the Basic Factors Affecting Successful Manufacturing and Distribution on the Pacific Coast.* Prepared by the chambers of commerce of communities surrounding San Francisco Bay, under the general supervision of

McCann-Erickson, Inc. (San Francisco? 1931.) Cover title: San Francisco–Oakland Metropolitan Area: An Industrial Study.

San Francisco Bay Area Council. *San Francisco Bay Area: Its People, Prospects and Problems.* San Francisco, 1947.

———— *San Francisco Bay Area: A Year of Action—1947.* San Francisco, 1948.

———— Planning Directors' Committee. *A Regional Planning Agency for the San Francisco Bay Area; a Report and Statutory Proposal.* Prepared under the supervision of the Regional Planning Subcommittee of the Bay Area Planning Directors' Committee. [Berkeley? 1956.]

San Francisco Bay Regional Development Council. *Minutes of Meeting at the Claremont Hotel, April 11, 1942.*

San Francisco Housing Association. *First Report.* San Francisco, 1911. (Langley Porter, "Report of the President" is pp. 6–10.)

San Jose. Chamber of Commerce. *Distinguished Neighbors.* San Jose, 1949.

San Jose Water Works. *What's Back of the Faucet.* San Jose, 1953.

San Mateo County. Planning Commission. *Industrial Survey of San Mateo County.* Redwood City, 1953. (Prepared for the Urban Land Institute.)

———— ———— *A Planned Program for Public Works.* Redwood City, 1942.

Santa Clara County. Planning Commission. *Flood Problems in Santa Clara County.* San Jose, 1952. (Monograph No. 3.)

Tomaschke-Elliott, Inc. *The Effect of Bridge Construction on Population Movement: A Study of Eastern Cities.* Prepared for the Residential Development Committee of the Oakland Chamber of Commerce. [Oakland,] 1934.

U. S. Bureau of Public Roads. *Report of a Study of the California Highway System.* Washington, 1922.

———— Circuit Court. *Opinions and Decrees . . . for the Northern District of California in the Case of the City of San Francisco vs. The United States: The Pueblo Case.* San Francisco, 1865. ("Opinion of Mr. Justice Field . . . Confirming the Claim of the City of San Francisco for Four Leagues of Pueblo Lands, Filed October 31st, 1864," is on pp. 4–13.)

———— Congress. House. Subcommittee of Naval Affairs Committee. Investigation of Congested Areas, Pt. 3: San Francisco, Calif., Area. Hearings, 78th Cong., 1st sess., pursuant to H. Res. 30. Washington, 1943.

———— ———— ———— ———— *Report on the San Francisco Bay Area by the Subcommittee Appointed to Investigate Congestion in Critical War-Production Areas.* [Washington, 1943.]

———— Executive Office of the President. Committee for Congested Production Areas. *San Francisco Bay Area, California.* San Francisco, 1944.

———— National Resources Planning Board. *Pacific Southwest Region—Industrial Development.* Washington, 1942.

———— ———— *Post-War Plan and Program.* Washington, 1943.

———— ———— *Post-War Planning.* Washington, 1942.

———— ———— Pacific Southwest Regional Office. *After the War—New Jobs in the Pacific Southwest.* Berkeley, 1943. (Mimeographed.)

University of California Conference on City and Regional Planning. *Proceedings of the Second Annual . . . Conference on City and Regional Planning.* Berkeley, 1954. (Norman Kennedy, "A Coordinated Attack on the Urban Transportation Problem" is on pp. 17–22.)

BOOKS

Aitken, Frank W., and Edward Hilton. *A History of the Earthquake and Fire in San Francisco: An Account of the Disaster of April 18, 1906, and Its Immediate Results.* San Francisco: Edward Hilton Co., 1906.

Altrocchi, Julia Cooley. *The Spectacular San Franciscans.* New York: Dutton, 1949.

Arbuckle, Clyde, and Roscoe D. Wyatt. *Historic Names, Persons, and Places in Santa Clara County.* San Jose: Chamber of Commerce, 1948.

Arnold, Bion J. *Report on the Improvement and Development of Transportation Facilities in San Francisco.* San Francisco: Hicks-Judd Co., 1913.

Baker, Joseph E. (ed.). *Past and Present of Alameda County, California.* 2 vols. Chicago: S. J. Clarke Publishing Co., 1914.

Bancroft, Hubert Howe. *History of California.* 7 vols. San Francisco, 1884–1890. (*Works*, Vols. XVIII–XXIV.)

Bartholomew, Harland. *The San Francisco Bay Region: A Statement Concerning the Nature and Importance of a Plan for Future Growth . . . to the Regional Plan Association.* (San Francisco: Regional Plan Association of the San Francisco Bay Counties, 1925.)

Bartholomew, Harland, and Associates. *A Major Street Plan for Oakland.* Oakland: Major Highway and Traffic Committee of One Hundred, 1927.

The Bay of San Francisco, the Metropolis of the Pacific Coast, and Its Suburban Cities: A History. 2 vols. Chicago: Lewis Publishing Co., 1892.

Bean, Walton. *Boss Ruef's San Francisco: The Story of the Union Labor Party, Big Business, and the Graft Prosecution.* Berkeley and Los Angeles: University of California Press, 1952.

Black, James B. *California: "Stored with Many Blessings Fit for the Use of Man."* New York: American Branch, Newcomen Society of England, 1949.

Beckman, Roy C. *The Romance of Oakland.* Oakland: Landis & Kelsey, 1932.

Blow, Ben. *California Highways: A Descriptive Record of Road Development by the State and by Such Counties As Have Paved Highways.* San Francisco: Ben Blow, 1920.

Bollens, John C. *The Problem of Government in the San Francisco Bay Region.* Berkeley: Bureau of Public Administration, University of California, 1948. (Processed.)

Bolton, Herbert Eugene. *Outpost of Empire: The Story of the Founding of San Francisco.* New York: Knopf, 1931.

Bolton, Herbert Eugene (ed.). *Font's Complete Diary: A Chronicle of the Founding of San Francisco.* Berkeley: University of California Press, 1931.

—— *Fray Juan Crespi, Missionary Explorer on the Pacific Coast, 1769–1774.* Berkeley: University of California Press, 1927.

Browne, J. Ross. *Letter from the Hon. J. Ross Browne, Late U. S. Minister to China, in Relation to the Proposed Town Site of Lower Berkeley and the Value of Property and Growth of Population in and Around Oakland.* San Francisco, 1870.

Burnham, Daniel Hudson, and Edward H. Bennett. *Report on a Plan for San Francisco.* Edited by Edward F. O'Day. Presented to the Mayor and Board of Supervisors by the Association for the Improvement and Adornment of San Francisco. San Francisco: Published by the City, 1905.

California Promotion Committee. *Sixth Annual Report.* San Francisco, 1908.

Caughey, John Walton. *Gold is the Cornerstone.* Berkeley and Los Angeles: University of California Press, 1948.

Chapman, Charles E. *A History of California: The Spanish Period.* New York: Macmillan, 1939.

Child, Stephen. *A Plan for the Development of Alum Rock Park (Reservation) at San Jose, California.* San Francisco, 1916.

Cleland, Robert Glass. *California in Our Time (1900–1940).* New York: Knopf, 1947.

—— *From Wilderness to Empire: A History of California, 1542–1900.* New York: Knopf, 1947.

Cleland, Robert Glass, and Osgood Hardy. *March of Industry* ("California Series.") Los Angeles: Powell Publishing Co., 1929.

Country Club of Washington Township. *History of Washington Township.* 2d ed. [Niles, Calif.] 1950.

Coy, Owen C. *California County Boundaries: A Study of the Division of the State into Counties and the Subsequent Changes in Their Boundaries.* Berkeley: California Historical Survey Commission, 1923.

Cummings, G. A., and E. S. Pladwell. *Oakland: A History.* Oakland: Grant D. Miller Mortuaries, 1942.

Daggett, Stuart. *Chapters on the History of the Southern Pacific.* New York: Ronald Press, 1922.

Davidson, George. *The Discovery of San Francisco Bay . . .* San Francisco, 1907. Transactions and Proceedings of the Geographical Society of the Pacific, Vol. IV, Ser. II. San Francisco, 1907.

Davis, William Heath. *Seventy-five Years in California.* San Francisco: John Howell, 1929.

Dawson, Nicholas "Cheyenne." *Overland to California in '41 and '49, and Texas in '51.* San Francisco: Grabhorn, 1933.

De Roos, Robert. *The Thirsty Land: The Story of the Central Valley Project.* Stanford: Stanford University Press, 1948.

Eldredge, Zoeth Skinner. *The Beginnings of San Francisco.* 2 vols. San Francisco: Published by the author, 1912.

—— *The March of Portolá and the Log of the San Carlos.* San Francisco: California Promotion Committee, 1909.

Elliott, Orrin Leslie. *Stanford University: The First Twenty-five Years.* Stanford: Stanford University Press, 1937.

Engelhardt, Fr. Zephyrin. *The Missions and Missionaries of California.* Vol. II, Upper California, Part I, General History. San Francisco: James H. Barry, 1912.

Ferrier, William Warren. *Berkeley, California: The Story of the Evolution of a Hamlet into a City of Culture and Commerce.* Berkeley: Published by the author, 1933.

Finley, Ernest Latimer (ed.). *History of Sonoma County, California, Its People and Its Resources.* Santa Rosa: Press Democrat Publishing Co., 1937.

Freeman, John R. *On the Proposed Use of a Portion of the Hetch Hetchy, Eleanor and Cherry Valleys Within and near to the Boundaries of the Stanislaus U. S. National Forest Reserve and the Yosemite National Park as Reservoirs for Impounding Tuolumne River Flood Waters and Appurtenant Works for the Water Supply of San Francisco, California, and Neighboring Cities.* San Francisco: Published by Authority of the Board of Supervisors, 1912.

Giffen, Guy, and Helen Giffen. *The Story of Golden Gate Park.* San Francisco: Published by the authors, 1949.

Goodwin, Cardinal. *The Establishment of State Government in California, 1846–1850.* New York: Macmillan, 1914.

Gregory, Thomas J., and others. *History of Sonoma County, Cali-*

fornia . . . Los Angeles: Historic Record Company, 1911.

Hall, Frederick. *The History of San Jose and Surroundings*. San Francisco, 1871.

Halley, William. *The Centennial Year Book of Alameda County, California*. Oakland, 1876.

Harlow, Neal. *The Maps of San Francisco Bay from the Spanish Discovery in 1769 to the American Occupation*. San Francisco: Book Club of California, 1950.

Hayler, Guy Wilfrid. *The San Francisco Bay Region of the Future: What the Great Regional Plan Means*. San Francisco, 1926. (Reprinted from the *Daily Commercial News Annual*, 1926.)

Heath, Erle. *Seventy-five Years of Progress: Historical Sketch of the Southern Pacific*. San Francisco: Southern Pacific Bureau of News, 1945.

Hegemann Werner. *Report on a City Plan for the Municipalities of Oakland and Berkeley. . . .* [Oakland], 1915.

Hinkel, Edgar J., and William E. McCann (eds.). *Oakland 1852–1938: Some Phases of the Social, Political and Economic History of Oakland, California*. 2 vols. Oakland: Oakland Public Library, 1939. (A Works Progress Administration project.) (Mimeographed.)

Littell, John Shertzer. *The Prospects of Vallejo; or, Evidences That Vallejo Will Become a Great City: A Re-Publication of a Series of Articles First Printed in the Vallejo* Evening Chronicle, *from March to July, 1871*. Vallejo, 1871.

Holterhoff, G., Jr. *Historical Review of the Atchison, Topeka and Santa Fe Railway Company (with Particular Reference to California Lines) as Furnished to the Railroad Commission of the State of California in Compliance with Its General Order No. 38.* Los Angeles, 1914.

Hulaniski, F. J. (ed.). *The History of Contra Costa County, California*. Berkeley: Elms Publishing Co., 1917.

Hunt, Marguerite, and Harry Lawrence Gunn. *History of Solano County . . . and Napa County, California . . .* Chicago: S. J. Clarke Publishing Co., 1926.

Hunt, Rockwell D., and Nellie van de Grift Sanchez. *A Short History of California*. New York: Thomas Y. Crowell, 1929.

Irwin, William Henry. *The City That Was: A Requiem of Old San Francisco*. New York: B. W. Huebsch, 1906.

James, William F., and George H. McMurray. *History of San Jose, California, Narrative and Biographical*. San Jose: A. H. Cawston, 1938.

Jennings, Rufus P. *Statement of Rufus P. Jennings, Executive Officer of the California Promotion Committee, at a Meeting Held April 4, 1905*. San Francisco: California Promotion Committee, 1905.

Langley, Henry G. (comp.). *The San Francisco Directory for the Year Commencing September, 1862*. San Francisco, 1862.

Langsdorff, G. H. von. *Voyages and Travels in Various Parts of the World During the Years 1803, 1804, 1805, 1806, and 1807*. London, 1813.

Lewis, Oscar. *Within the Golden Gate*. San Francisco: San Francisco Bay Area Council, 1945.

McEntire, Davis, and others. *The Population of California: A Report of a Research Study Made by Authorization of the Board of Governors of the Commonwealth Club of California*. San Francisco: Commonwealth Club of California, 1946.

McKittrick, Myrtle M. *Vallejo, Son of California*. Portland, Oregon: Binfords & Mort, 1944.

Marshall, James. *Santa Fe, the Railroad That Built an Empire*. New York: Random House, 1945.

Maybeck, Bernard R. *Palace of Fine Arts and Lagoon, Panama-Pacific International Exposition, 1915*. San Francisco: Paul Elder, 1915.

Merritt, Frank Clinton. *History of Alameda County, California . . .* 2 vols. Chicago: S. J. Clarke Publishing Co., 1928.

Moore, Charles. *Daniel H. Burnham, Architect, Planner of Cities*. 2 vols. Boston: Houghton Mifflin, 1921.

Mount Gregory Water and Mining Company. *Water Supply for San Francisco, Oakland, Vallejo, Sacramento, and Other Places*. Oakland, 1874.

Munro-Fraser. *History of Alameda County, California . . .* Oakland: M. W. Wood, 1883.

———— *History of Contra Costa County, California . . .* San Francisco: W. A. Slocum & Co., 1882.

———— *History of Marin County, California . . .* San Francisco: Alley, Bowen & Co., 1880.

———— *History of Santa Clara County, California . . .* San Francisco: Alley, Bowen & Co., 1881.

———— *History of Sonoma County . . .* San Francisco: Alley, Bowen & Co., 1880.

Murphy, Celeste G. *The People of the Pueblo: The Story of Sonoma*. Sonoma: W. L. and C. G. Murphy, 1937.

Oakland Daily Transcript. *Information Concerning the Terminus of the Railroad System of the Pacific Coast*. Oakland, 1871.

Ogden, Adele. *The California Sea Otter Trade, 1784–1848*. Berkeley and Los Angeles: University of California Press, 1941.

Olmsted, Frederick Law. *Berkeley Neighborhood: Report upon a Projected Improvement of the Estate of the College of California at Berkeley, near Oakland*. New York, 1866.

———— *Preliminary Report in Regard to a Plan of Public Pleasure Grounds for the City of San Francisco*. New York, 1866.

O'Shaughnessy, Michael M. *Hetch-Hetchy—Its Origin and History*. San Francisco: M. M. O'Shaughnessy, 1934.

Pacific Gas and Electric Company. *Pacific Gas and Electric Company—History, Facilities, Service*. San Francisco, 1936.

Palmer, Lyman L. *History of Napa and Lake Counties, California . . .* San Francisco: Slocum, Bowen & Co., 1881.

Palóu, Francisco. *Palóu's Life of Fray Junípero Serra*. Translated and annotated by Maynard J. Geiger, O.F.M. Washington, D.C.: Academy of American Franciscan History, 1955.

Peralta Associates and Vernon J. Sappers. *From Shore to Shore: The Key Route*. Oakland: Peralta Associates, 1948.

Purcell, Mae Fisher. *History of Contra Costa County, California*. Berkeley: Gillick Press, 1940.

Quiett, Glenn Chesney. *They Built the West: An Epic of Rails and Cities*. New York: Appleton-Century, 1934.

Reed, Albert S. *The San Francisco Conflagration of April, 1906*. New York: National Board of Fire Underwriters, 1906.

Robinson, Charles Mulford. *A Plan of Civic Improvement for the City of Oakland, California*. Oakland: Oakland Enquirer Publishing Co., 1906.

Robinson, W. W. *Land in California*. Berkeley and Los Angeles: University of California Press, 1948.

San Francisco Morning Call. *Fettered Commerce—How the Pacific Mail and the Railroads Have Bled San Francisco. A Series of Articles Reprinted from the San Francisco Morning Call*. San Francisco, 1892.

San Francisco Theatre Research [W.P.A.] Project. Edited by Lawrence Estevan. *The History of Opera in San Francisco*. Monograph XVIII, Pt. II. [First Series.] San Francisco, 1938.

San Francisco Water Company. *Reports of Engineers and Others on*

San Francisco Water Company (*Continued*)
a *Permanent Supply of Pure Fresh Water to the City of San Francisco*. San Francisco, 1872.

Santa Clara County and Its Resources: A Souvenir of the San Jose Mercury. San Jose, 1895.

Sherman, William T. *Memoirs of General William T. Sherman*. 2 vols. New York, 1875.

Shugg, Roger W., and H. A. DeWeerd. *World War II: A Concise History*. Washington: The Infantry Journal, 1946.

Soulé, Frank, John H. Gihon, and James Nisbet. *The Annals of San Francisco* . . . New York, 1855.

Souvenir of Golden Gate Park: Rehabilitation Edition of the Golden Gate Park News. San Francisco: Golden Gate Park News Company, 1907.

Stanger, Frank M. *History of San Mateo County, California*. San Mateo: Arthur H. Cawston, 1938.

Steele, Rufus. *The City That Is: The Story of the Rebuilding of San Francisco in Three Years*. San Francisco: A. M. Robertson, 1909.

Thompson, Frank R. *Electric Transportation*. Scranton, Pa.: International Textbook Co., 1940.

Todd, Frank Morton. *The Story of the Exposition* . . . *Official History of the International Celebration Held at San Francisco in 1915* . . . 5 vols. New York and London: Putnam, 1921.

Tunnard, Christopher. *The City of Man*. New York: Scribner, 1953.

Vancouver, George. *A Voyage of Discovery to the North Pacific Ocean and Round the World* . . . *in the Years 1790, 1791, 1792, 1793, 1794, and 1795* . . . 6 vols. London, 1801.

Vigness, Paul G. *Alameda Community Book*. Alameda: A. H. Cawston, 1952.

Wagner, H. Howe. *Mount Tamalpais State Park, Marin County*. California Historical Survey Series—Historic Landmarks, Monuments and State Parks. Edited by Clark Wing. [Sacramento, 1941.] (W.P.A. Project 665-08-3-147, sponsored by State of California Department of Natural Resources, Division of Parks.)

Walker, Robert A. *The Planning Function in Urban Government*. 2d ed. Chicago: University of Chicago Press, 1950.

Wheat, Carl I. *The Maps of the California Gold Region, 1848–1857: A Biblio-Cartography of an Important Decade*. San Francisco: Grabhorn, 1942.

Whitnah, Joseph C. *A History of Richmond, California*. Richmond: Richmond Chamber of Commerce, 1944.

Willey, Samuel H. *A History of the College of California*. San Francisco, 1887.

Winn, W. B. *Souvenir of Marin County, California*. San Rafael, 1893.

Winther, Oscar Osburn. *The Story of San Jose, California's First Pueblo, 1777–1869*. San Francisco: California Historical Society, 1935.

Wood, Dallas E. *History of Palo Alto*. Palo Alto: Arthur H. Cawston, 1939.

Writers Program of the Work Projects Administration in Northern California. *Berkeley: The First Seventy-five Years*. Berkeley: Gillick Press, 1941.

Young, John P. *San Francisco: A History of the Pacific Coast Metropolis*. 2 vols. San Francisco and Chicago: S. J. Clarke Publishing Co., 1912.

ARTICLES

Bauer, Catherine. "Outline of War Housing," *Task*, 1943 [?].

Bowman, Jacob N. "Weights and Measures of Provincial California," *California Historical Society Quarterly*, XXX (December 1951), 315–338.

Bradley, La Verne. "San Francisco: Gibraltar of the West Coast," *National Geographic Magazine*, LXXXIII (March, 1943), 279-308.

Cheney, Charles Henry. "How California Communities Can Profit by Active City Planning," *Pacific Municipalities*, XXVII (January, 1914), 31–35.

Douglas, J. R. "The City-Planning Movement in Berkeley," *Berkeley Civic Bulletin*, Aug. 22, 1916, pp. 2–5.

Greene, B. D. M. "Legal Aspect of the Zone Ordinance," *Berkeley Civic Bulletin*, Aug. 22, 1916, pp. 5 and 9.

Heizer, Robert F. "Indians of the San Francisco Bay Area," in *Geologic Guidebook of the San Francisco Bay Counties*, California Department of Natural Resources, Division of Mines, Bulletin 154, pp. 39–56. San Francisco, 1951.

Jenkins, Dorothy G. "Opening of the Golden Gate," in *Geologic Guidebook of the San Francisco Bay Counties*, California Department of Natural Resources, Division of Mines, Bulletin 154, pp. 11–29. San Francisco, 1951.

Lee, Charles H. "The Future Development of the Metropolitan Area Surrounding San Francisco Bay," *Bulletin of the Seismological Society of America*, XVI (June, 1926), 81–132.

Louderback, George D. "Geologic History of San Francisco Bay," in *Geologic Guidebook of the San Francisco Bay Counties*, California Department of Natural Resources, Division of Mines, Bulletin 154, pp. 75–92. San Francisco, 1951.

Macdonald, A. S. "The Beginnings of Richmond," *Bank News*, October, 1916, pp. 1–3. (Publication of First National Bank and Richmond Savings Bank, Richmond, Calif.)

McDuffie, Duncan. "City Planning in Berkeley," *Berkeley Civic Bulletin*, March 15, 1916, p. 108.

"Oakland's Municipal Airport," *Western City*, May, 1930, pp. 25–27.

Phelan, James D. "Historical Sketch of San Francisco," in Daniel H. Burnham and Edward H. Bennett, *Report on a Plan for San Francisco*, ed. Edward F. O'Day. San Francisco, 1905.

San Francisco Downtown Association. "Bay Area Gets Huge Defense Orders," *The Downtowner*, Nov. 20, 1940, p. [2].

——— "Bay Area Shipbuilding," *The Downtowner*, Dec. 26, 1940, p. [4].

Skeggs, John H. "The Bayshore Highway Dedication," *California Highways and Public Works*, November, 1929, pp. 9–10, 26.

Upton, M. G. "The Plan of San Francisco," *Overland Monthly*, I (February, 1869), 131–137.

NEWSPAPERS AND PERIODICALS

Benicia *Herald*, 1909, 1910, 1912.

Berkeley *Daily Gazette*, 1913, 1952.

California Real Estate Magazine, VII (February–December, 1927).

Commonwealth Club of California, *Transactions*, Vol. VII (1912), IX (1915), XI (1917), XII (1918), XVI (1921), XVII (1922), XVIII (1923), XIX (1924), XX (1925), XXIV (1929), XXV (1931).

Contra Costa Gazette, 1913, 1914.

The Golden Era (San Francisco) June 5–October 9, 1853.

Oakland Chamber of Commerce *Bulletin*. Vols. I (1910), II (1911), III (1912), V (1914).

Oakland *Enquirer*, 1906, 1907.

Oakland *Times*, 1906.

Oakland *Tribune*, 1906, 1907, 1910, 1912, 1913, 1914.

lo Alto *Times*, 1949, 1950, 1951.
ichmond *Independent*, 1928, 1939, 1954; Civic Center edition, Sept. 15, 1959.
n Francisco *Bulletin*, 1906, 1909, 1912.
n Francisco Business, June 3, Aug. 5, 1931.
un Francisco *Call*, 1909, 1911, 1915.
n Francisco Chamber of Commerce *Journal*, I, Nos. 8, 9 (June, July, 1912).
n Francisco *Chronicle*, 1906, 1909, 1910, 1912, 1913, 1924, 1932, 1937, 1942, 1943, 1949–1958.
n Francisco *Examiner*, 1909, 1924.
n Jose *Herald*, 1912, 1913.
un Jose *Mercury-Herald*, 1917, 1920, 1929.

Sausalito *News*, Souvenir edition, Feb. 27, 1941. Article: "Farewell to Northwestern Pacific Railroad Interurban Train-Ferry Service."
Vallejo *Times-Herald*, Sept. 16, 1954.

MAPS

Map of the City of Benicia Founded by Mariano G. Vallejo, Thomas O. Larkin & Robert Semple, 1847. Surveyed and drawn by Benjamin W. Barlow. San Francisco: Britton & Rey, [185–?]
Map of Holly Oak Park, Part of Suscol Rancho, Napa County. San Francisco: Britton & Rey, 1869. (Lots to be sold at auction by Maurice Dore & Co.)

Index